THIS SERIES OF BOOKS
IS DEDICATED TO THE MEMORY OF
ANNE-MARIE DALMAIS
WHOSE GREAT ENTHUSIASM
AND INSPIRATION MADE THIS
PROJECT COME TO LIFE

Four Little Friends

GYO FUJIKAWA

RAIN, SHINE, OR SNOW
and other tales

Modern Publishing
A Division of Unisystems, Inc.
New York, New York 10022
Printed in Italy

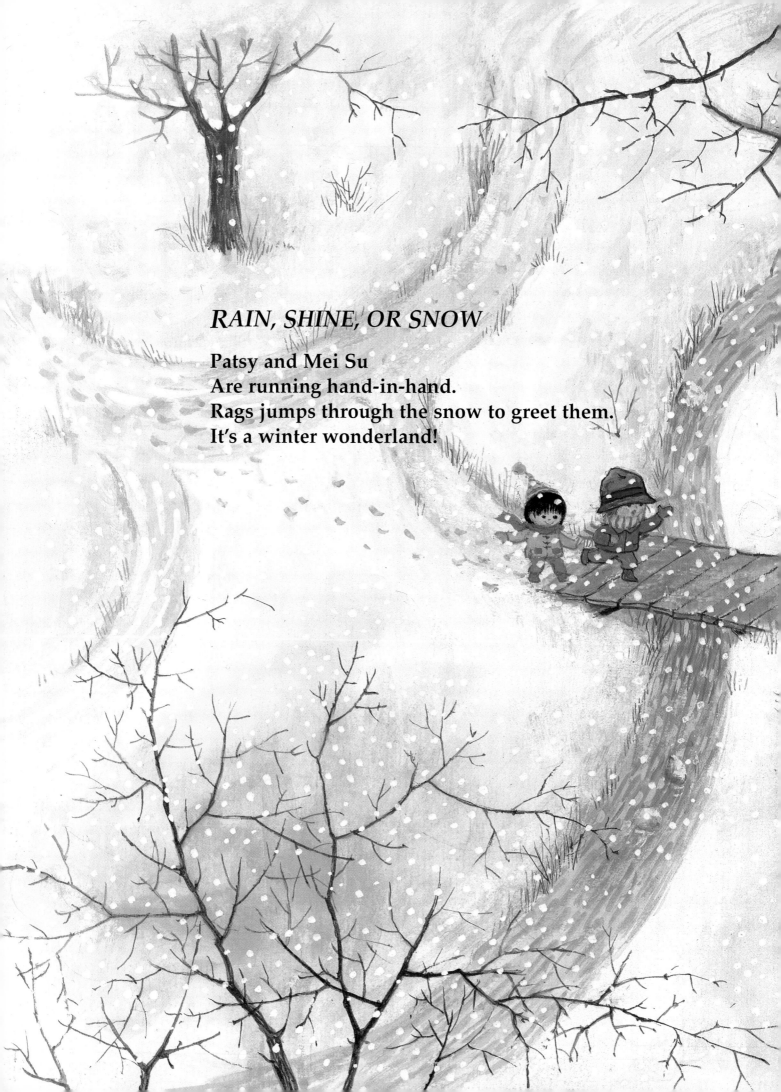

RAIN, SHINE, OR SNOW

Patsy and Mei Su
Are running hand-in-hand.
Rags jumps through the snow to greet them.
It's a winter wonderland!

Sam is standing at the door,
Waiting to go out and play.
They'll meet Brian and Mei Su
To have a snow-fun day.

The friends line up with their sleds.
Sleigh riding's such a thrill!
Rags waits on top and watches
As they all go down the hill.

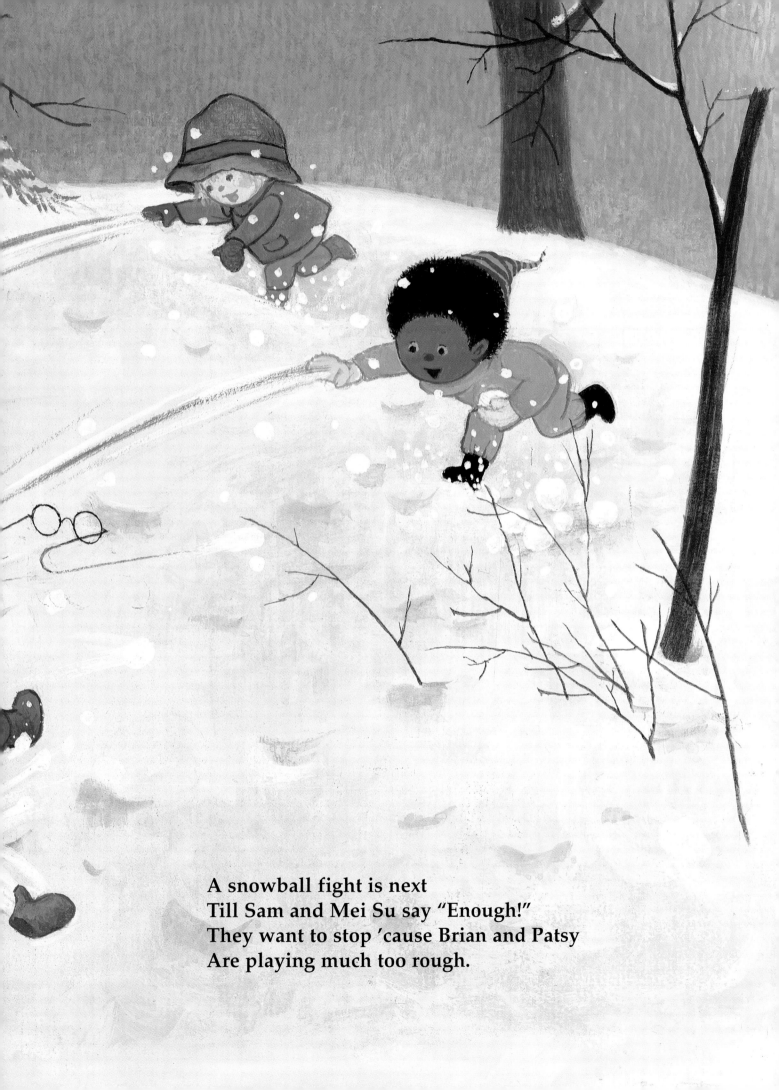

A snowball fight is next
Till Sam and Mei Su say "Enough!"
They want to stop 'cause Brian and Patsy
Are playing much too rough.

Patsy says they're sorry.
"Let's build a snowman, then."
It's just the thing to make the friends
Play happily again.

No matter what the weather,
Rain, shine, or snow,
The four little friends have good times
'Cause they like each other so.

AN INDOOR DAY

Patsy's sitting by the window,
Waiting for her friends.
It's raining, so they'll play inside.
It's a good day to pretend.

They'll have a Teddy Tea Party,
Draw lots of pictures, too.
Sam will show his friends the tricks
That his dog, Rags, can do.

They'll play in the house
And have lots of fun,
Doing rainy-day things
As they wait for the sun.

SAM'S DOG, RAGS

Sam's dog, Rags,
Is lots of fun.
When they go for a walk,
Rags likes to run.

Rags' bark can be fierce
When he's a watchdog on patrol.
But Rags is very friendly
When he's out for a stroll.

He sometimes barks a "woof"
When Sam wants Rags to speak.
If Sam says "Rags, roll over,"
Rags lies down and goes to sleep!

Rags can shake hands.
He can also sit up.
But whatever Rags does,
He's Sam's favorite pup!

I'M BOSS

Patsy wants to play
With her three friends today.
But only if they say
They'll do everything her way!

The three friends aren't happy.
Bossing and friends don't mix,
So Patsy must be lonely,
Or give up her bossy tricks.

HURRY, HURRY, HURRY!

The four little friends were ready to go.
They each had a question. They wanted to know:

"Is it time yet?"
"Can we go now?"
"Did it start?"
"Are we late?"
They all were so eager
They just couldn't wait!

So off they all went—
Their families, too.
Can you guess where they've gone?
They're waiting for you.

SO LONG, SUMMER

Rags chased a rabbit
Through the woods.
The little friends followed
As fast as they could.

The bunny hopped and hopped
Until it got away!
The little friends had fun
One last summer day.

Autumn leaves, harvest moon,
Winter will be coming soon.
Till it does, the friends will play
In the warm sun's golden rays!

Visual C#®

DEITEL®

HOW TO PROGRAM

SIXTH EDITION

Deitel® Series Page

How To Program Series

Android™ How to Program, 3/E
C++ How to Program, 10/E
C How to Program, 8/E
Java™ How to Program, Early Objects Version, 10/E
Java™ How to Program, Late Objects Version, 10/E
Internet & World Wide Web How to Program, 5/E
Visual Basic® 2012 How to Program, 6/E
Visual C#® How to Program, 6/E

Deitel® Developer Series

Android™ 6 for Programmers: An App-Driven
    Approach, 3/E
C for Programmers with an Introduction to C11
C++11 for Programmers
C# 6 for Programmers
iOS® 8 for Programmers: An App-Driven
    Approach with Swift™
Java™ for Programmers, 3/E
JavaScript for Programmers
Swift™ for Programmers

Simply Series

Simply Visual Basic® 2010: An App-Driven
    Approach, 4/E
Simply C++: An App-Driven Tutorial Approach

VitalSource Web Books

http://bit.ly/DeitelOnVitalSource
Android™ How to Program, 2/E and 3/E
C++ How to Program, 8/E and 9/E
Java™ How to Program, 9/E and 10/E
Simply C++: An App-Driven Tutorial Approach
Simply Visual Basic® 2010: An App-Driven
    Approach, 4/E
Visual Basic® 2012 How to Program, 6/E
Visual C#® How to Program, 6/E
Visual C#® 2012 How to Program, 5/E

LiveLessons Video Learning Products

http://deitel.com/books/LiveLessons/
Android™ 6 App Development Fundamentals, 3/E
C++ Fundamentals
Java™ Fundamentals, 2/E
C# 6 Fundamentals
C# 2012 Fundamentals
iOS® 8 App Development Fundamentals with
    Swift™, 3/E
JavaScript Fundamentals
Swift™ Fundamentals

REVEL™ Interactive Multimedia

REVEL™ for Deitel Java™

To receive updates on Deitel publications, Resource Centers, training courses, partner offers and more, please join the Deitel communities on

- Facebook®—http://facebook.com/DeitelFan
- Twitter®—http://twitter.com/deitel
- LinkedIn®—http://linkedin.com/company/deitel-&-associates
- YouTube™—http://youtube.com/DeitelTV
- Google+™—http://google.com/+DeitelFan

and register for the free *Deitel® Buzz Online* e-mail newsletter at:

    http://www.deitel.com/newsletter/subscribe.html

To communicate with the authors, send e-mail to:

    deitel@deitel.com

For information on programming-languages corporate training seminars offered by Deitel & Associates, Inc. worldwide, write to deitel@deitel.com or visit:

    http://www.deitel.com/training/

For continuing updates on Pearson/Deitel publications visit:

    http://www.deitel.com
    http://www.pearsonhighered.com/deitel/

Visit the Deitel Resource Centers, which will help you master programming languages, software development, Android™ and iOS® app development, and Internet- and web-related topics:

    http://www.deitel.com/ResourceCenters.html

Visual C#®

HOW TO PROGRAM

SIXTH EDITION

Paul Deitel
Harvey Deitel
Deitel & Associates, Inc.

PEARSON

Boston   Columbus   Hoboken   Indianapolis   New York   San Francisco
Amsterdam   Cape Town   Dubai   London   Madrid   Milan   Munich   Paris   Montreal
Toronto   Delhi   Mexico City   São Paulo   Sydney   Hong Kong   Seoul   Singapore   Taipei   Tokyo

Vice President, Editorial Director: *Marcia Horton*
Acquisitions Editor: *Tracy Johnson*
Editorial Assistant: *Kristy Alaura*
VP of Marketing: *Christy Lesko*
Field Marketing Manager: *Demetrius Hall*
Marketing Assistant: *Jon Bryant*
Director of Product Management: *Erin Gregg*
Team Lead, Program and Project Management: *Scott Disanno*
Program Manager: *Carole Snyder*
Project Manager: *Robert Engelhardt*
Manufacturing Buyer, Higher Ed | RR Donnelley: *Maura Zaldivar-Garcia*
Cover Design: *Paul Deitel, Harvey Deitel, Chuti Prasertsith*
R&P Manager: *Ben Ferrini*
Inventory Manager: *Ann Lam*
Cover Photo Credit: © *Kannanimages / Shutterstock*

Credits and acknowledgments borrowed from other sources and reproduced, with permission, in this textbook appear on page vi.

Library of Congress Cataloging-in-Publication Data on file.

4 18

ISBN-10:   0-13-460154-8
ISBN-13: 978-0-13-460154-0

PEARSON

*In memory of William Siebert, Professor Emeritus of
Electrical Engineering and Computer Science at MIT:*

*Your use of visualization techniques in
your Signals and Systems lectures inspired
the way generations of engineers, computer
scientists, educators and authors present
their work.*

Harvey and Paul Deitel

Trademarks

DEITEL and the double-thumbs-up bug are registered trademarks of Deitel and Associates, Inc.

Microsoft® Windows®, and Microsoft Visual C#® are registered trademarks of the Microsoft Corporation in the U.S.A. And other countries. This book is not sponsored or endorsed by or affiliated with the Microsoft Corporation.

UNIX is a registered trademark of The Open Group.

Throughout this book, trademarks are used. Rather than put a trademark symbol in every occurrence of a trademarked name, we state that we are using the names in an editorial fashion only and to the benefit of the trademark owner, with no intention of infringement of the trademark.

Contents

4 Introduction to Classes, Objects, Methods and `strings` 106

5 Algorithm Development and Control Statements: Part 1   142

8 Arrays; Introduction to Exception Handling 299

11 Object-Oriented Programming: Inheritance 435

12 OOP: Polymorphism and Interfaces 468

13 Exception Handling: A Deeper Look 507

14 Graphical User Interfaces with Windows Forms: Part 1   544

15 Graphical User Interfaces with Windows Forms: Part 2   597

22 Databases and LINQ 893

23 Asynchronous Programming with async and await 942

Chapters on the Web 975

A Operator Precedence Chart 976

B Simple Types 978

Online Topics

PDFs presenting additional topics for advanced college courses and professionals are available through the book's Companion Website:

        http://www.pearsonhighered.com/deitel

New copies of this book come with a Companion Website access code that's located on the book's inside front cover. If the access code is already visible or there is no card, you purchased a used book or an edition that does not come with an access code—you can purchase access directly from the Companion Website.

Web App Development with ASP.NET

XML and LINQ to XML

Universal Windows Platform (UWP) GUI, Graphics, Multimedia and XAML

REST Web Services

Cloud Computing with Microsoft Azure™

Windows Presentation Foundation (WPF) GUI, Graphics, Multimedia and XAML

ATM Case Study, Part 1: Object-Oriented Design with the UML

ATM Case Study, Part 2: Implementing an Object-Oriented Design in C#

Using the Visual Studio Debugger

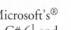Preface

Welcome to the world of desktop, mobile and web app development with Microsoft's®
Visual C#® programming language. *Visual C# How to Program, 6/e* is based on C# 6[1] and
related Microsoft software technologies. You'll be using the .NET platform and the Visual
Studio® Integrated Development Environment on which you'll conveniently write, test
and debug your applications and run them on Windows® devices. The Windows operating system runs on desktop and notebook computers, mobile phones and tablets, game
systems and a great variety of devices associated with the emerging "Internet of Things."

We believe that this book and its supplements for students and instructors will give
you an informative, engaging, challenging and entertaining introduction to Visual C#.
The book presents leading-edge computing technologies in a friendly manner appropriate
for introductory college course sequences, based on the curriculum recommendations of
two key professional organizations—the ACM and the IEEE.[2]

You'll study four of today's most popular programming paradigms:

- object-oriented programming,

- structured programming,

- generic programming and

- functional programming (new in this edition).

If you haven't already done so, please read the back cover and check out the additional
reviewer comments on the inside back cover and the facing page—these capture the
essence of the book concisely. In this Preface we provide more detail for students, instructors and professionals.

At the heart of the book is the Deitel signature *live-code approach*—rather than using
code snippets, we generally present concepts in the context of complete working programs
followed by sample executions. We include a broad range of example programs and exercises selected from computer science, business, education, social issues, personal utilities,
sports, mathematics, puzzles, simulation, game playing, graphics, multimedia and many
other areas. We also provide abundant tables, line drawings and UML diagrams for a more
visual learning experience.

---

1. At the time of this writing, Microsoft has not yet released the official C# 6 Specification. To view an
   unofficial copy, visit `https://github.com/ljw1004/csharpspec/blob/gh-pages/README.md`
2. These recommendations include *Computer Science Curricula 2013 Curriculum Guidelines for Undergraduate Degree Programs in Computer Science*, December 20, 2013, The Joint Task Force on Computing Curricula, Association for Computing Machinery (ACM), IEEE Computer Society.

Read the Before You Begin section after this Preface for instructions on setting up your computer to run the hundreds of code examples and to enable you to develop your own C# apps. The source code for all of the book's examples is available at

```
http://www.deitel.com/books/VCSharpHTP6
```

and

```
http://www.pearsonhighered.com/deitel
```

Use the source code we provide to compile and run each program as you study it—this will help you master Visual C# and related Microsoft technologies faster and at a deeper level. Most of the book's examples work in Visual Studio on Windows 7, 8 or 10 (there is no 9). The code examples for the online presentation of the Universal Windows Platform (UWP) and XAML specifically require Windows 10.

Contacting the Authors

As you read the book, if you have a question, we're easy to reach at

```
deitel@deitel.com
```

We'll respond promptly.

Join the Deitel & Associates, Inc. Social Media Communities

For book updates, visit

```
http://www.deitel.com/books/VCSharpHTP6
```

subscribe to the *Deitel® Buzz Online* newsletter

```
http://www.deitel.com/newsletter/subscribe.html
```

and join the Deitel social media communities on

- Facebook®—http://facebook.com/DeitelFan
- LinkedIn®—http://linkedin.com/company/deitel-&-associates
- YouTube®—http://youtube.com/DeitelTV
- Twitter®—http://twitter.com/Deitel
- Instagram®—http://instagram.com/DeitelFan
- Google+™—http://google.com/+DeitelFan

Object-Oriented Programming with an Early Objects Approach

The book introduces the basic concepts and terminology of object-oriented programming in Chapter 1. In Chapter 2, you'll *visually* manipulate objects, such as labels and images. In Chapter 3, Introduction to C# App Programming, you'll write Visual C# program code that manipulates preexisting objects. You'll develop your first customized classes and objects in Chapter 4. Presenting objects and classes early gets you "thinking about objects" immediately and mastering these concepts more thoroughly.

Our early objects presentation continues in Chapters 5–9 with a variety of straight-forward case studies. In Chapters 10–12, we take a deeper look at classes and objects, present inheritance, interfaces and polymorphism, then use those concepts throughout the remainder of the book.

New C# 6 Features

6 We introduce key new C# 6 language features throughout the book (Fig. 1)—each defining occurrence is marked with a "6" margin icon as shown next to this paragraph.

C# 6 new language feature	First introduced in
string interpolation	Section 3.5
expression bodied methods and get accessors	Section 7.15
auto-implemented property initializers	Section 8.6.1
getter-only auto-implemented properties	Section 8.6.1
nameof operator	Section 10.5.1
null-conditional operator (?.)	Section 13.9.1
when clause for exception filtering	Section 13.10
using static directive	Section 21.3.1
null conditional operator (?[])	Section 21.6
collection initializers for any collection with an Add extension method	Section 21.7
index initializers	Section 21.7

Fig. 1 | C# 6 new language features.

Interesting, Entertaining and Challenging Exercises

The book contains hundreds of exercises to practice the skills you learn. Extensive self-review exercises and answers are included for self-study. Also, each chapter concludes with a substantial set of exercises, which generally include

- simple recall of important terminology and concepts,
- identifying the errors in code samples,
- writing individual program statements,
- writing methods to perform specific tasks,
- writing C# classes,
- writing complete programs and
- implementing major projects.

Figure 2 lists only a sample of the book's hundreds of exercises, including selections from our *Making-a-Difference* exercises set, which encourage you to use computers and the Internet to research and work on significant social problems. We hope you'll approach these exercises in the context of your own values, politics and beliefs. The solutions to most of the book's exercises are available only to college instructors who have adopted the book for their courses. See "Instructor Supplements" later in this Preface.

A sampling of the book's exercises

Carbon Footprint Calculator
Body-Mass-Index Calculator
Attributes of Hybrid Vehicles
Gender Neutrality
Notepad GUI
Calendar and Appointments GUI
Calculator GUI
Alarm Clock GUI
Radio GUI
Displaying Shapes
Odd or Even?
Is a Number a Multiple of Another?
Separating an Integer's Digits
Table of Squares and Cubes
Account Class
Invoice Class
Employee Class
Date Class
Removing Duplicated Code
Target-Heart-Rate Calculator
Computerizing Health Records
Credit-Limit Calculator
Sales-Commission Calculator
Salary Calculator
Find the Two Largest Numbers
Dangling-else Problem
Palindromes
Decimal Equivalent of a Binary Number
Sides of a Right Triangle
Factorials
Infinite Series: Mathematical Constant *e*
World Population Growth
Enforcing Privacy with Cryptography
Bar Chart Display
Prime Numbers
Calculating Sales
Car-Pool Savings Calculator
Gas Mileage Calculator

Calculating the Value of π
Pythagorean Triples
Global Warming Facts Quiz
Tax Plan Alternative: The "FairTax"
Rounding to a Specific Decimal Place
Hypotenuse of a Right Triangle
Displaying a Square of Any Character
Separating Digits
Temperature Conversions
Perfect Numbers
Prime Numbers
Reversing Digits
Letter Grades to a Four-Point Scale
Coin Tossing
Guess-the-Number Game
Distance Between Two Points
Craps Game with Betting
Towers of Hanoi
Computer-Assisted Instruction
Sales Commissions
Duplicate Elimination
Dice Game of Craps
Airline Reservations System
Knight's Tour Chess Puzzle
Eight Queens Chess Puzzle
Sieve of Eratosthenes
Tortoise and the Hare
Card Shuffling and Dealing
Building Your Own Computer (Virtual Machine)
Polling
Querying an Array of Invoice Objects
Duplicate Word Removal
Rectangle Class
Savings-Account Class
Set of Integers
RationalNumber Class
HugeInteger Class
Tic-Tac-Toe

ComplexNumber Class
Shape Inheritance Hierarchy
Payroll System
Accounts Payable System
Polymorphic Banking Program
CarbonFootprint Interface: Polymorphism
Temperature Conversions
Painter
Guess the Number Game
Ecofont
Typing Tutor
Restaurant Bill Calculator
Story Writer
Pig Latin
Cooking with Healthier Ingredients
Spam Elimination
SMS Language
File of Student Grades
Telephone-Number Words
Student Poll
Phishing Scanner
Bucket Sort
Palindromes
Evaluating Expressions with a Stack
Building Your Own Compiler
Generic Linear Search
SortedDictionary of Colors
Prime Factorization
Bucket Sort with LinkedList<int>
Sieve of Eratosthenes with BitArray
Credit-Inquiry Program
Rolling a Die 60,000,000 Times
Baseball Database App
Parsing with LINQ to XML
I/O-Bound vs. Compute-Bound Apps
Recursive Fibonacci

Fig. 2 | A sampling of the book's exercises.

A Tour of the Book

This section discusses the book's modular organization to help instructors plan their syllabi.

Introduction to Computing, Visual C# and Visual Studio 2015 Community Edition
The chapters in this module of the book

- Chapter 1, Introduction to Computers, the Internet and Visual C#
- Chapter 2, Introduction to Visual Studio and Visual Programming

introduce hardware and software fundamentals, Microsoft's .NET platform and Visual Programming. The vast majority of the book's examples will run on Windows 7, 8 and 10 using the *Visual Studio 2015 Community* edition with which we test-drive a fun **Painter** app in Section 1.12. Chapter 1's introduction to object-oriented programming defines key terminology and discusses important concepts on which the rest of the book depends.

Introduction to C# Fundamentals
The chapters in this module of the book

- Chapter 3, Introduction to C# App Programming
- Chapter 4, Introduction to Classes, Objects, Methods and Strings
- Chapter 5, Algorithm Development and Control Statements: Part 1
- Chapter 6, Control Statements: Part 2
- Chapter 7, Methods: A Deeper Look
- Chapter 8, Arrays; Introduction to Exception Handling

present rich coverage of C# programming fundamentals (data types, operators, control statements, methods and arrays) and introduce object-oriented programming through a series of case studies. These chapters should be covered in order. Chapters 5 and 6 present a friendly treatment of control statements and problem solving. Chapters 7 and 8 present rich treatments of methods and arrays, respectively. Chapter 8 briefly introduces exception handling with an example that demonstrates attempting to access an element outside an array's bounds.

Object-Oriented Programming: A Deeper Look
The chapters in this module of the book

- Chapter 9, Introduction to LINQ and the List Collection
- Chapter 10, Classes and Objects: A Deeper Look
- Chapter 11, Object-Oriented Programming: Inheritance
- Chapter 12, OOP: Polymorphism and Interfaces
- Chapter 13, Exception Handling: A Deeper Look

provide a deeper look at object-oriented programming, including classes, objects, inheritance, polymorphism, interfaces and exception handling. An optional online two-chapter case study on designing and implementing the object-oriented software for a simple ATM is described later in this preface.

Chapter 9 introduces Microsoft's Language Integrated Query (LINQ) technology, which provides a uniform syntax for manipulating data from various data sources, such as arrays, collections and, as you'll see in later chapters, databases and XML. Chapter 9 is intentionally simple and brief to encourage instructors to begin covering LINQ technology early. Section 9.4 introduces the List collection, which we use in Chapter 12. Later in the book, we take a deeper look at LINQ, using LINQ to Entities (for querying databases) and LINQ to XML. Chapter 9's LINQ coverage can be deferred if you're in a course which either skips LINQ or defers coverage until later in the book—it's required for one example in Chapter 17 (Fig. 17.6) and many of the later chapters starting with Chapter 22, Databases and LINQ.

Windows *Forms* Graphical User Interfaces (GUIs)
The chapters in this module of the book

- Chapter 14, Graphical User Interfaces with Windows Forms: Part 1

- Chapter 15, Graphical User Interfaces with Windows Forms: Part 2

present a detailed introduction to building GUIs using Windows Forms—instructors teaching Visual C# still largely prefer Windows Forms for their classes. Many of the examples in GUI Chapters 14–15 can be presented after Chapter 4. We also use Windows Forms GUIs in several other print and online chapters.

There are two other GUI technologies in Windows—Windows Presentation Foundation (WPF) and Universal Windows Platform (UWP). We provide optional online treatments of both.[3]

Strings and Files
The chapters in this module of the book

- Chapter 16, Strings and Characters: A Deeper Look

- Chapter 17, Files and Streams

present string processing and file processing, respectively. We introduce strings beginning in Chapter 4 and use them throughout the book. Chapter 16 investigates strings in more detail. Most of Chapter 16's examples can be presented at any point after Chapter 4. Chapter 17 introduces text-file processing and object-serialization for inputting and outputting entire objects. Chapter 17 requires Windows Forms concepts presented in Chapter 14.

Searching, Sorting and Generic Data Structures
The chapters in this module of the book:

- Chapter 18, Searching and Sorting

- Chapter 19, Custom Linked Data Structures

- Chapter 20, Generics

- Chapter 21, Generic Collections; Functional Programming with LINQ/PLINQ

introduce searching, sorting and data structures. Most C# programmers should use .NET's *built-in* searching, sorting and generic collections (prepackaged data structures) capabilities, which are discussed in Chapter 21. For instructors who wish to present how to implement customized searching, sorting and data structures capabilities, we provide Chapters 18–20, which require the concepts presented in Chapters 3–8 and 10–13. Chapter 18 presents sev-

---

3. As of Summer 2016, Windows Forms, WPF and UWP apps all can be posted for distribution via the Windows Store. See http://bit.ly/DesktopToUWP for more information.

eral searching and sorting algorithms and uses Big O notation to help you compare how hard each algorithm works to do its job—the code examples use especially visual outputs to show how the algorithms work. In Chapter 19, we show how to implement your own custom data structures, including lists, stacks, queues and binary trees. The data structures in Chapter 19 store references to objects. Chapter 20 introduces C# generics and demonstrates how to create type-safe generic methods and a type-safe generic stack data structure.

Functional Programming with LINQ, PLINQ, Lambdas, Delegates and Immutability
In addition to generic collections, Chapter 21 now introduces functional programming, showing how to use it with LINQ to Objects to write code more concisely and with fewer bugs than programs written using previous techniques. In Section 21.12, with one additional method call, we'll demonstrate how PLINQ (Parallel LINQ) can improve LINQ to Objects performance substantially on multicore systems. The chapter's exercises also ask you to reimplement earlier examples using functional-programming techniques.

Database with LINQ to Entities and SQL Server
The chapter in this module

* Chapter 22, Databases and LINQ

presents a novice-friendly introduction to database programming with the ADO.NET Entity Framework, LINQ to Entities and Microsoft's free version of SQL Server that's installed with the Visual Studio 2015 Community edition. The chapter's examples require C#, object-oriented programming and Windows Forms concepts presented in Chapters 3–14. Several online chapters require the techniques presented in this chapter.

Asynchronous Programming
The chapter in this module

* Chapter 23, Asynchronous Programming with async and await

shows how to take advantage of multicore architectures by writing applications that can process tasks asynchronously, which can improve app performance and GUI responsiveness in apps with long-running or compute-intensive tasks. The async modifier and await operator greatly simplify asynchronous programming, reduce errors and enable your apps to take advantage of the processing power in today's multicore computers, smartphones and tablets. In this edition, we added a case study that uses the Task Parallel Library (TPL), async and await in a GUI app—we keep a progress bar moving along in the GUI thread in parallel with a lengthy, compute-intensive calculation in another thread.

A Tour of the Online Content

The printed book contains the core content (Chapters 1–23) for introductory and intermediate course sequences. Several optional online topics for advanced courses and professionals are available on the book's password-protected Companion Website

```
http://www.pearsonhighered.com/deitel
```

New copies of this book come with a Companion Website access code that's located on the book's inside front cover. If the access code is already visible or there isn't an access code, you purchased a used book or an edition that does not come with an access code. In this case, you can purchase access directly from the Companion Website. Figure 3 lists the online topics, and Figure 4 lists a sample of the associated exercises.

Online topics
Web App Development with ASP.NET
XML and LINQ to XML
Universal Windows Platform (UWP) GUI, Graphics, Multimedia and XAML
REST Web Services
Cloud Computing with Microsoft Azure™
Using the Visual Studio Debugger
(Optional) Windows Presentation Foundation (WPF) GUI, Graphics, Multimedia and XAML
(Optional) ATM Case Study, Part 1: Object-Oriented Design with the UML
(Optional) ATM Case Study, Part 2: Implementing an OO Design in C#

Fig. 3 | Online topics on the *Visual C# How to Program, 6/e* Companion Website.

A sampling of the online chapters' exercises		
Guestbook App	College Loan Payoff	Favorite Flickr Searches App
Web-Based Address Book	Calculator App	Flag Quiz App
Enhanced Painter App	Car Payment Calculator App	Phone Book App with Data
PhotoViewer App	Mileage Calculator App	Binding
Data Bindings to LINQ queries	Body Mass Index Calculator	Enhanced UsingGradients App
Snake PolyLine App	App	Enhanced DrawStars app
Drawing App	Target-Heart-Rate Calculator	Image Reflector App
Enhanced Tip Calculator App	App	Accessibility: Speech-
Mortgage Calculator App	Phone-Book Web Service	Controlled Drawing App

Fig. 4 | A sampling of the online chapters' exercises.

Web App Development with ASP.NET

Microsoft's .NET server-side technology, ASP.NET, enables you to create robust, scalable web-based apps. You'll build several apps, including a web-based guestbook that uses ASP.NET and the ADO .NET Entity Framework to store data in a database and display data in a web page.

Extensible Markup Language (XML)

The Extensible Markup Language (XML) is pervasive in the software-development industry, e-business and throughout the .NET platform. It's used in most of this book's online topics. XML is required to understand XAML—a Microsoft XML vocabulary that's used to describe graphical user interfaces, graphics and multimedia for Universal Windows Platform (UWP) GUI, graphics and multimedia apps, Windows 10 Mobile apps and Windows Presentation Foundation (WPF) apps. We present XML fundamentals, then discuss LINQ to XML, which allows you to query XML content using LINQ syntax.

Universal Windows Platform (UWP) for Desktop and Mobile Apps

The Universal Windows Platform (UWP) is designed to provide a common platform and user experience across all Windows devices, including personal computers, smartphones, tablets, Xbox and even Microsoft's new HoloLens virtual reality and augmented reality holographic headset—all using nearly identical code. We present GUI, graphics and multimedia apps, and demonstrate them on both personal computers and the smartphone emulator that comes with Visual Studio 2015 Community edition.

REST Web Services

Web services enable you to package app functionality in a manner that turns the web into a library of *reusable* services. We include a case study on building a math question generator web service that's called by a math tutor app.

Building a Microsoft Azure™ Cloud Computing App

Microsoft Azure's web services enable you to develop, manage and distribute your apps in "the cloud." We'll demonstrate how to use Azure web services to store an app's data online.

Windows Presentation Foundation (WPF) GUI, Graphics and Multimedia

Windows Presentation Foundation (WPF)—created after Windows Forms and before UWP—is another Microsoft technology for building robust GUI, graphics and multimedia desktop apps. WPF provides you with complete control over all aspects of a GUI's look-and-feel and includes multimedia capabilities that are not available in Windows Forms. We discuss WPF in the context of a painting app, a text editor, a color chooser, a book-cover viewer, a television video player, various animations, and speech synthesis and recognition apps.

We're moving away from WPF in favor of UWP for creating apps that can run on desktop, mobile and other Windows devices. For this reason, the WPF introduction is provided *as is* from the previous edition—we will no longer evolve this material.

Optional Case Study: Using the UML to Develop an Object-Oriented Design and C# Implementation of an ATM (Automated Teller Machine)

The UML™ (Unified Modeling Language™) is the industry-standard graphical language for visually modeling object-oriented systems. We introduce the UML in the early chapters and provide an optional online object-oriented design case study in which we use the UML to design and implement the software for a simple ATM. We analyze a typical *requirements document* that specifies the details of the system to be built. We determine the *classes* needed to implement that system, the *attributes* the classes need to have, the *behaviors* the classes' methods need to exhibit and we specify how the classes must *interact* with one another to meet the system requirements. From the design, we produce a complete working C# implementation. Students often report a "light bulb moment"—the case study helps them "tie it all together" and truly understand object orientation.

Teaching Approach

Visual C# How to Program, 6/e contains a rich collection of examples. We concentrate on building well-engineered software and stress program clarity.

Live-Code Approach. The book is loaded with "live-code" examples—most new concepts are presented in the context of complete working Visual C# apps, followed by one or more executions showing program inputs and outputs. In the few cases where we show a code snippet, to ensure correctness first we tested it in a complete working program then copied the code from the program and pasted it into the book.

Syntax Shading. For readability, we syntax shade the code, similar to the way Visual Studio colors the code. Our syntax-shading conventions are:

```
comments appear like this
keywords appear like this
constants and literal values appear like this
all other code appears in black
```

Code Highlighting. We emphasize key code segments by placing them in gray rectangles.

Using Fonts for Emphasis. We place the key terms and the index's page reference for each defining occurrence in colored **bold** text for easy reference. We show on-screen components in the **bold Helvetica** font (for example, the **File** menu) and Visual C# program text in the Lucida font (for example, int count = 5;). We use *italics* for emphasis.

Objectives. The chapter objectives preview the topics covered in the chapter.

Programming Tips. We include programming tips to help you focus on important aspects of program development. These tips and practices represent the best we've gleaned from a combined nine decades of programming and teaching experience.

Good Programming Practices

The Good Programming Practices *call attention to techniques that will help you produce programs that are clearer, more understandable and more maintainable.*

Common Programming Errors

Pointing out these Common Programming Errors *reduces the likelihood that you'll make them.*

Error-Prevention Tips

These tips contain suggestions for exposing and removing bugs from your programs; many of the tips describe aspects of Visual C# that prevent bugs from getting into programs.

Performance Tips

These tips highlight opportunities for making your programs run faster or minimizing the amount of memory that they occupy.

Portability Tips

These tips help you write code that will run on a variety of platforms.

Software Engineering Observations

The Software Engineering Observations *highlight architectural and design issues that affect the construction of software systems, especially large-scale systems.*

Look-and-Feel Observation 3.1

These observations help you design attractive, user-friendly graphical user interfaces that conform to industry norms.

Summary Bullets. We present a detailed bullet-list summary of each chapter.

Terminology. We include an alphabetized list of the important terms defined in each chapter.

Index. We've included an extensive index for reference. Defining occurrences of key terms in the index are highlighted with a colored bold page number. The printed book index covers only the printed material. The online index includes the content from the printed book and the online content.

Obtaining the Software Used in *Visual C# How to Program, 6/e*

We wrote the code examples in *Visual C# How to Program, 6/e* using Microsoft's free Visual Studio 2015 Community edition. See the Before You Begin section that follows this preface for download and installation instructions.

Instructor Supplements

The following supplements are available to *qualified instructors only* through Pearson Education's online Instructor Resource Center (`www.pearsonhighered.com/irc`):

- *Solutions Manual* contains solutions to *most* of the end-of-chapter exercises. We've included many *Making-a-Difference* exercises, most with solutions. **Please do not write to us requesting access to the Pearson Instructor's Resource Center. Access is restricted to college instructors who have adopted the book for their courses. Instructors can obtain access through their Pearson representatives.** If you're not a registered faculty member, contact your Pearson representative or visit `http://www.pearsonhighered.com/educator/replocator/`. Exercise Solutions are *not* provided for "project" exercises. Check out our Programming Projects Resource Center for lots of additional exercise and project possibilities:

    `http://www.deitel.com/ProgrammingProjects`

- *Test Item File* of multiple-choice questions (approximately two per top-level book section)

- *Customizable PowerPoint® slides* containing all the code and figures in the text, plus bulleted items that summarize the key points in the text.

Microsoft DreamSpark™

Microsoft provides many of its professional developer tools to students for free via a program called DreamSpark (`http://www.dreamspark.com`). See the website for details on verifying your student status so you take advantage of this program. To compile, test, debug and run this book's examples, you need only Windows 10 and the free Visual Studio 2015 Community edition. With the exception of the online UWP examples, the book's examples also will compile and run on Windows 7 and higher.

Acknowledgments

We'd like to thank Barbara Deitel of Deitel & Associates, Inc. She painstakingly researched the new capabilities of Visual C#, Visual Studio, .NET and other key technologies. We'd also like to acknowledge Frank McCown, Ph.D., Associate Professor of Computer Science, Harding University for his suggestion to include an example that used a `ProgressBar` with `async` and `await` in Chapter 23—so we ported to C# a similar example from our textbook *Java How to Program, 10/e*.

We're fortunate to have worked with the dedicated team of publishing professionals at Pearson Higher Education. We appreciate the guidance, wisdom, energy and mentorship of Tracy Johnson, Executive Editor, Computer Science. Kristy Alaura did an extraordinary job recruiting the book's reviewers and managing the review process. Bob Engelhardt did a wonderful job bringing the book to publication.

Reviewers

The book was scrutinized by academics teaching C# courses and industry C# experts. They provided countless suggestions for improving the presentation. Any remaining flaws in the book are our own.

Sixth Edition Reviewers: Qian Chen (Department of Engineering Technology: Computer Science Technology Program, Savannah State University), Octavio Hernandez (Microsoft Certified Solutions Developer, Principal Software Engineer at Advanced Bionics), José Antonio González Seco (Parliament of Andalusia, Spain), Bradley Sward (College of Dupage) and Lucian Wischik (Microsoft Visual C# Team).

Fifth Edition Post-Publication Reviewers: To help us prepare to write 6/e, the following academics reviewed 5/e and provided many helpful suggestions: Qian Chen (Savannah State University), Hongmei Chi (Florida A&M University), Kui Du (University of Massachusetts, Boston), James Leasure (Cuyahoga Community College West), Victor Miller (Ramapo College), Gary Savard (Champlain College) and Mohammad Yusuf (New Hampshire Technical Institute).

Other recent edition reviewers: Douglas B. Bock (MCSD.NET, Southern Illinois University Edwardsville), Dan Crevier (Microsoft), Shay Friedman (Microsoft Visual C# MVP), Amit K. Ghosh (University of Texas at El Paso), Marcelo Guerra Hahn (Microsoft), Kim Hamilton (Software Design Engineer at Microsoft and co-author of *Learning UML 2.0*), Huanhui Hu (Microsoft Corporation), Stephen Hustedde (South Mountain College), James Edward Keysor (Florida Institute of Technology), Narges Kasiri (Oklahoma State University), Helena Kotas (Microsoft), Charles Liu (University of Texas at San Antonio), Chris Lovett (Software Architect at Microsoft), Bashar Lulu (INETA Country Leader, Arabian Gulf), John McIlhinney (Spatial Intelligence; Microsoft MVP Visual Developer, Visual Basic), Ged Mead (Microsoft Visual Basic MVP, DevCity.net), Anand Mukundan (Architect, Polaris Software Lab Ltd.), Dr. Hamid R. Nemati (The University of North Carolina at Greensboro), Timothy Ng (Microsoft), Akira Onishi (Microsoft), Jeffrey P. Scott (Blackhawk Technical College), Joe Stagner (Senior Program Manager, Developer Tools & Platforms, Microsoft), Erick Thompson (Microsoft), Jesús Ubaldo Quevedo-Torrero (University of Wisconsin–Parkside, Department of Computer Science), Shawn Weisfeld (Microsoft MVP and President and Founder of UserGroup.tv) and Zijiang Yang (Western Michigan University).

As you read the book, we'd sincerely appreciate your comments, criticisms, corrections and suggestions for improving the text. Please address all correspondence to:

`deitel@deitel.com`

We'll respond promptly. It was fun writing *Visual C# How to Program, 6/e*—we hope you enjoy reading it!

Paul Deitel
Harvey Deitel

About the Authors

Paul Deitel, CEO and Chief Technical Officer of Deitel & Associates, Inc., has over 35 years of experience in computing. He is a graduate of MIT, where he studied Information Technology. Through Deitel & Associates, Inc., he has delivered hundreds of programming courses worldwide to clients, including Cisco, IBM, Boeing, Siemens, Sun Microsystems (now Oracle), Dell, Fidelity, NASA at the Kennedy Space Center, the National Severe Storm Laboratory, NOAA (National Oceanic and Atmospheric Administration), White Sands Missile Range, Rogue Wave Software, SunGard, Nortel Networks, Puma, iRobot, Invensys and many more. He and his co-author, Dr. Harvey Deitel, are the world's best-selling programming-language textbook/professional book/video authors.

Paul was named as a Microsoft® Most Valuable Professional (MVP) for C# in 2012–2014. According to Microsoft, "the Microsoft MVP Award is an annual award that recognizes exceptional technology community leaders worldwide who actively share their high quality, real-world expertise with users and Microsoft." He also holds the Java Certified Programmer and Java Certified Developer designations and is an Oracle Java Champion.

C# MVP 2012–2014

Dr. Harvey Deitel, Chairman and Chief Strategy Officer of Deitel & Associates, Inc., has over 55 years of experience in the computer field. Dr. Deitel earned B.S. and M.S. degrees in Electrical Engineering from MIT and a Ph.D. in Mathematics from Boston University—he studied computing in each of these programs before they spun off Computer Science programs. He has extensive college teaching experience, including earning tenure and serving as the Chairman of the Computer Science Department at Boston College before founding Deitel & Associates, Inc., in 1991 with his son, Paul. The Deitels' publications have earned international recognition, with translations published in Japanese, German, Russian, Spanish, French, Polish, Italian, Simplified Chinese, Traditional Chinese, Korean, Portuguese, Greek, Urdu and Turkish. Dr. Deitel has delivered hundreds of programming courses to academic, corporate, government and military clients.

About Deitel & Associates, Inc.

Deitel & Associates, Inc., founded by Paul Deitel and Harvey Deitel, is an internationally recognized authoring and corporate training organization, specializing in computer programming languages, object technology, Internet and web software technology, and Android and iOS app development. The company's clients include academic institutions, many of the world's largest corporations, government agencies and branches of the military. The company offers instructor-led training courses delivered at client sites worldwide on major programming languages and platforms, including Visual C#®, C++, C, Java™, Android app development, iOS app development, Swift™, Visual Basic® and Internet and web programming.

Through its 40-year publishing partnership with Prentice Hall/Pearson, Deitel & Associates, Inc., creates leading-edge programming college textbooks, professional books, *LiveLessons* video products, e-books and REVEL™ interactive multimedia courses with integrated labs and assessment (http://revel.pearson.com). Deitel & Associates, Inc. and the authors can be reached at:

`deitel@deitel.com`

To learn more about Deitel's corporate training curriculum, visit

```
http://www.deitel.com/training
```

To request a proposal for worldwide on-site, instructor-led training at your organization, send an e-mail to deitel@deitel.com.

Individuals wishing to purchase Deitel books can do so via

```
http://bit.ly/DeitelOnAmazon
```

Individuals wishing to purchase Deitel *LiveLessons* video training can do so at:

```
http://bit.ly/DeitelOnInformit
```

Deitel books and *LiveLessons* videos are generally available electronically to Safari Books Online subscribers at:

```
http://SafariBooksOnline.com
```

You can get a free 10-day Safari Books Online trial at:

```
https://www.safaribooksonline.com/register/
```

Bulk orders by corporations, the government, the military and academic institutions should be placed directly with Pearson. For more information, visit

```
http://www.informit.com/store/sales.aspx
```

Before You Begin

Please read this section before using the book to ensure that your computer is set up properly.

Font and Naming Conventions

We use fonts to distinguish between features, such as menu names, menu items, and other elements that appear in the program-development environment. Our convention is

- to emphasize Visual Studio features in a **sans-serif bold font** (e.g., **Properties** window) and

- to emphasize program text in a fixed-width `sans-serif font` (e.g., `bool x = true`).

Visual Studio 2015 Community Edition

This textbook uses Windows 10 and the free Microsoft Visual Studio 2015 Community edition—Visual Studio also can run on various older Windows versions. Ensure that your system meets Visual Studio 2015 Community edition's minimum hardware and software requirements listed at:

```
https://www.visualstudio.com/en-us/visual-studio-2015-system-
   requirements-vs
```

Next, download the installer from

```
https://www.visualstudio.com/products/visual-studio-express-vs
```

then execute it and follow the on-screen instructions to install Visual Studio.

Though we developed the book's examples on Windows 10, the examples will run on Windows 7 and higher—with the exception of those in our online Universal Windows Platform (UWP) presentation. Most examples without graphical user interfaces (GUIs) also will run on other C# and .NET implementations—see "If You're Not Using Microsoft Visual C#…" later in this Before You Begin for more information.

Viewing File Extensions

Several screenshots in *Visual C# How to Program, 6/e* display file names with file-name extensions (e.g., `.txt`, `.cs`, `.png`, etc.). You may need to adjust your system's settings to display file-name extensions. If you're using Windows 7:

1. Open **Windows Explorer**.

2. Press the *Alt* key to display the menu bar, then select **Folder Options…** from the **Tools** menu.

3. In the dialog that appears, select the **View** tab.

4. In the **Advanced settings** pane, *uncheck* the box to the left of the text **Hide extensions for known file types.**

5. Click **OK** to apply the setting and close the dialog.

If you're using Windows 8 or higher:

1. Open **File Explorer.**

2. Click the **View** tab.

3. Ensure that the **File name extensions** checkbox is *checked*.

Obtaining the Source Code

Visual C# How to Program, 6/e's source-code examples are available for download at

http://www.deitel.com/books/VCsharpHTP6

Click the **Examples** link to download the ZIP archive file to your computer—most browsers will save the file into your user account's Downloads folder. You can extract the ZIP file's contents using built-in Windows capabilities, or using a third-party archive-file tool such as WinZip (www.winzip.com) or 7-zip (www.7-zip.org).

Throughout the book, steps that require you to access our example code on your computer assume that you've extracted the examples from the ZIP file and placed them in your user account's Documents folder. You can extract them anywhere you like, but if you choose a different location, you'll need to update our steps accordingly. To extract the ZIP file's contents using the built-in Windows capabilities:

1. Open **Windows Explorer** (Windows 7) or **File Explorer** (Windows 8 and higher).

2. Locate the ZIP file on your system, typically in your user account's Downloads folder.

3. Right click the ZIP file and select **Extract All....**

4. In the dialog that appears, navigate to the folder where you'd like to extract the contents, then click the **Extract** button.

Configuring Visual Studio for Use with This Book

In this section, you'll use Visual Studio's **Options** dialog to configure several Visual Studio options. Setting these options is not required, but will make your Visual Studio match what we show in the book's Visual Studio screen captures.

Visual Studio Theme
Visual Studio has three color themes—**Blue, Dark** and **Light.** We used the **Blue** theme with light colored backgrounds to make the book's screen captures easier to read. To switch themes:

1. In the Visual Studio **Tools** menu, select **Options...** to display the **Options** dialog.

2. In the left column, select **Environment.**

3. Select the **Color theme** you wish to use.

Keep the **Options** dialog open for the next step.

Line Numbers

Throughout the book's discussions, we refer to code in our examples by line number. Many programmers find it helpful to display line numbers in Visual Studio as well. To do so:

1. Expand the **Text Editor** node in the **Options** dialog's left pane.

2. Select **All Languages**.

3. In the right pane, check the **Line numbers** checkbox.

Keep the **Options** dialog open for the next step.

Tab Size for Code Indents

Microsoft recommends four-space indents in source code, which is the Visual Studio default. Due to the fixed and limited width of code lines in print, we use three-space indents—this reduces the number of code lines that wrap to a new line, making the code a bit easier to read. If you wish to use three-space indents:

1. Expand the **C#** node in the **Options** dialog's left pane and select **Tabs**.

2. Ensure that **Insert spaces** is selected.

3. Enter **3** for both the **Tab size** and **Indent size** fields.

4. Click **OK** to save your settings.

If You're Not Using Microsoft Visual C#...

C# can be used on other platforms via two open-source projects managed by the .NET Foundation (`http://www.dotnetfoundation.org`)—the Mono Project and .NET Core.

Mono Project

The Mono Project is an open source, cross-platform C# and .NET Framework implementation that can be installed on Linux, OS X (soon to be renamed as macOS) and Windows. The code for most of the book's console (non-GUI) apps will compile and run using the Mono Project. Mono also supports Windows Forms GUI, which is used in Chapters 14–15 and several later examples. For more information and to download Mono, visit:

```
http://www.mono-project.com/
```

.NET Core

.NET Core is a new cross-platform .NET implementation for Windows, Linux, OS X and FreeBSD. The code for most of the book's console (non-GUI) apps will compile and run using .NET Core. At the time of this writing, a .NET Core version for Windows was available and versions were still under development for other platforms. For more information and to download .NET Core, visit:

```
https://dotnet.github.io/
```

You're now ready to learn C# and the .NET platform with *Visual C# How to Program, 6/e.* We hope you enjoy the book!

Introduction to Computers, the Internet and Visual C#

1

Objectives

In this chapter you'll:

- Learn basic computer hardware, software and data concepts.

- Be introduced to the different types of computer programming languages.

- Understand the history of the Visual C# programming language and the Windows operating system.

- Learn what cloud computing with Microsoft Azure is.

- Understand the basics of object technology.

- Be introduced to the history of the Internet and the World Wide Web.

- Understand the parts that Windows, .NET, Visual Studio and C# play in the C# ecosystem.

- Test-drive a Visual C# drawing app.

1.1 Introduction

Welcome to C#[1]—a powerful computer-programming language that's easy for novices to learn and that professionals use to build substantial computer applications. Using this book, you'll write instructions commanding computers to perform powerful tasks. *Software* (i.e., the instructions you write) controls *hardware* (i.e., computers and related devices).

There are billions of personal computers in use and an even larger number of mobile devices with computers at their core. Since it was released in 2001, C# has been used primarily to build applications for personal computers and systems that support them. The explosive growth of mobile phones, tablets and other devices also is creating significant opportunities for programming mobile apps. With this new sixth edition of *Visual C# How to Program*, you'll be able to use Microsoft's new Universal Windows Platform (UWP) with Windows 10 to build C# apps for both personal computers and Windows 10 Mobile devices. With Microsoft's purchase of Xamarin, you also can develop C# mobile apps for Android devices and for iOS devices, such as iPhones and iPads.

1.2 Computers and the Internet in Industry and Research

These are exciting times in the computer field! Many of the most influential and successful businesses of the last two decades are technology companies, including Apple, IBM, Hewlett Packard, Dell, Intel, Motorola, Cisco, Microsoft, Google, Amazon, Facebook, Twitter, eBay and many more. These companies are major employers of people who study computer science, computer engineering, information systems or related disciplines. At the time of this writing, Google's parent company, Alphabet, and Apple were the two most

---

1. The name C#, pronounced "C-sharp," is based on the musical # notation for "sharp" notes.

valuable companies in the world. Figure 1.1 provides a few examples of the ways in which computers are improving people's lives in research, industry and society.

Name	Description
Electronic health records	These might include a patient's medical history, prescriptions, immunizations, lab results, allergies, insurance information and more. Making these available to health-care providers across a secure network improves patient care, reduces the probability of error and increases the health-care system's overall efficiency, helping control costs.
Human Genome Project	The Human Genome Project was founded to identify and analyze the 20,000+ genes in human DNA. The project used computer programs to analyze complex genetic data, determine the sequences of the billions of chemical base pairs that make up human DNA and store the information in databases, which have been made available over the Internet to researchers in many fields.
AMBER™ Alert	The AMBER (America's Missing: Broadcast Emergency Response) Alert System helps find abducted children. Law enforcement notifies TV and radio broadcasters and state transportation officials, who then broadcast alerts on TV, radio, computerized highway signs, the Internet and wireless devices. AMBER Alert partners with Facebook, whose users can "Like" AMBER Alert pages by location to receive alerts in their news feeds.
World Community Grid	People worldwide can donate their unused computer processing power by installing a free secure software program that allows the World Community Grid (http://www.worldcommunitygrid.org) to harness unused capacity. This computing power, accessed over the Internet, is used in place of expensive supercomputers to conduct scientific research projects that are making a difference—providing clean water to third-world countries, fighting cancer, growing more nutritious rice for regions fighting hunger and more.
Cloud computing	Cloud computing allows you to use software, hardware and information stored in the "cloud"—i.e., accessed on remote computers via the Internet and available on demand—popular examples are Dropbox, Google Drive and Microsoft OneDrive. You can increase or decrease resources incrementally to meet your needs at any given time, so cloud services can be more cost effective than purchasing expensive hardware to ensure that you have enough storage and processing power to meet peak-level needs. Using cloud-computing services shifts the burden of managing these applications from the business to the service provider, saving businesses time, effort and money. In an online chapter, you'll use Microsoft Azure—a cloud-computing platform that allows you to develop, manage and distribute your apps in the cloud. With Microsoft Azure, your apps can store their data in the cloud so that it's available at all times from any of your desktop computers and mobile devices. For information on Microsoft Azure's free and paid services visit https://azure.microsoft.com.
Medical imaging	X-ray computed tomography (CT) scans, also called CAT (computerized axial tomography) scans, take X-rays of the body from hundreds of different angles. Computers are used to adjust the intensity of the X-rays, optimizing the scan for each type of tissue, then to combine all of the information to create a 3D image. MRI scanners use a technique called magnetic resonance imaging to produce internal images noninvasively.

Fig. 1.1 | Improving people's lives with computers. (Part 1 of 2.)

Name	Description
GPS	Global Positioning System (GPS) devices use a network of satellites to retrieve location-based information. Multiple satellites send time-stamped signals to the GPS device, which calculates the distance to each satellite, based on the time the signal left the satellite and the time the signal arrived. This information helps determine the device's exact location. GPS devices can provide step-by-step directions and help you locate nearby businesses (restaurants, gas stations, etc.) and points of interest. GPS is used in numerous location-based Internet services such as check-in apps to help you find your friends (e.g., Foursquare and Facebook), exercise apps such as Map My Ride+, Couch to 5K and RunKeeper that track the time, distance and average speed of your outdoor ride or jog, dating apps that help you find a match nearby and apps that dynamically update changing traffic conditions.
Robots	Robots can be used for day-to-day tasks (e.g., iRobot's Roomba vacuuming robot), entertainment (e.g., robotic pets), military combat, deep sea and space exploration (e.g., NASA's Mars rover Curiosity) and more. Researchers, such as those at Robo-How (http://robohow.eu), are working to create autonomous robots that perform complex human manipulation tasks (such as cooking) and that can learn additional tasks both from the robots' own experiences and from observing humans performing other tasks.
E-mail, Instant Messaging and Video Chat	Internet-based servers support all of your online messaging. E-mail messages go through a mail server that also stores the messages. Instant Messaging (IM) and Video Chat apps, such as Facebook Messenger, WhatsApp, AIM, Skype, Yahoo! Messenger, Google Hangouts, Trillian and others, allow you to communicate with others in real time by sending your messages and live video through servers.
E-commerce	This technology has exploded with companies like Amazon, eBay, Alibaba, Walmart and many others, causing a major shift away from brick-and-mortar retailers.
Internet TV	Internet TV set-top boxes (such as Apple TV, Android TV, Roku, Chromecast and TiVo) allow you to access an enormous amount of content on demand, such as games, news, movies, television shows and more, and they help ensure that the content is streamed to your TV smoothly.
Streaming music services	Streaming music services (such as Apple Music, Pandora, Spotify and more) allow you to listen to large catalogues of music over the web, create customized "radio stations" and discover new music based on your feedback.
Self-driving cars and smart homes	These are two enormous markets. Self-driving cars are under development by many technology companies and car manufacturers—they already have an impressive safety record and soon could be widely used saving lives and reducing injuries. Smart homes use computers for security, climate control, minimizing energy costs, automated lighting systems, fire detection, window control and more.
Game programming	Global video-game revenues are expected to reach $107 billion by 2017 (http://www.polygon.com/2015/4/22/8471789/worldwide-video-games-market-value-2015). The most sophisticated games can cost over $100 million to develop, with the most expensive costing half a billion dollars (http://www.gamespot.com/gallery/20-of-the-most-expensive-games-ever-made/2900-104/). Bethesda's *Fallout 4* earned $750 million in its first day of sales (http://fortune.com/2015/11/16/fallout4-is-quiet-best-seller/)!

Fig. 1.1 | Improving people's lives with computers. (Part 2 of 2.)

1.3 Hardware and Software

Computers can perform calculations and make logical decisions phenomenally faster than human beings can. Many of today's personal computers can perform billions of calculations in one second—more than a human can perform in a lifetime. *Supercomputers* are already performing *thousands of trillions (quadrillions) of instructions per second!* China's National University of Defense Technology's Tianhe-2 supercomputer can perform over 33 quadrillion calculations per second (33.86 *petaflops*)![2] To put that in perspective, *the Tianhe-2 supercomputer can perform in one second about 3 million calculations for every person on the planet!* And supercomputing upper limits are growing quickly.

Computers (i.e., hardware) process *data* under the control of sequences of instructions called computer programs. These programs guide the computer through *actions* specified by people called computer programmers. The programs that run on a computer are referred to as software. In this book, you'll learn several key programming methodologies that are enhancing programmer productivity, thereby reducing software development costs—*object-oriented programming, generic programming, functional programming* and *structured programming*. You'll build C# apps (short for applications) for a variety of environments including the *desktop*, mobile devices like *smartphones* and *tablets*, and even "the *cloud*."

Computers consist of devices referred to as hardware (e.g., the keyboard, screen, mouse, hard disks, memory, DVD drives and processing units). Computing costs are *dropping dramatically*, due to rapid developments in hardware and software technologies. Computers that filled large rooms and cost millions of dollars decades ago are now inscribed on silicon chips smaller than a fingernail, costing perhaps a few dollars each. Ironically, silicon is one of the most abundant materials on Earth—it's an ingredient in common sand. Silicon-chip technology has made computing so economical that computers have become a commodity.

1.3.1 Moore's Law

Every year, you probably expect to pay at least a little more for most products and services. The opposite has been the case in the computer and communications fields, especially with regard to the hardware supporting these technologies. For many decades, hardware costs have fallen rapidly.

Every year or two, the capacities of computers have approximately *doubled* inexpensively. This remarkable trend often is called Moore's Law, named for the person who identified it in the 1960s, Gordon Moore, co-founder of Intel—a leading manufacturer of the processors in today's computers and embedded systems. Moore's Law and related observations apply especially to the amount of memory that computers have for programs, the amount of secondary storage (such as disk storage) they have to hold programs and data over longer periods of time, and their processor speeds—the speeds at which they *execute* their programs (i.e., do their work). These increases make computers more capable, which puts greater demands on programming-language designers to innovate.

Similar growth has occurred in the communications field—costs have plummeted as enormous demand for communications *bandwidth* (i.e., information-carrying capacity) has attracted intense competition. We know of no other fields in which technology improves so quickly and costs fall so rapidly. Such phenomenal improvement is truly fostering the *Information Revolution*.

---

2. http://www.top500.org.

1.3.2 Computer Organization

Regardless of differences in *physical* appearance, computers can be envisioned as divided into various logical units or sections (Fig. 1.2).

Logical unit	Description
Input unit	This "receiving" section obtains information (data and computer programs) from input devices and places it at the disposal of the other units for processing. Most user input is entered into computers through keyboards, touch screens and mouse devices. Other forms of input include receiving voice commands, scanning images and barcodes, reading from secondary storage devices (such as hard drives, DVD drives, Blu-ray Disc™ drives and USB flash drives—also called "thumb drives" or "memory sticks"), receiving video from a webcam and having your computer receive information from the Internet (such as when you stream videos from You-Tube® or download e-books from Amazon). Newer forms of input include position data from a GPS device, motion and orientation information from an *accelerometer* (a device that responds to up/down, left/right and forward/backward acceleration) in a smartphone or game controller (such as Microsoft® Kinect® for Xbox®, Wii™ Remote and Sony® PlayStation® Move) and voice input from devices like Amazon Echo and the forthcoming Google Home.
Output unit	This "shipping" section takes information the computer has processed and places it on various output devices to make it available for use outside the computer. Most information that's output from computers today is displayed on screens (including touch screens), printed on paper ("going green" discourages this), played as audio or video on PCs and media players (such as Apple's iPods) and giant screens in sports stadiums, transmitted over the Internet or used to control other devices, such as robots and "intelligent" appliances. Information is also commonly output to secondary storage devices, such as solid-state drives (SSDs), hard drives, DVD drives and USB flash drives. Popular recent forms of output are smartphone and game-controller vibration, virtual reality devices like Oculus Rift and Google Cardboard and mixed reality devices like Microsoft's HoloLens.
Memory unit	This rapid-access, relatively low-capacity "warehouse" section retains information that has been entered through the input unit, making it immediately available for processing when needed. The memory unit also retains processed information until it can be placed on output devices by the output unit. Information in the memory unit is *volatile*—it's typically lost when the computer's power is turned off. The memory unit is often called either memory, primary memory or RAM (Random Access Memory). Main memories on desktop and notebook computers contain as much as 128 GB of RAM, though 2 to 16 GB is most common. GB stands for gigabytes; a gigabyte is approximately one billion bytes. A byte is eight bits. A bit is either a 0 or a 1.
Arithmetic and logic unit (ALU)	This "manufacturing" section performs *calculations*, such as addition, subtraction, multiplication and division. It also contains the *decision* mechanisms that allow the computer, for example, to compare two items from the memory unit to determine whether they're equal. In today's systems, the ALU is implemented as part of the next logical unit, the CPU.

Fig. 1.2 | Logical units of a computer. (Part 1 of 2.)

Logical unit	Description
Central processing unit (CPU)	This "administrative" section coordinates and supervises the operation of the other sections. The CPU tells the input unit when information should be read into the memory unit, tells the ALU when information from the memory unit should be used in calculations and tells the output unit when to send information from the memory unit to certain output devices. Many of today's computers have multiple CPUs and, hence, can perform many operations simultaneously. A multicore processor implements multiple processors on a single integrated-circuit chip—a *dual-core processor* has two CPUs, a *quad-core processor* has four and an *octa-core processor* has eight. Today's desktop computers have processors that can execute billions of instructions per second. Chapter 23 explores how to write apps that can take full advantage of multicore architecture.
Secondary storage unit	This is the long-term, high-capacity "warehousing" section. Programs or data not actively being used by the other units normally are placed on secondary storage devices (e.g., your *hard drive*) until they're again needed, possibly hours, days, months or even years later. Information on secondary storage devices is *persistent*—it's preserved even when the computer's power is turned off. Secondary storage information takes much longer to access than information in primary memory, but its cost per unit is much less. Examples of secondary storage devices include solid-state drives (SSDs), hard drives, DVD drives and USB flash drives, some of which can hold over 2 TB (TB stands for terabytes; a terabyte is approximately one trillion bytes). Typical hard drives on desktop and notebook computers hold up to 2 TB, and some desktop hard drives can hold up to 6 TB.

Fig. 1.2 | Logical units of a computer. (Part 2 of 2.)

1.4 Data Hierarchy

Data items processed by computers form a data hierarchy that becomes larger and more complex in structure as we progress from the simplest data items (called "bits") to richer data items, such as characters, fields, and so on. Figure 1.3 illustrates a portion of the data hierarchy.

Bits

The smallest data item in a computer can assume the value 0 or the value 1. It's called a bit (short for "binary digit"—a digit that can assume one of *two* values). Remarkably, the impressive functions performed by computers involve only the simplest manipulations of 0s and 1s—*examining a bit's value, setting a bit's value* and *reversing a bit's value* (from 1 to 0 or from 0 to 1).

Characters

It's tedious for people to work with data in the low-level form of bits. Instead, they prefer to work with *decimal digits* (0–9), *letters* (A–Z and a–z), and *special symbols* (e.g., $, @, %, &, *, (,), –, +, ", :, ? and /). Digits, letters and special symbols are known as characters. The computer's character set is the set of all the characters used to write programs and represent data items. Computers process only 1s and 0s, so a computer's character set represents every character as a pattern of 1s and 0s. C# supports various character sets (including Unicode®), with

Fig. 1.3 | Data hierarchy.

some requiring more than one byte per character. Unicode supports many of the world's languages, as well as emojis. See Appendix B for more information on the ASCII (American Standard Code for Information Interchange) character set—the popular subset of Unicode that represents uppercase and lowercase letters of the English alphabet, digits and some common special characters. We also provide an online appendix describing Unicode.

Fields

Just as characters are composed of bits, fields are composed of characters or bytes. A field is a group of characters or bytes that conveys meaning. For example, a field consisting of uppercase and lowercase letters can be used to represent a person's name, and a field consisting of decimal digits could represent a person's age.

Records

Several related fields can be used to compose a record. In a payroll system, for example, the record for an employee might consist of the following fields (possible types for these fields are shown in parentheses):

- Employee or student identification number (a whole number).
- Name (a string of characters).
- Address (a string of characters).

- Hourly pay rate (a number with a decimal point).

- Year-to-date earnings (a number with a decimal point).

- Amount of taxes withheld (a number with a decimal point).

Thus, a record is a group of related fields. In the preceding example, all the fields belong to the *same* employee. A company might have many employees and a payroll record for each.

To facilitate the retrieval of specific records from a file, at least one field in each record is chosen as a record key, which identifies a record as belonging to a particular person or entity and distinguishes that record from all others. For example, in a payroll record, the employee identification number normally would be the record key.

Files

A file is a group of related records. More generally, a file contains arbitrary data in arbitrary formats. In some operating systems, a file is viewed simply as a *sequence of bytes*—any organization of the bytes in a file, such as organizing the data into records, is a view created by the application programmer. It's not unusual for an organization to have many files, some containing billions, or even trillions, of characters of information.

Database

A database is a collection of data organized for easy access and manipulation. The most popular model is the *relational database*, in which data is stored in simple *tables*. A table includes *records* and *fields*. For example, a table of students might include first name, last name, major, year, student ID number and grade-point-average fields. The data for each student is a record, and the individual pieces of information in each record are the fields. You can *search*, *sort* and otherwise manipulate the data based on its relationship to multiple tables or databases. For example, a university might use data from the student database in combination with data from databases of courses, on-campus housing, meal plans, etc.

Big Data

The amount of data being produced worldwide is enormous and growing quickly. According to IBM, approximately 2.5 quintillion bytes (2.5 *exabytes*) of data are created daily,[3] and according to Salesforce.com, as of October 2015 90% of the world's data was created in just the prior 12 months![4] According to an IDC study, the global data supply will reach 40 *zettabytes* (equal to 40 trillion gigabytes) annually by 2020.[5] Figure 1.4 shows some common byte measurements. Big data applications deal with massive amounts of data and this field is growing quickly, creating lots of opportunity for software developers. According to a study by Gartner Group, over four million IT jobs globally were expected to support big data in 2015.[6]

---

3. http://www-01.ibm.com/software/data/bigdata/what-is-big-data.html.
4. https://www.salesforce.com/blog/2015/10/salesforce-channel-ifttt.html.
5. http://recode.net/2014/01/10/stuffed-why-data-storage-is-hot-again-really/.
6. http://fortune.com/2013/09/04/the-big-data-employment-boom/.

Unit	Bytes	Which is approximately
1 kilobyte (KB)	1024 bytes	10^3 (1024) bytes exactly
1 megabyte (MB)	1024 kilobytes	10^6 (1,000,000) bytes
1 gigabyte (GB)	1024 megabytes	10^9 (1,000,000,000) bytes
1 terabyte (TB)	1024 gigabytes	10^{12} (1,000,000,000,000) bytes
1 petabyte (PB)	1024 terabytes	10^{15} (1,000,000,000,000,000) bytes
1 exabyte (EB)	1024 petabytes	10^{18} (1,000,000,000,000,000,000) bytes
1 zettabyte (ZB)	1024 exabytes	10^{21} (1,000,000,000,000,000,000,000) bytes

Fig. 1.4 | Byte measurements.

1.5 Machine Languages, Assembly Languages and High-Level Languages

Programmers write instructions in various programming languages, some directly understandable by computers and others requiring intermediate *translation* steps.

Machine Languages
Any computer can directly understand only its own machine language (also called *machine code*), defined by its hardware architecture. Machine languages generally consist of numbers (ultimately reduced to 1s and 0s). Such languages are cumbersome for humans.

Assembly Languages
Programming in machine language was simply too slow and tedious for most programmers. Instead, they began using English-like *abbreviations* to represent elementary operations. These abbreviations formed the basis of assembly languages. *Translator programs* called assemblers were developed to convert assembly-language programs to machine language. Although assembly-language code is clearer to humans, it's incomprehensible to computers until translated to machine language. Assembly languages are still popular today in applications where minimizing memory use and maximizing execution efficiency is crucial.

High-Level Languages
To speed up the programming process further, high-level languages were developed in which single statements could be written to accomplish substantial tasks. High-level languages, such as C#, Visual Basic, C, C++, Java and Swift, allow you to write instructions that look more like everyday English and contain commonly used mathematical notations. Translator programs called compilers convert high-level language programs into machine language.

The process of compiling a large high-level-language program into machine language can take a considerable amount of computer time. Interpreter programs were developed to execute high-level language programs directly (without the need for compilation), although more slowly than compiled programs. Scripting languages such as the popular web languages JavaScript and PHP are processed by interpreters.

Performance Tip 1.1

Interpreters have an advantage over compilers in Internet scripting. An interpreted program can begin executing as soon as it's downloaded to the client's machine, without needing to be compiled before it can execute. On the downside, interpreted scripts generally run slower and consume more memory than compiled code. With a technique called JIT (just-in-time) compilation, interpreted languages can often run almost as fast as compiled ones.

1.6 Object Technology

C# is an object-oriented programming language. In this section we'll introduce the basics of object technology.

Building software quickly, correctly and economically remains an elusive goal at a time when demands for new and more powerful software are soaring. Objects, or more precisely—as we'll see in Chapter 4—the classes objects come from, are essentially *reusable* software components. There are date objects, time objects, audio objects, video objects, automobile objects, people objects, etc. Almost any *noun* can be reasonably represented as a software object in terms of *attributes* (e.g., name, color and size) and *behaviors* (e.g., calculating, moving and communicating). Software developers have discovered that using a modular, object-oriented design-and-implementation approach can make software-development groups much more productive than was possible with earlier techniques—object-oriented programs are often easier to understand, correct and modify.

The Automobile as an Object

Let's begin with a simple analogy. Suppose you want to *drive a car and make it go faster by pressing its accelerator pedal.* What must happen before you can do this? Well, before you can drive a car, someone has to *design* it. A car typically begins as engineering drawings, similar to the *blueprints* that describe the design of a house. These drawings include the design for an accelerator pedal. The pedal *hides* from the driver the complex mechanisms that actually make the car go faster, just as the brake pedal hides the mechanisms that slow the car, and the steering wheel *hides* the mechanisms that turn the car. This enables people with little or no knowledge of how engines, braking and steering mechanisms work to drive a car easily.

Before you can drive a car, it must be *built* from the engineering drawings that describe it. A completed car has an *actual* accelerator pedal to make the car go faster, but even that's not enough—the car won't accelerate on its own (hopefully!), so the driver must *press* the pedal to accelerate the car.

Methods and Classes

Let's use our car example to introduce some key object-oriented programming concepts. Performing a task in a program requires a method. The method houses the program statements that actually perform the task. It *hides* these statements from its user, just as a car's accelerator pedal hides from the driver the mechanisms of making the car go faster. In C#, we create a program unit called a class to house the set of methods that perform the class's tasks. For example, a class that represents a bank account might contain one method to *deposit* money to an account and another to *withdraw* money from an account. A class is similar in concept to a car's engineering drawings, which house the design of an accelerator pedal, steering wheel, and so on.

Making Objects from Classes

Just as someone has to *build a car* from its engineering drawings before you can actually drive a car, you must *build an object* from a class before a program can perform the tasks that the class's methods define. The process of doing this is called *instantiation*. An object is then referred to as an instance of its class.

Reuse

Just as a car's engineering drawings can be *reused* many times to build many cars, you can *reuse* a class many times to build many objects. Reuse of existing classes when building new classes and programs saves time and effort. Reuse also helps you build more reliable and effective systems, because existing classes and components often have gone through extensive *testing* (to locate problems), *debugging* (to correct those problems) and *performance tuning*. Just as the notion of *interchangeable parts* was crucial to the Industrial Revolution, reusable classes are crucial to the software revolution that's been spurred by object technology.

Messages and Method Calls

When you drive a car, pressing its gas pedal sends a *message* to the car to perform a task—that is, to go faster. Similarly, you *send messages to an object*. Each message is implemented as a method call that tells a method of the object to perform its task. For example, a program might call a particular bank-account object's *deposit* method to increase the account's balance.

Attributes and Instance Variables

A car, besides having capabilities to accomplish tasks, also has *attributes*, such as its color, its number of doors, the amount of gas in its tank, its current speed and its record of total miles driven (i.e., its odometer reading). Like its capabilities, the car's attributes are represented as part of its design in its engineering diagrams (which, for example, include an odometer and a fuel gauge). As you drive an actual car, these attributes are carried along with the car. Every car maintains its *own* attributes. For example, each car knows how much gas is in its own gas tank, but not how much is in the tanks of *other* cars.

An object, similarly, has attributes that it carries along as it's used in a program. These attributes are specified as part of the object's class. For example, a bank-account object has a *balance attribute* that represents the amount of money in the account. Each bank-account object knows the balance in the account it represents, but *not* the balances of the *other* accounts in the bank. Attributes are specified by the class's instance variables.

Properties, **get** Accessors and **set** Accessors

Attributes are not necessarily accessible directly. The car manufacturer does not want drivers to take apart the car's engine to observe the amount of gas in its tank. Instead, the driver can check the fuel gauge on the dashboard. The bank does not want its customers to walk into the vault to count the amount of money in an account. Instead, the customers talk to a bank teller or check personalized online bank accounts. Similarly, you do not need to have access to an object's instance variables in order to use them. You should use the properties of an object. Properties contain get accessors for reading the values of variables, and set accessors for storing values into them.

Encapsulation

Classes encapsulate (i.e., wrap) attributes and methods into objects created from those classes—an object's attributes and methods are intimately related. Objects may communicate with one another, but they're normally not allowed to know how other objects are implemented—implementation details are *hidden* within the objects themselves. This information hiding, as we'll see, is crucial to good software engineering.

Inheritance

A new class of objects can be created quickly and conveniently by inheritance—the new class absorbs the characteristics of an existing class, possibly customizing them and adding unique characteristics of its own. In our car analogy, an object of class "convertible" certainly *is an* object of the more *general* class "automobile," but more *specifically*, the roof can be raised or lowered.

Object-Oriented Analysis and Design (OOAD)

Soon you'll be writing programs in C#. How will you create the code (i.e., the program instructions) for your programs? Perhaps, like many programmers, you'll simply turn on your computer and start typing. This approach may work for small programs (like the ones we present in the early chapters of the book), but what if you were asked to create a software system to control thousands of automated teller machines for a major bank? Or suppose you were asked to work on a team of thousands of software developers building the next generation of the U.S. air traffic control system? For projects so large and complex, you should not simply sit down and start writing programs.

To create the best solutions, you should follow a detailed analysis process for determining your project's requirements (i.e., defining *what* the system is supposed to do) and developing a design that satisfies them (i.e., deciding *how* the system should do it). Ideally, you'd go through this process and carefully review the design (and have your design reviewed by other software professionals) before writing any code. If this process involves analyzing and designing your system from an object-oriented point of view, it's called an object-oriented analysis and design (OOAD) process. Languages like C# are object oriented—programming in such a language, called object-oriented programming (OOP), allows you to implement an object-oriented design as a working system.

The UML (Unified Modeling Language)

Although many different OOAD processes exist, a single graphical language for communicating the results of *any* OOAD process has come into wide use. This language, known as the Unified Modeling Language (UML), is now the most widely used graphical scheme for modeling object-oriented systems. We present our first UML diagrams in Chapters 4 and 5, then use them in our deeper treatment of object-oriented programming through Chapter 12. In our *optional* ATM Software Engineering Case Study in the online chapters, we present a simple subset of the UML's features as we guide you through an object-oriented design and implementation experience.

1.7 Internet and World Wide Web

In the late 1960s, ARPA—the Advanced Research Projects Agency of the United States Department of Defense—rolled out plans for networking the main computer systems of approximately a dozen ARPA-funded universities and research institutions. The computers were to be connected with communications lines operating at speeds on the order of 50,000 bits per second, a stunning rate at a time when most people (of the few who even had networking access) were connecting over telephone lines to computers at a rate of 110 bits per second. Academic research was about to take a giant leap forward. ARPA proceeded to implement what quickly became known as the ARPANET, the precursor to today's Internet. Today's fastest Internet speeds are on the order of billions of bits per second with trillion-bits-per-second speeds on the horizon!

Things worked out differently from the original plan. Although the ARPANET enabled researchers to network their computers, its main benefit proved to be the capability for quick and easy communication via what came to be known as electronic mail (e-mail). This is true even on today's Internet, with e-mail, instant messaging, file transfer and social media such as Facebook and Twitter enabling billions of people worldwide to communicate quickly and easily.

The protocol (set of rules) for communicating over the ARPANET became known as the Transmission Control Protocol (TCP). TCP ensured that messages, consisting of sequentially numbered pieces called *packets*, were properly routed from sender to receiver, arrived intact and were assembled in the correct order.

The Internet: A Network of Networks

In parallel with the early evolution of the Internet, organizations worldwide were implementing their own networks for both intraorganization (that is, within an organization) and interorganization (that is, between organizations) communication. A huge variety of networking hardware and software appeared. One challenge was to enable these different networks to communicate with each other. ARPA accomplished this by developing the Internet Protocol (IP), which created a true "network of networks," the current architecture of the Internet. The combined set of protocols is now called TCP/IP.

Businesses rapidly realized that by using the Internet, they could improve their operations and offer new and better services to their clients. Companies started spending large amounts of money to develop and enhance their Internet presence. This generated fierce competition among communications carriers and hardware and software suppliers to meet the increased infrastructure demand. As a result, bandwidth—the information-carrying capacity of communications lines—on the Internet has increased tremendously, while hardware costs have plummeted.

The World Wide Web: Making the Internet User-Friendly

The World Wide Web (simply called "the web") is a collection of hardware and software associated with the Internet that allows computer users to locate and view multimedia-based documents (documents with various combinations of text, graphics, animations, audios and videos) on almost any subject. In 1989, Tim Berners-Lee of CERN (the European Organization for Nuclear Research) began developing HyperText Markup Language (HTML)—the technology for sharing information via "hyperlinked" text documents. He also wrote communication protocols such as HyperText Transfer Protocol (HTTP) to form the backbone of his new hypertext information system, which he referred to as the World Wide Web.

In 1994, Berners-Lee founded the World Wide Web Consortium (W3C, http://www.w3.org), devoted to developing web technologies. One of the W3C's primary goals is to make the web universally accessible to everyone regardless of disabilities, language or culture.

Web Services

Web services are software components stored on one computer that can be accessed by an app (or other software component) on another computer over the Internet. With web services, you can create *mashups*, which enable you to rapidly develop apps by combining complementary web services, often from multiple organizations, and possibly other forms of information feeds. For example, 100 Destinations (http://www.100destinations.co.uk) combines the photos and tweets from Twitter with the mapping capabilities of Google Maps to allow you to explore countries around the world through the photos of others.

ProgrammableWeb (http://www.programmableweb.com/) provides a directory of over 15,000 APIs and 6,200 mashups, plus how-to guides and sample code for creating your own mashups. According to Programmableweb, the three most widely used APIs for mashups are Google Maps, Twitter and YouTube.

Ajax

Ajax technology helps Internet-based applications perform like desktop applications—a difficult task, given that such applications suffer transmission delays as data is shuttled back and forth between your computer and server computers on the Internet. Using Ajax, applications like Google Maps have achieved excellent performance, approaching the look-and-feel of desktop applications.

The Internet of Things

The Internet is no longer just a network of computers—it's an Internet of Things. A *thing* is any object with an IP address—a unique identifier that helps locate that *thing* on the Internet—and the ability to send data automatically over the Internet. Such things include:

- a car with a transponder for paying tolls,
- monitors for parking-space availability in a garage,
- a heart monitor implanted in a human,
- monitors for drinkable water quality,
- a smart meter that reports energy usage,
- radiation detectors,
- item trackers in a warehouse,
- mobile apps that can track your movement and location,
- smart thermostats that adjust room temperatures based on weather forecasts and activity in the home
- and many more.

1.8 C#

In 2000, Microsoft announced the C# programming language. C# has roots in the C, C++ and Java programming languages. It has similar capabilities to Java and is appropriate for the most demanding app-development tasks, especially for building today's desktop apps, large-scale enterprise apps, and web-based, mobile and cloud-based apps.

1.8.1 Object-Oriented Programming

C# is *object oriented*—we've discussed the basics of object technology and we present a rich treatment of object-oriented programming throughout the book. C# has access to the powerful .NET Framework Class Library—a vast collection of prebuilt classes that enable you to develop apps quickly (Fig. 1.5). We'll say more about .NET in Section 1.9.

Some key capabilities in the .NET Framework Class Library	
Database	Debugging
Building web apps	Multithreading
Graphics	File processing
Input/output	Security
Computer networking	Web communication
Permissions	Graphical user interface
Mobile	Data structures
String processing	Universal Windows Platform GUI

Fig. 1.5 | Some key capabilities in the .NET Framework Class Library.

1.8.2 Event-Driven Programming

C# graphical user interfaces (GUIs) are event driven. You can write programs that respond to user-initiated events such as mouse clicks, keystrokes, timer expirations and *touches* and *finger swipes*—gestures that are widely used on smartphones and tablets.

1.8.3 Visual Programming

Microsoft's Visual Studio enables you to use C# as a *visual programming language*—in addition to writing program statements to build portions of your apps, you'll also use Visual Studio to conveniently drag and drop predefined GUI objects like *buttons* and *textboxes* into place on your screen, and label and resize them. Visual Studio will write much of the GUI code for you.

1.8.4 Generic and Functional Programming

Generic Programming

It's common to write a program that processes a collection of things—e.g., a collection of numbers, a collection of contacts, a collection of videos, etc. Historically, you had to program separately to handle each type of collection. With *generic programming*, you write code that handles a collection "in the general" and C# handles the specifics for each different type of collection, saving you a great deal of work. We'll study generics and generic collections in Chapters 20 and 21.

Functional Programming

With *functional programming*, you specify *what* you want to accomplish in a task, but *not how* to accomplish it. For example, with Microsoft's LINQ—which we introduce in Chapter 9, then use in many later chapters—you can say, "Here's a collection of numbers, give me the sum of its elements." You do *not* need to specify the mechanics of walking through the elements and adding them into a running total one at a time—LINQ handles all that for you. Functional programming speeds application development and reduces errors. We take a deeper look at functional programming in Chapter 21.

1.8.5 An International Standard

C# has been standardized through ECMA International:

```
http://www.ecma-international.org
```

This enables other implementations of the language besides Microsoft's Visual C#. At the time of this writing, the C# standard document—ECMA-334—was still being updated for C# 6. For information on ECMA-334, visit

```
http://www.ecma-international.org/publications/standards/Ecma-
    334.htm
```

Visit the Microsoft download center to find the latest version of Microsoft's C# 6 specification, other documentation and software downloads.

1.8.6 C# on Non-Windows Platforms

Though C# was originally developed by Microsoft for the Windows platform, the language can be used on other platforms via the Mono Project and .NET Core—both are managed by the .NET Foundation

```
http://www.dotnetfoundation.org/
```

For more information, see the Before You Begin section after the Preface.

1.8.7 Internet and Web Programming

Today's apps can be written with the aim of communicating among the world's computers. As you'll see, this is the focus of Microsoft's .NET strategy. In online chapters, you'll build web-based apps with C# and Microsoft's ASP.NET technology.

1.8.8 Asynchronous Programming with async and await

In most programming today, each task in a program must finish executing before the next task can begin. This is called *synchronous programming* and is the style we use for most of this book. C# also allows *asynchronous programming* in which multiple tasks can be performed at the *same* time. Asynchronous programming can help you make your apps more responsive to user interactions, such as mouse clicks and keystrokes, among many other uses.

Asynchronous programming in early versions of Visual C# was difficult and error prone. C#'s async and await capabilities simplify asynchronous programming by enabling the compiler to hide much of the associated complexity from the developer. In Chapter 23, we provide an introduction to asynchronous programming with async and await.

1.8.9 Other Key Programming Languages

Figure 1.6 provides brief comments on several popular programming languages.

Programming language	Description
Ada	Ada, based on Pascal, was developed under the sponsorship of the U.S. Department of Defense (DOD) during the 1970s and early 1980s. The DOD wanted a single language that would fill most of its needs. The Pascal-based language was named after Lady Ada Lovelace, daughter of the poet Lord Byron. She's credited with writing the world's first computer program in the early 1800s (for the Analytical Engine mechanical computing device designed by Charles Babbage). Ada also supports object-oriented programming.
Basic	Basic was developed in the 1960s at Dartmouth College to familiarize novices with programming techniques. Many of its latest versions are object oriented.
C	C was developed in the early 1970s by Dennis Ritchie at Bell Laboratories. It initially became widely known as the UNIX operating system's development language. Today, most code for general-purpose operating systems is written in C or C++.
C++	C++, which is based on C, was developed by Bjarne Stroustrup in the early 1980s at Bell Laboratories. C++ provides several features that "spruce up" the C language, but more important, it provides capabilities for object-oriented programming.
COBOL	COBOL (COmmon Business Oriented Language) was developed in the late 1950s by computer manufacturers, the U.S. government and industrial computer users, based on a language developed by Grace Hopper, a career U.S. Navy officer and computer scientist. COBOL is still widely used for commercial applications that require precise and efficient manipulation of large amounts of data. Its latest version supports object-oriented programming.
Fortran	Fortran (FORmula TRANslator) was developed by IBM Corporation in the mid-1950s to be used for scientific and engineering applications that require complex mathematical computations. It's still widely used, and its latest versions support object-oriented programming.
Java	Sun Microsystems in 1991 funded an internal corporate research project led by James Gosling, which resulted in the C++-based object-oriented programming language called Java. A key goal of Java is to enable developers to write programs that will run on a great variety of computer systems and computer-controlled devices. This is sometimes called "write once, run anywhere." Java is used to develop large-scale enterprise applications, to enhance the functionality of web servers (the computers that provide the content we see in our web browsers), to provide applications for consumer devices (e.g., smartphones, tablets, television set-top boxes, appliances, automobiles and more) and for many other purposes. Java is also the key language for developing Android smartphone and tablet apps.
Objective-C	Objective-C is an object-oriented language based on C. It was developed in the early 1980s and later acquired by NeXT, which in turn was acquired by Apple. It became the key programming language for the OS X operating system and all iOS-powered devices (such as iPods, iPhones and iPads).

Fig. 1.6 | Some other programming languages. (Part 1 of 2.)

Programming language	Description
JavaScript	JavaScript is the most widely used scripting language. It's primarily used to add programmability to web pages—for example, animations and interactivity with the user. All major web browsers support it.
Pascal	Research in the 1960s resulted in *structured programming*—a disciplined approach to writing programs that are clearer, easier to test and debug and easier to modify than programs produced with previous techniques. The Pascal language, developed by Professor Niklaus Wirth in 1971, grew out of this research. It was popular for teaching structured programming for several decades.
PHP	PHP is an object-oriented, *open-source* "scripting" language supported by a community of developers and used by numerous websites. PHP is platform independent—implementations exist for all major UNIX, Linux, Mac and Windows operating systems.
Python	Python, another object-oriented scripting language, was released publicly in 1991. Developed by Guido van Rossum of the National Research Institute for Mathematics and Computer Science in Amsterdam (CWI), Python draws heavily from Modula-3—a systems programming language. Python is "extensible"—it can be extended through classes and programming interfaces.
Swift	Swift, which was introduced in 2014, is Apple's programming language of the future for developing iOS and OS X applications (apps). Swift is a contemporary language that includes popular programming-language features from languages such as Objective-C, Java, C#, Ruby, Python and others. In 2015, Apple released Swift 2 with new and updated features. According to the Tiobe Index, Swift has already become one of the most popular programming languages. Swift is now *open source*, so it can be used on non-Apple platforms as well.
Ruby on Rails	Ruby—created in the mid-1990s by Yukihiro Matsumoto—is an open-source, object-oriented programming language with a simple syntax that's similar to Python. Ruby on Rails combines the scripting language Ruby with the Rails web-application framework developed by the company 37Signals. Their book, *Getting Real* (free at `http://gettingreal.37signals.com/toc.php`), is a must-read for web developers. Many Ruby on Rails developers have reported productivity gains over other languages when developing database-intensive web applications.
Scala	Scala (`http://www.scala-lang.org/what-is-scala.html`)—short for "scalable language"—was designed by Martin Odersky, a professor at École Polytechnique Fédérale de Lausanne (EPFL) in Switzerland. Released in 2003, Scala uses both the object-oriented programming and functional programming paradigms and is designed to integrate with Java. Programming in Scala can reduce the amount of code in your applications significantly.
Visual Basic	Microsoft's Visual Basic language was introduced in the early 1990s to simplify the development of Microsoft Windows applications. Its latest versions support object-oriented programming.

Fig. 1.6 | Some other programming languages. (Part 2 of 2.)

1.9 Microsoft's .NET

In 2000, Microsoft announced its .NET initiative (www.microsoft.com/net), a broad vision for using the Internet and the web in the development, engineering, distribution and use of software. Rather than forcing you to use a single programming language, .NET permits you to create apps in *any* .NET-compatible language (such as C#, Visual Basic, Visual C++ and others). Part of the initiative includes Microsoft's ASP.NET technology for building web-based applications.

1.9.1 .NET Framework

The .NET Framework Class Library provides many capabilities that you'll use to build substantial C# apps quickly and easily. It contains *thousands* of valuable *prebuilt* classes that have been tested and tuned to maximize performance. You'll learn how to create your own classes, but you should *re-use* the .NET Framework classes whenever possible to speed up the software-development process, while enhancing the quality and performance of the software you develop.

1.9.2 Common Language Runtime

The Common Language Runtime (CLR), another key part of the .NET Framework, executes .NET programs and provides functionality to make them easier to develop and debug. The CLR is a virtual machine (VM)—software that manages the execution of programs and hides from them the underlying operating system and hardware. The source code for programs that are executed and managed by the CLR is called *managed code*. The CLR provides various services to managed code, such as

- integrating software components written in different .NET languages,
- error handling between such components,
- enhanced security,
- automatic memory management and more.

Unmanaged-code programs do not have access to the CLR's services, which makes unmanaged code more difficult to write.[7] Managed code is compiled into machine-specific instructions in the following steps:

1. First, the code is compiled into Microsoft Intermediate Language (MSIL). Code converted into MSIL from other languages and sources can be woven together by the CLR—this allows programmers to work in their preferred .NET programming language. The MSIL for an app's components is placed into the app's *executable file*—the file that causes the computer to perform the app's tasks.

2. When the app executes, another compiler (known as the just-in-time compiler or JIT compiler) in the CLR translates the MSIL in the executable file into machine-language code (for a particular platform).

3. The machine-language code executes on that platform.

---

7. http://msdn.microsoft.com/library/8bs2ecf4.

1.9.3 Platform Independence

If the .NET Framework exists and is installed for a platform, that platform can run *any* .NET program. The ability of a program to run without modification across multiple platforms is known as platform independence. Code written once can be used on another type of computer without modification, saving time and money. In addition, software can target a wider audience. Previously, companies had to decide whether converting their programs to different platforms—a process called porting—was worth the cost. With .NET, porting programs is no longer an issue, at least once .NET itself has been made available on the platforms.

1.9.4 Language Interoperability

The .NET Framework provides a high level of language interoperability. Because software components written in different .NET languages (such as C# and Visual Basic) are all compiled into MSIL, the components can be combined to create a single unified program. Thus, MSIL allows the .NET Framework to be language independent.

The .NET Framework Class Library can be used by any .NET language. The latest release of .NET includes .NET 4.6 and .NET Core:

- NET 4.6 introduces many improvements and new features, including ASP.NET 5 for web-based applications, improved support for today's high-resolution 4K screens and more.

- .NET Core is the cross-platform subset of .NET for Windows, Linux, OS X and FreeBSD.

1.10 Microsoft's Windows® Operating System

Microsoft's Windows is the most widely personal-computer, desktop operating system worldwide. Operating systems are software systems that make using computers more convenient for users, developers and system administrators. They provide *services* that allow each app to execute safely, efficiently and *concurrently* (i.e., in parallel) with other apps. Other popular desktop operating systems include Mac OS X and Linux. *Mobile operating systems* used in smartphones and tablets include Microsoft's Windows Phone, Google's Android, Apple's iOS (for iPhone, iPad and iPod Touch devices) and BlackBerry OS. Figure 1.7 presents the evolution of the Windows operating system.

Version	Description
Windows in the 1990s	In the mid-1980s, Microsoft developed the Windows operating system based on a graphical user interface with buttons, textboxes, menus and other graphical elements. The various versions released throughout the 1990s were intended for personal computing. Microsoft entered the corporate operating systems market with the 1993 release of *Windows NT.*

Fig. 1.7 | The evolution of the Windows operating system. (Part 1 of 2.)

Version	Description
Windows XP and Windows Vista	*Windows XP* was released in 2001 and combined Microsoft's corporate and consumer operating-system lines. At the time of this writing, it still holds more than 10% of the operating-systems market (`https://www.netmarketshare.com/operating-system-market-share.aspx`). *Windows Vista*, released in 2007, offered the attractive new Aero user interface, many powerful enhancements and new apps and enhanced security. But Vista never caught on.
Windows 7	*Windows 7* is currently the world's most widely used desktop operating system with over 47% of the operating-systems market (`https://www.netmarketshare.com/operating-system-market-share.aspx`). Windows added enhancements to the Aero user interface, faster startup times, further refinement of Vista's security features, touch-screen with multitouch support, and more.
Windows 8 for Desktops and Tablets	Windows 8, released in 2012, provided a similar platform (the underlying system on which apps run) and *user experience* across a wide range of devices including personal computers, smartphones, tablets *and* the Xbox Live online game service. Its new look-and-feel featured a Start screen with *tiles* representing each app, similar to that of *Windows Phone*—Microsoft's smartphone operating system. Windows 8 featured *multitouch* support for *touchpads* and *touchscreen* devices, enhanced security features and more.
Windows 8 UI (User Interface)	Windows 8 UI (previously called "Metro") introduced a clean look-and-feel with minimal distractions to the user. Windows 8 apps featured a *chromeless window* with no borders, title bars and menus. These elements were *hidden*, allowing apps to fill the *entire* screen—particularly helpful on smaller screens such as tablets and smartphones. The interface elements were displayed in the *app bar* when the user *swiped* the top or bottom of the screen by holding down the mouse button, moving the mouse in the swipe direction and releasing the mouse button; or using a *finger swipe* on a touchscreen device.
Windows 10 and the Universal Windows Platform	Windows 10, released in 2015, is the current version of Windows and currently holds a 15% (and growing) share of the operating-systems market (`https://www.netmarketshare.com/operating-system-market-share.aspx`). In addition to many user-interface and other updates, Windows 10 introduced the Universal Windows Platform (UWP), which is designed to provide a common platform (the underlying system on which apps run) and user experience across all Windows devices including personal computers, smartphones, tablets, Xbox and even Microsoft's new HoloLens augmented reality holographic headset—all using nearly identical code.

Fig. 1.7 | The evolution of the Windows operating system. (Part 2 of 2.)

Windows Store

You can sell apps or offer them for free in the Windows Store. At the time of this writing, the fee to become a registered developer is $19 for individuals and $99 for companies. Microsoft retains 30% of the purchase price (more in some markets). See the App Developer Agreement for more information:

```
https://msdn.microsoft.com/en-us/library/windows/apps/hh694058.aspx
```

The Windows Store offers several business models for monetizing your app. You can charge full price for your app before download, with prices starting at $1.49. You also can offer a time-limited trial or feature-limited trial that allows users to try the app before purchasing the full version, sell virtual goods (such as additional app features) using in-app purchases and more. To learn more about the Windows Store and monetizing your apps, visit

```
https://msdn.microsoft.com/windows/uwp/monetize/index
```

1.11 Visual Studio Integrated Development Environment

C# programs can be created using Microsoft's Visual Studio—a collection of software tools called an Integrated Development Environment (IDE). The Visual Studio Community edition IDE enables you to *write, run, test* and *debug* C# programs quickly and conveniently. It also supports Microsoft's Visual Basic, Visual C++ and F# programming languages and more. Most of this book's examples were built using *Visual Studio Community*, which runs on Windows 7, 8 and 10. A few of the book's examples require Windows 10.

1.12 Painter Test-Drive in Visual Studio Community

You'll now use *Visual Studio Community* to "test-drive" an existing app that enables you to draw on the screen using the mouse. The **Painter** app allows you to choose among several brush sizes and colors. The elements and functionality you see in this app are typical of what you'll learn to program in this text. The following steps walk you through test-driving the app. For this test drive, we assume that you placed the book's examples in your user account's Documents folder in a subfolder named examples.

Step 1: Checking Your Setup
Confirm that you've set up your computer and the software properly by reading the book's Before You Begin section that follows the Preface.

Step 2: Locating the Painter App's Directory
Open a **File Explorer** (Windows 8 and 10) or **Windows Explorer** (Windows 7) window and navigate to

```
C:\Users\yourUserName\Documents\examples\ch01
```

Double click the Painter folder to view its contents (Fig. 1.8), then double click the Painter.sln file to open the app's solution in Visual Studio. An app's *solution* contains all of the app's *code files, supporting files* (such as *images, videos, data files,* etc.) and configuration information. We'll discuss the contents of a solution in more detail in the next chapter.

Double click `Painter.sln` to open the project in Visual Studio

Fig. 1.8 | Contents of `C:\examples\ch01\Painter`.

Depending on your system configuration, **File Explorer** or **Windows Explorer** might display `Painter.sln` simply as `Painter`, without the filename extension `.sln`. To display the filename extensions in Windows 8 and higher:

1. Open **File Explorer**.

2. Click the **View** tab, then ensure that the **File name extensions** checkbox is checked.

To display them in Windows 7:

1. Open **Windows Explorer**.

2. Press *Alt* to display the menu bar, then select **Folder Options…** from **Windows Explorer**'s **Tools** menu.

3. In the dialog that appears, select the **View** tab.

4. In the **Advanced settings:** pane, uncheck the box to the left of the text **Hide extensions for known file types**. [*Note*: If this item is already unchecked, no action needs to be taken.]

5. Click **OK** to apply the setting and close the dialog.

Step 3: Running the Painter App

To see the running **Painter** app, click the **Start** button (Fig. 1.9)

or press the *F5* key.

Figure 1.10 shows the running app and labels several of the app's graphical elements—called controls. These include `GroupBoxes`, `RadioButtons`, `Buttons` and a `Panel`. These controls and many others are discussed throughout the text. The app allows you to draw with a **Red**, **Blue**, **Green** or **Black** brush of **Small**, **Medium** or **Large** size. As you drag the mouse on the white `Panel`, the app draws circles of the specified color and size at the mouse pointer's current position. The slower you drag the mouse, the closer the circles will be. Thus, dragging slowly draws a continuous line (as in Fig. 1.11) and dragging quickly draws individual circles with space in between. You also can **Undo** your previous operation or **Clear** the drawing to start from scratch by pressing the `Buttons` below the `RadioButtons` in the GUI. By using existing *controls*—which are *objects*—you can create powerful apps much faster than if you had to write all the code yourself. This is a key benefit of *software reuse*.

Press the **Start** button to begin executing the **Painter** app

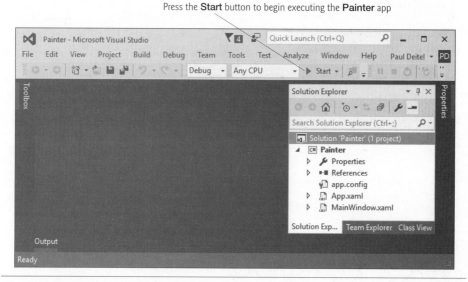

Fig. 1.9 | Running the **Painter** app.

Fig. 1.10 | **Painter** app running in Windows 10.

The brush's properties, selected in the RadioButtons labeled **Black** and **Medium**, are *default settings*—the initial settings you see when you first run the app. Programmers include default settings to provide *reasonable* choices that the app will use if the user *does not* change the settings. Default settings also provide visual cues for users to choose their own settings. Now you'll choose your own settings as a user of this app.

Step 4: Changing the Brush Color
Click the RadioButton labeled **Red** to change the brush color, then click the RadioButton labeled **Small** to change the brush size. Position the mouse over the white Panel, then drag the mouse to draw with the brush. Draw flower petals, as shown in Fig. 1.11.

Fig. 1.11 | Drawing flower petals with a small red brush.

Step 5: Changing the Brush Color and Size
Click the **Green** RadioButton to change the brush color. Then, click the **Large** RadioButton to change the brush size. Draw grass and a flower stem, as shown in Fig. 1.12.

Fig. 1.12 | Drawing the flower stem and grass with a large green brush.

Step 6: Finishing the Drawing
Click the **Blue** and **Medium** RadioButtons. Draw raindrops, as shown in Fig. 1.13, to complete the drawing.

Step 7: Stopping the App
When you run an app from Visual Studio, you can terminate it by clicking the stop button

Fig. 1.13 | Drawing rain drops with a medium blue brush.

on the Visual Studio toolbar or by clicking the close box

on the running app's window.

Now that you've completed the test-drive, you're ready to begin developing C# apps. In Chapter 2, Introduction to Visual Studio and Visual Programming, you'll use Visual Studio to create your first C# program using *visual programming* techniques. As you'll see, Visual Studio will generate for you the code that builds the app's GUI. In Chapter 3, Introduction to C# App Programming, you'll begin writing C# programs containing conventional program code that you write.

Self-Review Exercises

1.1   Fill in the blanks in each of the following statements:
   a) Computers process data under the control of sequences of instructions called _____.
   b) A computer consists of various devices referred to as _____, such as the keyboard, screen, mouse, hard disks, memory, DVD drives and processing units.
   c) Data items processed by computers form a(n) _____ that becomes larger and more complex in structure as we progress from the simplest data items (called "bits") to richer data items, such as characters, fields, and so on.
   d) Computers can directly understand only their _____ language, which is composed only of 1s and 0s.
   e) The three types of computer programming languages discussed in the chapter are machine languages, _____ and _____.
   f) Programs that translate high-level-language programs into machine language are called _____.
   g) A(n) _____ processor implements several processors on a single "microchip"—a dual-core processor has two CPUs and a quad-core processor has four CPUs.
   h) Windows 10 introduced the _____ for building Windows apps that run on desktop computers, notebook computers, tablets, phones, Xbox and even Microsoft's new HoloLens augmented reality holographic headset—all using nearly identical code.

1.2 Fill in the blanks in each of the following statements:

a) Objects, or more precisely the _____ that objects come from, are essentially reusable software components.

b) You send messages to an object. Each message is implemented as a method _____ that tells a method of the object to perform its task.

c) A new class of objects can be created quickly and conveniently by _____; the new class absorbs the characteristics of an existing class, possibly customizing them and adding unique characteristics of its own.

d) To create the best solutions, you should follow a detailed analysis process for determining your project's _____ (i.e., defining what the system is supposed to do) and developing a design that satisfies them (i.e., deciding how the system should do it).

e) Visual C# is _____ driven. You'll write programs that respond to mouse clicks, keystrokes, timer expirations and touches and finger swipes.

f) A key goal of Java is to be able to write programs that will run on a great variety of computer systems and computer-control devices. This is sometimes called _____.

1.3 Fill in the blanks in each of the following statements:

a) The _____ executes .NET programs.

b) The CLR provides various services to _____ code, such as integrating software components written in different .NET languages, error handling between such components, enhanced security and more.

c) The ability of a program to run without modification across multiple platforms is known as platform _____.

d) Visual Studio is a(n) _____ in which C# programs are developed.

e) You can sell your own Windows Phone apps in the _____.

1.4 State whether each of the following is *true* or *false*. If *false*, explain why.

a) Software objects model both abstract and real-world things.

b) The most popular database model is the *relational database* in which data is stored in simple *tables*. A table includes *records* and *fields*.

c) A database is a collection of data that's organized for easy access and manipulation.

d) Secondary storage data takes much longer to access than data in primary memory, but the cost per unit of secondary storage is much higher than that of primary memory.

e) High-level languages allow you to write instructions that look almost like everyday English and contain commonly used mathematical expressions.

f) An object has attributes that it carries along as it's used in a program.

g) The Transmission Control Protocol (TCP) ensures that messages, consisting of sequentially numbered pieces called bytes, were properly routed from sender to receiver, arrived intact and were assembled in the correct order

h) The information-carrying capacity of communications lines on the Internet has increased tremendously, while hardware costs have increased.

i) You can build web-based apps with C# and Microsoft's ASP.NET technology.

j) Java has become the key programming language for the Mac OS X desktop operating system and all iOS-based devices, such as iPods, iPhones and iPads.

k) Microsoft's ASP.WEB technology is used to create web apps.

l) Microsoft's Windows operating system is the most widely used desktop operating system worldwide.

1.5 Arrange these byte measurements in order from smallest to largest: terabyte, megabyte, petabyte, gigabyte and kilobyte.

1.6 Describe the two-step translation process for preparing your C# code to execute on your particular computer.

Answers to Self-Review Exercises

1.1   a) computer programs. b) hardware. c) data hierarchy. d) machine. e) assembly languages, high-level languages. f) compilers. g) multicore. h) Universal Windows Platform (UWP).

1.2   a) classes. b) call. c) inheritance. d) requirements. e) event. f) write once, run anywhere.

1.3   a) Common Language Runtime (CLR) of the .NET Framework. b) managed. c) independence. d) IDE. e) Windows Store.

1.4   a) True. b) True. c) True. d) False: The cost per unit of secondary storage is much lower than that of primary memory. e) True. f) True. g) False. The pieces are called packets, not bytes. h) False. Hardware costs have decreased. i) True. j) False. The language is Swift, not Java. k) False. It's ASP.NET technology. l) True.

1.5   kilobyte, megabyte, gigabyte, terabyte, petabyte.

1.6   C# code is first compiled into MSIL and placed in an executable file. When the app executes, another compiler called the JIT (just-in-time) compiler in the CLR translates the MSIL in the executable file into machine-language code (for a particular platform).

Exercises

1.7   Fill in the blanks in each of the following statements:
  a) The programs that run on a computer are referred to as _____.
  b) Systems such as smartphones, appliances, game controllers, cable set-top boxes and automobiles that contain small computers are called _____.
  c) Just as characters are composed of bits, _____ are composed of characters or bytes.
  d) Information on secondary storage devices is _____; it's preserved even when the computer's power is turned off.
  e) Translator programs called _____ convert high-level language code into machine-language code.
  f) In object-oriented programming languages, we create a program unit called a(n) _____ to house the set of methods that perform its tasks.
  g) Use a building-block approach to creating your programs. Avoid reinventing the wheel—use existing pieces wherever possible. Such software _____ is a key benefit of object-oriented programming.

1.8   Fill in the blanks in each of the following statements:
  a) Although many different OOAD processes exist, a single graphical language for communicating the results of *any* OOAD process has come into wide use. This language, known as the _____, is now the most widely used graphical scheme for modeling object-oriented systems.
  b) Tim Berners-Lee developed the _____ for sharing information via "hyperlinked" text documents on the web.
  c) The CLR is a(n) _____ machine. It is software that manages the execution of programs and hides from them the underlying operating system and hardware.
  d) Converting a program to run on a different platform from which it was originally intended is called _____.
  e) Microsoft's Windows _____ is a cloud-computing platform that allows you to develop, manage and distribute your apps in the cloud.
  f) By using existing controls—which are objects—you can create powerful apps much faster than if you had to write all the code yourself. This is a key benefit of software _____.

1.9 State whether each of the following is *true* or *false*. If *false*, explain why.

a)   The smallest data item in a computer can assume the value 1 or the value 2. Such a data item is called a bit (short for "binary digit"—a digit that can assume either of *two* values).

b)   The Unicode character set is a popular subset of ASCII that represents uppercase and lowercase letters, digits and some common special characters.

c)   Each of the following is a form of computer output: data displayed on screens, printed on paper, played as audio or video on PCs and media players, used to control other devices, such as robots, 3D printers and "intelligent" appliances.

d)   Reuse helps you build more reliable and effective systems, because existing classes and components often have gone through extensive testing, debugging and performance tuning.

e)   One of the W3C's primary goals is to make the web universally accessible to everyone regardless of disabilities, language or culture.

f)   C# is available only on Microsoft Windows.

g)   The .NET Framework Class Library has millions of valuable prebuilt classes that have been tested and tuned to maximize performance.

h)   .NET programs can run on any platform.

i)   The Universal Windows Platform (UWP) is designed to provide a common platform (the underlying system on which apps run) and user experience across all of your devices including personal computers, smartphones, tablets and Xbox Live.

1.10 What is a key advantage of interpreters over compilers? What is a key disadvantage?

1.11 What is the key advantage of using the new async feature in preference to using old-style multithreading?

1.12 What are operating systems?

1.13 Why is using cloud-computing resources sometimes preferable to purchasing all the hardware you need for your own computer?

1.14 Categorize each of the following items as either hardware or software:

a)   CPU

b)   Compiler

c)   Input unit

d)   A word-processor program

e)   A C# program

1.15 Translator programs, such as assemblers and compilers, convert programs from one language (referred to as the source language) to another language (referred to as the target language). Determine which of the following statements are *true* and which are *false*:

a)   An assembler translates source-language programs into machine-language programs.

b)   High-level languages are generally machine dependent.

c)   A machine-language program requires translation before it can be run on a computer.

d)   The C# compiler translates high-level-language programs into SMIL.

1.16 Expand each of the following acronyms:

a)   W3C

b)   OOP

c)   CLR

d)   MSIL

e)   UML

f)   IDE

1.17 What are the key benefits of the .NET Framework and the CLR? What are the drawbacks?

1.18   What are the advantages to using object-oriented techniques?

1.19   You are probably wearing on your wrist one of the world's most common types of objects—a watch. Discuss how each of the following terms and concepts applies to the notion of a watch: object, attributes and behaviors.

1.20   What is the key accomplishment of the UML?

1.21   What did the chief benefit of the early Internet prove to be?

1.22   What is the key capability of the web?

1.23   What is the key vision of Microsoft's .NET initiative?

1.24   How does the .NET Framework Class Library facilitate the development of .NET apps?

1.25   Besides the obvious benefits of reuse made possible by OOP, what do many organizations report as another key benefit of OOP?

Making-a-Difference Exercises

The Making-a-Difference exercises will ask you to work on problems that really matter to individuals, communities, countries and the world.

1.26   *(Test Drive: Carbon Footprint Calculator)* Some scientists believe that carbon emissions, especially from the burning of fossil fuels, contribute significantly to global warming and that this can be combatted if individuals take steps to limit their use of carbon-based fuels. Various organizations and individuals are increasingly concerned about their "carbon footprints." Websites such as TerraPass

```
http://www.terrapass.com/carbon-footprint-calculator-2/
```

and Carbon Footprint

```
http://www.carbonfootprint.com/calculator.aspx
```

provide carbon-footprint calculators. Test drive these calculators to determine your carbon footprint. Exercises in later chapters will ask you to program your own carbon-footprint calculator. To prepare for this, research the formulas for calculating carbon footprints.

1.27   *(Test Drive: Body-Mass-Index Calculator)* By recent estimates, two-thirds of the people in the United States are overweight and about half of those are obese. This causes significant increases in illnesses such as diabetes and heart disease. To determine whether a person is overweight or obese, you can use a measure called the body mass index (BMI). The United States Department of Health and Human Services provides a BMI calculator at `http://www.nhlbi.nih.gov/guidelines/obesity/BMI/bmicalc.htm`. Use it to calculate your own BMI. An exercise in Chapter 3 will ask you to program your own BMI calculator. To prepare for this, research the formulas for calculating BMI.

1.28   *(Attributes of Hybrid Vehicles)* In this chapter you learned the basics of classes. Now you'll begin "fleshing out" aspects of a class called "Hybrid Vehicle." Hybrid vehicles are becoming increasingly popular, because they often get much better mileage than purely gasoline-powered vehicles. Browse the web and study the features of four or five of today's popular hybrid cars, then list as many of their hybrid-related attributes as you can. For example, common attributes include city-miles-per-gallon and highway-miles-per-gallon. Also list the attributes of the batteries (type, weight, etc.).

1.29   *(Gender Neutrality)* Some people want to eliminate sexism in all forms of communication. You've been asked to create a program that can process a paragraph of text and replace gender-specific words with gender-neutral ones. Assuming that you've been given a list of gender-specific words and their gender-neutral replacements (e.g., replace "wife" with "spouse," "man" with "person," "daughter" with "child" and so on), explain the procedure you'd use to read through a paragraph of text and manually perform these replacements. How might your procedure generate a strange term like "woperchild," which is actually listed in the Urban Dictionary (www.urbandictionary.com)? In Chapter 5, you'll learn that a more formal term for "procedure" is "algorithm," and that an algorithm specifies the steps to be performed and the order in which to perform them.

Making-a-Difference Resources

The *Microsoft Imagine Cup* is a global competition in which students use technology to try to solve some of the world's most difficult problems, such as environmental sustainability, ending hunger, emergency response, literacy and more. For more information about the competition and to learn about previous winners' projects, visit https://www.imaginecup.com/Custom/Index/About. You can also find several project ideas submitted by worldwide charitable organizations. For additional ideas for programming projects that can make a difference, search the web for "making a difference" and visit the following websites:

http://www.un.org/millenniumgoals
The United Nations Millennium Project seeks solutions to major worldwide issues such as environmental sustainability, gender equality, child and maternal health, universal education and more.

http://www.ibm.com/smarterplanet
The IBM® Smarter Planet website discusses how IBM is using technology to solve issues related to business, cloud computing, education, sustainability and more.

http://www.gatesfoundation.org
The Bill and Melinda Gates Foundation provides grants to organizations that work to alleviate hunger, poverty and disease in developing countries.

http://nethope.org
NetHope is a collaboration of humanitarian organizations worldwide working to solve technology problems such as connectivity, emergency response and more.

http://www.rainforestfoundation.org
The Rainforest Foundation works to preserve rainforests and to protect the rights of the indigenous people who call the rainforests home. The site includes a list of things you can do to help.

http://www.undp.org
The United Nations Development Programme (UNDP) seeks solutions to global challenges such as crisis prevention and recovery, energy and the environment, democratic governance and more.

http://www.unido.org
The United Nations Industrial Development Organization (UNIDO) seeks to reduce poverty, give developing countries the opportunity to participate in global trade, and promote energy efficiency and sustainability.

http://www.usaid.gov/
USAID promotes global democracy, health, economic growth, conflict prevention, humanitarian aid and more.

Introduction to Visual Studio and Visual Programming

2

Outline

2.1 Introduction

Visual Studio is Microsoft's Integrated Development Environment (IDE) for creating, running and debugging apps (also called applications) written in C# and various other .NET programming languages. In this chapter, we overview the Visual Studio Community 2015 IDE, then show how to create a simple Visual C# app by dragging and dropping predefined building blocks into place—a technique known as visual app development.

2.2 Overview of the Visual Studio Community 2015 IDE

There are several versions of Visual Studio. This book's examples, screen captures and discussions are based on the free Visual Studio Community 2015 running on Windows 10. See the Before You Begin section that follows the Preface for information on installing the software. With few exceptions, this book's examples can be created and run on Windows 7, 8.x or 10—we'll point out any examples that require Windows 10.

The examples will work on full versions of Visual Studio as well—though some options, menus and instructions might differ. From this point forward, we'll refer to Visual Studio Community 2015 simply as "Visual Studio" or "the IDE." We assume that you have some familiarity with Windows.

2.2.1 Introduction to Visual Studio Community 2015

[*Note:* We use the **>** character to indicate when you should select a *menu item* from a *menu*. For example, notation **File > Save All** means that you should select the **Save All** menu item from the **File** menu.]

To begin, open Visual Studio. On Windows 10, click

then select **All Apps > Visual Studio 2015**. On Windows 7, click then select **All Programs > Visual Studio 2015**. On Windows 8's **Start** screen, locate and click the Visual Studio 2015 tile, which will contain the following icon:

Initially, Visual Studio displays the **Start Page** (Fig. 2.1). Depending on your version of Visual Studio, your **Start Page** may look different. The **Start Page** contains a list of links to Visual Studio resources and web-based resources. At any time, you can return to the **Start Page** by selecting **View > Start Page**.

2.2.2 Visual Studio Themes

Visual Studio supports three themes that specify the IDE's color scheme:

- a *dark theme* (with dark window backgrounds and light text)
- a *light theme* (with light window backgrounds and dark text) and
- a *blue theme* (with light window backgrounds and dark text).

We use the blue theme throughout this book. The Before You Begin section after the Preface explains how to set this option.

2.2.3 Links on the Start Page

The **Start Page** links are organized into two columns. The left column's **Start** section contains options for building new apps or working on existing ones. The left column's **Recent** section contains links to projects you've recently created or modified.

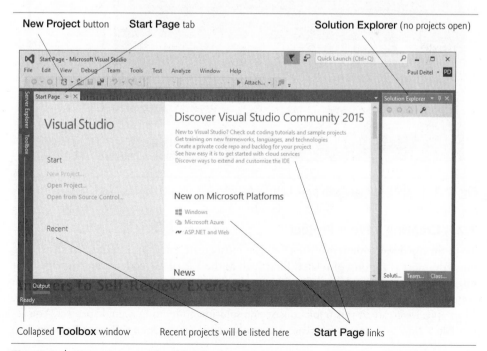

Fig. 2.1 | Start Page in Visual Studio Community 2015.

The **Start Page**'s right column—with **Discover Visual Studio Community 2015** at the top—contains links to various online documentation and resources to help you get started with Visual Studio and learn about Microsoft programming technologies. An Internet connection is required for the IDE to access most of this information.

To access more extensive information on Visual Studio, you can browse the MSDN (Microsoft Developer Network) Library at

```
https://msdn.microsoft.com/library/dd831853
```

The MSDN site contains articles, downloads and tutorials on technologies of interest to Visual Studio developers. You also can browse the web from the IDE by selecting **View > Other Windows > Web Browser.** To request a web page, type its URL into the location bar (Fig. 2.2) and press the *Enter* key—your computer, of course, must be connected to the Internet. The web page that you wish to view appears as another tab in the IDE— Figure 2.2 shows the browser tab after entering `http://msdn.microsoft.com/library`.

Web browser window tab   Location bar

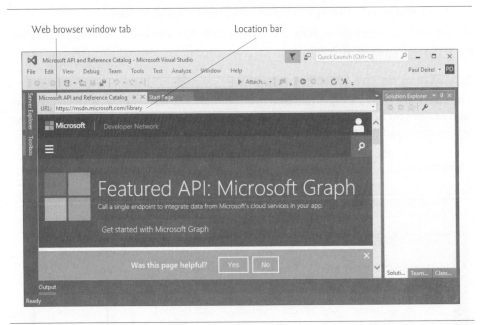

Fig. 2.2 | MSDN Library web page in Visual Studio.

2.2.4 Creating a New Project

To begin app development in Visual C#, you must create a new project or open an existing one. A project is a group of related files, such as the Visual C# code and any images that might make up an app. Visual Studio organizes apps into projects and solutions, which contain one or more projects. Multiple-project solutions are used to create large-scale apps. Most apps we create in this book consist of a solution containing a single project. You select **File > New > Project...** to create a new project or **File > Open > Project/Solution...** to open an existing one. You also can click the corresponding links in the **Start Page**'s **Start** section.

2.2.5 New Project Dialog and Project Templates

For the discussions in the next several sections, we'll create a new project. Select **File > New > Project...** to display the **New Project** dialog (Fig. 2.3). Dialogs are windows that facilitate user–computer communication.

Visual C# **Windows Forms Application** (selected)   Default project name (provided by Visual Studio)   Description of selected project (provided by Visual Studio)

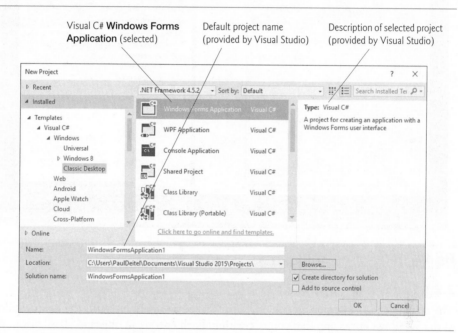

Fig. 2.3 | New Project dialog.

Visual Studio provides many templates (left column of Fig. 2.3)—the *project types* that users can create in Visual C# and other languages. The templates include Windows Forms apps, WPF apps and others—full versions of Visual Studio provide additional templates. In this chapter, you'll build a **Windows Forms Application**—an app that executes within a Windows operating system (such as Windows 7, 8 or 10) and typically has a graphical user interface (GUI). Users interact with this *visual* part of the app. GUI apps include Microsoft software products like Microsoft Word, Internet Explorer and Visual Studio, software products created by other vendors, and customized software that you and other app developers create. You'll create many Windows apps in this book.

To create a **Windows Forms Application**, under **Templates** select **Visual C# > Windows > Classic Desktop**, then in the middle column select **Windows Forms Application**. By default, Visual Studio assigns the name **WindowsFormsApplication1** to a new **Windows Forms Application** project and solution (Fig. 2.3). Click **OK** to display the IDE in **Design** view (Fig. 2.4), which contains the features that enable you to create an app's GUI.

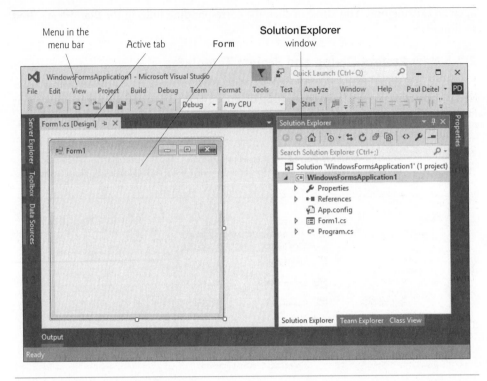

Fig. 2.4 | Design view of the IDE.

2.2.6 Forms and Controls

The rectangle in the **Design** area titled **Form1** (called a Form) represents the main window of the Windows Forms app that you're creating. Each Form is an object of class Form in the .NET Framework Class Library. Apps can have multiple Forms (windows)—however, the app you'll create in Section 2.6 and most other Windows Forms app you'll create later in this book will contain a single Form. You'll learn how to customize the Form by adding GUI controls—in Section 2.6, you'll add a Label and a PictureBox. A Label typically contains descriptive text (for example, "Welcome to Visual C#!"), and a PictureBox displays an image. Visual Studio has many preexisting controls and other components you can use to build and customize your apps. Many of these controls are discussed and used throughout the book. Other controls are available from third parties.

In this chapter, you'll work with preexisting controls from the .NET Framework Class Library. As you place controls on the Form, you'll be able to modify their properties (discussed in Section 2.4).

Collectively, the Form and controls make up the app's GUI. Users enter data into the app by typing at the keyboard, by clicking the mouse buttons and in a variety of other ways. Apps use the GUI to display instructions and other information for users to view. For example, the **New Project** dialog in Fig. 2.3 presents a GUI where the user clicks the mouse button to select a template type, then inputs a project name from the keyboard (the figure shows the default project name **WindowsFormsApplication1**).

Each open document's name is listed on a tab. To view a document when multiple documents are open, click its tab. The active tab (the tab of the currently displayed document) is highlighted (for example, **Form1.cs [Design]** in Fig. 2.4). The active tab's highlight color depends on the Visual Studio theme—the blue theme uses a yellow highlight and the light and dark themes use a blue highlight.

2.3 Menu Bar and Toolbar

Commands for managing the IDE and for developing, maintaining and executing apps are contained in menus, which are located on the menu bar of the IDE (Fig. 2.5). The set of menus displayed depends on what you're currently doing in the IDE.

| File | Edit | View | Project | Build | Debug | Team | Format | Tools | Test | Analyze | Window | Help |

Fig. 2.5 | Visual Studio menu bar.

Menus contain groups of related commands called *menu items* that, when selected, cause the IDE to perform specific actions—for example, open a window, save a file, print a file and execute an app. For example, selecting **File > New > Project...** tells the IDE to display the **New Project** dialog. The menus depicted in Fig. 2.5 are summarized in Fig. 2.6.

Menu	Contains commands for
File	Opening, closing, adding and saving projects, as well as printing project data and exiting Visual Studio.
Edit	Editing apps, such as cut, copy, paste, undo, redo, delete, find and select.
View	Displaying IDE windows (for example, **Solution Explorer**, **Toolbox**, **Properties** window) and for adding toolbars to the IDE.
Project	Managing projects and their files.
Build	Turning your app into an executable program.
Debug	Compiling, debugging (that is, identifying and correcting problems in apps) and running apps.
Team	Connecting to a Team Foundation Server—used by development teams that typically have multiple people working on the same app.
Format	Arranging and modifying a Form's controls. The **Format** menu appears *only* when a GUI component is selected in **Design** view.
Tools	Accessing additional IDE tools and options for customizing the IDE.
Test	Performing various types of automated testing on your app.
Analyze	Locating and reporting violations of the .NET Framework Design Guidelines (https://msdn.microsoft.com/library/ms229042).

Fig. 2.6 | Summary of Visual Studio menus that are displayed when a Form is in **Design** view. (Part 1 of 2.)

Menu	Contains commands for
Window	Hiding, opening, closing and displaying IDE windows.
Help	Accessing the IDE's help features.

Fig. 2.6 | Summary of Visual Studio menus that are displayed when a Form is in **Design** view. (Part 2 of 2.)

You can access many common menu commands from the toolbar (Fig. 2.7), which contains icons that graphically represent commands. By default, the standard toolbar is displayed when you run Visual Studio for the first time—it contains icons for the most commonly used commands, such as opening a file, saving files and running apps (Fig. 2.7). The icons that appear on the standard toolbar may vary, depending on the version of Visual Studio you're using. Some commands are initially disabled (grayed out or unavailable to use). These commands are enabled by Visual Studio only when you can use them. For example, Visual Studio enables the command for saving a file once you begin editing a file.

Fig. 2.7 | Standard Visual Studio toolbar.

You can customize which toolbars are displayed by selecting **View > Toolbars** then selecting a toolbar from the list in Fig. 2.8. Each toolbar you select is displayed with the other toolbars at the top of the Visual Studio window. You move a toolbar by dragging its handle

at the left side of the toolbar. To execute a command via the toolbar, click its icon.

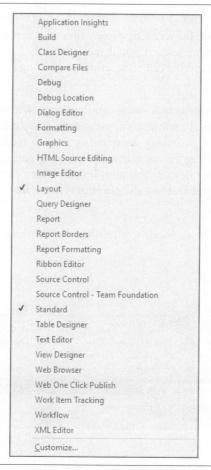

Fig. 2.8 | List of toolbars that can be added to the top of the IDE.

It can be difficult to remember what each toolbar icon represents. *Hovering* the mouse pointer over an icon highlights it and, after a brief pause, displays a description of the icon called a **tool tip** (Fig. 2.9)—these tips help you become familiar with the IDE's features and serve as useful reminders for each toolbar icon's functionality.

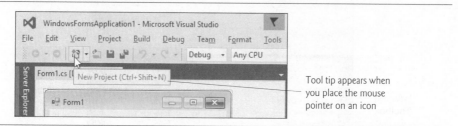

Tool tip appears when you place the mouse pointer on an icon

Fig. 2.9 | Tool tip for the **New Project** button.

2.4 Navigating the Visual Studio IDE

The IDE provides windows for accessing project files and customizing controls. This section introduces several windows that you'll use frequently when developing Visual C# apps. Each of the IDE's windows can be accessed by selecting its name in the **View** menu.

Auto-Hide

Visual Studio provides an auto-hide space-saving feature. When auto-hide is enabled for a window, a tab containing the window's name appears along the IDE window's left, right or bottom edge (Fig. 2.10). Clicking the name of an auto-hidden window displays that window (Fig. 2.11). Clicking the name again (or clicking outside) hides the window. To "pin down" a window (that is, to disable auto-hide and keep the window open), click the pin icon. When auto-hide is enabled, the pin icon is horizontal

as shown in Fig. 2.11. When a window is "pinned down," the pin icon is vertical

as shown in Fig. 2.12.

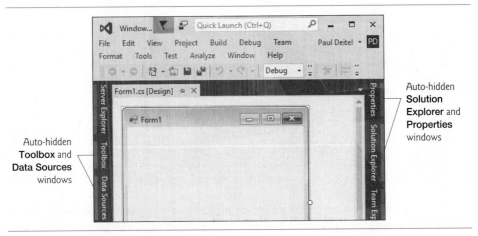

Fig. 2.10 | Auto-hide feature demonstration.

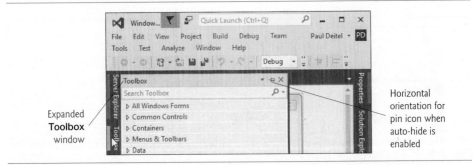

Fig. 2.11 | Displaying the hidden **Toolbox** window when auto-hide is enabled.

Toolbox
"pinned down"

Vertical
orientation for
pin icon when
window is
"pinned down"

Fig. 2.12 | Disabling auto-hide—"pinning down" a window.

The next few sections present three Visual Studio's windows that you'll use frequently—the **Solution Explorer**, the **Properties** window and the **Toolbox**. These windows display project information and include tools that help you build your apps.

2.4.1 Solution Explorer

The **Solution Explorer** window (Fig. 2.13) provides access to all of a solution's files. If it's not shown in the IDE, select **View > Solution Explorer**. When you open a new or existing solution, the **Solution Explorer** displays the solution's contents.

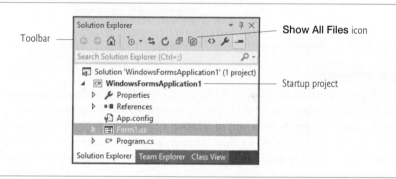

Toolbar

Show All Files icon

Startup project

Fig. 2.13 | Solution Explorer window showing the WindowsFormsApplication1 project.

The solution's startup project (shown in **bold** in the **Solution Explorer**) is the one that runs when you select **Debug > Start Debugging** (or press *F5*) or select **Debug > Start Without Debugging** (or press *Ctrl + F5* key). For a single-project solution like the examples in this book, the startup project is the only project (in this case, **WindowsFormsApplication1**). When you create an app for the first time, the **Solution Explorer** window appears as shown in Fig. 2.13. The Visual C# file that corresponds to the Form shown in Fig. 2.4 is named Form1.cs (selected in Fig. 2.13). Visual C# files use the .cs file-name extension, which is short for "C#."

By default, the IDE displays only files that you may need to edit—other files that the IDE generates are hidden. The **Solution Explorer** window includes a toolbar that contains several icons. Clicking the **Show All Files** icon (Fig. 2.13) displays all the solution's files, including those generated by the IDE. Clicking the arrow to the left of a node *expands* or *collapses* that node. Click the arrow to the left of **References** to display items grouped under that heading (Fig. 2.14). Click the arrow again to collapse the tree. Other Visual Studio windows also use this convention.

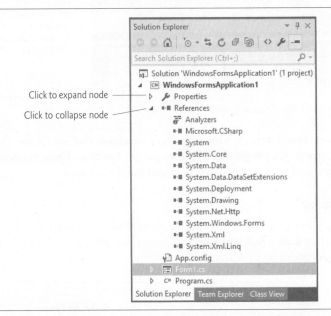

Fig. 2.14 | **Solution Explorer** with the **References** node expanded.

2.4.2 Toolbox

To display the **Toolbox** window, select **View > Toolbox**. The **Toolbox** contains the controls used to customize Forms (Fig. 2.15). With visual app development, you can "drag and drop" controls onto the Form and the IDE will write the code that creates the controls for you. This is faster and simpler than writing this code yourself. Just as you do not need to know how to build an engine to drive a car, you do not need to know how to build controls to use them. *Reusing* preexisting controls saves time and money when you develop apps. You'll use the **Toolbox** when you create your first app later in the chapter.

The **Toolbox** groups the prebuilt controls into categories—**All Windows Forms, Common Controls, Containers, Menus & Toolbars, Data, Components, Printing, Dialogs, Reporting, WPF Interoperability** and **General** are listed in Fig. 2.15. Again, note the use of arrows for expanding or collapsing a group of controls. We discuss many of the **Toolbox**'s controls and their functionality throughout the book.

2.4.3 Properties Window

If the **Properties** window is not displayed below the **Solution Explorer**, select **View > Properties Window** to display it—if the window is in auto-hide mode, pin down the window by clicking its horizontal pin icon

The **Properties** window contains the properties for the currently selected Form, control or file in the IDE. Properties specify information about the Form or control, such as its size,

Fig. 2.15 | **Toolbox** window displaying controls for the **Common Controls** group.

color and position. Each Form or control has its own set of properties. When you select a property, its description is displayed at the bottom of the **Properties** window.

Figure 2.16 shows Form1's **Properties** window—you can view by clicking anywhere in the **Form1.cs [Design]** window. The left column lists the Form's properties—the right column displays the current value of each property. You can sort the properties either

- *alphabetically* (by clicking the **Alphabetical** icon) or
- *categorically* (by clicking the **Categorized** icon).

Depending on the **Properties** window's size, some properties may be hidden from your view. You can scroll through the list of properties by dragging the scrollbox up or down inside the scrollbar, or by clicking the arrows at the top and bottom of the scrollbar. We show how to set individual properties later in this chapter.

Fig. 2.16 | Properties window.

The **Properties** window is crucial to visual app development—it allows you to quickly modify a control's properties and, rather than writing code yourself, lets the IDE write code for you "behind the scenes." You can see which properties are available for modification and, in many cases, can learn the range of acceptable values for a given property. The **Properties** window displays a brief description of the selected property, helping you understand its purpose.

2.5 Help Menu and Context-Sensitive Help

Microsoft provides extensive help documentation via the **Help** menu, which is an excellent way to get information quickly about Visual Studio, Visual C# and more. Visual Studio provides context-sensitive help pertaining to the "current content" (that is, the items around the location of the mouse cursor). To use context-sensitive help, click an item, then press the *F1* key. The help documentation is displayed in a web browser window. To return to the IDE, either close the browser window or select the IDE's icon in your Windows task bar.

2.6 Visual Programming: Creating a Simple App that Displays Text and an Image

Next, we create an app that displays the text "Welcome to C# Programming!" and an image of the Deitel & Associates bug mascot. The app consists of a Form that uses a Label and a PictureBox. Figure 2.17 shows the final app executing. The app and the bug image are available with this chapter's examples—see the Before You Begin section following the Preface for download instructions. We assume you placed the examples in your user account's Documents folder in a subfolder named examples.

Fig. 2.17 | Simple app executing.

In this example, you won't write any C# code. Instead, you'll use visual app-development techniques. Visual Studio processes your actions (such as mouse clicking, dragging and dropping) to generate app code. Chapter 3 begins our discussion of writing app code. Throughout the book, you'll produce increasingly substantial and powerful apps that will include code written by you and code generated by Visual Studio. The generated code can be difficult for novices to understand—but you'll rarely need to look at it.

Visual app development is useful for building GUI-intensive apps that require a significant amount of user interaction. To create, save, run and terminate this first app, perform the following steps.

Step 1: Closing the Open Project
If the project you were working with earlier in this chapter is still open, close it by selecting **File > Close Solution**.

Step 2: Creating the New Project
To create a new Windows Forms app:

1. Select **File > New > Project...** to display the **New Project** dialog (Fig. 2.18).

2. Select **Windows Forms Application**. Name the project **ASimpleApp**, specify the **Location** where you want to save it and click **OK**. We stored the app in the IDE's default location—in your user account's Documents folder under the Visual Studio 2015\Projects.

As you saw earlier in this chapter, when you first create a new Windows Forms app, the IDE opens in **Design** view (that is, the app is being designed and is not executing). The text **Form1.cs [Design]** in the tab containing the Form means that we're designing the Form *visually* rather than *programmatically*. An asterisk (*) at the end of the text in a tab indicates that you've changed the file and the changes have not yet been saved.

Type the project   Select the **Windows Forms**
name here   **Application** template

Fig. 2.18 | New Project dialog.

Step 3: Setting the Text in the Form's Title Bar

The text in the Form's title bar is determined by the Form's **Text** property (Fig. 2.19). If the **Properties** window is not open, select **View > Properties Window** and pin down the window so it doesn't auto hide. Click anywhere in the Form to display the Form's properties in the **Properties** window. In the textbox to the right of the Text property, type "A Simple App", as in Fig. 2.19. Press the *Enter* key—the Form's title bar is updated immediately (Fig. 2.20).

Fig. 2.19 | Setting the Form's Text property in the **Properties** window.

Fig. 2.20 | Form with updated title-bar text and enabled sizing handles.

Step 4: Resizing the Form

The Form's size is specified in pixels (that is, dots on the screen). By default, a Form is 300 pixels wide and 300 pixels tall. You can resize the Form by dragging one of its sizing handles (the small white squares that appear around the Form, as shown in Fig. 2.20). Using the mouse, select the bottom-right sizing handle and drag it down and to the right to make the Form larger. As you drag the mouse (Fig. 2.21), the IDE's status bar (at the bottom of the IDE) shows the current width and height in pixels. We set the Form to 400 pixels wide by 360 pixels tall. You also can do this via the Form's Size property in the **Properties** window.

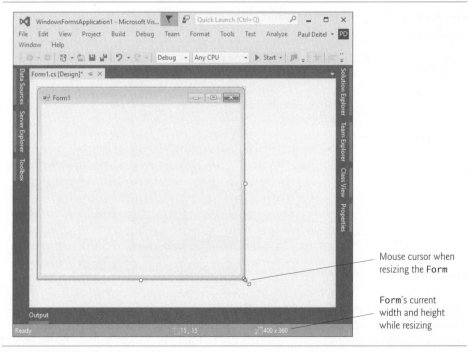

Fig. 2.21 | Resizing the Form.

Step 5: Changing the Form's Background Color

The `BackColor property` specifies a Form's or control's background color. Clicking `Back-Color` in the **Properties** window causes a down-arrow button to appear next to the value of the property (Fig. 2.22). Clicking the down-arrow button displays other options, which vary depending on the property. In this case, the arrow displays tabs for **Custom**, **Web** and **System** (the default). Click the **Custom** tab to display the palette (a grid of colors). Select the box that represents light blue. Once you select the color, the palette closes and the Form's background color changes to light blue (Fig. 2.23).

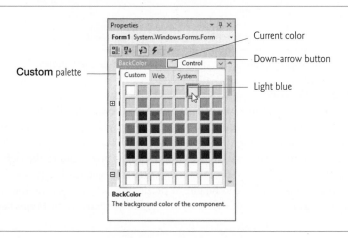

Fig. 2.22 | Changing the Form's `BackColor` property.

Fig. 2.23 | Form with new `BackColor` property applied.

Step 6: Adding a `Label` Control to the Form

For the app we're creating in this chapter, the typical controls we use are located in the **Toolbox**'s **Common Controls** group, and also can be found in the **All Windows Forms** group. If the **Toolbox** is *not* already open, select **View > Toolbox** to display the set of controls you'll use for creating your apps. If either group name is collapsed, expand it by clicking the arrow to the left of the group name (the **All Windows Forms** and **Common Controls** groups are shown in Fig. 2.15). Next, double click the Label control in the **Toolbox** to add a La-bel in the Form's upper-left corner (Fig. 2.24)—each Label you add to the Form is an object of class Label from the .NET Framework Class Library. [*Note:* If the Form is behind the **Toolbox**, you may need to hide or pin down the **Toolbox** to see the Label.] Although double clicking any **Toolbox** control places the control on the Form, you also can "drag" controls from the **Toolbox** to the Form—you may prefer dragging the control because you can position it wherever you want. The Label displays the text **label1** by default. By default, the Label's BackColor is the same as the Form's.

Label control ————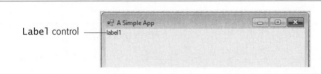

Fig. 2.24 | Adding a Label to the Form.

Step 7: Customizing the Label's Appearance
Click the Label's text in the Form to select it and display its properties in the **Properties** window. The Label's Text property determines the text that the Label displays. The Form and Label each have their own Text property—Forms and controls can have the *same* property names (such as Text, BackColor etc.) without conflict. Each common properties purpose can vary by control. Perform the following steps:

1. Set the Label's Text property to Welcome to C# Programming!. The Label resizes to fit all the typed text on one line.

2. By default, the **AutoSize property** of the Label is set to True so the Label can update its own size to fit all of its text. Set the AutoSize property to False so that you can change the Label's size, then resize the Label (using the sizing handles) so that the text fits.

3. Move the Label to the top center of the Form by dragging it or by using the keyboard's left and right arrow keys to adjust its position (Fig. 2.25). Alternatively, when the Label is selected, you can center it horizontally by selecting **Format > Center In Form > Horizontally.**

Sizing handles ———— 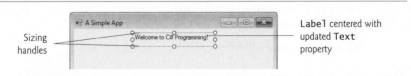 ———— Label centered with updated Text property

Fig. 2.25 | GUI after the Form and Label have been customized.

Step 8: Setting the Label's Font Size
To change the font type and appearance of the Label's text:

1. Select the value of the **Font property**, which causes an ellipsis button to appear next to the value (Fig. 2.26)—you can click this button to display a dialog of op-

tions for the property. Click the ellipsis button to display the **Font** dialog (Fig. 2.27).

Fig. 2.26 | **Properties** window displaying the Label's Font property.

Fig. 2.27 | **Font** dialog for selecting fonts, styles and sizes.

2. You can select the font name (the font options may be different, depending on your system), font style (**Regular, Italic, Bold,** etc.) and font size (**16, 18, 20,** etc.) in this dialog. The **Sample** text shows the selected font settings. Under **Font,** select **Segoe UI,** Microsoft's recommended font for user interfaces. Under **Size,** select **24** points and click **OK.**

3. If the Label's text does not fit on a single line, it *wraps* to the next line. Resize the Label so that the words "Welcome to" appear on the Label's first line and the words "C# Programming!" appear on the second line.

4. Re-center the Label horizontally.

Step 9: Aligning the Label's Text
Select the Label's **TextAlign** property, which determines how the text is aligned within the Label. A three-by-three grid of buttons representing alignment choices is displayed (Fig. 2.28). The position of each button corresponds to where the text appears in the Label. For this app, set the TextAlign property to MiddleCenter in the three-by-three grid—this selection centers the text horizontally and vertically within the Label. The other TextAlign values, such as TopLeft, TopRight, and BottomCenter, can be used to position

the text anywhere within a Label. Certain alignment values may require that you resize the Label to fit the text better.

Fig. 2.28 | Centering the Label's text.

Step 10: Adding a PictureBox to the Form
The PictureBox control displays images. Locate the PictureBox in the **Toolbox** (Fig. 2.15) and double click it to add it to the Form—each PictureBox you add to the Form is an object of class PictureBox from the .NET Framework Class Library. When the PictureBox appears, move it underneath the Label, either by dragging it or by using the arrow keys (Fig. 2.29).

Fig. 2.29 | Inserting and aligning a PictureBox.

Step 11: Inserting an Image
Click the PictureBox to display its properties in the **Properties** window (Fig. 2.30), then:

1. Locate and select the **Image property**, which displays a preview of the selected image or **(none)** if no image is selected.

2. Click the ellipsis button to display the **Select Resource** dialog (Fig. 2.31), which is used to import files, such as images, for use in an app.

Image property value
(no image selected)

Fig. 2.30 | Image property of the `PictureBox`.

Fig. 2.31 | Select Resource dialog to select an image for the `PictureBox`.

3. Click the **Import...** button to browse for an image, select the image file and click **OK** to add it to your project. We used `bug.png` from this chapter's examples folder. Supported image formats include PNG (Portable Network Graphics), GIF (Graphic Interchange Format), JPEG (Joint Photographic Experts Group) and BMP (Windows bitmap). Depending image's size, it's possible that only a portion of the image will be previewed in the **Select Resource** dialog—you can resize the dialog to see more of the image (Fig. 2.32). Click **OK** to use the image.

4. To scale the image to fit in the `PictureBox`, change the `SizeMode property` to `StretchImage` (Fig. 2.33). Resize the `PictureBox`, making it larger (Fig. 2.34), then re-center the `PictureBox` horizontally.

Step 12: Saving the Project
Select **File > Save All** to save the entire solution. The solution file (which has the filename extension `.sln`) contains the name and location of its project, and the project file (which has the filename extension `.csproj`) contains the names and locations of all the files in the project. If you want to reopen your project at a later time, simply open its `.sln` file.

Image resource name

Fig. 2.32 | Select Resource dialog displaying a preview of selected image.

SizeMode property

SizeMode property set to StretchImage

Fig. 2.33 | Scaling an image to the size of the PictureBox.

Newly inserted image

Fig. 2.34 | PictureBox displaying an image.

Step 13: Running the Project

Recall that up to this point we have been working in the IDE design mode (that is, the app being created is not executing). In **run mode**, the app is executing, and you can interact with only a few IDE features—features that are not available are disabled (grayed out). Select **Debug > Start Debugging** to execute the app (or press the *F5* key). The IDE enters run mode and displays "**(Running)**" next to the app's name in the IDE's title bar. Figure 2.35 shows the running app, which appears in its own window outside the IDE.

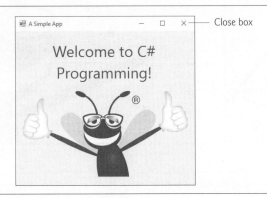

Fig. 2.35 | IDE in run mode, with the running app in the foreground.

Step 14: Terminating the App

You can terminate the app by clicking its close box

in the top-right corner of the running app's window. This action stops the app's execution and returns the IDE to design mode. You also can select **Debug > Stop Debugging** to terminate the app.

2.7 Wrap-Up

In this chapter, we introduced key features of the Visual Studio IDE. You visually designed a working Visual C# app without writing any code. Visual C# app development is a mixture of the two styles—visual app development allows you to develop GUIs easily and avoid tedious GUI programming and "conventional" programming (which we introduce in Chapter 3) allows you to specify the behavior of your apps.

You created a Visual C# Windows `Forms` app with one `Form`. You worked with the IDE's **Solution Explorer**, **Toolbox** and **Properties** windows, which are essential to developing Visual C# apps. We also demonstrated context-sensitive help, which displays help topics related to selected controls or text.

You used visual app development to design an app's GUI by adding a `Label` and a `PictureBox` control onto a `Form`. You used the **Properties** window to set a `Form`'s `Text` and `BackColor` properties. You learned that `Label` controls display text and that `PictureBox`es display images. You displayed text in a `Label` and added an image to a `PictureBox`. You also worked with the `Label`'s `AutoSize`, `TextAlign` and `Font` properties and the `PictureBox`'s `Image` and `SizeMode` properties.

In the next chapter, we discuss "nonvisual," or "conventional," programming—you'll create your first apps with C# code that you write, instead of having Visual Studio write the code. You'll learn memory concepts and write code that displays information on the screen, receives inputs from the user at the keyboard, performs arithmetic operations and makes decisions.

2.8 Web Resources

Please take a moment to visit each of these sites.

`https://www.visualstudio.com/`
The home page for Microsoft Visual Studio. The site includes news, documentation, downloads and other resources.

`https://social.msdn.microsoft.com/Forums/vstudio/en-US/home?forum=csharpgeneral`
This site provides access to the Microsoft Visual C# forums, which you can use to get your Visual C# language and IDE questions answered.

`https://msdn.microsoft.com/magazine/default.aspx`
This is the Microsoft Developer Network Magazine site. This site provides articles and code on many Visual C# and .NET app development topics. There is also an archive of past issues.

`http://stackoverflow.com/`
In addition to the Microsoft forums, StackOverflow is an excellent site for getting your programming questions answered for most programming languages and technologies.

Summary

Section 2.1 Introduction
- Visual Studio is Microsoft's Integrated Development Environment (IDE) for creating, running and debugging apps written in a variety of .NET programming languages.
- Creating simple apps by dragging and dropping predefined building blocks into place is called visual app development.

Section 2.2 Overview of the Visual Studio Community 2015 IDE
- The **Start Page** contains links to Visual Studio IDE resources and web-based resources.
- A project is a group of related files that compose a app.
- Visual Studio organizes apps into projects and solutions. A solution may contain one or more projects.
- Dialogs are windows that facilitate user–computer communication.
- Visual Studio provides templates for the project types you can create.
- A `Form` represents the main window of the Windows `Forms` app that you're creating.
- Collectively, the `Form` and controls constitute the app's graphical user interface (GUI), which is the visual part of the app with which the user interacts.

Section 2.3 Menu Bar and Toolbar
- Commands for managing the IDE and for developing, maintaining and executing apps are contained in the menus, which are located on the menu bar.

- Menus contain groups of commands (menu items) that, when selected, cause the IDE to perform actions (for example, open a window, save a file, print a file and execute an app).
- Tool tips help you become familiar with the IDE's features.

Section 2.4 Navigating the Visual Studio IDE
- The **Solution Explorer** window lists all the files in the solution.
- The **Toolbox** contains controls for customizing Forms.
- By using visual app development, you can place predefined controls onto the Form instead of writing the code yourself.
- Clicking an auto-hidden window's name opens that window. Clicking the name again hides it. To "pin down" a window (that is, to disable auto-hide), click its pin icon.
- The **Properties** window displays the properties for a Form, control or file (in **Design** view). Properties are information about a Form or control, such as size, color and position. The **Properties** window allows you to modify Forms and controls visually, without writing code.
- Each control has its own set of properties. The left column of the **Properties** window shows the property names and the right column displays the property values. This window's toolbar contains options for organizing properties alphabetically when the **Alphabetical** icon is selected or categorically (for example, **Appearance**, **Behavior**, **Design**) when the **Categorized** icon is selected.

Section 2.5 Help Menu and Context-Sensitive Help
- Extensive help documentation is available via the **Help** menu.
- Context-sensitive help brings up a list of relevant help articles. To use context-sensitive help, select an item and press the *F1* key.

Section 2.6 Visual Programming: Creating a Simple App that Displays Text and an Image
- Visual C# app development usually involves a combination of writing a portion of the app code and having Visual Studio generate the remaining code.
- The text that appears at the top of the Form (the title bar) is specified in the Form's Text property.
- To resize the Form, click and drag one of the Form's enabled sizing handles (the small squares around the Form). Enabled sizing handles appear as white boxes.
- The BackColor property specifies the background color of a Form. The Form's background color is the default background color for any controls added to the Form.
- Double clicking any **Toolbox** control icon places a control of that type on the Form. Alternatively, you can drag and drop controls from the **Toolbox** to the Form.
- The Label's Text property determines the text (if any) that the Label displays. The Form and Label each have their own Text property.
- A property's ellipsis button, when clicked, displays a dialog containing additional options.
- In the **Font** dialog, you can select the font for text in the user interface.
- The TextAlign property determines how the text is aligned within a Label's boundaries.
- The PictureBox control displays images. The Image property specifies the image to displayed.
- An app that is in design mode is not executing.
- In run mode, the app is executing—you can interact with only a few IDE features.
- When designing an app visually, the name of the Visual C# file appears in the project tab, followed by **[Design]**.
- Terminate an app's execution by clicking its close box.

Terminology

active tab
Alphabetical icon
auto-hide
`AutoSize` property of `Label`
`BackColor` property of `Form`
Categorized icon
component selection drop-down list
context-sensitive help
control
Custom tab
Design view
dialog
dragging
ellipsis button
Font dialog
`Font` property of `Label`
`Form`
graphical user interface (GUI)
Help menu
icon
`Image` property of `PictureBox`
`Label`
New Project dialog
palette

`PictureBox`
project
Properties window
property of a `Form` or control
run mode
scrollbar
scrollbox
Select Resource dialog
Show All Files icon
`SizeMode` property of `PictureBox`
sizing handle
solution
Solution Explorer in Visual Studio
Start Page
startup project
`StretchImage` value
templates for projects
`Text` property
`TextAlign` property of `Label`
tool tip
toolbar
visual app development
Visual Studio
Windows `Forms` app

Self-Review Exercises

2.1 Fill in the blanks in each of the following statements:
a) The technique of _____ allows you to create GUIs without writing any code.
b) A(n) _____ is a group of one or more projects that collectively form a Visual C# app.
c) The _____ feature hides a window in the IDE.
d) A(n) _____ appears when the mouse pointer hovers over an icon.
e) The _____ window allows you to browse solution files.
f) The properties in the **Properties** window can be sorted _____ or _____.
g) A Form's _____ property specifies the text displayed in the Form's title bar.
h) The _____ contains the controls that you can add to a Form.
i) _____ displays relevant help articles, based on the current context.
j) The _____ property specifies how text is aligned within a `Label`'s boundaries.

2.2 State whether each of the following is *true* or *false*. If *false*, explain why.
a) ✕ toggles auto-hide for a window.
b) The toolbar icons represent various menu commands.
c) The toolbar contains icons that represent controls you can drag onto a Form.
d) Both Forms and Labels have a title bar.
e) Control properties can be modified only by writing code.
f) PictureBoxes typically display images.
g) Visual C# files use the file extension `.csharp`.
h) A Form's background color is set using the `BackColor` property.

Answers to Self-Review Exercises

2.1 a) visual app development. b) solution. c) auto-hide. d) tool tip. e) **Solution Explorer**. f) alphabetically, categorically. g) Text. h) **Toolbox**. i) context-sensitive help. j) TextAlign.

2.2 a) False. The pin icon (⊟) toggles auto-hide. ✕ closes a window. b) True. c) False. The **Toolbox** contains icons that represent such controls. d) False. Forms have a title bar but Labels do not (although they do have Label text). e) False. Control properties can be modified using the **Properties** window. f) True. g) False. Visual C# files use the file extension .cs. h) True.

Exercises

2.3 Fill in the blanks in each of the following statements:
   a) When an ellipsis button is clicked, a(n) _____ is displayed.
   b) Using _____ help immediately displays a relevant help article.
   c) GUI is an acronym for _____.
   d) The _____ property specifies which image a PictureBox displays.
   e) The _____ menu contains commands for arranging and displaying windows.

2.4 State whether each of the following is *true* or *false*. If *false*, explain why.
   a) You can add a control to a Form by double clicking its control icon in the **Toolbox**.
   b) The Form, Label and PictureBox have identical properties.
   c) If your machine is connected to the Internet, you can browse websites from the Visual Studio IDE.
   d) Visual C# app developers usually create complex apps without writing any code.
   e) Sizing handles are visible during execution.

2.5 Some features that appear throughout Visual Studio perform similar actions in different contexts. Explain and give examples of how the ellipsis buttons, down-arrow buttons and tool tips act in this manner. Why do you think the Visual Studio IDE was designed this way?

2.6 Briefly describe each of the following terms:
   a) toolbar
   b) menu bar
   c) **Toolbox**
   d) control
   e) Form
   f) solution

Note Regarding Exercises 2.7–2.11

In the following exercises, you're asked to create GUIs using controls that we have not yet discussed in this book. These exercises give you practice with visual app development only—the apps do not perform any actions. You place controls from the **Toolbox** on a Form to familiarize yourself with what each control looks like. If you follow the step-by-step instructions, you should be able to recreate the sample GUIs we show.

2.7 *(Notepad GUI)* Create the GUI for the notepad as shown in Fig. 2.36.
   a) *Manipulating the Form's properties.* Change the Text property of the Form to My Notepad. Change the Font property to 9pt Segoe UI—the recommended font for Windows apps.
   b) *Adding a MenuStrip control to the Form.* Add a MenuStrip to the Form. After inserting the MenuStrip, add items by clicking the **Type Here** section, typing a menu name (for example, **File**, **Edit**, **View** and **About**) and then pressing *Enter*.

Fig. 2.36 | Notepad GUI.

c) *Adding a RichTextBox to the Form.* Drag this control onto the Form. Use the sizing handles to resize and position the RichTextBox as shown in Fig. 2.36. Change the Text property to Enter text here.

2.8 *(Calendar and Appointments GUI)* Create the GUI for the calendar as shown in Fig. 2.37.

Fig. 2.37 | Calendar and appointments GUI.

a) *Manipulating the Form's properties.* Change the Text property of the Form to My Scheduler. Change the Font property to 9pt Segoe UI. Set the Form's Size property to 275, 400.

b) *Adding Labels to the Form.* Add two Labels to the Form. Both should be of equal size (231, 23; remember to set the AutoSize property to False) and should be centered in the Form horizontally, as shown. Set the Label's Text properties to match Fig. 2.37. Use 12-point font size. Also, set the BackColor property to Yellow.

c) *Adding a MonthCalendar control to the Form.* Add this control to the Form and center it horizontally in the appropriate place between the two Labels.

d) *Adding a RichTextBox control to the Form.* Add a RichTextBox control to the Form and center it below the second Label. Resize the RichTextBox accordingly.

2.9   *(Calculator GUI)* Create the GUI for the calculator as shown in Fig. 2.38.

Fig. 2.38 | Calculator GUI.

a) *Manipulating the Form's properties.* Change the Text property of the Form to Calculator. Change the Font property to 9pt Segoe UI. Change the Size property of the Form to 258, 210.

b) *Adding a TextBox to the Form.* Set the TextBox's Text property in the **Properties** window to 0. Stretch the TextBox and position it as shown in Fig. 2.38. Set the TextAlign property to Right—this right aligns text displayed in the TextBox.

c) *Adding the first Panel to the Form.* Panel controls are used to group other controls. Add a Panel to the Form. Change the Panel's BorderStyle property to Fixed3D to make the inside of the Panel appear recessed. Change the Size property to 90, 120. This Panel will contain the calculator's numeric keys.

d) *Adding the second Panel to the Form.* Change the Panel's BorderStyle property to Fixed3D. Change the Size property to 62, 120. This Panel will contain the calculator's operator keys.

e) *Adding the third (and last) Panel to the Form.* Change the Panel's BorderStyle property to Fixed3D. Change the Size property to 54, 62. This Panel contains the calculator's **C** (clear) and **C/A** (clear all) keys.

f) *Adding Buttons to the Form.* There are 20 Buttons on the calculator. Add a Button to the Panel by dragging and dropping it on the Panel. Change the Text property of each Button to the calculator key it represents. The value you enter in the Text property will appear on the face of the Button. Finally, resize the Buttons, using their Size properties. Each Button labeled 0–9, *, /, -, = and . should have a size of 23, 23. The **00** Button has size 52, 23. The **OFF** Button has size 54, 23. The **+** Button is sized 23, 81. The **C** (clear) and **C/A** (clear all) Buttons are sized 44, 23.

2.10   *(Alarm Clock GUI)* Create the GUI for the alarm clock as shown in Fig. 2.39.

Fig. 2.39 | Alarm clock GUI.

a) *Manipulating the Form's properties.* Change the Text property of the Form to Alarm Clock. Change the Font property to 9pt Segoe UI. Change the Size property of the Form to 438, 170.

b) *Adding Buttons to the Form.* Add seven Buttons to the Form. Change the Text property of each Button to the appropriate text. Align the Buttons as shown.

c) *Adding a GroupBox to the Form.* GroupBoxes are like Panels, except that GroupBoxes display a title. Change the Text property to AM/PM, and set the Size property to 100, 50. Center the GroupBox horizontally on the Form.

d) *Adding AM/PM RadioButtons to the GroupBox.* Place two RadioButtons in the GroupBox. Change the Text property of one RadioButton to AM and the other to PM. Align the RadioButtons as shown.

e) *Adding the time Label to the Form.* Add a Label to the Form and change its Text property to 00:00:00. Change the BorderStyle property to Fixed3D and the BackColor to Black. Use the Font property to make the time bold and 12pt. Change the ForeColor to Silver (located in the **Web** tab) to make the time stand out against the black background. Position the Label as shown.

2.11   *(Radio GUI)* Create the GUI for the radio as shown in Fig. 2.40. [*Note:* The image used in this exercise is located in this chapter's examples folder.]

Fig. 2.40 | Radio GUI.

a) *Manipulating the Form's properties.* Change the Font property to 9pt Segoe UI. Change the Form's Text property to Radio and the Size to 427, 194.

b) *Adding the Pre-set Stations GroupBox and Buttons.* Set the GroupBox's Size to 180, 55 and its Text to Pre-set Stations. Add six Buttons to the GroupBox. Set each one's Size to 23, 23. Change the Buttons' Text properties to 1, 2, 3, 4, 5, 6, respectively.

c) *Adding the Speakers GroupBox and CheckBoxes.* Set the GroupBox's Size to 120, 55 and its Text to Speakers. Add two CheckBoxes to the GroupBox. Set the Text properties for the CheckBoxes to Rear and Front.

d) *Adding the Power On/Off Button.* Add a Button to the Form. Set its Text to Power On/Off and its Size to 75, 55.

e) *Adding the Volume Control GroupBox, the Mute CheckBox and the Volume TrackBar.* Add a GroupBox to the Form. Set its Text to Volume Control and its Size to 180, 70. Add a CheckBox to the GroupBox. Set its Text to Mute. Add a TrackBar to the GroupBox.

f) *Adding the* **Tuning** *GroupBox, the radio station* Label *and the* **AM/FM** *RadioButtons.* Add a GroupBox to the Form. Set its Text to Tuning and its Size to 120, 70. Add a Label to the GroupBox. Set its AutoSize to False, its Size to 50, 44, its BackColor to Black, its ForeColor to Silver, its font to 12pt bold and its TextAlign to MiddleCenter. Set its Text to 92.9. Place the Label as shown in the figure. Add two RadioButtons to the GroupBox. Set the Text of one to AM and of the other to FM.

g) *Adding the image.* Add a PictureBox to the Form. Set its SizeMode to StretchImage and its Size to 55, 70. Set the Image property to MusicNote.gif (located in this chapter's examples folder).

Introduction to C# App Programming

3

Objectives

In this chapter you'll:

- Write simple C# apps using code rather than visual programming.

- Input data from the keyboard and output data to the screen.

- Use C# 6's **string** interpolation to create formatted **string**s by inserting values into **string** literals.

- Declare and use data of various types.

- Store data in memory and retrieve it.

- Use arithmetic operators.

- Determine the order in which operators are applied.

- Write decision-making statements with equality and relational operators.

3.1 Introduction

We now introduce C# programming. Most of the C# apps you'll study in this book process information and display results. In this chapter, we introduce console apps—these input and output text in a *console window*, which in Windows is known as the Command Prompt.

We begin with several examples that simply display messages on the screen. We then demonstrate an app that obtains two numbers from a user, calculates their sum and displays the result. You'll perform various arithmetic calculations and save the results for later use. Many apps contain logic that makes *decisions*—the last example in this chapter demonstrates decision-making fundamentals by showing you how to compare numbers and display messages based on the comparison results. For example, the app displays a message indicating that two numbers are equal only if they have the same value. We analyze each code example one line at a time.

3.2 Simple App: Displaying a Line of Text

Let's consider a simple app that displays a line of text. Figure 3.1 shows the app's source code and its output. The app illustrates several important C# features. Each app we present in this book includes line numbers, which are *not* part of actual C# code. In the Before You Begin section following the Preface, we show how to display line numbers for your C# code in Visual Studio. We'll soon see that line 10 does the real work of the app—namely, displaying the phrase `Welcome to C# Programming!` on the screen. We now discuss each line of the app.

```
1   // Fig. 3.1: Welcome1.cs
2   // Text-displaying app.
3   using System;
4
5   class Welcome1
6   {
7      // Main method begins execution of C# app
8      static void Main()
9      {
10         Console.WriteLine("Welcome to C# Programming!");
11      } // end Main
12   } // end class Welcome1
```

```
Welcome to C# Programming!
```

Fig. 3.1 | Text-displaying app.

3.2.1 Comments

Line 1

```
// Fig. 3.1: Welcome1.cs
```

begins with `//`, indicating that the remainder of the line is a comment. You'll insert comments to document your apps and improve their readability. The C# compiler ignores comments, so they do *not* cause the computer to perform any action when the app executes. We begin every source-code file with a comment indicating the figure number and the name of the file in which the code is stored.

A comment that begins with `//` is called a single-line comment, because it terminates at the end of the line on which it appears. A `//` comment also can begin in the middle of a line and continue until the end of that line (as in lines 7, 11 and 12).

Delimited comments such as

```
/* This is a delimited comment.
   It can be split over many lines */
```

can be split over several lines. This type of comment begins with the delimiter `/*` and ends with the delimiter `*/`. All text between the delimiters is ignored by the compiler.

Common Programming Error 3.1

Forgetting one of the delimiters of a delimited comment is a syntax error. A programming language's syntax specifies the grammatical rules for writing code in that language. A syntax error occurs when the compiler encounters code that violates C#'s language rules. In this case, the compiler does not produce an executable file. Instead, it issues one or more error messages to help you identify and fix the incorrect code. Syntax errors are also called compiler errors, compile-time errors or compilation errors, because the compiler detects them during the compilation phase. You cannot execute your app until you correct all the compilation errors in it. We'll see that some compile-time errors are not syntax errors.

Error-Prevention Tip 3.1

When the compiler reports an error, the error may not be in the line indicated by the error message. First, check the line for which the error was reported. If that line does not contain syntax errors, check several preceding lines.

Line 2

```
// Text-displaying app.
```

is a single-line comment that describes the purpose of the app.

3.2.2 using Directive

Line 3

```
using System;
```

is a **using** directive that tells the compiler where to look for a class that's used in this app. A great strength of Visual C# is its rich set of predefined classes that you can *reuse* rather than "reinventing the wheel." These classes are organized under **namespaces**—named collections of related classes. Collectively, .NET's predefined namespaces are known as .NET Framework Class Library. Each **using** directive identifies a namespace containing classes that a C# app should be able to use. The **using** directive in line 3 indicates that this example intends to use classes from the System namespace, which contains the predefined Console class (discussed shortly) used in line 10, and many other useful classes.

Error-Prevention Tip 3.2

Forgetting to include a using directive for a namespace that contains a class used in your app typically results in a compilation error, containing a message such as "The name 'Console' does not exist in the current context." When this occurs, check that you provided the proper using directives and that the names in them are spelled correctly, including proper use of uppercase and lowercase letters. In the editor, when you hover over an error's red squiggly line, Visual Studio displays a box containing the link "Show potential fixes." If a using directive is missing, one potential fix shown is to add the using directive to your code—simply click that fix to have Visual Studio edit your code.

For each new .NET class we use, we indicate the namespace in which it's located. This information is important, because it helps you locate descriptions of each class in the .NET documentation. A web-based version of this documentation can be found at

```
https://msdn.microsoft.com/library/w0x726c2
```

This also can be accessed via the **Help** menu. You can click the name of any .NET class or method, then press the *F1* key to get more information. Finally, you can learn about the contents of a given namespace by going to

```
https://msdn.microsoft.com/namespace
```

So

```
https://msdn.microsoft.com/System
```

takes you to namespace System's documentation.

3.2.3 Blank Lines and Whitespace

Line 4 is simply a *blank line*. Blank lines and space characters make code easier to read, and together with tab characters are known as whitespace. Space characters and tabs are known specifically as whitespace characters. Whitespace is ignored by the compiler.

3.2.4 Class Declaration

Line 5

```
class Welcome1
```

begins a class declaration for the class named `Welcome1`. Every app consists of at least one class declaration that's defined by you—the programmer. These are known as user-defined classes. The `class` keyword introduces a class declaration and is immediately followed by the class name (`Welcome1`). Keywords (also called reserved words) are reserved for use by C#.

Class Name Convention

By convention, all class names begin with a capital letter and capitalize the first letter of each word they include (e.g., `SampleClassName`). This naming convention is known as camel case, because the uppercase letters stand out like a camel's humps. When the first letter is capitalized, it's known as Pascal Case. A class name is an identifier—a series of characters consisting of letters, digits and underscores (_) that does not begin with a digit and does not contain spaces. Some valid identifiers are `Welcome1`, `identifier`, `_value` and `m_inputField1`. The name `7button` is *not* a valid identifier because it begins with a digit, and the name `input field` is *not* a valid identifier because it contains a space. Normally, an identifier that does not begin with a capital letter is not the name of a class. C# is case sensitive—that is, uppercase and lowercase letters are distinct, so `a1` and `A1` are different (but both valid) identifiers. Keywords are always spelled with all lowercase letters. The complete list of C# keywords is shown in Fig. 3.2.[1]

Good Programming Practice 3.1

By convention, always begin a class name's identifier with a capital letter and start each subsequent word in the identifier with a capital letter.

Common Programming Error 3.2

C# is case sensitive. Not using the proper uppercase and lowercase letters for an identifier normally causes a compilation error.

Common Programming Error 3.3

Using a keyword as an identifier is a compilation error.

---

1. The contextual keywords at the bottom of Fig. 3.2 can be used as identifiers outside the contexts in which they're keywords, but for clarity this is not recommended.

Keywords and contextual keywords					
abstract	as	base	bool	break	byte
case	catch	char	checked	class	const
continue	decimal	default	delegate	do	double
else	enum	event	explicit	extern	false
finally	fixed	float	for	foreach	goto
if	implicit	in	int	interface	internal
is	lock	long	namespace	new	null
object	operator	out	override	params	private
protected	public	readonly	ref	return	sbyte
sealed	short	sizeof	stackalloc	static	string
struct	switch	this	throw	true	try
typeof	uint	ulong	unchecked	unsafe	ushort
using	virtual	void	volatile	while	
Contextual Keywords					
add	alias	ascending	async	await	by
descending	dynamic	equals	from	get	global
group	into	join	let	nameof	on
orderby	partial	remove	select	set	value
var	where	yield			

Fig. 3.2 | Keywords and contextual keywords.

Class Declaration's File Name

A class declaration's file name is usually the class name followed by the `.cs` file-name extension, though this is not required. For our app, the file name is `Welcome1.cs`.

Good Programming Practice 3.2

By convention, a file that contains a single class should have a name that's identical to the class name (plus the `.cs` extension) in both spelling and capitalization. This makes it easy to identify which file contains the class's declaration.

Body of a Class Declaration

A left brace, { (in line 6 in Fig. 3.1), begins each class declaration's body. A corresponding right brace, } (in line 12), must end each class declaration. Lines 7–11 are indented. This indentation is a *spacing convention*. We define each spacing convention and other conventions that improve program clarity as *Good Programming Practices*.

Good Programming Practice 3.3

Indent the entire body of each class declaration one "level" of indentation between the left and right braces that delimit the body of the class. This format emphasizes the class declaration's structure and makes it easier to read. You can let the IDE format your code by selecting Edit > Advanced > Format Document.

Good Programming Practice 3.4

Set a convention for the indent size you prefer, then uniformly apply that convention. The Tab *key may be used to create indents, but tab stops vary among text editors. Microsoft recommends four-space indents, which is the default in Visual Studio. Due to the limited width of code lines in print books, we use three-space indents—this reduces the number of code lines that wrap to a new line, making the code a bit easier to read. We show how to set the tab size in the Before You Begin section that follows the Preface.*

Error-Prevention Tip 3.3

Whenever you type an opening left brace, {, in your app, the IDE immediately inserts the closing right brace, }, then repositions the cursor between the braces so you can begin typing the body. This practice helps prevent errors due to missing braces.

Common Programming Error 3.4

It's a syntax error if braces do not occur in matching pairs.

3.2.5 Main Method

Line 7

```
// Main method begins execution of C# app
```

is a comment indicating the purpose of lines 8–11. Line 8

```
static void Main()
```

is where the app begins execution—this is known as the entry point. The parentheses after the identifier Main indicate that it's a building block called a method. Class declarations normally contain one or more methods. Method names usually follow the same capitalization conventions used for class names. For each app, one of the methods in a class *must* be called Main (which is typically defined as shown in line 8); otherwise, the app will not execute. A method is able to perform a task and return a value when it completes its task. Keyword void (line 8) indicates that Main will *not* return a value after it completes its task. Later, we'll see that most methods do return values. You'll learn more about methods in Chapters 4 and 7. We discuss the contents of Main's parentheses in Chapter 8. For now, simply mimic Main's first line in your apps.

Body of a Method Declaration

The left brace in line 9 begins the body of the method declaration. A corresponding right brace ends the body (line 11). Line 10 in the method body is indented between the braces.

Good Programming Practice 3.5

Indent each method declaration's body statements one level of indentation between the left and right braces that define the body.

3.2.6 Displaying a Line of Text

Line 10

```
Console.WriteLine("Welcome to C# Programming!");
```

instructs the computer to perform an action—namely, to display the string of characters between the double quotation marks, which delimit the string. A string is sometimes called a character string, a message or a string literal. We refer to them simply as strings. Whitespace characters in strings are *not* ignored by the compiler.

Class `Console` provides standard input/output capabilities that enable apps to read and display text in the console window from which the app executes. The `Console.Write-Line` method displays a line of text in the console window. The string in the parentheses in line 10 is the argument to the method. Method `Console.WriteLine` performs its task by displaying its argument in the console window. When `Console.WriteLine` completes its task, it positions the screen cursor (the blinking symbol indicating where the next character will be displayed) at the beginning of the next line in the console window. This movement of the cursor is similar to what happens when a user presses the *Enter* key while typing in a text editor—the cursor moves to the beginning of the next line in the file.

Statements

The entire line 10, including `Console.WriteLine`, the parentheses, the argument `"Welcome to C# Programming!"` in the parentheses and the semicolon (`;`), is called a statement. Most statements end with a semicolon. When the statement in line 10 executes, it displays the message `Welcome to C# Programming!` in the console window. A method is typically composed of one or more statements that perform the method's task.

3.2.7 Matching Left ({) and Right (}) Braces

You may find it difficult when reading or writing an app to match the left and right braces ({ and }) that delimit a class's or method's body. Visual Studio can help you locate matching braces in your code. Simply place the cursor immediately in front of the left brace or immediately after the right brace, and Visual Studio will highlight both.

3.3 Creating a Simple App in Visual Studio

Now that we've presented our first console app (Fig. 3.1), we provide a step-by-step explanation of how to create, compile and execute it using Visual Studio Community 2015, which we'll refer to simply as Visual Studio from this point forward.

3.3.1 Creating the Console App

After opening Visual Studio, select **File > New > Project…** to display the **New Project** dialog (Fig. 3.3). At the left side of the dialog, under **Installed > Templates > Visual C#** select the **Windows** category, then in the middle of the dialog select the **Console Application** template. In the dialog's **Name** field, type `Welcome1`—your project's name—then click **OK** to create the project. By default, the project's folder will be placed in your user account's documents folder under `visual studio 2015\Projects`.

The IDE now contains the open console app (Fig. 3.4). The editor window already contains some code provided by the IDE. Some of this code is similar to that of Fig. 3.1. Some is not and uses features that we have not yet discussed. The IDE inserts this extra code to help organize the app and to provide access to some common classes in the .NET Framework Class Library—at this point in the book, this code is neither required nor relevant to the discussion of this app; delete all of it.

Fig. 3.3 | Selecting **Console Application** in the **New Project** dialog.

Editor window

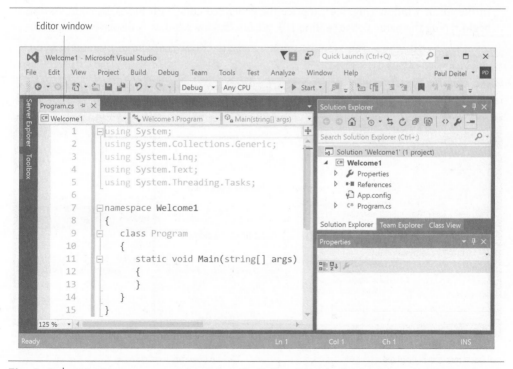

Fig. 3.4 | IDE with an open console app's code displayed in the editor and the project's contents shown in the **Solution Explorer** at the IDE's top-right side.

The code coloring scheme used by the IDE is called syntax-color highlighting and helps you visually differentiate code elements. For example, keywords appear in blue and comments appear in green. We syntax shade our code similarly as discussed in the Preface. One example of a literal is the string passed to `Console.WriteLine` in line 10 of Fig. 3.1. You can customize the colors shown in the code editor by selecting **Tools > Options...**. This displays the **Options** dialog. Then expand the **Environment** node and select **Fonts and Colors**. Here you can change the colors for various code elements. Visual Studio provides many ways to personalize your coding experience.

3.3.2 Changing the Name of the App File

For the apps we create in this book, we change the source-code file's default name (`Program.cs`) to a more descriptive name. To rename the file, right click `Program.cs` in the **Solution Explorer** and select **Rename** to make the file name editable. Windows automatically selects the file name's base part (i.e., `Program`). Type `Welcome1`, then press *Enter* to change the name to `Welcome1.cs`. Be sure to keep the `.cs` filename extension.

> **Error-Prevention Tip 3.4**
> *When changing a file name in a Visual Studio project, always do so in Visual Studio. Changing file names outside the IDE can break the project and prevent it from executing.*

3.3.3 Writing Code and Using *IntelliSense*

In the editor window (Fig. 3.4), replace the generated code with Fig. 3.1's code. As you begin typing the name `Console` (line 10), an *IntelliSense* window is displayed (Fig. 3.5).

a) *IntelliSense* window displayed as you type

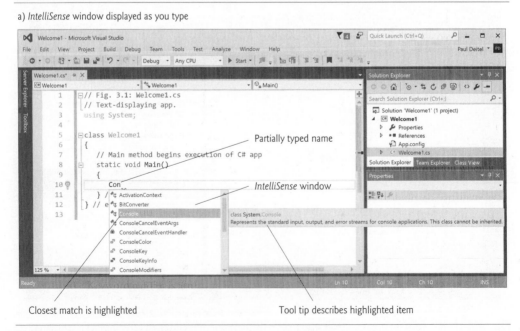

Closest match is highlighted   Tool tip describes highlighted item

Fig. 3.5 | *IntelliSense* window as you type "Con".

As you type, *IntelliSense* lists various items that start with or contain the letters you've typed so far. *IntelliSense* also displays a tool tip containing a description of the first matching item. You can either type the complete item name (e.g., `Console`), double click the item name in the member list or press the *Tab* key to complete the name. Once the complete name is provided, the *IntelliSense* window closes. While the *IntelliSense* window is displayed, pressing the *Ctrl* key makes the window transparent so you can see the code behind the window.

When you type the dot (.) after `Console`, the *IntelliSense* window reappears and initially shows only class `Console`'s members that can be used on the right of the dot—as you type, this list narrows to items containing what you've typed so far. Figure 3.6 shows the *IntelliSense* window narrowed down to only items that contain "`Write`". You also can type "`WL`" to find all items containing the capital letters "`W`" and "`L`" (such as `WriteLine`).

b) *IntelliSense* window showing method names that start with `Write`

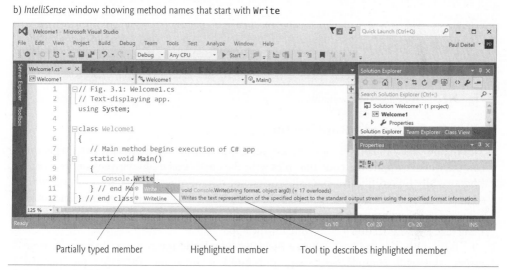

Partially typed member   Highlighted member   Tool tip describes highlighted member

Fig. 3.6 | *IntelliSense* window.

When you type the opening parenthesis character, (, after `Console.WriteLine`, the *Parameter Info* window is displayed (Fig. 3.7). This contains information about the method's parameters—the data methods require to perform their tasks. As you'll learn in Chapter 7, a method can have several versions. That is, a class can define several methods that have the *same* name, as long as they have *different* numbers and/or types of parameters—a concept known as *overloaded methods*. These methods normally all perform similar tasks. The *Parameter Info* window indicates how many versions of the selected method are available and provides up and down arrows for scrolling through the different versions. For example, there are many versions of the `WriteLine` method that enable you to display different types of data—we use the one that displays a string in our app. The *Parameter Info* window is one of many features provided by the IDE to facilitate app development. In the next several chapters, you'll learn more about the information displayed in these windows. The *Parameter Info* window is especially helpful when you want to see the different ways in which a method can be used. From the code in Fig. 3.1, we already know that we intend to display one string with WriteLine, so, because you know exactly which version of WriteLine you want to use, you can close the *Parameter Info* window by pressing the *Esc* key, or simply keep typing and ignore it. After you type the app's code, select **File > Save All** to save the project.

Parameter Info window

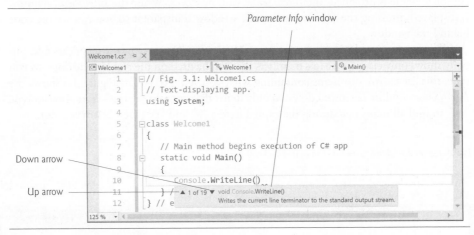

Down arrow

Up arrow

Fig. 3.7 | *Parameter Info* window.

3.3.4 Compiling and Running the App

You're now ready to compile and execute your app. Depending on the project's type, the compiler may compile the code into files with the **.exe** (executable) extension, the **.dll** (dynamically linked library) extension or one of several other extensions—you can find these files in project's subfolders on disk. Such files are called **assemblies** and are the packaging units for compiled C# code. These assemblies contain the Microsoft Intermediate Language (MSIL; Section 1.9.2) code for the app.

To compile the app, select **Build > Build Solution**. If the app contains no compile-time errors, this will compile your app and build it into an executable file (named Welcome1.exe, in one of the project's subdirectories). To execute it, type *Ctrl + F5*, which invokes the Main method (Fig. 3.1). If you attempt to run the app before building it, the IDE will build the app first, then run it only if there are no compilation errors. The statement in line 10 of Main displays Welcome to C# Programming!. Figure 3.8 shows the results of executing this app, displayed in a console (**Command Prompt**) window. Leave the app's project open in Visual Studio; we'll go back to it later in this section. [*Note:* The console window normally has a black background and white text. We reconfigured it to have a white background and black text for readability. If you'd like to do this, right click anywhere in the **Command Prompt** window's title bar, then select **Properties**. You can change the colors in the **Colors** tab of the dialog that appears.]

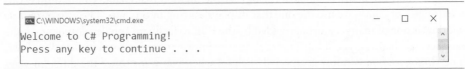

Fig. 3.8 | Executing the app shown in Fig. 3.1.

3.3.5 Errors, Error Messages and the Error List Window

Go back to the app in Visual Studio. As you type code, the IDE responds either by apply-ing syntax-color highlighting or by generating an error. When an error occurs, the IDE underlines the error's location with a red squiggly line and provides a description of it in the **Error List** window (Fig. 3.9). If the **Error List** window is not visible, select **View > Error List** to display it. In Fig. 3.9, we intentionally omitted the semicolon at the end of line 10. The error message indicates that the semicolon is missing. You can double click an error message in the **Error List** to jump to the error's location in the code.

Error-Prevention Tip 3.5

One compile-time error can lead to multiple entries in the Error List window. Each error you correct could eliminate several subsequent error messages when you recompile your app. So when you see an error you know how to fix, correct it—the IDE will recompile your code in the background, so fixing an error may make several other errors disappear.

Intentionally omitted semicolon (syntax error)

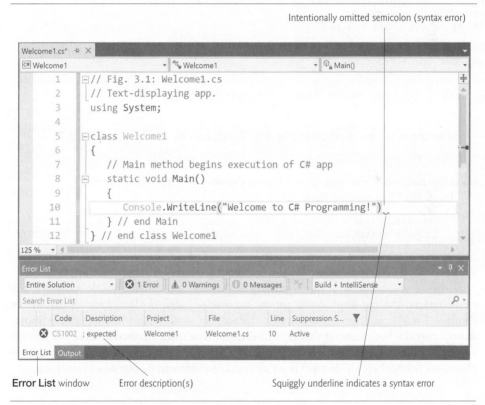

Error List window   Error description(s)   Squiggly underline indicates a syntax error

Fig. 3.9 | Syntax error indicated by the IDE.

3.4 Modifying Your Simple C# App

This section continues our introduction to C# programming with two examples that mod-ify the example of Fig. 3.1.

3.4.1 Displaying a Single Line of Text with Multiple Statements

Class `Welcome2`, shown in Fig. 3.10, uses two statements to produce the same output as that shown in Fig. 3.1. From this point forward, we highlight the new and key features in each code listing, as shown in lines 10–11 of Fig. 3.10.

```
1   // Fig. 3.10: Welcome2.cs
2   // Displaying one line of text with multiple statements.
3   using System;
4
5   class Welcome2
6   {
7      // Main method begins execution of C# app
8      static void Main()
9      {
10         Console.Write("Welcome to ");
11         Console.WriteLine("C# Programming!");
12      } // end Main
13   } // end class Welcome2
```

```
Welcome to C# Programming!
```

Fig. 3.10 | Displaying one line of text with multiple statements.

The app is almost identical to Fig. 3.1. We discuss the changes here. Line 2

```
   // Displaying one line of text with multiple statements.
```

states the purpose of this app. Line 5 begins the `Welcome2` class declaration.
Lines 10–11 of method `Main`

```
      Console.Write("Welcome to ");
      Console.WriteLine("C# Programming!");
```

display one line of text in the console window. The first statement uses `Console`'s method `Write` to display a string. Unlike `WriteLine`, after displaying its argument, `Write` does *not* position the screen cursor at the beginning of the next line in the console window—the next character the app displays will appear immediately after the last character that `Write` displays. Thus, line 11 positions the first character in its argument (the letter "C") immediately *after* the last character that line 10 displays (the space character before the string's closing double-quote character). Each `Write` or `WriteLine` statement resumes displaying characters from where the last `Write` or `WriteLine` statement displayed its last character.

3.4.2 Displaying Multiple Lines of Text with a Single Statement

A single statement can display multiple lines by using newline characters, which indicate to `Console` methods `Write` and `WriteLine` when they should position the screen cursor to the beginning of the next line. Like space characters and tab characters, newline characters are whitespace characters. The app of Fig. 3.11 outputs four lines of text, using newline characters to indicate when to begin each new line.

```
 1   // Fig. 3.11: Welcome3.cs
 2   // Displaying multiple lines with a single statement.
 3   using System;
 4
 5   class Welcome3
 6   {
 7      // Main method begins execution of C# app
 8      static void Main()
 9      {
10         Console.WriteLine("Welcome\nto\nC#\nProgramming!");
11      } // end Main
12   } // end class Welcome3
```

```
Welcome
to
C#
Programming!
```

Fig. 3.11 | Displaying multiple lines with a single statement.

Most of the app is identical to the apps of Fig. 3.1 and Fig. 3.10, so we discuss only the changes here. Line 2

```
   // Displaying multiple lines with a single statement.
```

states the purpose of this app. Line 5 begins the Welcome3 class declaration. Line 10

```
   Console.WriteLine("Welcome\nto\nC#\nProgramming!");
```

displays four separate lines of text in the console window. Normally, the characters in a string are displayed exactly as they appear in the double quotes. Note, however, that the two characters \ and n (repeated three times in the statement) do *not* appear on the screen. The backslash (\) is called an escape character. It indicates to C# that a "special character" is in the string. When a backslash appears in a string of characters, C# combines the next character with the backslash to form an escape sequence.[2]

The escape sequence \n represents the newline character. When a newline character appears in a string being output with Console methods, the newline character causes the screen cursor to move to the beginning of the next line in the console window. Figure 3.12 lists several common escape sequences and describes how they affect the display of characters in the console window.

---

2. There are also escape sequences that have four or eight hexadecimal characters following the \. These represent so-called Unicode characters. For more information, see the Lexical Structure section of Microsoft's C# 6 specification. For more information on the hexadecimal (base 16) number system, see our online Appendix D, Number Systems.

Escape sequence	Description
\n	Newline. Positions the screen cursor at the beginning of the next line.
\t	Horizontal tab. Moves the screen cursor to the next tab stop.
\"	Double quote. Used to place a double-quote character (") in a string—e.g., `Console.Write("\"in quotes\"");` displays `"in quotes"`.
\r	Carriage return. Positions the screen cursor at the beginning of the current line—does not advance the cursor to the next line. Any characters output after the carriage return overwrite the characters previously output on that line.
\\	Backslash. Used to place a backslash character in a string.

Fig. 3.12 | Common escape sequences.

3.5 String Interpolation

6 Many programs format data into strings. C# 6 introduces a mechanism called string interpolation that enables you to insert values in string literals to create formatted strings. Figure 3.13 demonstrates this capability.

```
 1   // Fig. 3.13: Welcome4.cs
 2   // Inserting content into a string with string interpolation.
 3   using System;
 4
 5   class Welcome4
 6   {
 7      // Main method begins execution of C# app
 8      static void Main()
 9      {
10         string person = "Paul"; // variable that stores the string "Paul"
11         Console.WriteLine($"Welcome to C# Programming, {person}!");
12      } // end Main
13   } // end class Welcome4
```

```
Welcome to C# Programming, Paul!
```

Fig. 3.13 | Inserting content into a `string` with `string` interpolation.

Declaring the string Variable person
Line 10

```
      string person = "Paul"; // variable that stores the string "Paul"
```

is a variable declaration statement (also called a declaration) that specifies the name (person) and type (string) of a variable used in this app. A variable is a location in the computer's memory where a value can be stored for later use (in this case, line 11). Variables are declared with a name and a type before they're used:

- A variable's name enables the app to access the corresponding value in memory—the name can be any valid identifier. (See Section 3.2 for identifier naming requirements.)

- A variable's type specifies what kind of information is stored at that location in memory. Variables of type `string` store character-based information, such as the contents of the string literal `"Paul"`. In fact, a string literal has type `string`. (From this point forward we'll use the type name `string` when referring to strings.)

Like other statements, declaration statements end with a semicolon (;).

string Interpolation
Line 11

```
Console.WriteLine($"Welcome to C# Programming, {person}!");
```

uses `string` interpolation to insert the variable person's value (`"Paul"`) into the `string` that `Console.WriteLine` is about to display. An interpolated `string` must begin with a $ (dollar sign). Then, you can insert interpolation expressions enclosed in braces, {} (e.g., {person}), anywhere between the quotes (""). When C# encounters an interpolated `string`, it replaces each braced interpolation expression with the corresponding value—in this case, {person} is replaced with Paul, so line 11 displays

```
Welcome to C# Programming, Paul!
```

3.6 Another C# App: Adding Integers

Our next app reads (or inputs) two integers (whole numbers, like –22, 7, 0 and 1024) typed by a user at the keyboard, computes the sum of the values and displays the result. This app must keep track of the numbers supplied by the user for the calculation later in the app, so once again we'll use variables. The app of Fig. 3.14 demonstrates these concepts. In the sample output, we highlight data the user enters at the keyboard in **bold**.

```
 1   // Fig. 3.14: Addition.cs
 2   // Displaying the sum of two numbers input from the keyboard.
 3   using System;
 4
 5   class Addition
 6   {
 7      // Main method begins execution of C# app
 8      static void Main()
 9      {
10         int number1; // declare first number to add
11         int number2; // declare second number to add
12         int sum; // declare sum of number1 and number2
13
14         Console.Write("Enter first integer: "); // prompt user
15         // read first number from user
16         number1 = int.Parse(Console.ReadLine());
```

Fig. 3.14 | Displaying the sum of two numbers input from the keyboard. (Part 1 of 2.)

```
17
18        Console.Write("Enter second integer: "); // prompt user
19        // read second number from user
20        number2 = int.Parse(Console.ReadLine());
21
22        sum = number1 + number2; // add numbers
23
24        Console.WriteLine($"Sum is {sum}"); // display sum
25     } // end Main
26  } // end class Addition
```

```
Enter first integer: 45
Enter second integer: 72
Sum is 117
```

Fig. 3.14 | Displaying the sum of two numbers input from the keyboard. (Part 2 of 2.)

Comments
Lines 1–2

```
// Fig. 3.14: Addition.cs
// Displaying the sum of two numbers input from the keyboard.
```

state the figure number, file name and purpose of the app.

Class **Addition**
Line 5

```
class Addition
```

begins the declaration of class Addition. Remember that the body of each class declaration starts with an opening left brace (line 6) and ends with a closing right brace (line 26).

Function **Main**
The app begins execution with Main (lines 8–25). The left brace (line 9) marks the beginning of Main's body, and the corresponding right brace (line 25) marks the end of Main's body. Method Main is indented one level within class Addition's body, and the code in the Main's body is indented another level for readability.

3.6.1 Declaring the int Variable number1
Line 10

```
int number1; // declare first number to add
```

is a variable declaration statement specifying that number1 has type int—it will hold integer values (whole numbers such as 7, –11, 0 and 31914). The range of values for an int is –2,147,483,648 (int.MinValue) to +2,147,483,647 (int.MaxValue). We'll soon discuss types float, double and decimal, for specifying numbers with decimal points (as in 3.4, 0.0 and –11.19), and type char, for specifying characters. Variables of type float and double store approximations of real numbers in memory. Variables of type decimal store numbers with decimal points *precisely* (to 28–29 significant digits[3]), so decimal variables are often used with *monetary calculations*—we use type decimal to represent the balance in our `Account` class in Chapter 4. Variables of type `char` represent individual characters, such as an uppercase letter (e.g., `A`), a digit (e.g., `7`), a special character (e.g., `*` or `%`) or an escape sequence (e.g., the newline character, `\n`). Types such as `int`, `float`, `double`, `decimal` and `char` are called simple types. Simple-type names are keywords and must appear in all lowercase letters. Appendix B summarizes the characteristics of the simple types (`bool`, `byte`, `sbyte`, `char`, `short`, `ushort`, `int`, `uint`, `long`, `ulong`, `float`, `double` and `decimal`), including the amount of memory required to store a value of each type.

3.6.2 Declaring Variables number2 and sum

The variable declaration statements at lines 11–12

```
int number2; // declare second number to add
int sum; // declare sum of number1 and number2
```

declare variables `number2` and `sum` to be of type `int`.

Good Programming Practice 3.6

Declare each variable on a separate line. This format allows a comment to be easily inserted next to each declaration.

Good Programming Practice 3.7

Choosing meaningful variable names helps code to be self-documenting (i.e., one can understand the code simply by reading it rather than by reading documentation manuals or viewing an excessive number of comments).

Good Programming Practice 3.8

By convention, variable-name identifiers begin with a lowercase letter, and every word in the name after the first word begins with a capital letter (e.g., `firstNumber`). This naming convention is known as camel case.

3.6.3 Prompting the User for Input

Line 14

```
Console.Write("Enter first integer: "); // prompt user
```

uses `Console.Write` to display the message `"Enter first integer: "`. This message is called a prompt because it directs the user to take a specific action.

3.6.4 Reading a Value into Variable number1

Line 16

```
number1 = int.Parse(Console.ReadLine());
```

works in two steps. First, it calls the `Console`'s `ReadLine` method, which waits for the user to type a string of characters at the keyboard and press the *Enter* key. As we mentioned, some methods perform a task, then return the result of that task. In this case, `ReadLine` returns the text the user entered. Then the returned `string` is used as an argument to type `int`'s `Parse` method, which converts this sequence of characters into data of type `int`.

---

3.   See Section 4.1.7 of the *C# Language Specification*.

Possible Erroneous User Input

Technically, the user can type anything as the input value. ReadLine will accept it and pass it off to int's Parse method. This method assumes that the string contains a valid integer value. In this app, if the user types a noninteger value, a runtime logic error called an *exception* will occur and the app will terminate. The string processing techniques you'll learn in Chapter 16 can be used to check that the input is in the correct format before attempting to convert the string to an int. C# also offers a technology called *exception handling* that will help you make your apps more robust by enabling them to handle exceptions and continue executing. This is also known as making your app fault tolerant. We introduce exception handling in Section 8.4, then use it again in Chapter 10. We take a deeper look at exception handling in Chapter 13 and throughout the book.

Assigning a Value to a Variable

In line 16, the result of the call to int's Parse method (an int value) is placed in variable number1 by using the assignment operator, =. The statement is read as "number1 gets the value returned by int.Parse." Operator = is a binary operator, because it works on two pieces of information. These are known as its operands—in this case, the operands are number1 and the result of the method call int.Parse. This statement is called an assignment statement, because it assigns a value to a variable. Everything to the right of the assignment operator, =, is always evaluated *before* the assignment is performed.

Good Programming Practice 3.9
Place spaces on either side of a binary operator to make the code more readable.

3.6.5 Prompting the User for Input and Reading a Value into number2

Line 18

```
Console.Write("Enter second integer: "); // prompt user
```

prompts the user to enter the second integer. Line 20

```
number2 = int.Parse(Console.ReadLine());
```

reads a second integer and assigns it to the variable number2.

3.6.6 Summing number1 and number2

Line 22

```
sum = number1 + number2; // add numbers
```

calculates the sum of number1 and number2 and assigns the result to variable sum by using the assignment operator, =. The statement is read as "sum *gets* the value of number1 + number2." When number1 + number2 is encountered, the values stored in the variables are used in the calculation. The addition operator is a binary operator—its two operands are number1 and number2. Portions of statements that contain calculations are called expressions. In fact, an expression is any portion of a statement that has a value associated with it. For example, the value of the expression number1 + number2 is the sum of the numbers. Similarly, the value of the expression Console.ReadLine() is the string of characters typed by the user.

3.6.7 Displaying the sum with string Interpolation

After the calculation has been performed, line 24

```
Console.WriteLine($"Sum is {sum}"); // display sum
```

uses method `Console.WriteLine` to display the sum. C# replaces the interpolation expression `{sum}` with the calculated sum from line 22. So method `WriteLine` displays "Sum is ", followed by the value of sum and a newline.

3.6.8 Performing Calculations in Output Statements

Calculations also can be performed in interpolation expressions. We could have combined the statements in lines 22 and 24 into the statement

```
Console.WriteLine($"Sum is {number1 + number2}");
```

3.7 Memory Concepts

Variable names such as number1, number2 and sum actually correspond to locations in the computer's memory. Every variable has a name, a type, a size (determined by the type) and a value.

In the addition app of Fig. 3.14, when the statement (line 16)

```
number1 = int.Parse(Console.ReadLine());
```

executes, the number typed by the user is placed into a memory location to which the name number1 has been assigned by the runtime. Suppose that the user enters 45. The computer places that integer value into location number1, as shown in Fig. 3.15. Whenever a value is placed in a memory location, the value *replaces* the previous value in that location—the previous value is destroyed.

number1   45

Fig. 3.15 | Memory location showing the name and value of variable number1.

When the statement (line 20)

```
number2 = int.Parse(Console.ReadLine());
```

executes, suppose that the user enters 72. The computer places that integer value into location number2. The memory now appears as shown in Fig. 3.16.

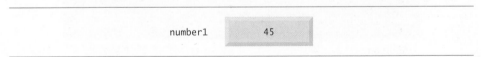

number1   45

number2   72

Fig. 3.16 | Memory locations after storing values for number1 and number2.

After the app of Fig. 3.14 obtains values for number1 and number2, it adds them and places the result into variable sum. The statement (line 22)

```
sum = number1 + number2; // add numbers
```

performs the addition, then *replaces* sum's previous value. After sum has been calculated, memory appears as shown in Fig. 3.17. The values of number1 and number2 appear exactly as they did *before* they were used in the calculation of sum. These values were used, but *not* destroyed, as the computer performed the calculation—when a value is *read* from a memory location, the process is *nondestructive*.

number1	45
number2	72
sum	117

Fig. 3.17 | Memory locations after calculating and storing the sum of number1 and number2.

3.8 Arithmetic

Most apps perform arithmetic calculations. The arithmetic operators are summarized in Fig. 3.18. Note the various special symbols not used in algebra. The asterisk (*) indicates multiplication, and the percent sign (%) is the remainder operator, which we'll discuss shortly. The arithmetic operators in Fig. 3.18 are binary operators—for example, the expression f + 7 contains the binary operator + and the two operands f and 7.

C# operation	Arithmetic operator	Algebraic expression	C# expression
Addition	+	$f + 7$	f + 7
Subtraction	–	$p - c$	p - c
Multiplication	*	$b \cdot m$	b * m
Division	/	x / y or $\frac{x}{y}$ or $x \div y$	x / y
Remainder	%	$r \bmod s$	r % s

Fig. 3.18 | Arithmetic operators.

If both operands of the division operator (/) are integers, integer division is performed and the result is an integer—for example, the expression 7 / 4 evaluates to 1, and the expression 17 / 5 evaluates to 3. Any fractional part in integer division is simply *truncated* (i.e., discarded)—*no rounding* occurs. C# provides the remainder operator, %, which yields the remainder after division. The expression x % y yields the remainder after x is divided by y. Thus, 7 % 4 yields 3, and 17 % 5 yields 2. This operator is most commonly used with integer operands but also can be used with floats, doubles, and decimals. In this chapter's exercises and in later chapters, we consider several interesting applications of the remainder operator, such as determining whether one number is a multiple of another.

3.8.1 Arithmetic Expressions in Straight-Line Form

Arithmetic expressions must be written in straight-line form to facilitate entering an app's code into the computer. Thus, expressions such as "a divided by b" must be written as a / b in a straight line. The following algebraic notation is not acceptable to the C# compiler and cannot be typed into the Visual Studio editor:

$$\frac{a}{b}$$

3.8.2 Parentheses for Grouping Subexpressions

Parentheses are used to group terms in C# expressions in the same manner as in algebraic expressions. For example, to multiply a times the quantity b + c, we write

```
a * (b + c)
```

If an expression contains nested parentheses, such as

```
((a + b) * c)
```

the expression in the *innermost* set of parentheses (a + b in this case) is evaluated first.

3.8.3 Rules of Operator Precedence

C# applies the operators in arithmetic expressions in a precise sequence determined by the following rules of operator precedence, which are generally the same as those followed in algebra (Fig. 3.19). These rules enable C# to apply operators in the correct order.[4]

Operators	Operations	Order of evaluation (associativity)
Evaluated first		
*	Multiplication	If there are several operators of this type,
/	Division	they're evaluated from left to right.
%	Remainder	
Evaluated next		
+	Addition	If there are several operators of this type,
-	Subtraction	they're evaluated from left to right.

Fig. 3.19 | Precedence of arithmetic operators.

When we say that operators are applied from left to right, we're referring to their associativity. You'll see that some operators associate from right to left. Figure 3.19 summa-

---

4. We discuss simple examples here to explain the order of evaluation. More subtle order of evaluation issues occur in the increasingly complex expressions you'll encounter later. For more details, see the following blog posts from Eric Lippert: https://ericlippert.com/2008/05/23/ and https://ericlippert.com/2007/08/14/.

rizes these rules of operator precedence. The table will be expanded as additional operators are introduced. Appendix A provides the complete precedence chart.

3.8.4 Sample Algebraic and C# Expressions

Now let's consider several expressions in light of the rules of operator precedence. Each example lists an algebraic expression and its C# equivalent. The following is an example of an arithmetic mean (average) of five terms:

Algebra: $m = \dfrac{a + b + c + d + e}{5}$

C#:   `m = (a + b + c + d + e) / 5;`

The parentheses are required because division has *higher* precedence than addition. The entire quantity (a + b + c + d + e) is to be divided by 5. If the parentheses are erroneously omitted, we obtain a + b + c + d + e / 5, which evaluates to the incorrect expression

$$a + b + c + d + \frac{e}{5}$$

The following is an example of the equation of a straight line:

Algebra: $y = mx + b$

C#:   `y = m * x + b;`

No parentheses are required. The multiplication operator is applied first, because multiplication has a *higher* precedence than addition. The assignment occurs last, because it has a *lower* precedence than multiplication or addition.

The following example contains remainder (%), multiplication, division, addition and subtraction operations:

Algebra: $z = pr\,\%q + w/x - y$

C#:   `z = p * r % q + w / x - y;`
              ⑥ ① ② ④ ③ ⑤

The circled numbers under the statement indicate the order in which C# applies the operators. The multiplication, remainder and division operations are evaluated first in left-to-right order (i.e., they associate from left to right), because they have *higher* precedence than addition and subtraction. The addition and subtraction operations are evaluated next. These operations are also applied from left to right.

Evaluation of a Second-Degree Polynomial
To develop a better understanding of the rules of operator precedence, consider the evaluation of a second-degree polynomial ($y = ax^2 + bx + c$):

`y = a * x * x + b * x + c;`
      ⑥ ① ② ④ ③ ⑤

The circled numbers indicate the order in which C# applies the operators. The multiplication operations are evaluated first in left-to-right order (i.e., they associate from left to right), because they have *higher* precedence than addition. The addition operations are evaluated next and are applied from left to right. There's no arithmetic operator for exponentiation in C#, so x^2 is represented as x * x. Section 6.6.1 shows an alternative for performing exponentiation in C#.

Suppose that a, b, c and x in the preceding second-degree polynomial are initialized (given values) as follows: a = 2, b = 3, c = 7 and x = 5. Figure 3.20 illustrates the order in which the operators are applied.

Step 1.	y = 2 * 5 * 5 + 3 * 5 + 7; 2 * 5 is 10	*(Leftmost multiplication)*
Step 2.	y = 10 * 5 + 3 * 5 + 7; 10 * 5 is 50	*(Leftmost multiplication)*
Step 3.	y = 50 + 3 * 5 + 7; 3 * 5 is 15	*(Multiplication before addition)*
Step 4.	y = 50 + 15 + 7; 50 + 15 is 65	*(Leftmost addition)*
Step 5.	y = 65 + 7; 65 + 7 is 72	*(Last addition)*
Step 6.	y = 72	*(Low-precedence assignment—place 72 in y)*

Fig. 3.20 | Order in which a second-degree polynomial is evaluated.

3.8.5 Redundant Parentheses

As in algebra, it's acceptable to place unnecessary parentheses in an expression to make the expression clearer. These are called redundant parentheses. For example, the preceding second-degree polynomial assignment statement might be parenthesized to highlight its terms as follows:

```
y = (a * x * x) + (b * x) + c;
```

3.9 Decision Making: Equality and Relational Operators

A condition is an expression that can be either true or false. This section introduces a simple version of C#'s if statement that allows an app to make a decision based on the value of a condition. For example, the condition "grade is greater than or equal to 60" determines whether a student passed a test. If the condition in an if statement is true, the body of the if statement executes. If the condition is false, the body is skipped—it does *not* execute. We'll see an example shortly.

Conditions in if statements can be formed by using the equality operators (== and !=) and relational operators (>, <, >= and <=) summarized in Fig. 3.21. The two equality operators (== and !=) each have the same level of precedence, the relational operators (>, <, >= and <=) each have the same level of precedence, and the equality operators have lower precedence than the relational operators. They all associate from left to right.

Common Programming Error 3.5

Confusing the equality operator, ==, with the assignment operator, =, can cause a logic error or a syntax error. The equality operator should be read as "is equal to," and the assignment operator should be read as "gets" or "gets the value of." To avoid confusion, some programmers read the equality operator as "double equals" or "equals equals."

Standard algebraic equality and relational operators	C# equality or relational operator	Sample C# condition	Meaning of C# condition
Relational operators			
>	>	x > y	x is greater than y
<	<	x < y	x is less than y
≥	>=	x >= y	x is greater than or equal to y
≤	<=	x <= y	x is less than or equal to y
Equality operators			
=	==	x == y	x is equal to y
≠	!=	x != y	x is not equal to y

Fig. 3.21 | Relational and equality operators.

Using the if Statement

Figure 3.22 uses six if statements to compare two integers entered by the user. If the condition in any of these if statements is true, the statement associated with that if statement executes. The app uses class Console to prompt for and read two lines of text from the user, extracts the integers from that text with int's Parse method, and stores them in variables number1 and number2. Then the app compares the numbers and displays the results of the comparisons that are true.

```
1   // Fig. 3.22: Comparison.cs
2   // Comparing integers using if statements, equality operators
3   // and relational operators.
4   using System;
5
```

Fig. 3.22 | Comparing integers using if statements, equality operators and relational operators. (Part 1 of 3.)

```
 6   class Comparison
 7   {
 8      // Main method begins execution of C# app
 9      static void Main()
10      {
11         // prompt user and read first number
12         Console.Write("Enter first integer: ");
13         int number1 = int.Parse(Console.ReadLine());
14
15         // prompt user and read second number
16         Console.Write("Enter second integer: ");
17         int number2 = int.Parse(Console.ReadLine());
18
19         if (number1 == number2)
20         {
21            Console.WriteLine($"{number1} == {number2}");
22         }
23
24         if (number1 != number2)
25         {
26            Console.WriteLine($"{number1} != {number2}");
27         }
28
29         if (number1 < number2)
30         {
31            Console.WriteLine($"{number1} < {number2}");
32         }
33
34         if (number1 > number2)
35         {
36            Console.WriteLine($"{number1} > {number2}");
37         }
38
39         if (number1 <= number2)
40         {
41            Console.WriteLine($"{number1} <= {number2}");
42         }
43
44         if (number1 >= number2)
45         {
46            Console.WriteLine($"{number1} >= {number2}");
47         }
48      } // end Main
49   } // end class Comparison
```

```
Enter first integer: 42
Enter second integer: 42
42 == 42
42 <= 42
42 >= 42
```

Fig. 3.22 | Comparing integers using if statements, equality operators and relational operators. (Part 2 of 3.)

```
Enter first integer: 1000
Enter second integer: 2000
1000 != 2000
1000 < 2000
1000 <= 2000
```

```
Enter first integer: 2000
Enter second integer: 1000
2000 != 1000
2000 > 1000
2000 >= 1000
```

Fig. 3.22 | Comparing integers using if statements, equality operators and relational operators. (Part 3 of 3.)

Class Comparison

The declaration of class Comparison begins at line 6

```
class Comparison
```

The class's Main method (lines 9–48) begins the execution of the app.

Reading the Inputs from the User

Lines 11–13

```
// prompt user and read first number
Console.Write("Enter first integer: ");
int number1 = int.Parse(Console.ReadLine());
```

prompt the user to enter the first integer and input the value. The input value is stored in variable number1. Line 13 also declares number1 as an int variable that stores the first value entered by the user.

Lines 15–17

```
// prompt user and read second number
Console.Write("Enter second integer: ");
int number2 = int.Parse(Console.ReadLine());
```

perform the same task, except that the input value is stored in variable number2, which is declared at line 17.

Comparing Numbers

The if statement in lines 19–22

```
if (number1 == number2)
{
    Console.WriteLine($"{number1} == {number2}");
}
```

compares the values of variables number1 and number2 to test for equality. The condition number1 == number2 is enclosed in required parentheses. If the values are equal, line 21 displays a line of text indicating that the numbers are equal. We used two interpolation expressions to insert the values of `number1` and `number2` in line 21's output. If the conditions are true in one or more of the `if` statements starting in lines 24, 29, 34, 39 and 44, the corresponding body statement displays an appropriate line of text.

Each `if` statement in Fig. 3.22 contains a single body statement that's indented. Also notice that we've enclosed each body statement in a pair of braces, { }, creating what's called a block.

Good Programming Practice 3.10
Indent the statement(s) in the body of an `if` statement to enhance readability.

Error-Prevention Tip 3.6
You don't need to use braces, { }, around single-statement bodies, but you must *include the braces around multiple-statement bodies. You'll see later that forgetting to enclose multiple-statement bodies in braces leads to errors. To avoid errors and make your code more readable, always enclose an `if` statement's body statement(s) in braces, even if it contains only a single statement.*

Common Programming Error 3.6
Placing a semicolon immediately after the right parenthesis after the condition in an `if` statement is often a logic error (although not a syntax error). The semicolon causes the body of the `if` statement to be empty, so the `if` statement performs no action, regardless of whether or not its condition is true. Worse yet, the original body statement of the `if` statement now becomes a statement in sequence *with the `if` statement and always* executes, *often causing the program to produce incorrect results.*

Whitespace

Note the use of whitespace in Fig. 3.22. Recall that whitespace characters, such as tabs, newlines and spaces, are normally ignored by the compiler. So, statements may be split over several lines and may be spaced according to your preferences without affecting the meaning of an app. It's incorrect to split identifiers, `strings`, and multicharacter operators (like >=). Ideally, statements should be kept small, but this is not always possible.

Good Programming Practice 3.11
A lengthy statement can be spread over several lines. If a single statement must be split across lines, choose breaking points that make sense, such as after a comma in a comma-separated list, or after an operator in a lengthy expression. If a statement is split across two or more lines, indent all lines after the first until the end of the statement.

Precedence and Associativity of the Operators We've Discussed So Far

Figure 3.23 shows the precedence of the operators introduced in this chapter. The operators are shown from top to bottom in decreasing order of precedence. All these operators, with the exception of the assignment operator, =, associate from left to right. Addition is left associative, so an expression like x + y + z is evaluated as if it had been written as (x + y) + z. The assignment operator, =, associates from right to left, so an expression like x = y = 0 is evaluated as if it had been written as x = (y = 0), which, as you'll soon see, first assigns the value 0 to variable y, then assigns the result of that assignment, 0, to x.

Good Programming Practice 3.12

Refer to the operator precedence chart (the complete chart is in Appendix A) when writing expressions containing many operators. Confirm that the operations in the expression are performed in the order you expect. If you're uncertain about the order of evaluation in a complex expression, use parentheses to force the order, as you would do in algebraic expressions. Some programmers also use parentheses to clarify the order. Observe that some operators, such as assignment, =, associate from right to left rather than left to right.

Operators				Associativity	Type
*	/	%		left to right	multiplicative
+	-			left to right	additive
<	<=	>	>=	left to right	relational
==	!=			left to right	equality
=				right to left	assignment

Fig. 3.23 | Precedence and associativity of operations discussed so far.

3.10 Wrap-Up

We presented many important features of C# in this chapter. First you learned how to display data on the screen in a **Command Prompt** using the `Console` class's `Write` and `WriteLine` methods. Next, we showed how to use C# 6's new `string`-interpolation capabilities to insert values into `string` literals. You learned how to input data from the keyboard using the `Console` class's `ReadLine` method and how to convert `strings` to `int` values with type `int`'s `Parse` method. We discussed how to perform calculations using C#'s arithmetic operators. Finally, you learned to make decisions using the `if` statement and the relational and equality operators. The apps presented here introduced you to basic programming concepts. As you'll see in Chapter 4, C# apps typically contain just a few lines of code in method `Main`—these statements normally create the objects that perform the work of the app. You'll learn how to implement your own classes and use objects of those classes in apps.

Summary

Section 3.2.1 Comments

- You may insert comments to document apps and improve their readability. The C# compiler ignores comments.
- A comment that begins with `//` is called a single-line comment, because it terminates at the end of the line on which it appears.
- Comments delimited by `/*` and `*/` can be spread over several lines.
- A programming language's syntax specifies rules for creating a proper app in that language.

Section 3.2.2 **using** Directive
- A using directive helps the compiler locate a type that's used in an app.
- C# provides a rich set of predefined classes that you can reuse rather than "reinventing the wheel." These classes are grouped into namespaces—named collections of classes.
- Collectively, C#'s predefined namespaces are referred to as the .NET Framework Class Library.

Section 3.2.3 Blank Lines and Whitespace
- You may use blank lines and space characters to make apps easier to read. Together, blank lines, space characters and tab characters are known as whitespace. Space characters and tabs are known specifically as whitespace characters. Whitespace is ignored by the compiler.

Section 3.2.4 Class Declaration
- Every app in C# consists of at least one class declaration that's defined by the programmer (also known as a user-defined class).
- Keywords are reserved for use by C# and are always spelled with all lowercase letters.
- Keyword class introduces a class declaration and is immediately followed by the class name.
- By convention, all class names in C# begin with a capital letter and capitalize the first letter of each word they include (e.g., SampleClassName). This convention is known as Pascal Case.
- A C# class name is an identifier—a series of characters consisting of letters, digits, and underscores (_) that does not begin with a digit and does not contain spaces.
- C# is case sensitive—that is, uppercase and lowercase letters are distinct.
- The body of every class declaration is delimited by braces, { and }.

Section 3.2.5 **Main** Method
- Method Main is the starting point of every C# app and is typically defined as:

```
static void Main()
```

- Methods are able to perform tasks and can return information when they complete their tasks. Keyword void indicates that a method will perform a task but will not return a value.

Section 3.2.6 Displaying a Line of Text
- Statements instruct the computer to perform actions.
- A sequence of characters in double quotation marks is called a string, a character string, a message or a string literal.
- The Console class allows C# apps to read and display characters in the console window.
- Method Console.WriteLine displays its argument in the console window, followed by a newline character to position the screen cursor to the beginning of the next line.
- Most statements end with a semicolon.

Section 3.3.1 Creating the Console App
- Visual Studio provides many ways to personalize your coding experience. You can modify the editor settings to display line numbers or set code indentation.

Section 3.3.3 Writing Code and Using **IntelliSense**
- As you type characters, in some contexts Visual Studio highlights the first member that matches all the characters typed, then displays a tool tip containing a description of that member. This IDE feature is called *IntelliSense*.
- When you type code, the IDE either applies syntax-color highlighting or generates a syntax error.

Section 3.4.1 Displaying a Single Line of Text with Multiple Statements
- `Console.Write` displays its argument and positions the screen cursor immediately after the last character displayed.

Section 3.4.2 Displaying Multiple Lines of Text with a Single Statement
- C# combines a backslash (\) in a string with the next character in the string to form an escape sequence. The escape sequence \n (newline) positions the cursor to the beginning of the next line.

Section 3.5 String Interpolation
- A variable declaration statement specifies the name and type of a variable.

- A variable is a location in the computer's memory where a value can be stored for use later in an app. Variables must be declared with a name and a type before they're used.

- A variable's name enables the app to access the value of the variable in memory. A variable name can be any valid identifier.

- Like other statements, variable declaration statements end with a semicolon (;).

- C# 6's `string` interpolation enables you to insert values into a `string` literal.

- An interpolated `string` must begin with a $ (dollar sign). Then, you can insert interpolation expressions enclosed in braces, {}, anywhere between the interpolated `string`'s quotes ("").

- When C# encounters an interpolated `string`, it replaces each braced interpolation expression with the corresponding value.

Section 3.6.1 Declaring the `int` Variable `number1`
- Integers are whole numbers, such as –22, 7, 0 and 1024.

- Type `int` is used to declare variables that will hold integer values. The range of values for an `int` is –2,147,483,648 to +2,147,483,647.

- Types `float`, `double`, and `decimal` specify real numbers, and type `char` specifies character data. Real numbers are numbers that may contain decimal points, such as 3.4, 0.0 and –11.19. Variables of type `char` data represent individual characters, such as an uppercase letter (e.g., A), a digit (e.g., 7), a special character (e.g., * or %) or an escape sequence (e.g., the newline character, \n).

- Types such as `int`, `float`, `double`, `decimal`, and `char` are often called simple types. Simple-type names are keywords; thus, they must appear in all lowercase letters.

Section 3.6.3 Prompting the User for Input
- A prompt directs the user to take a specific action.

- `Console` method `ReadLine` obtains a line of text from the keyboard for use in an app.

- `int` method `Parse` extracts an integer from a string of characters.

- The assignment operator, =, enables the app to give a value to a variable. Operator = is called a binary operator because it has two operands. An assignment statement uses an assignment operator to assign a value to a variable.

Section 3.6.6 Summing `number1` and `number2`
- Portions of statements that have values are called expressions.

Section 3.7 Memory Concepts
- Variable names correspond to locations in the computer's memory. Every variable has a name, a type, a size and a value.

- Whenever a value is placed in a memory location, the value replaces the previous value in that location. The previous value is lost.

Section 3.8 Arithmetic
- Most apps perform arithmetic calculations. The arithmetic operators are + (addition), - (subtraction), * (multiplication), / (division) and % (remainder).
- If both operands of the division operator (/) are integers, the result is an integer.
- The remainder operator, %, yields the remainder after division.

Section 3.8.1 Arithmetic Expressions in Straight-Line Form
- Arithmetic expressions in C# must be written in straight-line form.

Section 3.8.2 Parentheses for Grouping Subexpressions
- If an expression contains nested parentheses, the innermost set of parentheses is evaluated first.

Section 3.8.3 Rules of Operator Precedence
- C# applies the operators in arithmetic expressions in a precise sequence determined by the rules of operator precedence.
- Associativity determines whether operators are applied from left to right or right to left.

Section 3.8.5 Redundant Parentheses
- Redundant parentheses in an expression can make an expression clearer.

Section 3.9 Decision Making: Equality and Relational Operators
- A condition is an expression that can be either true or false. C#'s if statement allows an app to make a decision based on the value of a condition.
- Conditions in if statements can be formed by using the equality (== and !=) and relational (>, <, >= and <=) operators.
- An if statement always begins with keyword if, followed by a condition in parentheses and a body, which you should always enclose in braces ({}).
- An empty statement is a statement that does not perform a task.

Terminology

addition operator (+)
argument
arithmetic operators (*, /, %, + and -)
assignment operator (=)
associativity of operators
backslash (\) escape character
binary operator
body of a class declaration
body of a method declaration
camel case
char simple type
character string
class declaration
class keyword
class name

Command Prompt
comment
compilation error
condition
Console class
console window
.cs file-name extension
decimal simple type
decision
division operator (/)
double simple type
empty statement (;)
equality operators
   == "is equal to"
   != "is not equal to"

Error List window
escape character
escape sequence
.exe file-name extension
executable
expression
fault tolerant
float simple type
Framework Class Library
identifier
if statement
int (integer) simple type
integer
integer division
Intellisense
interpolated string
interpolation expression
left brace, {
literal
location of a variable
Main method
method
multiplication operator (*)
namespace
nested parentheses
newline character (\n)
operand
operator precedence
Parameter Info window
parentheses ()
Parse method of type int
Pascal Case
perform an action
precedence of operators
prompt

ReadLine method of class Console
redundant parentheses
relational operators
  < "is less than"
  <= "is less than or equal to"
  > "is greater than"
  >= "is greater than or equal to"
remainder operator (%)
reserved words
right brace, }
rules of operator precedence
semicolon (;) statement terminator
simple type
single-line comment (//)
standard input/output class (Console)
statement
straight-line form
string
string interpolation
string type
subtraction operator (-)
syntax-color highlighting
syntax error
using directive
variable
variable declaration
variable declaration statement
variable name
variable size
variable type
variable value
void keyword
whitespace
Write method of class Console
WriteLine method of class Console

Self-Review Exercises

3.1 Fill in the blanks in each of the following statements:

a) A(n) _____ begins the body of every method, and a(n) _____ ends the body of every method.

b) Most statements end with a(n) _____.

c) The _____ statement is used to make decisions.

d) _____ begins a single-line comment.

e) _____, _____ and _____ are called whitespace. Newline characters are also considered whitespace.

f) _____ are reserved for use by C#.

g) C# apps begin execution at method _____.

h) Methods _____ and _____ display information in the console window.

i) _____ enables you to insert values directly into a string literal.

3.2   State whether each of the following is *true* or *false*. If *false*, explain why.
   a) Comments cause the computer to display the text after the `//` on the screen when the
       app executes.
   b) C# considers the variables `number` and `NuMbEr` to be identical.
   c) The remainder operator (`%`) can be used only with integer operands.
   d) The arithmetic operators `*`, `/`, `%`, `+` and `-` all have the same level of precedence.
   e) An interpolated string must begin with a `$` before the string literal.

3.3   Write statements to accomplish each of the following tasks:
   a) Declare variables `c`, `thisIsAVariable`, `q76354` and `number` to be of type `int`.
   b) Prompt the user to enter an integer.
   c) Input an integer and assign the result to `int` variable `value`.
   d) If the variable `number` is not equal to 7, display `"The variable number is not equal to 7"`.
   e) Display `"This is a C# app"` on one line in the console window.
   f) Display `"This is a C# app"` on two lines in the console window. The first line should
       end with `C#`. Use method `Console.WriteLine`.
   g) Write a statement that uses `string` interpolation to display the sum of the variables `x`
       and `y`. Assume variables `x` and `y` of type `int` exist and already have values.

3.4   Identify and correct the errors in each of the following statements:
   a)
```
if (c < 7);
{
    Console.WriteLine("c is less than 7");
}
```
   b)
```
if (c => 7)
{
    Console.WriteLine("c is equal to or greater than 7");
}
```

3.5   Write declarations, statements or comments that accomplish each of the following tasks:
   a) State that an app will calculate the product of three integers.
   b) Declare the variables `x`, `y`, `z` and `result` to be of type `int`.
   c) Prompt the user to enter the first integer.
   d) Read the first integer from the user and store it in the variable `x`.
   e) Prompt the user to enter the second integer.
   f) Read the second integer from the user and store it in the variable `y`.
   g) Prompt the user to enter the third integer.
   h) Read the third integer from the user and store it in the variable `z`.
   i) Compute the product of the three integers contained in variables `x`, `y` and `z`, and assign
       the result to the variable `result`.
   j) Display the message `"Product is"`, followed by the value of the variable `result`—use
       `string` interpolation.

3.6   Using the statements you wrote in Exercise 3.5, write a complete app that calculates and
displays the product of three integers.

Answers to Self-Review Exercises

3.1   a) left brace (`{`), right brace (`}`). b) semicolon (`;`). c) `if`. d) `//`. e) Blank lines, space characters, tab characters. f) Keywords. g) `Main`. h) `Console.WriteLine` and `Console.Write`. i) `string` interpolation.

3.2   The answers to Self-Review Exercise 3.2 are as follows:
   a) False. Comments do not cause any action to be performed when the app executes. They're used to document apps and improve their readability.
   b) False. C# is case sensitive, so these variables are distinct.
   c) False. The remainder operator also can be used with noninteger operands in C#.
   d) False. The operators *, / and % are on the same level of precedence, and the operators + and - are on a lower level of precedence.
   e) True.

3.3   The answers to Self-Review Exercise 3.3 are as follows:
   a)
```
int c;
int thisIsAVariable;
int q76354;
int number;
```
   b) `Console.Write("Enter an integer: ");`
   c) `value = int.Parse(Console.ReadLine());`
   d)
```
if (number != 7)
{
    Console.WriteLine("The variable number is not equal to 7");
}
```
   e) `Console.WriteLine("This is a C# app");`
   f) `Console.WriteLine("This is a C#\napp");`
   g) `Console.WriteLine($"The sum of {x} and {y} is {x + y}");`

3.4   The answers to Self-Review Exercise 3.4 are as follows:
   a) *Error:* Semicolon after the right parenthesis of the condition (c < 7) in the if statement. *Correction:* Remove the semicolon after the right parenthesis. [*Note:* With the semicolon, the output statement executes regardless of whether the condition in the if is true.]
   b) *Error:* The relational operator => is incorrect. *Correction:* Change => to >=.

3.5   The answers to Self-Review Exercise 3.5 are as follows:
   a) `// Calculating the product of three integers`
   b)
```
int x;
int y;
int z;
int result;
```
   c) `Console.Write("Enter first integer: ");`
   d) `x = int.Parse(Console.ReadLine());`
   e) `Console.Write("Enter second integer: ");`
   f) `y = int.Parse(Console.ReadLine());`
   g) `Console.Write("Enter third integer: ");`
   h) `z = int.Parse(Console.ReadLine());`
   i) `result = x * y * z;`
   j) `Console.WriteLine($"Product is {result}");`

3.6   The solution to Self-Review Exercise 3.6 is as follows:

```
1    // Exercise 3.6: Product.cs
2    // Calculating the product of three integers.
3    using System;
```

Fig. 3.24 | Solution to Exercise 3.6. (Part 1 of 2.)

```
4
5    class Product
6    {
7       static void Main()
8       {
9          int x; // stores first number to be entered by user
10         int y; // stores second number to be entered by user
11         int z; // stores third number to be entered by user
12         int result; // product of numbers
13
14         Console.Write("Enter first integer: "); // prompt for input
15         x = int.Parse(Console.ReadLine()); // read first integer
16
17         Console.Write("Enter second integer: "); // prompt for input
18         y = int.Parse(Console.ReadLine()); // read second integer
19
20         Console.Write("Enter third integer: "); // prompt for input
21         z = int.Parse(Console.ReadLine()); // read third integer
22
23         result = x * y * z; // calculate the product of the numbers
24         Console.WriteLine($"Product is {result}");
25      } // end Main
26   } // end class Product
```

```
Enter first integer: 10
Enter second integer: 20
Enter third integer: 30
Product is 6000
```

Fig. 3.24 | Solution to Exercise 3.6. (Part 2 of 2.)

Exercises

3.7   Fill in the blanks in each of the following statements:
   a) _____ are used to document an app and improve its readability.
   b) A decision can be made in a C# app with a(n) _____.
   c) Calculations are normally performed by _____ statements.
   d) The arithmetic operators with the same precedence as multiplication are _____ and
       _____.
   e) When parentheses in an arithmetic expression are nested, the _____ set of parenthe-
       ses is evaluated first.
   f) A location in the computer's memory that may contain different values at various times
       throughout the execution of an app is called a(n) _____.

3.8   Write C# statements that accomplish each of the following tasks:
   a) Display the message "Enter an integer: ", leaving the cursor on the same line.
   b) Assign the product of variables b and c to variable a.
   c) State that an app performs a simple payroll calculation (i.e., use text that helps to doc-
       ument an app).

3.9   State whether each of the following is *true* or *false*. If *false*, explain why.
   a) C# operators are evaluated from left to right.
   b) The following are all valid variable names: _under_bar_, m928134, t5, j7, her_sales,
       his_account_total, a, b, c, z and z2.
   c) A valid C# arithmetic expression with no parentheses is evaluated from left to right.
   d) The following are all invalid variable names: 3g, 87, 67h2, h22 and 2h.

3.10   Assuming that x = 2 and y = 3, what does each of the following statements display?

a) `Console.WriteLine($"x = {x}");`
b) `Console.WriteLine($"Value of {x} + {x} is {x + x}");`
c) `Console.Write("x =");`
d) `Console.WriteLine($"{x + y} = {y + x}");`

3.11   Which of the following C# statements contain variables whose values are modified?

a) `p = i + j + k + 7;`
b) `Console.WriteLine("variables whose values are modified");`
c) `Console.WriteLine("a = 5");`
d) `value = int.Parse(Console.ReadLine());`

3.12   Given that $y = ax^3 + 7$, which of the following are correct C# statements for this equation?

a) `y = a * x * x * x + 7;`
b) `y = a * x * x * (x + 7);`
c) `y = (a * x) * x * (x + 7);`
d) `y = (a * x) * x * x + 7;`
e) `y = a * (x * x * x) + 7;`
f) `y = a * x * (x * x + 7);`

3.13   *(Order of Evaluation)* State the order of evaluation of the operators in each of the following C# statements and show the value of x after each statement is performed:

a) `x = 7 + 3 * 6 / 2 - 1;`
b) `x = 2 % 2 + 2 * 2 - 2 / 2;`
c) `x = (3 * 9 * (3 + (9 * 3 / (3))));`

3.14   *(Displaying Numbers)* Write an app that displays the numbers 1 to 4 on the same line, with each pair of adjacent numbers separated by one space. Write the app using the following techniques:

a)   Use one `Console.WriteLine` statement.
b)   Use four `Console.Write` statements.
c)   Use one `Console.WriteLine` statement with four `int` variables and string interpolation.

3.15   *(Arithmetic)* Write an app that asks the user to enter two integers, obtains them from the user and displays their sum, product, difference and quotient (division). Use the techniques shown in Fig. 3.14.

3.16   *(Comparing Integers)* Write an app that asks the user to enter two integers, obtains them from the user and displays the larger number followed by the words `"is larger"`. If the numbers are equal, display the message `"These numbers are equal."` Use the techniques shown in Fig. 3.22.

3.17   *(Arithmetic, Smallest and Largest)* Write an app that inputs three integers from the user and displays the sum, average, product, and smallest and largest of the numbers. Use the techniques from Fig. 3.22. [*Note:* The average calculation in this exercise should result in an integer representation of the average. So, if the sum of the values is 7, the average should be 2, not 2.3333….]

3.18   *(Displaying Shapes with Asterisks)* Write an app that displays a box, an oval, an arrow and a diamond using asterisks (*), as in Fig. 3.25.

3.19   What does the following code display?

```
Console.WriteLine("*\n**\n***\n****\n*****");
```

3.20   What does the following code display?

```
Console.WriteLine("*");
Console.WriteLine("***");
Console.WriteLine("*****");
Console.WriteLine("****");
Console.WriteLine("**");
```

```
*********     ***       *        *
*       *   *     *    ***      * *
*       *  *       *  *****    *   *
*       *  *       *    *     *     *
*       *  *       *    *    *       *
*       *  *       *    *     *     *
*       *  *       *    *      *   *
*       *   *     *     *       * *
*********     ***       *        *
```

Fig. 3.25 | Sample output for Exercise 3.18.

3.21 What does the following code display?

```
Console.Write("*");
Console.Write("***");
Console.Write("*****");
Console.Write("****");
Console.WriteLine("**");
```

3.22 What does the following code display?

```
Console.Write("*");
Console.WriteLine("***");
Console.WriteLine("*****");
Console.Write("****");
Console.WriteLine("**");
```

3.23 What does the following code display?

```
string s1 = "*";
string s2 = "***";
string s3 = "*****";
Console.WriteLine($"{s1}\n{s2}\n{s3}");
```

3.24 ***(Odd or Even)*** Write an app that reads an integer, then determines and displays whether it's odd or even. [*Hint:* Use the remainder operator. An even number is a multiple of 2. Any multiple of 2 leaves a remainder of 0 when divided by 2.]

3.25 ***(Multiples)*** Write an app that reads two integers, determines whether the first is a multiple of the second and displays the result. [*Hint:* Use the remainder operator.]

3.26 ***(Diameter, Circumference and Area of a Circle)*** Here's a peek ahead. In this chapter, you have learned about integers and the type `int`. C# also can represent floating-point numbers that contain decimal points, such as 3.14159. Write an app that inputs from the user the radius of a circle as an integer and displays the circle's diameter, circumference and area using the floating-point value 3.14159 for π. Use the techniques shown in Fig. 3.14. [*Note:* You may also use the predefined constant `Math.PI` for the value of π. This constant is more precise than the value 3.14159. Class `Math` is defined in namespace `System`]. Use the following formulas (r is the radius):

$$diameter = 2r$$
$$circumference = 2\pi r$$
$$area = \pi r^2$$

Don't store each calculation's result in a variable. Rather, specify each calculation as the value to be output in a `Console.WriteLine` statement. The values produced by the circumference and area calculations are floating-point numbers. You'll learn more about these in Chapter 5.

3.27 ***(Integer Equivalent of a Character)*** Here's another peek ahead. In this chapter, you have learned about integers and the type `int`. C# also can represent uppercase letters, lowercase letters

and a considerable variety of special symbols. Every character has a corresponding integer representation. The set of characters a computer uses and the corresponding integer representations for those characters is called that computer's character set. You can indicate a character value in an app simply by enclosing that character in single quotes, as in `'A'`.

You can determine the integer equivalent of a character by preceding that character with `(int)`, as in

```
(int) 'A'
```

The keyword `int` in parentheses is known as a cast operator, and the entire expression is called a cast expression. (You'll learn about cast operators in Chapter 5.) The following statement outputs a character and its integer equivalent:

```
Console.WriteLine($"The character {'A'} has the value {(int)'A'}");
```

When the preceding statement executes, it displays the character A and the value 65 as part of the string. See Appendix C for a list of characters and their integer equivalents.

Using statements similar to the one shown earlier in this exercise, write an app that displays the integer equivalents of some uppercase letters, lowercase letters, digits and special symbols. Display the integer equivalents of the following: A B C a b c 0 1 2 $ * + / and the space character.

3.28 *(Digits of an Integer)* Write an app that inputs one number consisting of five digits from the user, separates the number into its individual digits and displays the digits separated from one another by three spaces each. For example, if the user types 42339, the app should display

```
4   2   3   3   9
```

Assume that the user enters the correct number of digits. What happens when you execute the app and type a number with more than five digits? What happens when you execute the app and type a number with fewer than five digits? [*Hint:* It's possible to do this exercise with the techniques you learned in this chapter. You'll need to use both division and remainder operations to "pick off" each digit.]

3.29 *(Table of Squares and Cubes)* Using only the programming techniques you learned in this chapter, write an app that calculates the squares and cubes of the numbers from 0 to 10 and displays the resulting values in table format, as shown in. All calculations should be done in terms of a variable x. [*Note:* This app does not require any input from the user.]

```
number  square  cube
0       0       0
1       1       1
2       4       8
3       9       27
4       16      64
5       25      125
6       36      216
7       49      343
8       64      512
9       81      729
10      100     1000
```

Fig. 3.26 | Sample output for Exercise 3.29.

3.30 *(Counting Negative, Positive and Zero Values)* Write an app that inputs five numbers and determines and displays the number of negative numbers input, the number of positive numbers input and the number of zeros input.

Making-a-Difference Exercises

3.31 *(Body Mass Index Calculator)* We introduced the body mass index (BMI) calculator in Exercise 1.27. The formulas for calculating the BMI are

$$BMI = \frac{weightInPounds \times 703}{heightInInches \times heightInInches}$$

or

$$BMI = \frac{weightInKilograms}{heightInMeters \times heightInMeters}$$

Create a BMI calculator app that reads the user's weight in pounds and height in inches (or, if you prefer, the user's weight in kilograms and height in meters), then calculates and displays the user's body mass index. The app should also display the following information from the Department of Health and Human Services/National Institutes of Health so the user can evaluate his/her BMI:

```
BMI VALUES
Underweight: less than 18.5
Normal:      between 18.5 and 24.9
Overweight:  between 25 and 29.9
Obese:       30 or greater
```

3.32 *(Car-Pool Savings Calculator)* Research several car-pooling websites. Create an app that calculates your daily driving cost, so that you can estimate how much money could be saved by car pooling, which also has other advantages such as reducing carbon emissions and reducing traffic congestion. The app should input the following information and display the user's cost per day of driving to work:

a) Total miles driven per day.
b) Cost per gallon of gasoline (in cents).
c) Average miles per gallon.
d) Parking fees per day (in cents).
e) Tolls per day (in cents).

4

Introduction to Classes, Objects, Methods and strings

Objectives

In this chapter you'll:

- Begin programming with the object-oriented concepts introduced in Section 1.6.

- Declare a class and use it to create an object.

- Implement a class's attributes as instance variables and a class's behaviors as methods.

- Call an object's methods to make them perform their tasks.

- Understand what local variables of a method are and how they differ from instance variables of a class.

- Use validation to prevent bad data from being stored in an object.

- Understand the software engineering benefits of **private** instance variables and **public** access methods.

- Use properties to provide a friendlier notation for storing and retrieving data.

- Use a constructor to initialize an object's data when the object is created.

- Use type **decimal** for precise monetary amounts and calculations.

4.1 Introduction

[*Note:* This chapter depends on the terminology and concepts introduced in Section 1.6, Object Technology.]

Section 1.6 presented a friendly introduction to object-oriented programming concepts, including classes, objects, instance variables, properties and methods. In this chapter's examples, we make those concepts real by building a simple bank-account class. The final version of the class maintains a bank account's name and balance, and provides *properties* (Name and Balance) and *methods* (Deposit and Withdraw) for behaviors including

- querying the balance (with the Balance property),
- making deposits that increase the balance (with the Deposit method) and
- making withdrawals that decrease the balance (with the Withdraw method).

We'll build the Balance property and Deposit method into the chapter's examples. You'll add the Withdraw method in Exercise 4.9.

Each *class* you create becomes a new *type* you can use to create objects, so C# is an extensible programming language. Major development teams in industry work on applications that contain hundreds, or even thousands, of classes.

4.2 Test-Driving an Account Class

A person drives a car by telling it what to do (go faster, go slower, turn left, turn right, etc.)—without having to know how the car's internal mechanisms work. Similarly, a method (such as `Main`) "drives" an `Account` object by calling its methods—without having to know how the class's internal mechanisms work. In this sense, the class containing method `Main` is referred to as a *driver class*. We show the `Main` method and its output first, so you can see an `Account` object in action.

To help you prepare for the larger programs you'll encounter later in this book and in industry, we define class `AccountTest` and its `Main` method in the file `AccountTest.cs` (Fig. 4.1). We define the `Account` class in its own file as well (file `Account.cs`, Fig. 4.2). After we present classes `AccountTest` (in this section) and `Account` (in Section 4.3), Section 4.4 discusses how to create and build a project that contains multiple `.cs` source-code files. First, let's walk through the `AccountTest` class.

```csharp
1   // Fig. 4.1: AccountTest.cs
2   // Creating and manipulating an Account object.
3   using System;
4
5   class AccountTest
6   {
7      static void Main()
8      {
9         // create an Account object and assign it to myAccount
10        Account myAccount = new Account();
11
12        // display myAccount's initial name (there isn't one yet)
13        Console.WriteLine($"Initial name is: {myAccount.GetName()}");
14
15        // prompt for and read the name, then put the name in the object
16        Console.Write("Enter the name: "); // prompt
17        string theName = Console.ReadLine(); // read the name
18        myAccount.SetName(theName); // put theName in the myAccount object
19
20        // display the name stored in the myAccount object
21        Console.WriteLine($"myAccount's name is: {myAccount.GetName()}");
22     }
23  }
```

```
Initial name is:
Enter the name: Jane Green
myAccount's name is: Jane Green
```

Fig. 4.1 | Creating and manipulating an Account object.

4.2.1 Instantiating an Object—Keyword new

Typically, you cannot call a method of a class until you *create an object* of that class.[1] Line 10

```csharp
Account myAccount = new Account();
```

---

1. You'll see in Section 10.9 that `static` methods (and other `static` class members) are an exception.

uses an object-creation expression

```
new Account()
```

to create an Account object, then assigns it to the variable myAccount. The variable's type is Account—the class we'll define in Fig. 4.2. Keyword new creates a new object of the specified class—in this case, Account. The parentheses to the right of Account are required (we'll discuss these in Section 4.8).

4.2.2 Calling Class Account's GetName Method

The Account class's GetName method returns the account name stored in a particular Account object. Line 13

```
Console.WriteLine($"Initial name is: {myAccount.GetName()}");
```

displays myAccount's initial name by calling the object's GetName method with the expression myAccount.GetName(). To call this method for a specific object, you specify

- the object's name (myAccount) followed by
- the member access operator (.),
- the method name (GetName) and
- a set of parentheses.

The *empty* parentheses indicate that GetName does not require any additional information to perform its task. Soon, you'll see the SetName method that does require additional information to perform its task.

When Main calls the GetName method:

1. The app transfers execution from the expression myAccount.GetName() (line 13 in Main) to method GetName's declaration (which we'll study in Section 4.3). Because GetName was accessed via the object myAccount, GetName knows which object's data to manipulate.

2. Next, method GetName performs its task—that is, it returns the myAccount object's name to line 13 where the method was called.

3. Console.WriteLine displays the string returned by GetName—the name is inserted into the interpolated string in place of the call to GetName—then the program continues executing at line 16 in Main.

Because we have not yet stored a name in the myAccount object, line 13 does not display a name.

4.2.3 Inputting a Name from the User

Next, lines 16–17 prompt for and input a name. Line 17

```
string theName = Console.ReadLine(); // read a line of text
```

uses Console method ReadLine to read the name from the user and assign it to the string variable theName. The user types the name (in this case, Jane Green) and presses *Enter* to submit it to the app. Method ReadLine reads a *whole* line, including all the characters the user types until the newline that the user typed by pressing *Enter*—the newline is discarded. Pressing *Enter* also positions the output cursor to the beginning of the next line in the console window, so the program's next output begins on the line below the user's input.

4.2.4 Calling Class Account's SetName Method

The `Account` class's `SetName` method stores (*sets*) an account name in a particular `Account` object. Line 18

```
myAccount.SetName(theName); // put theName in the myAccount object
```

calls `myAccounts`'s `SetName` method, passing `theName`'s value as `SetName`'s argument. The method stores this value in the object `myAccount`—we'll see exactly where it's stored in the next section.

When `Main` calls the `SetName` method:

1. The app transfers program execution from line 18 in `Main` to method `SetName`'s declaration. Because method `SetName` was accessed via the `myAccount` object, `SetName` "knows" which object to manipulate.

2. Next, method `SetName` stores the argument's value in the `myAccount` object (we'll see exactly where in Section 4.3).

3. When `SetName` completes execution, program control returns to where method `SetName` was called (line 18 in `Main`), then execution continues at line 21.

Displaying the Name That Was Entered by the User
To demonstrate that `myAccount` now contains the name the user entered, line 21

```
Console.WriteLine($"myAccount's name is: {myAccount.GetName()}");
```

calls `myAccounts`'s `GetName` method again. As you can see in the last line of the program's output, the name entered by the user in line 17 is displayed. When the preceding statement completes execution, the end of `Main` is reached, so the app terminates.

4.3 Account Class with an Instance Variable and *Set* and *Get* Methods

The fact that in Fig. 4.1 we could create and manipulate an `Account` object without knowing its implementation details is called abstraction. This is one of the most powerful software-engineering benefits of object-oriented programming. Now that we've seen class `Account` in action (Fig. 4.1), in the next several sections we'll explain its implementation in detail. Then, we present a UML diagram that summarizes class `Account`'s *attributes* and *operations* in a concise graphical representation.

4.3.1 Account Class Declaration

Class `Account` (Fig. 4.2) contains a `name` *instance variable* (line 7) that stores the account holder's name—each `Account` object has its own copy of the `name` *instance variable*. In Section 4.9, we'll add a `balance` instance variable to keep track of the current balance in each `Account`. Class `Account` also contains method `SetName` that a program can call to store a name in an Account object, and method GetName that a program can call to obtain the name from an Account object.

```
 1   // Fig. 4.2: Account.cs
 2   // A simple Account class that contains a private instance
 3   // variable name and public methods to Set and Get name's value.
 4
 5   class Account
 6   {
 7      private string name; // instance variable
 8
 9      // method that sets the account name in the object
10      public void SetName(string accountName)
11      {
12         name = accountName; // store the account name
13      }
14
15      // method that retrieves the account name from the object
16      public string GetName()
17      {
18         return name; // returns name's value to this method's caller
19      }
20   }
```

Fig. 4.2 | A simple Account class that contains a `private` instance variable name and `public` methods to *Set* and *Get* name's value.

4.3.2 Keyword class and the Class Body

The class declaration begins in line 5 with

```
class Account
```

As we mentioned in Chapter 3, every class declaration contains the keyword class followed immediately by the class's name—in this case, Account. Also, each class declaration is typically stored in a file having the same name as the class and ending with the .cs filename extension, so we've placed class Account in the file Account.cs. The class's body is enclosed in a pair of braces (lines 6 and 20 of Fig. 4.2).

Identifiers and Camel-Case Naming

Class, property, method and variable names are all *identifiers* and by convention all use the naming schemes we discussed in Chapter 3:

- class, property and method names begin with an initial *uppercase* letter (i.e., Pascal case)
- variable names begin with an initial *lowercase* letter (i.e., camel case).

4.3.3 Instance Variable name of Type string

Recall from Section 1.6 that a class has attributes, implemented as instance variables. Objects of the class carry these instance variables with them throughout their lifetimes. Each object has its own copy of the class's instance variables. Normally, a class also contains methods and properties. These manipulate the instance variables belonging to particular objects of the class.

Instance variables are declared *inside* a class declaration but *outside* the bodies of the class's methods and properties. Line 7

```
private string name; // instance variable
```

declares instance variable name of type `string` *outside* the bodies of methods `SetName` and `GetName`. If there are many `Account` objects, each has its own `name`. Because `name` is an instance variable, it can be manipulated by each of the class's methods and properties. Clients of class `Account`—that is, any other code that calls the class's methods (such as class `AccountTest`'s `Main` method in Fig. 4.1)—cannot access the `name` instance variable because it's declared `private`. However, clients *can* access `Account`'s `public` methods `SetName` and `GetName`. These methods *can* access `private` instance variable `name`. We discuss `private` and `public` in Section 4.3.6, then discuss why this architecture of `private` instance variables and `public` *access methods* is powerful in more detail in Section 4.5.

Good Programming Practice 4.1

We prefer to list a class's instance variables first in the class's body, so that you see the names and types of the variables before they're used in the class's methods and properties. You can list the class's instance variables anywhere in the class outside its method (and property) declarations, but scattering the instance variables can lead to hard-to-read code.

`null`—the Default Initial Value for `string` Variables

Every instance variable has a default initial value—a value provided by C# if you do not specify the instance variable's initial value. Thus, instance variables are not required to be explicitly initialized before they're used in a program—unless they must be initialized to values *other* than their default values. The default value for an instance variable of type `string` (like `name` in this example) is `null`, which we discuss further in Chapter 7 when we consider so-called *reference types*. When you use `Console.Write` or `Console.WriteLine` to display a `string` variable that contains the value `null`, no text is displayed on the screen—this is why line 13 in `Main` (Fig. 4.1) did not display a name the first time we called `myAccount`'s `GetName` method.

4.3.4 SetName Method

Let's walk through the code of method `SetName`'s declaration (Fig. 4.2, lines 10–13):

```
public void SetName(string accountName)
{
    name = accountName; // store the account name
}
```

The first line of each method declaration (line 10) is the *method header*. The method's return type (which appears to the left of the method's name) specifies the type of data the method returns to its *caller* after performing its task. The return type `void` (line 10) indicates that when `SetName` completes its task, it does not return (i.e., give back) any information to its calling method—in this example, line 18 of the `Main` method (Fig. 4.1). As you'll soon see, `Account` method `GetName` *does* return a value.

SetName's Parameter

Our car analogy from Section 1.6 mentioned that pressing a car's gas pedal sends a message to the car to perform a task—make the car go faster. But *how fast* should the car accelerate? The farther down you press the pedal, the faster the car accelerates. So the message to the car includes both the task to perform and information that helps the car perform that task. This information is known as a parameter—the parameter's value helps the car determine how fast to accelerate. Similarly, a method can require one or more parameters that represent the data it needs to perform its task.

Method SetName declares the string parameter accountName—which receives the name that's passed to SetName as an argument. When line 18 in Fig. 4.1

```
myAccount.SetName(theName); // put theName in the myAccount object
```

executes, the *argument value* in the call's parentheses (i.e., the value stored in theName) is copied into the corresponding *parameter* (accountName) in the method's header (line 10 of Fig. 4.2). In Fig. 4.1's sample execution, we entered "Jane Green" for theName, so "Jane Green" was copied into the accountName parameter.

SetName Parameter List

Parameters like accountName are declared in a parameter list located in the *required* parentheses following the method's name. Each parameter *must* specify a type (e.g., string) followed by a parameter name (e.g., accountName). When there are multiple parameters, they are placed in a comma-separated list, as in

```
(type1 name1, type2 name2, ...)
```

The number and order of *arguments* in a method call *must match* the number and order of *parameters* in the method declaration's parameter list.

SetName Method Body

Every method body is delimited by an opening left brace (Fig. 4.2, line 11) and a closing right brace (line 13). Within the braces are one or more statements that perform the method's task(s). In this case, the method body contains a single statement (line 12)

```
name = accountName; // store the account name
```

that assigns the accountName parameter's value (a string) to the class's name instance variable, thus storing the account name in the object for which SetName was called—myAccount in this example's Main program.[2] After line 12 executes, program execution reaches the method's closing brace (line 13), so the method returns to its *caller*.

Parameters Are Local Variables

In Chapter 3, we declared all of an app's variables in the Main method. Variables declared in a particular method's body (such as Main) are local variables which can be used *only* in that method. Each method can access only its own local variables, not those of other methods. When a method terminates, the values of its local variables are lost. A method's parameters also are local variables of the method.

---

2. We used different names for the SetName method's parameter (accountName) and the instance variable (name). It's common idiom in industry to use the same name for both. We'll show you how to do this without ambiguity in Section 10.4.

4.3.5 GetName Method

Method `GetName` (lines 16–19)

```
public string GetName()
{
    return name; // returns name's value to this method's caller
}
```

returns a particular `Account` object's name to the caller—a `string`, as specified by the method's return type. The method has an empty parameter list, so it does not require additional information to perform its task. When a method with a return type other than `void` is called and completes its task, it *must* return a result to its caller. A statement that calls method `GetName` on an `Account` object expects to receive the `Account`'s name.

The `return` statement in line 18

```
return name; // returns name's value to this method's caller
```

passes the `string` value of instance variable name back to the caller, which can then use the returned value. For example, the statement in line 21 of Fig. 4.1

```
Console.WriteLine($"myAccount's name is: {myAccount.GetName()}");
```

uses the value returned by `GetName` to output the name stored in the `myAccount` object.

4.3.6 Access Modifiers `private` and `public`

The keyword `private` (line 7 of Fig. 4.2)

```
private string name; // instance variable
```

is an access modifier. Instance variable name is `private` to indicate that name is accessible *only* to class `Account`'s methods (and other members, like properties, as you'll see in subsequent examples). This is known as information hiding—the instance variable name is hidden and can be used *only* in class `Account`'s methods (`SetName` and `GetName`). Most instance variables are declared `private`.

This class also contains the `public` access modifier (line 10)

```
public void SetName(string accountName)
```

and line 16

```
public string GetName()
```

Methods (and other class members) that are declared `public` are "available to the public." They can be used

- by methods (and other members) of the class in which they're declared,
- by the class's clients—that is, methods (and other members) of any other classes (in this app, class `AccountTest`'s `Main` method is the client of class `Account`).

In Chapter 11, we'll introduce the `protected` access modifier.

Default Access for Class Members
By default, everything in a class is `private`, unless you specify otherwise by providing access modifiers.

Error-Prevention Tip 4.1

Making a class's instance variables private *and its methods (and as you'll see, properties)* public *and accessing those instance variables only through the class's methods and properties facilitates debugging, because problems with data manipulations are localized to the methods (and properties).*

Common Programming Error 4.1

An attempt by a method that's not a member of a particular class to access a private *member of that class is a compilation error.*

4.3.7 Account UML Class Diagram

We'll often use UML class diagrams to summarize a class's *attributes* and *operations*. In industry, UML diagrams help systems designers specify systems in a concise, graphical, programming-language-independent manner, before programmers implement the systems in specific programming languages. Figure 4.3 presents a UML class diagram for class Account of Fig. 4.2.

Account
– name : string
+ SetName(accountName : string) + GetName() : string

Fig. 4.3 | UML class diagram for class Account of Fig. 4.2.

Top Compartment
In the UML, each class is modeled in a class diagram as a rectangle with three compartments. In this diagram the top compartment contains the *class name* Account centered horizontally in boldface type.

Middle Compartment
The middle compartment contains the class's attribute names, which correspond to the instance variables of the same names in C#. The single instance variable name in Fig. 4.2 is private in C#, so the UML class diagram lists a *minus sign (–) UML access modifier* before the attribute's name. Following the attribute's name are a *colon* and the *attribute type*, in this case string.

Bottom Compartment
The bottom compartment contains the class's operations, SetName and GetName, which correspond to the methods of the same names in C#. The UML models operations by listing the operation name preceded by a UML access modifier, for example, + SetName. This plus sign (+) indicates that SetName is a public operation in the UML (because it's a public method in C#). Operation GetName is also a public operation.

Return Types

The UML indicates an operation's return type by placing a colon and the return type *after* the parentheses following the operation name. Method `SetName` does not return a value (because it returns `void` in C#), so the UML class diagram does not specify a return type after the parentheses of this operation. Method `GetName` has a `string` return type. The UML has its own data types similar to those of C#—for simplicity, we use the C# types.

Parameters

The UML models a parameter by listing the parameter name, followed by a colon and the parameter type in the parentheses after the operation name. `Account` method `SetName` has a `string` parameter called `accountName`, so the class diagram lists

```
accountName : string
```

between the parentheses following the method name. Operation `GetName` does not have any parameters, so the parentheses following the operation name in the class diagram are empty, just as they are in the method's declaration in line 16 of Fig. 4.2.

4.4 Creating, Compiling and Running a Visual C# Project with Two Classes

When you create the project for this app, you should rename `Program.cs` to `Account-Test.cs` and add the `Account.cs` file to the project. To set up a project with two classes:

1. Create a **Console Application** as you did in Chapter 3. We named this chapter's projects `Account1`, `Account2`, `Account3` and `Account4`, respectively.

2. Rename the project's `Program.cs` file to `AccountTest.cs`. Replace the autogenerated code with class `AccountTest`'s code (Fig. 4.1).

3. Right click the project name in the **Solution Explorer** and select **Add > Class...** from the pop-up menu.

4. In the **Add New Item** dialog's **Name** field, enter the new file's name (`Account.cs`), then click **Add**. In the new `Account.cs` file, replace the auto-generated code with class `Account`'s code from Fig. 4.2.

You can open each class in the Visual Studio editor by double clicking the filename in the **Solution Explorer** window.

You must compile the classes in Figs. 4.1 and 4.2 before you can *execute* the app. This is the first time you've created an app with *multiple* classes. Class `AccountTest` has a `Main` method; class `Account` does not. The IDE automatically recognizes as the app's entry point the class that contains `Main`. When you select **Build > Build Solution** in Visual Studio, the IDE compiles all the files in the project to create the executable app. If both classes compile correctly—that is, no compilation errors are displayed—you can then run the app by typing *Ctrl* + *F5* to execute the `AccountTest` class's `Main` method. If you do not build the app before running it, typing *Ctrl* + *F5* will build the app first and run the app only if there are no compilation errors.

Common Programming Error 4.2

In a given project, declaring a Main *method in more than exactly one class results in the compilation error, "Program has more than one entry point defined."*

4.5 Software Engineering with *Set* and *Get* Methods

Set and *Get* methods can *validate* attempts to modify `private` data and control how that data is presented to the caller, respectively. These are compelling software engineering benefits. If an instance variable were `public`, any client of the class could see the data and modify it, including setting it to an *invalid* value. Also, `public` data allows client-code programmers to write code that depends on the class's data format. If the class's owner changes that format, any client code dependent on it would "break" and would need to be adjusted to the new format, making it subject to break again.

You might think that even though a client of the class cannot directly access a `private` instance variable, the client can nevertheless do whatever it wants with the variable through `public` *Set* and *Get* methods. You'd think that you could peek at the `private` data (and see exactly how it's stored in the object) any time with the `public` *Get* method and that you could modify the `private` data at will through the `public` *Set* method.

Actually, *Set* methods can be programmed to *validate* their arguments and reject any attempts to *Set* the data to bad values, such as

- a negative body temperature
- a day in March outside the range 1 through 31
- a product code not in the company's product catalog, etc.

A *Get* method can present the data in a different form, while the actual data representation remains hidden from the user. For example, a `Grade` class might store a `grade` instance variable as an `int` between 0 and 100, but a `GetGrade` method might return a letter grade as a `string`, such as `"A"` for grades between 90 and 100, `"B"` for grades between 80 and 89, …—we'll do this in Section 5.7 with a property. Tightly controlling the *access* to and *presentation* of `private` data can greatly reduce errors, while increasing the robustness, security and usability of your programs.

Conceptual View of an **Account** *Object with* `private` *Data*

You can think of an `Account` object as shown in Fig. 4.4. The `private` instance variable name is *hidden inside* the object (represented by the inner circle containing `name`) and *guarded by an outer layer* of `public` methods (represented by the outer circle containing `GetName` and `SetName`). Any client code that needs to interact with the `Account` object can do so *only* by calling the `public` methods of the protective outer layer.

Software Engineering Observation 4.1

Generally, instance variables should be private *and methods* public.

Software Engineering Observation 4.2

Change is the rule rather than the exception. You should anticipate that your code will be modified, and possibly often. Using public *Set and* Get *methods to control access to* private *data makes programs clearer and easier to maintain.*

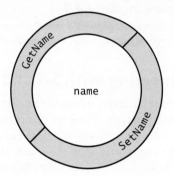

Fig. 4.4 | Conceptual view of an Account object with its private instance variable name and guarding layer of public methods.

4.6 Account Class with a Property Rather Than *Set* and *Get* Methods

Our first Account class contained a private instance variable name and public methods SetName and GetName that enabled a client to assign to and retrieve from an Account's name, respectively. C# provides a more elegant solution—called properties—to accomplish the same tasks. A property encapsulates a **set** accessor for storing a value into a variable and a **get** accessor for getting the value of a variable.[3] In this section, we'll revisit the AccountTest class to demonstrate how to interact with an Account object containing a public Name *property*, then we'll present the updated Account class and take a detailed look at properties.

4.6.1 Class AccountTest Using Account's Name Property

Figure 4.5 shows the updated AccountTest class that uses class Account's Name property (declared in Fig. 4.6) to **get** and **set** an Account's name instance variable. This app produces the same output as the one in Fig. 4.1, assuming the user once again enters Jane Green when prompted to enter a name.

```
1   // Fig. 4.5: AccountTest.cs
2   // Creating and manipulating an Account object with properties.
3   using System;
4
5   class AccountTest
6   {
7      static void Main()
8      {
9         // create an Account object and assign it to myAccount
10        Account myAccount = new Account();
```

Fig. 4.5 | Creating and manipulating an Account object with properties. (Part 1 of 2.)

---

3. In subsequent chapters, you'll see that properties are not required to have both a **set** and a **get**.

```
11
12          // display myAccount's initial name
13          Console.WriteLine($"Initial name is: {myAccount.Name}");
14
15          // prompt for and read the name, then put the name in the object
16          Console.Write("Please enter the name: "); // prompt
17          string theName = Console.ReadLine(); // read a line of text
18          myAccount.Name = theName; // put theName in myAccount's Name
19
20          // display the name stored in object myAccount
21          Console.WriteLine($"myAccount's name is: {myAccount.Name}");
22       }
23    }
```

```
Initial name is:
Please enter the name: Jane Green
myAccount's name is: Jane Green
```

Fig. 4.5 | Creating and manipulating an Account object with properties. (Part 2 of 2.)

Invoking Class *Account's* **Name** *Property to Get the Name*

The get accessor of the Account class's Name property *gets* the account name stored in a particular Account object. Line 13

```
Console.WriteLine($"Initial name is: {myAccount.Name}");
```

displays myAccount's initial name by accessing the object's Name property with the expression myAccount.Name. To access a property, you specify the object's name (myAccount), followed by the member-access operator (.) and the property's name (Name). When used to get the account's name, this notation *implicitly* executes the property's get accessor, which returns the account's name.

When Main accesses the Name property in line 13:

1. The app transfers program execution from the expression myAccount.Name (line 13 in Main) to the property Name's get accessor).

2. Next, the Name property's get accessor performs its task—that is, it *returns* (i.e., gives back) the value of myAccount's name instance variable to line 13 where the property was accessed.

3. Console.WriteLine displays the string returned by the Name property's get accessor—which was inserted into the interpolated string in place of the expression myAccount.Name—then the program continues executing at line 16 in Main.

As in Fig. 4.1, line 13 does not display a name, because we have not yet stored a name in the myAccount object.

Invoking Class *Account's* **Name** *Property to Set the Name*

Next, lines 16–17 prompt for and input a name. The set accessor Account class's Name property *sets* an account name in a particular Account object. Line 18

```
myAccount.Name = theName; // put theName in myAccount's Name
```

assigns to myAccounts's Name property the `string` entered by the user in line 17. When property Name is invoked by the expression myAccount.Name on the left of an assignment:

1. The app transfers program execution from line 18 in Main to Name's `set` accessor.

2. Property Name's `set` accessor performs its task—that is, it stores in the myAccount object's name instance variable the `string` value that was assigned to property Name in Main (line 18).

3. When Name's `set` accessor completes execution, program execution returns to where the Name property was accessed (line 18 in Main), then execution continues at line 21.

To demonstrate that myAccount now contains the name the user entered, line 21

```
Console.WriteLine($"myAccount's name is: {myAccount.Name}");
```

accesses myAccounts's Name property again, which uses the property's get accessor to obtain the name instance variable's new value. As you can see, the last line of the program's output displays the name input from the user in line 17.

4.6.2 Account Class with an Instance Variable and a Property

The updated Account class replaces the GetName and SetName methods from Fig. 4.2 with the property Name (lines 10–20 of Fig. 4.6). The property's get and set accessors handle the details of *getting* and *setting* data, respectively. Unlike method names, the accessor names get and set each begin with a lowercase letter.

```
1   // Fig. 4.6: Account.cs
2   // Account class that replaces public methods SetName
3   // and GetName with a public Name property.
4
5   class Account
6   {
7      private string name; // instance variable
8
9      // property to get and set the name instance variable
10     public string Name
11     {
12        get // returns the corresponding instance variable's value
13        {
14           return name; // returns the value of name to the client code
15        }
16        set // assigns a new value to the corresponding instance variable
17        {
18           name = value; // value is implicitly declared and initialized
19        }
20     }
21  }
```

Fig. 4.6 | Account class that replaces `public` methods SetName and GetName with a `public` Name property.

*Property **Name**'s Declaration*
Line 10

```
    public string Name
```

begins the Name property declaration, which specifies that

- the property is public so it can be used by the class's clients,
- the property's type is string and
- the property's name is Name.

By convention, a property's identifier is the capitalized identifier of the instance variable that it manipulates—Name is the property that represents instance variable name. C# is case sensitive, so Name and name are distinct identifiers. The property's body is enclosed in the braces at lines 11 and 20.

*Property **Name**'s **get** Accessor*
The get accessor (lines 12–15) performs the same task as method GetName in Fig. 4.2. A get accessor begins with the keyword get, and its body is delimited by braces (lines 13 and 15). Like method GetName, the get accessor's body contains a return statement (line 14) that returns the value of an Account's name instance variable. So, in line 13 of Fig. 4.5

```
    Console.WriteLine($"Initial name is: {myAccount.Name}");
```

the expression myAccount.Name gets the value of myAccount's instance variable name. The property notation allows the client to *think of the property as the underlying data*, but the client still *cannot* directly manipulate the private instance variable name. Keyword get is a *contextual keyword*, because it's a keyword only in a property's context (that is, its body)—in other contexts, get can be used as an identifier.

*Property **Name**'s **set** Accessor*
The set accessor (lines 16–19, Fig. 4.6) begins with the identifier set followed by its body, which is delimited by braces (lines 17 and 19). Method SetName (Fig. 4.2) declared a parameter accountName to receive the new name to store in an Account object—a set accessor uses the keyword value (line 18, Fig. 4.6) for the same purpose. value is *implicitly* declared and initialized for you with the value that the client code *assigns* to the property. So, in line 18 of Fig. 4.5

```
    myAccount.Name = theName; // put theName in myAccount's Name
```

value is initialized with theName (the string entered by the user). Property Name's set accessor simply assigns value to the instance variable name—we'll show a set accessor that performs *validation* in Fig. 4.11. Like get, the keywords set and value are *contextual keywords*—set is a keyword only in a property's context and value is a keyword only in a set accessor's context.

Error-Prevention Tip 4.2
Although contextual keywords, like value in a set accessor, can be used as identifiers in some contexts, we prefer not to do so.

The statements inside the property in lines 14 and 18 (Fig. 4.6) each access name even though it was declared outside the property declaration. We can use instance variable name in class `Account`'s property (and other properties and methods, if there are any), because name is an instance variable in the same class.

4.6.3 Account UML Class Diagram with a Property

Figure 4.7 presents a UML class diagram for class `Account` of Fig. 4.6. We model C# properties in the UML as attributes. The property `Name` is listed as a *public* attribute—as indicated by the plus (+) sign—followed by the word "property" in guillemets (« and »). Using descriptive words in guillemets (called stereotypes in the UML) helps distinguish properties from other attributes and operations. The UML indicates the type of the property by placing a colon and a type after the property name.

Fig. 4.7 | UML class diagram for class `Account` of Fig. 4.6.

A class diagram helps you *design* a class, so it's not required to show every *implementation* detail. Since an instance variable that's manipulated by a property is really an implementation detail of that property, our class diagram does *not* show the name instance variable. A programmer implementing the `Account` class based on this class diagram would create the instance variable name as part of the implementation process (as we did in Fig. 4.6). Similarly, a property's `get` and `set` accessors are implementation details, so they're not listed in the UML diagram.

4.7 Auto-Implemented Properties

In Fig. 4.6, we created an `Account` class with a `private` name instance variable and a `public` property `Name` to enable client code to access the name. When you look at the `Name` property's definition (Fig. 4.6, lines 10–20), notice that the `get` accessor simply returns `private` instance variable name's value and the `set` accessor simply assigns a value to the instance variable—no other logic appears in the accessors. For such simple cases, C# provides auto-implemented properties.

With an auto-implemented property, the C# compiler automatically creates a *hidden* `private` instance variable, and the `get` and `set` accessors for *getting* and *setting* that hidden instance variable. This enables you to implement the property trivially, which is handy when you're first designing a class. If you later decide to include other logic in the `get` or `set` accessors, you can simply implement the property and an instance variable using the techniques shown in Fig. 4.6. To use an auto-implemented property in the `Account` class of Fig. 4.6, you'd replace the `private` instance variable at line 7 and the property at lines 10–20 with the following *single* line of code:

```
public string Name { get; set; }
```

We'll use this technique for the `Name` property in Fig. 4.8.

> **Software Engineering Observation 4.3**
> *In programming languages that do not have property syntax, you think of a class's attributes as instance variables. With C# property syntax, you should think of the properties themselves as the class's attributes.*

4.8 Account Class: Initializing Objects with Constructors

As mentioned in Section 4.6, when an object of class Account (Fig. 4.6) is created, its string instance variable name is initialized to null by *default*. But what if you want to provide an actual name when you *create* an Account object?

Each class you declare optionally can provide a *constructor* with parameters that can be used to initialize an object when it's created. C# *requires* a constructor call for *every* object that's created, so this is the ideal point to initialize an object's instance variables. The next example enhances class Account (Fig. 4.8) with a constructor that can receive a name and use it to initialize the Name property when an Account object is created (Fig. 4.9). Now that you've seen class Account in action, this chapter's two remaining examples present class Account before class AccountTest.

This version of class Account replaces the private name instance variable and the public Name property from Fig. 4.6 with a public *auto-implemented* Name property (Fig. 4.8, line 6). This property automatically creates a hidden private instance variable to store the property's value.

```
1   // Fig. 4.8: Account.cs
2   // Account class with a constructor that initializes an Account's name.
3
4   class Account
5   {
6      public string Name { get; set; } // auto-implemented property
7
8      // constructor sets the Name property to parameter accountName's value
9      public Account(string accountName) // constructor name is class name
10     {
11        Name = accountName;
12     }
13  }
```

Fig. 4.8 | Account class with a constructor that initializes an Account's name.

4.8.1 Declaring an Account Constructor for Custom Object Initialization

When you declare a class, you can provide your own constructor to specify *custom initialization* for objects of your class. For example, you might want to specify a name for an Account object when the object is created, as in line 11 of Fig. 4.9:

```
Account account1 = new Account("Jane Green");
```

In this case, the string argument "Jane Green" is passed to the Account object's constructor and used to initialize the Account's name. A constructor's identifier *must* be the class's name. The preceding statement requires an `Account` constructor that can receive a `string`. Figure 4.8 contains a modified `Account` class with such a constructor.

***Account* Constructor Declaration**
Let's walk through the code of the constructor's declaration (Fig. 4.8, lines 9–12):

```
public Account(string accountName) // constructor name is class name
{
    Name = accountName;
}
```

We refer to the first line of each constructor declaration (line 9 in this case) as the *constructor header*. This constructor receives the `string` parameter `accountName`—which represents the name that's passed to the constructor as an argument. An important difference between constructors and methods is that *constructors cannot specify a return type* (not even `void`). Normally, constructors are declared `public` so they can be used by the class's client code to initialize objects of the class.

Constructor Body
A constructor's *body* is delimited by a pair of *braces* (lines 10 and 12 of Fig. 4.8) containing one or more statements that perform the constructor's task(s). In this case, the body contains one statement (line 11) that assigns parameter `accountName`'s value (a `string`) to the class's `Name` *property*, thus storing the account name in the object. After line 11 executes, the constructor has completed its task, so it returns to the line of code containing the object-creation expression that invoked the constructor. As you'll soon see, the statements in lines 11–12 of `Main` (Fig. 4.9) each call this constructor.

4.8.2 Class `AccountTest`: Initializing `Account` Objects When They're Created

The `AccountTest` program (Fig. 4.9) initializes two `Account` objects using the constructor. Line 11 creates and initializes the `Account` object `account1`. Keyword `new` requests memory from the system to store the `Account` object, then implicitly calls the class's constructor to *initialize* the object. The call is indicated by the parentheses after the class name, which contain the *argument* `"Jane Green"` that's used to initialize the new object's name. Line 11 then assigns the initialized object to the variable `account1`. Line 12 repeats this process, passing the argument `"John Blue"` to initialize the name for `account2`. Lines 15–16 use each object's `Name` property to obtain the names and show that they were indeed initialized when the objects were *created*. The output shows *different* names, confirming that each `Account` maintains its *own* name.

```
1   // Fig. 4.9: AccountTest.cs
2   // Using the Account constructor to set an Account's name
3   // when an Account object is created.
4   using System;
5
```

Fig. 4.9 | Using the `Account` constructor to set an `Account`'s name when an `Account` object is created. (Part 1 of 2.)

```
 6   class AccountTest
 7   {
 8      static void Main()
 9      {
10         // create two Account objects
11         Account account1 = new Account("Jane Green");
12         Account account2 = new Account("John Blue");
13
14         // display initial value of name for each Account
15         Console.WriteLine($"account1 name is: {account1.Name}");
16         Console.WriteLine($"account2 name is: {account2.Name}");
17      }
18   }
```

```
account1 name is: Jane Green
account2 name is: John Blue
```

Fig. 4.9 | Using the Account constructor to set an Account's name when an Account object is created. (Part 2 of 2.)

Default Constructor
Recall that line 10 of Fig. 4.5

```
Account myAccount = new Account();
```

used new to create an Account object. The *empty* parentheses in the expression

```
new Account()
```

indicate a call to the class's **default constructor**—in any class that does *not* explicitly declare a constructor, the compiler provides a public default constructor (which always has no parameters). When a class has only the default constructor, the class's instance variables are initialized to their *default values*:

- 0 for numeric simple types,
- false for simple type bool and
- null for all other types.

In Section 10.5, you'll learn that classes can have multiple constructors through a process called overloading.

There's No Default Constructor in a Class That Declares a Constructor
If you declare one or more constructors for a class, the compiler will *not* create a *default constructor* for that class. In that case, you will not be able to create an Account object with the expression new Account() as we did in Fig. 4.5—unless one of the custom constructors you declare takes *no* parameters.

 Software Engineering Observation 4.4
Unless default initialization of your class's instance variables is acceptable, provide a custom constructor to ensure that your instance variables are properly initialized with meaningful values when each new object of your class is created.

*Adding the Constructor to Class **Account**'s UML Class Diagram*
The UML class diagram of Fig. 4.10 models class `Account` of Fig. 4.8, which has a constructor with a `string accountName` parameter. The UML models constructors as operations in the *third* compartment of a class diagram. To distinguish a constructor from the class's other operations, the UML requires that the word "constructor" be enclosed in guillemets (« and ») and placed before the constructor's name. It's customary to list constructors *before* other operations in the third compartment. In Fig. 4.14, you'll see a class diagram with both a constructor and an operation in the third compartment.

Account

+ «property» Name : string

+ «constructor» Account(accountName: string)

Fig. 4.10 | UML class diagram for Account class of Fig. 4.8.

4.9 Account Class with a Balance; Processing Monetary Amounts

In this section, we'll declare an `Account` class that maintains an `Account`'s *balance* in addition to its name. Most account balances are not whole numbers (such as 0, –22 and 1024), rather they're numbers that include a decimal point, such as 99.99 or –20.15. For this reason, class `Account` represents the account balance using type `decimal`, which is designed to precisely represent numbers with decimal points, especially *monetary amounts*.

4.9.1 Account Class with a `decimal balance` Instance Variable

A typical bank services *many* accounts, each with its *own* balance, so our next `Account` class (Fig. 4.11) maintains a bank account's

- name—as the auto-implemented `Name` property (line 6)—and

- balance—as the `private decimal` instance variable `balance` (line 7) and a corresponding `public Balance` property (lines 17–32). We use a fully implemented `Balance` property here so we can ensure that the `set` accessor's argument is valid before assigning it to the `balance` instance variable.

A `decimal` instance variable is initialized to zero by default. Every instance (i.e., object) of class `Account` contains its *own* name and balance.

```
1   // Fig. 4.13: Account.cs
2   // Account class with a balance and a Deposit method.
3
4   class Account
5   {
```

Fig. 4.11 | Account class with a `decimal` instance variable `balance` and a `Balance` property and `Deposit` method that each perform validation. (Part 1 of 2.)

```
 6      public string Name { get; set; } // auto-implemented property
 7      private decimal balance; // instance variable
 8
 9      // Account constructor that receives two parameters
10      public Account(string accountName, decimal initialBalance)
11      {
12         Name = accountName;
13         Balance = initialBalance; // Balance's set accessor validates
14      }
15
16      // Balance property with validation
17      public decimal Balance
18      {
19         get
20         {
21            return balance;
22         }
23         private set // can be used only within the class
24         {
25            // validate that the balance is greater than 0.0; if it's not,
26            // instance variable balance keeps its prior value
27            if (value > 0.0m) // m indicates that 0.0 is a decimal literal
28            {
29               balance = value;
30            }
31         }
32      }
33
34      // method that deposits (adds) only a valid amount to the balance
35      public void Deposit(decimal depositAmount)
36      {
37         if (depositAmount > 0.0m) // if the depositAmount is valid
38         {
39            Balance = Balance + depositAmount; // add it to the balance
40         }
41      }
42   }
```

Fig. 4.11 | Account class with a `decimal` instance variable `balance` and a `Balance` property and `Deposit` method that each perform validation. (Part 2 of 2.)

Account Class Two-Parameter Constructor

It's common for someone opening an account to deposit money immediately, so the constructor (lines 10–14) now receives a second parameter—`initialBalance` of type decimal that represents the starting balance. Line 13 assigns `initialBalance` to the property `Balance`, invoking `Balance`'s set accessor to ensure that the `initialBalance` argument is valid before assigning a value to the instance variable `balance`.

Account Property Balance

Property `Balance` (lines 17–32) of type `decimal` provides a get accessor, which allows clients of the class to obtain a particular `Account` object's `balance`. The property also provides a set accessor.

In Fig. 4.6, class `Account` defined a `Name` property in which the `set` accessor simply assigned the value received in its implicit parameter `value` to class `Account`'s instance variable name. The `Name` property did *not* ensure that name contains only *valid* data.

The `Balance` property's `set` accessor performs validation (also known as validity checking). Line 27 (Fig. 4.11) ensures that the `set` accessor's implicit `value` parameter is greater than `0.0m`—the letter m (or M) indicates that 0.0 is a **decimal literal**.[4] If `value` is greater than `0.0m`, the amount stored in `value` is assigned to instance variable `balance` (line 29). Otherwise, `balance` is left unchanged—we'll say more about error processing throughout the book.

Though we validated the balance in this example, we did not validate the name. Names are normally quite "free form"—there's a wide variety of acceptable name formats. Often when you fill out a form, you're asked to limit a name to a certain number of characters. In Chapter 16, Strings and Characters: A Deeper Look, you'll learn how to check a `string`'s length, so that you can validate `strings` by checking that they're not too long.

set *and* get *Accessors with Different Access Modifiers*

By default, a property's `get` and `set` accessors have the *same* access as the property—e.g., `public` property `Name`'s accessors are `public`. It's possible to declare the `get` and `set` accessors with *different* access modifiers. In this case, one of the accessors must *implicitly* have the *same* access as the property and the other must be *explicitly declared* with a *more restrictive* access modifier than the property. We declared the `Balance` property's `set` accessor `private`—this indicates that it may be used only in class `Account`, not by the class's clients. This enables us to ensure that once an `Account` object exists, its `balance` can be modified *only* by method `Deposit` (and in the exercises, by method `Withdraw` as well).

Error-Prevention Tip 4.3
The benefits of data integrity are not automatic simply because instance variables are made `private`—you must provide appropriate validity checking and report the errors.

Error-Prevention Tip 4.4
`set` accessors that set the values of `private` data should verify that the intended new values are proper; if they're not, the `set` accessors should leave the instance variables unchanged and indicate an error. We demonstrate how to indicate errors by throwing exceptions in Chapter 10.

Account *Class* Deposit *Method*

The `public` method `Deposit` (lines 35–41) enables the client code to deposit money into an `Account`, thus increasing its `balance`. Line 35 indicates that

- the method does not return any information to its caller (as indicated by the return type `void`) and
- receives one parameter named `depositAmount`—a `decimal` value.

The `depositAmount` is *added* to the `balance` *only* if the parameter's value is *valid*—that is, it's greater than `0.0m` as specified in line 37. Line 39 first adds the current `Balance` and

---

4.   The m is required to indicate a `decimal` literal. C# treats numeric literals with decimal points as type `double` by default, and `double`s and `decimal`s cannot be intermixed. We introduce type `double` in Chapter 5.

depositAmount, forming a *temporary* sum which is *then* assigned to the Balance property. The property's set accessor then *replaces* instance variable balance's prior value (recall that addition has a *higher* precedence than the assignment operator). So line 39 uses the Balance property's get accessor on the right side of the assignment and the set accessor on the left side. It's important to understand that the calculation on the right side of the assignment operator in line 39 does *not* modify the instance variable balance—that's why the assignment is necessary.

Software Engineering Observation 4.5

When implementing a method of a class, although it's possible for the method to access the class's instance variables directly, always use the class's properties for that purpose. In Chapter 10, we'll take a deeper look at this issue.

4.9.2 AccountTest Class That Uses Account Objects with Balances

Class AccountTest (Fig. 4.12) creates two Account objects (lines 9–10) and initializes them with a *valid* balance of 50.00m and an *invalid* balance of -7.53m, respectively—for the purpose of our examples, we assume that balances must be greater than or equal to zero. The calls to method Console.WriteLine in lines 13–16 output the account names and initial balances, which are obtained from each Account's Name and Balance properties.

```csharp
1   // Fig. 4.12: AccountTest.cs
2   // Reading and writing monetary amounts with Account objects.
3   using System;
4
5   class AccountTest
6   {
7      static void Main()
8      {
9         Account account1 = new Account("Jane Green", 50.00m);
10        Account account2 = new Account("John Blue", -7.53m);
11
12        // display initial balance of each object
13        Console.WriteLine(
14           $"{account1.Name}'s balance: {account1.Balance:C}");
15        Console.WriteLine(
16           $"{account2.Name}'s balance: {account2.Balance:C}");
17
18        // prompt for then read input
19        Console.Write("\nEnter deposit amount for account1: ");
20        decimal depositAmount = decimal.Parse(Console.ReadLine());
21        Console.WriteLine(
22           $"adding {depositAmount:C} to account1 balance\n");
23        account1.Deposit(depositAmount); // add to account1's balance
24
25        // display balances
26        Console.WriteLine(
27           $"{account1.Name}'s balance: {account1.Balance:C}");
28        Console.WriteLine(
29           $"{account2.Name}'s balance: {account2.Balance:C}");
```

Fig. 4.12 | Reading and writing monetary amounts with Account objects. (Part 1 of 2.)

```
30
31          // prompt for then read input
32          Console.Write("\nEnter deposit amount for account2: ");
33          depositAmount = decimal.Parse(Console.ReadLine());
34          Console.WriteLine(
35              $"adding {depositAmount:C} to account2 balance\n");
36          account2.Deposit(depositAmount); // add to account2's balance
37
38          // display balances
39          Console.WriteLine(
40              $"{account1.Name}'s balance: {account1.Balance:C}");
41          Console.WriteLine(
42              $"{account2.Name}'s balance: {account2.Balance:C}");
43      }
44  }
```

```
Jane Green's balance: $50.00
John Blue's balance: $0.00

Enter deposit amount for account1: 25.53
adding $25.53 to account1 balance

Jane Green's balance: $75.53
John Blue's balance: $0.00

Enter deposit amount for account2: 123.45
adding $123.45 to account2 balance

Jane Green's balance: $75.53
John Blue's balance: $123.45
```

Fig. 4.12 | Reading and writing monetary amounts with `Account` objects. (Part 2 of 2.)

*Displaying the **Account** Objects' Initial Balances*

When line 14 accesses account1's `Balance` property, the value of account1's `balance` instance variable is returned from line 21 of Fig. 4.11 and inserted into the interpolated `string` at line 14 of Fig. 4.12 for display. Similarly, when line 16 accesses account2's `Balance` property, the value of account2's `balance` instance variable is returned from line 21 of Fig. 4.11 and inserted into the interpolated `string` at line 16 of Fig. 4.12 for display. The `balance` of account2 is initially `0.00`, because the constructor rejected the attempt to start account2 with a *negative* `balance`, so the `balance` instance variable retains its default initial value.

`string` Interpolation Expressions with Formatting

This app displays each `Account`'s `balance` as a monetary amount. You can specify formatting in a C# 6 `string` interpolation expression by following the value in the braces with a colon and a format specifier. For example, in line 14, the interpolation expression

```
{account1.Balance:C}
```

uses the format specifier C to format account1.`Balance` as *currency*. The Windows culture settings on the user's machine determine the format for displaying currency amounts, such as the commas vs. periods for separating thousands, millions, etc. For example,

6

- 50 displays as $50.00 in the United States (U.S.), as 50,00 e (e for euros) in Germany and as ¥50 in Japan.

- 4382.51 displays as $4,382.51 in the U.S., as 4.382,51 e in Germany and as ¥4,382 in Japan.

- 1254827.40 displays as $1,254,827.40 in the U.S., as 1.254.827,40 e in Germany and as ¥1,254,827 in Japan.

Figure 4.13 lists additional format specifiers.

Format specifier	Description
C or c	Formats the string as currency. Includes an appropriate currency symbol ($ in the U.S.) next to the number. Separates digits with an appropriate *separator character* (in the U.S. its a comma between every three digits for thousands, millions, etc.) and sets the number of decimal places to two by default.
D or d	Formats the string as a whole number (integer types only).
N or n	Formats the string with a thousands separator and a default of two decimal places.
E or e	Formats the number using scientific notation with a default of six decimal places.
F or f	Formats the string with a fixed number of decimal places (two by default).
G or g	Formats the number normally with decimal places or using scientific notation, depending on context. If a format item does not contain a format specifier, format G is assumed implicitly.
X or x	Formats the string as hexadecimal (base 16 numbers; we discuss these in the online Number Systems appendix).

Fig. 4.13 | string format specifiers.

Reading a *decimal* Value from the User

Line 19 (Fig. 4.12) prompts the user to enter a deposit amount for account1. Line 20 declares *local* variable depositAmount to store each deposit amount entered by the user. Unlike *instance* variables (such as name and balance in class Account), *local* variables (like depositAmount in Main) are *not* initialized by default, so they normally must be initialized explicitly. As you'll learn momentarily, variable depositAmount's initial value will be determined by the user's input.

Common Programming Error 4.3

The C# compiler will issue the compilation error "Use of unassigned local variable 'variableName'" if you attempt to use the value of an uninitialized local variable—in the error message, variableName will be the actual variable name. This helps you avoid dangerous execution-time logic errors. It's always better to get the errors out of your programs at compilation time rather than execution time.

Line 20 obtains the input from the user by calling the Console class's ReadLine method, then passing the string entered by the user to type decimal's Parse method, which returns the decimal value in this string. Lines 21–22 display the deposit amount in currency format.

Making a Deposit
Line 23 calls object account1's `Deposit` method and supplies `depositAmount` as the method's argument. The method then adds the parameter's value to the `Balance` property (line 39 of Fig. 4.11). Then lines 26–29 in Fig. 4.12 output the balances of both `Accounts` again to show that *only* account1's `balance` instance variable changed.

Reading a `decimal` *Value and Depositing into* `account2`
Line 32 prompts the user to enter a deposit amount for account2. Line 33 obtains the input from the user by calling method `Console.ReadLine` and passing the return value to type `decimal`'s `Parse` method. Lines 34–35 display the deposit amount. Line 36 calls object account2's `Deposit` method and supplies `depositAmount` as the method's argument. Then, the method adds that value to account2's `Balance` property. Finally, lines 39–42 output the `Balances` of both `Accounts` again to show that *only* account2's `balance` instance variable changed.

Duplicated Code in Method `Main`
The six statements at lines 13–14, 15–16, 26–27, 28–29, 39–40 and 41–42 are almost *identical*—they each output an `Account`'s `name` and `balance`. They differ only in the name of the `Account` object—account1 or account2. Duplicate code like this can create code-maintenance problems when it needs to be updated—if six copies of the same code require an error correction or update, you must make that change six times, without making errors. Exercise 4.13 asks you to modify Fig. 4.12 to include a `DisplayAccount` method that takes as a parameter an `Account` object and outputs the object's `name` and `balance`, and contains only *one* copy of the output code. You'll then replace `Main`'s duplicated statements with six calls to `DisplayAccount`.

Software Engineering Observation 4.6
Replacing duplicated code with calls to a method that contains one copy of that code can reduce the size of your program and improve its maintainability.

UML Class Diagram for Class `Account`
The class diagram in Fig. 4.14 concisely models class Account of Fig. 4.11. The diagram models in its second compartment the `public` properties `Name` of type `string` and `Balance` of type `decimal`. Class Account's constructor is modeled in the third compartment with parameters `name` of type `string` and `initialBalance` of type `decimal`. The class's `public` `Deposit` operation also is modeled in the third compartment—`Deposit` has a `depositAmount` parameter of type `decimal`. Method `Deposit` does not return a value (because it returns `void` in C#), so the UML class diagram does not specify a return type for this operation.

Fig. 4.14 | UML class diagram for Account class of Fig. 4.11.

4.10 Wrap-Up

In this chapter, you learned basic object-oriented programming concepts of classes, objects, methods, instance variables, properties and constructors—these will be used in most substantial C# apps you create. You declared instance variables of a class to maintain data for each object of the class and declared *Set* and *Get* methods for operating on that data. We demonstrated how to call methods to perform their tasks and how to pass information to methods as arguments. Next, we showed C#'s more elegant property syntax for setting and getting data, and we demonstrated how to access properties to execute their set and get accessors. We discussed the differences between local variables of a method and instance variables of a class and that only instance variables are initialized automatically. You learned how to create auto-implemented properties that simply get or set an instance variable without any additional logic in the accessors' declarations. You learned about type decimal for precise manipulation of numbers with decimal points, such as monetary amounts.

We showed how to create UML class diagrams that model the constructors, methods, properties and attributes of classes. You learned the value of declaring instance variables private and using public properties to manipulate them. For example, we demonstrated how set accessors in properties can be used to validate an instance variable's potential new value before modifying the variable's value.

In Chapter 5, we begin our introduction to control statements, which specify the order in which an app's actions are performed. You'll use these in your methods and properties to specify how they should perform their tasks.

Summary

Section 4.1 Introduction
- Each class you create becomes a new type you can use to create objects, so C# is an extensible programming language.

Section 4.2 Test-Driving an **Account** Class
- Classes cannot execute by themselves.
- A class containing a method that tests another class's capabilities is referred to as a driver class.

Section 4.2.1 Instantiating an Object—Keyword **new** and Constructors
- Typically, you cannot call a method of a class until you create an object of that class.
- An object-creation expression uses the new operator to create an object.

Section 4.2.2 Calling Class **Account's** GetName Method
- To call a method for a specific object, you specify the object's name, followed by the member-access operator (.), then the method name and a set of parentheses. Empty parentheses indicate that a method does not require any additional information to perform its task.
- When a method is called, the app transfers execution from the method call to the method's declaration, the method performs its task, then control returns to the point of the method call.

Section 4.2.3 Inputting a Name from the User

- `Console` method `ReadLine` reads characters until it encounters the newline, then returns a `string` containing the characters up to, but not including, the newline, which is discarded.

Section 4.2.4 Calling Class `Account`'s `SetName` *Method*

- A method call can supply arguments that help the method perform its task. You place the arguments in the method call's parentheses.

Section 4.3 `Account` *Class with an Instance Variable and* Set *and* Get *Methods*

- The fact that you can create and manipulate an object of a class without knowing the class's implementation details is called abstraction.

Section 4.3.1 `Account` *Class Declaration*

- A class's instance variables maintain data for each object of the class.

Section 4.3.2 Keyword `class` *and the Class Body*

- Every class declaration contains the keyword `class` followed immediately by the class's name.
- Each class declaration is typically stored in a file having the same name as the class and ending with the `.cs` filename extension.
- The class's body is enclosed in a pair of braces.
- Class, property, method and variable names are all identifiers and by convention all use the camel-case naming scheme. Class, property and method names begin with an initial uppercase letter and variable names begin with an initial lowercase letter.

Section 4.3.3 Instance Variable `name` *of Type* `string`

- Each object has its own copy of the class's instance variables.
- Instance variables exist before an app calls methods or accesses properties on an object, while the methods and properties are executing, and after the methods and properties complete execution.
- Instance variables are declared inside a class declaration but outside the bodies of the class's methods and properties.
- Clients of a class—that is, any other code that calls the class's methods (or accesses its properties)—cannot access the class's `private` instance variables. However, clients can access a class's `public` methods (and properties).
- Every instance variable has a default initial value—a value provided by C# when you do not specify the instance variable's initial value.
- Instance variables are not required to be explicitly initialized before they're used in a program—unless they must be initialized to values other than their default values.
- The default value for an instance variable of type `string` is `null`.
- When you display the value of a `string` variable that contains the value `null`, no text is displayed on the screen.

Section 4.3.4 `SetName` *Method*

- The return type `void` indicates that a method does not return any information to its caller.
- A method can require one or more parameters that represent the data it needs to perform its task.
- Parameters are declared in a parameter list located in the required parentheses following the method's name.
- Each parameter *must* specify a type followed by a parameter name. When there are multiple parameters, each is separated from the next by a comma.

- Each argument value in a method call's parentheses is copied into the method declaration's corresponding parameter.

- The number and order of arguments in a method call must match the number and order of parameters in the method declaration's parameter list.

- Every method body is delimited by an opening left brace and a closing right brace. Within the braces are one or more statements that perform the method's task(s).

- Variables declared in a particular method's body are local variables which can be used only in that method. A method's parameters also are local variables of that method.

Section 4.3.5 `GetName` Method

- When a method with a return type other than void is called and completes its task, it must return a result to its caller via a return statement.

Section 4.3.6 Access Modifiers `private` and `public`

- The keyword private is an access modifier.

- A private instance variable is accessible only to methods (and other members, like properties) of the instance variable's class. This is known as information hiding.

- Most instance variables are declared private.

- Methods (and other class members) that are declared public can be used by methods (and other members) of the class in which they're declared, by the class's clients.

- By default, class members are private, unless you specify otherwise with access modifiers.

Section 4.3.7 `Account` UML Class Diagram

- UML class diagrams summarize a class's attributes and operations.

- UML diagrams help systems designers specify systems in a concise, graphical, programming-language-independent manner, before programmers implement the systems in specific programming languages.

- In the UML, each class is modeled in a class diagram as a rectangle with three compartments.

- The top compartment contains the class name centered horizontally in boldface type.

- The middle compartment contains the class's attributes.

- A minus sign (–) access modifier an the attribute name indicates that the attribute is private.

- Following an attribute name are a colon and the attribute type.

- The bottom compartment contains the class's operations.

- The UML models operations by listing the operation name preceded by an access modifier.

- A plus sign (+) indicates a public operation.

- The UML indicates the return type of an operation by placing a colon and the return type after the parentheses following the operation name.

- The UML models a parameter by listing the parameter name, followed by a colon and the parameter type in the parentheses after the operation name.

Section 4.4 Creating, Compiling and Running a Visual C# Project with Two Classes

- You can open each class in the Visual Studio editor by double clicking the file's name in the **Solution Explorer** window.

- When you select **Build > Build Solution** in Visual Studio, the IDE compiles all the files in the project to create the executable app.

Section 4.5 Software Engineering with Set *and* Get *Methods*

- *Set* and *Get* methods can validate attempts to modify private data and control how that data is presented to the caller, respectively.

Section 4.6 **Account** *Class with a Property Rather Than* Set *and* Get *Methods*

- A property contains a set accessor for storing a value into a variable and a get accessor for getting the value of a variable.

Section 4.6.1 Class **AccountTest** *Using Account's* **Name** *Property*

- To access a property to get its value, specify the object's name, followed by the member-access operator (.) and the property's name—this implicitly executes the property's get accessor, unless the expression is on the left side of an assignment.
- Accessing a property on the left of an assignment implicitly executes the property's set accessor.

Section 4.6.2 **Account** *Class with an Instance Variable and a Property*

- A property declaration specifies the property's access specifier, type, name and body.
- By convention, a property's identifier is the capitalized identifier of the instance variable that it manipulates.
- A get accessor begins with the contextual keyword get followed by a body, which contains a return statement that returns the value of a corresponding instance variable.
- The property notation allows the client to think of the property as the underlying data.
- A set accessor begins with the contextual keyword set followed by its body.
- A set accessor's contextual keyword value is implicitly declared and initialized for you with the value that the client code assigns to the property.

Section 4.6.3 **Account** *UML Class Diagram with a Property*

- C# properties are modeled in the UML as attributes. A public property is indicated by the plus (+) sign followed by the word "property" in guillemets (« and »), then the property's name, a colon and the property's type.
- Using descriptive words in guillemets (called stereotypes in the UML) helps distinguish properties from other attributes and operations.
- A class diagram helps you design a class, so it's not required to show every implementation detail.
- Since an instance variable that's manipulated by a property is really an implementation detail of that property, a class diagram does not show a property's corresponding instance variable.
- Similarly, a property's get and set accessors are implementation details, so they're not listed in a UML diagram.

Section 4.7 Auto-Implemented Properties

- For properties in which the get accessor simply returns an instance variable's value and a set accessor simply assigns a value to the instance variable, C# provides auto-implemented properties.
- With an auto-implemented property, the C# compiler creates a hidden private instance variable, and the get and set accessors for getting and setting that instance variable.

Section 4.8 **Account** *Class: Initializing Objects with Constructors*

- Each class you declare optionally can provide a constructor with parameters that can be used to initialize an object when it's created.

- C# requires a constructor call for every object that's created, so this is the ideal point to initialize an object's instance variables.

Section 4.8.1 Declaring an **Account** Constructor for Custom Object Initialization

- A constructor must have the same name as its class.
- An important difference between constructors and methods is that constructors cannot specify a return type (not even void).
- Normally, constructors are declared public so they can be used by the class's client code to initialize objects of the class.

Section 4.8.2 Class **AccountTest**: Initializing **Account** Objects When They're Created

- Creating an object with new implicitly calls the class's constructor to initialize the object.
- In any class that does not explicitly declare a constructor, the compiler provides a public default constructor with no parameters.
- When a class has only the default constructor, the class's instance variables are initialized to their default values—0 for numeric simple types, false for simple type bool and null for all other types.
- If you declare one or more constructors for a class, the compiler will not create a default constructor.
- The UML models constructors as operations in the third compartment of a class diagram. To distinguish a constructor from the class's other operations, the UML requires that the word "constructor" be enclosed in guillemets (« and ») and placed before the constructor's name.
- It's customary to list constructors before other operations in the third compartment.

Section 4.9 **Account** Class with a Balance; Processing Monetary Amounts

- Type decimal is designed to precisely represent numbers with decimal points, such as monetary amounts.

Section 4.9.1 **Account** Class with a **decimal balance** Instance Variable

- A decimal instance variable is initialized to zero by default.
- A property's set accessor can performs validation (also known as validity checking).
- The letter m appended to a numeric literal indicates the number is a decimal literal.
- By default, the get and set accessors of a property have the same access as the property.
- get and set accessors can have different access modifiers. One of the accessors must implicitly have the same access as the property and the other must be declared with more restrictive access.
- A property's private set accessor may be used only by the property's class, not by the class's clients.

Section 4.9.2 **AccountTest** Class That Creates and Uses **Account** Objects

- You can specify formatting in a C# 6 string interpolation expression by following the value in the braces with a colon and a format specifier.
- The format specifier C formats a numeric value as currency (C is for currency)—typically with two digits to the right of the decimal point.
- The Windows culture settings on the user's machine determine the format for displaying currency amounts, such as the commas vs. periods for separating thousands, millions, etc.
- Unlike instance variables, local variables are not initialized by default.
- Type decimal's Parse method converts a string to a decimal value.

Terminology

abstraction

access modifier

attribute (UML)

auto-implemented property

`C` format specifier

calling method

class declaration

`class` keyword

client of a class

comma-separated list

compartment in a class diagram (UML)

constructor

constructor header

create (or instantiate) an object

`decimal` literal (M)

`decimal` simple type

default constructor

default initial value

driver class

extensible programming language

format specifier

get accessor

guillemets, « and » (UML)

information hiding

instance variable

invoke a method

local variable

member access operator (.)

method

method header

`new` operator

`null` keyword

object (or instance)

object-creation expression

operation (UML)

parameter

parameter list

`Parse` method of type `decimal`

property

property declaration

`private` access modifier

`public` access modifier

`public` default constructor

`public` method

`public` property

`return` statement

return type

set accessor

UML class diagram

UML visibility symbol

validation

validity checking

`value` contextual keyword

`void` keyword

Self-Review Exercises

4.1   Fill in the blanks in each of the following:

a) The format specifier _____ is used to display values in a monetary format.

b) Every class declaration contains keyword _____ followed immediately by the class's name.

c) Operator _____ creates an object of the class specified to the right of the keyword.

d) Each parameter must specify both a(n) _____ and a(n) _____.

e) Return type _____ indicates that a method will not return any information when it completes its task.

f) When each object of a class maintains its own copy of an attribute, the attribute is known as a(n) _____.

g) For a(n) _____, the compiler automatically generates a `private` instance variable and set and get accessors.

h) Variables of type _____ are typically used to represent monetary amounts.

i) `decimal` method _____ converts a `string` to a `decimal` value.

j) Keyword `public` is a(n) _____.

4.2   State whether each of the following is *true* or *false*. If *false*, explain why.

a) By convention, method names begin with a lowercase first letter and all subsequent words in the name begin with a capital first letter.

b) A property's get accessor enables a client to modify the value of the instance variable associated with the property.

c) All instance variables are initialized by default to null.

d) Empty parentheses following a method name in a method declaration indicate that the method does not require any parameters to perform its task.

e) The number of arguments in the method call must match the number of required parameters in the method declaration's parameter list.

f) Variables or methods declared with access modifier private are accessible only to members of the class in which they're declared.

g) Variables declared in the body of a particular method are known as instance variables and can be used in all methods of the class.

h) A property declaration must contain both a get accessor and a set accessor.

i) The body of any method or property is delimited by left and right braces.

j) Local variables are initialized by default.

4.3   What is the difference between a local variable and an instance variable?

4.4   Explain the purpose of a method parameter. What is the difference between a parameter and an argument?

Answers to Self-Review Exercises

4.1   a) C. b) class. c) new. d) type, name. e) void. f) instance variable. g) auto-implemented property. h) decimal. i) Parse. j) access modifier.

4.2   a) False. By convention, method names begin with an uppercase first letter and all subsequent words in the name begin with an uppercase first letter. b) False. A property's get accessor enables a client to retrieve the value of the instance variable associated with the property. A property's set accessor enables a client to modify the value of the instance variable associated with the property. c) False. Numeric simple-type instance variables are initialized to 0, bool simple-type instance variables are initialized to false and instance variables of all other types are initialized to null. d) True. e) True. f) True. g) False. Such variables are called local variables and can be used only in the method in which they're declared. h) False. A property declaration can contain a get accessor, a set accessor or both. i) True. j) False. Instance variables are initialized by default.

4.3   A local variable is declared in the body of a method and can be used only in the method in which it's declared. An instance variable is declared in a class, but not in the body of any of the class's members. Every object (instance) of a class has a separate copy of the class's instance variables. Also, instance variables are accessible to all members of the class. (We'll see an exception to this in Chapter 10.)

4.4   A parameter represents additional information that a method requires to perform its task. Each parameter required by a method is specified in the method's declaration. An argument is the actual value that's passed to a method parameter when a method is called.

Exercises

4.5   *(Keyword **new**)* What is the purpose of operator new? Explain what happens when this keyword is used in an app.

4.6   *(Default Constructor)* What is a default constructor? How are an object's instance variables initialized if a class has only a default constructor?

4.7   *(Instance Variable)* Explain the purpose of an instance variable.

4.8   *(Properties)* Explain why a class might provide a property for an instance variable.

4.9   *(Account Modification)* Modify class Account (Fig. 4.11) to provide a `Withdraw` method that withdraws money from an Account. Ensure that the withdrawal amount doesn't exceed the balance. If it does, the balance should not be changed and the method should display a message indicating "`Withdrawal amount exceeded account balance.`" Modify class AccountTest (Fig. 4.12) to test method `Withdraw`.

4.10   *(Invoice Class)* Create a class called Invoice that a hardware store might use to represent an invoice for an item sold at the store. An Invoice should include four pieces of information as either instance variables or auto-implemented properties—a part number (type string), a part description (type string), a quantity of the item being purchased (type int) and a price per item (decimal). Your class should have a constructor that initializes the four values. Provide a property with a get and set accessor for any instance variables. For the Quantity and PricePerItem properties, if the value passed to the set accessor is negative, the value of the instance variable should be left unchanged. Also, provide a method named GetInvoiceAmount that calculates the invoice amount (i.e., multiplies the quantity by the price per item), then returns the amount as a decimal value. Write a test app named InvoiceTest that demonstrates class Invoice's capabilities.

4.11   *(Employee Class)* Create a class called Employee that includes three pieces of information as either instance variables or auto-implemented properties—a first name (type string), a last name (type string) and a monthly salary (decimal). Your class should have a constructor that initializes the three values. Provide a property with a get and set accessor for any instance variables. If the monthly salary is negative, the set accessor should leave the instance variable unchanged. Write a test app named EmployeeTest that demonstrates class Employee's capabilities. Create two Employee objects and display each object's *yearly* salary. Then give each Employee a 10% raise and display each Employee's yearly salary again.

4.12   *(Date Class)* Create a class called Date that includes three pieces of information as auto-implemented properties—a month (type int), a day (type int) and a year (type int). Your class should have a constructor that initializes the three automatic properties and assumes that the values provided are correct. Provide a method DisplayDate that displays the month, day and year separated by forward slashes (/). Write a test app named DateTest that demonstrates class Date's capabilities.

4.13   *(Removing Duplicated Code in Method Main)* In the AccountTest class of Fig. 4.12, method Main contains six statements (lines 13–14, 15–16, 26–27, 29–29, 39–40 and 41–42) that each display an Account object's Name and Balance. Study these statements and you'll notice that they differ only in the Account object being manipulated—account1 or account2. In this exercise, you'll define a new DisplayAccount method that contains *one* copy of that output statement. The method's parameter will be an Account object and the method will output the object's Name and Balance. You'll then replace the six duplicated statements in Main with calls to DisplayAccount, passing as an argument the specific Account object to output.

Modify class AccountTest class of Fig. 4.12 to declare the following DisplayAccount method after the closing right brace of Main and before the closing right brace of class AccountTest:

```
static void DisplayAccount(Account accountToDisplay)
{
   // place the statement that displays
   // accountToDisplay's Name and Balance here
}
```

Replace the comment in the member function's body with a statement that displays accountToDisplay's Name and Balance.

Note that Main is a static method. We also declared method DisplayAccount as a static method. When Main needs to call another method in the same class without first creating an object of that class, the other method *also* must be declared static.

Once you've completed `DisplayAccount`'s declaration, modify `Main` to replace the statements that display each `Account`'s `Name` and `Balance` with calls to `DisplayAccount`—each receiving as its argument the `account1` or `account2` object, as appropriate. Then, test the updated `AccountTest` class to ensure that it produces the same output as shown in Fig. 4.12.

Making-a-Difference Exercises

4.14 *(Target-Heart-Rate Calculator)* While exercising, you can use a heart-rate monitor to see that your heart rate stays within a safe range suggested by your trainers and doctors. According to the American Heart Association (AHA) (`http://bit.ly/AHATargetHeartRates`), the formula for calculating your *maximum heart rate* in beats per minute is 220 minus your age in years. Your *target heart rate* is a range that is 50–85% of your maximum heart rate. [*Note:* **These formulas are esti-mates provided by the AHA. Maximum and target heart rates may vary based on the health, fit-ness and gender of the individual. Always consult a physician or qualified health care professional before beginning or modifying an exercise program.**] Create a class called `HeartRates`. The class attributes should include the person's first name, last name, year of birth and the current year. Your class should have a constructor that receives this data as parameters. For each attribute provide a property with `set` and `get` accessors. The class also should include a property that calculates and returns the person's age (in years), a property that calculates and returns the person's maximum heart rate and properties that calculate and return the person's minimum and maximum target heart rates. Write an app that prompts for the person's information, instantiates an object of class `Heart-Rates` and displays the information from that object—including the person's first name, last name and year of birth—then calculates and displays the person's age in years, maximum heart rate and target-heart-rate range.

4.15 *(Computerization of Health Records)* A health-care issue that has been in the news lately is the computerization of health records. This possibility is being approached cautiously because of sensitive privacy and security concerns, among others. [We address such concerns in later exercises.] Computerizing health records could make it easier for patients to share their health profiles and his-tories among their various health-care professionals. This could improve the quality of health care, help avoid drug conflicts and erroneous drug prescriptions, reduce costs and, in emergencies, could save lives. In this exercise, you'll design a "starter" `HealthProfile` class for a person. The class attri-butes should include the person's first name, last name, gender, date of birth (consisting of separate attributes for the month, day and year of birth), height (in inches) and weight (in pounds). Your class should have a constructor that receives this data. For each attribute provide a property with `set` and `get` accessors. The class also should include methods that calculate and return the user's age in years, maximum heart rate and target-heart-rate range (see Exercise 4.14), and body mass index (BMI; see Exercise 3.31). Write an app that prompts for the person's information, instantiates an object of class `HealthProfile` for that person and displays the information from that object—including the person's first name, last name, gender, date of birth, height and weight—then calculates and dis-plays the person's age in years, BMI, maximum heart rate and target-heart-rate range. It should also display the "BMI values" chart from Exercise 3.31.

5

Algorithm Development and Control Statements: Part 1

Objectives

In this chapter you'll:

- Learn basic problem-solving techniques.

- Develop algorithms through the process of top-down, stepwise refinement with pseudocode.

- Use the `if` and `if...else` selection statements to choose between actions.

- Use the `while` statement to execute statements repeatedly.

- Use counter-controlled iteration and sentinel-controlled iteration.

- Use nested control statements.

- Use the increment, decrement and compound assignment operators.

- Learn about the simple types.

- Understand the elements of structured programming with the sequence, selection and iteration control structures.

5.1 Introduction

Before writing a program to solve a problem, you should have a thorough understanding of the problem and a carefully planned approach to solving it. When writing a program, you also should understand the available building blocks and employ proven program-construction techniques. In this chapter and the next, we discuss these issues in presenting the theory and principles of structured programming. The concepts presented here are crucial in building classes and manipulating objects. We discuss C#'s if statement in additional detail and introduce the if...else and while statements—all of these building blocks allow you to specify the logic required for methods and properties to perform their tasks. We also introduce the compound assignment operators and the increment and decrement operators. Finally, we discuss additional details of C#'s simple types.

5.2 Algorithms

Any computing problem can be solved by executing a series of actions in a specific order. A *procedure* for solving a problem in terms of

1. the actions to execute and
2. the order in which these actions execute

is called an algorithm. The following example demonstrates that correctly specifying the order in which the actions execute is important.

Consider the "rise-and-shine algorithm" one executive follows for getting out of bed and going to work: (1) Get out of bed; (2) take off pajamas; (3) take a shower; (4) get dressed; (5) eat breakfast; (6) carpool to work. This routine gets the executive to work well prepared to make critical decisions. Suppose that the same steps are performed in a slightly different order: (1) Get out of bed; (2) take off pajamas; (3) get dressed; (4) take a shower; (5) eat breakfast; (6) carpool to work. In this case, our executive shows up for work soaking wet. Specifying the order in which statements (actions) execute in a program is called program control. This chapter investigates program control using control statements.

5.3 Pseudocode

Pseudocode is an informal language that helps you develop algorithms without having to worry about the strict details of C# language syntax. The pseudocode we present is particularly useful for developing algorithms that will be converted to structured portions of C# apps. Pseudocode is similar to everyday English (or other natural language)—it's convenient and user friendly, but it's not an actual computer programming language. You'll see an algorithm written in pseudocode in Fig. 5.1. You may, of course, use your own native language(s) to develop your own pseudocode style.

Pseudocode does not execute on computers. Rather, it helps you "think out" an app before attempting to write it in a programming language, such as C#. This chapter provides several examples of using pseudocode to develop C# apps.

The style of pseudocode we present consists purely of characters, so you can type pseudocode conveniently, using any text editor. Carefully prepared pseudocode can easily be converted to a corresponding C# app.

Pseudocode normally describes only statements representing the *actions* that occur after you convert from pseudocode to a C# app and run the app on a computer. Such actions might include *input, output, assignments* or *calculations*. In our pseudocode, we typically do not include variable declarations, but some programmers choose to list variables and mention their purposes.

Addition-Program Pseudocode

Let's look at an example of pseudocode that may be written to help a programmer create the addition program of Fig. 3.14. This pseudocode (Fig. 5.1) corresponds to the algorithm that inputs two integers from the user, adds these integers and displays their sum. We show the complete pseudocode listing here—we'll show how to create pseudocode from a problem statement later in the chapter.

Notice that the pseudocode statements are simply English statements that convey what task is to be performed in C#. Lines 1–2 correspond to the C# statements in lines 14

1	*Prompt the user to enter the first integer*
2	*Input the first integer*
3	
4	*Prompt the user to enter the second integer*
5	*Input the second integer*
6	
7	*Add first integer and second integer, store result*
8	*Display result*

Fig. 5.1 | Pseudocode for the addition program of Fig. 3.14.

and 16 of Fig. 3.14. Lines 4–5 correspond to the statements in lines 18 and 20, and lines 7–8 correspond to the statements in lines 22 and 24.

5.4 Control Structures

Normally, statements execute one after the other in the order in which they're written. This process is called sequential execution. Various C# statements enable you to specify that the next statement to execute is *not* necessarily the next one in sequence. This is called transfer of control.

During the 1960s, it became clear that the indiscriminate use of transfers of control was the root of much difficulty experienced by software development groups. The blame was pointed at the goto statement (used in most programming languages of the time), which allows you to specify a transfer of control to one of a wide range of destinations in a program.

The research of Bohm and Jacopini[1] had demonstrated that programs could be written *without* any goto statements. The challenge for programmers of the era was to shift their styles to "goto-less programming." The term structured programming became almost synonymous with "goto elimination." Not until the 1970s did most programmers start taking structured programming seriously. The results were impressive. Software development groups reported shorter development times, more frequent on-time delivery of systems and more frequent within-budget completion of software projects. The key to these successes was that structured programs were clearer, easier to debug and modify, and more likely to be bug free in the first place.

Bohm and Jacopini's work demonstrated that all programs could be written in terms of only three control structures—the sequence structure, the selection structure and the iteration structure. We'll discuss how each of these is implemented in C#.

5.4.1 Sequence Structure

The *sequence structure* is built into C#. Unless directed otherwise, the computer executes C# statements one after the other in the order in which they're written—that is, in sequence. The UML activity diagram in Fig. 5.2 illustrates a typical sequence structure in which two calculations are performed in order. C# lets you have as many actions as you want in a sequence structure.

---

1. C. Bohm and G. Jacopini, "Flow Diagrams, Turing Machines, and Languages with Only Two Formation Rules," *Communications of the ACM*, Vol. 9, No. 5, May 1966, pp. 336–371.

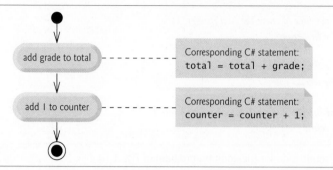

Fig. 5.2 | Sequence structure activity diagram.

An activity diagram models the workflow (also called the activity) of a portion of a software system. Such workflows may include a portion of an algorithm, like the sequence structure in Fig. 5.2. Activity diagrams are composed of symbols, such as action-state symbols (rectangles with their left and right sides replaced with outward arcs), diamonds and small circles. These symbols are connected by transition arrows, which represent the *flow of the activity*—that is, the *order* in which the actions should occur.

Like pseudocode, activity diagrams help you develop and represent algorithms. Activity diagrams clearly show how control structures operate. We use the UML in this chapter and the next to show the flow of control in control statements.

Consider the sequence-structure activity diagram in Fig. 5.2. It contains two action states, each containing an action expression—for example, "add grade to total" or "add 1 to counter"—that specifies a particular action to perform. The arrows in the activity diagram represent transitions, which indicate the *order* in which the actions represented by the action states occur. The portion of the app that implements the activities illustrated in Fig. 5.2 first adds grade to total, then adds 1 to counter.

The solid circle at the top of the activity diagram represents the initial state—the *beginning* of the workflow *before* the app performs the modeled actions. The solid circle surrounded by a hollow circle at the bottom of the diagram represents the final state—the *end* of the workflow *after* the app performs its actions.

Figure 5.2 also includes rectangles with the upper-right corners folded over. These are UML notes (like comments in C#) that describe the purpose of symbols in the diagram. Figure 5.2 uses UML notes to show the C# code associated with each action state. A dotted line connects each note with the element that the note describes. Activity diagrams normally do *not* show the C# code that implements the activity. We do this here to illustrate how the diagram relates to C# code.

5.4.2 Selection Statements

C# has three types of selection structures, which from this point forward we shall refer to as selection statements. The if statement performs (selects) an action if a condition is *true* or skips the action if the condition is *false*. The if...else statement performs an action if a condition is *true* or performs a different action if the condition is *false*. The switch statement (Chapter 6) performs one of many different actions, depending on the value of an expression.

The if statement is called a single-selection statement because it selects or ignores a single action (or, as we'll soon see, a single group of actions). The if...else statement is called a double-selection statement because it selects between *two* different actions (or groups of actions). The switch statement is called a multiple-selection statement because it selects among *many* different actions (or groups of actions).

5.4.3 Iteration Statements

C# provides four iteration statements (sometimes called repetition statements or looping statements) that enable programs to perform statements repeatedly as long as a condition (called the loop-continuation condition) remains *true*. The iteration statements are the while, do...while, for and foreach statements. (Chapter 6 presents the do...while and for statements. Chapter 8 discusses the foreach statement.) The while, for and foreach statements perform the action (or group of actions) in their bodies *zero or more times*—if the loop-continuation condition is initially *false*, the action (or group of actions) will not execute. The do...while statement performs the action (or group of actions) in its body *one or more times*. The words if, else, switch, while, do, for and foreach are C# keywords.

5.4.4 Summary of Control Statements

C# has only three kinds of control statements: the *sequence*, *selection* (three types) and *iteration* (four types). Every app is formed by combining as many of these statements as is appropriate for the algorithm the app implements. We can model each control statement as an activity diagram. Like Fig. 5.2, each diagram contains an initial state and a final state that represent a control statement's entry point and exit point, respectively. Single-entry/single-exit control statements make it easy to build programs—we simply connect the exit point of one to the entry point of the next. We call this control-statement stacking. We'll learn that there's only one other way in which control statements may be connected—control-statement nesting—in which one control statement appears *inside* another. Thus, algorithms in C# apps are constructed from only three kinds of control statements, combined in only two ways. This is the essence of simplicity.

5.5 if Single-Selection Statement

We introduced the if single-selection statement briefly in Section 3.9. Apps use selection statements to choose among alternative courses of action. For example, suppose that the passing grade on an exam is 60. The pseudocode statement

> *If student's grade is greater than or equal to 60*
> *Display "Passed"*

represents an if statement that determines whether the *condition* "student's grade is greater than or equal to 60" is *true*. If so, "Passed" is displayed, and the next pseudocode statement in order is "performed." (Remember, pseudocode is not a real programming language.) If the condition is *false*, the *Display* statement is ignored, and the next pseudocode statement in order is performed. The indentation of the second line of this selection statement is optional, but recommended, because it emphasizes the inherent structure of structured programs.

The preceding pseudocode *if* statement may be written in C# as

```
if (studentGrade >= 60)
{
    Console.WriteLine("Passed");
}
```

The C# code corresponds closely to the pseudocode. This is one of the characteristics of pseudocode that makes it such a useful app-development tool.

bool *Simple Type*

You saw in Chapter 3 that decisions can be based on conditions containing relational or equality operators. Actually, a decision can be based on *any* expression that evaluates to `true` or `false`. C# provides the simple type `bool` for Boolean variables that can hold only the values `true` and `false`—each of these is a C# keyword.

UML Activity Diagram for an if *Statement*

Figure 5.3 illustrates the single-selection `if` statement. This figure contains the most important symbol in an activity diagram—the diamond, or decision symbol, which indicates that a *decision* is to be made. The workflow continues along a path determined by the symbol's associated guard conditions, which can be *true* or *false*. Each transition arrow emerging from a decision symbol has a guard condition specified in *square brackets* next to the arrow. If a guard condition is *true*, the workflow enters the action state to which the transition arrow points. In Fig. 5.3, if the student's grade is greater than or equal to 60, the app displays "Passed," then transitions to the final state of this activity. If the grade is less than 60, the app immediately transitions to the final state without displaying a message.

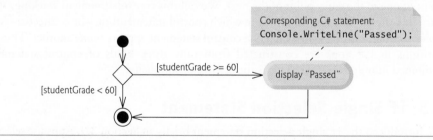

Corresponding C# statement:
`Console.WriteLine("Passed");`

[studentGrade >= 60]   display "Passed"

[studentGrade < 60]

Fig. 5.3 | `if` single-selection statement UML activity diagram.

The `if` statement is a *single-entry/single-exit* control statement. We'll see that the activity diagrams for the remaining control statements also contain initial states, transition arrows, action states that indicate actions to perform, decision symbols (with associated guard conditions) that indicate decisions to be made, and final states.

5.6 if...else **Double-Selection Statement**

The `if` single-selection statement performs an indicated action *only* when the condition is true; otherwise, the action is skipped. The `if...else` double-selection statement allows you to specify an action to perform when the condition is *true* and a different action when the condition is *false*. For example, the pseudocode statement

> *If student's grade is greater than or equal to 60*
> *Display "Passed"*
> *Else*
> *Display "Failed"*

represents an `if...else` statement that displays "Passed" if the student's grade is greater than or equal to 60, but displays "Failed" if it's less than 60. In either case, after "Passed" or "Failed" is displayed, the next pseudocode statement in sequence is "performed."

The preceding *if...else* pseudocode statement can be written in C# as

```csharp
if (grade >= 60)
{
    Console.WriteLine("Passed");
}
else
{
    Console.WriteLine("Failed");
}
```

The body of the `else` part is also indented. Whatever indentation convention you choose should be applied consistently throughout your apps.

Good Programming Practice 5.1

Indent both body statements of an if...else statement. Visual Studio does this for you.

Good Programming Practice 5.2

If there are several levels of indentation, each level should be indented the same additional amount of space. Again, we use three-space indents for book-publication purposes, but Microsoft recommends four-space indents—the default in Visual Studio.

UML Activity Diagram for an *if...else* Statement

Figure 5.4 illustrates the flow of control in the preceding `if...else` statement. Once again, the symbols in the UML activity diagram (besides the initial state, transition arrows and final state) represent action states and decisions.

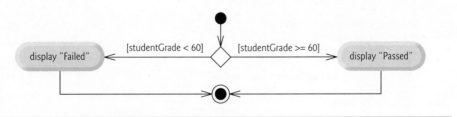

Fig. 5.4 | `if...else` double-selection statement UML activity diagram.

5.6.1 Nested `if...else` Statements

An app can test multiple cases by placing `if...else` statements *inside* other `if...else` statements to create **nested if...else statements**. For example, the following pseudocode represents a nested if...else statement that displays A for exam grades greater than or equal to 90, B for 80 to 89, C for 70 to 79, D for 60 to 69 and F for all other grades:

If student's grade is greater than or equal to 90
  Display "A"
Else
  If student's grade is greater than or equal to 80
    Display "B"
  Else
    If student's grade is greater than or equal to 70
      Display "C"
    Else
      If student's grade is greater than or equal to 60
        Display "D"
      Else
        Display "F"

We use shading to highlight the nesting. This pseudocode may be written in C# as

```
if (studentGrade >= 90)
{
   Console.WriteLine("A")
}
else
{
   if (studentGrade >= 80)
   {
      Console.WriteLine("B")
   }
   else
   {
      if (studentGrade >= 70)
      {
         Console.WriteLine("C")
      }
      else
      {
         if (studentGrade >= 60)
         {
            Console.WriteLine("D")
         }
         else
         {
            Console.WriteLine("F")
         }
      }
   }
}
```

If variable studentGrade is greater than or equal to 90, the first four conditions in the nested if...else statement will be true, but only the statement in the if part of the first if...else statement will execute. After that statement executes, the else part of the "outermost" if...else statement is skipped. Many programmers prefer to write the preceding nested if...else statement in the following form, which is identical except for the spacing and indentation that the compiler ignores:

```
if (studentGrade >= 90)
{
    Console.WriteLine("A");
}
else if (studentGrade >= 80)
{
    Console.WriteLine("B");
}
else if (studentGrade >= 70)
{
    Console.WriteLine("C");
}
else if (studentGrade >= 60)
{
    Console.WriteLine("D");
}
else
{
    Console.WriteLine("F");
}
```

The latter form avoids deep indentation of the code to the right. Such indentation often leaves little room on a line of code, forcing lines to wrap.

Error-Prevention Tip 5.1

In a nested if...else statement, ensure that you test for all possible cases.

5.6.2 Dangling-else Problem

Throughout the text, we always enclose control statement bodies in braces ({ and }). This avoids a logic error called the "dangling-else" problem. We investigate this problem in Exercises 5.27–5.29.

5.6.3 Blocks

The if statement normally expects only *one* statement in its body. To include *several* statements in the body of an if (or the body of an else for an if...else statement), you must enclose the statements in braces. As we've done throughout the text, it's good practice to always use the braces. Statements contained in a pair of braces (such as the body of a control statement, property or method) form a block. A block can be placed anywhere in a control statement, property or method that a single statement can be placed.

The following example includes a block of *multiple* statements in the else part of an if...else statement:

```
if (studentGrade >= 60)
{
   Console.WriteLine("Passed");
}
else
{
   Console.WriteLine("Failed");
   Console.WriteLine("You must take this course again.");
}
```

In this case, if studentGrade is less than 60, the program executes *both* statements in the body of the else and prints

```
Failed
You must take this course again.
```

Without the braces surrounding the two statements in the else clause, the statement

```
Console.WriteLine("You must take this course again.");
```

would be outside the body of the else part of the if...else statement and would execute *regardless* of whether the grade was less than 60.

Syntax and Logic Errors

Syntax errors (such as when one brace in a block is left out of the program) are caught by the compiler. A logic error (such as the problem above or an incorrect calculation) has its effect at execution time. A fatal logic error causes a program to fail and terminate prematurely. A nonfatal logic error allows a program to continue executing but causes it to produce incorrect results.

Empty Statement

Just as a block can be placed anywhere a single statement can be placed, it's also possible to have an empty statement, which is represented by placing a semicolon (;) where a statement would normally be.

Common Programming Error 5.1

Placing a semicolon after the parenthesized condition in an if or if...else statement leads to a logic error in single-selection if statements and a syntax error in double-selection if...else statements (when the if-part contains a body statement).

5.6.4 Conditional Operator (?:)

C# provides the conditional operator (?:) that can be used in place of an if...else statement. This can make your code shorter and clearer. The conditional operator is C#'s only ternary operator—it takes three operands. Together, the operands and the ?: symbols form a conditional expression:

- The first operand (to the left of the ?) is a bool expression that evaluates to true or false.

- The second operand (between the ? and :) is the value of the conditional expression if the `bool` expression is `true`.

- The third operand (to the right of the :) is the value of the conditional expression if the `bool` expression is `false`.

For now, the second and third operands should have the same type. In Section 7.6, we'll discuss implicit conversions that may occur if these operands do not have the same type.

For example, the statement

```
Console.WriteLine(studentGrade >= 60 ? "Passed" : "Failed");
```

displays the value of `WriteLine`'s conditional-expression argument. The conditional expression in the preceding statement evaluates to the `string` "Passed" if the condition

```
studentGrade >= 60
```

is `true` and to the `string` "Failed" if it's `false`. Thus, this statement with the conditional operator performs essentially the same task as the first `if...else` statement shown in Section 5.6. The precedence of the conditional operator is low, so the entire conditional expression is normally placed in parentheses. We'll see that conditional expressions can be used in some situations where `if...else` statements cannot.

5.7 Student Class: Nested if...else Statements

The example of Figs. 5.5–5.6 demonstrates a nested `if...else` statement that determines a student's letter grade based on the student's average in a course.

Class **Student**

Class `Student` (Fig. 5.5) stores a student's name and average and provides properties for manipulating these values. The class contains:

- Auto-implemented `string` property `Name` (line 7) to store a `Student`'s name.

- Instance variable `average` of type `int` (line 8) to store a `Student`'s average in a course and a corresponding `Average` property (lines 18–36) to *get* and *set* the Student's average. Average's `set` accessor uses *nested if statements* (lines 28–34) to validate the value that's assigned to the `Average` property. These statements ensure that the value is greater than 0 *and* less than or equal to 100; otherwise, instance variable `average`'s value is left unchanged. Each `if` statement contains a *simple condition*—i.e., one that makes only a single test. In Section 6.11, you'll see how to use *logical operators* to write *compound conditions* that conveniently combine several simple conditions. If the condition in line 28 is `true`, only then will the condition in line 30 be tested, and *only* if the conditions in both lines 28 *and* 30 are `true` will the statement in line 32 execute.

- A constructor (lines 11–15) that sets the `Name` and `Average` properties.

- Read-only property `LetterGrade` (lines 39–68), which uses *nested if...else statements* to determine the `Student`'s letter grade based on the `Student`'s average. A read-only property provides only a `get` accessor. Note that the local variable `letterGrade` is initialized to `string.Empty` (line 43), which represents the empty string (that is, a `string` containing no characters).

```csharp
1  // Fig. 5.5: Student.cs
2  // Student class that stores a student name and average.
3  using System;
4
5  class Student
6  {
7     public string Name { get; set; } // property
8     private int average; // instance variable
9
10    // constructor initializes Name and Average properties
11    public Student(string studentName, int studentAverage)
12    {
13       Name = studentName;
14       Average = studentAverage; // sets average instance variable
15    }
16
17    // property to get and set instance variable average
18    public int Average
19    {
20       get // returns the Student's average
21       {
22          return average;
23       }
24       set  // sets the Student's average
25       {
26          // validate that value is > 0 and <= 100; otherwise,
27          // keep instance variable average's current value
28          if (value > 0)
29          {
30             if (value <= 100)
31             {
32                average = value; // assign to instance variable
33             }
34          }
35       }
36    }
37
38    // returns the Student's letter grade, based on the average
39    string LetterGrade
40    {
41       get
42       {
43          string letterGrade = string.Empty; // string.Empty is ""
44
45          if (average >= 90)
46          {
47             letterGrade = "A";
48          }
49          else if (average >= 80)
50          {
51             letterGrade = "B";
52          }
```

Fig. 5.5 | Student class that stores a student name and average. (Part 1 of 2.)

```
53              else if (average >= 70)
54              {
55                  letterGrade = "C";
56              }
57              else if (average >= 60)
58              {
59                  letterGrade = "D";
60              }
61              else
62              {
63                  letterGrade = "F";
64              }
65
66              return letterGrade;
67          }
68      }
69  }
```

Fig. 5.5 | Student class that stores a student name and average. (Part 2 of 2.)

Class StudentTest

To demonstrate the nested if statements and nested if...else statements in class Student's Average and LetterGrade properties, respectively, method Main (Fig. 5.6) creates two Student objects (lines 9–10). Next, lines 12–15 display each Student's name, average and letter grade by accessing the objects' Name, Average and LetterGrade properties, respectively.

```
 1  // Fig. 5.6: StudentTest.cs
 2  // Create and test Student objects.
 3  using System;
 4
 5  class StudentTest
 6  {
 7      static void Main()
 8      {
 9          Student student1 = new Student("Jane Green", 93);
10          Student student2 = new Student("John Blue", 72);
11
12          Console.Write($"{student1.Name}'s letter grade equivalent of ");
13          Console.WriteLine($"{student1.Average} is {student1.LetterGrade}");
14          Console.Write($"{student2.Name}'s letter grade equivalent of ");
15          Console.WriteLine($"{student2.Average} is {student2.LetterGrade}");
16      }
17  }
```

```
Jane Green's letter grade equivalent of 93 is A
John Blue's letter grade equivalent of 72 is C
```

Fig. 5.6 | Create and test Student objects.

5.8 `while` Iteration Statement

An iteration statement allows you to specify that a program should repeat an action while some condition remains *true*. The pseudocode statement

> *While there are more items on my shopping list*
> *Purchase next item and cross it off my list*

describes the iteration during a shopping trip. The condition "there are more items on my shopping list" may be *true* or *false*. If it's *true*, then the action "Purchase next item and cross it off my list" is performed. This action will be performed *repeatedly* while the condition remains *true*. The statement(s) contained in the *While* iteration statement constitute its body, which may be a single statement or a block. Eventually, the condition will become *false* (when the shopping list's last item has been purchased and crossed off). At this point, the iteration terminates, and the first statement after the iteration statement executes.

As an example of C#'s while iteration statement, consider a code segment designed to find the first power of 3 larger than 100. When the following `while` statement finishes executing, `product` contains the result:

```
int product = 3;

while (product <= 100)
{
    product = 3 * product;
}
```

When this `while` statement begins execution, variable `product` contains the value 3. Each iteration of the `while` statement multiplies `product` by 3, so `product` takes on the values 9, 27, 81 and 243 successively. When `product` becomes 243, `product <= 100` becomes `false`. This terminates the iteration, so the final value of `product` is 243. At this point, program execution continues with the next statement after the `while` statement.

Common Programming Error 5.2

Not providing in the body of a `while` statement an action that eventually causes the condition in the `while` to become false results in a logic error called an infinite loop (the loop never terminates). This often will make your program appear to "hang."

`while` Iteration Statement Activity Diagram

The UML activity diagram in Fig. 5.7 illustrates the flow of control in the preceding `while` statement. Once again, the symbols in the diagram (besides the initial state, transition arrows, a final state and three notes) represent an action state and a decision. This diagram introduces the UML's merge symbol. The UML represents *both* the merge symbol and the decision symbol as diamonds. The merge symbol joins multiple flows of activity into one. In this diagram, the merge symbol joins the transitions from the initial state and from the action state, so they both flow into the decision that determines whether the loop should begin (or continue) executing.

The decision and merge symbols can be distinguished by the number of "incoming" and "outgoing" transition arrows. A decision symbol has *one* transition arrow pointing *to* the diamond and *two or more* pointing out *from* it to indicate possible transitions from that point. In addition, each transition arrow pointing out of a decision symbol has a guard

Fig. 5.7 | `while` iteration statement UML activity diagram.

condition next to it. A merge symbol has two or more transition arrows pointing to the diamond and only one pointing from the diamond, to indicate multiple activity flows merging to continue the activity. None of the transition arrows associated with a merge symbol has a guard condition.

Figure 5.7 clearly shows the iteration of the `while` statement discussed earlier in this section. The transition arrow emerging from the action state points back to the merge, from which program flow transitions back to the decision that's tested at the beginning of each iteration of the loop. The loop continues executing until the guard condition `product > 100` becomes *true*. Then the `while` statement exits (reaches its final state), and control passes to the next statement in sequence in the app.

5.9 Formulating Algorithms: Counter-Controlled Iteration

To illustrate how algorithms are developed, we solve two variations of a problem that averages student grades. Consider the following problem statement:

> *A class of 10 students took a quiz. The grades (integers in the range 0 to 100) for this quiz are available to you. Determine the class average on the quiz.*

The class average is equal to the sum of the grades divided by the number of students. The algorithm for solving this problem on a computer must input each grade, keep track of the total of all grades entered, perform the averaging calculation and print the result.

5.9.1 Pseudocode Algorithm with Counter-Controlled Iteration

Let's use pseudocode to list the actions to execute and specify the order in which they should execute. We use counter-controlled iteration to input the grades one at a time. This technique uses a variable called a counter (or control variable) to control the number of times a set of statements will execute. Counter-controlled iteration is often called definite iteration, because the number of iterations is known *before* the loop begins executing. In this example, iteration terminates when the counter exceeds 10. This section presents a fully developed pseudocode algorithm (Fig. 5.8) and a corresponding C# app (Fig. 5.9) that implements the algorithm. In Section 5.10, we demonstrate how to develop pseudo-code algorithms from scratch.

I	*Set total to zero*
2	*Set grade counter to one*
3	
4	*While grade counter is less than or equal to 10*
5	*Prompt the user to enter the next grade*
6	*Input the next grade*
7	*Add the grade into the total*
8	*Add one to the grade counter*
9	
10	*Set the class average to the total divided by 10*
II	*Display the class average*

Fig. 5.8 | Pseudocode algorithm that uses counter-controlled iteration to solve the class-average problem.

Note the mentions in the algorithm of Fig. 5.8 to a total and a counter. A total is a variable used to accumulate the sum of several values. A counter is a variable used to count—in this case, the grade counter indicates which of the 10 grades is about to be entered by the user. Variables used to store totals normally are initialized to zero before being used in a program. In pseudocode, we do *not* use braces around the statements that form the body of the pseudocode *while* structure, but you could.

Software Engineering Observation 5.1

Experience has shown that the most difficult part of solving a problem on a computer is developing the algorithm for the solution. Once a correct algorithm has been specified, producing a working C# program from it is usually straightforward.

5.9.2 Implementing Counter-Controlled Iteration

In Fig. 5.9, method `Main` implements the class-averaging algorithm described by the pseudocode in Fig. 5.8—it allows the user to enter 10 grades, then calculates and displays the average.

```
 I  // Fig. 5.9: ClassAverage.cs
 2  // Solving the class-average problem using counter-controlled iteration.
 3  using System;
 4
 5  class ClassAverage
 6  {
 7     static void Main()
 8     {
 9        // initialization phase
10        int total = 0; // initialize sum of grades entered by the user
II        int gradeCounter = 1; // initialize grade # to be entered next
```

Fig. 5.9 | Solving the class-average problem using counter-controlled iteration. (Part 1 of 2.)

```
12
13          // processing phase uses counter-controlled iteration
14          while (gradeCounter <= 10) // loop 10 times
15          {
16              Console.Write("Enter grade: "); // prompt
17              int grade = int.Parse(Console.ReadLine()); // input grade
18              total = total + grade; // add the grade to total
19              gradeCounter = gradeCounter + 1; // increment the counter by 1
20          }
21
22          // termination phase
23          int average = total / 10; // integer division yields integer result
24
25          // display total and average of grades
26          Console.WriteLine($"\nTotal of all 10 grades is {total}");
27          Console.WriteLine($"Class average is {average}");
28      }
29  }
```

```
Enter grade: 88
Enter grade: 79
Enter grade: 95
Enter grade: 100
Enter grade: 48
Enter grade: 88
Enter grade: 92
Enter grade: 83
Enter grade: 90
Enter grade: 85

Total of all 10 grades is 848
Class average is 84
```

Fig. 5.9 | Solving the class-average problem using counter-controlled iteration. (Part 2 of 2.)

Local Variables in Main

Lines 10, 11, 17 and 23 declare local variables total, gradeCounter, grade and average, respectively. A variable declared in a method body is a local variable and can be used only from the line of its declaration to the closing right brace of the block in which the variable is declared. A local variable's declaration must appear *before* the variable is used; otherwise, a compilation error occurs. Variable grade—declared in the body of the while loop—can be used only in that block.

Initialization Phase: Initializing Variables total and gradeCounter

C# requires local variables to be definitely assigned—that is, each local variable must be assigned a value before the variable's value is used. Lines 10–11 declare and initialize total to 0 and gradeCounter to 1 before their values are used, so these variables are definitely assigned (as are grade and average in lines 17 and 23, respectively).

Common Programming Error 5.3

All local variables must be definitely assigned before their values are used in expressions. Using a local variable's value before it's definitely assigned results in a compilation error.

Error-Prevention Tip 5.2
Initializing local variables when they're declared helps you avoid compilation errors that might arise from attempts to use uninitialized data. While C# does not require that local-variable initializations be incorporated into declarations, it does require that local variables be initialized before their values are used in an expression.

Error-Prevention Tip 5.3
Initialize each counter and total, either in its declaration or in an assignment statement. Totals are normally initialized to 0. Counters are normally initialized to 0 or 1, depending on how they're used (we'll show examples of each).

Processing Phase: Reading 10 Grades from the User

Line 14 indicates that the while statement should continue looping (also called iterating) as long as gradeCounter's value is less than or equal to 10. While this condition remains *true*, the while statement repeatedly executes the statements between the braces that delimit its body (lines 15–20).

Line 16 displays the prompt "Enter grade: ". Line 17 inputs the grade entered by the user and assigns it to variable grade. Then line 18 adds the new grade entered by the user to the total and assigns the result to total, replacing its previous value.

Line 19 adds 1 to gradeCounter to indicate that the program has processed a grade and is ready to input the next grade from the user. Incrementing gradeCounter eventually causes it to exceed 10. Then the loop terminates, because its condition (line 14) becomes false.

Termination Phase: Calculating and Displaying the Class Average

When the loop terminates, line 23 performs the averaging calculation in the average variable's initializer. Line 26 displays the text "Total of all 10 grades is " followed by variable total's value. Then, line 27 displays the text "Class average is " followed by variable average's value. When execution reaches line 28, the program terminates.

Notice that this example contains only one class, with method Main performing all the work. In this chapter and in Chapter 3, you've seen examples consisting of two classes:

- one containing instance variables, properties and methods that perform tasks using the instance variables and properties, and

- one containing method Main, which creates an object of the other class and calls its methods and accesses its properties.

Occasionally, when it does not make sense to create a separate class to demonstrate a concept, we'll place the program's statements entirely within a single class's Main method.

5.9.3 Integer Division and Truncation

The averaging calculation performed in line 23 produces an integer result. The app's output indicates that the sum of the grade values in the sample execution is 848, which, when divided by 10, should yield 84.8. However, the result of the calculation total / 10 is the integer 84, because total and 10 are *both* integers. Dividing two integers results in integer division—any fractional part of the calculation is lost (i.e., truncated, not rounded). We'll see how to obtain a floating-point result from the averaging calculation in the next section.

Common Programming Error 5.4

Assuming that integer division rounds (rather than truncates) can lead to incorrect results. For example, 7 ÷ 4, which yields 1.75 in conventional arithmetic, truncates to 1 in integer arithmetic, rather than rounding to 2.

5.10 Formulating Algorithms: Sentinel-Controlled Iteration

Let us generalize Section 5.9's class-average problem. Consider the following problem:

Develop a class-averaging app that processes grades for an arbitrary number of students each time it's run.

In the previous class-average example, the problem statement specified the number of students, so the number of grades (10) was known in advance. In this example, no indication is given of how many grades the user will enter during the program's execution. The program must process an *arbitrary* number of grades. How can it determine when to stop the input of grades? How will it know when to calculate and print the class average?

One way to solve this problem is to use a special value called a sentinel value (also called a signal value, a dummy value or a flag value) to indicate "end of data entry." The user enters grades until all legitimate grades have been entered. The user then types the sentinel value to indicate that no more grades will be entered. Sentinel-controlled iteration is often called indefinite iteration because the number of iterations is *not* known before the loop begins executing. Clearly, a sentinel value must be chosen that cannot be confused with an acceptable input value. Grades on a quiz are nonnegative integers, so –1 is an acceptable sentinel value for this problem. Thus, a run of the class-averaging program might process a stream of inputs such as 95, 96, 75, 74, 89 and –1. The program would then compute and print the class average for the grades 95, 96, 75, 74 and 89; since –1 is the sentinel value, it should *not* enter into the averaging calculation.

5.10.1 Top-Down, Stepwise Refinement: The Top and First Refinement

We approach this class-averaging program with a technique called top-down, stepwise refinement, which is essential to the development of well-structured programs. We begin with a pseudocode representation of the top—a single statement that conveys the overall purpose of the program:

Determine the class average for the quiz

The top is, in effect, a *complete* representation of a program. Unfortunately, the top rarely conveys sufficient detail from which to write a C# app. So we now begin the refinement process. We divide the top into a series of smaller tasks and list these in the order in which they'll be performed. This results in the following first refinement:

Initialize variables
Input, sum and count the quiz grades
Calculate and print the class average

This refinement uses only the *sequence structure*—the steps listed should execute in order, one after the other.

> **Software Engineering Observation 5.2**
> *Each refinement, as well as the top itself, is a complete specification of the algorithm—only the level of detail varies.*

> **Software Engineering Observation 5.3**
> *Many programs can be divided logically into three phases: an* initialization phase *that initializes the variables; a* processing phase *that inputs data values and adjusts program variables accordingly; and a* termination phase *that calculates and outputs the final results.*

5.10.2 Second Refinement

The preceding Software Engineering Observation is often all you need for the first refinement in the top-down process. To proceed to the next level of refinement—that is, the second refinement—we commit to specific variables. In this example, we need a running total of the numbers, a count of how many numbers have been processed, a variable to receive the value of each grade as it's entered by the user and a variable to hold the calculated average. The pseudocode statement

> *Initialize variables*

can be refined as follows:

> *Initialize total to zero*
> *Initialize counter to zero*

Only the variables *total* and *counter* need to be initialized before they're used. The variables *average* and *grade* (for the calculated average and the user input, respectively) need not be initialized, because their values will be replaced as they're calculated or input.

The pseudocode statement

> *Input, sum and count the quiz grades*

requires *iteration* to successively input each grade. We do not know in advance how many grades will be entered, so we'll use sentinel-controlled iteration. The user enters grades one at a time. After entering the last grade, the user enters the sentinel value. The program tests for the sentinel value after each grade is input and terminates the loop when the user enters the sentinel value. The second refinement of the preceding pseudocode statement is then

> *Prompt the user to enter the first grade*
> *Input the first grade (possibly the sentinel)*
>
> *While the user has not yet entered the sentinel*
>   *Add this grade into the running total*
>   *Add one to the grade counter*
>   *Prompt the user to enter the next grade*
>   *Input the next grade (possibly the sentinel)*

We simply indent the statements under the *While* to show that they belong to the *While*. Again, pseudocode is only an informal program-development aid.

The pseudocode statement

> *Calculate and print the class average*

can be refined as follows:

> *If the counter is not equal to zero*
> > *Set the average to the total divided by the counter*
> > *Print the average*
> *Else*
> > *Print "No grades were entered"*

We're careful here to test for the possibility of *division by zero*—a *logic error* that, if undetected, would cause the program to fail or produce invalid output. The complete second refinement of the pseudocode for the class-average problem is shown in Fig. 5.10.

Error-Prevention Tip 5.4

When performing division by an expression whose value could be zero, explicitly test for this possibility and handle it appropriately in your app (e.g., by displaying an error message) rather than allowing the error to occur.

1	*Initialize total to zero*
2	*Initialize counter to zero*
3	
4	*Prompt the user to enter the first grade*
5	*Input the first grade (possibly the sentinel)*
6	
7	*While the user has not yet entered the sentinel*
8	*Add this grade into the running total*
9	*Add one to the grade counter*
10	*Prompt the user to enter the next grade*
11	*Input the next grade (possibly the sentinel)*
12	
13	*If the counter is not equal to zero*
14	*Set the average to the total divided by the counter*
15	*Print the average*
16	*Else*
17	*Print "No grades were entered"*

Fig. 5.10 | Class-averaging pseudocode algorithm with sentinel-controlled iteration.

In Fig. 5.8 and Fig. 5.10, we included blank lines and indentation in the pseudocode to make it more readable. The blank lines separate the algorithms into their phases and set off control statements; the indentation emphasizes the bodies of the control statements.

The pseudocode algorithm in Fig. 5.10 solves the more general class-average problem. This algorithm was developed after two refinements. Sometimes more are needed.

Software Engineering Observation 5.4

Terminate the top-down, stepwise refinement process when you've specified the pseudocode algorithm in sufficient detail for you to convert the pseudocode to C#.

Software Engineering Observation 5.5

Some programmers do not use program-development tools like pseudocode. They feel that their ultimate goal is to solve the problem on a computer and that writing pseudocode merely delays the production of final outputs. Although this may work for simple and familiar problems, it can lead to serious errors and delays in large, complex projects.

5.10.3 Implementing Sentinel-Controlled Iteration

In Fig. 5.11, method Main implements the pseudocode algorithm of Fig. 5.10. Although each grade entered by the user is an integer, the averaging calculation is likely to produce a number with a decimal point—in other words, a real number or floating-point number (e.g., 7.33, 0.0975 or 1000.12345). The type int cannot represent such a number, so this example must use another type to do so. C# provides data types float and double to store floating-point numbers in memory. The primary difference between these types is that double variables can typically store numbers with larger magnitude and finer detail (i.e., more digits to the right of the decimal point—also known as the number's precision). We say more about floating-point types in Chapter 6.

```csharp
 1   // Fig. 5.11: ClassAverage.cs
 2   // Solving the class-average problem using sentinel-controlled iteration.
 3   using System;
 4
 5   class ClassAverage
 6   {
 7      static void Main()
 8      {
 9         // initialization phase
10         int total = 0; // initialize sum of grades
11         int gradeCounter = 0; // initialize # of grades entered so far
12
13         // processing phase
14         // prompt for input and read grade from user
15         Console.Write("Enter grade or -1 to quit: ");
16         int grade = int.Parse(Console.ReadLine());
17
18         // loop until sentinel value is read from the user
19         while (grade != -1)
20         {
21            total = total + grade; // add grade to total
22            gradeCounter = gradeCounter + 1; // increment counter
23
24            // prompt for input and read grade from user
25            Console.Write("Enter grade or -1 to quit: ");
26            grade = int.Parse(Console.ReadLine());
27         }
28
```

Fig. 5.11 | Solving the class-average problem using sentinel-controlled iteration. (Part 1 of 2.)

```
29          // termination phase
30          // if the user entered at least one grade...
31          if (gradeCounter != 0)
32          {
33              // use number with decimal point to calculate average of grades
34              double average = (double) total / gradeCounter;
35
36              // display the total and average (with two digits of precision)
37              Console.WriteLine(
38                  $"\nTotal of the {gradeCounter} grades entered is {total}");
39              Console.WriteLine($"Class average is {average:F}");
40          }
41          else // no grades were entered, so output error message
42          {
43              Console.WriteLine("No grades were entered");
44          }
45      }
46  }
```

```
Enter grade or -1 to quit: 97
Enter grade or -1 to quit: 88
Enter grade or -1 to quit: 72
Enter grade or -1 to quit: -1

Total of the 3 grades entered is 257
Class average is 85.67
```

Fig. 5.11 | Solving the class-average problem using sentinel-controlled iteration. (Part 2 of 2.)

Recall that integer division produces an integer result. This program introduces a special operator called a cast operator to *force* the averaging calculation to produce a floating-point numeric result. This program also *stacks* control statements on top of one another (in sequence)—the while statement (lines 19–27) is followed in sequence by an if...else statement (lines 31–44). Much of the code in this program is identical to that in Fig. 5.9, so we concentrate on the new concepts.

5.10.4 Program Logic for Sentinel-Controlled Iteration

Line 11 initializes gradeCounter to 0, because no grades have been entered yet. Remember that this program uses *sentinel-controlled iteration* to input the grades. The program increments gradeCounter only when the user enters a valid grade. Line 34 declares double variable average, which stores the class average as a floating-point number.

Compare the program logic for sentinel-controlled iteration in this program with that for counter-controlled iteration in Fig. 5.9. In counter-controlled iteration, each iteration of the while statement (lines 14–20 of Fig. 5.9) reads a value from the user, for the specified number of iterations. In sentinel-controlled iteration, the program prompts for and reads the first value (lines 15–16 of Fig. 5.11) before reaching the while. This value determines whether the program's flow of control should enter the body of the while. If the condition of the while is false (line 19), the user entered the sentinel value, so the body of the while does not execute (i.e., no grades were entered). If, on the other hand, the condition is true, the body begins execution, and the loop adds the grade value to the total and increments the gradeCounter (lines 21–22). Then lines 25–26 in the loop body input the next value from the user. Next, program control reaches the closing right brace of the loop body at line 27, so execution continues with the test of the while's condition (line 19). The condition uses the most recent grade entered by the user to determine whether the loop body should execute again.

The value of variable grade is always input from the user immediately *before* the program tests the while condition. This allows the program to determine whether the value just input is the sentinel value *before* the program processes that value (i.e., adds it to the total). If the sentinel value is input, the loop terminates, and the program does not add –1 to the total.

Good Programming Practice 5.3

In a sentinel-controlled loop, prompts should remind the user of the sentinel.

After the loop terminates, the if...else statement at lines 31–44 executes. Line 31 determines whether any grades were input. If none were input, the if...else statement's else part executes and displays the message "No grades were entered".

5.10.5 Braces in a while Statement

Notice the while statement's block in Fig. 5.11 (lines 20–27). Without the braces, the loop would consider its body to be *only* the first statement, which adds the grade to the total. The last three statements in the block would fall outside the loop's body, causing the computer to interpret the code incorrectly as follows:

```
while (grade != -1)
    total = total + grade; // add grade to total
gradeCounter = gradeCounter + 1; // increment counter

// prompt for input and read grade from user
Console.Write("Enter grade or -1 to quit: ");
grade = int.Parse(Console.ReadLine());
```

The preceding code would cause an *infinite loop* if the user did not enter the sentinel -1 at line 16 (before the while statement).

Error-Prevention Tip 5.5

Omitting the braces that delimit a block can lead to logic errors, such as infinite loops. To prevent this and other problems, we always enclose the body of every control statement in braces even if the body contains only a single statement.

5.10.6 Converting Between Simple Types Explicitly and Implicitly

If at least one grade was entered, line 34 of Fig. 5.11

```
double average = (double) total / gradeCounter;
```

calculates the average. Recall from Fig. 5.9 that integer division yields an integer result. Even though variable average is declared as a double, if we had written line 34 as

```
double average = total / gradeCounter;
```

it would lose the fractional part of the quotient *before* the result of the division was used to initialize average.

Cast Operator

To perform a floating-point calculation with integers in this example, you first create a *temporary* floating-point value using the unary cast operator. Line 34 uses the (double) unary cast operator—which has higher precedence than the arithmetic operators—to create a temporary double *copy* of its operand total, which appears to the right of the operator. The value stored in total is still an integer. Using a cast operator in this manner is called explicit conversion.

Promotions

After the cast operation, the calculation consists of the temporary double copy of total divided by the integer gradeCounter. For arithmetic, the compiler knows how to evaluate only expressions in which the operand types are *identical*. To ensure this, the compiler performs an operation called promotion (also called implicit conversion) on selected operands. In an expression containing values of types int and double, the compiler promotes int operands to double values. So, in line 34, the compiler creates a temporary copy of gradeCounter's value of type double, then performs the floating-point division. Finally, average is initialized with the floating-point result. Section 7.6.1 discusses the allowed simple-type promotions.

Cast Operators for Any Type

Cast operators are available for all simple types. We'll discuss cast operators for other types in Chapter 12. The cast operator is formed by placing parentheses around the name of a type. This operator is a unary operator—it takes only one operand. C# also supports unary versions of the plus (+) and minus (–) operators, so you can write expressions like +5 or – 7. Cast operators have the second highest precedence. (See the operator precedence chart in Appendix A.)

5.10.7 Formatting Floating-Point Numbers

Line 39

```
Console.WriteLine($"Class average is {average:F}");
```

outputs the class average. In this example, we decided that we'd like to display the class average *rounded to the nearest hundredth* and output the average with exactly two digits to the right of the decimal point. The format specifier F in the interpolation expression

```
{average:F}
```

typically formats average's value with two digits to the right of the decimal point—again, the Windows culture settings on the user's machine determine the actual format, including the digits to the right of the decimal point, whether commas or periods are used for separating thousands, millions, etc.

Rounding Floating-Point Numbers

When the F format specifier is used to format a floating-point value, the formatted value is rounded to a specific decimal position, although the value in memory remains unaltered. In many cultures a floating-point value output with F will be rounded to the hundredths position—for example, 123.457 will be rounded to 123.46, and 27.333 will be rounded to 27.33—though in some cultures these values are rounded to whole numbers. In this app, the three grades entered during the sample execution total 257, which yields the average 86.66666…. In the United States, the F format specifier rounds average to the hundredths position, so the average is displayed as 85.67.

5.11 Formulating Algorithms: Nested Control Statements

For the next example, we once again formulate an algorithm by using pseudocode and top-down, stepwise refinement, and write a corresponding C# app. We've seen that control statements can be *stacked* on top of one another (in sequence). In this case study, we examine the only other structured way control statements can be connected, namely, by nesting one control statement within another.

5.11.1 Problem Statement

Consider the following problem statement:

> *A college offers a course that prepares students for the state licensing exam for real-estate brokers. Last year, 10 of the students who completed this course took the exam. The college wants to know how well its students did on the exam. You've been asked to write an app to summarize the results. You've been given a list of these 10 students. Next to each name is written a 1 if the student passed the exam or a 2 if the student failed.*
>
> *Your app should analyze the results of the exam as follows:*
>
> 1. *Input each test result (i.e., a 1 or a 2). Display the message "Enter result" on the screen each time the app requests a test result.*
>
> 2. *Count the number of test results of each type.*
>
> 3. *Display a summary of the test results, indicating the number of students who passed and the number who failed.*
>
> 4. *If more than eight students passed the exam, display the message "Bonus to instructor!"*

Problem Statement Observations

After reading the problem statement, we make the following observations:

1. The app must process test results for 10 students. A *counter-controlled loop* can be used because the number of test results is known in advance.

2. Each test result has a numeric value—either a 1 or a 2. Each time the app reads a test result, the app must determine whether the number is a 1 or a 2. We test for a 1 in our algorithm. If the number is not a 1, we assume that it's a 2. (Exercise 5.24 considers the consequences of this assumption.)

3. Two counters are used to keep track of the exam results—one to count the number of students who passed the exam and one to count the number of students who failed the exam.

4. After the app has processed all the results, it must determine whether more than eight students passed the exam.

5.11.2 Top-Down, Stepwise Refinement: Pseudocode Representation of the Top

Let's proceed with top-down, stepwise refinement. We begin with a pseudocode representation of the top:

> *Analyze exam results and decide whether the instructor should receive a bonus*

Once again, the top is a *complete* representation of the app, but several refinements are likely to be needed before the pseudocode can evolve naturally into a C# app.

5.11.3 Top-Down, Stepwise Refinement: First Refinement

Our first refinement is

> *Initialize variables*
> *Input the 10 exam results, and count passes and failures*
> *Display a summary of the exam results and decide if the instructor should*
>   *receive a bonus*

Here, too, even though we have a complete representation of the entire app, further refinement is necessary. We now specify individual variables. Counters are needed to record the passes and failures, a counter will be used to control the looping process and a variable is needed to store the user input. The variable in which the user input will be stored is not initialized at the start of the algorithm, because its value is read from the user during each iteration of the loop.

5.11.4 Top-Down, Stepwise Refinement: Second Refinement

The pseudocode statement

> *Initialize variables*

can be refined as follows:

> *Initialize passes to zero*
> *Initialize failures to zero*
> *Initialize student counter to one*

Notice that only the counters are initialized at the start of the algorithm.
   The pseudocode statement

> *Input the 10 exam results, and count passes and failures*

requires a loop that successively inputs the result of each exam. We know in advance that there are precisely 10 exam results, so counter-controlled looping is appropriate. Inside the loop (i.e., nested within the loop), a double-selection statement will determine whether each exam result is a pass or a failure and will increment the appropriate counter. The refinement of the preceding pseudocode statement is then

> *While student counter is less than or equal to 10*
>   *Prompt the user to enter the next exam result*
>   *Input the next exam result*
>
>   *If the student passed*
>   *Add one to passes*
>   *Else*
>   *Add one to failures*
>
>   *Add one to student counter*

We use blank lines to isolate the *if...else* control statement, which improves readability. The pseudocode statement

> *Display a summary of the exam results and decide if the instructor should*
>   *receive a bonus*

can be refined as follows:

> *Display the number of passes*
> *Display the number of failures*
>
> *If more than eight students passed*
>   *Display "Bonus to instructor!"*

5.11.5 Complete Second Refinement of the Pseudocode

The complete second refinement of the pseudocode appears in Fig. 5.12. Notice that blank lines are also used to set off the *while* statement for readability. This pseudocode is now sufficiently refined for conversion to C#. The program that implements the pseudocode algorithm and sample outputs are shown in Fig. 5.13.

```
 1   Initialize passes to zero
 2   Initialize failures to zero
 3   Initialize student counter to one
 4
 5   While student counter is less than or equal to 10
 6       Prompt the user to enter the next exam result
 7       Input the next exam result
 8
 9       If the student passed
10           Add one to passes
11       Else
12           Add one to failures
13
14       Add one to student counter
15
```

Fig. 5.12 | Pseudocode for the examination-results problem. (Part 1 of 2.)

```
16    Display the number of passes
17    Display the number of failures
18
19    If more than eight students passed
20        Display "Bonus to instructor!"
```

Fig. 5.12 | Pseudocode for the examination-results problem. (Part 2 of 2.)

5.11.6 App That Implements the Pseudocode Algorithm

The program that implements the pseudocode algorithm and two sample executions are shown in Fig. 5.13. Lines 10–12 and 19 declare the local variables that method Main uses to process the examination results.

```csharp
1   // Fig. 5.13: Analysis.cs
2   // Analysis of examination results, using nested control statements.
3   using System;
4
5   class Analysis
6   {
7      static void Main()
8      {
9         // initialize variables in declarations
10        int passes = 0; // number of passes
11        int failures = 0; // number of failures
12        int studentCounter = 1; // student counter
13
14        // process 10 students using counter-controlled iteration
15        while (studentCounter <= 10)
16        {
17           // prompt user for input and obtain a value from the user
18           Console.Write("Enter result (1 = pass, 2 = fail): ");
19           int result = int.Parse(Console.ReadLine());
20
21           // if...else is nested in the while statement
22           if (result == 1)
23           {
24              passes = passes + 1; // increment passes
25           }
26           else
27           {
28              failures = failures + 1; // increment failures
29           }
30
31           // increment studentCounter so loop eventually terminates
32           studentCounter = studentCounter + 1;
33        }
34
35        // termination phase; prepare and display results
36        Console.WriteLine($"Passed: {passes}\nFailed: {failures}");
```

Fig. 5.13 | Analysis of examination results, using nested control statements. (Part 1 of 2.)

```
37
38          // determine whether more than 8 students passed
39          if (passes > 8)
40          {
41              Console.WriteLine("Bonus to instructor!");
42          }
43      }
44  }
```

```
Enter result (1 = pass, 2 = fail): 1
Enter result (1 = pass, 2 = fail): 2
Enter result (1 = pass, 2 = fail): 1
Enter result (1 = pass, 2 = fail): 1
Enter result (1 = pass, 2 = fail): 1
Enter result (1 = pass, 2 = fail): 1
Enter result (1 = pass, 2 = fail): 1
Enter result (1 = pass, 2 = fail): 1
Enter result (1 = pass, 2 = fail): 1
Enter result (1 = pass, 2 = fail): 1
Passed: 9
Failed: 1
Bonus to instructor!
```

```
Enter result (1 = pass, 2 = fail): 1
Enter result (1 = pass, 2 = fail): 2
Enter result (1 = pass, 2 = fail): 2
Enter result (1 = pass, 2 = fail): 2
Enter result (1 = pass, 2 = fail): 1
Enter result (1 = pass, 2 = fail): 1
Enter result (1 = pass, 2 = fail): 1
Enter result (1 = pass, 2 = fail): 1
Enter result (1 = pass, 2 = fail): 2
Enter result (1 = pass, 2 = fail): 2
Passed: 5
Failed: 5
```

Fig. 5.13 | Analysis of examination results, using nested control statements. (Part 2 of 2.)

The while statement (lines 15–33) loops 10 times. During each iteration, the loop inputs and processes one exam result. Notice that the if...else statement (lines 22–29) for processing each result is *nested* in the while statement. If the result is 1, the if...else statement increments passes; otherwise, it *assumes* the result is 2 and increments failures. Line 32 increments studentCounter before the loop condition is tested again at line 15. After 10 values have been input, the loop terminates and line 36 displays the number of passes and the number of failures. Lines 39–42 determine whether more than eight students passed the exam and, if so, output the message "Bonus to instructor!".

Figure 5.13 shows the input and output from two sample executions of the app. During the first, the condition at line 39 is true—more than eight students passed the exam, so the app outputs a message to bonus the instructor.

5.12 Compound Assignment Operators

The compound assignment operators abbreviate assignment expressions. Statements like

> *variable = variable   operator   expression*;

where *operator* is one of the binary operators +, -, *, / or % (or others we discuss later in the text) can be written in the form

> *variable   operator= expression*;

For example, you can abbreviate the statement

```
c = c + 3;
```

with the addition compound assignment operator, +=, as

```
c += 3;
```

The += operator adds the value of the expression on its right to the value of the variable on its left and stores the result in the variable on the left of the operator. Thus, the assignment expression c += 3 adds 3 to c. Figure 5.14 shows the arithmetic compound assignment operators, sample expressions using the operators and explanations of what the operators do.

Assignment operator	Sample expression	Explanation	Assigns
Assume: int c = 3, d = 5, e = 4, f = 6, g = 12;			
+=	c += 7	c = c + 7	10 to c
-=	d -= 4	d = d - 4	1 to d
*=	e *= 5	e = e * 5	20 to e
/=	f /= 3	f = f / 3	2 to f
%=	g %= 9	g = g % 9	3 to g

Fig. 5.14 | Arithmetic compound assignment operators.

5.13 Increment and Decrement Operators

C# provides two unary operators for adding 1 to or subtracting 1 from the value of a numeric variable (summarized in Fig. 5.15). These are the unary increment operator, ++, and the unary decrement operator, --, respectively. An app can increment by 1 the value of a variable called c using the increment operator, ++, rather than the expression c = c + 1 or c += 1. An increment or decrement operator that's prefixed to (placed *before*) a variable is referred to as the prefix increment operator or prefix decrement operator, respectively. An increment or decrement operator that's postfixed to (placed *after*) a variable is referred to as the postfix increment operator or postfix decrement operator, respectively.

Using the prefix increment (or decrement) operator to add 1 to (or subtract 1 from) a variable is known as preincrementing (or predecrementing). This causes the variable to be incremented (decremented) by 1; then the new value of the variable is used in the expression in which it appears.

Operator	Sample expression	Explanation
++ (prefix increment)	++a	Increments a by 1 and uses the new value of a in the expression in which a resides.
++ (postfix increment)	a++	Increments a by 1, but uses the original value of a in the expression in which a resides.
-- (prefix decrement)	--b	Decrements b by 1 and uses the new value of b in the expression in which b resides.
-- (postfix decrement)	b--	Decrements b by 1 but uses the original value of b in the expression in which b resides.

Fig. 5.15 | Increment and decrement operators.

Using the postfix increment (or decrement) operator to add 1 to (or subtract 1 from) a variable is known as postincrementing (or postdecrementing). This causes the current value of the variable to be used in the expression in which it appears; then the variable's value is incremented (decremented) by 1.

Good Programming Practice 5.4

Unlike binary operators, the unary increment and decrement operators as a matter of style should be placed next to their operands, with no intervening spaces.

5.13.1 Prefix Increment vs. Postfix Increment

Figure 5.16 demonstrates the difference between the prefix-increment and postfix-increment versions of the ++ increment operator. The decrement operator (--) works similarly.

```
1   // Fig. 5.16: Increment.cs
2   // Prefix increment and postfix increment operators.
3   using System;
4
5   class Increment
6   {
7      static void Main()
8      {
9         // demonstrate postfix increment operator
10        int c = 5; // assign 5 to c
11        Console.WriteLine($"c before postincrement: {c}"); // displays 5
12        Console.WriteLine($"    postincrementing c: {c++}"); // displays 5
13        Console.WriteLine($" c after postincrement: {c}"); // displays 6
14
```

Fig. 5.16 | Prefix-increment and postfix-increment operators. (Part 1 of 2.)

```
15          Console.WriteLine(); // skip a line
16
17          // demonstrate prefix increment operator
18          c = 5; // assign 5 to c
19          Console.WriteLine($" c before preincrement: {c}"); // displays 5
20          Console.WriteLine($"     preincrementing c: {++c}"); // displays 6
21          Console.WriteLine($"  c after preincrement: {c}"); // displays 6
22       }
23    }
```

```
c before postincrement: 5
    postincrementing c: 5
 c after postincrement: 6

c before preincrement: 5
    preincrementing c: 6
 c after preincrement: 6
```

Fig. 5.16 | Prefix-increment and postfix-increment operators. (Part 2 of 2.)

Line 10 initializes the variable c to 5, and line 11 outputs c's initial value. Line 12 outputs the value of the expression c++. This expression postincrements the variable c, so c's *original* value (5) is output, then c's value is incremented (to 6). Thus, line 12 outputs c's initial value (5) again. Line 13 outputs c's new value (6) to prove that the variable's value was indeed incremented in line 12.

Line 18 resets c's value to 5, and line 19 outputs c's value. Line 20 outputs the value of the expression ++c. This expression preincrements c, so its value is incremented; then the *new* value (6) is output. Line 21 outputs c's value again to show that the value of c is still 6 after line 20 executes.

5.13.2 Simplifying Increment Statements

The arithmetic compound assignment operators and the increment and decrement operators can be used to simplify statements. For example, the three assignment statements in Fig. 5.13 (lines 24, 28 and 32)

```
passes = passes + 1;
failures = failures + 1;
studentCounter = studentCounter + 1;
```

can be written more concisely with compound assignment operators as

```
passes += 1;
failures += 1;
studentCounter += 1;
```

and even more concisely with prefix-increment operators as

```
++passes;
++failures;
++studentCounter;
```

or with postfix-increment operators as

```
passes++;
failures++;
studentCounter++;
```

When incrementing or decrementing a variable in a statement by itself, the prefix increment and postfix increment forms have the *same* effect, and the prefix decrement and postfix decrement forms have the *same* effect. It's only when a variable appears in the context of a larger expression that the prefix increment and postfix increment have *different* results (and similarly for the prefix decrement and postfix decrement).

 Common Programming Error 5.5

Attempting to use the increment or decrement operator on an expression other than one to which a value can be assigned is a syntax error. For example, writing ++(x + 1) is a syntax error, because (x + 1) is not an expression to which a value can be assigned.

5.13.3 Operator Precedence and Associativity

Figure 5.17 shows the precedence and associativity of the operators introduced to this point. The operators are shown from top to bottom in decreasing order of precedence. The second column describes the associativity of the operators at each level of precedence. The conditional operator (?:); the unary operators prefix increment (++), prefix decrement (--), plus (+) and minus (-); the cast operators; and the assignment operators =, +=, -=, *=, /= and %= associate from right to left. All the other operators in the operator precedence chart in Fig. 5.17 associate from left to right. The third column names the groups of operators.

Operators						Associativity	Type
.	new	++*(postfix)*	--*(postfix)*			left to right	highest precedence
++	--	+	-	*(type)*		right to left	unary prefix
*	/	%				left to right	multiplicative
+	-					left to right	additive
<	<=	>	>=			left to right	relational
==	!=					left to right	equality
?:						right to left	conditional
=	+=	-=	*=	/=	%=	right to left	assignment

Fig. 5.17 | Precedence and associativity of the operators discussed so far.

5.14 Simple Types

The table in Appendix B lists C#'s 13 simple types. Like its predecessor languages C and C++, C# requires *all* variables to have a type.

In C and C++, you frequently have to write separate versions of apps to support different computer platforms, because the simple types are *not* guaranteed to be identical from computer to computer. For example, an `int` value on one machine might be represented by 16 bits (2 bytes) of storage, while an `int` value on another machine might be represented by 32 bits (4 bytes) of storage. In C#, `int` values are always 32 bits (4 bytes). In fact, *all* C# numeric types have fixed sizes, as is shown in Appendix B.

Each type in Appendix B is listed with its size in bits (there are eight bits to a byte) and its range of values. Because the designers of C# want it to be maximally portable, they use internationally recognized standards for both character formats (Unicode; `http://unicode.org`) and floating-point numbers (IEEE 754; `http://grouper.ieee.org/groups/754/`).

Recall that variables of *simple types* declared *outside* of a method as instance variables of a class are automatically assigned default values unless explicitly initialized. Instance variables of types `char`, `byte`, `sbyte`, `short`, `ushort`, `int`, `uint`, `long`, `ulong`, `float`, `double`, and `decimal` are all given the value 0 by default. Instance variables of type `bool` are given the value `false` by default. Similarly, reference-type instance variables are initialized by default to the value `null`.

5.15 Wrap-Up

This chapter presented basic problem-solving techniques that you'll use in building classes and developing methods for these classes. We demonstrated how to construct an algorithm, then how to refine the algorithm through several phases of pseudocode development, resulting in C# code that can be executed as part of a method. The chapter showed how to use top-down, stepwise refinement to plan out the specific actions that a method must perform and the order in which the method must perform these actions.

Only three types of control statements—sequence, selection and iteration—are needed to develop any algorithm. Specifically, we demonstrated the `if` and `if...else` selection statements and the `while` iteration statement. These are some of the building blocks used to construct apps. We used control-statement stacking to compute the total and the average of a set of student grades with counter- and sentinel-controlled iteration, and we used control-statement nesting to analyze and make decisions based on a set of exam results. We introduced C#'s compound assignment, unary cast, conditional (`?:`), increment and decrement operators. Finally, we discussed the simple types. In Chapter 6, we continue our discussion of control statements, introducing the `for`, `do...while` and `switch` statements.

Summary

Section 5.2 Algorithms
- An algorithm is a procedure for solving a problem in terms of the actions to execute and the order in which these actions execute.
- Specifying the order in which statements (actions) execute in an app is called program control.

Section 5.3 Pseudocode
- Pseudocode is an informal language that helps you develop algorithms without having to worry about the strict details of C# language syntax.
- Carefully prepared pseudocode can easily be converted to a corresponding C# app.

Section 5.4 Control Structures
- There are three types of control structures—sequence, selection and iteration.

Section 5.4.1 Sequence Structure
- The sequence structure is built into C#. Unless directed otherwise, the computer executes C# statements one after the other in the order in which they're written.
- Activity diagrams are part of the UML. An activity diagram models the workflow of a portion of a software system.
- Activity diagrams are composed of special-purpose symbols, such as action-state symbols, diamonds and small circles. These symbols are connected by transition arrows, which represent the flow of the activity.
- Like pseudocode, activity diagrams help you develop and represent algorithms. Activity diagrams clearly show how control structures operate.
- Action-state symbols (rectangles with their left and right sides replaced with arcs curving outward) represent actions to perform.
- The arrows in an activity diagram represent transitions, which indicate the order in which the actions represented by the action states occur.
- The solid circle in an activity diagram represents the activity's initial state. The solid circle surrounded by a hollow circle represents the final state.
- Rectangles with the upper-right corners folded over are UML notes (like comments in C#)—explanatory remarks that describe the purpose of symbols in the diagram.

Section 5.4.2 Selection Statements
- C# has three types of selection statements: the `if` statement, the `if...else` statement and the `switch` statement.
- The `if` statement is called a single-selection statement because it selects or ignores a single action (or group of actions).
- The `if...else` statement is called a double-selection statement because it selects between two different actions (or groups of actions).
- The `switch` statement is called a multiple-selection statement because it selects among many different actions (or groups of actions).

Section 5.4.3 Iteration Statements
- C# provides four iteration statements: the `while`, `do...while`, `for` and `foreach` statements.
- The `while`, `for` and `foreach` statements perform the actions in their bodies zero or more times.
- The `do...while` statement performs the actions in its body one or more times.

Section 5.4.4 Summary of Control Statements
- Control statements may be connected in two ways: control-statement stacking and control-statement nesting.

Section 5.5 `if` Single-Selection Statement
- The `if` single-selection statement performs an indicated action (or group of actions) only when the condition is true; otherwise, the action is skipped.

- In an activity diagram, the diamond symbol indicates that a decision is to be made. The workflow will continue along a path determined by the symbol's associated guard conditions.
- When modelled by a UML activity diagram, all control statements contain initial states, transition arrows, action states and decision symbols.

Section 5.6 `if...else` Double-Selection Statement
- The `if...else` statement allows you to specify an action (or group of actions) to perform when the condition is true and a different action (or group of actions) when the condition is false.

Section 5.6.3 Blocks
- To include several statements in the body of an `if` (or the body of an `else` for an `if...else` statement), enclose the statements in braces (`{` and `}`).
- A set of statements contained within a pair of braces is called a block. A block can be placed anywhere in an app that a single statement can be placed.

Section 5.6.4 Conditional Operator (`?:`)
- C# provides the conditional operator (`?:`), which can be used in place of an `if...else` statement. The conditional expression evaluates to the second operand if the first operand evaluates to `true`, and evaluates to the third operand if the first operand evaluates to `false`.

Section 5.7 `Student` Class: Nested `if...else` Statements
- A read-only property contains only a `get` accessor.

Section 5.8 `while` Iteration Statement
- An iteration statement allows you to specify that an app should repeat an action while some condition remains true.
- The format for the `while` iteration statement is

```
while (condition)
{
    statement
}
```

- The UML represents both the merge symbol and the decision symbol as diamonds. The merge symbol joins two flows of activity into one.

Section 5.9.1 Pseudocode Algorithm with Counter-Controlled Iteration
- Counter-controlled iteration is a technique that uses a variable called a counter to control the number of times a set of statements will execute.

Section 5.9.2 Implementing Counter-Controlled Iteration
- C# requires local variables to be definitely assigned before their values are used.

Section 5.9.3 Integer Division and Truncation
- Dividing two integers results in integer division—any fractional part of the calculation is lost.

Section 5.10 Formulating Algorithms: Sentinel-Controlled Iteration
- Sentinel-controlled iteration is a technique that uses a special value called a sentinel value to indicate "end of data entry."
- Sentinel-controlled iteration is often called indefinite iteration, because the number of iterations is not known in advance.

Section 5.10.1 Top-Down, Stepwise Refinement: The Top and First Refinement

- Top-down, stepwise refinement is essential to the development of well-structured apps.

- Begin with a pseudocode representation of the top—a single statement that, in effect, is a complete representation of an app.

- The top rarely conveys sufficient detail from which to write an app. So in the first refinement, we refine the top into a series of smaller tasks and list these in the order in which they'll be performed. This refinement uses only tasks in sequence.

Section 5.10.2 Second Refinement

- In the second refinement, we commit to specific variables and logic.

Section 5.10.3 Implementing Sentinel-Controlled Iteration

- A number with a decimal point is called a real number or floating-point number (e.g., 7.33, 0.0975 or 1000.12345).

- Types `float` and `double` represent floating-point numbers.

- `double` variables can typically store numbers with larger magnitude and finer detail (i.e., more precision).

Section 5.10.6 Converting Between Simple Types Explicitly and Implicitly

- The unary cast operator (`double`) creates a *temporary* floating-point copy of its operand. Using a cast operator in this manner is called explicit conversion.

- To ensure that both operands of a binary operator are of the same type, C# performs promotion on selected operands.

Section 5.10.7 Formatting Floating-Point Numbers

- The format specifier F is used to format floating-point numbers—typically rounded to two digits to the right of the decimal point.

Section 5.12 Compound Assignment Operators

- C# provides several compound assignment operators for abbreviating assignment expressions, including +=, -=, *=, /= and %=.

Section 5.13 Increment and Decrement Operators

- C# provides the unary increment operator, ++, and the unary decrement operator, --, for adding 1 to or subtracting 1 from the value of a numeric variable.

- Incrementing (or decrementing) a variable with the prefix increment (or prefix decrement) operator increments (or decrements) the variable by 1 and uses the new variable value in the expression in which the variable appears. Incrementing (or decrementing) a variable with the postfix increment (or postfix decrement) operator increments (or decrements) the variable by 1 but uses the original variable value in the expression in which the variable appears.

Section 5.14 Simple Types

- C# requires all variables to have a type.

- Variables of simple types declared outside a method as fields of a class are automatically assigned default values. Instance variables of types char, byte, sbyte, short, ushort, int, uint, long, ulong, float, double, and decimal are all given the value 0 by default. Instance variables of type bool are given the value false by default. Reference-type instance variables are initialized by default to the value null.

Terminology

-- operator
?: operator
++ operator
action
action expression (in the UML)
action state (in the UML)
action-state symbol (in the UML)
activity (in the UML)
activity diagram (in the UML)
addition compound assignment operator (+=)
algorithm
arithmetic compound assignment operators:
    +=, -=, *=, /= and %=
block
body of a loop
bool simple type
cast operator, (*type*)
compound assignment operator
conditional operator (?:)
control statement
control-statement nesting
control-statement stacking
control structure
control variable
counter
counter-controlled iteration
dangling-else problem
decision
decision symbol (in the UML)
decrement operator (--)
definite assignment
definite iteration
diamond (in the UML)
dotted line
double-selection statement
dummy value
explicit conversion
false
fatal logic error
final state (in the UML)
flag value
goto statement
guard condition (in the UML)
if selection statement
if...else selection statement
implicit conversion
increment operator (++)
indefinite iteration
infinite loop

initial state (in the UML)
integer division
iteration
iteration statement
logic error
loop
loop-continuation condition
merge symbol (in the UML)
multiple-selection statement
multiplicative operators
nested control statements
nested if...else statements
nonfatal logic error
note (in the UML)
order in which actions should execute
postfix decrement operator
postfix increment operator
prefix decrement operator
prefix increment operator
procedure
program control
promotion
pseudocode
refinement
selection statement
sentinel-controlled iteration
sentinel value
sequence structure
sequential execution
signal value
simple types
single-entry/single-exit control structures
single-selection statement
small circle (in the UML)
solid circle (in the UML)
solid circle surrounded by a hollow circle
    (in the UML)
stacked control statements
structured programming
syntax error
ternary operator
top-down stepwise refinement
total
transfer of control
transition (in the UML)
transition arrow (in the UML)
true
truncate
unary cast operator

unary operator   workflow
while iteration statement

Self-Review Exercises

5.1 Fill in the blanks in each of the following statements:
a) All apps can be written in terms of three types of control structures: _____, _____ and _____.
b) The _____ statement is used to execute one action when a condition is true and another when that condition is false.
c) Repeating a set of instructions a specific number of times is called _____ iteration.
d) When it's not known in advance how many times a set of statements will be repeated, a(n) _____ value can be used to terminate the iteration.
e) The _____ structure is built into C#—by default, statements execute in the order in which they appear.
f) Instance variables of type int are given the value _____ by default.
g) C# requires all variables to have a(n) _____.
h) If the increment operator is _____ to a variable, the variable is incremented by 1 and its new value is used in the expression.

5.2 State whether each of the following is *true* or *false*. If *false*, explain why.
a) An algorithm is a procedure for solving a problem in terms of the actions to execute and the order in which these actions execute.
b) A set of statements contained within a pair of parentheses is called a block.
c) A selection statement specifies that an action is to be repeated while some condition remains true.
d) A nested control statement appears in the body of another control statement.
e) C# provides the arithmetic compound assignment operators +=, -=, *=, /= and %= for abbreviating assignment expressions.
f) Specifying the order in which statements (actions) execute in an app is called program control.
g) The unary cast operator (double) creates a temporary integer copy of its operand.
h) Instance variables of type bool are given the value true by default.
i) Pseudocode helps you think out an app before attempting to write it in a programming language.

5.3 Write four different C# statements that each add 1 to int variable x.

5.4 Write C# statements to accomplish each of the following tasks:
a) Assign the sum of x and y to z, and increment x by 1 with ++. Use only one statement and ensure that the original value of x is used in the statement.
b) Test whether variable count is greater than 10. If it is, display "Count is greater than 10".
c) Decrement the variable x by 1, then subtract it from the variable total. Use only one statement.
d) Calculate the remainder after q is divided by divisor, and assign the result to q. Write this statement in two different ways.

5.5 Write a C# statement to accomplish each of the following tasks:
a) Declare the int variable sum and initialize it to 0.
b) Declare the int variable x and initialize it to 1.
c) Add variable x to variable sum, and assign the result to variable sum.
d) Display "The sum is: ", followed by the value of variable sum.

5.6   Combine the statements that you wrote in Exercise 5.5 into a C# app that calculates and displays the sum of the integers from 1 to 10. Use a `while` statement to loop through the calculation and increment statements. The loop should terminate when the value of x becomes 11.

5.7   Determine the values of the variables in the following statement after it executes. Assume that when the statement begins executing, all variables are type `int` and have the value 5.

```
product *= x++;
```

5.8   Identify and correct the errors in each of the following sets of code:

a)
```
while (c <= 5)
{
    product *= c;
    ++c;
```

b)
```
if (gender == 1)
{
    Console.WriteLine("Woman");
}
else;
{
    Console.WriteLine("Man");
}
```

5.9   What is wrong with the following `while` statement?

```
while (z >= 0)
{
    sum += z;
}
```

Answers to Self-Review Exercises

5.1   a) sequence, selection, iteration. b) if...else. c) counter-controlled (or definite). d) sentinel, signal, flag or dummy. e) sequence. f) 0 (zero). g) type. h) prefixed.

5.2   a) True. b) False. A set of statements contained within a pair of braces ({ and }) is called a block. c) False. An iteration statement specifies that an action is to be repeated while some condition remains true. A selection statement determines whether an action is performed based on the truth or falsity of a condition. d) True. e) True. f) True. g) False. The unary cast operator (`double`) creates a temporary floating-point copy of its operand. h) False. Instance variables of type `bool` are given the value `false` by default. i) True.

5.3
```
x = x + 1;
x += 1;
++x;
x++;
```

5.4   The answers to Self-Review Exercise 5.4 are as follows:

a)
```
z = x++ + y;
```

b)
```
if (count > 10)
{
    Console.WriteLine("Count is greater than 10");
}
```

c)
```
total -= --x;
```

d)
```
q %= divisor;
q = q % divisor;
```

5.5   The answers to Self-Review Exercise 5.5 are as follows:
   a) `int sum = 0;`
   b) `int x = 1;`
   c) `sum += x;` or `sum = sum + x;`
   d) `Console.WriteLine($"The sum is: {sum}");`

5.6   The app is as follows:

```
 1   // Ex. 5.6: Calculate.cs
 2   // Calculate the sum of the integers from 1 to 10
 3   using System;
 4
 5   class Calculate
 6   {
 7      static void Main()
 8      {
 9         int sum = 0; // initialize sum to 0 for totaling
10         int x = 1; // initialize x to 1 for counting
11
12         while (x <= 10) // while x is less than or equal to 10
13         {
14            sum += x; // add x to sum
15            ++x; // increment x
16         } // end while
17
18         Console.WriteLine($"The sum is: {sum}");
19      }
20   }
```

```
The sum is: 55
```

5.7   product = 25, x = 6

5.8   The answers to Self-Review Exercise 5.8 are as follows:
   a) *Error:* The closing right brace of the `while` statement's body is missing.
       Correction: Add a closing right brace after the statement ++c;.
   b) *Error:* The semicolon after `else` results in a logic error. The second output statement
       will always execute.
       Correction: Remove the semicolon after `else`.

5.9   The value of the variable z is never changed in the `while` statement. Therefore, an infinite
loop occurs if the loop-continuation condition (z >= 0) is initially true. To prevent an infinite loop,
z must be decremented so that it eventually becomes less than 0.

Exercises

5.10   Compare and contrast the `if` single-selection statement and the `while` iteration statement.
How are these two statements similar? How are they different?

5.11   *(Integer Division)* Explain what happens when a C# app attempts to divide one integer by
another. What happens to the fractional part of the calculation? How can you avoid that outcome?

5.12   *(Combining Control Statements)* Describe the two ways in which control statements can be
combined.

5.13   *(Choosing Iteration Statements)* What type of iteration would be appropriate for calculating
the sum of the first 100 positive integers? What type of iteration would be appropriate for calculat-

ing the sum of an arbitrary number of positive integers? Briefly describe how each of these tasks could be performed.

5.14   *(Prefix vs. Postfix Increment Operators)* What is the difference between the prefix increment operator and the postfix increment operator?

5.15   *(Find the Error)* Identify and correct the errors in each of the following pieces of code. [*Note:* There may be more than one error in each piece of code.]

a)
```
if (age >= 65);
    {
        Console.WriteLine("Age greater than or equal to 65");
    }
    else
    {
        Console.WriteLine("Age is less than 65)";
    }
```

b)
```
int x = 1, total;
while (x <= 10)
    {
        total += x;
        ++x;
    }
```

c)
```
while (x <= 100)
    total += x;
    ++x;
```

d)
```
while (y > 0)
    {
        Console.WriteLine(y);
        ++y;
```

5.16   *(What Does This Program Do?)* What does the following app display?

```
 1   // Ex. 5.16: Mystery.cs
 2   using System;
 3
 4   class Mystery
 5   {
 6      static void Main()
 7      {
 8         int x = 1;
 9         int total = 0;
10
11         while (x <= 10)
12         {
13            int y = x * x;
14            Console.WriteLine(y);
15            total += y;
16            ++x;
17         }
18
19         Console.WriteLine($"Total is {total}");
20      }
21   }
```

For Exercises 5.17–5.20, perform each of the following steps:
   a) Read the problem statement.
   b) Formulate the algorithm using pseudocode and top-down, stepwise refinement.
   c) Write a C# app.
   d) Test, debug and execute the C# app.
   e) Process three complete sets of data.

5.17   *(Gas Mileage)* Drivers are concerned with the mileage their automobiles get. One driver has kept track of several tankfuls of gasoline by recording the miles driven and gallons used for each tankful. Develop a C# app that will input the miles driven and gallons used (both as integers) for each tankful. The app should calculate and display the miles per gallon obtained for each tankful and display the combined miles per gallon obtained for all tankfuls up to this point. All averaging calculations should produce floating-point results. Display the results rounded to the nearest hundredth. Use the Console class's ReadLine method and sentinel-controlled iteration to obtain the data from the user.

5.18   *(Credit-Limit Calculator)* Develop a C# app that will determine whether any of several department-store customers has exceeded the credit limit on a charge account. For each customer, the following facts are available:
   a) account number,
   b) balance at the beginning of the month,
   c) total of all items charged by the customer this month,
   d) total of all credits applied to the customer's account this month and
   e) allowed credit limit.

The app should input all these facts as integers, calculate the new balance (= *beginning balance* + *charges – credits*), display the new balance and determine whether the new balance exceeds the customer's credit limit. For those whose credit limit is exceeded, the app should display the message "Credit limit exceeded". Use sentinel-controlled iteration to obtain the data for each account.

5.19   *(Sales-Commission Calculator)* A large company pays its salespeople on a commission basis. The salespeople receive $200 per week plus 9% of their gross sales for that week. For example, a salesperson who sells $5,000 worth of merchandise in a week receives $200 plus 9% of $5,000, or a total of $650. You've been supplied with a list of the items sold by each salesperson. The values of these items are as follows:

Item	Value
1	239.99
2	129.75
3	99.95
4	350.89

Develop a C# app that inputs one salesperson's items sold for the last week, then calculates and displays that salesperson's earnings. There's no limit to the number of items that can be sold by a salesperson.

5.20   *(Salary Calculator)* Develop a C# app that will determine the gross pay for each of three employees. The company pays straight time for the first 40 hours worked by each employee and time-and-a-half for all hours worked in excess of 40 hours. You're given a list of the three employees of the company, the number of hours each employee worked last week and the hourly rate of each employee. Your app should input this information for each employee, then should determine and display the employee's gross pay. Use the Console class's ReadLine method to input the data.

5.21   *(Find the Largest Number)* The process of finding the maximum value (i.e., the largest of a group of values) is used frequently in computer applications. For example, an app that determines the winner of a sales contest would input the number of units sold by each salesperson. The salesperson who sells the most units wins the contest. Write pseudocode, then a C# app that inputs a series of 10 integers, then determines and displays the largest integer. Your app should use at least the following three variables:

    a) counter: A counter to count to 10 (i.e., to keep track of how many numbers have been input and to determine when all 10 numbers have been processed).

    b) number: The integer most recently input by the user.

    c) largest: The largest number found so far.

5.22 *(Tabular Output)* Write a C# app that uses looping to display the following table of values:

N	10*N	100*N	1000*N
1	10	100	1000
2	20	200	2000
3	30	300	3000
4	40	400	4000
5	50	500	5000

5.23 *(Find the Two Largest Numbers)* Using an approach similar to that for Exercise 5.21, find the *two* largest values of the 10 values entered. [*Note:* You may input each number only once.]

5.24 *(Validating User Input)* Modify the app in Fig. 5.13 to validate its inputs. For any input, if the value entered is other than 1 or 2, display the message "Invalid input," then keep looping until the user enters a correct value.

5.25 *(What Does This Program Do?)* What does the following app display?

```
 1   // Ex. 5.25: Mystery2.cs
 2   using System;
 3
 4   class Mystery2
 5   {
 6      static void Main()
 7      {
 8         int count = 1;
 9
10         while (count <= 10)
11         {
12            Console.WriteLine(count % 2 == 1 ? "****" : "++++++++");
13            ++count;
14         }
15      }
16   }
```

5.26 *(What Does This Program Do?)* What does the following app display?

```
 1   // Ex. 5.26: Mystery3.cs
 2   using System;
 3
 4   class Mystery3
 5   {
 6      static void Main()
 7      {
 8         int row = 10;
 9         int column;
10                                          (continued...)
```

```
11        while (row >= 1)
12        {
13            column = 1;
14
15            while (column <= 10)
16            {
17                Console.Write(row % 2 == 1 ? "<" : ">");
18                ++column;
19            }
20
21            --row;
22            Console.WriteLine();
23        }
24    }
25 }
```

5.27 *(Dangling-else Problem)* The C# compiler always associates an else with the immediately preceding if unless told to do otherwise by the placement of braces ({ and }). This behavior can lead to what is referred to as the dangling-else problem. The indentation of the nested statement

```
if (x > 5)
    if (y > 5)
        Console.WriteLine("x and y are > 5");
else
    Console.WriteLine("x is <= 5");
```

appears to indicate that if x is greater than 5, the nested if statement determines whether y is also greater than 5. If so, the statement outputs the string "x and y are > 5". Otherwise, it appears that if x is not greater than 5, the else part of the if...else outputs the string "x is <= 5". Beware! This nested if...else statement does *not* execute as it appears. The compiler actually interprets the statement as

```
if (x > 5)
    if (y > 5)
        Console.WriteLine("x and y are > 5");
    else
        Console.WriteLine("x is <= 5");
```

in which the body of the first if is a *nested* if...else. The outer if statement tests whether x is greater than 5. If so, execution continues by testing whether y is also greater than 5. If the second condition is true, the proper string—"x and y are > 5"—is displayed. However, if the second condition is false, the string "x is <= 5" is displayed, even though we know that x is greater than 5. Equally bad, if the outer if statement's condition is false, the inner if...else is skipped and nothing is displayed. For this exercise, add braces to the preceding code snippet to force the nested if...else statement to execute as it was originally intended.

5.28 *(Another Dangling-else Problem)* Based on the dangling-else discussion in Exercise 5.27, state the output for each of the following code snippets when x is 9 and y is 11 and when x is 11 and y is 9. We eliminated the indentation from the following code to make the problem more challenging. [*Hint:* Apply indentation conventions you've learned.]

a)
```
if (x < 10)
if (y > 10)
Console.WriteLine("*****");
else
Console.WriteLine("#####");
Console.WriteLine("$$$$$");
```

```
b)  if (x < 10)
    {
    if (y > 10)
    Console.WriteLine("******");
    }
    else
    {
    Console.WriteLine("#####");
    Console.WriteLine("$$$$$");
    }
```

5.29   *(Another Dangling-else Problem)* Based on the dangling-else discussion in Exercise 5.27, modify the given code to produce the output shown in each part of the problem. Use proper indentation techniques. You must not make any additional changes other than inserting braces. We eliminated the indentation from the following code to make the problem more challenging. [*Note:* It's possible that no modification is necessary.]

```
if (y == 8)
if (x == 5)
Console.WriteLine("@@@@@");
else
Console.WriteLine("#####");
Console.WriteLine("$$$$$");
Console.WriteLine("&&&&&");
```

a) Assuming that x = 5 and y = 8, the following output is produced:

```
@@@@@
$$$$$
&&&&&
```

b) Assuming that x = 5 and y = 8, the following output is produced:

```
@@@@@
```

c) Assuming that x = 5 and y = 8, the following output is produced:

```
@@@@@
&&&&&
```

d) Assuming that x = 5 and y = 7, the following output is produced.

```
#####
$$$$$
&&&&&
```

5.30   *(Square of Asterisks)* Write an app that prompts the user to enter the size of the side of a square, then displays a hollow square of that size made of asterisks. Your app should work for squares of all side lengths between 1 and 20. If the user enters a number less than 1 or greater than 20, your app should display a square of size 1 or 20, respectively.

5.31   *(Palindromes)* A palindrome is a sequence of characters that reads the same backward as forward. For example, each of the following five-digit integers is a palindrome: 12321, 55555, 45554 and 11611. Write an app that reads in a five-digit integer and determines whether it's a palindrome. If the number is not five digits long, display an error message and allow the user to enter a new value. [*Hint:* Use the remainder and division operators to pick off the number's digits one at a time, from right to left.]

5.32   *(Displaying the Decimal Equivalent of a Binary Number)* Write an app that inputs an integer containing only 0s and 1s (i.e., a binary integer) and displays its decimal equivalent. [*Hint:* Picking the digits off a binary number is similar to picking the digits off a decimal number, which you did in Exercise 5.31. In the decimal number system, the rightmost digit has a positional value of 1 and the next digit to the left has a positional value of 10, then 100, then 1000 and so on. The decimal number 234 can be interpreted as 4 * 1 + 3 * 10 + 2 * 100. In the binary number system, the rightmost digit has a positional value of 1, the next digit to the left has a positional value of 2, then 4, then 8 and so on. The decimal equivalent of binary 1101 is 1 * 1 + 0 * 2 + 1 * 4 + 1 * 8, or 1 + 0 + 4 + 8, or 13.]

5.33 *(Checkerboard Pattern of Asterisks)* Write an app that uses only the output statements

```
Console.Write("* ");
Console.Write(" ");
Console.WriteLine();
```

to display the checkerboard pattern that follows. A `Console.WriteLine` method call with no arguments outputs a single newline character. [*Hint:* Iteration statements are required.]

```
* * * * * * * *
 * * * * * * * *
* * * * * * * *
 * * * * * * * *
* * * * * * * *
 * * * * * * * *
* * * * * * * *
 * * * * * * * *
```

5.34 *(Multiples of 2)* Write an app that keeps displaying in the console window the powers of the integer 2—namely, 2, 4, 8, 16, 32, 64 and so on. Loop 40 times. What happens when you run this app?

5.35 *(What's Wrong with This Code?)* What is wrong with the following statement? Provide the correct statement to add 1 to the sum of x and y.

```
Console.WriteLine(++(x + y));
```

5.36 *(Sides of a Triangle)* Write an app that reads three nonzero values entered by the user, then determines and displays whether they could represent the sides of a triangle.

5.37 *(Sides of a Right Triangle)* Write an app that reads three nonzero integers, then determines and displays whether they could represent the sides of a right triangle.

5.38 *(Factorials)* The factorial of a nonnegative integer n is written as $n!$ (pronounced "n factorial") and is defined as follows:

$$n! = n \cdot (n-1) \cdot (n-2) \cdot \ldots \cdot 1 \quad \text{(for values of } n \text{ greater than or equal to 1)}$$

and

$$n! = 1 \quad \text{(for } n = 0\text{)}$$

For example, $5! = 5 \cdot 4 \cdot 3 \cdot 2 \cdot 1$, which is 120. Write an app that reads a nonnegative integer and computes and displays its factorial.

5.39 *(Infinite Series: Mathematical Constant e)* Write an app that estimates the value of the mathematical constant e by using the formula

$$e = 1 + \frac{1}{1!} + \frac{1}{2!} + \frac{1}{3!} + \ldots$$

The predefined constant `Math.E` (class `Math` is in the `System` namespace) provides a good approximation of e. Use the `WriteLine` method to output both your estimated value of e and `Math.E` for comparison.

5.40   *(Infinite Series: e^x)* Write an app that computes the value of e^x by using the formula

$$e^x = 1 + \frac{x}{1!} + \frac{x^2}{2!} + \frac{x^3}{3!} + \dots$$

Compare the result of your calculation to the return value of the method call

```
Math.Pow(Math.E, x)
```

[*Note:* The predefined method `Math.Pow` takes two arguments and raises the first argument to the power of the second. We discuss `Math.Pow` in Section 6.6.]

Making-a-Difference Exercises

5.41   *(World Population Growth)* World population has grown considerably over the centuries. Continued growth could eventually challenge the limits of breathable air, drinkable water, arable cropland and other limited resources. There's evidence that growth has been slowing in recent years and that world population could peak some time this century, then start to decline.

For this exercise, research world-population-growth issues online. *Be sure to investigate various viewpoints.* Get estimates for the current world population and its growth rate (the percentage by which it is likely to increase this year). Write a program that calculates world population growth each year for the next 75 years, *using the simplifying assumption that the current growth rate will stay constant.* When displaying the results, the first column should display the year from year 1 to year 75. The second column should display the anticipated world population at the end of that year. The third column should display the numerical increase in the world population that would occur that year. Using your results, determine the year in which the population would be double what it is today, if this year's growth rate were to persist. [*Hint:* Use `double` variables because `int` variables can store values only up to approximately two billion. Display the `double` values using the format `F0`, which displays the values rounded to the closest whole number—0 means no digits to the right of the decimal point.]

5.42   *(Enforcing Privacy with Cryptography)* The explosive growth of Internet communications and data storage on Internet-connected computers has greatly increased privacy concerns. The field of cryptography is concerned with coding data to make it difficult (and hopefully—with the most advanced schemes—impossible) for unauthorized users to read. In this exercise you'll investigate a simple scheme for encrypting and decrypting data. A company that wants to send data over the Internet has asked you to write a program that will encrypt it so that it may be transmitted more securely. All the data is transmitted as four-digit integers. Your app should read a four-digit integer entered by the user and encrypt it as follows: Replace each digit with the result of adding 7 to the digit and getting the remainder after dividing the new value by 10. Then swap the first digit with the third, and swap the second digit with the fourth. Then display the encrypted integer. Write a separate app that inputs an encrypted four-digit integer and decrypts it (by reversing the encryption scheme) to form the original number. Use the format specifier `D4` to display the encrypted value in case the number starts with a `0`. The format specifier `D` is used to format integer values, and `D4` indicates that the value should be formatted with a minimum of four digit positions, possibly with leading zeros.

6

Control Statements: Part 2

6.1 Introduction

This chapter continues our presentation of structured-programming theory and principles by introducing all but one of C#'s remaining control statements. We demonstrate C#'s for, do...while and switch statements. Through examples using while and for, we explore the essentials of counter-controlled iteration. We use a switch statement to count the number of A, B, C, D and F grade equivalents in a set of numeric grades entered by the user. We introduce the break and continue program-control statements. We discuss C#'s logical operators, which enable you to combine simple conditions in control statements. Finally, we summarize C#'s control statements and the proven problem-solving techniques presented in this chapter and Chapter 5.

6.2 Essentials of Counter-Controlled Iteration

This section uses the while iteration statement introduced in Chapter 5 to formalize the elements of counter-controlled iteration:

1. a control variable (or loop counter),

2. the control variable's initial value,

3. the control variable's increment that's applied during each iteration of the loop,

4. the loop-continuation condition that determines if looping should continue.

Consider the application of Fig. 6.1, which uses a loop to display the numbers from 1 through 10.

```csharp
1   // Fig. 6.1: WhileCounter.cs
2   // Counter-controlled iteration with the while iteration statement.
3   using System;
4
5   class WhileCounter
6   {
7      static void Main()
8      {
9         int counter = 1; // declare and initialize control variable
10
11        while (counter <= 10) // loop-continuation condition
12        {
13           Console.Write($"{counter}   ");
14           ++counter; // increment control variable
15        }
16
17        Console.WriteLine();
18     }
19  }
```

```
1  2  3  4  5  6  7  8  9  10
```

Fig. 6.1 | Counter-controlled iteration with the `while` iteration statement.

In Fig. 6.1, the elements of counter-controlled iteration are defined in lines 9, 11 and 14. Line 9 declares the control variable (`counter`) as an `int`, reserves space for it in memory and sets its initial value to 1.

Line 13 displays control variable `counter`'s value per iteration of the loop. Line 14 increments the control variable by 1 for each iteration of the loop. The `while`'s loop-continuation condition (line 11) tests whether the value of the control variable is less than or equal to 10 (the final value for which the condition is `true`). The program performs the `while`'s body even when the control variable is 10. The loop terminates when the control variable exceeds 10 (that is, when `counter` becomes 11).

Error-Prevention Tip 6.1

Floating-point values are approximate, so controlling counting loops with floating-point variables of types `float` or `double` can result in imprecise counter values and inaccurate tests for termination. Use integer values to control counting loops.

6.3 for Iteration Statement

Section 6.2 presented the essentials of counter-controlled iteration. The while statement can be used to implement any counter-controlled loop. C# also provides the **for iteration statement**, which specifies the elements of counter-controlled iteration in a single line of code. Typically, for statements are used for counter-controlled iteration, and while statements for sentinel-controlled iteration. However, while and for can each be used for either iteration type. Figure 6.2 reimplements the app in Fig. 6.1 using the for statement.

```csharp
1  // Fig. 6.2: ForCounter.cs
2  // Counter-controlled iteration with the for iteration statement.
3  using System;
4
5  class ForCounter
6  {
7     static void Main()
8     {
9        // for statement header includes initialization,
10       // loop-continuation condition and increment
11       for (int counter = 1; counter <= 10; ++counter)
12       {
13          Console.Write($"{counter}   ");
14       }
15
16       Console.WriteLine();
17    }
18 }
```

```
1  2  3  4  5  6  7  8  9  10
```

Fig. 6.2 | Counter-controlled iteration with the for iteration statement.

When the for statement (lines 11–14) begins executing, the control variable counter is *declared* and *initialized* to 1. (Recall from Section 6.2 that the first two elements of counter-controlled iteration are the *control variable* and its *initial value*.) Next, the program checks the *loop-continuation condition*, counter <= 10, which is between the two required semicolons. Because counter's initial value is 1, the condition is true. So, the body statement (line 13) displays control variable counter's value (1). After executing the loop's body, the program increments counter in the expression ++counter, which appears to the right of the second semicolon. Then the program performs the loop-continuation test again to determine whether to continue with the loop's next iteration. At this point, counter's value is 2, so the condition is still true (the *final value* of 10 is not exceeded)— thus, the program executes the body statement again. This process continues until the numbers 1–10 have been displayed and the counter's value becomes 11. At this point, the loop-continuation test fails, iteration terminates and the program continues executing at the first statement after the for (line 16).

Figure 6.2 uses (in line 11) the loop-continuation condition counter <= 10. If you incorrectly specified counter < 10 as the condition, the loop would iterate only nine times—a common logic error called an off-by-one error.

Common Programming Error 6.1
Using an incorrect relational operator or an incorrect final value of a loop counter in the loop-continuation condition of an iteration statement can cause an off-by-one error.

Error-Prevention Tip 6.2
Using the final value and operator <= in a loop's condition helps avoid off-by-one errors. For a loop that outputs 1 to 10, the loop-continuation condition should be counter <= 10 *rather than* counter < 10 *(which causes an off-by-one error) or* counter < 11 *(which is correct). Many programmers prefer zero-based counting in which, to count 10 times, you'd initialize* counter *to zero and use the loop-continuation test* counter < 10.

6.3.1 A Closer Look at the for Statement's Header

Figure 6.3 takes a closer look at the for statement in Fig. 6.2. The first line—including the keyword for and everything in parentheses after for (line 11 in Fig. 6.2)—is sometimes called the for statement header. The for header "does it all"—it specifies each item needed for counter-controlled iteration with a control variable.

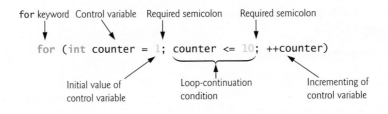

Fig. 6.3 | for statement header components.

6.3.2 General Format of a for Statement

The general format of the for statement is

```
for (initialization; loopContinuationCondition; increment)
{
    statement
}
```

where the *initialization* expression names the loop's control variable and provides its initial value, the *loopContinuationCondition* determines whether looping should continue and the *increment* modifies the control variable's value (whether an increment or decrement), so that the loop-continuation condition eventually becomes false. The two semicolons in the for header are required. We don't include a semicolon after *statement*, because the semicolon is already assumed to be included in the notion of a *statement*.

6.3.3 Scope of a for Statement's Control Variable

If the *initialization* expression in the for header declares the control variable (i.e., the control variable's type is specified before the variable name, as in Fig. 6.2), the control variable can be used *only* in that for statement—it will not exist outside it. This restricted use of the name of the control variable is known as the variable's scope. The scope of a variable defines where it can be used in an app. For example, a local variable can be used only in the method that declares the variable and *only* from the point of declaration through the end of the block in which the variable has been declared. Scope is discussed in detail in Chapter 7, Methods: A Deeper Look.

Common Programming Error 6.2

When a for statement's control variable is declared in the initialization section of a for's header, using the control variable after the for's body is a compilation error.

6.3.4 Expressions in a for Statement's Header Are Optional

All three expressions in a for header are *optional*. If the *loopContinuationCondition* is omitted, C# assumes that it's *always true*, thus creating an *infinite loop*. You can omit the *initialization* expression if the app initializes the control variable *before* the loop—in this case, the scope of the control variable will *not* be limited to the loop. You can omit the *increment* expression if the app calculates the increment with statements in the loop's body or if no increment is needed. The increment expression in a for acts as if it were a standalone statement at the end of the for's body. Therefore, the expressions

```
counter = counter + 1
counter += 1
++counter
counter++
```

are equivalent increment expressions in a for statement. Many programmers prefer counter++ because it's concise and because a for loop evaluates its increment expression after its body executes—so the postfix increment form *seems* more natural. In this case, the variable being incremented does not appear in a larger expression, so the prefix and postfix increment operators have the *same* effect.

Performance Tip 6.1

There's a slight performance advantage to using the prefix increment operator, but if you choose the postfix increment operator because it seems more natural (as in a for header), optimizing compilers are likely to generate code that uses the more efficient form anyway.

Error-Prevention Tip 6.3

Infinite loops occur when the loop-continuation condition in an iteration statement never becomes false. To prevent this situation in a counter-controlled loop, ensure that the control variable is incremented (or decremented) during each iteration of the loop. In a sentinel-controlled loop, ensure that the sentinel value is eventually entered.

6.3.5 Placing Arithmetic Expressions in a for Statement's Header

The initialization, loop-continuation condition and increment portions of a for statement can contain arithmetic expressions. For example, assume that x = 2 and y = 10; if x and y are not modified in the body of the loop, then the statement

```
for (int j = x; j <= 4 * x * y; j += y / x)
```

is equivalent to the statement

```
for (int j = 2; j <= 80; j += 5)
```

The increment of a for statement may also be *negative*, in which case it's actually a *decrement*, and the loop counts downward.

6.3.6 Using a for Statement's Control Variable in the Statement's Body

Apps frequently display the control variable value or use it in calculations in the loop body, but this use is not required. The control variable is commonly used to control iteration without being mentioned in the body of the for.

Error-Prevention Tip 6.4

Although the value of the control variable can be changed in the body of a for loop, avoid doing so, because this practice can lead to subtle errors. If a program must modify the control variable's value in the loop's body, use while rather than for.

6.3.7 UML Activity Diagram for the for Statement

Figure 6.4 shows the activity diagram of the for statement in Fig. 6.2. The diagram makes it clear that initialization occurs only once—*before* the loop-continuation test is evaluated the first time—and that incrementing occurs *each* time through the loop *after* the body statement executes.

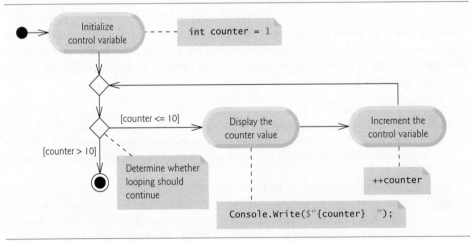

Fig. 6.4 | UML activity diagram for the for statement in Fig. 6.2.

6.4 Examples Using the for Statement

The following examples show techniques for varying the control variable in a for statement. In each case, we write only the appropriate for header. Note the change in the relational operator for loops that decrement the control variable.

a) Vary the control variable from 1 to 100 in increments of 1.

```
for (int i = 1; i <= 100; ++i)
```

b) Vary the control variable from 100 to 1 in decrements of 1.

```
for (int i = 100; i >= 1; --i)
```

c) Vary the control variable from 7 to 77 in increments of 7.

```
for (int i = 7; i <= 77; i += 7)
```

d) Vary the control variable from 20 to 2 in decrements of 2.

```
for (int i = 20; i >= 2; i -= 2)
```

e) Vary the control variable over the sequence 2, 5, 8, 11, 14, 17, 20.

```
for (int i = 2; i <= 20; i += 3)
```

f) Vary the control variable over the sequence 99, 88, 77, 66, 55, 44, 33, 22, 11, 0.

```
for (int i = 99; i >= 0; i -= 11)
```

Common Programming Error 6.3

Using an incorrect relational operator in the loop-continuation condition of a loop that counts downward (e.g., using i <= 1 instead of i >= 1 in a loop counting down to 1) is usually a logic error.

Common Programming Error 6.4

Do not use equality operators (!= or ==) in a loop-continuation condition if the loop's control variable increments or decrements by more than 1. For example, consider the for *statement header* for (int counter = 1; counter != 10; counter += 2). *The loop-continuation test* counter != 10 *never becomes false (resulting in an* infinite loop*) because* counter *increments by 2 after each iteration (and never becomes 10).*

6.5 App: Summing Even Integers

We now consider a sample app that demonstrates a simple use of for. The app in Fig. 6.5 uses a for statement to sum the even integers from 2 to 20 and store the result in an int variable called total. Each iteration of the loop (lines 12–15) adds control variable number's value to variable total.

```
1   // Fig. 6.5: Sum.cs
2   // Summing integers with the for statement.
3   using System;
4
5   class Sum
6   {
7      static void Main()
8      {
9         int total = 0; // initialize total
```

Fig. 6.5 | Summing integers with the for statement. (Part 1 of 2.)

```
10
11          // total even integers from 2 through 20
12          for (int number = 2; number <= 20; number += 2)
13          {
14              total += number;
15          }
16
17          Console.WriteLine($"Sum is {total}"); // display results
18      }
19  }
```

```
Sum is 110
```

Fig. 6.5 | Summing integers with the for statement. (Part 2 of 2.)

The *initialization* and *increment* expressions can be comma-separated lists that enable you to use multiple initialization expressions or multiple increment expressions. For example, although this is discouraged, you could merge the for's body statement (line 14) into the increment portion of the for header by using a comma as follows:

```
total += number, number += 2
```

6.6 App: Compound-Interest Calculations

The next app uses the for statement to compute compound interest. Consider the following problem:

> *A person invests $1,000 in a savings account yielding 5% interest. Assuming that all the interest is left on deposit, calculate and print the amount of money in the account at the end of each year for 10 years. Use the following formula to determine the amounts:*
>
> $$a = p \, (1 + r)^n$$
>
> *where*
>
> *p* is the original amount invested (i.e., the principal)
> *r* is the annual interest rate (e.g., use 0.05 for 5%)
> *n* is the number of years
> *a* is the amount on deposit at the end of the *n*th year.

The solution to this problem (Fig. 6.6) involves a loop that performs the indicated calculation for each of the 10 years the money remains on deposit.

```
1  // Fig. 6.6: Interest.cs
2  // Compound-interest calculations with for.
3  using System;
4
5  class Interest
6  {
```

Fig. 6.6 | Compound-interest calculations with for. (Part 1 of 2.)

```
 7      static void Main()
 8      {
 9          decimal principal = 1000; // initial amount before interest
10          double rate = 0.05; // interest rate
11
12          // display headers
13          Console.WriteLine("Year    Amount on deposit");
14
15          // calculate amount on deposit for each of ten years
16          for (int year = 1; year <= 10; ++year)
17          {
18              // calculate new amount for specified year
19              decimal amount = principal *
20                  ((decimal) Math.Pow(1.0 + rate, year));
21
22              // display the year and the amount
23              Console.WriteLine($"{year,4}{amount,20:C}");
24          }
25      }
26  }
```

```
Year    Amount on deposit
   1        $1,050.00
   2        $1,102.50
   3        $1,157.63
   4        $1,215.51
   5        $1,276.28
   6        $1,340.10
   7        $1,407.10
   8        $1,477.46
   9        $1,551.33
  10        $1,628.89
```

Fig. 6.6 | Compound-interest calculations with `for`. (Part 2 of 2.)

Lines 9 and 19 declare `decimal` variables `principal` and `amount`, and line 10 declares `double` variable `rate`. Lines 9–10 also initialize `principal` to 1000 (i.e., $1,000.00) and `rate` to 0.05. C# treats numeric literals like 0.05 as type `double`. Similarly, C# treats whole-number literals like 7 and 1000 as type `int`—unlike `double` values, `int` values *can* be assigned to `decimal` variables. When `principal` is initialized to 1000, the `int` value 1000 is *promoted* to type `decimal` *implicitly*—no cast is required. Line 13 outputs the headers for the app's two columns of output. The first column displays the year, and the second displays the amount on deposit at the end of that year.

6.6.1 Performing the Interest Calculations with Math Method pow

Classes provide methods that perform common tasks on objects. Most methods must be called on a specific object. For example, to deposit money into bank accounts in Fig. 4.12, we called method `Deposit` on the `Account` objects `account1` and `account2`. Many classes also provide methods to perform common tasks that do not require specific objects—they *must* be called using a class name. Such methods are called `static` methods. You've used several `static` methods of class `Console`—methods `Write`, `WriteLine` and `ReadLine`. You call a static method by specifying the class name followed by the member-access operator (.) and the method name, as in

ClassName.MethodName(arguments)

C# does not include an exponentiation operator, so we use class Math's static method Pow to perform the compound-interest calculation. The expression

```
Math.Pow(x, y)
```

calculates the value of *x* raised to the *y*th power. The method receives two double arguments and returns a double value. Lines 19–20 in Fig. 6.6 perform the calculation

$$a = p \, (1 + r)^n$$

from the problem statement, where *a* is the amount, *p* is the principal, *r* is the rate and *n* is the year. In this calculation, we need to multiply the decimal value principal by a double value (the value returned by the call to Math.Pow). C# will not *implicitly* convert double to a decimal type, or vice versa, because of the *possible loss of information* in either conversion, so line 20 contains a (decimal) cast operator that *explicitly* converts Math.Pow's double return value to a decimal.

The for statement's body contains the calculation 1.0 + rate, which appears as an argument to the Math.Pow method. In fact, this calculation produces the same result each time through the loop, so repeating the calculation in every iteration of the loop is wasteful.

 Performance Tip 6.2
In loops, avoid calculations for which the result never changes—such calculations should typically be placed before the loop. Optimizing compilers will typically do this for you.

6.6.2 Formatting with Field Widths and Alignment

After each calculation, line 23

```
Console.WriteLine($"{year,4}{amount,20:C}");
```

displays the year and the amount on deposit at the end of that year. The interpolation expression

```
{year,4}
```

formats the year. The integer 4 after the comma indicates that the value output should be displayed with a field width of 4—that is, WriteLine displays the value with at least four character positions. If the value to be output is *fewer than* four character positions wide (one or two characters in this example), the value is right-aligned in the field by default—in this case the value is preceded by two or three spaces, depending on the year value. If the value to be output were *more* than four character positions wide, the field width would be *extended to the right* to accommodate the entire value—this would push the amount column to the right, upsetting the neat columns of our tabular output. Similarly, the interpolation expression

```
{amount,20:C}
```

formats the amount as currency (C) right-aligned in a field of at least 20 characters. To left align a value, simply use a *negative* field width.

6.6.3 Caution: Do Not Use `float` or `double` for Monetary Amounts

Section 4.9 introduced the simple type `decimal` for precise monetary representation and calculations. You might be tempted to use the floating-point types `float` or `double` for such calculations. However, for certain values types `float` or `double` suffer from what we call representational error. For example, floating-point numbers often arise as a result of calculations—when we divide 10 by 3, the result is 3.3333333…, with the sequence of 3s repeating infinitely. The computer allocates only a *fixed* amount of space to hold such a value, so clearly the stored floating-point value can be only an *approximation*.

Common Programming Error 6.5
Using floating-point numbers in a manner that assumes they're represented exactly (e.g., using them in comparisons for equality) can lead to incorrect results. Floating-point numbers are represented only approximately.

Error-Prevention Tip 6.5
Do not use variables of type `double` (or `float`) to perform precise monetary calculations—use type `decimal` instead. The imprecision of floating-point numbers can cause errors that will result in incorrect monetary values.

Applications of Floating-Point Numbers
Floating-point numbers have numerous applications, especially for measured values. For example, when we speak of a "normal" body temperature of 98.6 degrees Fahrenheit, we need not be precise to a large number of digits. When we read the temperature on a thermometer as 98.6, it may actually be 98.5999473210643. Calling this number simply 98.6 is fine for most applications involving body temperatures. Similarly, we used type `double` to perform class-average calculations in Chapter 5. Due to the imprecise nature of floating-point numbers, type `double` is preferred over type `float`, because `double` variables can represent floating-point numbers more precisely. For this reason, we use type `double` throughout the book, unless we're manipulating monetary amounts, in which case we use type `decimal`.

A Warning About Displaying Rounded Values
Two `double` dollar amounts stored in the machine could be 14.234 (which would normally be rounded to 14.23 for display purposes) and 18.673 (which would normally be rounded to 18.67 for display purposes). When these amounts are added, they produce the internal sum 32.907, which would normally be rounded to 32.91 for display purposes. Thus, your output could appear as

```
    14.23
  + 18.67
  -------
    32.91
```

but a person adding the individual numbers as displayed would expect the sum to be 32.90. You've been warned! For people who work with programming languages that do not support a type like decimal for precise monetary calculations, Exercise 6.18 explores the use of integers to perform such calculations.

6.7 do...while Iteration Statement

The do...while iteration statement is similar to the while statement. In the while, the app tests the loop-continuation condition at the beginning of the loop, *before* executing the loop's body. If the condition is false, the body *never* executes. The do...while statement tests the loop-continuation condition *after* executing the loop's body; therefore, the body always executes *at least once*. When a do...while statement terminates, execution continues with the next statement in sequence. Figure 6.7 uses a do...while (lines 11–15) to output the numbers 1–10.

```
1   // Fig. 6.7: DoWhileTest.cs
2   // do...while iteration statement.
3   using System;
4
5   class DoWhileTest
6   {
7      static void Main()
8      {
9         int counter = 1; // initialize counter
10
11         do
12         {
13            Console.Write($"{counter}   ");
14            ++counter;
15         } while (counter <= 10); // required semicolon
16
17         Console.WriteLine();
18      }
19   }
```

```
1  2  3  4  5  6  7  8  9  10
```

Fig. 6.7 | do...while iteration statement.

Line 9 declares and initializes control variable counter. Upon entering the do...while statement, line 13 outputs counter's value, and line 14 increments counter. Then the app evaluates the loop-continuation test at the *bottom* of the loop (line 15). If the condition is true, the loop continues from the first body statement (line 13). If the condition is false, the loop terminates, and the app continues with the next statement after the loop (line 17).

*UML Activity Diagram for the **do...while** Iteration Statement*
Figure 6.8 contains the UML activity diagram for the do...while statement. This diagram makes it clear that the loop-continuation condition is not evaluated until *after* the loop performs the action state *at least once*. Compare this activity diagram with that of the while statement (Fig. 5.7).

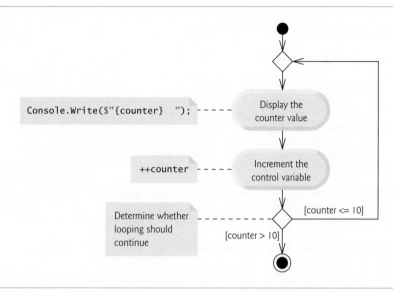

Fig. 6.8 | do...while iteration statement UML activity diagram.

6.8 switch Multiple-Selection Statement

We discussed the if and if...else selection statements in Chapter 5. C# provides the switch multiple-selection statement to perform different actions based on the possible values of an expression, known as the switch expression. Each action is associated with one or more of the switch expression's possible values. These are specified as constant integral expressions or a constant string expressions:

- A constant integral expression is any expression involving character and integer constants that evaluates to an integer value—i.e., values of type sbyte, byte, short, ushort, int, uint, long, ulong and char, or a constant from an enum type (enum is discussed in Section 7.9).

- A constant string expression is any expression composed of string literals or const string variables that always results in the same string.

6.8.1 Using a switch Statement to Count A, B, C, D and F Grades.

Figure 6.9 calculates the class average of a set of numeric grades entered by the user, and uses a switch statement to determine whether each grade is the equivalent of an A, B, C, D or F and to increment the appropriate grade counter. The program also displays a summary of the number of students who received each grade.

```
1   // Fig. 6.9: LetterGrades.cs
2   // Using a switch statement to count letter grades.
3   using System;
```

Fig. 6.9 | Using a switch statement to count letter grades. (Part 1 of 3.)

```
4
5    class LetterGrades
6    {
7        static void Main()
8        {
9            int total = 0; // sum of grades
10           int gradeCounter = 0; // number of grades entered
11           int aCount = 0; // count of A grades
12           int bCount = 0; // count of B grades
13           int cCount = 0; // count of C grades
14           int dCount = 0; // count of D grades
15           int fCount = 0; // count of F grades
16
17           Console.WriteLine("Enter the integer grades in the range 0-100.");
18           Console.WriteLine(
19              "Type <Ctrl> z and press Enter to terminate input:");
20
21           string input = Console.ReadLine(); // read user input
22
23           // loop until user enters the end-of-file indicator (<Ctrl> z)
24           while (input != null)
25           {
26               int grade = int.Parse(input); // read grade off user input
27               total += grade; // add grade to total
28               ++gradeCounter; // increment number of grades
29
30               // determine which grade was entered
31               switch (grade / 10)
32               {
33                   case 9: // grade was in the 90s
34                   case 10: // grade was 100
35                       ++aCount; // increment aCount
36                       break; // necessary to exit switch
37                   case 8: // grade was between 80 and 89
38                       ++bCount; // increment bCount
39                       break; // exit switch
40                   case 7: // grade was between 70 and 79
41                       ++cCount; // increment cCount
42                       break; // exit switch
43                   case 6: // grade was between 60 and 69
44                       ++dCount; // increment dCount
45                       break; // exit switch
46                   default: // grade was less than 60
47                       ++fCount; // increment fCount
48                       break; // exit switch
49               }
50
51               input = Console.ReadLine(); // read user input
52           }
53
54           Console.WriteLine("\nGrade Report:");
55
```

Fig. 6.9 | Using a switch statement to count letter grades. (Part 2 of 3.)

```
56              // if user entered at least one grade...
57              if (gradeCounter != 0)
58              {
59                  // calculate average of all grades entered
60                  double average = (double) total / gradeCounter;
61
62                  // output summary of results
63                  Console.WriteLine(
64                      $"Total of the {gradeCounter} grades entered is {total}");
65                  Console.WriteLine($"Class average is {average:F}");
66                  Console.WriteLine("Number of students who received each grade:");
67                  Console.WriteLine($"A: {aCount}"); // display number of A grades
68                  Console.WriteLine($"B: {bCount}"); // display number of B grades
69                  Console.WriteLine($"C: {cCount}"); // display number of C grades
70                  Console.WriteLine($"D: {dCount}"); // display number of D grades
71                  Console.WriteLine($"F: {fCount}"); // display number of F grades
72              }
73              else // no grades were entered, so output appropriate message
74              {
75                  Console.WriteLine("No grades were entered");
76              }
77          }
78      }
```

```
Enter the integer grades in the range 0-100.
Type <Ctrl> z and press Enter to terminate input:
99
92
45
57
63
71
76
85
90
100
^Z

Grade Report:
Total of the 10 grades entered is 778
Class average is 77.80
Number of students who received each grade:
A: 4
B: 1
C: 2
D: 1
F: 2
```

Fig. 6.9 | Using a switch statement to count letter grades. (Part 3 of 3.)

Lines 9 and 10 declare and initialize to 0 local variables total and gradeCounter to keep track of the sum of the grades entered by the user and the number of grades entered, respectively. Lines 11–15 declare and initialize to 0 counter variables for each grade category. The Main method has two key parts. Lines 21–52 read an arbitrary number of integer grades from the user using sentinel-controlled iteration, update variables total and gradeCounter, and increment an appropriate letter-grade counter for each grade entered. Lines 54–76 output a report containing the total of all grades entered, the average grade and the number of students who received each letter grade.

Reading Grades from the User

Lines 17–19 prompt the user to enter integer grades and to type *Ctrl* + *z*, then press *Enter* to terminate the input. The notation *Ctrl* + *z* means to hold down the *Ctrl* key and tap the *z* key when typing in a **Command Prompt**. *Ctrl* + *z* is the Windows key sequence for typing the end-of-file indicator. This is one way to inform an app that there's no more data to input. If *Ctrl* + *z* is entered while the app is awaiting input with a ReadLine method, null is returned. (The end-of-file indicator is a system-dependent keystroke combination. On many non-Windows systems, end-of-file is entered by typing *Ctrl* + *d*.) In Chapter 17, Files and Streams, we'll see how the end-of-file indicator is used when an app reads its input from a file. Windows typically displays the characters ^Z in a **Command Prompt** when the end-of-file indicator is typed, as shown in the program's output.

Line 21 uses Console's ReadLine method to get the first line that the user entered and store it in variable input. The while statement (lines 24–52) processes this user input. The condition at line 24 checks whether the value of input is null—Console's ReadLine method returns null only if the user typed an end-of-file indicator. As long as the end-of-file indicator has not been typed, input will not be null and the condition will pass.

Line 26 converts the string in input to an int type. Line 27 adds grade to total. Line 28 increments gradeCounter.

Processing the Grades

The switch statement (lines 31–49) determines which counter to increment. In this example, we assume that the user enters a valid grade in the range 0–100. A grade in the range 90–100 represents A, 80–89 represents B, 70–79 represents C, 60–69 represents D and 0–59 represents F. The switch statement consists of a block that contains a sequence of case labels and an optional default label. These are used in this example to determine which counter to increment based on the grade.

The switch Statement

When control reaches the switch statement, the app evaluates the expression grade / 10 in the parentheses—this is the switch expression. The app attempts to match the value of the switch expression with one of the case labels. The switch expression in line 31 performs integer division, which *truncates* the fractional part of the result. Thus, when we divide any value in the range 0–100 by 10, the result is always a value from 0 to 10. We use several of these values in our case labels. For example, if the user enters the integer 85, the switch expression evaluates to int value 8. If a match occurs between the switch expression and a case (case 8: at line 37), the app executes the statements for that case. For the integer 8, line 38 increments bCount, because a grade in the 80s is a B.

The break statement (line 39) causes program control to proceed with the first statement after the switch (line 51), which reads the next line entered by the user and assigns it to the variable input. Line 52 marks the end of the body of the while statement that inputs grades, so control flows to the while's condition (line 24) to determine whether the loop should continue executing based on the value just assigned to the variable input.

Consecutive **case** Labels

The switch's cases explicitly test for the values 10, 9, 8, 7 and 6. Lines 33–34 test for the values 9 and 10 (both of which represent the grade A). Listing case labels consecutively in this manner with no statements between them enables the cases to perform the same set of statements—when the switch expression evaluates to 9 or 10, the statements in lines 35–36 execute. The switch statement does not provide a mechanism for testing ranges of values, so every value to be tested must be listed in a separate case label. Each case can have multiple statements. The switch statement differs from other control statements in that it does *not* require braces around multiple statements in each case.

The **default** Case

If *no match* occurs between the switch expression's value and a case label, the statements after the default label (lines 47–48) execute. We use the default label in this example to process all switch-expression values that are less than 6—that is, all failing grades. If no match occurs and the switch does *not* contain a default label, program control simply continues with the first statement (if there's one) after the switch statement.

Good Programming Practice 6.1
Although each case and the default *label in a switch can occur in any order, place the* default *label last for clarity.*

No "Fall Through" in the C# **switch** Statement

In many other programming languages containing switch, the break statement *is not* required at the end of a case. In those languages, without break statements, each time a match occurs in the switch, the statements for that case and subsequent cases execute until a break statement or the end of the switch is encountered. This is often referred to as "falling through" to the statements in subsequent cases. This leads to logic errors when you forget the break statement. C# is different from other programming languages—after the statements in a case, you're *required* to include a statement that terminates the case, such as a break, a return or a throw;[1] otherwise, a compilation error occurs.[2]

Displaying the Grade Report

Lines 54–76 output a report based on the grades entered (as shown in the input/output window in Fig. 6.9). Line 57 determines whether the user entered at least one grade—this helps us avoid dividing by zero. If so, line 60 calculates the average of the grades. Lines 63–71 then output the total of all the grades, the class average and the number of students who received each letter grade. If no grades were entered, line 75 outputs an appropriate message. The output in Fig. 6.9 shows a sample grade report based on 10 grades.

6.8.2 switch Statement UML Activity Diagram

Figure 6.10 shows the UML activity diagram for the general switch statement. Every set of statements after a case label normally ends its execution with a break or return state-

---

1. We discuss the throw statement in Chapter 13, Exception Handling: A Deeper Look.
2. You can implement fall through by replacing the break statement after a case's or default's actions with a statement of the form goto case *value*; (where *value* is a literal or constant in one of the switch's cases) or goto default;.

ment to terminate the switch statement after processing the case. Typically, you'll use break statements. Figure 6.10 emphasizes this by including break statements in the activity diagram. The diagram makes it clear that the break statement at the end of a case causes control to exit the switch statement immediately.

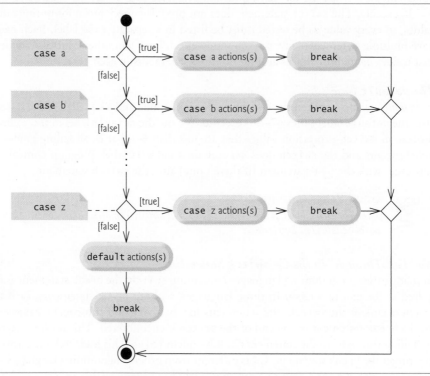

Fig. 6.10 | switch multiple-selection statement UML activity diagram with break statements.

6.8.3 Notes on the Expression in Each case of a switch

In the switch statements cases, *constant integral expressions* can be character constants—specific characters in single quotes, such as 'A', '7' or '$'—which represent the integer values of characters. (Appendix C shows the integer values of the characters in the ASCII character set, which is a popular subset of the Unicode character set used by C#.) A *string constant* (or *string literal*) is a sequence of characters in double quotes, such as "Welcome to C# Programming!" or a const string variable. For strings, you also can use null or string.Empty.

The expression in each case also can be a constant—a value which does not change for the entire app. Constants are declared with the keyword const (discussed in Chapter 7). C# also has a feature called *enumerations*, which we also present in Chapter 7. Enumeration constants also can be used in case labels. In Chapter 12, we present a more elegant way to implement switch logic—we use a technique called *polymorphism* to create apps that are often clearer, easier to maintain and easier to extend than apps using switch logic.

6.9 Class AutoPolicy Case Study: `strings` in `switch` Statements

`strings` can be used in `switch` expressions, and `string` literals can be used in `case` labels. To demonstrate this, we'll implement an app that meets the following requirements:

> *You've been hired by an auto insurance company that serves these northeast states—Connecticut, Maine, Massachusetts, New Hampshire, New Jersey, New York, Pennsylvania, Rhode Island and Vermont. The company would like you to create a program that produces a report indicating for each of their auto insurance policies whether the policy is held in a state with "no-fault" auto insurance—Massachusetts, New Jersey, New York and Pennsylvania.*

The app contains two classes—AutoPolicy (Fig. 6.11) and AutoPolicyTest (Fig. 6.12).

Class *AutoPolicy*

Class AutoPolicy (Fig. 6.11) represents an auto insurance policy. The class contains:

- auto-implemented `int` property AccountNumber (line 5) to store the policy's account number,

- auto-implemented `string` property MakeAndModel (line 6) to store the car's make and model (such as a `"Toyota Camry"`),

- auto-implemented `string` property State (line 7) to store a two-character state abbreviation representing the state in which the policy is held (e.g., `"MA"` for Massachusetts),

- a constructor (lines 10–15) that initializes the class's properties and

- read-only property IsNoFaultState (lines 18–37) to return a `bool` value indicating whether the policy is held in a no-fault auto insurance state; note the property name—a common naming convention for a `bool` property is to begin the name with `"Is"`.

In property IsNoFaultState, the `switch` expression (line 25) is the `string` returned by AutoPolicy's State property. The `switch` statement compares the `switch` expression's value with the `case` labels (line 27) to determine whether the policy is held in Massachusetts, New Jersey, New York or Pennsylvania (the no-fault states). If there's a match, then line 28 sets local variable noFaultState to `true` and the `switch` statement terminates; otherwise, the `default` case sets noFaultState to `false` (line 31). Then IsNoFaultState's get accessor returns local variable noFaultState's value.

```
1   // Fig. 6.11: AutoPolicy.cs
2   // Class that represents an auto insurance policy.
3   class AutoPolicy
4   {
5      public int AccountNumber { get; set; } // policy account number
6      public string MakeAndModel { get; set; } // car that policy applies to
7      public string State { get; set; } // two-letter state abbreviation
8
```

Fig. 6.11 | Class that represents an auto insurance policy. (Part 1 of 2.)

```
 9        // constructor
10        public AutoPolicy(int accountNumber, string makeAndModel, string state)
11        {
12           AccountNumber = accountNumber;
13           MakeAndModel = makeAndModel;
14           State = state;
15        }
16
17        // returns whether the state has no-fault insurance
18        public bool IsNoFaultState
19        {
20           get
21           {
22              bool noFaultState;
23
24              // determine whether state has no-fault auto insurance
25              switch (State) // get AutoPolicy object's state abbreviation
26              {
27                 case "MA": case "NJ": case "NY": case "PA":
28                    noFaultState = true;
29                    break;
30                 default:
31                    noFaultState = false;
32                    break;
33              }
34
35              return noFaultState;
36           }
37        }
38    }
```

Fig. 6.11 | Class that represents an auto insurance policy. (Part 2 of 2.)

For simplicity, we do not validate an AutoPolicy's properties, and we assume that state abbreviations are always two uppercase letters. In addition, a real AutoPolicy class would likely contain many other properties and methods for data such as the account holder's name, address, birth date, etc. In Exercise 6.28, you'll be asked to enhance class AutoPolicy by validating its state abbreviation using techniques that you'll learn in Section 6.11.

Class AutoPolicyTest

Class AutoPolicyTest (Fig. 6.12) creates two AutoPolicy objects (lines 10–11 in Main). Lines 14–15 pass each object to static method policyInNoFaultState (lines 20–28), which uses AutoPolicy methods to determine and display whether the object it receives represents a policy in a no-fault auto insurance state.

```
1    // Fig. 6.12: AutoPolicyTest.cs
2    // Demonstrating strings in switch.
3    using System;
4
```

Fig. 6.12 | Demonstrating strings in switch. (Part 1 of 2.)

```
 5    class AutoPolicyTest
 6    {
 7       static void Main()
 8       {
 9          // create two AutoPolicy objects
10          AutoPolicy policy1 = new AutoPolicy(11111111, "Toyota Camry", "NJ");
11          AutoPolicy policy2 = new AutoPolicy(22222222, "Ford Fusion", "ME");
12
13          // display whether each policy is in a no-fault state
14          PolicyInNoFaultState(policy1);
15          PolicyInNoFaultState(policy2);
16       }
17
18       // method that displays whether an AutoPolicy
19       // is in a state with no-fault auto insurance
20       public static void PolicyInNoFaultState(AutoPolicy policy)
21       {
22          Console.WriteLine("The auto policy:");
23          Console.Write($"Account #: {policy.AccountNumber}; ");
24          Console.WriteLine($"Car: {policy.MakeAndModel};");
25          Console.Write($"State {policy.State}; ");
26          Console.Write($"({policy.IsNoFaultState ? "is": "is not"})");
27          Console.WriteLine(" a no-fault state\n");
28       }
29    }
```

```
The auto policy:
Account #: 11111111; Car: Toyota Camry;
State NJ is a no-fault state

The auto policy:
Account #: 22222222; Car: Ford Fusion;
State ME is not a no-fault state
```

Fig. 6.12 | Demonstrating strings in switch. (Part 2 of 2.)

6.10 break and continue Statements

In addition to selection and iteration statements, C# provides statements break and continue to alter the flow of control. The preceding section showed how break can be used to terminate a switch statement's execution. This section discusses how to use break to terminate any iteration statement.

6.10.1 break Statement

The break statement, when executed in a while, for, do...while, switch, or foreach, causes immediate exit from the loop or switch. Execution continues with the first statement after the control statement. Figure 6.13 demonstrates a break statement exiting a for. When the if nested at line 13 in the for statement (lines 11–19) determines that count is 5, the break statement at line 15 executes. This terminates the for statement, and the app proceeds to line 21 (immediately after the for statement), which displays a message indicating the value of the control variable when the loop terminated. The loop fully executes its body only four times instead of 10 because of the `break`.

```
1   // Fig. 6.13: BreakTest.cs
2   // break statement exiting a for statement.
3   using System;
4
5   class BreakTest
6   {
7       static void Main()
8       {
9           int count; // control variable also used after loop terminates
10
11          for (count = 1; count <= 10; ++count) // loop 10 times
12          {
13              if (count == 5) // if count is 5,
14              {
15                  break; // terminate loop
16              }
17
18              Console.Write($"{count} ");
19          }
20
21          Console.WriteLine($"\nBroke out of loop at count = {count}");
22      }
23  }
```

```
1 2 3 4
Broke out of loop at count = 5
```

Fig. 6.13 | `break` statement exiting a `for` statement.

6.10.2 continue Statement

The **continue statement**, when executed in a `while`, `for`, `do...while`, or `foreach`, skips the remaining statements in the loop body and proceeds with the next iteration of the loop. In `while` and `do...while` statements, the app evaluates the loop-continuation test *immediately after* the `continue` statement executes. In a `for` statement, the increment expression normally executes next, then the app evaluates the loop-continuation test.

Figure 6.14 uses the `continue` statement in a `for` to skip the statement at line 16 when the nested `if` (line 11) determines that the value of `count` is 5. When the `continue` statement executes, program control continues with the increment of the control variable in the `for` statement (line 9).

Software Engineering Observation 6.1

Some programmers feel that break and continue statements violate structured programming. Since the same effects are achievable with structured-programming techniques, these programmers prefer not to use break or continue statements.

Software Engineering Observation 6.2

There's a tension between achieving quality software engineering and achieving the best-performing software. Often, one of these goals is achieved at the expense of the other. For all but the most performance-intensive situations, apply the following rule: First, make your code simple and correct; then make it fast, but only if necessary.

```csharp
1   // Fig. 6.14: ContinueTest.cs
2   // continue statement skipping an iteration of a for statement.
3   using System;
4
5   class ContinueTest
6   {
7      static void Main()
8      {
9         for (int count = 1; count <= 10; ++count) // loop 10 times
10        {
11           if (count == 5) // if count is 5,
12           {
13              continue; // skip remaining code in loop
14           }
15
16           Console.Write($"{count} ");
17        }
18
19        Console.WriteLine("\nUsed continue to skip displaying 5");
20     }
21  }
```

```
1 2 3 4 6 7 8 9 10
Used continue to skip displaying 5
```

Fig. 6.14 | continue statement skipping an iteration of a for statement.

6.11 Logical Operators

The if, if...else, while, do...while and for statements each require a condition to determine how to continue an app's flow of control. So far, we've studied only simple conditions, such as count <= 10, number != sentinelValue and total > 1000. Simple conditions are expressed in terms of the relational operators >, <, >= and <=, and the equality operators == and !=. Each expression tests only one condition. To test *multiple* conditions in the process of making a decision, we performed these tests in separate statements or in nested if or if...else statements. Sometimes, control statements require more complex conditions to determine an app's flow of control.

C# provides logical operators to enable you to form more complex conditions by combining simple conditions. The logical operators are && (conditional AND), || (conditional OR), & (boolean logical AND), | (boolean logical inclusive OR), ∧ (boolean logical exclusive OR) and ! (logical negation).

6.11.1 Conditional AND (&&) Operator

Suppose that we wish to ensure at some point in an app that two conditions are *both* true before we choose a certain path of execution. In this case, we can use the && (conditional AND) operator, as follows:

```
if (gender == 'F' && age >= 65)
{
    ++seniorFemales;
}
```

This if statement contains two simple conditions. The condition gender == 'F' determines whether a person is female. The condition age >= 65 might be evaluated to determine whether a person is a senior citizen. The if statement considers the combined condition

```
gender == 'F' && age >= 65
```

which is true if and only if *both* simple conditions are true. If the combined condition is true, the if statement's body increments seniorFemales by 1. If either or both of the simple conditions are false, the app skips the increment. Some programmers find that the preceding combined condition is more readable when redundant parentheses are added, as in

```
(gender == 'F') && (age >= 65)
```

The table in Fig. 6.15 summarizes the && operator. The table shows all four possible combinations of false and true values for *expression1* and *expression2*. Such tables are called truth tables. C# evaluates all expressions that include relational operators, equality operators or logical operators to bool values—which are either true or false.

expression1	expression2	expression1 && expression2
false	false	false
false	true	false
true	false	false
true	true	true

Fig. 6.15 | && (conditional AND) operator truth table.

6.11.2 Conditional OR (||) Operator

Now suppose we wish to ensure that *either or both* of two conditions are true before we choose a certain path of execution. In this case, we use the || (conditional OR) operator, as in the following app segment:

```
if ((semesterAverage >= 90) || (finalExam >= 90))
{
    Console.WriteLine ("Student grade is A");
}
```

This statement also contains two simple conditions. The condition semesterAverage >= 90 is evaluated to determine whether the student deserves an A in the course because of a solid performance throughout the semester. The condition finalExam >= 90 is evaluated to determine whether the student deserves an A in the course because of an outstanding performance on the final exam. The `if` statement then considers the combined condition

```
(semesterAverage >= 90) || (finalExam >= 90)
```

and awards the student an A if either or both of the simple conditions are true. The only time the message "`Student grade is A`" is *not* displayed is when *both* of the simple conditions are *false*. Figure 6.16 is a truth table for operator conditional OR (`||`). Operator `&&` has a higher precedence than operator `||`. Both operators associate from left to right.

expression1	expression2	expression1 `||` expression2
false	false	false
false	true	true
true	false	true
true	true	true

Fig. 6.16 | `||` (conditional OR) operator truth table.

6.11.3 Short-Circuit Evaluation of Complex Conditions

The parts of an expression containing `&&` or `||` operators are evaluated *only* until it's known whether the condition is true or false. Thus, evaluation of the expression

```
(gender == 'F') && (age >= 65)
```

stops immediately if `gender` is not equal to `'F'` (i.e., at that point, it's certain that the entire expression is `false`) and continues *only* if `gender` *is* equal to `'F'` (i.e., the entire expression could still be `true` if the condition `age >= 65` is `true`). This feature of conditional AND and conditional OR expressions is called short-circuit evaluation.

Common Programming Error 6.6

In expressions using operator &&, a condition—known as the dependent condition—may require another condition to be true for the evaluation of the dependent condition to be meaningful. In this case, the dependent condition should be placed after the other one, or an error might occur. For example, in the expression (i != 0) && (10 / i == 2), the second condition must appear after the first condition, or a divide-by-zero error might occur.

6.11.4 Boolean Logical AND (&) and Boolean Logical OR (|) Operators

The boolean logical AND (`&`) and boolean logical inclusive OR (`|`) operators work identically to the `&&` (conditional AND) and `||` (conditional OR) operators, with one exception—the boolean logical operators *always* evaluate both of their operands (i.e., they do *not* perform short-circuit evaluation). Therefore, the expression

```
(gender == 'F') & (age >= 65)
```

evaluates `age >= 65` regardless of whether `gender` is equal to `'F'`. This is useful if the right operand of the `&` or `|` operator has a required side effect—such as a modification of a variable's value. For example, the expression

```
(birthday == true) | (++age >= 65)
```

guarantees that the condition ++age >= 65 will be evaluated. Thus, the variable age is incremented in the preceding expression, *regardless* of whether the overall expression is true or false.

Error-Prevention Tip 6.6

For clarity, avoid expressions with side effects in conditions. The side effects may appear clever, but they can make it harder to understand code and can lead to subtle logic errors.

6.11.5 Boolean Logical Exclusive OR (^)

A complex condition containing the boolean logical exclusive OR (^) operator (also called the logical XOR operator) is true *if and only if one of its operands is* true *and the other is* false. If both operands are true or both are false, the entire condition is false. Figure 6.17 is a truth table for the boolean logical exclusive OR operator. This operator is also guaranteed to evaluate *both* of its operands.

expression1	expression2	expression1 ^ expression2
false	false	false
false	true	true
true	false	true
true	true	false

Fig. 6.17 | ^ (boolean logical exclusive OR) operator truth table.

6.11.6 Logical Negation (!) Operator

The ! (logical negation or **not**) operator enables you to "reverse" the meaning of a condition. Unlike the logical operators &&, ||, &, | and ^, which are *binary* operators that combine two conditions, the logical negation operator is a *unary* operator that has only a single condition as an operand. The logical negation operator is placed before a condition to choose a path of execution if the original condition (without the logical negation operator) is false, as in the code segment

```
if (! (grade == sentinelValue))
{
    Console.WriteLine($"The next grade is {grade}");
}
```

which executes the WriteLine call *only if* grade is not equal to sentinelValue. The parentheses around the condition grade == sentinelValue are needed because the logical negation operator has a higher precedence than the equality operator.

In most cases, you can avoid using logical negation by expressing the condition differently with an appropriate relational or equality operator. For example, the previous statement may also be written as

```
    if (grade != sentinelValue)
    {
        Console.WriteLine($"The next grade is {grade}");
    }
```

This flexibility can help you express a condition in a more convenient manner. Figure 6.18 is a truth table for the logical negation operator.

expression	!expression
false	true
true	false

Fig. 6.18 | ! (logical negation) operator truth table.

6.11.7 Logical Operators Example

Figure 6.19 demonstrates the logical operators and boolean logical operators by producing their truth tables. The output shows the expression that was evaluated and the bool result of that expression. Lines 10–14 produce the truth table for && (conditional AND). Lines 17–21 produce the truth table for || (conditional OR). Lines 24–28 produce the truth table for & (boolean logical AND). Lines 31–35 produce truth table for | (boolean logical inclusive OR). Lines 38–42 produce the truth table for ∧ (boolean logical exclusive OR). Lines 45–47 produce the truth table for ! (logical negation).

```
 1  // Fig. 6.19: LogicalOperators.cs
 2  // Logical operators.
 3  using System;
 4
 5  class LogicalOperators
 6  {
 7      static void Main()
 8      {
 9          // create truth table for && (conditional AND) operator
10          Console.WriteLine("Conditional AND (&&)");
11          Console.WriteLine($"false && false: {false && false}");
12          Console.WriteLine($"false && true: {false && true}");
13          Console.WriteLine($"true && false: {true && false}");
14          Console.WriteLine($"true && true: {true && true}\n");
15
16          // create truth table for || (conditional OR) operator
17          Console.WriteLine("Conditional OR (||)");
18          Console.WriteLine($"false || false: {false || false}");
19          Console.WriteLine($"false || true: {false || true}");
20          Console.WriteLine($"true || false: {true || false}");
21          Console.WriteLine($"true || true: {true || true}\n");
22
```

Fig. 6.19 | Logical operators. (Part 1 of 3.)

```
23          // create truth table for & (boolean logical AND) operator
24          Console.WriteLine("Boolean logical AND (&)");
25          Console.WriteLine($"false & false: {false & false}");
26          Console.WriteLine($"false & true: {false & true}");
27          Console.WriteLine($"true & false: {true & false}");
28          Console.WriteLine($"true & true: {true & true}\n");
29
30          // create truth table for | (boolean logical inclusive OR) operator
31          Console.WriteLine("Boolean logical inclusive OR (|)");
32          Console.WriteLine($"false | false: {false | false}");
33          Console.WriteLine($"false | true: {false | true}");
34          Console.WriteLine($"true | false: {true | false}");
35          Console.WriteLine($"true | true: {true | true}\n");
36
37          // create truth table for ^ (boolean logical exclusive OR) operator
38          Console.WriteLine("Boolean logical exclusive OR (^)");
39          Console.WriteLine($"false ^ false: {false ^ false}");
40          Console.WriteLine($"false ^ true: {false ^ true}");
41          Console.WriteLine($"true ^ false: {true ^ false}");
42          Console.WriteLine($"true ^ true: {true ^ true}\n");
43
44          // create truth table for ! (logical negation) operator
45          Console.WriteLine("Logical negation (!)");
46          Console.WriteLine($"!false: {!false}");
47          Console.WriteLine($"!true: {!true}");
48      }
49  }
```

```
Conditional AND (&&)
false && false: False
false && true: False
true && false: False
true && true: True

Conditional OR (||)
false || false: False
false || true: True
true || false: True
true || true: True

Boolean logical AND (&)
false & false: False
false & true: False
true & false: False
true & true: True

Boolean logical inclusive OR (|)
false | false: False
false | true: True
true | false: True
true | true: True

Boolean logical exclusive OR (^)
false ^ false: False
```

Fig. 6.19 | Logical operators. (Part 2 of 3.)

```
false ∧ true: True
true ∧ false: True
true ∧ true: False

Logical negation (!)
!false: True
!true: False
```

Fig. 6.19 | Logical operators. (Part 3 of 3.)

Precedence and Associativity of the Operators Presented So Far
Figure 6.20 shows the precedence and associativity of the C# operators introduced so far. The operators are shown from top to bottom in decreasing order of precedence.

Operators					Associativity	Type
. new ++*(postfix)* --*(postfix)*					left to right	highest precedence
++ -- + - ! *(type)*					right to left	unary prefix
* / %					left to right	multiplicative
+ -					left to right	additive
< <= > >=					left to right	relational
== !=					left to right	equality
&					left to right	boolean logical AND
∧					left to right	boolean logical exclusive OR
|					left to right	boolean logical inclusive OR
&&					left to right	conditional AND
||					left to right	conditional OR
?:					right to left	conditional
= += -= *= /= %=					right to left	assignment

Fig. 6.20 | Precedence/associativity of the operators discussed so far.

6.12 Structured-Programming Summary

Just as architects design buildings by employing the collective wisdom of their profession, so should programmers design apps. Our field is younger than architecture, and our collective wisdom is sparser but growing quickly. We've learned that structured programming produces apps that are easier than unstructured apps to understand, test, debug, modify and even prove correct in a mathematical sense.

Control Statements Are Single-Entry/Single-Exit
Figure 6.21 uses UML activity diagrams to summarize C#'s control statements. The initial and final states indicate the *single entry point* and the *single exit point* of each control statement. Arbitrarily connecting individual symbols in an activity diagram can lead to unstructured apps. Therefore, a limited set of control statements can be combined in only two simple ways to build structured apps.

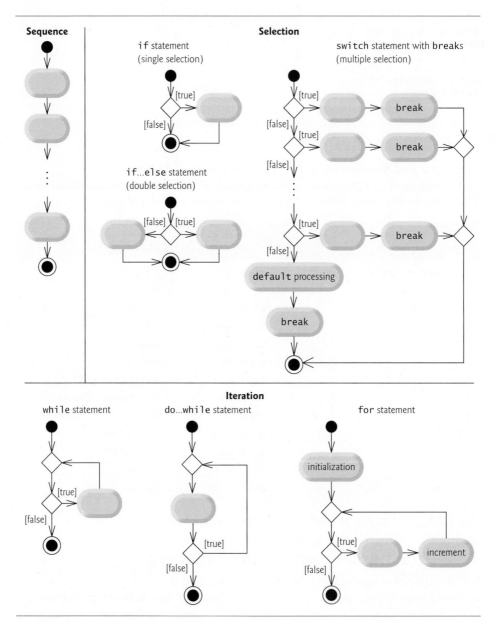

Fig. 6.21 | C#'s sequence, selection and iteration statements.

For simplicity, only **single-entry/single-exit control statements** are used—there's *only one* way to enter and *only one* way to exit each control statement. Connecting control statements in sequence to form structured apps is simple. The final state of one control statement is connected to the initial state of the next—that is, the control statements are placed one after another in an app in sequence. We call this *control-statement stacking*. The rules for forming structured apps also allow for control statements to be *nested*.

Rules for Forming Structured Programs

Figure 6.22 shows the rules for forming structured apps. The rules assume that action states may be used to indicate any action. The rules also assume that we begin with the simplest activity diagram (Fig. 6.23) consisting of only an initial state, an action state, a final state and transition arrows.

Rules for forming structured apps
1   Begin with the simplest activity diagram (Fig. 6.23).
2   Any action state can be replaced by two action states in sequence.
3   Any action state can be replaced by any control statement (sequence of action states, `if`, `if...else`, `switch`, `while`, `do...while`, `for` or `foreach`, which we'll see in Chapter 8).
4   Rules 2 and 3 can be applied as often as necessary in any order.

Fig. 6.22 | Rules for forming structured apps.

Fig. 6.23 | Simplest activity diagram.

Applying the rules in Fig. 6.22 always results in a properly structured activity diagram with a neat, building-block appearance. For example, repeatedly applying Rule 2 to the simplest activity diagram results in an activity diagram containing many action states in sequence (Fig. 6.24). Rule 2 generates a stack of control statements, so let us call Rule 2 the stacking rule. [*Note:* The vertical dashed lines in Fig. 6.24 are not part of the UML—we use them to separate the four activity diagrams that demonstrate the application of Rule 2 of Fig. 6.22.]

Rule 3 is called the nesting rule. Repeatedly applying Rule 3 to the simplest activity diagram results in an activity diagram with neatly nested control statements. For example, in Fig. 6.25, the action state in the simplest activity diagram is replaced with a double-selection (`if...else`) statement. Then Rule 3 is applied again to the action states in the double-selection statement, replacing each of these action states with a double-selection statement. The dashed action-state symbols around each of the double-selection statements represent the action state that was replaced. The dashed arrows and dashed action-state symbols shown in Fig. 6.25 are not part of the UML—they're used here to illustrate that any action state can be replaced with any control statement.

Rule 4 generates larger, more involved and more deeply nested statements. The diagrams that emerge from applying the rules in Fig. 6.22 constitute the set of all possible structured activity diagrams and hence the set of all possible structured apps. The beauty

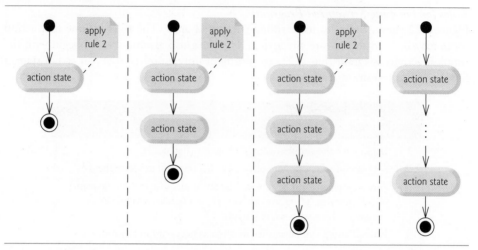

Fig. 6.24 | Repeatedly applying the stacking rule (Rule 2) of Fig. 6.22 to the simplest activity diagram.

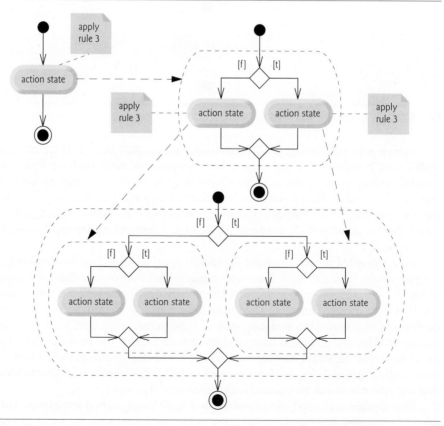

Fig. 6.25 | Repeatedly applying Rule 3 of Fig. 6.22 to the simplest activity diagram.

of the structured approach is that we use only eight simple single-entry/single-exit control statements (counting the `foreach` statement, which we introduce in Section 8.4.5) and assemble them in only two simple ways.

If the rules in Fig. 6.22 are followed, an "unstructured" activity diagram (like the one in Fig. 6.26) cannot be created. If you're uncertain about whether a particular diagram is structured, apply the rules of Fig. 6.22 *in reverse* to reduce the diagram to the simplest activity diagram. If you *can* reduce it, the original diagram is structured; otherwise, it's not.

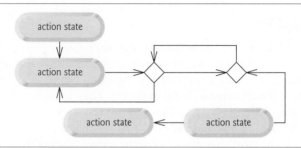

Fig. 6.26 | "Unstructured" activity diagram.

Three Forms of Control

Structured programming promotes simplicity. Research has shown that only three forms of control are needed to implement any algorithm:

- sequence
- selection
- iteration

Sequence is trivial. Simply list the statements of the sequence in the order in which they should execute. Selection is implemented in one of three ways:

- `if` statement (single selection)
- `if...else` statement (double selection)
- `switch` statement (multiple selection)

In fact, it's straightforward to prove that the simple `if` statement is sufficient to provide any form of selection—everything that can be done with the `if...else` statement and the `switch` statement can be done by combining `if` statements (although perhaps not as clearly and conveniently).

Iteration is implemented in one of four ways:

- `while` statement
- `do...while`
- `for` statement
- `foreach` statement

It's straightforward to prove that `while` is sufficient to provide any form of iteration. Everything that can be done with `do...while`, `for` and `foreach` can be done with `while` (although perhaps not as clearly and conveniently).

Combining these results illustrates that any form of control ever needed in a C# app can be expressed in terms of

- sequence structure
- if statement (selection)
- while statement (iteration)

and these can be combined in only two ways—stacking and nesting.

6.13 Wrap-Up

Chapter 5 discussed the if, if...else and while control statements. In Chapter 6, we discussed the for, do...while and switch control statements. (We'll discuss the foreach statement in Chapter 8.) You learned that any algorithm can be developed using combinations of sequence (i.e., statements listed in the order in which they should execute), the three selection statements—if, if...else and switch—and the four iteration statements—while, do...while, for and foreach. You saw that the for and do...while statements are simply more convenient ways to express certain types of iteration. Similarly, we showed that the switch statement is a convenient notation for multiple selection, rather than using nested if...else statements. We discussed how you can combine various control statements by stacking and nesting them. We showed how to use the break and continue statements to alter the flow of control in iteration statements. You learned about the logical operators, which enable you to use more complex conditional expressions in control statements. In Chapter 7, we examine methods in greater depth.

Summary

Section 6.2 Essentials of Counter-Controlled Iteration
- Counter-controlled iteration requires a control variable, the initial value of the control variable, the increment (or decrement) by which the control variable is modified each time through the loop and the loop-continuation condition that determines whether looping should continue.

Section 6.3 **for** Iteration Statement
- Typically, for statements are used for counter-controlled iteration, and while statements for sentinel-controlled iteration.

Section 6.3.1 A Closer Look at the **for** Statement's Header
- The for header "does it all"—it specifies each of the items needed for counter-controlled iteration with a control variable.

Section 6.3.2 General Format of a **for** Statement
- The general format of the for statement is

```
for (initialization; loopContinuationCondition; increment)
{
    statement
}
```

where the *initialization* expression names the loop's control variable and provides its initial value, the *loopContinuationCondition* is the condition that determines whether looping should continue and the *increment* modifies the control variable's value so that the loop-continuation condition eventually becomes `false`.

Section 6.3.3 Scope of a **for** Statement's Control Variable
- The scope of a variable defines where it can be used in an app. A local variable can be used only in the method that declares the variable and only from the point of declaration through the end of the block in which the variable is declared. A control variable declared in the initialization expression of a `for` statement is only that statement.

Section 6.3.5 Placing Arithmetic Expressions in a **for** Statement's Header
- The increment of a `for` statement may also be negative, in which case it's a decrement, and the loop counts downward.

Section 6.6 App: Compound-Interest Calculations
- When a variable of type `decimal` is initialized to an `int` value, the value of type `int` is promoted to a `decimal` type implicitly—no cast is required.

Section 6.6.1 Performing the Interest Calculations with Math Method **pow**
- Methods that must be called using a class name are called `static` methods.
- C# does not include an exponentiation operator. Instead, `Math.Pow(x, y)` calculates the value of *x* raised to the *y*th power. The method receives two `double` arguments and returns a `double` value.
- C# will not implicitly convert a `double` to a `decimal` type, or vice versa, because of the possible loss of information in either conversion. To perform this conversion, a cast operator is required.

Section 6.6.2 Formatting with Field Widths and Alignment
- Values are right-aligned in a field by default. To indicate that values should be output left-aligned, simply use a negative field width.
- In a format item, an integer *n* after a comma indicates that the value output should be displayed with a field width of *n*—that is, with at least *n* character positions, using spaces as fill characters.

Section 6.6.3 Caution: Do Not Use **float** or **double** for Monetary Amounts
- Floating-point numbers of type `double` (or `float`) can cause trouble in monetary calculations; use type `decimal` instead.

Section 6.7 **do...while** Iteration Statement
- The do...while statement tests the loop-continuation condition *after* executing the loop's body; therefore, the body always executes at least once.
- The do...while statement has the form:

```
do
{
    statement
} while (condition);
```

Section 6.8 **switch** Multiple-Selection Statement
- The switch multiple-selection statement performs different actions based on the possible values of an expression.

Section 6.8.1 Using a **switch** Statement to Count A, B, C, D and F Grades.
- Method `Console.ReadLine` returns `null` when the end-of-file key sequence is encountered.
- The switch statement's block contains a sequence of case labels and an optional `default` label.

- The expression in parentheses following keyword switch is the switch expression. The app attempts to match the value of the switch expression to a case label. If a match occurs, the app executes the statements for that case.

- The switch statement does not provide a mechanism for testing ranges of values, so every value to be tested must be listed in a separate case label.

- After the statements in a case execute, you're required to include a statement that terminates the case, such as a break or a return.

- If no match occurs between the switch expression's value and a case label, the statements after the default label execute. If no match occurs and the switch does not contain a default label, program control continues with the first statement after the switch statement.

Section 6.10.1 **break** *Statement*
- The break statement causes immediate exit from a while, for, do...while, switch or foreach statement. Execution continues with the first statement after the control statement.

Section 6.10.2 **continue** *Statement*
- The continue statement, when executed in a while, for, do...while or foreach, skips the remaining statements in the loop body and proceeds with the next iteration of the loop. In a for statement, the increment is performed before the loop-continuation condition is tested.

Section 6.11 *Logical Operators*
- Logical operators enable you to form more complex conditions by combining simple conditions. The logical operators are && (conditional AND), || (conditional OR), & (boolean logical AND), | (boolean logical inclusive OR), ∧ (boolean logical exclusive OR) and ! (logical negation).

Section 6.11.1 *Conditional AND (&&) Operator*
- The && (conditional AND) operator ensures that two conditions are *both* true before we choose a certain path of execution.

Section 6.11.2 *Conditional OR (||) Operator*
- The || (conditional OR) operator ensures that *either or both* of two conditions are true before we choose a certain path of execution.

Section 6.11.3 *Short-Circuit Evaluation of Complex Conditions*
- The parts of an expression containing && or || operators are evaluated only until it's known whether the condition is true or false. This feature of conditional AND and conditional OR expressions is called short-circuit evaluation.

Section 6.11.4 *Boolean Logical AND (&) and Boolean Logical OR (|) Operators*
- The boolean logical AND (&) and boolean logical inclusive OR (|) operators work identically to the && (conditional AND) and || (conditional OR) operators, but the boolean logical operators always evaluate both of their operands (i.e., they do not perform short-circuit evaluation).

Section 6.11.5 *Boolean Logical Exclusive OR (∧)*
- A complex condition containing the boolean logical exclusive OR (∧) operator is true if and only if one of its operands is true and the other is false. If both operands are true or both are false, the entire condition is false.

Section 6.11.6 *Logical Negation (!) Operator*
- The ! (logical negation) operator enables you to "reverse" the meaning of a condition. The logical negation operator is placed before a condition to choose a path of execution if the original

condition is `false`. In most cases, you can avoid using logical negation by expressing the condition differently with an appropriate relational or equality operator.

Section 6.12 Structured-Programming Summary
- Any form of control ever needed in a C# app can be expressed in terms of sequence, the `if` statement (selection) and the `while` statement (iteration). These can be combined in only two ways—stacking and nesting.

Terminology

`!`, logical negation operator	increment a control variable
`&`, boolean logical AND operator	initial value of a control variable
`&&`, conditional AND operator	iteration of a loop
`|`, boolean logical OR operator	left-aligned
`||`, conditional OR operator	logical operators
`^`, boolean logical exclusive OR operator	loop-continuation condition
`break` statement	multiple-selection statement
`case` label in `switch`	nested control statements
character constant	nesting rule
`const` keyword	off-by-one error
constant	iteration statement
constant integral expression	right-aligned
constant string expression	scope of a variable
`continue` statement	short-circuit evaluation
control variable	side effect
decrement a control variable	simple condition
`default` label in `switch`	single-entry/single-exit control statements
`do...while` iteration statement	stacked control statements
end-of-file indicator	stacking rule
field width	`static` method
`for` header	`switch` expression
`for` iteration statement	`switch` multiple-selection statement
`for` statement header	truth table

Self-Review Exercises

6.1 Fill in the blanks in each of the following statements:

a) Typically, _____ statements are used for counter-controlled iteration and _____ statements are used for sentinel-controlled iteration.

b) The `do...while` statement tests the loop-continuation condition _____ executing the loop's body; therefore, the body always executes at least once.

c) The _____ statement selects among multiple actions based on the possible values of an integer variable or expression.

d) The _____ statement, when executed in an iteration statement, skips the remaining statements in the loop body and proceeds with the next iteration of the loop.

e) The _____ operator can be used to ensure that two conditions are *both* true before choosing a certain path of execution.

f) If the loop-continuation condition in a `for` header is initially _____, the `for` statement's body does not execute.

g) Methods that perform common tasks and cannot be called on objects are called _____ methods.

6.2   State whether each of the following is *true* or *false*. If *false*, explain why.

a) The default label is required in the switch selection statement.

b) The break statement is required in every case of a switch statement.

c) The expression ((x > y) && (a < b)) is true if either (x > y) is true or (a < b) is true.

d) An expression containing the || operator is true if either or both of its operands are true.

e) The integer after the comma (,) in a format item (e.g., {0,4}) indicates the field width of the displayed string.

f) To test for a range of values in a switch statement, use a hyphen (-) between the start and end values of the range in a case label.

g) Listing cases consecutively with no statements between them enables the cases to perform the same set of statements.

6.3   Write a C# statement or a set of C# statements to accomplish each of the following tasks:

a) Sum the odd integers between 1 and 99, using a for statement. Assume that the integer variables sum and count have been declared.

b) Calculate the value of 2.5 raised to the power of 3, using the Pow method.

c) Display the integers from 1 to 20 using a while loop and the counter variable i. Assume that the variable i has been declared, but not initialized. Display only five integers per line. [*Hint:* Use the calculation i % 5. When the value of this expression is 0, display a newline character; otherwise, display a tab character. Use the Console.WriteLine() method to output the newline character, and use the Console.Write('\t') method to output the tab character.]

d) Repeat part (c), using a for statement.

6.4   Find the error(s) in each of the following code segments and explain how to correct it:

a)
```
i = 1;
while (i <= 10);
    ++i;
}
```

b)
```
for (k = 0.1; k != 1.0; k += 0.1)
{
    Console.WriteLine(k);
}
```

c)
```
switch (n)
{
    case 1:
        Console.WriteLine("The number is 1");
    case 2:
        Console.WriteLine("The number is 2");
        break;
    default:
        Console.WriteLine("The number is not 1 or 2");
        break;
}
```

d) The following code should display the values 1 to 10:
```
n = 1;
while (n < 10)
{
    Console.WriteLine(n++);
}
```

Answers to Self-Review Exercises

6.1   a) for, while. b) after. c) switch. d) continue. e) && (conditional AND) or & (boolean logical AND). f) false. g) static.

6.2   a) False. The default label is optional. If no default action is needed, then there's no need for a default label. b) False. You could terminate the case with other statements, such as a return. c) False. Both of the relational expressions must be true for this entire expression to be true when using the && operator. d) True. e) True. f) False. The switch statement does not provide a mechanism for testing ranges of values, so you must list every value to test in a separate case label. g) True.

6.3   The answers to Self-Review Exercise 6.3 are as follows:

a)
```
sum = 0;
for (count = 1; count <= 99; count += 2)
{
    sum += count
}
```

b)
```
double result = Math.Pow(2.5, 3);
```

c)
```
i = 1;

while (i <= 20)
{
    Console.Write(i);

    if (i % 5 == 0)
    {
        Console.WriteLine();
    }
    else
    {
        Console.Write('\t');
    }

    ++i;
}
```

d)
```
for (i = 1; i <= 20; ++i)
{
    Console.Write(i);

    if (i % 5 == 0)
    {
        Console.WriteLine();
    }
    else
    {
        Console.Write('\t');
    }
}
```

6.4   The answers to Self-Review Exercise 6.4 are as follows:

a) *Error:* The semicolon after the while header causes an infinite loop, and there's a missing left brace for the body of the while statement.
Correction: Remove the semicolon and add a { before the loop's body.

b) *Error:* Using a floating-point number to control a for statement may not work, because floating-point numbers are represented only approximately by most computers.
Correction: Use an integer, and perform the proper calculation in order to get the values you desire:

```
for (k = 1; k < 10; ++k)
{
    Console.WriteLine((double) k / 10);
}
```

c) *Error:* case 1 cannot fall through into case 2.
Correction: Terminate the case in some way, such as adding a break statement at the end of the statements for the first case.

d) *Error:* The wrong operator is used in the while iteration-continuation condition.
Correction: Use <= rather than <, or change 10 to 11.

Exercises

6.5 Describe the four basic elements of counter-controlled iteration.

6.6 Compare and contrast the while and for iteration statements.

6.7 Discuss a situation in which it would be more appropriate to use a do...while statement than a while statement. Explain why.

6.8 Compare and contrast the break and continue statements.

6.9 Find and correct the error(s) in each of the following segments of code:

a)
```
For (i = 100, i >= 1, ++i)
{
    Console.WriteLine(i);
}
```

b) The following code should display whether integer value is odd or even:

```
switch (value % 2)
{
    case 0:
        Console.WriteLine("Even integer");
    case 1:
        Console.WriteLine("Odd integer");
}
```

c) The following code should output the odd integers from 19 to 1:

```
for (int i = 19; i >= 1; i += 2)
{
    Console.WriteLine(i);
}
```

d) The following code should output the even integers from 2 to 100:

```
counter = 2;

do
{
    Console.WriteLine(counter);
    counter += 2;
} While (counter < 100);
```

6.10 *(What Does This Code Do?)* What does the following app do?

```
// Exercise 6.10 Solution: Printing.cs
using System;

class Printing
{
   static void Main()
   {
      for (int i = 1; i <= 10; ++i)
      {
         for (int j = 1; j <= 5; ++j)
         {
            Console.Write('@');
         }

         Console.WriteLine();
      }
   }
}
```

6.11 *(Find the Smallest Value)* Write an app that finds the smallest of several integers. Assume that the first value read specifies the number of values to input from the user.

6.12 *(Product of Odd Integers)* Write an app that calculates the product of the odd integers from 1 to 7.

6.13 *(Factorials)* *Factorials* are used frequently in probability problems. The factorial of a positive integer *n* (written *n!* and pronounced "*n* factorial") is equal to the product of the positive integers from 1 to *n*. Write an app that evaluates the factorials of the integers from 1 to 5. Display the results in tabular format. What difficulty might prevent you from calculating the factorial of 20?

6.14 *(Modified Compound-Interest Program)* Modify the compound-interest app (Fig. 6.6) to repeat its steps for interest rates of 5, 6, 7, 8, 9 and 10%. Use a for loop to vary the rate.

6.15 *(Displaying Triangles)* Write an app that displays the following patterns separately, one below the other. Use for loops to generate the patterns. All asterisks (*) should be displayed by a single statement of the form Console.Write('*'); which causes the asterisks to display side by side. A statement of the form Console.WriteLine(); can be used to move to the next line. A statement of the form Console.Write(' '); can be used to display a space for the last two patterns. There should be no other output statements in the app. [*Hint:* The last two patterns require that each line begin with an appropriate number of blank spaces.]

(a)	(b)	(c)	(d)
*	**********	**********	*
**	*********	*********	**
***	********	********	***
****	*******	*******	****
*****	******	******	*****
******	*****	*****	******
*******	****	****	*******
********	***	***	********
*********	**	**	*********
**********	*	*	**********

6.16 *(Displaying a Bar Chart)* One interesting application of computers is to display graphs and bar charts. Write an app that reads three numbers between 1 and 30. For each number that's read, your app should display the same number of adjacent asterisks. For example, if your app reads the number 7, it should display *******.

6.17 *(Calculating Sales)* A website sells three products whose retail prices are as follows: product 1, $2.98; product 2, $4.50; and product 3, $9.98. Write an app that reads a series of pairs of numbers as follows:
    a) product number
    b) quantity sold

Your app should use a switch statement to determine the retail price for each product. It should calculate and display the total retail value of all products sold. Use a sentinel-controlled loop to determine when the app should stop looping and display the final results.

6.18 *(Modified Compound-Interest Program)* In the future, you may work with other programming languages that do not have a type like decimal which supports precise monetary calculations. In those languages, you should perform such calculations using integers. Modify the app in Fig. 6.6 to use only integers to calculate the compound interest. Treat all monetary amounts as integral numbers of pennies. Then break the result into its dollars and cents portions by using the division and remainder operations, respectively. Insert a period between the dollars and the cents portions when you display the results.

6.19 Assume that i = 1, j = 2, k = 3 and m = 2. What does each of the following statements display?
    a) `Console.WriteLine(i == 1);`
    b) `Console.WriteLine(j == 3);`
    c) `Console.WriteLine((i >= 1) && (j < 4));`
    d) `Console.WriteLine((m <= 99) & (k < m));`
    e) `Console.WriteLine((j >= i) || (k == m));`
    f) `Console.WriteLine((k + m < j) | (3 - j >= k));`
    g) `Console.WriteLine(!(k > m));`

6.20 *(Calculating the Value of π)* Calculate the value of π from the infinite series

$$\pi = 4 - \frac{4}{3} + \frac{4}{5} - \frac{4}{7} + \frac{4}{9} - \frac{4}{11} + \cdots$$

Display a table that shows the value of π approximated by computing one term of this series, by two terms, by three terms, and so on. How many terms of this series do you have to use before you first get 3.14? 3.141? 3.1415? 3.14159?

6.21 *(Pythagorean Triples)* A right triangle can have sides whose lengths are all integers. The set of three integer values for the side lengths of a right triangle is called a Pythagorean triple (http://en.wikipedia.org/wiki/Pythagorean_triple). The side lengths must satisfy the relationship that the sum of the squares of two of the sides is equal to the square of the hypotenuse. Write an app to find all Pythagorean triples for side1, side2 and the hypotenuse, all no larger than 500. Use a triple-nested for loop that tries all possibilities. This method is an example of "brute-force" computing. You'll learn in more advanced computer science courses that there are many interesting problems for which there's no known algorithmic approach other than using sheer brute force.

6.22 *(Modified Triangle Program)* Modify Exercise 6.15 to combine your code from the four separate triangles of asterisks such that all four patterns display side by side. Make clever use of nested for loops.

6.23 *(Displaying a Diamond)* Write an app that displays the following diamond shape. You may use output statements that display a single asterisk (*), a single space or a single newline character. Maximize your use of iteration (with nested `for` statements) and minimize the number of output statements.

```
    *
   ***
  *****
 *******
*********
 *******
  *****
   ***
    *
```

6.24 *(Modified Diamond Program)* Modify the app you wrote in Exercise 6.23 to read an odd number in the range 1 to 19 to specify the number of rows in the diamond. Your app should then display a diamond of the appropriate size.

6.25 *(Structured Equivalent of **break** Statement)* A criticism of the `break` statement and the `continue` statement (in a loop) is that each is unstructured. Actually, `break` and `continue` statements can always be replaced by structured statements, although doing so can be awkward. Describe in general how you would remove any `break` statement from a loop in an app and replace it with a structured equivalent. [*Hint:* The `break` statement exits a loop from the body of the loop. The other way to exit is by failing the loop-continuation test. Consider using in the loop-continuation test a second test that indicates "early exit because of a 'break' condition."] Use the technique you develop here to remove the `break` statement from the app in Fig. 6.13.

6.26 *(What Does This Code Do?)* What does the following code segment do?

```
for (int i = 1; i <= 5; ++i)
{
   for (int j = 1; j <= 3; ++j)
   {
      for (int k = 1; k <= 4; ++k)
      {
         Console.Write('*');
      }

      Console.WriteLine();
   }
   Console.WriteLine();
}
```

6.27 *(Structured Equivalent of **continue** Statement)* Describe in general how you would remove any `continue` statement from a loop in an app and replace it with some structured equivalent. Use the technique you develop here to remove the `continue` statement from the app in Fig. 6.14.

6.28 *(Modified `AutoPolicy` Class)* Modify class `AutoPolicy` in Fig. 6.11 to validate the two-letter state codes for the northeast states. The codes are: CT for Connecticut, MA for Massachusetts, ME for Maine, NH for New Hampshire, NJ for New Jersey, NY for New York, PA for Pennsylvania and VT for Vermont. In the `State` property's `set` accessor, use the logical OR (`||`) operator (Section 6.11.2) to create a compound condition in an `if...else` statement that compares the method's argument with each two-letter code. If the code is incorrect, the `else` part of the `if...else` statement should display an error message. In later chapters, you'll learn how to use exception handling to indicate that a method received an invalid value.

Making-a-Difference Exercises

6.29   *(Global Warming Facts Quiz)* The controversial issue of global warming has been widely publicized by the film *An Inconvenient Truth*, featuring former Vice President Al Gore. Mr. Gore and a U.N. network of scientists, the Intergovernmental Panel on Climate Change, shared the 2007 Nobel Peace Prize in recognition of "their efforts to build up and disseminate greater knowledge about man-made climate change." Research *both* sides of the global warming issue online (you might want to search for phrases like "global warming skeptics"). Create a five-question multiple-choice quiz on global warming, each question having four possible answers (numbered 1–4). Be objective and try to fairly represent both sides of the issue. Next, write an app that administers the quiz, calculates the number of correct answers (zero through five) and returns a message to the user. If the user correctly answers five questions, display "Excellent"; if four, display "Very good"; if three or fewer, display "Time to brush up on your knowledge of global warming," and include a list of some of the websites where you found your facts.

6.30   *(Tax Plan Alternatives; The "FairTax")* There are many proposals to make taxation fairer. Check out the FairTax initiative in the United States at

        http://www.fairtax.org

Research how the proposed FairTax works. One suggestion is to eliminate income taxes and most other taxes in favor of a 23% consumption tax on all products and services that you buy. Some FairTax opponents question the 23% figure and say that because of the way the tax is calculated, it would be more accurate to say the rate is 30%—check this carefully. Write a program that prompts the user to enter expenses in various expense categories they have (e.g., housing, food, clothing, transportation, education, health care, vacations), then displays the estimated FairTax that person would pay.

Methods: A Deeper Look

Outline

7.1 Introduction

In this chapter, we take a deeper look at methods. We'll discuss the difference between non-static and static methods. You'll see that the Math class in the .NET Framework Class Library provides many static methods to perform mathematical calculations. We'll also discuss static variables (known as class variables) and why method Main is declared static.

You'll declare a method with multiple parameters and learn how to use operator + to perform `string` concatenations. We'll discuss C#'s argument promotion rules for implicitly converting simple-type values to other types and when these rules are applied by the compiler. We'll also present several commonly used Framework Class Library namespaces.

We'll take a brief, and hopefully entertaining, diversion into simulation techniques with random-number generation and develop a version of a popular casino dice game that uses most of the programming techniques you've learned so far. You'll declare named constants with the `const` keyword and with `enum` types. We'll then present C#'s scope rules, which determine where identifiers can be referenced in an app.

We'll discuss how the method-call stack enables C# to keep track of which method is currently executing, how local variables of methods are maintained in memory and how a method knows where to return after it completes execution. You'll overload methods in a class by providing methods with the same name but different numbers and/or types of parameters, and learn how to use optional and named parameters.

We'll introduce C# 6's expression-bodied methods, which provide a concise notation for methods that simply return a value to their caller. We'll also use this expression-bodied notation for a read-only property's `get` accessor.

We'll discuss how recursive methods call themselves, breaking larger problems into smaller subproblems until eventually the original problem is solved. Finally, we'll provide more insight into how value-type and reference-type arguments are passed to methods.

7.2 Packaging Code in C#

So far, we've used properties, methods and classes to package code. We'll present additional packaging mechanisms in later chapters. C# apps are written by combining your properties, methods and classes with predefined properties, methods and classes available in the .NET Framework Class Library and in other class libraries. Related classes are often grouped into namespaces and compiled into class libraries so that they can be reused in other apps. You'll learn how to create your own namespaces and class libraries in Chapter 15. The Framework Class Library provides many *predefined* classes that contain methods for performing common mathematical calculations, string manipulations, character manipulations, input/output operations, graphical user interfaces, graphics, multimedia, printing, file processing, database operations, networking operations, error checking, web-app development, accessibility (for people with disabilities) and more.

Software Engineering Observation 7.1

Don't try to "reinvent the wheel." When possible, reuse Framework Class Library classes and methods (`https://msdn.microsoft.com/library/mt472912`). This reduces app development time and errors, contributes to good performance and often enhances security.

7.2.1 Modularizing Programs

Methods (called functions or procedures in other programming languages) allow you to modularize an app by separating its tasks into self-contained units. You've declared methods in every app you've written. The actual statements in the method bodies are written only *once*, can be reused from several locations in an app and are *hidden* from other methods.

There are several motivations for modularizing an app with methods:

- Software reuse. For example, in previous apps, we did not have to define how to read a line of text from the keyboard—C# provides this capability via the Console class's ReadLine method.

- Avoiding code repetition.

- Making programs easier to test, debug and maintain.

 Software Engineering Observation 7.2

To promote software reusability, every method should be limited to performing a single, well-defined task, and the name of the method should express that task effectively.

7.2.2 Calling Methods

As you know, a method is invoked by a method call, and when the called method completes its task, it returns control and possibly a result to its caller. An analogy to the method-call-and-return structure is the hierarchical form of management (Fig. 7.1).

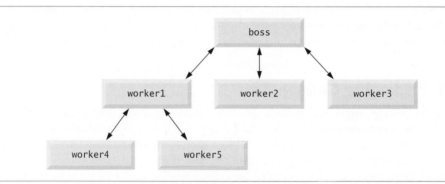

Fig. 7.1 | Hierarchical boss-method/worker-method relationship.

A boss (the caller) asks a worker (the called method) to perform a task and report back (i.e., return) the results after completing the task. The boss method does not need to know how the worker method performs its designated tasks. The worker may call other worker methods, including ones unknown to the boss. As we'll see, this *hiding* of implementation details promotes good software engineering. Figure 7.1 shows the boss method communicating with several worker methods in a hierarchical manner. The boss divides the responsibilities among the various workers. Note that worker1 also acts as a "boss" to worker4 and worker5. The relationship does not need to be hierarchical, but often it is, which makes it easier to test, debug and update programs.

7.3 static Methods, static Variables and Class Math

As we mentioned in Section 6.6.1, although most methods are called to operate on the data of specific objects, this is not always the case. Sometimes a method performs a task that does *not* depend on the data of any object (other than the method's arguments). Such a method applies to the class in which it's declared as a whole and is known as a static method.

It's common for a class to contain a group of static methods to perform common tasks. For example, recall that we used static method Pow of class Math to raise a value to a power in Fig. 6.6. To declare a method as static, place the keyword static before the return type in the method's declaration. You call any static method by specifying the name of the class in which the method is declared, followed by the member-access operator (.) and the method name, as in

ClassName . MethodName(arguments)

7.3.1 Math Class Methods

We use various methods of the Math class here to present the concept of static methods. Class Math (from the System namespace) provides a collection of methods that enable you to perform common mathematical calculations. For example, you can calculate the square root of 900.0 with the static method call

```
double value = Math.Sqrt(900.0);
```

The expression Math.Sqrt(900.0) evaluates to 30.0. Method Sqrt takes an argument of type double and returns a result of type double. The following statement displays in the console window the value of the preceding method call:

```
Console.WriteLine(Math.Sqrt(900.0));
```

Here, the value that Sqrt returns becomes the argument to WriteLine. We did not create a Math object before calling Sqrt, nor did we create a Console object before calling Write-Line. Also, *all* of Math's methods are static—therefore, each is called by preceding the name of the method with the class name Math and the member-access operator (.).

Method arguments may be constants, variables or expressions. If c = 13.0, d = 3.0 and f = 4.0, then the statement

```
Console.WriteLine(Math.Sqrt(c + d * f));
```

calculates and displays the square root of 13.0 + 3.0 * 4.0 = 25.0—namely, 5.0. Figure 7.2 summarizes several Math class methods. In the figure, x and y are of type double.

Method	Description	Example
Abs(x)	absolute value of x	Abs(23.7) is 23.7 Abs(0.0) is 0.0 Abs(-23.7) is 23.7
Ceiling(x)	rounds x to the smallest integer not less than x	Ceiling(9.2) is 10.0 Ceiling(-9.8) is -9.0
Floor(x)	rounds x to the largest integer not greater than x	Floor(9.2) is 9.0 Floor(-9.8) is -10.0
Cos(x)	trigonometric cosine of x (x in radians)	Cos(0.0) is 1.0
Sin(x)	trigonometric sine of x (x in radians)	Sin(0.0) is 0.0
Tan(x)	trigonometric tangent of x (x in radians)	Tan(0.0) is 0.0

Fig. 7.2 | Math class methods. (Part 1 of 2.)

Method	Description	Example
Exp(x)	exponential method e^x	Exp(1.0) is 2.71828 Exp(2.0) is 7.38906
Log(x)	natural logarithm of x (base e)	Log(Math.E) is 1.0 Log(Math.E * Math.E) is 2.0
Max(x, y)	larger value of x and y	Max(2.3, 12.7) is 12.7 Max(-2.3, -12.7) is -2.3
Min(x, y)	smaller value of x and y	Min(2.3, 12.7) is 2.3 Min(-2.3, -12.7) is -12.7
Pow(x, y)	x raised to the power y (i.e., x^y)	Pow(2.0, 7.0) is 128.0 Pow(9.0, 0.5) is 3.0
Sqrt(x)	square root of x	Sqrt(900.0) is 30.0

Fig. 7.2 | Math class methods. (Part 2 of 2.)

7.3.2 Math Class Constants PI and E

Recall from Section 4.3 that each object of a class maintains its own copy of each of the class's *instance variables*. There are also variables for which each object of a class does *not* need its own separate copy (as you'll see momentarily). Such variables are declared static and are also known as class variables. When objects of a class containing static variables are created, all the objects of that class share *one* copy of those variables. Together a class's static variables and instance variables are known as its fields. You'll learn more about static fields in Section 10.9.

Class Math also declares two double constants for commonly used mathematical values:

- Math.PI (3.1415926535897931) is the ratio of a circle's circumference to its diameter, and

- Math.E (2.7182818284590451) is the base value for natural logarithms (calculated with static Math method Log).

These constants are declared in class Math with the modifiers public and const. Making them public allows other programmers to use these variables in their own classes. A constant is declared with the keyword const—its value cannot be changed after the constant is declared. Fields declared const are implicitly static, so you can access them via the class name Math and the member-access operator (.), as in Math.PI and Math.E.

Common Programming Error 7.1

Constants declared in a class, but not inside a method or property, are implicitly static—it's a syntax error to declare such a constant with keyword static explicitly.

7.3.3 Why Is Main Declared static?

Why must Main be declared static? During app *startup*, when *no objects* of the class have been created, the Main method must be called to begin program execution. Main is sometimes called the app's entry point. Declaring Main as static allows the execution environment to invoke Main without creating an instance of the class. Method Main is typically declared with the header:

```
static void Main()
```

but also can be declared with the header:

```
static void Main(string[] args)
```

which we'll discuss and demonstrate in Section 8.12, Using Command-Line Arguments. In addition, you can declare `Main` with return type `int` (instead of `void`)—this can be useful if an app is executed by another app and needs to return an indication of success or failure to that other app.

7.3.4 Additional Comments About `Main`

Most earlier examples have one class that contained only `Main`, and some examples had a second class that was used by `Main` to create and manipulate objects. Actually, *any* class can contain a `Main` method. In fact, each of our two-class examples could have been implemented as one class. For example, in the app in Figs. 4.11–4.12, method `Main` (lines 7–43 of Fig. 4.12) could have been moved into class `Account` (Fig. 4.11). The app results would have been identical to those of the two-class version. You can place a `Main` method in every class you declare. Some programmers take advantage of this to build a small test app into each class they declare. However, if you declare more than one `Main` method among the classes of your project, you'll need to indicate to the IDE which one you would like to be the *app's* entry point. To do so:

1. With the project open in Visual Studio, select **Project > [ProjectName] Properties...** (where **[ProjectName]** is the name of your project).

2. Select the class containing the `Main` method that should be the entry point from the **Startup object** list box.

7.4 Methods with Multiple Parameters

We now consider how to write a method with multiple parameters. Figure 7.3 defines `Maximum` method that determines and returns the largest of *three* `double` values. When the app begins execution, the `Main` method (lines 8–23) executes. Line 19 calls method `Maximum` (declared in lines 26–43) to determine and return the largest of its three `double` arguments. In Section 7.4.3, we'll discuss the use of the + operator in line 22. The sample outputs show that `Maximum` determines the largest value regardless of whether that value is the first, second or third argument.

```
1   // Fig. 7.3: MaximumFinder.cs
2   // Method Maximum with three parameters.
3   using System;
4
5   class MaximumFinder
6   {
7      // obtain three floating-point values and determine maximum value
8      static void Main()
9      {
```

Fig. 7.3 | Method `Maximum` with three parameters. (Part 1 of 2.)

```
10          // prompt for and input three floating-point values
11          Console.Write("Enter first floating-point value: ");
12          double number1 = double.Parse(Console.ReadLine());
13          Console.Write("Enter second floating-point value: ");
14          double number2 = double.Parse(Console.ReadLine());
15          Console.Write("Enter third floating-point value: ");
16          double number3 = double.Parse(Console.ReadLine());
17
18          // determine the maximum of three values
19          double result = Maximum(number1, number2, number3);
20
21          // display maximum value
22          Console.WriteLine("Maximum is: " + result);
23       }
24
25    // returns the maximum of its three double parameters
26    static double Maximum(double x, double y, double z)
27    {
28       double maximumValue = x; // assume x is the largest to start
29
30       // determine whether y is greater than maximumValue
31       if (y > maximumValue)
32       {
33          maximumValue = y;
34       }
35
36       // determine whether z is greater than maximumValue
37       if (z > maximumValue)
38       {
39          maximumValue = z;
40       }
41
42       return maximumValue;
43    }
44 }
```

```
Enter first floating-point values: 3.33
Enter second floating-point values: 1.11
Enter third floating-point values: 2.22
Maximum is: 3.33
```

```
Enter first floating-point values: 2.22
Enter second floating-point values: 3.33
Enter third floating-point values: 1.11
Maximum is: 3.33
```

```
Enter first floating-point values: 2.22
Enter second floating-point values: 1.11
Enter third floating-point values: 3.33
Maximum is: 3.33
```

Fig. 7.3 | Method Maximum with three parameters. (Part 2 of 2.)

7.4.I Keyword `static`

Method `Maximum`'s declaration begins with keyword `static`, which enables the `Main` method (another `static` method) to call `Maximum` as shown in line 19 without creating an object of class `MaximumFinder` and without qualifying the method name with the class name `MaximumFinder`—`static` methods in the *same* class can call each other directly.

7.4.2 Method `Maximum`

Consider the declaration of method `Maximum` (lines 26–43). Line 26 indicates that the method returns a `double` value, that the method's name is `Maximum` and that the method requires *three* `double` parameters (x, y and z) to accomplish its task. When a method has more than one parameter, the parameters are specified as a *comma-separated list*. When `Maximum` is called in line 19, the parameter x is initialized with the value of the argument `number1`, the parameter y is initialized with the value of the argument `number2` and the parameter z is initialized with the value of the argument `number3`. There must be one argument in the method call for each required parameter in the method declaration. Also, each argument must be *consistent* with the type of the corresponding parameter. For example, a parameter of type `double` can receive values like 7.35 (a double), 22 (an int) or -0.03456 (a double), but not `strings` like "hello". Section 7.6 discusses the argument types that can be provided in a method call for each parameter of a simple type. Note the use of type `double`'s **Parse** method in lines 12, 14 and 16 to convert into `double` values the `strings` typed by the user.

Common Programming Error 7.2

Declaring method parameters of the same type as `double x, y` *instead of* `double x, double y` *is a syntax error—a type is required for each parameter in the parameter list.*

Logic of Determining the Maximum Value

To determine the maximum value, we begin with the assumption that parameter x contains the largest value, so line 28 declares local variable `maximumValue` and initializes it with the value of parameter x. Of course, it's possible that parameter y or z contains the largest value, so we must compare each of these values with `maximumValue`. The `if` statement at lines 31–34 determines whether y is greater than `maximumValue`. If so, line 33 assigns y to `maximumValue`. The `if` statement at lines 37–40 determines whether z is greater than `maximumValue`. If so, line 39 assigns z to `maximumValue`. At this point, the largest of the three values resides in `maximumValue`, so line 42 returns that value to line 19 where it's assigned to the variable `result`. When program control returns to the point in the app where `Maximum` was called, `Maximum`'s parameters x, y and z are no longer accessible. Methods can return *at most one* value; the returned value can be a value type that contains one or more values (implemented as a `struct`; Section 10.13) or a reference to an object that contains one or more values.

7.4.3 Assembling `strings` with Concatenation

C# allows `string` objects to be created by assembling smaller `strings` into larger `strings` using operator + (or the compound assignment operator +=). This is known as **string concatenation**. When both operands of operator + are `string` objects, the + operator creates a *new* `string` object containing copies of the characters in its left operand followed by copies of the characters in its right operand. For example, the expression "hello " + "there" creates the string "hello there" without disturbing the original strings.

In line 22, the expression "Maximum is: " + result uses operator + with operands of types string and double. Every simple-type value has a string representation. When one of the + operator's operands is a string, the other is implicitly converted to a string, then the two strings are *concatenated*. So, in line 22, the double value is converted to its string representation and placed at the end of "Maximum is: ". If there are any trailing zeros in a double value, these are *discarded*. Thus, the string representation of 9.3500 is "9.35".

Anything Can Be Converted to a *string*

If a bool is concatenated with a string, the bool is converted to the string "True" or "False" (each is capitalized). In addition, every object has a ToString method that returns a string representation of that object. When an object is concatenated with a string, the object's ToString method is called *implicitly* to obtain the string representation of the object. If the object is null, an *empty string* is written.

If a type does not define a ToString method, the default ToString implementation returns a string containing the type's fully qualified name—that is, the namespace in which the type is defined followed by a dot (.) and the type name (e.g., System.Object for the .NET class Object). Each type you create can declare a custom ToString method, as you'll do in Chapter 8 for a Card class that represents a playing card in a deck of cards.

Formatting *strings* with *string* Interpolation

Line 22 of Fig. 7.3, of course, could also be written using string interpolation as

```
Console.WriteLine($"Maximum is: {result}");
```

As with string concatenation, using string interpolation to insert an *object* into a string *implicitly* calls the object's ToString method to obtain the object's string representation.

7.4.4 Breaking Apart Large *string* Literals

When a large string literal or interpolated string is typed into an app's source code, you can break that string into several smaller strings and place them on multiple lines for readability. The strings can be reassembled using string concatenation. We discuss the details of strings in Chapter 16.

Common Programming Error 7.3

It's a syntax error to break a string literal or interpolated string across multiple lines of code. If a string does not fit on one line, you can split it into several smaller strings and use concatenation to form the desired string.

Common Programming Error 7.4

Confusing the string concatenation + operator with the addition + operator can lead to strange results. The + operator is left-associative. For example, if y has the int value 5, the expression "y + 2 = " + y + 2 results in the string "y + 2 = 52", not "y + 2 = 7", because first the value of y (5) is concatenated with the string "y + 2 = ", then the value 2 is concatenated with the new larger string "y + 2 = 5". The expression "y + 2 = " + (y + 2) produces the desired result "y + 2 = 7". Using C# 6 string interpolation eliminates this problem.

7.4.5 When to Declare Variables as Fields

Variable `result` is a local variable in method `Main` because it's declared in the block that represents the method's body. Variables should be declared as fields of a class (i.e., as either instance variables or `static` variables) *only* if they're required for use in more than one method of the class or if the app should save their values between calls to a given method.

7.4.6 Implementing Method `Maximum` by Reusing Method `Math.Max`

Recall from Fig. 7.2 that class `Math`'s `Max` method can determine the larger of two values. The entire body of our maximum method could also be implemented with nested calls to `Math.Max`, as follows:

```
return Math.Max(x, Math.Max(y, z));
```

The leftmost `Math.Max` call has the arguments x and `Math.Max(y, z)`. Before any method can be called, the runtime evaluates *all* the arguments to determine their values. If an argument is a method call, the call must be performed to determine its return value. So, in the preceding statement, `Math.Max(y, z)` is evaluated first to determine the larger of y and z. Then the result is passed as the second argument to the first call to `Math.Max`, which returns the larger of its two arguments. Using `Math.Max` in this manner is a good example of *software reuse*—we find the largest of three values by reusing `Math.Max`, which finds the larger of two values. Note how concise this code is compared to lines 28–42 of Fig. 7.3.

7.5 Notes on Using Methods

Three Ways to Call a Method
You've seen three ways to call a method:

1. Using a method name by itself to call a method of the *same* class—as in line 19 of Fig. 7.3, which calls `Maximum(number1, number2, number3)` from `Main`.

2. Using a reference to an object, followed by the member-access operator (.) and the method name to call a non-`static` method of the referenced object—as in line 23 of Fig. 4.12, which called `account1.Deposit(depositAmount)` from the `Main` method of class `AccountTest`.

3. Using the class name and the member-access operator (.) to call a `static` method of a class—as in lines 12–14 of Fig. 7.3, which each call `Console.ReadLine()`, or as in `Math.Sqrt(900.0)` in Section 7.3.

Three Ways to Return from a Method
You've seen three ways to return control to the statement that calls a method:

- Reaching the method-ending right brace in a method with return type `void`.

- When the following statement executes in a method with return type `void`

```
return;
```

- When a method returns a result with a statement of the following form in which the *expression* is evaluated and its result (and control) are returned to the caller:

```
return expression;
```

Common Programming Error 7.5

Declaring a method outside the body of a class declaration or inside the body of another method is a syntax error.

Common Programming Error 7.6

Redeclaring a method parameter as a local variable in the method's body is a compilation error.

Common Programming Error 7.7

Forgetting to return a value from a method that should return one is a compilation error. If a return type other than void *is specified, the method must use a* return *statement to return a value, and that value must be consistent with the method's return type. Returning a value from a method whose return type has been declared* void *is a compilation error.*

static *Members Can Access Only the Class's Other* static *Members Directly*

A static method or property can call *only* other static methods or properties of the same class directly (i.e., using the method name by itself) and can manipulate *only* static variables in the same class directly. To access a class's non-static members, a static method or property must use a reference to an object of that class. Recall that static methods relate to a class as a whole, whereas non-static methods are associated with a specific object (instance) of the class and may manipulate the instance variables of that object (as well as the class's static members).

Many objects of a class, each with its own copies of the instance variables, may exist at the same time. Suppose a static method were to invoke a non-static method directly. How would the method know which object's instance variables to manipulate? What would happen if no objects of the class existed at the time the non-static method was invoked?

Software Engineering Observation 7.3

A static *method cannot access non-static members of the same class directly.*

7.6 Argument Promotion and Casting

Another important feature of method calls is argument promotion—implicitly converting an argument's value to the type that the method expects to receive (if possible) in its corresponding parameter. For example, an app can call Math method Sqrt with an integer argument even though the method expects to receive a double argument. The statement

```
Console.WriteLine(Math.Sqrt(4));
```

correctly evaluates Math.Sqrt(4) and displays the value 2.0. Sqrt's parameter list causes C# to convert the int value 4 to the double value 4.0 before passing the value to Sqrt. Such conversions may lead to compilation errors if C#'s promotion rules are not satisfied. The promotion rules specify which conversions are allowed—that is, which conversions can be performed *without losing data*. In the Sqrt example above, an int is converted to a `double` without changing its value. However, converting a `double` to an `int` *truncates* the fractional part of the `double` value—thus, part of the value is lost. Also, `double` variables can hold values much larger (and much smaller) than `int` variables, so assigning a `double` to an `int` can cause a loss of information when the `double` value doesn't fit in the `int`. Converting large integer types to small integer types (e.g., `long` to `int`) also can produce incorrect results.

7.6.1 Promotion Rules

The promotion rules apply to expressions containing values of two or more simple types and to simple-type values passed as arguments to methods. Each value is promoted to the appropriate type in the expression. (Actually, the expression uses a *temporary* copy of each promoted value—the types of the original values remain unchanged.) Figure 7.4 lists the simple types alphabetically and the types to which each can be promoted. Values of all simple types also can be implicitly converted to type `object`. We demonstrate such implicit conversions in Chapter 19.

Type	Conversion types
`bool`	no possible implicit conversions to other simple types
`byte`	`ushort`, `short`, `uint`, `int`, `ulong`, `long`, `decimal`, `float` or `double`
`char`	`ushort`, `int`, `uint`, `long`, `ulong`, `decimal`, `float` or `double`
`decimal`	no possible implicit conversions to other simple types
`double`	no possible implicit conversions to other simple types
`float`	`double`
`int`	`long`, `decimal`, `float` or `double`
`long`	`decimal`, `float` or `double`
`sbyte`	`short`, `int`, `long`, `decimal`, `float` or `double`
`short`	`int`, `long`, `decimal`, `float` or `double`
`uint`	`ulong`, `long`, `decimal`, `float` or `double`
`ulong`	`decimal`, `float` or `double`
`ushort`	`uint`, `int`, `ulong`, `long`, `decimal`, `float` or `double`

Fig. 7.4 | Implicit conversions between simple types.

7.6.2 Sometimes Explicit Casts Are Required

By default, C# does not allow you to implicitly convert values between simple types if the target type cannot represent every value of the original type (e.g., the `int` value 2000000 cannot be represented as a `short`, and any floating-point number with nonzero digits after its decimal point cannot be represented in an integer type such as `long`, `int` or `short`).

To prevent a compilation error in cases where information may be lost due to an implicit conversion between simple types, the compiler requires you to use a *cast operator* to *force* the conversion. This enables you to "take control" from the compiler. You essentially say, "I know this conversion might cause loss of information, but for my purposes here, that's fine." Suppose you create a method `Square` that calculates the square of an `int` argument. To call `Square` with the whole part of a `double` argument named `doubleValue`, you'd write `Square((int) doubleValue)`. This method call explicitly casts (converts) the value of `doubleValue` to an integer for use in method `Square`. Thus, if `doubleValue`'s value is 4.5, the method receives the value 4 and returns 16, not 20.25.

> **Common Programming Error 7.8**
>
> *Converting a simple-type value to a value of another simple type may change the value if the promotion is not allowed. For example, converting a floating-point value to an integral value may introduce truncation errors (loss of the fractional part) in the result.*

7.7 The .NET Framework Class Library

Many predefined classes are grouped into categories of related classes called *namespaces*. Together, these namespaces are referred to as the .NET Framework Class Library.

using Directives and Namespaces

Throughout the text, `using` directives allow us to use library classes from the Framework Class Library without specifying their namespace names. For example, an app would include the declaration

```
using System;
```

in order to use the class names from the `System` namespace without fully qualifying their names. This allows you to use the *unqualified* name `Console`, rather than the *fully qualified* name `System.Console`, in your code.

> **Software Engineering Observation 7.4**
>
> *The C# compiler does not require `using` declarations in a source-code file if the fully qualified class name is specified every time a class name is used. Most programmers prefer the more concise programming style enabled by `using` declarations.*

You might have noticed in each project containing multiple classes that in each class's source-code file we did not need additional `using` directives to use the other classes in the project. There's a special relationship between classes in a project—by default, such classes are in the same namespace and can be used by other classes in the project. Thus, a `using` declaration is not required when one class in a project uses another in the same project—such as when class `AccountTest` used class `Account` in Chapter 4's examples. Also, any classes that are not *explicitly* placed in a namespace are *implicitly* placed in the so-called global namespace.

.NET Namespaces

A strength of C# is the large number of classes in the namespaces of the .NET Framework Class Library. Some key Framework Class Library namespaces are described in Fig. 7.5, which represents only a small portion of the reusable classes in the .NET Framework Class Library.

Namespace	Description
`System.Windows.Forms`	Contains the classes required to create and manipulate GUIs. (Various classes in this namespace are discussed in Chapter 14, Graphical User Interfaces with Windows Forms: Part 1, and Chapter 15, Graphical User Interfaces with Windows Forms: Part 2.)
`System.Windows.Controls` `System.Windows.Input` `System.Windows.Media` `System.Windows.Shapes`	Contain the classes of the Windows Presentation Foundation for GUIs, 2-D and 3-D graphics, multimedia and animation. (See the online WPF chapters.)
`System.Linq`	Contains the classes that support Language Integrated Query (LINQ). (See Chapter 9, Introduction to LINQ and the List Collection, and several other chapters throughout the book.)
`System.Data.Entity`	Contains the classes for manipulating data in databases (i.e., organized collections of data), including support for LINQ to Entities. (See Chapter 22, Databases and LINQ.)
`System.IO`	Contains the classes that enable programs to input and output data. (See Chapter 17, Files and Streams.)
`System.Web`	Contains the classes used for creating and maintaining web apps, which are accessible over the Internet. (See the online ASP.NET Web App Development chapter.)
`System.Xml`	Contains the classes for creating and manipulating XML data. Data can be read from or written to XML files. (See the online XML and LINQ to XML chapter.)
`System.Xml.Linq`	Contains the classes that support Language Integrated Query (LINQ) for XML documents. (See the online XML and LINQ to XML chapter, and several other chapters throughout the book.)
`System.Collections` `System.Collections.Generic`	Contain the classes that define data structures for maintaining collections of data. (See Chapter 21, Generic Collections; Functional Programming with LINQ/PLINQ.)
`System.Text`	Contains classes that enable programs to manipulate characters and strings. (See Chapter 16, Strings and Characters: A Deeper Look.)

Fig. 7.5 | .NET Framework Class Library namespaces (a subset).

Locating Additional Information About a .NET Class's Methods

You can locate additional information about a .NET class's methods in the *.NET Framework Class Library* reference

```
https://msdn.microsoft.com/library/mt472912
```

When you visit this site, you'll see an alphabetical listing of all the namespaces in the Framework Class Library. Locate the namespace and click its link to see an alphabetical listing of all its classes, with a brief description of each. Click a class's link to see a more complete description of the class. Click the **Methods** link in the left-hand column to see a listing of the class's methods.

Good Programming Practice 7.1
The online .NET Framework documentation is easy to search and provides many details about each class. As you learn each class in this book, you should review the class in the online documentation for additional information.

7.8 Case Study: Random-Number Generation

In this and the next section, we develop a nicely structured game-playing app with multiple methods. The app uses most of the control statements presented thus far in the book and introduces several new programming concepts.

There's something in the air of a casino that invigorates people—from the high rollers at the plush mahogany-and-felt craps tables to the quarter poppers at the one-armed bandits. It's the element of chance, the possibility that luck will convert a pocketful of money into a mountain of wealth. The element of chance can be introduced in an app via an object of class Random (of namespace System). Objects of class Random can produce random byte, int and double values. In the next several examples, we use objects of class Random to produce random numbers.

Secure Random Numbers
According to Microsoft's documentation for class Random, the random values it produces "are not completely random because a mathematical algorithm is used to select them, but they are sufficiently random for practical purposes." Such values should not be used, for example, to create randomly selected passwords. If your app requires so-called cryptographically secure random numbers, use class RNGCryptoServiceProvider[1] from namespace System.Security.Cryptography) to produce random values:

```
https://msdn.microsoft.com/library/system.security.cryptography.
    rngcryptoserviceprovider
```

7.8.1 Creating an Object of Type Random

A new random-number generator object can be created with class Random (from the System namespace) as follows:

```
Random randomNumbers = new Random();
```

The Random object can then be used to generate random byte, int and double values—we discuss only random int values here.

7.8.2 Generating a Random Integer

Consider the following statement:

```
int randomValue = randomNumbers.Next();
```

---

1. Class RNGCryptoServiceProvider produces arrays of bytes. We discuss arrays in Chapter 8.

When called with no arguments, method `Next` of class `Random` generates a random `int` value in the range 0 to +2,147,483,646, inclusive. If the `Next` method truly produces values at random, then every value in that range should have an equal chance (or probability) of being chosen each time method `Next` is called. The values returned by `Next` are actually pseudorandom numbers—a sequence of values produced by a complex mathematical calculation. The calculation uses the current time of day (which, of course, changes constantly) to seed the random-number generator such that each execution of an app yields a different sequence of random values.

7.8.3 Scaling the Random-Number Range

The range of values produced directly by method `Next` often differs from the range of values required in a particular C# app. For example, an app that simulates coin tossing might require only 0 for "heads" and 1 for "tails." An app that simulates the rolling of a six-sided die might require random integers in the range 1–6. A video game that randomly predicts the next type of spaceship (out of four possibilities) that will fly across the horizon might require random integers in the range 1–4. For cases like these, class `Random` provides versions of method `Next` that accept arguments. One receives an `int` argument and returns a value from 0 up to, but not including, the argument's value. For example, you might use the statement

```
int randomValue = randomNumbers.Next(6); // 0, 1, 2, 3, 4 or 5
```

which returns 0, 1, 2, 3, 4 or 5. The argument 6—called the scaling factor—represents the number of unique values that `Next` should produce (in this case, six—0, 1, 2, 3, 4 and 5). This manipulation is called scaling the range of values produced by `Random` method `Next`.

7.8.4 Shifting Random-Number Range

Suppose we wanted to simulate a six-sided die that has the numbers 1–6 on its faces, not 0–5. Scaling the range of values alone is not enough. So we shift the range of numbers produced. We could do this by adding a shifting value—in this case 1—to the result of method `Next`, as in

```
int face = 1 + randomNumbers.Next(6); // 1, 2, 3, 4, 5 or 6
```

The shifting value (1) specifies the first value in the desired set of random integers. The preceding statement assigns to `face` a random integer in the range 1–6.

7.8.5 Combining Shifting and Scaling

The third alternative of method `Next` provides a more intuitive way to express both shifting and scaling. This method receives two `int` arguments and returns a value from the first argument's value up to, but not including, the second argument's value. We could use this method to write a statement equivalent to our previous statement, as in

```
int face = randomNumbers.Next(1, 7); // 1, 2, 3, 4, 5 or 6
```

7.8.6 Rolling a Six-Sided Die

To demonstrate random numbers, let's develop an app that simulates 20 rolls of a six-sided die and displays each roll's value. Figure 7.6 shows two sample outputs, which confirm that the results of the preceding calculation are integers in the range 1–6 and that each run of the app can produce a *different* sequence of random numbers. Line 9 creates the Random object randomNumbers to produce random values. Line 15 executes 20 times in a loop to roll the die and line 16 displays the value of each roll.

```
1   // Fig. 7.6: RandomIntegers.cs
2   // Shifted and scaled random integers.
3   using System;
4
5   class RandomIntegers
6   {
7      static void Main()
8      {
9         Random randomNumbers = new Random(); // random-number generator
10
11         // loop 20 times
12         for (int counter = 1; counter <= 20; ++counter)
13         {
14            // pick random integer from 1 to 6
15            int face = randomNumbers.Next(1, 7);
16            Console.Write($"{face}  "); // display generated value
17         }
18
19         Console.WriteLine();
20      }
21   }
```

```
3  3  3  1  1  2  1  2  4  2  2  3  6  2  5  3  4  6  6  1
```

```
6  2  5  1  3  5  2  1  6  5  4  1  6  1  3  3  1  4  3  4
```

Fig. 7.6 | Shifted and scaled random integers.

Rolling a Six-Sided Die 60,000,000 Times
To show that the numbers produced by Next occur with approximately equal likelihood, let's simulate 60,000,000 rolls of a die (Fig. 7.7). Each integer from 1 to 6 should appear approximately 10,000,000 times.

```
1   // Fig. 7.7: RollDie.cs
2   // Roll a six-sided die 60,000,000 times.
3   using System;
4
5   class RollDie
6   {
7      static void Main()
8      {
```

Fig. 7.7 | Roll a six-sided die 60,000,000 times. (Part 1 of 3.)

```csharp
 9          Random randomNumbers = new Random(); // random-number generator
10
11      int frequency1 = 0; // count of 1s rolled
12      int frequency2 = 0; // count of 2s rolled
13      int frequency3 = 0; // count of 3s rolled
14      int frequency4 = 0; // count of 4s rolled
15      int frequency5 = 0; // count of 5s rolled
16      int frequency6 = 0; // count of 6s rolled
17
18      // summarize results of 60,000,000 rolls of a die
19      for (int roll = 1; roll <= 60000000; ++roll)
20      {
21          int face = randomNumbers.Next(1, 7); // number from 1 to 6
22
23          // determine roll value 1-6 and increment appropriate counter
24          switch (face)
25          {
26              case 1:
27                  ++frequency1; // increment the 1s counter
28                  break;
29              case 2:
30                  ++frequency2; // increment the 2s counter
31                  break;
32              case 3:
33                  ++frequency3; // increment the 3s counter
34                  break;
35              case 4:
36                  ++frequency4; // increment the 4s counter
37                  break;
38              case 5:
39                  ++frequency5; // increment the 5s counter
40                  break;
41              case 6:
42                  ++frequency6; // increment the 6s counter
43                  break;
44          }
45      }
46
47      Console.WriteLine("Face\tFrequency"); // output headers
48      Console.WriteLine($"1\t{frequency1}\n2\t{frequency2}");
49      Console.WriteLine($"3\t{frequency3}\n4\t{frequency4}");
50      Console.WriteLine($"5\t{frequency5}\n6\t{frequency6}");
51  }
52 }
```

```
Face    Frequency
1       10006774
2       9993289
3       9993438
4       10006520
5       9998762
6       10001217
```

Fig. 7.7 | Roll a six-sided die 60,000,000 times. (Part 2 of 3.)

```
Face      Frequency
1         10002183
2         9997815
3         9999619
4         10006012
5         9994806
6         9999565
```

Fig. 7.7 | Roll a six-sided die 60,000,000 times. (Part 3 of 3.)

As the two sample outputs show, the values produced by method `Next` enable the app to realistically simulate rolling a six-sided die. The app uses nested control statements (the `switch` is nested inside the `for`) to determine the number of times each side of the die occurred. The `for` statement (lines 19–45) iterates 60,000,000 times. During each iteration, line 21 produces a random value from 1 to 6. This `face` value is then used as the `switch` expression (line 24). Based on the `face` value, the `switch` statement increments one of the six counter variables during each iteration of the loop. (In Section 8.4.7, we show an elegant way to replace the entire `switch` statement in this app with a single statement.) The `switch` statement has no `default` label because we have a `case` label for every possible die value that the expression in line 21 can produce. Run the app several times and observe the results. You'll see that every time you execute this app, it produces different results.

7.8.7 Scaling and Shifting Random Numbers

Previously, we demonstrated the statement

```
int face = randomNumbers.Next(1, 7);
```

which simulates the rolling of a six-sided die. This statement always assigns to variable `face` an integer in the range $1 \le$ `face` < 7. The width of this range (i.e., the number of consecutive integers in the range) is 6, and the starting number in the range is 1. Referring to the preceding statement, we see that the width of the range is determined by the difference between the two integers passed to `Random` method `Next`, and the starting number of the range is the value of the first argument. We can generalize this result as

```
int number = randomNumbers.Next(shiftingValue, shiftingValue + scalingFactor);
```

where *shiftingValue* specifies the first number in the desired range of consecutive integers and *scalingFactor* specifies how many numbers are in the range.

It's also possible to choose integers at random from sets of values *other* than ranges of consecutive integers. For this purpose, it's simpler to use the version of the `Next` method that takes only *one* argument. For example, to obtain a random value from the sequence 2, 5, 8, 11 and 14, you could use the statement

```
int number = 2 + 3 * randomNumbers.Next(5);
```

In this case, `randomNumbers.Next(5)` produces values in the range 0–4. Each value produced is multiplied by 3 to produce a number in the sequence 0, 3, 6, 9 and 12. We then add 2 to that value to *shift* the range of values and obtain a value from the sequence 2, 5, 8, 11 and 14. We can generalize this result as

```
int number = shiftingValue +
    differenceBetweenValues * randomNumbers.Next(scalingFactor);
```

where *shiftingValue* specifies the first number in the desired range of values, *difference-BetweenValues* represents the difference between consecutive numbers in the sequence and *scalingFactor* specifies how many numbers are in the range.

7.8.8 Repeatability for Testing and Debugging

As we mentioned earlier in this section, the methods of class Random actually generate *pseudorandom* numbers based on complex mathematical calculations. Repeatedly calling any of Random's methods produces a sequence of numbers that appears to be random. The calculation that produces the pseudorandom numbers uses the time of day as a seed value to change the sequence's starting point. Each new Random object seeds itself with a value based on the computer system's clock at the time the object is created, enabling each execution of an app to produce a *different* sequence of random numbers.

When debugging an app, it's sometimes useful to repeat the *same* sequence of pseudorandom numbers during each execution of the app. This repeatability enables you to prove that your app is working for a specific sequence of random numbers before you test the app with different sequences of random numbers. When repeatability is important, you can create a Random object as follows:

```
Random randomNumbers = new Random(seedValue);
```

The seedValue argument (an int) seeds the random-number calculation—using the *same* seedValue every time produces the *same* sequence of random numbers. Different seed values, of course, produce *different* sequences of random numbers.

7.9 Case Study: A Game of Chance; Introducing Enumerations

One popular game of chance is the dice game known as "craps," which is played in casinos and back alleys throughout the world. The rules of the game are straightforward:

> *You roll two dice. Each die has six faces, which contain one, two, three, four, five and six spots, respectively. After the dice have come to rest, the sum of the spots on the two upward faces is calculated. If the sum is 7 or 11 on the first throw, you win. If the sum is 2, 3 or 12 on the first throw (called "craps"), you lose (i.e., "the house" wins). If the sum is 4, 5, 6, 8, 9 or 10 on the first throw, that sum becomes your "point." To win, you must continue rolling the dice until you "make your point" (i.e., roll that same point value). You lose by rolling a 7 before making your point.*

The app in Fig. 7.8 simulates the game of craps, using methods to define the logic of the game. The Main method (lines 24–80) calls the static RollDice method (lines 83–94) as needed to roll the two dice and compute their sum. The four sample outputs show winning on the first roll, losing on the first roll, winning on a subsequent roll and losing on a subsequent roll, respectively. Variable randomNumbers (line 8) is declared static, so it can be created once during the program's execution and used in method RollDice.

```csharp
 1   // Fig. 7.8: Craps.cs
 2   // Craps class simulates the dice game craps.
 3   using System;
 4
 5   class Craps
 6   {
 7      // create random-number generator for use in method RollDice
 8      private static Random randomNumbers = new Random();
 9
10      // enumeration with constants that represent the game status
11      private enum Status {Continue, Won, Lost}
12
13      // enumeration with constants that represent common rolls of the dice
14      private enum DiceNames
15      {
16         SnakeEyes = 2,
17         Trey = 3,
18         Seven = 7,
19         YoLeven = 11,
20         BoxCars = 12
21      }
22
23      // plays one game of craps
24      static void Main()
25      {
26         // gameStatus can contain Continue, Won or Lost
27         Status gameStatus = Status.Continue;
28         int myPoint = 0; // point if no win or loss on first roll
29
30         int sumOfDice = RollDice(); // first roll of the dice
31
32         // determine game status and point based on first roll
33         switch ((DiceNames) sumOfDice)
34         {
35            case DiceNames.Seven; // win with 7 on first roll
36            case DiceNames.YoLeven: // win with 11 on first roll
37               gameStatus = Status.Won;
38               break;
39            case DiceNames.SnakeEyes: // lose with 2 on first roll
40            case DiceNames.Trey: // lose with 3 on first roll
41            case DiceNames.BoxCars: // lose with 12 on first roll
42               gameStatus = Status.Lost;
43               break;
44            default: // did not win or lose, so remember point
45               gameStatus = Status.Continue; // game is not over
46               myPoint = sumOfDice; // remember the point
47               Console.WriteLine($"Point is {myPoint}");
48               break;
49         }
50
51         // while game is not complete
52         while (gameStatus == Status.Continue) // game not Won or Lost
53         {
```

Fig. 7.8 | Craps class simulates the dice game craps. (Part 1 of 3.)

```
54              sumOfDice = RollDice(); // roll dice again
55
56              // determine game status
57              if (sumOfDice == myPoint) // win by making point
58              {
59                  gameStatus = Status.Won;
60              }
61              else
62              {
63                  // lose by rolling 7 before point
64                  if (sumOfDice == (int) DiceNames.Seven)
65                  {
66                      gameStatus = Status.Lost;
67                  }
68              }
69          }
70
71          // display won or lost message
72          if (gameStatus == Status.Won)
73          {
74              Console.WriteLine("Player wins");
75          }
76          else
77          {
78              Console.WriteLine("Player loses");
79          }
80      }
81
82      // roll dice, calculate sum and display results
83      static int RollDice()
84      {
85          // pick random die values
86          int die1 = randomNumbers.Next(1, 7); // first die roll
87          int die2 = randomNumbers.Next(1, 7); // second die roll
88
89          int sum = die1 + die2; // sum of die values
90
91          // display results of this roll
92          Console.WriteLine($"Player rolled {die1} + {die2} = {sum}");
93          return sum; // return sum of dice
94      }
95  }
```

```
Player rolled 2 + 5 = 7
Player wins
```

```
Player rolled 2 + 1 = 3
Player loses
```

Fig. 7.8 | Craps class simulates the dice game craps. (Part 2 of 3.)

```
Player rolled 4 + 6 = 10
Point is 10
Player rolled 1 + 3 = 4
Player rolled 1 + 3 = 4
Player rolled 2 + 3 = 5
Player rolled 4 + 4 = 8
Player rolled 6 + 6 = 12
Player rolled 4 + 4 = 8
Player rolled 4 + 5 = 9
Player rolled 2 + 6 = 8
Player rolled 6 + 6 = 12
Player rolled 6 + 4 = 10
Player wins
```

```
Player rolled 2 + 4 = 6
Point is 6
Player rolled 3 + 1 = 4
Player rolled 5 + 5 = 10
Player rolled 6 + 1 = 7
Player loses
```

Fig. 7.8 | Craps class simulates the dice game craps. (Part 3 of 3.)

7.9.1 Method RollDice

In the rules of the game, the player must roll two dice on the first roll and must do the same on all subsequent rolls. We declare method RollDice (lines 83–94) to roll the dice and compute and display their sum. Method RollDice is declared once, but it's called from two places (lines 30 and 54) in method Main, which contains the logic for one complete game of craps. Method RollDice takes no arguments, so it has an empty parameter list. Each time it's called, RollDice returns the sum of the dice as an int. Although lines 86 and 87 look the same (except for the die names), they do not necessarily produce the same result. Each of these statements produces a random value in the range 1–6. Variable randomNumbers (used in lines 86–87) is *not* declared in the method. Rather it's declared as a private static variable of the class and initialized in line 8. This enables us to create *one* Random object that's reused in each call to RollDice.

7.9.2 Method Main's Local Variables

The game is reasonably involved. The player may win or lose on the first roll or may win or lose on any subsequent roll. Method Main (lines 24–80) uses local variable gameStatus (line 27) to keep track of the overall game status, local variable myPoint (line 28) to store the "point" if the player does not win or lose on the first roll and local variable sumOfDice (line 30) to maintain the sum of the dice for the most recent roll. Variable myPoint is initialized to 0 to ensure that the app will compile. If you do not initialize myPoint, the compiler issues an error, because myPoint is not assigned a value in every case of the switch statement—thus, the app could try to use myPoint before it's definitely assigned a value. By contrast, gameStatus does not require initialization because it's assigned a value in every branch of the switch statement—thus, it's guaranteed to be initialized before it's used. However, as good practice, we initialize it anyway.

7.9.3 enum Type Status

Local variable gameStatus (line 27) is declared to be of a new type called Status, which we declared in line 11. Status is a user-defined type called an enumeration, which declares a set of *constants* represented by identifiers. An enumeration is introduced by the keyword enum and a type name (in this case, Status). As with a class, braces ({ and }) delimit the body of an enum declaration. Inside the braces is a comma-separated list of enumeration constants—by default, the first constant has the value 0 and each subsequent constant's value is incremented by 1. The enum constant names must be *unique*, but the value associated with each constant need not be. Type Status is declared as a private member of class Craps, because Status is used only in that class.

Variables of type Status should be assigned only one of the three constants declared in the enumeration. When the game is won, the app sets local variable gameStatus to Status.Won (lines 37 and 59). When the game is lost, the app sets gameStatus to Status.Lost (lines 42 and 66). Otherwise, the app sets gameStatus to Status.Continue (line 45) to indicate that the dice must be rolled again.

Good Programming Practice 7.2

Using enumeration constants (like Status.Won, Status.Lost and Status.Continue) rather than literal integer values (such as 0, 1 and 2) can make code easier to read and maintain.

7.9.4 The First Roll

Line 30 in method Main calls RollDice, which picks two random values from 1 to 6, displays the value of the first die, the value of the second die and the sum of the dice, and returns the sum of the dice. Method Main next enters the switch statement at lines 33–49, which uses the sumOfDice value to determine whether the game has been won or lost, or whether it should continue with another roll.

7.9.5 enum Type DiceNames

The sums of the dice that would result in a win or loss on the first roll are declared in the DiceNames enumeration in lines 14–21. These are used in the switch statement's cases. The identifier names use casino parlance for these sums. In the DiceNames enumeration, we assign a value explicitly to each identifier name. When the enum is declared, each constant in the enum declaration is a constant value of type int. If you do not assign a value to an identifier in the enum declaration, the compiler will do so. If the first enum constant is unassigned, the compiler gives it the value 0. If any other enum constant is unassigned, the compiler gives it a value one higher than that of the preceding enum constant. For example, in the Status enumeration, the compiler implicitly assigns 0 to Status.Continue, 1 to Status.Won and 2 to Status.Lost.

7.9.6 Underlying Type of an enum

You could also declare an enum's underlying type to be byte, sbyte, short, ushort, int, uint, long or ulong by writing

```
private enum MyEnum : typeName {Constant1, Constant2, ...}
```

where *typeName* represents one of the integral simple types.

7.9.7 Comparing Integers and enum Constants

If you need to compare a simple integral type value to the underlying value of an enumeration constant, you must use a cast operator to make the two types match—there are no implicit conversions between enum and integral types. In the switch expression (line 33), we use the cast operator to convert the int value in sumOfDice to type DiceNames and compare it to each of the constants in DiceNames. Lines 35–36 determine whether the player won on the first roll with Seven (7) or YoLeven (11). Lines 39–41 determine whether the player lost on the first roll with SnakeEyes (2), Trey (3) or BoxCars (12). After the first roll, if the game is not over, the default case (lines 44–48) saves sumOfDice in myPoint (line 46) and displays the point (line 47).

Additional Rolls of the Dice
If we're still trying to "make our point" (i.e., the game is continuing from a prior roll), the loop in lines 52–69 executes. Line 54 rolls the dice again. If sumOfDice matches myPoint in line 57, line 59 sets gameStatus to Status.Won, and the loop terminates because the game is complete. In line 64, we use the cast operator (int) to obtain the underlying value of DiceNames.Seven so that we can compare it to sumOfDice. If sumOfDice is equal to Seven (7), line 66 sets gameStatus to Status.Lost, and the loop terminates because the game is over. When the game completes, lines 72–79 display a message indicating whether the player won or lost, and the app terminates.

*Control Statements in the **Craps** Example*
Note the use of the various program-control mechanisms we've discussed. The Craps class uses two methods—Main and RollDice (called twice from Main)—and the switch, while, if...else and nested if control statements. Also, notice that we use multiple case labels in the switch statement to execute the same statements for sums of Seven and YoLeven (lines 35–36) and for sums of SnakeEyes, Trey and BoxCars (lines 39–41).

Code Snippets for Auto-Implemented Properties
Visual Studio has a feature called code snippets that allows you to insert *predefined code templates* into your source code. One such snippet enables you to easily create a switch statement with cases for all possible values for an enum type. Type switch in the C# code then press *Tab* twice. If you specify a variable of an enum type in the switch statement's expression and press *Enter*, a case for each enum constant will be generated automatically.

To get a list of all available code snippets, type *Ctrl + k, Ctrl + x*. This displays the **Insert Snippet** window in the code editor. You can navigate through the Visual C# snippet folders with the mouse to see the snippets. This feature also can be accessed by *right clicking* in the source code editor and selecting the **Insert Snippet...** menu item.

7.10 Scope of Declarations

You've seen declarations of C# entities, such as classes, methods, properties, variables and parameters. Declarations introduce names that can be used to refer to such C# entities. The scope of a declaration is the portion of the app that can refer to the declared entity by its unqualified name. Such an entity is said to be "in scope" for that portion of the app. This section introduces several important scope issues. The basic scope rules are as follows:

1. The scope of a parameter declaration is the body of the method in which the declaration appears.

2. The scope of a local-variable declaration is from the point at which the declaration appears to the end of the block containing the declaration.

3. The scope of a local-variable declaration that appears in the initialization section of a `for` statement's header is the body of the `for` statement and the other expressions in the header.

4. The scope of a method, property or field of a class is the entire body of the class. This enables non-`static` methods and properties of a class to use any of the class's fields, methods and properties, regardless of the order in which they're declared. Similarly, `static` methods and properties can use any of the `static` members of the class.

Any block may contain variable declarations. If a local variable or parameter in a method has the same name as a field, the field is hidden until the block terminates—in Chapter 10, we discuss how to access hidden fields. A compilation error occurs if a *nested block* in a method contains a variable with the same name as a local variable in an *outer block* of the method. The app in Fig. 7.9 demonstrates scoping issues with fields and local variables.

Error-Prevention Tip 7.1

Use different names for fields and local variables to help prevent subtle logic errors that occur when a method is called and a local variable of the method hides a field of the same name in the class.

```
1   // Fig. 7.9: Scope.cs
2   // Scope class demonstrates static and local variable scopes.
3   using System;
4
5   class Scope
6   {
7      // static variable that's accessible to all methods of this class
8      private static int x = 1;
9
10     // Main creates and initializes local variable x
11     // and calls methods UseLocalVariable and UseStaticVariable
12     static void Main()
13     {
14        int x = 5; // method's local variable x hides static variable x
15
16        Console.WriteLine($"local x in method Main is {x}");
17
18        // UseLocalVariable has its own local x
19        UseLocalVariable();
20
21        // UseStaticVariable uses class Scope's static variable x
22        UseStaticVariable();
```

Fig. 7.9 | Scope class demonstrates static- and local-variable scopes. (Part 1 of 2.)

```
23
24          // UseLocalVariable reinitializes its own local x
25          UseLocalVariable();
26
27          // class Scope's static variable x retains its value
28          UseStaticVariable();
29
30          Console.WriteLine($"\nlocal x in method Main is {x}");
31      }
32
33      // create and initialize local variable x during each call
34      static void UseLocalVariable()
35      {
36          int x = 25; // initialized each time UseLocalVariable is called
37
38          Console.WriteLine(
39              $"\nlocal x on entering method UseLocalVariable is {x}");
40          ++x; // modifies this method's local variable x
41          Console.WriteLine(
42              $"local x before exiting method UseLocalVariable is {x}");
43      }
44
45      // modify class Scope's static variable x during each call
46      static void UseStaticVariable()
47      {
48          Console.WriteLine("\nstatic variable x on entering method " +
49              $"UseStaticVariable is {x}");
50          x *= 10; // modifies class Scope's static variable x
51          Console.WriteLine("static variable x before exiting " +
52              $"method UseStaticVariable is {x}");
53      }
54  }
```

```
local x in method Main is 5

local x on entering method UseLocalVariable is 25
local x before exiting method UseLocalVariable is 26

static variable x on entering method UseStaticVariable is 1
static variable x before exiting method UseStaticVariable is 10

local x on entering method UseLocalVariable is 25
local x before exiting method UseLocalVariable is 26

static variable x on entering method UseStaticVariable is 10
static variable x before exiting method UseStaticVariable is 100

local x in method Main is 5
```

Fig. 7.9 | Scope class demonstrates static- and local-variable scopes. (Part 2 of 2.)

Line 8 declares and initializes the static variable x to 1. This static variable is *hidden* in any block (or method) that declares a local variable named x. Method Main (lines 12–31) declares local variable x (line 14) and initializes it to 5. This local variable's value is output to show that static variable x (whose value is 1) is hidden in method Main. The app declares two other methods—UseLocalVariable (lines 34–43) and UseStaticVariable (lines 46–53)—that each take no arguments and do not return results. Method Main calls each method twice (lines 19–28). Method UseLocalVariable declares local variable x (line 36). When UseLocalVariable is first called (line 19), it creates local variable x and initializes it to 25 (line 36), outputs the value of x (lines 38–39), increments x (line 40) and outputs the value of x again (lines 41–42). When UseLocalVariable is called a second time (line 25), it re-creates local variable x and reinitializes it to 25, so the output of each call to UseLocalVariable is identical.

Method UseStaticVariable does not declare any local variables. Therefore, when it refers to x, static variable x (line 8) of the class is used. When method UseStaticVariable is first called (line 22), it outputs the value (1) of static variable x (lines 48–49), multiplies the static variable x by 10 (line 50) and outputs the value (10) of static variable x again (lines 51–52) before returning. The next time method UseStaticVariable is called (line 28), the static variable has its modified value, 10, so the method outputs 10, then 100. Finally, in method Main, the app outputs the value of local variable x again (line 30) to show that none of the method calls modified Main's local variable x, because the methods all referred to variables named x in other scopes.

7.11   Method-Call Stack and Activation Records

To understand how C# performs method calls, we first need to consider a data structure (i.e., collection of related data items) known as a stack. Think of a stack as analogous to a pile of dishes. When a dish is placed on the pile, it's placed at the *top*—referred to as pushing the dish onto the stack. Similarly, when a dish is removed from the pile, it's removed from the top—referred to as popping the dish off the stack. Stacks are known as last-in, first-out (LIFO) data structures—the last item pushed (inserted) on the stack is the first item popped (removed) from the stack.

7.11.1 Method-Call Stack

One of the most important mechanisms for computer science students to understand is the method-call stack (sometimes referred to as the program-execution stack). This data structure—working "behind the scenes"—supports the method call/return mechanism. It also supports the creation, maintenance and destruction of each called method's local variables. As we'll see in Figs. 7.11–7.13, last-in, first-out (LIFO) behavior is *exactly* what a method needs in order to return to the method that called it.

7.11.2 Stack Frames

As each method is called, it may, in turn, call other methods, which may, in turn, call other methods—all *before* any of the methods return. Each method eventually must return control to the method that called it. So, somehow, the system must keep track of the *return addresses* that each method needs in order to return control to the method that called it. The method-call stack is the perfect data structure for handling this information. Each time a method calls another method, an entry is *pushed* onto the stack. This entry, called a stack frame or an activation record, contains the *return address* that the called method needs in order to return to the calling method. It also contains some additional information we'll soon discuss. If the called method returns instead of calling another method before returning, the stack frame for the method call is *popped*, and control transfers to the return address in the popped stack frame. The same techniques apply when a method accesses a property or when a property calls a method.

The beauty of the call stack is that each called method *always* finds the information it needs to return to its caller at the *top* of the call stack. And, if a method makes a call to another method, a stack frame for the new method call is simply *pushed* onto the call stack. Thus, the return address required by the newly called method to return to its caller is now located at the *top* of the stack.

7.11.3 Local Variables and Stack Frames

The stack frames have another important responsibility. Most methods have local variables—parameters and any local variables the method declares. Local variables need to exist while a method is executing. They need to remain active if the method makes calls to other methods. But when a called method returns to its caller, the called method's local variables need to "go away." The called method's stack frame is a perfect place to reserve the memory for the called method's local variables. That stack frame exists as long as the called method is active. When that method returns—and no longer needs its local variables—its stack frame is *popped* from the stack, and those local variables no longer exist.

7.11.4 Stack Overflow

Of course, the amount of memory in a computer is finite, so only a certain amount of memory can be used to store activation records on the method-call stack. If more method calls occur than can have their activation records stored on the method-call stack, a fatal error known as **stack overflow** occurs[2]—typically caused by infinite recursion (Section 7.16).

7.11.5 Method-Call Stack in Action

Now let's consider how the call stack supports the operation of a `Square` method (lines 15–18 of Fig. 7.10) called by `Main` (lines 8–12).

```
1   // Fig. 7.10: SquareTest.cs
2   // Square method used to demonstrate the method
3   // call stack and activation records.
4   using System;
5
6   class Program
7   {
8      static void Main()
9      {
10         int x = 10; // value to square (local variable in main)
11         Console.WriteLine($"x squared: {Square(x)}");
12      }
13
```

Fig. 7.10 | Square method used to demonstrate the method-call stack and activation records. (Part 1 of 2.)

---

2. This is how the website `stackoverflow.com` got its name. This is a great website for getting answers to your programming questions.

```
14      // returns the square of an integer
15      static int Square(int y) // y is a local variable
16      {
17          return y * y; // calculate square of y and return result
18      }
19   }
```

x squared: 100

Fig. 7.10 | Square method used to demonstrate the method-call stack and activation records. (Part 2 of 2.)

First, the operating system calls Main—this *pushes* an activation record onto the stack (Fig. 7.11). This tells Main how to return to the operating system (i.e., transfer to return address R1) and contains the space for Main's local variable x, which is initialized to 10.

Step 1: Operating system calls Main to begin program execution

Operating system

```
static void Main()
{
    int x = 10;
    Console.WriteLine(
        $"x squared: {Square(x)}");
}
```

Return location **R1**

Method call stack after operating system calls Main

Top of stack

Activation record for method Main

Return location: **R1**

Local variables:

x   10

Key

⎯⎯⎯ Lines that represent the operating
⎯⎯⎯ system executing instructions

Fig. 7.11 | Method-call stack after the operating system calls main to execute the program.

Method Main—before returning to the operating system—calls method Square in line 11 of Fig. 7.10. This causes a stack frame for Square (lines 15–18) to be pushed onto the method-call stack (Fig. 7.12). This stack frame contains the return address that Square needs to return to Main (i.e., R2) and the memory for Square's local variable y.

After Square performs its calculation, it needs to return to Main—and no longer needs the memory for y. So Square's stack frame is *popped* from the stack—giving Square the return location in Main (i.e., R2) and losing Square's local variable (*Step 3*). Figure 7.13 shows the method-call stack *after* Square's activation record has been *popped*.

Method Main now displays the result of calling Square (Fig. 7.10, line 11). Reaching the closing right brace of Main causes its stack frame to be *popped* from the stack, giving Main the address it needs to return to the operating system (i.e., R1 in Fig. 7.11)—at this point, Main's local variable x no longer exists.

Step 2: Main calls method Square to perform calculation

Fig. 7.12 | Method-call stack after Main calls square to perform the calculation.

Step 3: Square returns its result to Main

Fig. 7.13 | Method-call stack after method square returns to Main.

You've now seen how valuable the stack data structure is in implementing a key mechanism that supports program execution. Data structures have many important applications in computer science. We discuss stacks, queues, lists, trees and other data structures in Chapter 19, Custom Linked Data Structures, and Chapter 21, Generic Collections; Functional Programming with LINQ/PLINQ.

7.12 Method Overloading

Methods of the same name can be declared in the same class, as long as they have different sets of parameters (determined by the number, types and order of the parameters). This is called method overloading. When an overloaded method is called, the C# compiler selects the appropriate method by examining the number, types and order of the arguments in the call. Method overloading is commonly used to create several methods with the *same name* that perform the same or similar tasks, but on *different types* or *different numbers of arguments*. For example, Random method Next (Section 7.8) has overloads that accept different numbers of arguments, and Math method Max has overloads that accept different types of arguments (ints vs. doubles). These find the minimum and maximum, respectively, of two values of each of the numeric simple types. Our next example demonstrates declaring and invoking overloaded methods. You'll see examples of overloaded constructors in Chapter 10.

7.12.1 Declaring Overloaded Methods

In class MethodOverload (Fig. 7.14), we include two overloaded versions of a method called Square—one that calculates the square of an int (and returns an int) and one that calculates the square of a double (and returns a double). Although these methods have the same name and similar parameter lists and bodies, you can think of them simply as *different* methods. It may help to think of the method names as "Square of int" and "Square of double," respectively.

```csharp
1   // Fig. 7.14: MethodOverload.cs
2   // Overloaded method declarations.
3   using System;
4
5   class MethodOverload
6   {
7      // test overloaded square methods
8      static void Main()
9      {
10         Console.WriteLine($"Square of integer 7 is {Square(7)}");
11         Console.WriteLine($"Square of double 7.5 is {Square(7.5)}");
12      }
13
14      // square method with int argument
15      static int Square(int intValue)
16      {
17         Console.WriteLine($"Called square with int argument: {intValue}");
18         return intValue * intValue;
19      }
20
```

Fig. 7.14 | Overloaded method declarations. (Part 1 of 2.)

```
21      // square method with double argument
22      static double Square(double doubleValue)
23      {
24         Console.WriteLine(
25            $"Called square with double argument: {doubleValue}");
26         return doubleValue * doubleValue;
27      }
28   }
```

```
Called square with int argument: 7
Square of integer 7 is 49
Called square with double argument: 7.5
Square of double 7.5 is 56.25
```

Fig. 7.14 | Overloaded method declarations. (Part 2 of 2.)

Line 10 in Main invokes method Square with the argument 7. Literal integer values are treated as type int, so the method call in line 10 invokes the version of Square at lines 15–19 that specifies an int parameter. Similarly, line 11 invokes method Square with the argument 7.5. Literal real-number values are treated as type double, so the method call in line 11 invokes the version of Square at lines 22–27 that specifies a double parameter. Each method first outputs a line of text to prove that the proper method was called in each case.

The overloaded methods in Fig. 7.14 perform the same calculation, but with two different types. C#'s generics feature provides a mechanism for writing a single "generic method" that can perform the same tasks as an entire set of overloaded methods. We discuss generic methods in Chapter 20.

7.12.2 Distinguishing Between Overloaded Methods

The compiler distinguishes overloaded methods by their signature—a combination of the method's name and the number, types and order of its parameters. The signature also includes the way those parameters are passed, which can be modified by the ref and out keywords (discussed in Section 7.18). If the compiler looked only at method names during compilation, the code in Fig. 7.14 would be *ambiguous*—the compiler would not know how to distinguish between the Square methods (lines 15–19 and 22–27). Internally, the compiler uses signatures to determine whether a class's methods are unique in that class.

For example, in Fig. 7.14, the compiler will use the method signatures to distinguish between the "Square of int" method (the Square method that specifies an int parameter) and the "Square of double" method (the Square method that specifies a double parameter). As another example, if Method1's declaration begins as

```
void Method1(int a, float b)
```

then that method will have a different signature than a method that begins with

```
void Method1(float a, int b)
```

The *order* of the parameter types is important—the compiler considers the preceding two Method1 headers to be distinct.

7.12.3 Return Types of Overloaded Methods

In discussing the logical names of methods used by the compiler, we did not mention the methods' return types. Methods *cannot* be distinguished by return type. If in a class named `MethodOverloadError` you define overloaded methods with the following headers:

```
int Square(int x)
double Square(int x)
```

which each have the *same* signature but *different* return types, the compiler generates the following error for the second `Square` method:

```
Type 'MethodOverloadError' already defines a member called 'Square'
with the same parameter types
```

Overloaded methods can have the *same* or *different* return types if the parameter lists are *different*. Also, overloaded methods need not have the same number of parameters.

Common Programming Error 7.9

Declaring overloaded methods with identical parameter lists is a compilation error regardless of whether the return types are different.

7.13 Optional Parameters

Methods can have optional parameters that allow the calling method to *vary the number of arguments* to pass. An optional parameter specifies a default value that's assigned to the parameter if the optional argument is omitted. You can create methods with one or more optional parameters. *All optional parameters must be placed to the right of the method's non-optional parameters*—that is, at the end of the parameter list.

Common Programming Error 7.10

Declaring a non-optional parameter to the right of an optional one is a compilation error.

When a parameter has a default value, the caller has the *option* of passing that particular argument. For example, the method header

```
static int Power(int baseValue, int exponentValue = 2)
```

specifies an optional second parameter. Each call to `Power` must pass at least a `baseValue` argument, or a compilation error occurs. Optionally, a second argument (for the `exponentValue` parameter) can be passed to `Power`. Each optional parameter must specify a default value by using an equal (=) sign followed by the value. For example, the header for `Power` sets 2 as `exponentValue`'s default value. Consider the following calls to `Power`:

- `Power()`—This call generates a compilation error because this method requires a minimum of one argument.
- `Power(10)`—This call is valid because one argument (10) is being passed. The optional `exponentValue` is not specified in the method call, so the compiler uses 2 for the `exponentValue`, as specified in the method header.
- `Power(10, 3)`—This call is also valid because 10 is passed as the required argument and 3 is passed as the optional argument.

Figure 7.15 demonstrates an optional parameter. The program calculates the result of raising a base value to an exponent. Method `Power` (lines 15–25) specifies that its second parameter is optional. In `Main`, lines 10–11 call method `Power`. Line 10 calls the method without the optional second argument. In this case, the compiler provides the second argument, 2, using the default value of the optional argument, which is not visible to you in the call.

```
1    // Fig. 7.15: CalculatePowers.cs
2    // Optional parameter demonstration with method Power.
3    using System;
4
5    class CalculatePowers
6    {
7       // call Power with and without optional arguments
8       static void Main()
9       {
10          Console.WriteLine($"Power(10) = {Power(10)}") ;
11          Console.WriteLine($"Power(2, 10) = {Power(2, 10)}");
12       }
13
14       // use iteration to calculate power
15       static int Power(int baseValue, int exponentValue = 2)
16       {
17          int result = 1;
18
19          for (int i = 1; i <= exponentValue; ++i)
20          {
21             result *= baseValue;
22          }
23
24          return result;
25       }
26    }
```

```
Power(10) = 100
Power(2, 10) = 1024
```

Fig. 7.15 | Optional parameter demonstration with method `Power`.

7.14 Named Parameters

Normally, when calling a method, the argument values—in order—are assigned to the parameters from left to right in the parameter list. Consider a `Time` class that stores the time of day in 24-hour clock format as `int` values representing the hour (0–23), minute (0–59) and second (0–59). Such a class might provide a `SetTime` method with optional parameters like

```
public void SetTime(int hour = 0, int minute = 0, int second = 0)
```

In the preceding method header, all three of `SetTime`'s parameters are optional. Assuming that we have a `Time` object named `t`, consider the following calls to `SetTime`:

- t.SetTime()—This call specifies no arguments, so the compiler assigns the default value 0 to each parameter. The resulting time is 12:00:00 AM.

- t.SetTime(12)—This call specifies the argument 12 for the first parameter, hour, and the compiler assigns the default value 0 to the minute and second parameters. The resulting time is 12:00:00 PM.

- t.SetTime(12, 30)—This call specifies the arguments 12 and 30 for the parameters hour and minute, respectively, and the compiler assigns the default value 0 to the parameter second. The resulting time is 12:30:00 PM.

- t.SetTime(12, 30, 22)—This call specifies the arguments 12, 30 and 22 for the parameters hour, minute and second, respectively, so the compiler does not provide any default values. The resulting time is 12:30:22 PM.

What if you wanted to specify only arguments for the hour and second? You might think that you could call the method as follows:

```
t.SetTime(12, , 22); // COMPILATION ERROR
```

C# doesn't allow you to skip an argument as shown above. C# provides a feature called named parameters, which enable you to call methods that receive optional parameters by providing *only* the optional arguments you wish to specify. To do so, you explicitly specify the parameter's name and value—separated by a colon (:)—in the argument list of the method call. For example, the preceding statement can be written as follows:

```
t.SetTime(hour: 12, second: 22); // sets the time to 12:00:22
```

In this case, the compiler assigns parameter hour the argument 12 and parameter second the argument 22. The parameter minute is not specified, so the compiler assigns it the default value 0. It's also possible to specify the arguments *out of order* when using named parameters. The arguments for the required parameters must always be supplied. The *argumentName*: *value* syntax may be used with any method's required parameters.

7.15 C# 6 Expression-Bodied Methods and Properties

C# 6 introduces a new concise syntax for:

- methods that contain only a return statement that returns a value
- read-only properties in which the get accessor contains only a return statement
- methods that contain single statement bodies.

Consider the following Cube method:

```
static int Cube(int x)
{
    return x * x * x;
}
```

In C# 6, this can be expressed with an expression-bodied method as

```
static int Cube(int x) => x * x * x;
```

The value of x * x * x is returned to Cube's caller implicitly. The symbol => follows the method's parameter list and introduces the method's body—no braces or return statement are required and this can be used with static and non-static methods alike. If the expression to the right of => does not have a value (e.g., a call to a method that returns void), the expression-bodied method must return void. Similarly, a read-only property can be implemented as an expression-bodied property. The following reimplements the IsNoFaultState property in Fig. 6.11 to return the result of a logical expression:

```
public bool IsNoFaultState =>
    State == "MA" || State == "NJ" || State == "NY" || State == "PA";
```

7.16 Recursion

The apps we've discussed thus far are generally structured as methods that call one another in a disciplined, hierarchical manner. For some problems, however, it's useful to have a method call itself. A recursive method is a method that calls itself, either *directly* or *indirectly through another method*. We consider recursion conceptually first. Then we examine an app containing a recursive method.

7.16.1 Base Cases and Recursive Calls

Recursive problem-solving approaches have a number of elements in common. When a recursive method is called to solve a problem, it actually is capable of solving *only* the simplest case(s), or base case(s). If the method is called with a base case, it returns a result. If the method is called with a more complex problem, it divides the problem into two conceptual pieces (often called *divide and conquer*): a piece that the method knows how to do and a piece that it does not know how to do. To make recursion feasible, the latter piece must resemble the original problem, but be a slightly simpler or slightly smaller version of it. Because this new problem looks like the original problem, the method calls a fresh copy (or several fresh copies) of itself to work on the smaller problem; this is referred to as a recursive call and is also called the recursion step. The recursion step normally includes a return statement, because its result will be combined with the portion of the problem the method knew how to solve to form a result that will be passed back to the original caller.

The recursion step executes while the original call to the method is still active (i.e., while it has not finished executing). The recursion step can result in many more recursive calls, as the method divides each new subproblem into two conceptual pieces. For the recursion to *terminate* eventually, each time the method calls itself with a slightly simpler version of the original problem, the sequence of smaller and smaller problems must converge on the base case(s). At that point, the method recognizes the base case and returns a result to the previous copy of the method. A sequence of returns ensues until the original method call returns the result to the caller. This process sounds complex compared with the conventional problem solving we've performed to this point.

7.16.2 Recursive Factorial Calculations

Let's write a recursive app to perform a popular mathematical calculation. The factorial of a nonnegative integer n, written $n!$ (and pronounced "n factorial"), is the product

$$n \cdot (n-1) \cdot (n-2) \cdot \ldots \cdot 1$$

1! is equal to 1 and 0! is defined to be 1. For example, 5! is the product $5 \cdot 4 \cdot 3 \cdot 2 \cdot 1$, which is equal to 120.

The factorial of an integer, number, greater than or equal to 0 can be calculated iteratively (nonrecursively) using the for statement as follows:

```
long factorial = 1;

for (long counter = number; counter >= 1; --counter)
{
    factorial *= counter;
}
```

A recursive declaration of the factorial method is arrived at by observing the following relationship:

$$n! = n \cdot (n - 1)!$$

For example, 5! is clearly equal to 5 · 4!, as is shown by the following equations:

$$5! = 5 \cdot 4 \cdot 3 \cdot 2 \cdot 1$$
$$5! = 5 \cdot (4 \cdot 3 \cdot 2 \cdot 1)$$
$$5! = 5 \cdot (4!)$$

The evaluation of 5! would proceed as shown in Fig. 7.16. Figure 7.16(a) shows how the succession of recursive calls proceeds until 1! is evaluated to be 1, which terminates the recursion. Figure 7.16(b) shows the values returned from each recursive call to its caller until the value is calculated and returned.

(a) Sequence of recursive calls   (b) Values returned from each recursive call

Fig. 7.16 | Recursive evaluation of 5!.

7.16.3 Implementing Factorial Recursively

Figure 7.17 uses recursion to calculate and display the factorials of the integers from 0 to 10. The recursive method Factorial (lines 17–28) first tests to determine whether a terminating condition (line 20) is true. If number is less than or equal to 1 (the base case), Factorial returns 1 and no further recursion is necessary. If number is greater than 1, line

26 expresses the problem as the product of number and a recursive call to Factorial evaluating the factorial of number - 1, which is a slightly simpler problem than the original calculation, Factorial(number).

```
1   // Fig. 7.17: FactorialTest.cs
2   // Recursive Factorial method.
3   using System;
4
5   class FactorialTest
6   {
7      static void Main()
8      {
9         // calculate the factorials of 0 through 10
10        for (long counter = 0; counter <= 10; ++counter)
11        {
12           Console.WriteLine($"{counter}! = {Factorial(counter)}");
13        }
14     }
15
16     // recursive declaration of method Factorial
17     static long Factorial(long number)
18     {
19        // base case
20        if (number <= 1)
21        {
22           return 1;
23        }
24        else // recursion step
25        {
26           return number * Factorial(number - 1);
27        }
28     }
29  }
```

```
0! = 1
1! = 1
2! = 2
3! = 6
4! = 24
5! = 120
6! = 720
7! = 5040
8! = 40320
9! = 362880
10! = 3628800
```

Fig. 7.17 | Recursive Factorial method.

Method Factorial (lines 17–28) receives a parameter of type long and returns a result of type long. As you can see in Fig. 7.17, factorial values become large quickly. We chose type long (which can represent relatively large integers) so that the app could calculate factorials greater than 20!. Unfortunately, the Factorial method produces large values so quickly that factorial values soon exceed even the maximum value that can be stored in a `long` variable. Due to the restrictions on the integral types, variables of type `float`, `double` or `decimal` might ultimately be needed to calculate factorials of larger numbers. This situation points to a weakness in some programming languages—the languages are *not easily extended* to handle the unique requirements of various apps. As you know, C# allows you to create new types. For example, you could create a type `HugeInteger` for arbitrarily large integers (as you'll do in Exercise 10.9). This class would enable an app to calculate the factorials of larger numbers. The .NET Framework's `BigInteger` type (from namespace `System.Numerics`) supports arbitrarily large integers.

> **Common Programming Error 7.11**
>
> *Either omitting the base case or writing the recursion step incorrectly so that it does not converge on the base case will cause infinite recursion, eventually exhausting memory. This error is analogous to the problem of an infinite loop in an iterative (nonrecursive) solution.*

7.17 Value Types vs. Reference Types

Types in C# are divided into two categories—*value types* and *reference types*.

Value Types
C#'s simple types (like `int`, `double` and `decimal`) are all value types. A variable of a value type simply contains a *value* of that type. For example, Fig. 7.18 shows an `int` variable named count that contains the value 7.

`int count = 7;`

count

7

A variable (`count`) of a value type (`int`) contains a value (7) of that type

Fig. 7.18 | Value-type variable.

Reference Types
By contrast, a variable of a reference type (also called a reference) contains the *location* where the data referred to by that variable is stored. Such a variable is said to refer to an object in the program. For example, the statement

```
Account myAccount = new Account();
```

creates an object of our class `Account` (presented in Chapter 4), places it in memory and stores the object's reference in variable myAccount of type `Account`, as shown in Fig. 7.19. The `Account` object is shown with its name instance variable.

Reference-Type Instance Variables Are Initialized to **null** by Default
Reference-type instance variables (such as myAccount in Fig. 7.19) are initialized by default to null. The type `string` is a reference type. For this reason, `string` instance variable name is shown in Fig. 7.19 with an empty box representing the null-valued variable. A `string` variable with the value null is *not* an empty `string`, which is represented by "" or `string.Empty`. Rather, the value null represents a reference that does *not* refer to an

Fig. 7.19 | Reference-type variable.

object, whereas the empty string is a string object that does not contain any characters. In Section 7.18, we discuss value types and reference types in more detail.

> **Software Engineering Observation 7.5**
>
> *A variable's declared type (e.g., int or Account) indicates whether the variable is of a value type or a reference type. If a variable's type is one of the simple types (Appendix B), an enum type or a struct type (which we introduce in Section 10.13), then it's a value type. Classes like Account are reference types.*

7.18 Passing Arguments By Value and By Reference

Two ways to pass arguments to methods in many programming languages are pass-by-value and pass-by-reference. When an argument is passed by *value* (the default in C#), a *copy* of its value is made and passed to the called method. Changes to the copy do *not* affect the original variable's value in the caller. This prevents the accidental side effects that so greatly hinder the development of correct and reliable software systems. Each argument that's been passed in the programs so far has been passed by value. When an argument is passed by *reference*, the caller gives the method the ability to access and modify the caller's original variable—no copy is passed.

To pass an object by reference into a method, simply provide as an argument in the method call the variable that refers to the object. Then, in the method body, reference the object using the corresponding parameter name. The parameter refers to the original object in memory, so the called method can access the original object directly.

In the previous section, we began discussing the differences between *value types* and *reference types*. A major difference is that:

- *value-type variables store values*, so specifying a value-type variable in a method call passes a *copy* of that variable's value to the method, whereas

- *reference-type variables store references to objects*, so specifying a reference-type variable as an argument passes the method a *copy of the reference* that refers to the object.

Even though the reference itself is passed by value, the method can still use the reference it receives to interact with—and possibly modify—the original object. Similarly, when returning information from a method via a return statement, the method returns a copy of the value stored in a value-type variable or a copy of the reference stored in a reference-type variable. When a reference is returned, the calling method can use that reference to interact with the referenced object.

Performance Tip 7.1
A disadvantage of pass-by-value is that, if a large data item is being passed, copying that data can take a considerable amount of execution time and memory space.

Performance Tip 7.2
Pass-by-reference improves performance by eliminating the pass-by-value overhead of copying large objects.

Software Engineering Observation 7.6
Pass-by-reference can weaken security; the called method can corrupt the caller's data.

7.18.1 ref and out Parameters

What if you would like to pass a variable by reference so the called method can modify the variable's value in the caller? To do this, C# provides keywords `ref` and `out`.

ref Parameters

Applying the `ref` keyword to a parameter declaration allows you to pass a variable to a method by reference—the method will be able to modify the original variable in the caller. Keyword `ref` is used for variables that already have been initialized in the calling method.

Common Programming Error 7.12
When a method call contains an uninitialized variable as an argument to a `ref` parameter, the compiler generates an error.

out Parameters

Preceding a parameter with keyword `out` creates an **output parameter**. This indicates to the compiler that the argument will be passed into the called method by reference and that the called method will assign a value to the original variable in the caller. This also prevents the compiler from generating an error message for an uninitialized variable that's passed as an argument to a method.

Common Programming Error 7.13
If the method does not assign a value to the `out` parameter in every possible path of execution, the compiler generates an error. Also, reading an `out` parameter before it's assigned a value is also a compilation error.

Software Engineering Observation 7.7
A method can return only one value to its caller via a return statement, but can return many values by specifying multiple output (`ref` and/or `out`) parameters.

Passing Reference-Type Variables by Reference

You also can pass a reference-type variable by reference, which allows you to modify it so that it refers to a new object. Passing a reference by reference is a tricky but powerful technique that we discuss in Section 8.13.

Software Engineering Observation 7.8

By default, C# does not allow you to choose whether to pass each argument by value or by reference. Value types are passed by value. Objects are not passed to methods; rather, references to objects are passed—the references themselves are passed by value. When a method receives a reference to an object, the method can manipulate the object directly, but the reference value cannot be changed to refer to a new object.

7.18.2 Demonstrating ref, out and Value Parameters

The app in Fig. 7.20 uses the `ref` and `out` keywords to manipulate integer values. The class contains three methods that calculate the square of an integer.

```
 1   // Fig. 7.20: ReferenceAndOutputParameters.cs
 2   // Reference, output and value parameters.
 3   using System;
 4
 5   class ReferenceAndOutputParameters
 6   {
 7      // call methods with reference, output and value parameters
 8      static void Main()
 9      {
10         int y = 5; // initialize y to 5
11         int z; // declares z, but does not initialize it
12
13         // display original values of y and z
14         Console.WriteLine($"Original value of y: {y}");
15         Console.WriteLine("Original value of z: uninitialized\n");
16
17         // pass y and z by reference
18         SquareRef(ref y); // must use keyword ref
19         SquareOut(out z); // must use keyword out
20
21         // display values of y and z after they're modified by
22         // methods SquareRef and SquareOut, respectively
23         Console.WriteLine($"Value of y after SquareRef: {y}");
24         Console.WriteLine($"Value of z after SquareOut: {z}\n");
25
26         // pass y and z by value
27         Square(y);
28         Square(z);
29
30         // display values of y and z after they're passed to method Square
31         // to demonstrate that arguments passed by value are not modified
32         Console.WriteLine($"Value of y after Square: {y}");
33         Console.WriteLine($"Value of z after Square: {z}");
34      }
35
36      // uses reference parameter x to modify caller's variable
37      static void SquareRef(ref int x)
38      {
```

Fig. 7.20 | Reference, output and value parameters. (Part 1 of 2.)

```
39           x = x * x; // squares value of caller's variable
40       }
41
42       // uses output parameter x to assign a value
43       // to an uninitialized variable
44       static void SquareOut(out int x)
45       {
46           x = 6; // assigns a value to caller's variable
47           x = x * x; // squares value of caller's variable
48       }
49
50       // parameter x receives a copy of the value passed as an argument,
51       // so this method cannot modify the caller's variable
52       static void Square(int x)
53       {
54           x = x * x;
55       }
56   }
```

```
Original value of y: 5
Original value of z: uninitialized

Value of y after SquareRef: 25
Value of z after SquareOut: 36

Value of y after Square: 25
Value of z after Square: 36
```

Fig. 7.20 | Reference, output and value parameters. (Part 2 of 2.)

Method SquareRef (lines 37–40) multiplies its parameter x by itself and assigns the new value to x. SquareRef's parameter is declared as ref int, which indicates that the argument passed to this method must be an integer that's passed by reference. Because the argument is passed by reference, the assignment at line 39 modifies the original argument's value in the caller.

Method SquareOut (lines 44–48) assigns its parameter the value 6 (line 46), then squares that value. SquareOut's parameter is declared as out int, which indicates that the argument passed to this method must be an integer that's passed by reference and that the argument does *not* need to be initialized in advance.

Method Square (lines 52–55) multiplies its parameter x by itself and assigns the new value to x. When this method is called, a *copy* of the argument is passed to the parameter x. Thus, even though parameter x is modified in the method, the original value in the caller is *not* modified.

Method Main (lines 8–34) invokes methods SquareRef, SquareOut and Square. We begin by initializing variable y to 5 and declaring, but *not* initializing, variable z. Lines 18–19 call methods SquareRef and SquareOut. Notice that when you pass a variable to a method with a reference parameter, you must precede the argument with the same keyword (ref or out) that was used to declare the reference parameter. Lines 23–24 display the values of y and z after the calls to SquareRef and SquareOut. Notice that y has been changed to 25 and z has been set to 36.

Lines 27–28 call method Square with y and z as arguments. In this case, both variables are passed by *value*—only *copies* of their values are passed to Square. As a result, the values of y and z remain 25 and 36, respectively. Lines 32–33 output the values of y and z to show that they were *not* modified.

Common Programming Error 7.14

The ref and out arguments in a method call must match the ref and out parameters specified in the method declaration; otherwise, a compilation error occurs.

7.19 Wrap-Up

In this chapter, we discussed the difference between non-static and static methods, and we showed how to call static methods by preceding the method name with the name of the class in which it appears and the member-access operator (.). You saw that the Math class in the .NET Framework Class Library provides many static methods to perform mathematical calculations. We also discussed static class members and why method Main is declared static.

We presented several commonly used Framework Class Library namespaces. You learned how to use operator + to perform string concatenations. You also learned how to declare constants with the const keyword and how to define sets of named constants with enum types. We demonstrated simulation techniques and used class Random to generate sets of random numbers. We discussed the scope of fields and local variables in a class. You saw how to overload methods in a class by providing methods with the same name but different signatures. You learned how to use optional and named parameters.

We showed the concise notation of C# 6's expression-bodied methods and read-only properties for implementing methods and read-only property get accessors that contain only a return statement. We discussed how recursive methods call themselves, breaking larger problems into smaller subproblems until eventually the original problem is solved. You learned the differences between value types and reference types with respect to how they're passed to methods, and how to use the ref and out keywords to pass arguments by reference.

In Chapter 8, you'll learn how to maintain lists and tables of data in arrays. You'll see a more elegant implementation of the app that rolls a die 60,000,000 times and two versions of a GradeBook case study. You'll also learn how to access an app's command-line arguments that are passed to method Main when a console app begins execution.

Summary

Section 7.1 Introduction

• Experience has shown that the best way to develop and maintain a large app is to construct it from small, simple pieces. This technique is called divide and conquer.

Section 7.2 Packaging Code in C#

• Three common ways of packaging code are methods, classes and namespaces.

Section 7.2.1 Modularizing Programs
- Methods allow you to modularize an app by separating its tasks into self-contained units.
- Dividing an app into meaningful methods makes it easier to debug and maintain.

Section 7.3 `static` Methods, `static` Variables and Class `Math`
- You can call any `static` method by specifying the name of the class in which it's declared, followed by the member-access operator (`.`) and the method name, as in

   ClassName.*MethodName*(*arguments*)

Section 7.3.1 `Math` Class Methods
- Method arguments may be constants, variables or expressions.

Section 7.3.2 `Math` Class Constants `PI` and `E`
- A constant is declared with the keyword `const`—its value cannot be changed after the constant is declared.
- `Math.PI` (3.1415926535897931) is the ratio of a circle's circumference to its diameter. `Math.E` (2.7182818284590451) is the base value for natural logarithms.
- When each object of a class maintains its own copy of an attribute, each object (instance) of the class has a separate instance of the variable. When objects of a class containing `static` variables are created, all objects of that class share one copy of the class's `static` variables.
- Together the `static` variables and instance variables represent the fields of a class.

Section 7.3.4 Additional Comments About `Main`
- If you declare more than one `Main` method among all the classes of your project, you'll need to indicate which one you would like to be the app's entry point. You can do this by clicking the menu **Project > [ProjectName] Properties...** and selecting the class containing the `Main` method that should be the entry point from the **Startup object** list box.

Section 7.4.2 Method `Maximum`
- Multiple parameters are specified as a comma-separated list.
- When a method is called, each parameter is initialized with the value of the corresponding argument. There must be one argument in the method call for each required parameter in the method declaration. Each argument must be consistent with the type of the corresponding parameter.
- When program control returns to the point in the app where a method was called, the method's parameters are no longer accessible.
- Methods can return at most one value; the returned value can be a value type that contains many values (implemented as a `struct`) or a reference to an object that contains many values.

Section 7.4.3 Assembling `string`s with Concatenation
- C# allows `string` objects to be created by assembling smaller `string`s into larger `string`s using operator +. This is known as `string` concatenation.
- Every value of a simple type in C# has a `string` representation. When one of the + operator's operands is a `string`, the other is implicitly converted to a `string`, then the two are concatenated.

Section 7.4.4 Breaking Apart Large `string` Literals
- All objects have a `ToString` method that returns a `string` representation of the object. When an object is concatenated with a `string`, the object's `ToString` method is implicitly called to obtain the `string` representation of the object, then the two `string`s are concatenated.

Section 7.5 Notes on Declaring and Using Methods

- You've seen three ways to call a method—using a method name by itself to call another method of the same class; using a variable that contains a reference to an object, followed by the member-access operator (.) and the method name to call a non-static method of the referenced object; and using the class name and the member-access operator (.) to call a static method of a class.

- A static method can call only other static methods of the same class and can manipulate only static variables in the same class.

- You've seen three ways to return control to the statement that calls a method—when the method-ending right brace in a method with return type void is reached, when the following statement executes in a method with return type void:

    ```
    return;
    ```

    and when a method returns a result with a statement of the following form in which the *expression* is evaluated and its result (and control) are returned to the caller:

    ```
    return expression;
    ```

Section 7.6 Argument Promotion and Casting

- Another important feature of method calls is argument promotion—implicitly converting an argument's value to the type that the method expects to receive in its corresponding parameter.

Section 7.6.1 Promotion Rules

- The argument-promotion rules apply to expressions containing values of two or more simple types and to simple-type values passed as arguments to methods.

Section 7.6.2 Sometimes Explicit Casts Are Required

- In cases where information may be lost due to conversion between simple types, the compiler requires you to use a cast operator to explicitly force the conversion.

Section 7.7 The .NET Framework Class Library

- Many predefined classes are grouped into categories of related classes called namespaces. Together, these namespaces are referred to as the .NET Framework Class Library.

Section 7.8.2 Generating a Random Integer

- Random method Next() generates a random int value in the range 0 to +2,147,483,646, inclusive.

- The methods of class Random actually generate pseudorandom numbers based on complex mathematical calculations. The calculation that produces the pseudorandom numbers uses the time of day as a seed value to change the sequence's starting point.

Section 7.8.3 Scaling the Random-Number Range

- Class Random provides other versions of method Next. One receives an int and returns a value from 0 up to, but not including, the argument's value. The other receives two ints and returns a value from the first argument's value up to, but not including, the second argument's value.

Section 7.8.8 Repeatability for Testing and Debugging

- If the same seed value is used every time, the Random object produces the same sequence of random numbers. Class Random's constructor can receive the seed value as an argument.

Section 7.9.3 enum Type Status

- An enumeration is introduced by the keyword enum and a type name. Braces delimit the body of an enum declaration. Inside the braces is a comma-separated list of enumeration constants.

- Variables of an enum type should be assigned only constants of that enum type.

Section 7.9.5 enum Type `DiceNames`

- When an enum is declared, each constant in the enum declaration is a constant value of type int. If you do not assign a value to an identifier in the enum declaration, the compiler will do so. If the first enum constant is unassigned, the compiler gives it the value 0. If any other enum constant is unassigned, the compiler gives it a value equal to one more than the value of the preceding enum constant. The enum constant names must be unique, but their underlying values need not be.

Section 7.9.6 Underlying Type of an **enum**

- If you need to compare a simple integral type value to the underlying value of an enumeration constant, you must use a cast operator to make the two types match.

Section 7.10 Scope of Declarations

- The scope of a declaration is the portion of the app that can refer to the declared entity by its unqualified name.
- The scope of a parameter declaration is the body of the method in which the declaration appears.
- A local variable's scope is from the point at which the declaration appears to the end of that block.
- The scope of a local-variable declaration that appears in the initialization section of a for statement's header is the body of the for statement and the other expressions in the header.
- The scope of a method, property or field of a class is the entire body of the class.
- Any block may contain variable declarations. If a local variable or parameter in a method has the same name as a field, the field is hidden until the block terminates execution.

Section 7.11 Method-Call Stack and Activation Records

- Stacks are known as last-in, first-out (LIFO) data structures—the last item pushed (inserted) on the stack is the first item popped off (removed from) the stack.

Section 7.11.1 Method-Call Stack

- The method-call stack (sometimes referred to as the program-execution stack) is a data structure that supports the method call/return mechanism. It also supports the creation, maintenance and destruction of each called method's local variables.

Section 7.11.2 Stack Frames

- Each method eventually must return control to the method that called it. The method-call stack is the perfect data structure for handling this information.
- Each time a method calls another method, an entry (called a stack frame or an activation record) is pushed onto the stack. This entry contains the return address that the called method needs in order to return to the calling method.
- If a called method returns instead of calling another method before returning, the stack frame for the method call is popped, and control transfers to the return address in the popped stack frame.
- The same techniques apply when a method accesses a property or when a property calls a method.

Section 7.11.3 Local Variables and Stack Frames

- Stack frames also contain the memory for parameters and any local variables a method declares.
- When a method returns—and no longer needs its local variables—its stack frame is popped from the stack, and those local variables no longer exist.

Section 7.11.4 Stack Overflow

- If more method calls occur than can have their activation records stored on the method-call stack, a fatal error known as stack overflow occurs.

Section 7.12.1 Declaring Overloaded Methods
• Methods of the same name can be declared in the same class, as long as they have different sets of parameters. This is called method overloading. When an overloaded method is called, the C# compiler selects the appropriate method by examining the number, types and order of the arguments in the call.

Section 7.12.2 Distinguishing Between Overloaded Methods
• The compiler distinguishes overloaded methods by their signature—a combination of the method's name and the number, types and order of its parameters. The signature also includes the way those parameters are passed, which can be modified by the ref and out keywords.

Section 7.12.3 Return Types of Overloaded Methods
• The compiler will generate an error when two methods have the same signature but different return types. Overloaded methods can have the same or different return types if the methods have different parameter lists.

Section 7.13 Optional Parameters
• Methods can have optional parameters, which allow the calling method to vary the number of arguments to pass. An optional parameter specifies a default value that's assigned to the parameter if the optional argument is omitted.

• Methods can have one or more optional parameters. All optional parameters must be placed to the right of the method's non-optional parameters.

• When a parameter has a default value, the caller has the option of passing that particular argument.

Section 7.14 Named Parameters
• Normally, when calling a method, the argument values—in order—are assigned to the parameters from left to right in the parameter list.

• C# provides a feature called named parameters, which enable you to call methods that receive optional parameters by providing only the optional arguments you wish to specify. To do so, you explicitly specify the parameter's name and value—separated by a colon (:)—in the argument list of the method call.

Section 7.15 C# 6 Expression-Bodied Methods and Properties
• C# 6 introduces a new expression-bodied method syntax for methods that contain only a return statement that returns a value or a single-statement body, and a new expression-bodied property syntax for read-only properties in which the get accessor contains only a return statement.

• In a method, the symbol => follows the method's parameter list and introduces the body—no braces or return statement are required.

• A read-only property can be implemented as an expression-bodied property with the syntax

    modifiers returnType PropertyName => *expression*;

Section 7.16 Recursion
• A recursive method calls itself, either directly or indirectly through another method.

Section 7.16.1 Base Cases and Recursive Calls
• When a recursive method is called to solve a problem, the method actually is capable of solving only the simplest case(s), or base case(s). If the method is called with a base case, the method returns a result.

- If the method is called with a more complex problem, the method divides the problem into two conceptual pieces: a piece that the method knows how to do and a piece that it does not know how to do. Because this new problem looks like the original problem, the method calls a fresh copy of itself to work on the smaller problem; this procedure is referred to as a recursive call and is also called the recursion step.

Section 7.16.2 Recursive Factorial Calculations
- A recursive declaration of the factorial method is arrived at by observing the relationship:

$$n! = n \cdot (n - 1)!$$

Section 7.17 Value Types vs. Reference Types
- Types in C# are divided into value types and reference types.
- C#'s simple types (like int), enum types and struct types are all value types.
- A variable of a value type simply contains a value of that type.
- A reference-type variable (sometimes called a reference) contains the location where the data referred to by that variable is stored. Such a variable is said to refer to an object.
- Reference-type instance variables are initialized by default to null.
- Type string is a reference type. A string variable with the value null is not an empty string, which is represented by "" or string.Empty.
- The value null represents a reference that does not refer to an object.
- The empty string is a string object that does not contain any characters.

Section 7.18 Passing Arguments by Value and by Reference
- Two ways to pass arguments to methods in many programming languages are pass-by-value and pass-by-reference.
- When an argument is passed by value (the default), a *copy* of the argument's value is passed to the called method. Changes to the copy do not affect the original variable's value in the caller.
- When an argument is passed by reference, the caller gives the method the ability to access and modify the caller's original data directly.
- Value-type variables store values, so specifying a value-type variable in a method call passes a copy of that variable's value to the method. Reference-type variables store references to objects, so specifying a reference-type variable as an argument passes the method a copy of the actual reference that refers to the object.
- When returning information from a method via a return statement, the method returns a copy of the value stored in a value-type variable or a copy of the reference stored in a reference-type variable.

Section 7.18.1 ref and out Parameters
- C# provides the keywords ref and out to pass variables by reference.
- A ref parameter indicates that an argument will be passed to the method by reference—the called method will be able to modify the original variable in the caller.
- An out parameter indicates that a possibly uninitialized variable will be passed into the method by reference and that the called method will assign a value to the original variable in the caller.
- A method can return only one value to its caller via a return statement, but can return many values by specifying multiple output (ref and/or out) parameters.
- When a variable is passed to a method with a reference parameter, you must precede the variable with the same keyword (ref or out) that was used to declare the reference parameter.

Terminology

=> in an expression-bodied method or read-only property	pop data from a stack
activation record	program-execution stack
argument promotion	push data onto a stack
base case in recursion	pseudorandom number
const keyword to declare a named constant	Random class
default value	random number
divide-and-conquer approach	ref keyword
element of chance	recursion
enum type to declare named constants	recursion step
enumeration	recursive call
enumeration constant	recursive method
expression-bodied method	refer to an object
expression-bodied property	reference
field of a class	reference type
fully qualified name	reusable software components
implicit conversion	scaling factor (with random numbers)
infinite recursion	scope of a declaration
last-in, first-out (LIFO) data structure	seed value (with random numbers)
Math.PI constant	shift a range (with random numbers)
Math.E constant	shifting value (with random numbers)
method-call stack	signature of a method
named parameter	simulation
Next method of class Random	simple-type promotion rules
optional parameter	stack
out keyword	stack frame
output parameter	stack overflow
overloaded method	string concatenation
pass-by-reference	string.Empty
pass-by-value	unqualified name
	value type

Self-Review Exercises

7.1 Fill in the blanks in each of the following statements:

a) A method is invoked with a(n) _____.

b) A variable known only within the method in which it's declared is called a(n) _____.

c) The _____ statement in a called method can be used to pass the value of an expression back to the calling method.

d) The keyword _____ indicates that a method does not return a value.

e) Data can be added to or removed from only the _____ of a stack.

f) Stacks are known as _____ data structures—the last item pushed (inserted) on the stack is the first item popped off (removed from) the stack.

g) The three ways to return control from a called method to a caller are _____, _____ and _____.

h) An object of class _____ produces pseudorandom numbers.

i) The program-execution stack contains the memory for local variables on each invocation of a method during an app's execution. This data, stored as a portion of the program-execution stack, is known as the _____ or _____ of the method call.

j) If there are more method calls than can be stored on the program-execution stack, an error known as a(n) _____ occurs.

k) The _____ of a declaration is the portion of an app that can refer to the entity in the declaration by its unqualified name.

l) It's possible to have several methods with the same name that each operate on different types or numbers of arguments. This feature is called method _____.

m) The program-execution stack is also referred to as the _____ stack.

n) A method that calls itself either directly or indirectly is a(n) _____ method.

o) A recursive method typically has two components: one that provides a means for the recursion to terminate by testing for a(n) _____ case and one that expresses the problem as a recursive call for a slightly simpler problem than does the original call.

p) In an expression-bodied method or read-only property, the symbol _____ introduces the method's or read-only-property get accessor's body.

q) Types are either _____ types or _____ types.

7.2   For the class `Craps` in Fig. 7.8, state the scope of each of the following entities:

a) the variable `randomNumbers`.

b) the variable `die1`.

c) the method `RollDice`.

d) the method `Main`.

e) the variable `sumOfDice`.

7.3   Write an app that tests whether the examples of the `Math` class method calls shown in Fig. 7.2 actually produce the indicated results.

7.4   Give the method header for each of the following methods:

a) Method `Hypotenuse`, which takes two double-precision, floating-point arguments `side1` and `side2` and returns a double-precision, floating-point result.

b) Method `Smallest`, which takes three integers `x`, `y` and `z` and returns an integer.

c) Method `Instructions`, which does not take any arguments and does not return a value. [*Note:* Such methods are commonly used to display instructions to a user.]

d) Method `IntToDouble`, which takes integer argument `number` and returns a `double` value.

7.5   Find the error(s) in each of the following code segments. Explain how to correct the error.

a)
```
void G()
{
   Console.WriteLine("Inside method G");

   void H()
   {
      Console.WriteLine("Inside method H");
   }
}
```

b)
```
int Sum(int x, int y)
{
   int result;
   result = x + y;
}
```

c)
```
void F(float a);
{
   float a;
   Console.WriteLine(a);
}
```

```
d) void Product()
   {
       int a = 6, b = 5, c = 4, result;
       result = a * b * c;
       Console.WriteLine("Result is " + result);
       return result;
   }
```

7.6 Write a complete C# app to prompt the user for the double radius of a sphere, and call method SphereVolume to calculate and display the volume of the sphere. Write an expression-bodied method containing the following expression to calculate the volume:

```
(4.0 / 3.0) * Math.PI * Math.Pow(radius, 3)
```

Answers to Self-Review Exercises

7.1 a) method call. b) local variable. c) return. d) void. e) top. f) last-in, first-out (LIFO). g) return; or return *expression*; or encountering the closing right brace of a method. h) Random. i) activation record, stack frame. j) stack overflow. k) scope. l) overloading. m) method call. n) recursive. o) base. p) =>. q) value, reference.

7.2 a) class body. b) block that defines method RollDice's body. c) class body. d) class body. e) block that defines method Main's body.

7.3 Figure 7.21 demonstrates the Math class methods in Fig. 7.2:

```
 1   // Exercise 7.3 Solution: MathTest.cs
 2   // Testing the Math class methods.
 3   using System;
 4
 5   class MathTest
 6   {
 7       static void Main()
 8       {
 9           Console.WriteLine($"Math.Abs(23.7) = {Math.Abs(23.7)}");
10           Console.WriteLine($"Math.Abs(0.0) = {Math.Abs(0.0)}");
11           Console.WriteLine($"Math.Abs(-23.7) = {Math.Abs(-23.7)}");
12           Console.WriteLine($"Math.Ceiling(9.2) = {Math.Ceiling(9.2)}");
13           Console.WriteLine($"Math.Ceiling(-9.8) = {Math.Ceiling(-9.8)}");
14           Console.WriteLine($"Math.Cos(0.0) = {Math.Cos(0.0)}");
15           Console.WriteLine($"Math.Exp(1.0) = {Math.Exp(1.0)}");
16           Console.WriteLine($"Math.Exp(2.0) = {Math.Exp(2.0)}");
17           Console.WriteLine($"Math.Floor(9.2) = {Math.Floor(9.2)}");
18           Console.WriteLine($"Math.Floor(-9.8) = {Math.Floor(-9.8)}");
19           Console.WriteLine($"Math.Log(Math.E) = {Math.Log(Math.E)}");
20           Console.WriteLine($"Math.Log(Math.E * Math.E) = {Math.Log(Math.E * Math.E)}");
21           Console.WriteLine($"Math.Max(2.3, 12.7) = {Math.Max(2.3, 12.7)}");
22           Console.WriteLine($"Math.Max(-2.3, -12.7) = {Math.Max(-2.3, -12.7)}");
23           Console.WriteLine($"Math.Min(2.3, 12.7) = {Math.Min(2.3, 12.7)}");
24           Console.WriteLine($"Math.Min(-2.3, -12.7) = {Math.Min(-2.3, -12.7)}");
25           Console.WriteLine($"Math.Pow(2.0, 7.0) = {Math.Pow(2.0, 7.0)}");
26           Console.WriteLine($"Math.Pow(9.0, 0.5) = {Math.Pow(9.0, 0.5)}");
27           Console.WriteLine($"Math.Sin(0.0) = {Math.Sin(0.0)}");
28           Console.WriteLine($"Math.Sqrt(900.0) = {Math.Sqrt(900.0)}");
29           Console.WriteLine($"Math.Tan(0.0) = {Math.Tan(0.0)}");
30       }
31   }
```

Fig. 7.21 | Solution to Exercise 7.3. (Part I of 2.)

```
Math.Abs(23.7) = 23.7
Math.Abs(0.0) = 0
Math.Abs(-23.7) = 23.7
Math.Ceiling(9.2) = 10
Math.Ceiling(-9.8) = -9
Math.Cos(0.0) = 1
Math.Exp(1.0) = 2.71828182845905
Math.Exp(2.0) = 7.38905609893065
Math.Floor(9.2) = 9
Math.Floor(-9.8) = -10
Math.Log(Math.E) = 1
Math.Log(Math.E * Math.E) = 2
Math.Max(2.3, 12.7) = 12.7
Math.Max(-2.3, -12.7) = -2.3
Math.Min(2.3, 12.7) = 2.3
Math.Min(-2.3, -12.7) = -12.7
Math.Pow(2.0, 7.0) = 128
Math.Pow(9.0, 0.5) = 3
Math.Sin(0.0) = 0
Math.Sqrt(900.0) = 30
Math.Tan(0.0) = 0
```

Fig. 7.21 | Solution to Exercise 7.3. (Part 2 of 2.)

7.4   The answers to Self-Review Exercise 7.4 are as follows:
   a) `double Hypotenuse(double side1, double side2)`
   b) `int Smallest(int x, int y, int z)`
   c) `void Instructions()`
   d) `double IntToDouble(int number)`

7.5   The answers to Self-Review Exercise 7.5 are as follows:
   a) *Error:* Method H is declared within method G.
       Correction: Move the declaration of H outside the declaration of G.
   b) *Error:* The method is supposed to return an integer, but does not.
       Correction: Delete the method's body statements and place the statement
          `return x + y;`
       in the method, or add the following statement at the end of the method body:
          `return result;`
   c) *Error:* The semicolon after the right parenthesis of the parameter list is incorrect, and
       the parameter a should not be redeclared in the method.
       Correction: Delete the semicolon after the right parenthesis of the parameter list, and de-
       lete the declaration `float a;`.
   d) *Error:* The method returns a value when it's not supposed to.
       Correction: Change the return type from void to int.

7.6   Figure 7.22 contains the solution to Exercise 7.6.

```
1   // Exercise 7.6 Solution: Sphere.cs
2   // Calculate the volume of a sphere.
3   using System;
4
5   class Sphere
6   {
7      // obtain radius from user and display volume of sphere
8      static void Main()
9      {
```

Fig. 7.22 | Solution to Exercise 7.6. (Part 1 of 2.)

```
10          Console.Write("Enter radius of sphere: ");
11          double radius = double.Parse(Console.ReadLine());
12          Console.WriteLine("Volume is {SphereVolume(radius):F3}");
13      }
14
15      // calculate and return sphere volume
16      static double SphereVolume(double radius) =>
17          (4.0 / 3.0) * Math.PI * Math.Pow(radius, 3);
18  }
```

```
Enter radius of sphere: 4
Volume is 268.083
```

Fig. 7.22 | Solution to Exercise 7.6. (Part 2 of 2.)

Exercises

7.7   What is the value of the double variable x after each of the following statements is executed?

a) x = Math.Abs(7.5);
b) x = Math.Floor(7.5);
c) x = Math.Abs(0.0);
d) x = Math.Ceiling(0.0);
e) x = Math.Abs(-6.4);
f) x = Math.Ceiling(-6.4);
g) x = Math.Ceiling(-Math.Abs(-8 + Math.Floor(-5.5)));

7.8   *(Parking Charges)* A parking garage charges a $2.00 minimum fee to park for up to three hours. The garage charges an additional $0.50 per hour for each hour *or part thereof* in excess of three hours. The maximum charge for any given 24-hour period is $10.00. Assume that no car parks for longer than 24 hours at a time. Write an app that calculates and displays the parking charges for each customer who parked in the garage yesterday. You should enter the hours parked for each customer. The app should display the charge for the current customer and should calculate and display the running total of yesterday's receipts. The app should use method CalculateCharges to determine the charge for each customer.

7.9   *(Rounding to Nearest Integer)* An app of method Math.Floor is rounding a value to the nearest integer. The statement

        y = Math.Floor(x + 0.5);

will round the number x to the nearest integer and assign the result to y. Write an app that reads double values and uses the preceding statement to round each of the numbers to the nearest integer. For each number processed, display both the original number and the rounded number.

7.10   *(Rounding to a Specific Decimal Place)* Math.Floor may be used to round a number to a specific decimal place. The statement

        y = Math.Floor(x * 10 + 0.5) / 10;

rounds x to the tenths position (i.e., the first position to the right of the decimal point). The statement

        y = Math.Floor(x * 100 + 0.5) / 100;

rounds x to the hundredths position (i.e., the second position to the right of the decimal point). Write an app that defines four *expression-bodied methods* for rounding a number x in various ways:

a) RoundToInteger(number)
b) RoundToTenths(number)

    c) RoundToHundredths(number)
    d) RoundToThousandths(number)

For each value read, your app should display the original value, the number rounded to the nearest integer, the number rounded to the nearest tenth, the number rounded to the nearest hundredth and the number rounded to the nearest thousandth.

7.11   Answer each of the following questions:
    a) What does it mean to choose numbers "at random"?
    b) Why is the Random class useful for simulating games of chance?
    c) Why is it often necessary to scale or shift the values produced by a Random object?
    d) Why is computerized simulation of real-world situations a useful technique?

7.12   Write statements that assign random integers to the variable n in the following ranges. Assume Random randomNumbers = new Random() has been defined and use the two-parameter version of the method Random.Next.
    a) $1 \le n \le 2$
    b) $1 \le n \le 100$
    c) $0 \le n \le 9$
    d) $1000 \le n \le 1112$
    e) $-1 \le n \le 1$
    f) $-3 \le n \le 11$

7.13   For each of the following sets of integers, write a single statement that will display a number at random from the set. Assume Random randomNumbers = new Random() has been defined and use the one-parameter version of method Random.Next.
    a) 2, 4, 6, 8, 10.
    b) 3, 5, 7, 9, 11.
    c) 6, 10, 14, 18, 22.

7.14   *(Exponentiation)* Write a method IntegerPower(base, exponent) that returns the value of

$$base^{\,exponent}$$

For example, IntegerPower(3, 4) calculates 3^4 (or 3 * 3 * 3 * 3). Assume that exponent is a positive integer and that base is an integer. Method IntegerPower should use a for or while loop to control the calculation. Do not use any Math-library methods. Incorporate this method into an app that reads integer values for base and exponent and performs the calculation with the IntegerPower method.

7.15   *(Hypotenuse of a Right Triangle)* Write *expression-bodied method* Hypotenuse that calculates the length of the hypotenuse of a right triangle when the lengths of the other two sides are given. The method should take two double arguments and return the hypotenuse as a double. Incorporate this method into an app that reads values for side1 and side2 and performs the calculation with the Hypotenuse method. Determine the length of the hypotenuse for each of the triangles in Fig. 7.23.

Triangle	Side 1	Side 2
1	3.0	4.0
2	5.0	12.0
3	8.0	15.0

Fig. 7.23 | Values for the sides of triangles in Exercise 7.15.

7.16   *(Multiples)* Write *expression-bodied method* Multiple that determines, for a pair of integers, whether the second integer is a multiple of the first. The method should take two integer arguments and return true if the second is a multiple of the first and false otherwise. Incorporate this method into an app that inputs a series of pairs of integers (one pair at a time) and determines whether the second value in each pair is a multiple of the first.

7.17   *(Even or Odd)* Write *expression-bodied method* IsEven that uses the remainder operator (%) to determine whether an integer is even. The method should take an integer argument and return true if the integer is even and false otherwise. Incorporate this method into an app that inputs a sequence of integers (one at a time) and determines whether each is even or odd.

7.18   *(Displaying a Square of Asterisks)* Write method SquareOfAsterisks that displays a solid square (the same number of rows and columns) of asterisks whose side length is specified in integer parameter side. For example, if side is 4, the method should display

```
****
****
****
****
```

Incorporate this method into an app that reads an integer value for side from the user and outputs the asterisks with the SquareOfAsterisks method.

7.19   *(Displaying a Square of Any Character)* Modify the method created in Exercise 7.18 to form the square out of whatever character is contained in character parameter fillCharacter and provide '*' as the default value. If side is 5 and fillCharacter is '#', the method should display

```
#####
#####
#####
#####
#####
```

[*Hint:* Use the expression char.Parse(Console.ReadLine()) to read a character from the user. A variable of type char can store a single character's value.]

7.20   *(Circle Area)* Write an app that prompts the user for the radius of a circle and uses *expression-bodied method* CircleArea to calculate the area of the circle.

7.21   *(Separating Digits)* Write code segments that accomplish each of the following tasks:
   a)   Calculate the integer part of the quotient when integer a is divided by integer b.
   b)   Calculate the integer remainder when integer a is divided by integer b.
   c)   Use the app pieces developed in parts (a) and (b) to write a method DisplayDigits that receives an integer between 1 and 99999 and displays it as a sequence of digits, separating each pair of digits by two spaces. For example, the integer 4562 should appear as:
        4 5 6 2.
   d)   Incorporate the method developed in part (c) into an app that inputs an integer and calls DisplayDigits by passing the method the integer entered. Display the results.

7.22   *(Temperature Conversions)* Implement the following integer methods:
   a)   *Expression-bodied method* Celsius returns the Celsius equivalent of a Fahrenheit temperature, using the calculation

        5.0 / 9.0 * (f - 32);

   b)   *Expression-bodied method* Fahrenheit returns the Fahrenheit equivalent of a Celsius temperature, using the calculation

        9.0 / 5.0 * c + 32;

   c)   Use the methods from parts (a) and (b) to write an app that enables the user either to enter a Fahrenheit temperature and display the Celsius equivalent or to enter a Celsius temperature and display the Fahrenheit equivalent.

7.23 *(Find the Minimum)* Write a method `Minimum3` that returns the smallest of three floating-point numbers. Use the `Math.Min` method to implement `Minimum3`. Incorporate the method into an app that reads three values from the user, determines the smallest value and displays the result.

7.24 *(Perfect Numbers)* An integer number is said to be a *perfect number* if its factors, including 1 (but not the number itself), sum to the number. For example, 6 is a perfect number, because 6 = 1 + 2 + 3. Write method `Perfect` that determines whether parameter `value` is a perfect number. Use this method in an app that determines and displays all the perfect numbers between 2 and 1000. Display the factors of each perfect number to confirm that the number is indeed perfect.

7.25 *(Prime Numbers)* An integer is said to be *prime* if it's greater than 1 and divisible by only 1 and itself. For example, 2, 3, 5 and 7 are prime, but 4, 6, 8 and 9 are not.

  a) Write a method that determines whether a number is prime.

  b) Use this method in an app that displays all the prime numbers less than 10,000.

  c) Initially, you might think that *n*/2 is the upper limit for which you must test to see whether a number is prime, but you need go only as high as the square root of *n*. Rewrite the app, and run it both ways.

7.26 *(Reversing Digits)* Write a method that takes an integer value and returns the number with its digits reversed. For example, given the number 7631, the method should return 1367. Incorporate the method into an app that reads a value from the user and displays the method's result.

7.27 *(Greatest Common Divisor)* The *greatest common divisor* (*GCD*) of two integers is the largest integer that evenly divides each of the two numbers. Write method `Gcd` that returns the greatest common divisor of two integers. Incorporate the method into an app that reads two values from the user and displays the result.

7.28 *(Converting Grade Averages to a Four-Point Scale)* Write method `QualityPoints` that inputs a student's average and returns 4 if the student's average is 90–100, 3 if the average is 80–89, 2 if the average is 70–79, 1 if the average is 60–69 and 0 if the average is lower than 60. Incorporate the method into an app that reads a value from the user and displays the result.

7.29 *(Coin Tossing)* Write an app that simulates coin tossing. Let the app toss a coin each time the user chooses the "`Toss Coin`" menu option. Count the number of times each side of the coin appears. Display the results. The app should call a separate method `Flip` that takes no arguments and returns `false` for tails and `true` for heads. [*Note:* If the app realistically simulates coin tossing, each side of the coin should appear approximately half the time.]

7.30 *(Guess-the-Number Game)* Write an app that plays "guess the number" as follows: Your app chooses the number to be guessed by selecting a random integer in the range 1 to 1000. The app displays the prompt `Guess a number between 1 and 1000`. The player inputs a first guess. If the player's guess is incorrect, your app should display `Too high. Try again.` or `Too low. Try again.` to help the player "zero in" on the correct answer. The app should prompt the user for the next guess. When the user enters the correct answer, display `Congratulations. You guessed the number!` and allow the user to choose whether to play again. [*Note:* The guessing technique employed in this problem is similar to a binary search, which is discussed in Chapter 18.]

7.31 *(Enhanced Guess-the-Number Game)* Modify the app of Exercise 7.30 to count the number of guesses the player makes. If the number is 10 or fewer, display `Either you know the secret or you got lucky!` If the player guesses the number in 10 tries, display `Aha! You know the secret!` If the player makes more than 10 guesses, display `You should be able to do better!` Why should it take no more than 10 guesses? Well, with each "good guess," the player should be able to eliminate half of the numbers. Now show why any number from 1 to 1000 can be guessed in 10 or fewer tries.

7.32 *(Distance Between Two Points)* Write method `Distance` to calculate the distance between two points *(x1, y1)* and *(x2, y2)*. All numbers and return values should be of type `double`. Incorporate this method into an app that enables the user to enter the coordinates of the points.

7.33 *(Craps Game Modification)* Modify the craps app of Fig. 7.8 to allow wagering. Initialize variable balance to 1000 dollars. Prompt the player to enter a wager. Check that wager is less than or equal to balance, and if it's not, have the user reenter wager until a valid wager is entered. After a correct wager is entered, run one game of craps. If the player wins, increase balance by wager and display the new balance. If the player loses, decrease balance by wager, display the new balance, check whether balance has become zero and, if so, display the message "Sorry. You busted!"

7.34 *(Binary, Octal and Hexadecimal)* Write an app that displays a table of the binary, octal, and hexadecimal equivalents of the decimal numbers in the range 1–256. If you're not familiar with these number systems, read online Appendix D first.

7.35 *(Recursive Power Calculation)* Write recursive method Power(base, exponent) that, when called, returns

$$base^{exponent}$$

For example, Power(3, 4) = 3 * 3 * 3 * 3. Assume that exponent is an integer greater than or equal to 1. The recursion step should use the relationship

$$base^{exponent} = base \cdot base^{exponent-1}$$

The terminating condition occurs when exponent is equal to 1, because

$$base^1 = base$$

Incorporate this method into an app that enables the user to enter the base and exponent.

7.36 *(Towers of Hanoi)* Every budding computer scientist must grapple with certain classic problems, and the *Towers of Hanoi* (see Fig. 7.24) is one of the most famous. Legend has it that in a temple in the Far East, priests are attempting to move a stack of disks from one peg to another. The initial stack has 64 disks threaded onto one peg and arranged from bottom to top by decreasing size. The priests are attempting to move the stack from this peg to a second peg under the constraints that exactly one disk is moved at a time and at no time may a larger disk be placed above a smaller disk. A third peg is available for temporarily holding disks. Supposedly, the world will end when the priests complete their task, so there's little incentive for us to facilitate their efforts.

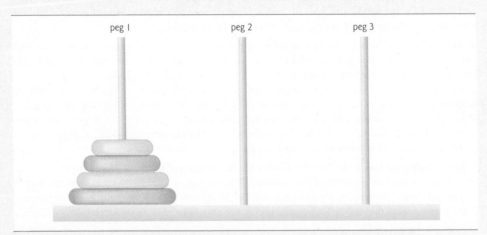

Fig. 7.24 | The Towers of Hanoi for the case with four disks.

Let's assume that the priests are attempting to move the disks from peg 1 to peg 3. We wish to develop an algorithm that will display the precise sequence of peg-to-peg disk transfers.

If we were to approach this problem with conventional methods, we'd rapidly find ourselves hopelessly knotted up in managing the disks. Instead, if we attack the problem with recursion in mind, it immediately becomes tractable. Moving *n* disks can be viewed in terms of moving only *n* – 1 disks (hence the recursion) as follows:

a) Move *n* – 1 disks from peg 1 to peg 2, using peg 3 as a temporary holding area.

b) Move the last disk (the largest) from peg 1 to peg 3.

c) Move the *n* – 1 disks from peg 2 to peg 3, using peg 1 as a temporary holding area.

The process ends when the last task involves moving *n* = 1 disk (i.e., the base case). This task is accomplished by simply moving the disk, without the need for a temporary holding area.

Write an app to solve the Towers of Hanoi problem. Allow the user to enter the number of disks. Use a recursive `Tower` method with four parameters:

a) the number of disks to be moved,

b) the peg on which these disks are initially threaded,

c) the peg to which this stack of disks is to be moved, and

d) the peg to be used as a temporary holding area.

Your app should display the precise instructions it will take to move the disks from the starting peg to the destination peg. For example, to move a stack of three disks from peg 1 to peg 3, your app should display the following series of moves:

```
1 --> 3 (This notation means "Move one disk from peg 1 to peg 3.")
1 --> 2
3 --> 2
1 --> 3
2 --> 1
2 --> 3
1 --> 3
```

7.37   *(What Does This Code Do?)* What does the following method do?

```
// Parameter b must be positive to prevent infinite recursion
static int Mystery(int a, int b)
{
   if (b == 1)
      return a;
   else
      return a + Mystery(a, b - 1);
}
```

7.38   *(Find the Error)* Find the error(s) in the following recursive method, and explain how to correct it:

```
static int Sum(int n)
{
   if (n == 0)
   {
      return 0;
   }
   else
   {
      return n + Sum(n);
   }
}
```

Making-a-Difference Exercises

As computer costs decline, it becomes feasible for every student, regardless of economic circumstance, to have a computer and use it in school. This creates exciting possibilities for improving the educational experience of all students worldwide as suggested by the next two exercises. [*Note:*

Check out initiatives such as the One Laptop Per Child Project (http://one.laptop.org). Also, research "green" laptops—and note the key "going green" characteristics of these devices. Look into the Electronic Product Environmental Assessment Tool (http://www.epeat.net) which can help you assess the "greenness" of desktops, notebooks and monitors to help you decide which products to purchase.]

7.39 *(Computer-Assisted Instruction)* The use of computers in education is referred to as *computer-assisted instruction (CAI)*. Write a program that will help an elementary-school student learn multiplication. Use a Random object to produce two positive one-digit integers. The program should then prompt the user with a question, such as

    How much is 6 times 7?

The student then inputs the answer. Next, the program checks the student's answer. If it's correct, display the message "Very good!" and ask another multiplication question. If the answer is wrong, display the message "No. Please try again." and let the student try the same question repeatedly until the student gets it right. A separate method should be used to generate each new question. This method should be called once when the app begins execution and each time the user answers the question correctly.

7.40 *(Computer-Assisted Instruction: Reducing Student Fatigue)* One problem in CAI environments is student fatigue. This can be reduced by varying the computer's responses to hold the student's attention. Modify the program of Exercise 7.39 so that various comments are displayed for each answer. Possible responses to a correct answer:

    Very good!
    Excellent!
    Nice work!
    Keep up the good work!

Possible responses to an incorrect answer:

    No. Please try again.
    Wrong. Try once more.
    Don't give up!
    No. Keep trying.

Use random-number generation to choose a number from 1 to 4 that will be used to select one of the four appropriate responses to each correct or incorrect answer. Use a switch statement to issue the responses.

Arrays; Introduction to Exception Handling

8

8.1 Introduction

This chapter introduces the important topic of data structures—collections of related data items. Arrays are data structures consisting of related data items of the *same* type. Arrays are *fixed-length* entities—they remain the same length once they're created, although an array variable may be reassigned so that it refers to a new array of a different length.

We'll discuss how to declare, create and initialize arrays, then show several examples of common array manipulations. We'll present the `foreach` iteration statement, which provides a concise notation for accessing data in arrays (and collections, as you'll see in Section 9.4, Introduction to Collections, and in Chapter 21, Generic Collections; Functional Programming with LINQ/PLINQ).

You'll use the `var` keyword to declare implicitly typed local variables—as you'll see, the compiler can determine a local variable's type, based on its initializer value. We'll introduce *exception handling* for detecting and processing problems that occur during an app's execution.

Many of the chapter's examples manipulate arrays of `int` simple-type values. To demonstrate that arrays also can store reference types, we'll create a card-shuffling-and-dealing simulation that manipulates an array of `Card` objects. In that example, we'll introduce

C# 6's getter-only auto-implemented properties, which define properties that can be used to get, but not set, a value.

We present two versions of an instructor GradeBook case study that use arrays to maintain sets of student grades *in memory* and analyze them. We'll also demonstrate how to define methods that receive variable-length argument lists (which are implemented by C# as arrays) and a version of method Main that can receive a string array containing an app's so-called command-line arguments.

8.2 Arrays

An array is a group of variables—called elements—containing values of the *same type*. Arrays are reference types—an array variable is actually a reference to an array object. An array's elements can be either value types or reference types, including other arrays—e.g., every element of an int array is an int *value*, and every element of a string array is a *reference* to a string object. Array names follow the same conventions as other variable names.

Logical Representation of an Array; Array-Access Expressions
Figure 8.1 shows a logical representation of an integer array called c that contains 12 elements. An app refers to any one of these elements with an array-access expression that includes the name of the reference to the array, c, followed by the index (i.e., *position number*) of the particular element in square brackets ([]). The first element in every array has index zero (0) and is sometimes called the zeroth element. Thus, the names of array c's elements are c[0], c[1], c[2] and so on. The highest index in array c is 11—one less than the array's number of elements, because indices begin at 0.

Fig. 8.1 | A 12-element array.

Indices Must Be Nonnegative Integer Values
An index must be a nonnegative integer or integer expression with a value of type int, uint, long or ulong—or a value of a type that can be implicitly promoted to one of these

types (as discussed in Section 7.6.1). If we assume that variable a is 5 and variable b is 6, then the statement

```
c[a + b] += 2;
```

evaluates the expression a + b to determine the index and in this case adds 2 to element c[11]. Array-access expressions can be used on the left side of an assignment to place a new value into an array element.

Examining Array c in More Detail

Let's examine array c in Fig. 8.1 more closely. The name of the variable that references the array is c. Every array instance knows its own length and provides access to this information with the Length property. For example, the expression c.Length returns array c's length (that is, 12). The Length property of an array is *read only*, so it *cannot* be changed. The array's 12 elements are referred to as c[0], c[1], c[2], ..., c[11]. Referring to elements *outside* of this range, such as c[-1] or c[12], is a runtime error (as we'll demonstrate in Fig. 8.9). The value of c[0] is -45, the value of c[1] is 6, the value of c[2] is 0, the value of c[7] is 62 and the value of c[11] is 78. To calculate the sum of the values contained in the first three elements of array c and store the result in variable sum, we'd write

```
sum = c[0] + c[1] + c[2];
```

To divide the value of c[6] by 2 and assign the result to the variable x, we'd write

```
x = c[6] / 2;
```

8.3 Declaring and Creating Arrays

Arrays occupy space in memory. Since they're objects, they're typically created with keyword new.[1] To create an array object, you specify the type and the number of array elements in an array-creation expression that uses keyword new and returns a reference that can be stored in an array variable. The following statement creates an array object containing 12 int elements—each initialized to 0 by default—and stores the array's reference in variable c:

```
int[] c = new int[12];
```

When you create an array with new, each element of the array receives the default value for the array's element type—0 for the numeric simple-type elements, false for bool elements and null for references. The preceding statement creates the memory for the array in Fig. 8.1 but does not populate the array with the values shown in that figure. In Section 8.4.2, we'll provide specific, nondefault initial values when we create an array.

Common Programming Error 8.1

In an array variable declaration, specifying the number of elements in the square brackets (e.g., int[12] c;) is a syntax error.

---

1. Section 8.4.2 shows a case in which new is not required.

Creating the array c also can be performed as follows:

```
int[] c; // declare the array variable
c = new int[12]; // create the array; assign to array variable
```

In the declaration, the square brackets following int indicate that c will refer to an array of ints (i.e., c will store a reference to an array object). In the assignment statement, the array variable c receives the reference to a new array object of 12 int elements. The number of elements also can be specified as an expression that's calculated at execution time.

Resizing an Array
Though arrays are fixed-length entities, you can use the static Array method Resize to create a new array with the specified length—class Array defines many methods for common array manipulations. This method takes as arguments

- the array to be resized and
- the new length

and copies the contents of the old array into the new one, then sets the variable it receives as its first argument to reference the new array. For example, in the following statements:

```
int[] newArray = new int[5];
Array.Resize(ref newArray, 10);
```

newArray initially refers to a five-element array. The Resize method then sets newArray to refer to a new 10-element array containing the original array's element values. If the new array is *smaller* than the old array, any content that cannot fit into the new array is *truncated without warning*. The old array's memory is reclaimed by the runtime if there are no other array variables referring to that array.[2]

8.4 Examples Using Arrays

This section presents several examples that demonstrate declaring arrays, creating arrays, initializing arrays and manipulating array elements.

8.4.1 Creating and Initializing an Array

In Fig. 8.2, line 10 of uses an array-creation expression to create a five-element int array with values initialized to 0 by default. The resulting array's reference initializes the variable array to refer to the new array object.

```
1  // Fig. 8.2: InitArray.cs
2  // Creating an array.
3  using System;
4
5  class InitArray
6  {
7     static void Main()
8     {
```

Fig. 8.2 | Creating an array. (Part 1 of 2.)

---

2. Section 10.8 discusses how the runtime reclaims the memory of objects that are no longer used.

```
 9          // create the space for array and initialize to default zeros
10          int[] array = new int[5]; // array contains 5 int elements
11
12          Console.WriteLine($"{"Index"}{"Value",8}"); // headings
13
14          // output each array element's value
15          for (int counter = 0; counter < array.Length; ++counter)
16          {
17              Console.WriteLine($"{counter,5}{array[counter],8}");
18          }
19      }
20  }
```

```
Index    Value
    0        0
    1        0
    2        0
    3        0
    4        0
```

Fig. 8.2 | Creating an array. (Part 2 of 2.)

Line 12 displays column headings for the app's output. The first column will display each array element's index (0–4 for a five-element array), and the second column contains each element's default value (0). The column head `"Value"` is right-aligned in a field width of 8, as specified in the string-interpolation expression

```
{"Value",8}
```

The `for` statement (lines 15–18) displays each array element's index (represented by `counter`) and value (represented by `array[counter]`). The loop-control variable `counter` is initially 0—index values start at 0, so zero-based counting allows the loop to access *every* element. The loop-continuation condition uses the property `array.Length` (line 15) to obtain `array`'s length. In this example, the length is 5, so the loop continues executing as long as `counter`'s value is less than 5. The highest index in a five-element array is 4, so using the less-than operator in the loop-continuation condition guarantees that the loop does not attempt to access an element beyond the end of the array (i.e., during the *final* iteration of the loop, `counter` is 4). We'll soon see what happens when an *out-of-range index* is encountered at execution time.

8.4.2 Using an Array Initializer

An app can create an array and initialize its elements with an array initializer—a comma-separated list of expressions (called an initializer list) enclosed in braces. The array length is determined by the number of elements in the initializer list. For example, the declaration

```
int[] n = {10, 20, 30, 40, 50};
```

creates a five-element array with index values 0, 1, 2, 3 and 4. Element `n[0]` is initialized to 10, `n[1]` is initialized to 20 and so on. This statement does *not* require new to create the array object—the compiler counts the number of initializers (5) to determine the array's size, then sets up the appropriate new operation "behind the scenes." The app in Fig. 8.3

initializes an integer array with 5 values (line 10) and displays the array in tabular format. Lines 15–18 for displaying the array's contents are identical to lines 15–18 of Fig. 8.2.

```
1   // Fig. 8.3: InitArray.cs
2   // Initializing the elements of an array with an array initializer.
3   using System;
4
5   class InitArray
6   {
7      static void Main()
8      {
9         // initializer list specifies the value of each element
10        int[] array = {32, 27, 64, 18, 95};
11
12        Console.WriteLine($"{"Index"}{"Value",8}"); // headings
13
14        // output each array element's value
15        for (int counter = 0; counter < array.Length; ++counter)
16        {
17           Console.WriteLine($"{counter,5}{array[counter],8}");
18        }
19     }
20  }
```

```
Index    Value
    0       32
    1       27
    2       64
    3       18
    4       95
```

Fig. 8.3 | Initializing the elements of an array with an array initializer.

8.4.3 Calculating a Value to Store in Each Array Element

Figure 8.4 creates a 5-element array and assigns to its elements the even integers from 2 to 10 (2, 4, 6, 8 and 10). Then the app displays the array in tabular format. Lines 13–16 calculate an array element's value by multiplying the current value of the for loop's control variable counter by 2, then adding 2.

```
1   // Fig. 8.4: InitArray.cs
2   // Calculating values to be placed into the elements of an array.
3   using System;
4
5   class InitArray
6   {
7      static void Main()
8      {
9         const int ArrayLength = 5; // create a named constant
10        int[] array = new int[ArrayLength]; // create array
```

Fig. 8.4 | Calculating values to be placed into the elements of an array. (Part 1 of 2.)

```
11
12          // calculate value for each array element
13          for (int counter = 0; counter < array.Length; ++counter)
14          {
15              array[counter] = 2 + 2 * counter;
16          }
17
18          Console.WriteLine($"{"Index"}{"Value",8}"); // headings
19
20          // output each array element's value
21          for (int counter = 0; counter < array.Length; ++counter)
22          {
23              Console.WriteLine($"{counter,5}{array[counter],8}");
24          }
25      }
26  }
```

```
Index   Value
    0       2
    1       4
    2       6
    3       8
    4      10
```

Fig. 8.4 | Calculating values to be placed into the elements of an array. (Part 2 of 2.)

Declaring a Named Constant with const

Line 9 uses the modifier const to declare the constant ArrayLength, which is initialized to 5. Constants must be initialized in their declarations and cannot be modified thereafter. Constants use the same Pascal Case naming conventions as classes, methods and properties.

Good Programming Practice 8.1

Constants are also called named constants. Apps using constants often are more readable than those that use literal values (e.g., 5)—a named constant such as ArrayLength clearly indicates its purpose, whereas the literal value 5 could have different meanings based on the context in which it's used. Another advantage to using named constants is that if the constant's value must be changed, the change is necessary only in the declaration, thus reducing code-maintenance costs.

Good Programming Practice 8.2

Defining the size of an array as a named constant instead of a literal makes code clearer. This technique eliminates so-called magic numbers. For example, repeatedly mentioning the size 5 in array-processing code for a five-element array gives the number 5 an artificial significance and can be confusing when the program includes other 5s that have nothing to do with the array size.

Common Programming Error 8.2

Assigning a value to a named constant after it's been initialized is a compilation error.

Common Programming Error 8.3

Attempting to declare a named constant without initializing it is a compilation error.

8.4.4 Summing the Elements of an Array

Often, the elements of an array represent a series of values to be used in a calculation. For example, if the elements of an array represent exam grades, an instructor may wish to sum the elements then use the sum to calculate the class average. The GradeBook examples later in the chapter (Sections 8.8 and 8.10) use this technique. Figure 8.5 sums the values contained in a 10-element int array, which is declared and initialized in line 9. The for statement performs the calculations by adding each element's value to the total (line 15).[3]

```
 1   // Fig. 8.5: SumArray.cs
 2   // Computing the sum of the elements of an array.
 3   using System;
 4
 5   class SumArray
 6   {
 7      static void Main()
 8      {
 9         int[] array = {87, 68, 94, 100, 83, 78, 85, 91, 76, 87};
10         int total = 0;
11
12         // add each element's value to total
13         for (int counter = 0; counter < array.Length; ++counter)
14         {
15            total += array[counter]; // add element value to total
16         }
17
18         Console.WriteLine($"Total of array elements: {total}");
19      }
20   }
```

```
Total of array elements: 849
```

Fig. 8.5 | Computing the sum of the elements of an array.

8.4.5 Iterating Through Arrays with foreach

So far, we've used counter-controlled for statements to iterate through array elements. In this section, we introduce the **foreach** statement, which iterates through an entire array's elements (or the elements of a collection, as you'll see in Section 9.4). The syntax of a foreach statement is

---

3. The values supplied as array initializers are often read into an app, rather than specified in an initializer list. For example, an app could input the values from a user at the keyboard or from a file on disk (as discussed in Chapter 17, Files and Streams). This makes the app more reusable, because it can be used with different data sets.

```
foreach (type identifier in arrayName)
{
    statement
}
```

where *type* and *identifier* are the type and name (e.g., int number) of the iteration variable, and *arrayName* is the array through which to iterate. The iteration variable's type must be consistent with the array's element type. The iteration variable represents successive values in the array on successive iterations of the foreach statement.

Figure 8.6 uses the foreach statement (lines 13–16) to calculate the sum of array's elements. The iteration variable number's type is declared as int (line 13), because array contains int values. The foreach statement iterates through successive int values in array one by one, starting with the first element. The foreach header can be read concisely as "for each iteration, assign array's next element to int variable number, then execute the following statement." Lines 13–16 are equivalent to the counter-controlled iteration used in lines 13–16 of Fig. 8.5.

Common Programming Error 8.4

Any attempt to change the iteration variable's value in the body of a foreach statement results in a compilation error.

```
 1   // Fig. 8.6: ForEachTest.cs
 2   // Using the foreach statement to total integers in an array.
 3   using System;
 4
 5   class ForEachTest
 6   {
 7      static void Main()
 8      {
 9         int[] array = {87, 68, 94, 100, 83, 78, 85, 91, 76, 87};
10         int total = 0;
11
12         // add each element's value to total
13         foreach (int number in array)
14         {
15            total += number;
16         }
17
18         Console.WriteLine($"Total of array elements: {total}");
19      }
20   }
```

```
Total of array elements: 849
```

Fig. 8.6 | Using the foreach statement to total integers in an array.

foreach vs. for

The foreach statement can be used in place of the for statement whenever code looping through an array does *not* require access to the current array element's *index*. For example, totaling the integers in an array requires access only to the element values—each element's index is irrelevant. If an app must use a counter for some reason other than simply to loop through an array (e.g., to calculate an element's value based on the counter's value, as in Fig. 8.4), you should use the for statement.

Common Programming Error 8.5

Attempting to modify an array element's value using a foreach statement's iteration variable is a logic error—the iteration variable can be used only to access each array element's value, not modify it.

8.4.6 Using Bar Charts to Display Array Data Graphically; Introducing Type Inference with var

Many apps present data to users in a graphical manner. For example, numeric values are often displayed as bars in a bar chart. In such a chart, longer bars represent proportionally larger numeric values. One simple way to display numeric data graphically is with a bar chart that shows each numeric value as a bar of asterisks (*).

An instructor might graph the number of grades in each of several categories to visualize the grade distribution for an exam. Suppose the grades on an exam were 87, 68, 94, 100, 83, 78, 85, 91, 76 and 87. Included were one grade of 100, two grades in the 90s, four grades in the 80s, two grades in the 70s, one grade in the 60s and no grades below 60. Our next app (Fig. 8.7) stores this grade-distribution data in an array of 11 elements, each corresponding to a category of grades. For example, array[0] indicates the number of grades in the range 0–9, array[7] the number of grades in the range 70–79 and array[10] the number of 100 grades. The two versions of class GradeBook in Sections 8.8 and 8.10 contain code that calculates these grade frequencies based on a set of grades. For now, we manually create array and initialize it with the number of grades in each range (Fig. 8.7, line 9). We discuss the keyword var (lines 14 and 27) after we present the app's logic.

```
1   // Fig. 8.7: BarChart.cs
2   // Bar chart displaying app.
3   using System;
4
5   class BarChart
6   {
7      static void Main()
8      {
9         int[] array = {0, 0, 0, 0, 0, 0, 1, 2, 4, 2, 1}; // distribution
10
11        Console.WriteLine("Grade distribution:");
12
13        // for each array element, output a bar of the chart
14        for (var counter = 0; counter < array.Length; ++counter)
15        {
16           // output bar labels ("00-09: ", ..., "90-99: ", "100: ")
17           if (counter == 10)
18           {
19              Console.Write("  100: ");
20           }
```

Fig. 8.7 | Bar chart displaying app. (Part 1 of 2.)

```
21              else
22              {
23                  Console.Write($"{counter * 10:D2}-{counter * 10 + 9:D2}: ");
24              }
25
26              // display bar of asterisks
27              for (var stars = 0; stars < array[counter]; ++stars)
28              {
29                  Console.Write("*");
30              }
31
32              Console.WriteLine(); // start a new line of output
33          }
34      }
35  }
```

```
Grade distribution:
00-09:
10-19:
20-29:
30-39:
40-49:
50-59:
60-69: *
70-79: **
80-89: ****
90-99: **
  100: *
```

Fig. 8.7 | Bar chart displaying app. (Part 2 of 2.)

The app reads the numbers from the array and graphs the information as a bar chart. Each grade range is followed by a bar of asterisks indicating the number of grades in that range. To label each bar, lines 17–24 display a grade range (e.g., "70-79: ") based on the current value of counter. When counter is 10, line 19 displays "   100: " to align the colon with the other bar labels. When counter is not 10, line 23 uses the string-interpolation expressions

```
{counter * 10:D2}
```

and

```
{counter * 10 + 9:D2}
```

to format the label of the grade range. The format specifier D indicates that the value should be formatted as an integer, and the number after the D indicates how many digits this formatted integer must contain. The 2 indicates that values with fewer than two digits should begin with a leading 0.

The nested for statement (lines 27–30) displays the bars. Note the loop-continuation condition at line 27 (stars < array[counter]). Each time the app reaches the inner for, the loop counts from 0 up to one less than array[counter], thus using a value in array to determine the number of asterisks to display. In this example, array[0]–array[5] contain 0s because no students received a grade below 60. Thus, the app displays no asterisks next to the first six grade ranges.

Implicitly Typed Local Variables and Keyword **var**
In line 14

```
for (var counter = 0; counter < array.Length; ++counter)
```

notice **var** keyword rather than a type preceding the variable counter. This declares the variable and lets the *compiler* determine the variable's type, based on the variable's *initializer*. This process is known as type inference and local variables declared in this manner are known as implicitly typed local variables. Here, the compiler *infers* that counter's type is int, because it's initialized with the literal 0, which is an int.

Similarly, consider line 11 of Fig. 4.9:

```
Account account1 = new Account("Jane Green");
```

Notice that the type Account appears twice—once to declare variable account1's type and once to specify the type of the new object being created. From this point forward, the preferred way to write this statement is

```
var account1 = new Account("Jane Green");
```

Here, the compiler *infers* that account1's type is Account, because the compiler can determine the type from the expression

```
new Account("Jane Green")
```

which creates an Account object.

The Microsoft C# Coding Conventions

```
https://msdn.microsoft.com/library/ff926074
```

recommend using type inference when a local variable's type is *obvious*, based on its initial value.[4] These coding conventions are just *guidelines*, not requirements. In industry, your employer might have its own coding requirements that differ from Microsoft's guidelines.

More on Implicitly Typed Local Variables
Implicitly typed local variables also can be used to initialize an array variable via an initializer list. In the following statement, the type of values is inferred as int[]:

```
var values = new[] {32, 27, 64, 18, 95, 14, 90, 70, 60, 37};
```

new[] specifies that the initializer list is for an array. The array's element type, int, is inferred from the initializers. The following statement—in which values is initialized directly *without* new[]—generates a compilation error:

```
var values = {32, 27, 64, 18, 95, 14, 90, 70, 60, 37};
```

 Common Programming Error 8.6

Initializer lists can be used with both arrays and collections. If an implicitly typed local variable is initialized via an initializer list without new[]*, a compilation error occurs, because the compiler cannot infer whether the variable should be an array or a collection. We use a* List *collection in Chapter 9 and cover collections in detail in Chapter 21.*

---

4. You'll see in Chapter 9 that type inference is particularly helpful with anonymous types—that is, types that are created as the result of an expression and that do not have names.

8.4.7 Using the Elements of an Array as Counters

Sometimes, apps use counter variables to summarize data, such as the results of a survey. In Fig. 7.7, we used separate counters in our die-rolling app to track the number of times each face of a six-sided die appeared as the app rolled the die 60,000,000 times. An array version of the app in Fig. 7.7 is shown in Fig. 8.8.

```csharp
1   // Fig. 8.8: RollDie.cs
2   // Roll a six-sided die 60,000,000 times.
3   using System;
4
5   class RollDie
6   {
7      static void Main()
8      {
9         var randomNumbers = new Random(); // random-number generator
10        var frequency = new int[7]; // array of frequency counters
11
12        // roll die 60,000,000 times; use die value as frequency index
13        for (var roll = 1; roll <= 60000000; ++roll)
14        {
15           ++frequency[randomNumbers.Next(1, 7)];
16        }
17
18        Console.WriteLine($"{"Face"}{"Frequency",10}");
19
20        // output each array element's value
21        for (var face = 1; face < frequency.Length; ++face)
22        {
23           Console.WriteLine($"{face,4}{frequency[face],10}");
24        }
25     }
26  }
```

```
Face Frequency
   1  10004131
   2   9998200
   3  10003734
   4   9999332
   5   9999792
   6   9994811
```

Fig. 8.8 | Roll a six-sided die 60,000,000 times.

The app uses array frequency (line 10) to count the occurrences of each roll. *The single statement in line 15 replaces lines 24–44 of Fig. 7.7.* Line 15 of Fig. 8.8 uses the random value to determine which frequency array element to increment. The call to Next produces a random number from 1 to 6, so frequency must be large enough to store six counters. We use a seven-element array in which we ignore frequency[0]—it's more logical to have the face value 1 increment frequency[1] than frequency[0]. Thus, each face value is used directly as an index for array frequency. We also replaced lines 48–50 of Fig. 7.7 by looping through array frequency to output the results (Fig. 8.8, lines 21–24).

8.5 Using Arrays to Analyze Survey Results; Intro to Exception Handling

Our next example uses arrays to summarize data collected in a survey. Consider the following problem statement:

> *Twenty students were asked to rate on a scale of 1 to 5 the quality of the food in the student cafeteria, with 1 being "awful" and 5 being "excellent." Place the 20 responses in an integer array and determine the frequency of each rating.*

This is a typical array-processing app (Fig. 8.9). We wish to summarize the number of responses of each type (that is, 1–5). Array `responses` (lines 10–11) is a 20-element integer array containing the students' survey responses. The last value in the array is intentionally an incorrect response (14). When a C# program executes, the runtime checks array element indices for *validity*—all indices must be greater than or equal to 0 and less than the length of the array. Any attempt to access an element *outside* that range of indices results in a runtime error known as an `IndexOutOfRangeException`. At the end of this section, we'll discuss the invalid response, demonstrate array bounds checking and introduce C#'s exception-handling mechanism, which can be used to detect and handle an `IndexOutOfRangeException`.

```
 1   // Fig. 8.9: StudentPoll.cs
 2   // Poll analysis app.
 3   using System;
 4
 5   class StudentPoll
 6   {
 7      static void Main()
 8      {
 9         // student response array (more typically, input at runtime)
10         int[] responses = {1, 2, 5, 4, 3, 5, 2, 1, 3, 3, 1, 4, 3, 3, 3,
11            2, 3, 3, 2, 14};
12         var frequency = new int[6]; // array of frequency counters
13
14         // for each answer, select responses element and use that value
15         // as frequency index to determine element to increment
16         for (var answer = 0; answer < responses.Length; ++answer)
17         {
18            try
19            {
20               ++frequency[responses[answer]];
21            }
22            catch (IndexOutOfRangeException ex)
23            {
24               Console.WriteLine(ex.Message);
25               Console.WriteLine(
26                  $"   responses[{answer}] = {responses[answer]}\n");
27            }
28         }
```

Fig. 8.9 | Poll analysis app. (Part 1 of 2.)

```
29
30          Console.WriteLine($"{"Rating"}{"Frequency",10}");
31
32          // output each array element's value
33          for (var rating = 1; rating < frequency.Length; ++rating)
34          {
35              Console.WriteLine($"{rating,6}{frequency[rating],10}");
36          }
37      }
38  }
```

```
Index was outside the bounds of the array.
  responses[19] = 14

Rating Frequency
    1        3
    2        4
    3        8
    4        2
    5        2
```

Fig. 8.9 | Poll analysis app. (Part 2 of 2.)

*The **frequency** Array*

We use the *six-element* array frequency (line 12) to count the number of occurrences of each response. Each element is used as a counter for one of the possible types of survey responses—frequency[1] counts the number of students who rated the food as 1, frequency[2] counts the number of students who rated the food as 2, and so on.

8.5.1 Summarizing the Results

Lines 16–28 read the responses from the array responses one at a time and increments on of the counters frequency[1] to frequency[5]; we ignore frequency[0] because the survey responses are limited to the range 1–5. The key statement in the loop appears in line 20. This statement increments the appropriate frequency counter as determined by the value of responses[answer].

Let's step through the first few iterations of the foreach statement:

- When the counter answer is 0, responses[answer] is the value of responses[0] (that is, 1—see line 10). In this case, frequency[responses[answer]] is interpreted as frequency[1], and the counter frequency[1] is incremented by one. To evaluate the expression, we begin with the value in the *innermost* set of brackets (answer, currently 0). The value of answer is plugged into the expression, and the next set of brackets (responses[answer]) is evaluated. That value is used as the index for the frequency array to determine which counter to increment (in this case, frequency[1]).

- The next time through the loop answer is 1, responses[answer] is the value of responses[1] (that is, 2—see line 10), so frequency[responses[answer]] is interpreted as frequency[2], causing frequency[2] to be incremented.

- When answer is 2, responses[answer] is the value of responses[2] (that is, 5— see line 10), so frequency[responses[answer]] is interpreted as frequency[5], causing frequency[5] to be incremented, and so on.

Regardless of the number of responses processed in the survey, only a six-element array (in which we *ignore* element zero) is required to summarize the results, because all the correct response values are between 1 and 5, and the index values for a six-element array are 0–5. In the output in Fig. 8.9, the frequency column summarizes only 19 of the 20 values in the responses array—the last element of the array responses contains an *incorrect* response that was *not* counted. Lines 16–28 could be simplified, by changing line 16 to

```
foreach (var response in responses)
```

line 20 to

```
++frequency[response];
```

and modifying the error message displayed by lines 25–26.

8.5.2 Exception Handling: Processing the Incorrect Response

An exception indicates a problem that occurs while a program executes. Exception handling enables you to create fault-tolerant programs that can resolve (or handle) exceptions. In many cases, this allows a program to continue executing as if no problems were encountered. For example, the **Student Poll** app still displays results (Fig. 8.9), even though one of the responses was out of range. More severe problems might prevent a program from continuing normal execution, instead requiring the program to notify the user of the problem, then terminate. When the runtime or a method detects a problem, such as an invalid array index or an invalid method argument, it throws an exception—that is, an exception occurs. The exception here is thrown by the runtime. In Section 10.2, you'll see how to throw your own exceptions.

8.5.3 The try Statement

To handle an exception, place any code that might throw an exception in a **try** statement (Fig. 8.9, lines 18–27). The **try** block (lines 18–21) contains the code that might *throw* an exception, and the **catch** block (lines 22–27) contains the code that *handles* the exception if one occurs. You can have many catch blocks to handle different types of exceptions that might be thrown in the corresponding try block. When line 20 correctly increments an element of the frequency array, lines 22–27 are ignored. The braces that delimit the bodies of the try and catch blocks are required.

8.5.4 Executing the catch Block

When the program encounters the value 14 in the responses array, it attempts to add 1 to frequency[14], which does *not* exist—the frequency array has only six elements. Because the runtime performs array bounds checking, it generates an exception—specifically line 20 throws an **IndexOutOfRangeException** to notify the program of this problem. At this point the try block *terminates* and the catch block begins executing—if you declared any variables in the try block, they no longer exist, so they're *not accessible* in the catch block.

The catch block declares an exception parameter's type (IndexOutOfRangeException) and name (ex). The catch block can handle exceptions of the specified type. Inside the catch block, you can use the parameter's identifier to interact with a caught exception object.

> **Error-Prevention Tip 8.1**
> *When writing code to access an array element, ensure that the array index remains greater than or equal to 0 and less than the length of the array. This will help prevent Index-OutOfRangeExceptions in your program.*

8.5.5 Message Property of the Exception Parameter

When lines 22–27 *catch* the exception, the program displays a message indicating the problem that occurred. Line 24 uses the exception object's built-in **Message** property to get the error message and display it. Once the message is displayed, the exception is considered handled and the program continues with the next statement after the catch block's closing brace. In this example, the end of the foreach statement is reached (line 28), so the program continues with the next iteration of the loop. We use exception handling again in Chapter 10, then Chapter 13 presents a deeper look at exception handling.

8.6 Case Study: Card Shuffling and Dealing Simulation

So far, this chapter's examples have used arrays of value-type elements. This section uses random-number generation and an *array of reference-type elements*—namely, *objects* representing playing cards—to develop a class that simulates card shuffling and dealing. This class can then be used to implement apps that play card games. The exercises at the end of the chapter use the techniques developed here to build a poker app.

We first develop class Card (Fig. 8.10), which represents a playing card that has a face (e.g., "Ace", "Deuce", "Three", ..., "Jack", "Queen", "King") and a suit (e.g., "Hearts", "Diamonds", "Clubs", "Spades"). Next, we develop class DeckOfCards (Fig. 8.11), which creates a deck of 52 playing cards in which each element is a Card object. Then we build an app (Fig. 8.12) that uses class DeckOfCards's card shuffling and dealing capabilities.

8.6.1 Class Card and Getter-Only Auto-Implemented Properties

Class Card (Fig. 8.10) contains two auto-implemented string properties—Face and Suit—that store references to the *face value* and *suit name* for a specific Card. Prior to C# 6, auto-implemented properties required both a get and a set accessor. Face and Suit are declared as C# 6 getter-only auto-implemented properties, which client code can use only to *get* each property's value. Such properties are *read only*. Getter-only auto-implemented properties can be initialized *only* either in their declarations or in all of the type's constructors. Initializing an auto-implemented property in its declaration is another C# 6 feature known as auto-property initializers. To do so, follow the property declaration with an = and the initial value, as in

Type PropertyName { **get**; **set**; } = *initializer*;

You can also initialize instance variables in their declarations.

The constructor (lines 9–13) receives two strings that it uses to initialize the class's properties. Method ToString (line 16)—implemented here as an expression-bodied

```
 1    // Fig. 8.10: Card.cs
 2    // Card class represents a playing card.
 3    class Card
 4    {
 5       private string Face { get; } // Card's face ("Ace", "Deuce", ...)
 6       private string Suit { get; } // Card's suit ("Hearts", "Diamonds", ...)
 7
 8       // two-parameter constructor initializes card's Face and Suit
 9       public Card(string face, string suit)
10       {
11          Face = face; // initialize face of card
12          Suit = suit; // initialize suit of card
13       }
14
15       // return string representation of Card
16       public override string ToString() => $"{Face} of {Suit}";
17    }
```

Fig. 8.10 | Card class represents a playing card.

method—creates a string consisting of the Face of the card, the string " of " and the Suit of the card (e.g., "Ace of Spades"). An object's ToString method is called *implicitly* in many cases when the object is used where a string is expected, such as

- when Write or WriteLine outputs the object,
- when the object is *concatenated* to a string using the + operator, or
- when the object is inserted into a string-interpolation expression.

ToString also can be invoked *explicitly* to obtain a string representation of an object.

ToString must be declared with the header exactly as shown in line 16 of Fig. 8.10. We'll explain the purpose of the override keyword in Section 11.4.1.

8.6.2 Class DeckOfCards

Class DeckOfCards (Fig. 8.11) creates and manages an array of Card references. The named constant NumberOfCards (line 10) specifies the number of Cards in a deck (52). Line 11 declares an instance-variable named deck that refers to an array of Card objects with Number-OfCards (52) elements—the elements of the deck array are null by default. Like simple-type array-variable declarations, the declaration of a variable for an array of objects (e.g., Card[] deck) includes the type of the array's elements, followed by square brackets and the name of the array variable. Class DeckOfCards also declares int instance variable current-Card (line 12), representing the next Card to be dealt from the deck array. Note that we cannot use var for type inference with NumberOfCards, deck and currentCard, because they are not local variables of a method or property.

```
 1    // Fig. 8.11: DeckOfCards.cs
 2    // DeckOfCards class represents a deck of playing cards.
 3    using System;
```

Fig. 8.11 | DeckOfCards class represents a deck of playing cards. (Part 1 of 3.)

```
4
5    class DeckOfCards
6    {
7        // create one Random object to share among DeckOfCards objects
8        private static Random randomNumbers = new Random();
9
10       private const int NumberOfCards = 52; // number of cards in a deck
11       private Card[] deck = new Card[NumberOfCards];
12       private int currentCard = 0; // index of next Card to be dealt (0-51)
13
14       // constructor fills deck of Cards
15       public DeckOfCards()
16       {
17           string[] faces = {"Ace", "Deuce", "Three", "Four", "Five", "Six",
18               "Seven", "Eight", "Nine", "Ten", "Jack", "Queen", "King"};
19           string[] suits = {"Hearts", "Diamonds", "Clubs", "Spades"};
20
21           // populate deck with Card objects
22           for (var count = 0; count < deck.Length; ++count)
23           {
24               deck[count] = new Card(faces[count % 13], suits[count / 13]);
25           }
26       }
27
28       // shuffle deck of Cards with one-pass algorithm
29       public void Shuffle()
30       {
31           // after shuffling, dealing should start at deck[0] again
32           currentCard = 0; // reinitialize currentCard
33
34           // for each Card, pick another random Card and swap them
35           for (var first = 0; first < deck.Length; ++first)
36           {
37               // select a random number between 0 and 51
38               var second = randomNumbers.Next(NumberOfCards);
39
40               // swap current Card with randomly selected Card
41               Card temp = deck[first];
42               deck[first] = deck[second];
43               deck[second] = temp;
44           }
45       }
46
47       // deal one Card
48       public Card DealCard()
49       {
50           // determine whether Cards remain to be dealt
51           if (currentCard < deck.Length)
52           {
53               return deck[currentCard++]; // return current Card in array
54           }
55           else
56           {
```

Fig. 8.11 | DeckOfCards class represents a deck of playing cards. (Part 2 of 3.)

```
57                    return null; // indicate that all Cards were dealt
58            }
59        }
60    }
```

Fig. 8.11 | DeckOfCards class represents a deck of playing cards. (Part 3 of 3.)

Class *DeckOfCards: Constructor*

The constructor uses a for statement (lines 22–25) to fill the deck array with Cards. The for statement initializes count to 0 and loops while count is less than deck.Length, causing count to take on each integer value from 0 to 51 (the indices of the deck array). Each Card is instantiated and initialized with two strings—one from the faces array at lines 17–18 (which contains the strings "Ace" through "King") and one from the suits array at line 19 (which contains the strings "Hearts", "Diamonds", "Clubs" and "Spades"). The calculation count % 13 (line 24) always results in a value from 0 to 12—the 13 indices of array faces. Similarly, the calculation count / 13 always results in a value from 0 to 3—the four indices of array suits. When the deck array is initialized, it contains the Cards with faces "Ace" through "King" in order for each suit. Note that we cannot use a foreach loop in lines 22–25, because we need to modify each element of deck.

Class *DeckOfCards: Shuffle Method*

Method Shuffle (lines 29–45) shuffles the Cards in the deck. The method loops through all 52 Cards and performs the following tasks:

- For each Card, a random number between 0 and 51 is picked to select another Card.

- Next, the current Card object and the randomly selected Card object are swapped in the array. This exchange is performed by the three assignments in lines 41–43. The extra variable temp temporarily stores one of the two Card objects being swapped.

The swap cannot be performed with only the two statements

```
deck[first] = deck[second];
deck[second] = deck[first];
```

If deck[first] is the "Ace" of "Spades" and deck[second] is the "Queen" of "Hearts", then after the first assignment, both array elements contain the "Queen" of "Hearts", and the "Ace" of "Spades" is lost—hence, the extra variable temp is needed. After the for loop terminates, the Card objects are randomly ordered. Only 52 swaps are made in a single pass of the entire array, and the array of Card objects is shuffled.

Recommendation: *Use an Unbiased Shuffling Algorithm*

It's recommended that you use a so-called unbiased shuffling algorithm for real card games. Such an algorithm ensures that all possible shuffled card sequences are equally likely to occur. A popular unbiased shuffling algorithm is the Fisher-Yates algorithm

```
http://en.wikipedia.org/wiki/Fisher-Yates_shuffle
```

This page also uses pseudocode to shows how to implement the algorithm.

Class **DeckOfCards: DealCard** Method

Method DealCard (lines 48–59) deals one Card in the array. Recall that currentCard indicates the index of the next Card to be dealt (i.e., the Card at the top of the deck). Thus, line 51 compares currentCard to the length of the deck array. If the deck is not empty (i.e., currentCard is less than 52), line 53 returns the top Card and increments current-Card to prepare for the next call to DealCard—otherwise, line 57 returns null to indicate that the end of deck has been reached.

8.6.3 Shuffling and Dealing Cards

Figure 8.12 demonstrates the card shuffling and dealing capabilities of class DeckOfCards (Fig. 8.11). Line 10 of Fig. 8.12 creates a DeckOfCards object named myDeckOfCards and uses type inference to determine the variable's type. Recall that the DeckOfCards constructor creates the deck with the 52 Card objects in order by suit and face. Line 11 invokes myDeckOfCards's Shuffle method to rearrange the Card objects. The for statement in lines 14–22 deals all 52 Cards in the deck and displays them in four columns of 13 Cards each. Line 16 deals and displays a Card object by invoking myDeckOfCards's DealCard method. When a Card object is placed in a string-interpolation expression, the Card's To-String method is invoked implicitly. Because the field width is *negative*, the result is displayed *left*-aligned in a field of width 19.

```
 1   // Fig. 8.12: DeckOfCardsTest.cs
 2   // Card shuffling and dealing app.
 3   using System;
 4
 5   class DeckOfCardsTest
 6   {
 7      // execute app
 8      static void Main()
 9      {
10         var myDeckOfCards = new DeckOfCards();
11         myDeckOfCards.Shuffle(); // place Cards in random order
12
13         // display all 52 Cards in the order in which they are dealt
14         for (var i = 0; i < 52; ++i)
15         {
16            Console.Write($"{myDeckOfCards.DealCard(),-19}");
17
18            if ((i + 1) % 4 == 0)
19            {
20               Console.WriteLine();
21            }
22         }
23      }
24   }
```

```
Eight of Clubs      Ten of Clubs      Ten of Spaces     Four of Spades
Ace of Spades       Jack of Spades    Three of Spades   Seven of Spades
Three of Diamonds   Five of Clubs     Eight of Spades   Five of Hearts
```

Fig. 8.12 | Card-shuffling-and-dealing app. (Part 1 of 2.)

Ace of Hearts	Ten of Hearts	Deuce of Hearts	Deuce of Clubs
Jack of Hearts	Nine of Spades	Four of Hearts	Seven of Clubs
Queen of Spades	Seven of Diamonds	Five of Diamonds	Ace of Clubs
Four of Clubs	Ten of Diamonds	Jack of Clubs	Six of Diamonds
Eight of Diamonds	King of Hearts	Three of Clubs	King of Spades
King of Diamonds	Six of Spades	Deuce of Spades	Five of Spades
Queen of Clubs	King of Clubs	Queen of Hearts	Seven of Hearts
Ace of Diamonds	Deuce of Diamonds	Four of Diamonds	Nine of Clubs
Queen of Diamonds	Jack of Diamonds	Six of Hearts	Nine of Diamonds
Nine of Hearts	Three of Hearts	Six of Clubs	Eight of Hearts

Fig. 8.12 | Card-shuffling-and-dealing app. (Part 2 of 2.)

8.7 Passing Arrays and Array Elements to Methods

To pass an array argument to a method, specify the name of the array *without any brackets*. For example, if `hourlyTemperatures` is declared as

```
var hourlyTemperatures = new double[24];
```

then the method call

```
ModifyArray(hourlyTemperatures);
```

passes the reference of array `hourlyTemperatures` to method `ModifyArray`. Every array object "knows" its own length (and makes it available via its `Length` property). Thus, when we pass an array object's reference to a method, we need not pass the array length as an additional argument.

Specifying an Array Parameter
For a method to receive an array reference through a method call, the method's parameter list must specify an array parameter. For example, the method header for method `Modify-Array` might be written as

```
void ModifyArray(double[] b)
```

indicating that `ModifyArray` receives the reference of an array of `double`s in parameter `b`. The method call passes array `hourlyTemperatures`' reference, so when the called method uses the array variable `b`, it refers to the same array object as `hourlyTemperatures` in the calling method.

Pass-By-Value vs. Pass-By-Reference
When an argument is an entire array or an individual array element *of a reference type*, the called method receives a *copy of the reference*. However, when an argument to a method is an individual array element *of a value type*, the called method receives a *copy of the element's value*. To pass an individual array element to a method, use the indexed name of the array as an argument (e.g., `hourlyTemperatures[2]`). If you want to pass a value-type array element to a method by reference, you must use the `ref` keyword as shown in Section 7.18.

Passing an Entire Array vs. Passing a Single Array Element
Figure 8.13 demonstrates the difference between passing an entire array and passing a value-type array element to a method. The `foreach` statement at lines 16–19 outputs the five

int elements of array. Line 21 invokes method ModifyArray, passing array as an argument. Method ModifyArray (lines 38–44) receives a *copy* of array's *reference* and uses the reference to multiply each of array's elements by 2. To prove that array's elements (in Main) were modified, the foreach statement at lines 25–28 outputs the five elements of array again. As the output shows, method ModifyArray doubled the value of each element.

```
 1   // Fig. 8.13: PassArray.cs
 2   // Passing arrays and individual array elements to methods.
 3   using System;
 4
 5   class PassArray
 6   {
 7      // Main creates array and calls ModifyArray and ModifyElement
 8      static void Main()
 9      {
10         int[] array = {1, 2, 3, 4, 5};
11
12         Console.WriteLine("Effects of passing reference to entire array:");
13         Console.WriteLine("The values of the original array are:");
14
15         // output original array elements
16         foreach (var value in array)
17         {
18            Console.Write($"   {value}");
19         }
20
21         ModifyArray(array); // pass array reference
22         Console.WriteLine("\n\nThe values of the modified array are:");
23
24         // output modified array elements
25         foreach (var value in array)
26         {
27            Console.Write($"   {value}");
28         }
29
30         Console.WriteLine("\n\nEffects of passing array element value:\n" +
31            $"array[3] before ModifyElement: {array[3]}");
32
33         ModifyElement(array[3]); // attempt to modify array[3]
34         Console.WriteLine($"array[3] after ModifyElement: {array[3]}");
35      }
36
37      // multiply each element of an array by 2
38      static void ModifyArray(int[] array2)
39      {
40         for (var counter = 0; counter < array2.Length; ++counter)
41         {
42            array2[counter] *= 2;
43         }
44      }
45
```

Fig. 8.13 | Passing arrays and individual array elements to methods. (Part 1 of 2.)

```
46      // multiply argument by 2
47      static void ModifyElement(int element)
48      {
49          element *= 2;
50          Console.WriteLine($"Value of element in ModifyElement: {element}");
51      }
52  }
```

```
Effects of passing reference to entire array:
The values of the original array are:
   1   2   3   4   5

The values of the modified array are:
   2   4   6   8   10

Effects of passing array element value:
array[3] before ModifyElement: 8
Value of element in ModifyElement: 16
array[3] after ModifyElement: 8
```

Fig. 8.13 | Passing arrays and individual array elements to methods. (Part 2 of 2.)

Figure 8.13 next demonstrates that when a copy of an individual value-type array element is passed to a method, modifying the copy in the called method does *not* affect the original value of that element in the calling method's array. To show the value of array[3] before invoking method ModifyElement, lines 30–31 display the value of array[3], which is 8. Line 33 calls method ModifyElement (lines 47–51) and passes array[3] as an argument. Remember that array[3] is actually one int value (8) in array. Therefore, the app passes a copy of the value of array[3]. Method ModifyElement multiplies the value received as an argument by 2, stores the result in its parameter element, then outputs the value of element (16). Since method parameters, like local variables, cease to exist when the method in which they're declared completes execution, the method parameter element is destroyed when method ModifyElement terminates. When the app returns control to Main, line 34 displays the unmodified value of array[3] (i.e., 8).

8.8 Case Study: GradeBook Using an Array to Store Grades

We now present the first version of a GradeBook class that instructors can use to maintain students' grades on an exam and display a grade report that includes the grades, class average, lowest grade, highest grade and a grade distribution bar chart. The version of class GradeBook presented in this section stores the grades for one exam in a one-dimensional array. In Section 8.10, we present a second version of class GradeBook that uses a two-dimensional array to store students' grades for *several* exams.

Storing Student Grades in an **array** in Class **GradeBook**

Figure 8.14 shows the output that summarizes the 10 grades we store in an object of class GradeBook (Fig. 8.15), which uses an array of integers to store the grades of 10 students for a single exam. The array grades is declared as an instance variable in line 7 of Fig. 8.15—therefore, each GradeBook object maintains its own set of grades.

```
Welcome to the grade book for
CS101 Introduction to C# Programming!

The grades are:

Student  1:  87
Student  2:  68
Student  3:  94
Student  4: 100
Student  5:  83
Student  6:  78
Student  7:  85
Student  8:  91
Student  9:  76
Student 10:  87

Class average is 84.90
Lowest grade is 68
Highest grade is 100

Grade distribution:
00-09:
10-19:
20-29:
30-39:
40-49:
50-59:
60-69: *
70-79: **
80-89: ****
90-99: **
  100: *
```

Fig. 8.14 | Output of the GradeBook example that stores one exam's grades in an array.

```csharp
 1  // Fig. 8.15: GradeBook.cs
 2  // Grade book using an array to store test grades.
 3  using System;
 4
 5  class GradeBook
 6  {
 7     private int[] grades; // array of student grades
 8
 9     // getter-only auto-implemented property CourseName
10     public string CourseName { get; }
11
12     // two-parameter constructor initializes
13     // auto-implemented property CourseName and grades array
14     public GradeBook(string name, int[] gradesArray)
15     {
16        CourseName = name; // set CourseName to name
17        grades = gradesArray; // initialize grades array
18     }
```

Fig. 8.15 | Grade book using an array to store test grades. (Part 1 of 4.)

```
19
20      // display a welcome message to the GradeBook user
21      public void DisplayMessage()
22      {
23         // auto-implemented property CourseName gets the name of course
24         Console.WriteLine(
25            $"Welcome to the grade book for\n{CourseName}!\n");
26      }
27
28      // perform various operations on the data
29      public void ProcessGrades()
30      {
31         // output grades array
32         OutputGrades();
33
34         // call method GetAverage to calculate the average grade
35         Console.WriteLine($"\nClass average is {GetAverage():F}");
36
37         // call methods GetMinimum and GetMaximum
38         Console.WriteLine($"Lowest grade is {GetMinimum()}");
39         Console.WriteLine($"Highest grade is {GetMaximum()}\n");
40
41         // call OutputBarChart to display grade distribution chart
42         OutputBarChart();
43      }
44
45      // find minimum grade
46      public int GetMinimum()
47      {
48         var lowGrade = grades[0]; // assume grades[0] is smallest
49
50         // loop through grades array
51         foreach (var grade in grades)
52         {
53            // if grade lower than lowGrade, assign it to lowGrade
54            if (grade < lowGrade)
55            {
56               lowGrade = grade; // new lowest grade
57            }
58         }
59
60         return lowGrade; // return lowest grade
61      }
62
63      // find maximum grade
64      public int GetMaximum()
65      {
66         var highGrade = grades[0]; // assume grades[0] is largest
67
68         // loop through grades array
69         foreach (var grade in grades)
70         {
```

Fig. 8.15 | Grade book using an array to store test grades. (Part 2 of 4.)

```
71              // if grade greater than highGrade, assign it to highGrade
72              if (grade > highGrade)
73              {
74                  highGrade = grade; // new highest grade
75              }
76          }
77
78      return highGrade; // return highest grade
79  }
80
81  // determine average grade for test
82  public double GetAverage()
83  {
84      var total = 0.0; // initialize total as a double
85
86      // sum students' grades
87      foreach (var grade in grades)
88      {
89          total += grade;
90      }
91
92      // return average of grades
93      return total / grades.Length;
94  }
95
96  // output bar chart displaying grade distribution
97  public void OutputBarChart()
98  {
99      Console.WriteLine("Grade distribution:");
100
101     // stores frequency of grades in each range of 10 grades
102     var frequency = new int[11];
103
104     // for each grade, increment the appropriate frequency
105     foreach (var grade in grades)
106     {
107         ++frequency[grade / 10];
108     }
109
110     // for each grade frequency, display bar in chart
111     for (var count = 0; count < frequency.Length; ++count)
112     {
113         // output bar label ("00-09: ", ..., "90-99: ", "100: ")
114         if (count == 10)
115         {
116             Console.Write("  100: ");
117         }
118         else
119         {
120             Console.Write($"{count * 10:D2}-{count * 10 + 9:D2}: ");
121         }
122
```

Fig. 8.15 | Grade book using an array to store test grades. (Part 3 of 4.)

```
123                // display bar of asterisks
124                for (var stars = 0; stars < frequency[count]; ++stars)
125                {
126                    Console.Write("*");
127                }
128
129                Console.WriteLine(); // start a new line of output
130            }
131        }
132
133        // output the contents of the grades array
134        public void OutputGrades()
135        {
136            Console.WriteLine("The grades are:\n");
137
138            // output each student's grade
139            for (var student = 0; student < grades.Length; ++student)
140            {
141                Console.WriteLine(
142                    $"Student {student + 1, 2}: {grades[student],3}");
143            }
144        }
145    }
```

Fig. 8.15 | Grade book using an array to store test grades. (Part 4 of 4.)

The constructor (lines 14–18) receives the name of the course and an array of grades. When an app (e.g., class GradeBookTest in Fig. 8.16) creates a GradeBook object, the app passes an existing int array to the constructor, which assigns the array's reference to instance variable grades (Fig. 8.15, line 17). The size of grades is determined by the class that passes the array to the constructor. Thus, a GradeBook can process a variable number of grades— as many as are in the array in the caller. The grade values in the passed array could have been input from a user at the keyboard or read from a file on disk (as discussed in Chapter 17). In our test app, we simply initialize an array with a set of grade values (Fig. 8.16, line 9). Once the grades are stored in instance variable grades of class GradeBook, all the class's methods can access the elements of grades as needed to perform various calculations.

Methods *ProcessGrades* and *OutputGrades*

Method ProcessGrades (Fig. 8.15, lines 29–43) contains a series of method calls that result in the output of a report summarizing the grades. Line 32 calls method OutputGrades to display the contents of array grades. Lines 139–143 in method OutputGrades use a for statement to output the student grades. We use a for statement, rather than a foreach, because lines 141–142 use counter variable student's value to output each grade next to a particular student number (see Fig. 8.14). Although array indices start at 0, an instructor would typically number students starting at 1. Thus, lines 141–142 output student + 1 as the student number to produce grade labels "Student 1: ", "Student 2: " and so on.

Method *GetAverage*

Method ProcessGrades next calls method GetAverage (line 35) to obtain the average of the grades in the array. Method GetAverage (lines 82–94) uses a foreach statement to total the values in array grades before calculating the average. The iteration variable in the foreach's header indicates that for each iteration, grade takes on a value in array grades. The average calculation in line 93 uses grades.Length to determine the number of grades being averaged. Note that we initialized total as a double (0.0), so no cast is necessary.

Methods *GetMinimum* and *GetMaximum*

Lines 38–39 in method ProcessGrades call methods GetMinimum and GetMaximum to determine the lowest and highest grades of any student on the exam, respectively. Each of these methods uses a foreach statement to loop through array grades. Lines 51–58 in method GetMinimum loop through the array, and lines 54–57 compare each grade to lowGrade. If a grade is less than lowGrade, lowGrade is set to that grade. When line 60 executes, lowGrade contains the lowest grade in the array. Method GetMaximum (lines 64–79) works the same way as method GetMinimum.

Method *OutputBarChart*

Finally, line 42 in method ProcessGrades calls method OutputBarChart to display a distribution chart of the grade data, using a technique similar to that in Fig. 8.7. In that example, we manually calculated the number of grades in each category (i.e., 0–9, 10–19, …, 90–99 and 100) by simply looking at a set of grades. In this example, lines 102–108 use a technique similar to that in Figs. 8.8 and 8.9 to calculate the frequency of grades in each category. Line 102 declares variable frequency and initializes it with an array of 11 ints to store the frequency of grades in each grade category. For each grade in array grades, lines 105–108 increment the appropriate element of the frequency array. To determine which element to increment, line 107 divides the current grade by 10, using integer division. For example, if grade is 85, line 107 increments frequency[8] to update the count of grades in the range 80–89. Lines 111–130 next display the bar chart (see Fig. 8.7) based on the values in array frequency. Like lines 27–30 of Fig. 8.7, lines 124–127 of Fig. 8.15 use a value in array frequency to determine the number of asterisks to display in each bar.

Class *GradeBookTest* That Demonstrates Class *GradeBook*

Lines 11–12 of Fig. 8.16 create an object of class GradeBook (Fig. 8.15) using int array gradesArray (declared and initialized in line 9 of Fig. 8.16). Line 13 displays a welcome message, and line 14 invokes the GradeBook object's ProcessGrades method. The output reveals the summary of the 10 grades in myGradeBook.

Software Engineering Observation 8.1

A test harness (or test app) creates an object of the class to test and provides it with data, which could be placed directly into an array with an array initializer, come from the user at the keyboard or come from a file (as you'll see in Chapter 17). After initializing an object, the test harness uses the object's members to manipulate the data. Gathering data in the test harness like this allows the class to manipulate data from several sources.

```
1   // Fig. 8.16: GradeBookTest.cs
2   // Create a GradeBook object using an array of grades.
3   class GradeBookTest
4   {
```

Fig. 8.16 | Create a GradeBook object using an array of grades. (Part 1 of 2.)

```
5      // Main method begins app execution
6      static void Main()
7      {
8         // one-dimensional array of student grades
9         int[] gradesArray = {87, 68, 94, 100, 83, 78, 85, 91, 76, 87};
10
11        var myGradeBook = new GradeBook(
12           "CS101 Introduction to C# Programming", gradesArray);
13        myGradeBook.DisplayMessage();
14        myGradeBook.ProcessGrades();
15     }
16  }
```

Fig. 8.16 | Create a GradeBook object using an array of grades. (Part 2 of 2.)

8.9 Multidimensional Arrays

Two-dimensional arrays are often used to represent tables of values consisting of information arranged in rows and columns. To identify a particular table element, we must specify *two* indices. By convention, the first identifies the element's row and the second its column. (Multidimensional arrays can have more than two dimensions, but such arrays are beyond the scope of this book.) C# supports two types of two-dimensional arrays—rectangular arrays and jagged arrays.

8.9.1 Rectangular Arrays

Rectangular arrays are used to represent tables of information in the form of rows and columns, where each row has the same number of columns. Figure 8.17 illustrates a rectangular array named a containing three rows and four columns—a three-by-four array. In general, an array with *m* rows and *n* columns is called an *m-by-n* array.

Fig. 8.17 | Rectangular array with three rows and four columns.

Array-Access Expression for a Two-Dimensional Rectangular Array
Every element in array a is identified in Fig. 8.17 by an array-access expression of the form a[*row*, *column*]; a is the name of the array, and *row* and *column* are the indices that uniquely identify each element in array a by row and column number. The names of the elements in row 0 all have a first index of 0, and the names of the elements in column 3 all have a second index of 3.

Array Initializer for a Two-Dimensional Rectangular Array
Like one-dimensional arrays, multidimensional arrays can be initialized with array initializers in declarations. A rectangular array b with two rows and two columns could be declared and initialized with nested array initializers as follows:

```
int[,] b = {{1, 2}, {3, 4}};
```

The initializer values are grouped by row in braces. So, 1 and 2 initialize b[0, 0] and b[0, 1], respectively, and 3 and 4 initialize b[1, 0] and b[1, 1], respectively. The compiler counts the number of nested array initializers (represented by sets of two inner braces within the outer braces) in the initializer list to determine the number of rows in array b. The compiler counts the initializer values in the nested array initializer for a row to determine the number of columns (two) in that row. The compiler will generate an error if the number of initializers in each row is not the same, because every row of a rectangular array must have the *same* length (i.e., the same number of columns).

8.9.2 Jagged Arrays

A jagged array is maintained as a one-dimensional array in which each element refers to a one-dimensional array. The manner in which jagged arrays are represented makes them quite flexible, because the lengths of the rows in the array need *not* be the same. For example, jagged arrays could be used to store a single student's exam grades across multiple courses, where the number of exams may vary from course to course.

Array Initializer for a Two-Dimensional Jagged Array
We can access the elements in a jagged array by an array-access expression of the form *arrayName*[*row*] [*column*]—similar to the array-access expression for rectangular arrays, but with a separate set of square brackets for each dimension. A jagged array with three rows of different lengths could be declared and initialized as follows:

```
int[][] jagged = {new int[] {1, 2},
                  new int[] {3},
                  new int[] {4, 5, 6}};
```

In this statement, 1 and 2 initialize jagged[0][0] and jagged[0][1], respectively; 3 initializes jagged[1][0]; and 4, 5 and 6 initialize jagged[2][0], jagged[2][1] and jagged[2][2], respectively. Therefore, array jagged in the preceding declaration is actually composed of four separate one-dimensional arrays—one that represents the rows, one containing the values in the first row ({1, 2}), one containing the value in the second row ({3}) and one containing the values in the third row ({4, 5, 6}). Thus, array jagged itself is an array of three elements, each a reference to a one-dimensional array of int values.

Diagram of a Two-Dimensional Jagged Array in Memory
Observe the differences between the array-creation expressions for rectangular arrays and for jagged arrays. Two sets of square brackets follow the type of jagged, indicating that this is an array of int arrays. Furthermore, in the array initializer, C# requires the keyword new to create an array object for each row. Figure 8.18 illustrates the array reference jagged after it's been declared and initialized.

Fig. 8.18 | Jagged array with three rows of different lengths.

Creating Two-Dimensional Arrays with Array-Creation Expressions
A rectangular array can be created with an array-creation expression. For example, the following lines declare variable b and assign it a reference to a three-by-four rectangular array:

```
int[,] b;
b = new int[3, 4];
```

In this case, we use the literal values 3 and 4 to specify the number of rows and number of columns, respectively, but this is *not* required—apps also can use variables and expressions to specify array dimensions. As with one-dimensional arrays, the elements of a rectangular array are initialized when the array object is created.

A jagged array cannot be completely created with a single array-creation expression. The following statement is a syntax error:

```
int[][] c = new int[2][5]; // error
```

Instead, each one-dimensional array in the jagged array must be initialized separately. A jagged array can be created as follows:

```
int[][] c;
c = new int[2][]; // create 2 rows
c[0] = new int[5]; // create 5 columns for row 0
c[1] = new int[3]; // create 3 columns for row 1
```

The preceding statements create a jagged array with two rows. Row 0 has five columns, and row 1 has three columns.

8.9.3 Two-Dimensional Array Example: Displaying Element Values

Figure 8.19 demonstrates initializing rectangular and jagged arrays with array initializers and using nested for loops to traverse the arrays (i.e., visit every element of each array). Class InitArray's Main method creates two arrays. Line 12 uses nested array initializers to initialize variable rectangular with an array in which row 0 has the values 1, 2 and 3, and row 1 has the values 4, 5 and 6. Lines 17–19 use nested initializers of different lengths to initialize variable jagged. In this case, the initializer uses the keyword new to create a one-dimensional array for each row. Row 0 is initialized to have two elements with values 1 and 2, respectively. Row 1 is initialized to have one element with value 3. Row 2 is initialized to have three elements with the values 4, 5 and 6, respectively.

```
 1   // Fig. 8.19: InitArray.cs
 2   // Initializing rectangular and jagged arrays.
 3   using System;
 4
 5   class InitArray
 6   {
 7      // create and output rectangular and jagged arrays
 8      static void Main()
 9      {
10         // with rectangular arrays,
11         // every row must be the same length.
12         int[,] rectangular = {{1, 2, 3}, {4, 5, 6}};
13
14         // with jagged arrays,
15         // we need to use "new int[]" for every row,
16         // but every row does not need to be the same length.
17         int[][] jagged = {new int[] {1, 2},
18                           new int[] {3},
19                           new int[] {4, 5, 6}};
20
21         OutputArray(rectangular); // displays array rectangular by row
22         Console.WriteLine(); // output a blank line
23         OutputArray(jagged); // displays array jagged by row
24      }
25
26      // output rows and columns of a rectangular array
27      static void OutputArray(int[,] array  )
28      {
29         Console.WriteLine("Values in the rectangular array by row are");
30
31         // loop through array's rows
32         for (var row = 0; row < array.GetLength(0); ++row)
33         {
34            // loop through columns of current row
35            for (var column = 0; column < array.GetLength(1); ++column)
36            {
37               Console.Write($"{array[row, column]}  ");
38            }
39
40            Console.WriteLine(); // start new line of output
41         }
42      }
43
44      // output rows and columns of a jagged array
45      static void OutputArray(int[][] array)
46      {
47         Console.WriteLine("Values in the jagged array by row are");
48
49         // loop through each row
50         foreach (var row in array)
51         {
```

Fig. 8.19 | Initializing jagged and rectangular arrays. (Part 1 of 2.)

```
52              // loop through each element in current row
53              foreach (var element in row)
54              {
55                  Console.Write($"{element}  ");
56              }
57
58              Console.WriteLine(); // start new line of output
59          }
60      }
61  }
```

```
Values in the rectangular array by row are
1  2  3
4  5  6

Values in the jagged array by row are
1  2
3
4  5  6
```

Fig. 8.19 | Initializing jagged and rectangular arrays. (Part 2 of 2.)

Overloaded Method `OutputArray`

Method OutputArray is overloaded. The first version (lines 27–42) specifies the array parameter as int[,] array to indicate that it takes a rectangular array. The second version (lines 45–60) takes a jagged array, because its array parameter is listed as int[][] array.

Method `OutputArray` for Rectangular Arrays

Line 21 invokes method OutputArray with argument rectangular, so the version of OutputArray at lines 27–42 is called. The nested for statement (lines 32–41) outputs the rows of a rectangular array. The loop-continuation condition of each for statement (lines 32 and 35) uses the rectangular array's GetLength method to obtain the length of each dimension. Dimensions are numbered starting from 0, so the method call GetLength(0) on array returns the size of the first dimension of the array (the number of rows), and the call GetLength(1) returns the size of the second dimension (the number of columns). A foreach statement also can iterate through all the elements in a rectangular array. In this case, foreach iterates through all the rows and columns starting from row 0, as if the elements were in a one-dimensional array.

Method `OutputArray` for Jagged Arrays

Line 23 invokes method OutputArray with argument jagged, so OutputArray at lines 45–60 is called. The nested foreach statement (lines 50–59) outputs the rows of a jagged array. The inner foreach statement (lines 53–56) iterates through each element in the current row. This allows the loop to determine the exact number of columns in each row. Since the jagged array is created as an array of arrays, we can use nested foreach statements to output the elements in the console window. The outer loop iterates through the elements of array, which are references to one-dimensional arrays of int values that represent each row. The inner loop iterates through the elements of the current row.

Common Multidimensional-Array Manipulations Performed with **for** *Statements*
Many common array manipulations use for statements. As an example, the following for statement sets all the elements in row 2 of rectangular array a in Fig. 8.17 to 0:

```
for (int column = 0; column < a.GetLength(1); ++column)
{
    a[2, column] = 0;
}
```

We specified row 2; therefore, we know that the first index is always 2 (0 is the first row, and 1 is the second row). This for loop varies only the second index (i.e., the column index). The preceding for statement is equivalent to the assignment statements

```
a[2, 0] = 0;
a[2, 1] = 0;
a[2, 2] = 0;
a[2, 3] = 0;
```

The following nested for statement totals the values of all the elements in array a:

```
int total = 0;

for (int row = 0; row < a.GetLength(0); ++row)
{
    for (int column = 0; column < a.GetLength(1); ++column)
    {
        total += a[row, column];
    }
}
```

These nested for statements total the array elements one row at a time. The outer for statement begins by setting the row index to 0 so that row 0's elements can be totaled by the inner for statement. The outer for then increments row to 1 so that row 1's elements can be totaled. Then the outer for increments row to 2 so that row 2's elements can be totaled. The variable total can be displayed when the outer for statement terminates. In the next example, we show how to process a rectangular array in a more concise manner using foreach statements.

8.10 Case Study: GradeBook Using a Rectangular Array

In Section 8.8, we presented class GradeBook (Fig. 8.15), which used a one-dimensional array to store student grades on a single exam. In most courses, students take several exams. Instructors are likely to want to analyze grades across the entire course, both for a single student and for the class as a whole.

Storing Student Grades in a Rectangular Array in Class **GradeBook**
Figure 8.20 shows the output that summarizes 10 students' grades on three exams. Figure 8.21 contains a version of class GradeBook that uses a rectangular array grades to store the grades of a number of students on multiple exams. Each row of the array represents a single student's grades for the entire course, and each column represents the grades for the whole class on one of the exams the students took during the course. An app such as GradeBookTest (Fig. 8.22) passes the array as an argument to the GradeBook constructor. In this example, we use a 10-by-3 array containing 10 students' grades on three exams.

```
Welcome to the grade book for
CS101 Introduction to C# Programming!

The grades are:

            Test 1  Test 2  Test 3  Average
Student  1      87      96      70    84.33
Student  2      68      87      90    81.67
Student  3      94     100      90    94.67
Student  4     100      81      82    87.67
Student  5      83      65      85    77.67
Student  6      78      87      65    76.67
Student  7      85      75      83    81.00
Student  8      91      94     100    95.00
Student  9      76      72      84    77.33
Student 10      87      93      73    84.33

Lowest grade in the grade book is 65
Highest grade in the grade book is 100

Overall grade distribution:
00-09:
10-19:
20-29:
30-39:
40-49:
50-59:
60-69: ***
70-79: ******
80-89: ************
90-99: *******
  100: ***
```

Fig. 8.20 | Output of GradeBook that uses two-dimensional arrays.

```csharp
 1   // Fig. 8.21: GradeBook.cs
 2   // Grade book using a rectangular array to store grades.
 3   using System;
 4
 5   class GradeBook
 6   {
 7      private int[,] grades; // rectangular array of student grades
 8
 9      // auto-implemented property CourseName
10      public string CourseName { get; }
11
12      // two-parameter constructor initializes
13      // auto-implemented property CourseName and grades array
14      public GradeBook(string name, int[,] gradesArray)
15      {
16         CourseName = name; // set CourseName to name
17         grades = gradesArray; // initialize grades array
18      }
```

Fig. 8.21 | Grade book using a rectangular array to store grades. (Part 1 of 4.)

```
19
20      // display a welcome message to the GradeBook user
21      public void DisplayMessage()
22      {
23         // auto-implemented property CourseName gets the name of course
24         Console.WriteLine(
25            $"Welcome to the grade book for\n{CourseName}!\n");
26      }
27
28      // perform various operations on the data
29      public void ProcessGrades()
30      {
31         // output grades array
32         OutputGrades();
33
34         // call methods GetMinimum and GetMaximum
35         Console.WriteLine(
36            $"\nLowest grade in the grade book is {GetMinimum()}" +
37            $"\nHighest grade in the grade book is {GetMaximum()}\n");
38
39         // output grade distribution chart of all grades on all tests
40         OutputBarChart();
41      }
42
43      // find minimum grade
44      public int GetMinimum()
45      {
46         // assume first element of grades array is smallest
47         var lowGrade = grades[0, 0];
48
49         // loop through elements of rectangular grades array
50         foreach (var grade in grades)
51         {
52            // if grade less than lowGrade, assign it to lowGrade
53            if (grade < lowGrade)
54            {
55               lowGrade = grade;
56            }
57         }
58
59         return lowGrade; // return lowest grade
60      }
61
62      // find maximum grade
63      public int GetMaximum()
64      {
65         // assume first element of grades array is largest
66         var highGrade = grades[0, 0];
67
68         // loop through elements of rectangular grades array
69         foreach (var grade in grades)
70         {
```

Fig. 8.21 | Grade book using a rectangular array to store grades. (Part 2 of 4.)

```
71              // if grade greater than highGrade, assign it to highGrade
72              if (grade > highGrade)
73              {
74                  highGrade = grade;
75              }
76          }
77
78          return highGrade; // return highest grade
79      }
80
81      // determine average grade for particular student
82      public double GetAverage(int student)
83      {
84          // get the number of grades per student
85          var gradeCount = grades.GetLength(1);
86          var total = 0.0; // initialize total
87
88          // sum grades for one student
89          for (var exam = 0; exam < gradeCount; ++exam)
90          {
91              total += grades[student, exam];
92          }
93
94          // return average of grades
95          return total / gradeCount;
96      }
97
98      // output bar chart displaying overall grade distribution
99      public void OutputBarChart()
100     {
101         Console.WriteLine("Overall grade distribution:");
102
103         // stores frequency of grades in each range of 10 grades
104         var frequency = new int[11];
105
106         // for each grade in GradeBook, increment the appropriate frequency
107         foreach (var grade in grades)
108         {
109             ++frequency[grade / 10];
110         }
111
112         // for each grade frequency, display bar in chart
113         for (var count = 0; count < frequency.Length; ++count)
114         {
115             // output bar label ("00-09: ", ..., "90-99: ", "100: ")
116             if (count == 10)
117             {
118                 Console.Write("  100: ");
119             }
120             else
121             {
122                 Console.Write($"{count * 10:D2}-{count * 10 + 9:D2}: ");
123             }
```

Fig. 8.21 | Grade book using a rectangular array to store grades. (Part 3 of 4.)

```
124
125              // display bar of asterisks
126              for (var stars = 0; stars < frequency[count]; ++stars)
127              {
128                  Console.Write("*");
129              }
130
131              Console.WriteLine(); // start a new line of output
132          }
133      }
134
135      // output the contents of the grades array
136      public void OutputGrades()
137      {
138          Console.WriteLine("The grades are:\n");
139          Console.Write("                 "); // align column heads
140
141          // create a column heading for each of the tests
142          for (var test = 0; test < grades.GetLength(1); ++test)
143          {
144              Console.Write($"Test {test + 1}   ");
145          }
146
147          Console.WriteLine("Average"); // student average column heading
148
149          // create rows/columns of text representing array grades
150          for (var student = 0; student < grades.GetLength(0); ++student)
151          {
152              Console.Write($"Student {student + 1,2}");
153
154              // output student's grades
155              for (var grade = 0; grade < grades.GetLength(1); ++grade)
156              {
157                  Console.Write($"{grades[student, grade],8}");
158              }
159
160              // call method GetAverage to calculate student's average grade;
161              // pass row number as the argument to GetAverage
162              Console.WriteLine($"{GetAverage(student),9:F}");
163          }
164      }
165  }
```

Fig. 8.21 | Grade book using a rectangular array to store grades. (Part 4 of 4.)

Five methods perform array manipulations to process the grades. Each method is similar to its counterpart in the one-dimensional-array GradeBook (Fig. 8.15). Method Get-Minimum (lines 44–60 in Fig. 8.21) determines the lowest grade of any student. Method GetMaximum (lines 63–79) determines the highest grade of any student. Method Get-Average (lines 82–96) determines a particular student's semester average. Method OutputBarChart (lines 99–133) outputs a bar chart of the distribution of all student grades for the semester. Method OutputGrades (lines 136–164) outputs the two-dimensional array in tabular format, along with each student's semester average.

Processing a Two-Dimensional Array with a **foreach** *Statement*

Methods GetMinimum, GetMaximum and OutputBarChart each loop through array grades using the foreach statement—for example, the foreach statement from method GetMinimum (lines 50–57). To find the lowest overall grade, this foreach statement iterates through rectangular array grades and compares each element to variable lowGrade. If a grade is less than lowGrade, lowGrade is set to that grade.

When the foreach statement traverses the elements of array grades, it looks at each element of the first row in order by index, then each element of the second row in order by index and so on. The foreach statement (lines 50–57) traverses the elements of grades in the same order as the following equivalent code, expressed with nested for statements:

```
for (var row = 0; row < grades.GetLength(0); ++row)
{
    for (var column = 0; column < grades.GetLength(1); ++column)
    {
        if (grades[row, column] < lowGrade)
        {
            lowGrade = grades[row, column];
        }
    }
}
```

When the foreach statement completes, lowGrade contains the lowest grade in the rectangular array. Method GetMaximum works similarly to method GetMinimum. Note the simplicity of using foreach vs. the preceding nested for statement.

Software Engineering Observation 8.2

"Keep it simple" is good advice for most of the code you'll write.

Method **OutputBarChart**

Method OutputBarChart (lines 99–133) displays the grade distribution as a bar chart. The syntax of the foreach statement (lines 107–110) is identical for one-dimensional and two-dimensional arrays.

Method **OutputGrades**

Method OutputGrades (lines 136–164) uses nested for statements to output grades' values, in addition to each student's semester average. The output in Fig. 8.20 shows the result, which resembles the tabular format of an instructor's physical grade book. Lines 142–145 (in Fig. 8.21) display the column headings for each test. We use the for statement rather than the foreach statement here so that we can identify each test with a number. Similarly, the for statement in lines 150–163 first outputs a row label using a counter variable to identify each student (line 152). Although array indices start at 0, lines 144 and 152 output test + 1 and student + 1, respectively, to produce test and student numbers starting at 1 (see Fig. 8.20). The inner for statement in lines 155–158 of Fig. 8.21 uses the outer for statement's counter variable student to loop through a specific row of array grades and output each student's test grade. Finally, line 162 obtains each student's semester average by passing the row index of grades (i.e., student) to method GetAverage.

Method **GetAverage**

Method GetAverage (lines 82–96) takes one argument—the row index for a particular student. When line 162 calls GetAverage, the argument is int value student, which specifies the particular row of rectangular array grades. Method GetAverage calculates the sum of the array elements on this row, divides the total by the number of test results and returns the floating-point result as a double value (line 95).

Class **GradeBookTest** *That Demonstrates Class* **GradeBook**

Figure 8.22 creates an object of class GradeBook (Fig. 8.21) using the two-dimensional array of ints that gradesArray references (Fig. 8.22, lines 9–18). Lines 20–21 pass a course name and gradesArray to the GradeBook constructor. Lines 22–23 then invoke myGrade-Book's DisplayMessage and ProcessGrades methods to display a welcome message and obtain a report summarizing the students' grades for the semester, respectively.

```
1   // Fig. 8.22: GradeBookTest.cs
2   // Create a GradeBook object using a rectangular array of grades.
3   class GradeBookTest
4   {
5      // Main method begins app execution
6      static void Main()
7      {
8         // rectangular array of student grades
9         int[,] gradesArray = {{87, 96, 70},
10                              {68, 87, 90},
11                              {94, 100, 90},
12                              {100, 81, 82},
13                              {83, 65, 85},
14                              {78, 87, 65},
15                              {85, 75, 83},
16                              {91, 94, 100},
17                              {76, 72, 84},
18                              {87, 93, 73}};
19
20         GradeBook myGradeBook = new GradeBook(
21            "CS101 Introduction to C# Programming", gradesArray);
22         myGradeBook.DisplayMessage();
23         myGradeBook.ProcessGrades();
24      }
25   }
```

Fig. 8.22 | Create a GradeBook object using a rectangular array of grades.

8.11 Variable-Length Argument Lists

Variable-length argument lists allow you to create methods that receive an arbitrary number of arguments. A one-dimensional array-type argument preceded by the keyword params in a method's parameter list indicates that the method receives a variable number of arguments with the type of the array's elements. This use of a params modifier can occur only in the parameter list's last parameter. While you can use method overloading and array passing to accomplish much of what is accomplished with variable-length argument lists, using the params modifier is more concise.

Figure 8.23 demonstrates method Average (lines 8–19), which receives a variable-length sequence of doubles (line 8). C# treats the variable-length argument list as a one-dimensional array whose elements are all of the same type. Hence, the method body can manipulate the parameter numbers as an array of doubles. Lines 13–16 use the foreach loop to walk through the array and calculate the total of the doubles in the array. Line 18 accesses numbers.Length to obtain the size of the numbers array for use in the averaging calculation. Lines 30, 32 and 34 in Main call method Average with two, three and four arguments, respectively. Method Average has a variable-length argument list, so it can average as many double arguments as the caller passes. The output reveals that each call to method Average returns the correct value.

Common Programming Error 8.7
The params modifier may be used only with the last parameter of the parameter list.

```
1   // Fig. 8.23: ParamArrayTest.cs
2   // Using variable-length argument lists.
3   using System;
4
5   class ParamArrayTest
6   {
7      // calculate average
8      static double Average(params double[] numbers)
9      {
10        var total = 0.0; // initialize total
11
12        // calculate total using the foreach statement
13        foreach (var d in numbers)
14        {
15           total += d;
16        }
17
18        return numbers.Length != 0 ? total / numbers.Length : 0.0;
19     }
20
21     static void Main()
22     {
23        var d1 = 10.0;
24        var d2 = 20.0;
25        var d3 = 30.0;
26        var d4 = 40.0;
27
28        Console.WriteLine(
29           $"d1 = {d1:F1}\nd2 = {d2:F1}\nd3 = {d3:F1}\nd4 = {d4:F1}\n");
30        Console.WriteLine($"Average of d1 and d2 is {Average(d1, d2):F1}");
31        Console.WriteLine(
32           $"Average of d1, d2 and d3 is {Average(d1, d2, d3):F1}");
33        Console.WriteLine(
34           $"Average of d1, d2, d3 and d4 is {Average(d1, d2, d3, d4):F1}");
35     }
36  }
```

Fig. 8.23 | Using variable-length argument lists. (Part 1 of 2.)

```
d1 = 10.0
d2 = 20.0
d3 = 30.0
d4 = 40.0

Average of d1 and d2 is 15.0
Average of d1, d2 and d3 is 20.0
Average of d1, d2, d3 and d4 is 25.0
```

Fig. 8.23 | Using variable-length argument lists. (Part 2 of 2.)

8.12 Using Command-Line Arguments

On many systems, it's possible to pass arguments from the command line (these are known as command-line arguments) to an app by including a parameter of type string[] (i.e., an array of strings) in the parameter list of Main. By convention, this parameter is named args (Fig. 8.24, line 7). You can execute an app directly from the **Command Prompt** by changing to the directory containing the app's .exe file, typing the file's name (possibly followed by command-line arguments) and pressing *Enter*. When you do this, the execution environment passes any command-line arguments that appear after the app name to the app's Main method as strings in the one-dimensional array args. The number of arguments passed from the command line is obtained by accessing the array's Length property. For example, the command "MyApp a b" passes two command-line arguments to app MyApp. You must enter command-line arguments separated by whitespace, not commas. When the preceding command executes, the Main method entry point receives the two-element array args (i.e., args.Length is 2) in which args[0] contains the string "a" and args[1] contains the string "b". Common uses of command-line arguments include passing options and filenames to apps.

```
 1   // Fig. 8.24: InitArray.cs
 2   // Using command-line arguments to initialize an array.
 3   using System;
 4
 5   class InitArray
 6   {
 7      static void Main(string[] args)
 8      {
 9         // check number of command-line arguments
10         if (args.Length != 3)
11         {
12            Console.WriteLine(
13               "Error: Please re-enter the entire command, including\n" +
14               "an array size, initial value and increment.");
15         }
16         else
17         {
18            // get array size from first command-line argument
19            var arrayLength = int.Parse(args[0]);
```

Fig. 8.24 | Using command-line arguments to initialize an array. (Part 1 of 2.)

```
20              var array = new int[arrayLength]; // create array
21
22              // get initial value and increment from command-line argument
23              var initialValue = int.Parse(args[1]);
24              var increment = int.Parse(args[2]);
25
26              // calculate value for each array element
27              for (var counter = 0; counter < array.Length; ++counter)
28              {
29                  array[counter] = initialValue + increment * counter;
30              }
31
32              Console.WriteLine($"{"Index"}{"Value",8}");
33
34              // display array index and value
35              for (int counter = 0; counter < array.Length; ++counter)
36              {
37                  Console.WriteLine($"{counter,5}{array[counter],8}");
38              }
39          }
40      }
41  }
```

```
C:\Users\PaulDeitel\Documents\examples\ch08\fig08_24>InitArray.exe
Error: Please re-enter the entire command, including
an array size, initial value and increment.
```

```
C:\Users\PaulDeitel\Documents\examples\ch08\fig08_24>InitArray.exe 5 0 4
Index    Value
    0        0
    1        4
    2        8
    3       12
    4       16
```

```
C:\Users\PaulDeitel\Documents\examples\ch08\fig08_24>InitArray.exe 10 1 2
Index    Value
    0        1
    1        3
    2        5
    3        7
    4        9
    5       11
    6       13
    7       15
    8       17
    9       19
```

Fig. 8.24 | Using command-line arguments to initialize an array. (Part 2 of 2.)

Figure 8.24 uses three command-line arguments to initialize an array. When the app executes, if args.Length is not 3, the app displays an error message and terminates (lines 10–15). Otherwise, lines 16–39 initialize and display the array based on the values of the command-line arguments.

The command-line arguments become available to Main as strings in args. Line 19 gets args[0]—a string that specifies the array size—and converts it to an int value, which the app uses to create the array in line 20.

Lines 23–24 convert the args[1] and args[2] command-line arguments to int values and store them in initialValue and increment, respectively—as always, these lines could result in exceptions if the user does not enter valid integers. Line 29 calculates the value for each array element.

The first sample execution indicates that the app received an insufficient number of command-line arguments. The second sample execution uses command-line arguments 5, 0 and 4 to specify the size of the array (5), the value of the first element (0) and the increment of each value in the array (4), respectively. The corresponding output indicates that these values create an array containing the integers 0, 4, 8, 12 and 16. The output from the third sample execution illustrates that the command-line arguments 10, 1 and 2 produce an array whose 10 elements are the nonnegative odd integers from 1 to 19.

Specifying Command-Line Arguments in Visual Studio
We ran this example from a **Command Prompt** window. You also can supply command-line arguments in the IDE. To do so, right click the project's **Properties** node in the **Solution Explorer**, then select **Open**. Select the **Debug** tab, then enter the arguments in the text box labeled **Command line arguments**. When you run the app, the IDE will pass the command-line arguments to the app.

8.13 (Optional) Passing Arrays by Value and by Reference

In C#, a variable that "stores" an object, such as an array, does not actually store the object itself. Instead, such a variable stores a *reference* to the object. The distinction between reference-type variables and value-type variables raises some subtle issues that you must understand to create secure, stable programs.

As you know, when an app passes an argument to a method, the called method receives a *copy* of that argument's value. Changes to the *local copy* in the called method do *not* affect the original variable in the caller. If the argument is a *reference* type, the method makes a *copy* of the *reference*, *not* a *copy* of the actual object that's referenced. The local copy of the reference also refers to the original object, which means that changes to the object in the called method affect the original object.

Performance Tip 8.1
Passing references to arrays and other objects makes sense for performance reasons. If arrays were passed by value, a copy of each element would be passed. For large, frequently passed arrays, this would waste time and consume considerable storage for the copies of the arrays.

In Section 7.18, you learned that C# allows variables to be passed by reference with keyword ref. You also can use keyword ref to pass a *reference-type variable* by reference, which allows the called method to modify the original variable in the caller and make that variable refer to a different object. This is a capability, which, if misused, can lead to subtle problems. For instance, when a reference-type object like an array is passed with ref, the called method actually gains control over the *reference itself*, allowing the called method to replace the original reference in the caller with a reference to a different object, or even with null. Such behavior can lead to *unpredictable effects*, which can be disastrous in mission-critical apps.

Figure 8.25 demonstrates the subtle difference between passing a reference by value and passing a reference by reference with keyword ref. Lines 11 and 14 declare two integer array variables, firstArray and firstArrayCopy. Line 11 initializes firstArray with the values 1, 2 and 3. The assignment statement at line 14 copies the reference stored in firstArray to variable firstArrayCopy, causing these variables to reference the same array object. We make the copy of the reference so that we can determine later whether reference firstArray gets overwritten. The foreach statement at lines 21–24 displays the contents of firstArray before it's passed to method FirstDouble (line 27) so that we can verify that the called method indeed changes the array's contents.

```csharp
1   // Fig. 8.25: ArrayReferenceTest.cs
2   // Testing the effects of passing array references
3   // by value and by reference.
4   using System;
5
6   class ArrayReferenceTest
7   {
8      static void Main(string[] args)
9      {
10         // create and initialize firstArray
11         int[] firstArray = {1, 2, 3};
12
13         // copy the reference in variable firstArray
14         int[] firstArrayCopy = firstArray;
15
16         Console.WriteLine("Test passing firstArray reference by value");
17         Console.Write(
18            "Contents of firstArray before calling FirstDouble:\n\t");
19
20         // display contents of firstArray
21         foreach (var element in firstArray)
22         {
23            Console.Write($"{element} ");
24         }
25
26         // pass variable firstArray by value to FirstDouble
27         FirstDouble(firstArray);
28
29         Console.Write(
30            "\nContents of firstArray after calling FirstDouble\n\t");
31
```

Fig. 8.25 | Testing the effects of passing an array reference by value and by reference. (Part 1 of 3.)

```
32        // display contents of firstArray
33        foreach (var element in firstArray)
34        {
35            Console.Write($"{element} ");
36        }
37
38        // test whether reference was changed by FirstDouble
39        if (firstArray == firstArrayCopy)
40        {
41            Console.WriteLine("\n\nThe references refer to the same array");
42        }
43        else
44        {
45            Console.WriteLine(
46                "\n\nThe references refer to different arrays");
47        }
48
49        // create and initialize secondArray
50        int[] secondArray = {1, 2, 3};
51
52        // copy the reference in variable secondArray
53        int[] secondArrayCopy = secondArray;
54
55        Console.WriteLine(
56            "\nTest passing secondArray reference by reference");
57        Console.Write(
58            "Contents of secondArray before calling SecondDouble:\n\t");
59
60        // display contents of secondArray before method call
61        foreach (var element in secondArray)
62        {
63            Console.Write($"{element} ");
64        }
65
66        // pass variable secondArray by reference to SecondDouble
67        SecondDouble(ref secondArray);
68
69        Console.Write(
70            "\nContents of secondArray after calling SecondDouble:\n\t");
71
72        // display contents of secondArray after method call
73        foreach (var element in secondArray)
74        {
75            Console.Write($"{element} ");
76        }
77
78        // test whether reference was changed by SecondDouble
79        if (secondArray == secondArrayCopy)
80        {
81            Console.WriteLine("\n\nThe references refer to the same array");
82        }
83        else
84        {
```

Fig. 8.25 | Testing the effects of passing an array reference by value and by reference. (Part 2 of 3.)

```
85                 Console.WriteLine(
86                    "\n\nThe references refer to different arrays");
87             }
88       }
89
90       // modify elements of array and attempt to modify reference
91       static void FirstDouble(int[] array)
92       {
93          // double each element's value
94          for (var i = 0; i < array.Length; ++i)
95          {
96             array[i] *= 2;
97          }
98
99          // create new object and assign its reference to array
100         array = new int[] {11, 12, 13};
101      }
102
103      // modify elements of array and change reference array
104      // to refer to a new array
105      static void SecondDouble(ref int[] array)
106      {
107         // double each element's value
108         for (var i = 0; i < array.Length; ++i)
109         {
110            array[i] *= 2;
111         }
112
113         // create new object and assign its reference to array
114         array = new int[] {11, 12, 13};
115      }
116  }
```

```
Test passing firstArray reference by value
Contents of firstArray before calling FirstDouble:
       1 2 3
Contents of firstArray after calling FirstDouble
       2 4 6

The references refer to the same array

Test passing secondArray reference by reference
Contents of secondArray before calling SecondDouble:
       1 2 3
Contents of secondArray after calling SecondDouble:
       11 12 13

The references refer to different arrays
```

Fig. 8.25 | Testing the effects of passing an array reference by value and by reference. (Part 3 of 3.)

Method *FirstDouble*

The for statement in method FirstDouble (lines 94–97) multiplies the values of all the elements in the array by 2. Line 100 creates a new array containing the values 11, 12 and

13, and assigns the array's reference to parameter `array` in an attempt to overwrite reference `firstArray` in the caller—this, of course, does not happen, because the reference was passed by value. After method `FirstDouble` executes, the `foreach` statement at lines 33–36 displays `firstArray`'s contents, demonstrating that the values of the elements have been changed by the method. The `if...else` statement at lines 39–47 uses the `==` operator to compare references `firstArray` (which we just attempted to overwrite) and `firstArrayCopy`. The expression in line 39 evaluates to `true` if the operands of operator `==` reference the same object. In this case, the object represented by `firstArray` is the array created in line 11—not the array created in method `FirstDouble` (line 100)—so the original reference stored in `firstArray` was not modified.

Method *SecondDouble*

Lines 50–87 perform similar tests, using array variables `secondArray` and `secondArrayCopy`, and method `SecondDouble` (lines 105–115). Method `SecondDouble` performs the same operations as `FirstDouble`, but receives its array argument using keyword `ref`. In this case, the reference stored in `secondArray` after the method call is a reference to the array created in line 114 of `SecondDouble`, demonstrating that a variable passed with keyword `ref` can be modified by the called method so that the variable in the caller actually points to a *different* object—in this case, an array created in `SecondDouble`. The `if...else` statement in lines 79–87 confirms that `secondArray` and `secondArrayCopy` no longer refer to the same array.

Software Engineering Observation 8.3

When a method receives a reference-type parameter by value, a copy of the object's reference is passed. This prevents a method from overwriting references passed to that method. In the vast majority of cases, protecting the caller's reference from modification is the desired behavior. If you encounter a situation where you truly want the called procedure to modify the caller's reference, pass the reference-type parameter using keyword ref—*but, again, such situations are rare.*

Software Engineering Observation 8.4

In C#, references to objects (including arrays) are passed to called methods. A called method—receiving a reference to an object in a caller—can interact with, and possibly change, the caller's object.

8.14 Wrap-Up

This chapter began our introduction to data structures, using arrays to store data in and retrieve data from lists and tables of values. You saw how arrays are declared, created and initialized. We presented examples demonstrating common array manipulations. We introduced C#'s last control statement—the `foreach` iteration statement—which provides a concise and less error-prone notation for accessing data in arrays and other data structures.

We demonstrated implicitly typed local variables (with keyword `var`) for which the compiler determines variable types, based on their initializer values. We introduced the exception-handling mechanism and used it to allow a program to continue executing when it attempted to access an array element outside the array's bounds.

We used arrays to simulate shuffling and dealing playing cards. In that example, we introduced C# 6's getter-only auto-implemented properties, which define properties that can be used to get, but not set, a value. We also discussed auto-property initialization for auto-implemented properties.

We presented two versions of an instructor GradeBook case study that used arrays to maintain sets of student grades in memory and analyze student grades. Finally, we demonstrate how to define methods that receive variable-length argument lists and how to process command-line arguments passed to Main as a string array.

We continue our coverage of data structures in Chapter 9, where we discuss List, which is a dynamically resizable array-based collection. Chapter 18 discusses searching and sorting algorithms. Chapter 19 introduces dynamic data structures, such as lists, queues, stacks and trees, that can grow and shrink as apps execute. Chapter 20 presents generics, which provide the means to create general models of methods and classes that can be declared once, but used with many different data types. Chapter 21 introduces the data-structure classes provided by the .NET Framework, some of which use generics to allow you to specify the exact types of objects that a particular data structure will store. You should almost always use these predefined data structures instead of building your own. Chapter 21 discusses many data-structures classes that can grow and shrink in response to an app's changing storage requirements. The .NET Framework also provides class Array, which contains utility methods for array manipulation, such as the Resize method introduced in this chapter. Chapter 21 uses several static methods of class Array to perform such manipulations as sorting and searching the data in an array.

We've now introduced the basic concepts of classes, objects, control statements, methods and arrays. In Chapter 9, we introduce Language Integrated Query (LINQ), which enables you to write expressions that can retrieve information from a wide variety of data sources, such as arrays. You'll see how to search, sort and filter data using LINQ.

Summary

Section 8.1 Introduction
• Arrays are data structures consisting of related data items of the same type. Arrays are fixed-length entities—they remain the same length once they're created.

Section 8.2 Arrays
• Arrays are reference types.
• The elements of an array can be either value or reference types (including other arrays).
• An app refers to an array element with an array-access expression that includes the name of the array, followed by the index of the particular element in square brackets ([]).
• The first element in every array has index zero and is sometimes called the zeroth element.
• An array's Length property returns the number of elements in the array.

Section 8.3 Declaring and Creating Arrays
• To create an array instance, you specify the type and the number of array elements as part of an array-creation expression that uses keyword new, such as

```
int[] a = new int[12];
```

- When an array is created, each element of the array receives a default value.
- Every element of a value-type array contains a value of the array's declared type. In an array of a reference type, every element is a reference to an object of the array's declared type or null.

Section 8.4.2 Using an Array Initializer
- An app can create an array and initialize its elements with an array initializer, which is a comma-separated list of expressions (called an initializer list) enclosed in braces.

Section 8.4.3 Calculating a Value to Store in Each Array Element
- Constants must be initialized when they're declared and cannot be modified thereafter.

Section 8.4.5 Iterating Through Arrays with **foreach**
- The foreach statement iterates through the elements of an entire array or collection. The syntax of a foreach statement is:

```
foreach (type identifier in arrayName)
{
    statement
}
```

where *type* and *identifier* are the type and name of the iteration variable, and *arrayName* is the array through which to iterate.
- The foreach header can be read concisely as "for each iteration, assign the next element of the array to the iteration variable, then execute the following statement."
- The foreach statement's iteration variable can be used only to access array elements, not to modify them. Any attempt to change the value of the iteration variable in the body of a foreach statement will cause a compilation error.

Section 8.4.6 Using Bar Charts to Display Array Data Graphically; Introducing Type Inference with **var**
- In a format item, a D format specifier indicates that the value should be formatted as an integer, and the number after the D indicates how many digits this formatted integer must contain.
- The var keyword declares a local variable and lets the compiler determine the variable's type, based on the variable's initializer. This process is known as type inference, and local variables declared in this manner are known as implicitly typed local variables.
- The var keyword cannot be used to declare an array that's initialized via an initializer list—such initializers also can be used with collections, so the compiler cannot infer whether the variable should be an array or collection.

Section 8.5.2 Exception Handling: Processing the Incorrect Response
- An exception indicates a problem that occurs while a program executes. "
- Exception handling enables you to create fault-tolerant programs that can resolve exceptions.

Section 8.5.3 The **try** Statement
- To handle an exception, place any code that might throw an exception in a try statement.
- The try block contains the code that might throw an exception, and the catch block contains the code that handles the exception if one occurs.
- You can have many catch blocks to handle different types of exceptions that might be thrown in the corresponding try block.
- When a try block terminates, any variables declared in the try block go out of scope.

Section 8.5.4 Executing the **catch** Block
- A catch block declares a type and an exception parameter. Inside the catch block, you can use the parameter's identifier to interact with a caught exception object.
- When a program is executed, array element indices are checked for validity—all indices must be greater than or equal to 0 and less than the length of the array. If an attempt is made to use an invalid index to access an element, an IndexOutOfRangeException exception occurs.

Section 8.5.5 **Message** Property of the Exception Parameter
- An exception object's Message property returns the exception's error message.

Section 8.6.1 Class **Card** and Getter-Only Auto-Implemented Properties
- Prior to C# 6 auto-implemented properties required both a get and a set accessor.
- C# 6 supports getter-only auto-implemented properties that are read only.
- Getter-only auto-implemented properties must be initialized either in their declarations or in all of the type's constructors.
- Initializing an auto-implemented property in its declaration is another C# 6 feature known as auto-property initializers.
- The ToString method of an object is called implicitly in many cases when the object is used where a string is expected, such as concatenating an object to a **string**.

Section 8.7 Passing Arrays and Array Elements to Methods
- When a method's argument is an array or an individual array element of a reference type, the called method receives a copy of the reference. However, when an argument to a method is an individual array element of a value type, the called method receives a copy of the element's value.

Section 8.9 Multidimensional Arrays
- Two-dimensional arrays are often used to represent tables of values consisting of information arranged in rows and columns. To identify a particular table element, we must specify two indices.
- C# supports two types of two-dimensional arrays—rectangular arrays and jagged arrays.
- Rectangular arrays are used to represent tables of information in the form of rows and columns, where each row has the same number of columns.
- Elements in rectangular array a are identified by an expression of the form a[row, column].
- A rectangular array could be declared and initialized with array initializers of the form

     arrayType[,] *arrayName* = {{*row0 initializer*}, {*row1 initializer*}, ...};

  provided that each row of the rectangular array must have the same length.
- A rectangular array can be created with an array-creation expression of the form

     arrayType[,] *arrayName* = new *arrayType*[*numRows*, *numColumns*];

- A jagged array is maintained as a one-dimensional array in which each element refers to a one-dimensional array.
- The lengths of the rows in a jagged array need not be the same.
- We can access the elements in a jagged array *arrayName* by an array-access expression of the form *arrayName*[*row*][*column*].
- A jagged array can be declared and initialized in the form:

     arrayType[][] *arrayName* = {new *arrayType*[] {*row0 initializer*},
                          new *arrayType*[] {*row1 initializer*}, ...};

Section 8.10 Case Study: **GradeBook** Using a Rectangular Array

- When the `foreach` statement traverses a rectangular array's elements, it looks at each element of the first row in order by index, then each element of the second row in order by index and so on.

Section 8.11 Variable-Length Argument Lists

- A one-dimensional array parameter preceded by `params` in a method's parameter list indicates that the method receives a variable number of arguments with the type of the array's elements.

- The `params` modifier can appear only in the last entry of the parameter list.

- C# treats a variable-length argument list as a one-dimensional array.

Section 8.12 Using Command-Line Arguments

- When an app is executed from the **Command Prompt**, the execution environment passes the command-line arguments that appear after the app name to the app's `Main` method as `strings` in a one-dimensional array.

Section 8.13 (Optional) Passing Arrays by Value and by Reference

- When a reference-type object is passed with `ref`, the called method actually gains control over the reference itself, allowing the called method to replace the original reference in the caller with a different object or even with `null`.

- If you encounter a situation where you truly want the called procedure to modify the caller's reference, pass the reference-type parameter using keyword `ref`—but such situations are rare.

Terminology

array	jagged array
array-access expression	leading 0
array-creation expression	`Length` property of an array
array initializer	*m*-by-*n* array
auto-property initializer	magic number
bounds checking	`Message` property of an exception
catch block	multidimensional array
column index	name of an array
column of an array	named constant
command-line arguments	nested array initializers
const keyword	`params` modifier
element of an array	rectangular array
exception	row index
exception handling	row of an array
fault-tolerant program	square brackets, []
`foreach` statement	table of values
getter-only auto-implemented property	test harness
index	traverse an array
index zero	`try` statement
`IndexOutOfRangeException`	two-dimensional array
initializer list	variable-length argument list
iteration variable	zeroth element

Self-Review Exercises

8.1 Fill in the blank(s) in each of the following statements:
   a) Lists and tables of values can be stored in _____.

b) An array is a group of _____ (called elements) containing values that all have the same _____.

c) The _____ statement allows you to iterate through the elements in an array without using a counter.

d) The number that refers to a particular array element is called the element's _____.

e) An array that uses two indices is referred to as a(n) _____ array.

f) Use the foreach header _____ to iterate through double array numbers.

g) Command-line arguments are stored in _____.

h) Use the expression _____ to receive the total number of arguments in a command line. Assume that command-line arguments are stored in args.

i) Given the command MyApp test, the first command-line argument is _____.

j) A(n) _____ in the parameter list of a method indicates that the method can receive a variable number of arguments.

k) As of C# 6, you can declare _____ auto-implemented properties, which are read-only properties.

8.2 Determine whether each of the following is *true* or *false*. If *false*, explain why.

a) A single array can store values of many different types.

b) An array index should normally be of type float.

c) An individual array element that's passed to a method and modified in that method will contain the modified value when the called method completes execution.

d) Command-line arguments are separated by commas.

e) Auto-implemented properties cannot be initialized in their declarations.

8.3 Perform the following tasks for an array called fractions:

a) Declare constant ArraySize initialized to 10.

b) Declare variable fractions which will reference an array with ArraySize elements of type double. Initialize the elements to 0.

c) Name the element of the array with index 3.

d) Assign the value 1.667 to the array element with index 9.

e) Assign the value 3.333 to the array element with index 6.

f) Sum all the elements of the array, using a for statement. Declare integer variable x as a control variable for the loop.

g) Sum all the elements of the array, using a foreach statement. Declare double variable element as a control variable for the loop.

8.4 Perform the following tasks for an array called table:

a) Declare the variable and initialize it with a rectangular integer array that has three rows and three columns. Assume that constant ARRAY_SIZE has been declared to be 3.

b) How many elements does the array contain?

c) Use a nested for statement to initialize each element of the array to the sum of its indices.

8.5 Find and correct the error in each of the following code segments:

```
a) const int ArraySize = 5;
   ArraySize = 10;
b) Assume var b = new int[10];
   for (var i = 0; i <= b.Length; ++i)
   {
      b[i] = 1;
   }
c) Assume int[,] a = {{1, 2}, {3, 4}};
   a[1][1] = 5;
```

Answers to Self-Review Exercises

8.1   a) arrays. b) variables, type. c) foreach. d) index (or position number). e) two-dimensional. f) foreach (double d in numbers). g) an array of strings, usually called args. h) args.Length. i) test. j) params modifier. k) getter-only.

8.2   The answers to Self-Review Exercise 8.2 are:
   a) False. An array can store only values of the same type.
   b) False. An array index must be an integer or an integer expression.
   c) For individual value-type elements of an array: False. A called method receives and manipulates a copy of the value of such an element, so modifications do not affect the original value. If the reference of an array is passed to a method, however, modifications to the array elements made in the called method are indeed reflected in the original. For individual elements of a reference type: True. A called method receives a copy of the reference of such an element, and changes to the referenced object will be reflected in the original array element.
   d) False. Command-line arguments are separated by whitespace.
   e) False. As of C# 6, you can use auto-property initialization in auto-implemented property declarations.

8.3   The answers to Self-Review Exercise 8.3 are:
   a) `const int ArraySize = 10;`
   b) `var fractions = new double[ArraySize];`
   c) `fractions[3]`
   d) `fractions[9] = 1.667;`
   e) `fractions[6] = 3.333;`
   f)
```
var total = 0.0;
for (var x = 0; x < fractions.Length; ++x)
{
    total += fractions[x];
}
```
   g)
```
var total = 0.0;
foreach (var element in fractions)
{
    total += element;
}
```

8.4   The answers to Self-Review Exercise 8.4 are:
   a) `var table = new int[ArraySize, ArraySize];`
   b) Nine.
   c)
```
for (var x = 0; x < table.GetLength(0); ++x)
{
    for (var y = 0; y < table.GetLength(1); ++y)
    {
        table[x, y] = x + y;
    }
}
```

8.5   The answers to Self-Review Exercise 8.5 are:
   a) *Error:* Assigning a value to a constant after it's been initialized.
       Correction: Assign the correct value to the constant in the const declaration.
   b) *Error:* Referencing an array element outside the bounds of the array (b[10]).
       Correction: Change the <= operator to <.

c) *Error:* Array indexing is performed incorrectly.
Correction: Change the statement to a[1, 1] = 5;.

Exercises

8.6 Fill in the blanks in each of the following statements:
a) One-dimensional array p contains four elements. The names of those elements are
_____, _____, _____ and _____.
b) Naming an array's variable, stating its type and specifying the number of dimensions in the array is called _____ the array.
c) In a two-dimensional array, the first index identifies the _____ of an element and the second index identifies the _____ of an element.
d) An *m*-by-*n* array contains _____ rows, _____ columns and _____ elements.
e) The name of the element in row 3 and column 5 of jagged array d is _____.

8.7 Determine whether each of the following is *true* or *false*. If *false*, explain why.
a) To refer to a particular location or element within an array, we specify the name of the array's variable and the value of the particular element.
b) The declaration of a variable that references an array reserves memory for the array.
c) To indicate that 100 locations should be reserved for integer array p, the programmer writes the declaration

    p[100];

d) An app that initializes the elements of a 15-element array to 0 must contain at least one for statement.
e) To total the elements of a two-dimensional array you must use nested for statements.

8.8 Write C# statements to accomplish each of the following tasks:
a) Display the value of the element of character array f with index 6.
b) Initialize each of the five elements of one-dimensional integer array g to 8.
c) Total the 100 elements of floating-point array c.
d) Copy 11-element array a into the first portion of array b, which contains 34 elements.
e) Determine and display the smallest and largest values contained in 99-element floating-point array w.

8.9 Consider the two-by-three rectangular integer array t.
a) Write a statement that declares t and creates the array.
b) How many rows does t have?
c) How many columns does t have?
d) How many elements does t have?
e) Write the names of all the elements in row 1 of t.
f) Write the names of all the elements in column 2 of t.
g) Write a single statement that sets the element of t in row 0 and column 1 to zero.
h) Write a sequence of statements that initializes each element of t to 1. Do not use an iteration statement.
i) Write a nested for statement that initializes each element of t to 3.
j) Write a nested for statement that inputs values for the elements of t from the user.
k) Write a sequence of statements that determines and displays the smallest value in t.
l) Write a statement that displays the elements of row 0 of t.
m) Write a statement that totals the elements of column 2 of t.
n) Write a sequence of statements that displays the contents of t in tabular format. List the column indices as headings across the top, and list the row indices at the left of each row.

8.10 *(Sales Commissions)* Use a one-dimensional array to solve the following problem: A company pays its salespeople on a commission basis. The salespeople receive $200 per week plus 9% of their gross sales for that week. For example, a salesperson who grosses $5,000 in sales in a week receives $200 plus 9% of $5,000, or a total of $650. Write an app (using an array of counters) that determines how many of the salespeople earned salaries in each of the following ranges (assume that each salesperson's salary is an integer). Summarize the results in tabular format.

    a) $200–299
    b) $300–399
    c) $400–499
    d) $500–599
    e) $600–699
    f) $700–799
    g) $800–899
    h) $900–999
    i) $1,000 and over

8.11 *(Array Manipulations)* Write statements that perform the following one-dimensional-array operations:

    a) Set the three elements of integer array `counts` to 0.
    b) Add 1 to each of the four elements of integer array `bonus`.
    c) Display the five values of integer array `bestScores` in column format.

8.12 *(Duplicate Elimination)* Use a one-dimensional array to solve the following problem: Write an app that inputs five numbers, each between 10 and 100, inclusive. As each number is read, display it only if it's not a duplicate of a number already read. Provide for the "worst case," in which all five numbers are different. Use the smallest possible array to solve this problem. Display the complete set of unique values input after the user inputs each new value.

8.13 *(Jagged Arrays)* List the elements of the three-by-five jagged array `sales` in the order in which they're set to 0 by the following code segment:

```
for (var row = 0; row < sales.Length; ++row)
{
    for (var col = 0; col < sales[row].Length; ++col)
    {
        sales[row][col] = 0;
    }
}
```

8.14 *(Variable-Length Argument List)* Write an app that calculates the product of a series of integers that are passed to method `product` using a variable-length argument list. Test your method with several calls, each with a different number of arguments.

8.15 *(Command-Line Arguments)* Rewrite Fig. 8.2 so that the array's size is specified by the first command-line argument. If no command-line argument is supplied, use 10 as the default size.

8.16 *(Using the `foreach` Statement)* Write an app that uses a `foreach` statement to sum the double values passed by the command-line arguments. [*Hint:* Use `static double` method `Parse` to convert a `string` to a `double` value.]

8.17 *(Dice Rolling)* Write an app to simulate the rolling of two dice. The app should use an object of class `Random` once to roll the first die and again to roll the second die. The sum of the two values should then be calculated. Each die can show an integer value from 1 to 6, so the sum of the values will vary from 2 to 12, with 7 being the most frequent sum and 2 and 12 the least frequent sums. Figure 8.26 shows the 36 possible combinations of the two dice. Your app should roll the dice 36,000 times. Use a one-dimensional array to tally the number of times each possible sum appears.

Display the results in tabular format. Determine whether the totals are reasonable (e.g., there are six ways to roll a 7, so approximately one-sixth of the rolls should be 7).

	1	2	3	4	5	6
1	2	3	4	5	6	7
2	3	4	5	6	7	8
3	4	5	6	7	8	9
4	5	6	7	8	9	10
5	6	7	8	9	10	11
6	7	8	9	10	11	12

Fig. 8.26 | The 36 possible sums of two dice.

8.18 *(Game of Craps)* Write an app that runs 1,000,000 games of craps (Fig. 7.8) and answers the following questions:
   a) How many games are won on the first roll, second roll, …, twentieth roll and after the twentieth roll?
   b) How many games are lost on the first roll, second roll, …, twentieth roll and after the twentieth roll?
   c) What are the chances of winning at craps? [*Note:* You should discover that craps is one of the fairest casino games.]
   d) What is the average length of a game of craps?

8.19 *(Airline Reservations System)* A small airline has just purchased a computer for its new automated reservations system. You have been asked to develop the new system. You're to write an app to assign seats on each flight of the airline's only plane (capacity: 10 seats).

Display the following alternatives: `Please type 1 for First Class` and `Please type 2 for Economy`. If the user types 1, your app should assign a seat in the first-class section (seats 1–5). If the user types 2, your app should assign a seat in the economy section (seats 6–10).

Use a one-dimensional array of type `bool` to represent the seating chart of the plane. Initialize all the elements of the array to `false` to indicate that all the seats are empty. As each seat is assigned, set the corresponding element of the array to `true` to indicate that the seat is no longer available.

Your app should never assign a seat that has already been assigned. When the economy section is full, your app should ask the person if it's acceptable to be placed in the first-class section (and vice versa). If yes, make the appropriate seat assignment. If no, display the message `"Next flight leaves in 3 hours."`

8.20 *(Total Sales)* Use a rectangular array to solve the following problem: A company has three salespeople (1 to 3) who sell five different products (1 to 5). Once a day, each salesperson passes in a slip for each type of product sold. Each slip contains the following:
   a) The salesperson number
   b) The product number
   c) The total dollar value of that product sold that day

Thus, each salesperson passes in between 0 and 5 sales slips per day. Assume that the information from all of the slips for last month is available. Write an app that will read all the information for last month's sales and summarize the total sales by salesperson and by product. All totals should be stored in rectangular array `sales`. After processing all the information for last month, display the results in tabular format, with each column representing a particular salesperson and each row representing a particular product. Cross-total each row to get the total sales of each product for last month. Cross-total each column to get the total sales by salesperson for last month. Your tabular output should include these cross-totals to the right of the totaled rows and below the totaled columns.

8.21 *(Turtle Graphics)* The Logo language made the concept of *turtle graphics* famous. Imagine a mechanical turtle that walks around the room under the control of a C# app. The turtle holds a pen in one of two positions—up or down. While the pen is down, the turtle traces out shapes as it moves, and while the pen is up, the turtle moves about freely without writing anything. In this problem, you'll simulate the operation of the turtle and create a computerized sketchpad.

Use a 20-by-20 rectangular array floor that's initialized to 0. Read commands from an array that contains them. Keep track at all times of the current position of the turtle and whether the pen is currently up or down. Assume that the turtle always starts at position (0, 0) of the floor with its pen up and move to the right by default. The set of turtle commands your app must process are shown in Fig. 8.27.

Suppose that the turtle is somewhere near the center of the floor. The following "app" would draw and display a 12-by-12 square, leaving the pen in the up position:

```
2
5,12
3
5,12
3
5,12
3
5,12
1
6
9
```

As the turtle moves with the pen down, set the appropriate elements of array floor to 1s. When the 6 command (display the array) is given, wherever there's a 1 in the array, display an asterisk or any character you choose. Wherever there's a 0, display a blank.

Write an app to implement the turtle graphics capabilities discussed here. Write several turtle graphics apps to draw interesting shapes. Add other commands to increase the power of your turtle graphics language.

Command	Meaning
1	Pen up
2	Pen down
3	Turn right
4	Turn left
5,10	Move forward 10 spaces (replace 10 for a different number of spaces)
6	Display the 20-by-20 array
9	End of data (sentinel)

Fig. 8.27 | Turtle graphics commands.

8.22 *(Knight's Tour)* One of the more interesting puzzlers for chess buffs is the Knight's Tour problem, originally proposed by the mathematician Euler. Can the chess piece called the knight move around an empty chessboard and touch each of the 64 squares once and only once? We study this intriguing problem in depth here.

The knight makes only L-shaped moves (two spaces in one direction and one space in a perpendicular direction). Thus, as shown in Fig. 8.28, from a square near the middle of an empty chessboard, the knight (labeled K) can make eight different moves (numbered 0 through 7).

a) Draw an eight-by-eight chessboard on a sheet of paper, and attempt a Knight's Tour by hand. Put a 1 in the starting square, a 2 in the second square, a 3 in the third and so on. Before starting the tour, estimate how far you think you'll get, remembering that a full tour consists of 64 moves. How far did you get? Was this close to your estimate?

b) Now let's develop an app that will move the knight around a chessboard. The board is represented by an eight-by-eight rectangular array board. Each square is initialized to zero. We describe each of the eight possible moves in terms of their horizontal and vertical components. For example, a move of type 0, as shown in Fig. 8.28, consists of moving two squares horizontally to the right and one square vertically upward. A move of type 2 consists of moving one square horizontally to the left and two squares vertically upward. Horizontal moves to the left and vertical moves upward are indicated with negative numbers. The eight moves may be described by two one-dimensional arrays, horizontal and vertical, as follows:

Fig. 8.28 | The eight possible moves of the knight.

```
horizontal[0] = 2        vertical[0] = -1
horizontal[1] = 1        vertical[1] = -2
horizontal[2] = -1       vertical[2] = -2
horizontal[3] = -2       vertical[3] = -1
horizontal[4] = -2       vertical[4] = 1
horizontal[5] = -1       vertical[5] = 2
horizontal[6] = 1        vertical[6] = 2
horizontal[7] = 2        vertical[7] = 1
```

Let variables currentRow and currentColumn indicate the row and column, respectively, of the knight's current position. To make a move of type moveNumber, where moveNumber is between 0 and 7, your app should use the statements

```
currentRow += vertical[moveNumber];
currentColumn += horizontal[moveNumber];
```

Write an app to move the knight around the chessboard. Keep a counter that varies from 1 to 64. Record the latest count in each square the knight moves to. Test each potential move to see if the knight has already visited that square. Test every potential move to ensure that the knight does not land off the chessboard. Run the app. How many moves did the knight make?

c) After attempting to write and run a Knight's Tour app, you have probably developed some valuable insights. We'll use these insights to develop a *heuristic* for moving the knight. Heuristics do not guarantee success, but a carefully developed heuristic greatly improves the chance of success. You may have observed that the outer squares are more troublesome than the squares nearer the center of the board. In fact, the most troublesome and inaccessible squares are the four corners.

Intuition may suggest that you should attempt to move the knight to the most troublesome squares first and leave open those that are easiest to get to, so that when the board gets congested near the end of the tour, there will be a greater chance of success.

We could develop an "accessibility heuristic" by classifying each of the squares according to how accessible it is and always moving the knight (using the knight's L-shaped moves) to the most inaccessible square. We label two-dimensional array `accessibility` with numbers indicating from how many squares each particular square is accessible. On a blank chessboard, each of the 16 squares nearest the center is rated as 8, each corner square is rated as 2, and the other squares have accessibility numbers of 3, 4 or 6 as follows:

```
2  3  4  4  4  4  3  2
3  4  6  6  6  6  4  3
4  6  8  8  8  8  6  4
4  6  8  8  8  8  6  4
4  6  8  8  8  8  6  4
4  6  8  8  8  8  6  4
3  4  6  6  6  6  4  3
2  3  4  4  4  4  3  2
```

Write a new version of the Knight's Tour, using the accessibility heuristic. The knight should always move to the square with the lowest accessibility number. In case of a tie, the knight may move to any of the tied squares. Therefore, the tour may begin in any of the four corners. [*Note:* As the knight moves around the chessboard and more squares become occupied, your app should reduce the accessibility numbers. In this way, at any given time during the tour, each available square's accessibility number will remain equal to precisely the number of squares from which that square may be reached.] Run this version of your app. Did you get a full tour? Modify the app to run 64 tours, one starting from each square of the chessboard. How many full tours did you get?

d) Write a version of the Knight's Tour app that, when encountering a tie between two or more squares, decides what square to choose by looking ahead to those squares reachable from the "tied" squares. Your app should move to the tied square for which the next move would arrive at the square with the lowest accessibility number.

8.23 *(Knight's Tour: Brute-Force Approaches)* In *Part c* of Exercise 8.22, we developed a solution to the Knight's Tour problem using the "accessibility heuristic," which generates many solutions and executes efficiently. As computers continue to increase in power, we'll be able to solve more problems with sheer computer power and relatively unsophisticated algorithms. Let's call this approach "brute-force" problem solving.

a) Use random-number generation to enable the knight to walk around the chessboard (in its legitimate L-shaped moves) at random. Your app should run one tour and display the final chessboard. How far did the knight get?

b) Most likely, the app in *Part a* produced a relatively short tour. Now modify your app to attempt 1000 tours. Use a one-dimensional array to keep track of the number of tours of each length. When your app finishes attempting the 1000 tours, it should display this information in neat tabular format. What was the best result?

c) Most likely, the app in *Part b* gave you some "respectable" tours, but no full tours. Now let your app run until it produces a full tour. Once again, keep a table of the number of tours of each length, and display this table when the first full tour is found. How many tours did your app attempt before producing a full tour?

d) Compare the brute-force version of the Knight's Tour with the accessibility-heuristic version. Which required a more careful study of the problem? Which algorithm was more difficult to develop? Which required more computer power? Could we be certain (in advance) of obtaining a full tour with the accessibility-heuristic approach? Could we be certain (in advance) of obtaining a full tour with the brute-force approach? Argue the pros and cons of brute-force problem solving in general.

8.24 *(Eight Queens)* Another puzzler for chess buffs is the Eight Queens problem, which asks: Is it possible to place eight queens on an empty chessboard so that no queen is "attacking" any other (i.e., no two queens are in the same row, in the same column or along the same diagonal)? Use the thinking developed in Exercise 8.22 to formulate a heuristic for solving the Eight Queens problem. Run your app. [*Hint:* It's possible to assign a value to each square of the chessboard to indicate how many squares of an empty chessboard are "eliminated" if a queen is placed in that square. Each of the corners would be assigned the value 22, as demonstrated by Fig. 8.29. Once these "elimination numbers" are placed in all 64 squares, an appropriate heuristic might be as follows: Place the next queen in the square with the smallest elimination number. Why is this strategy intuitively appealing?]

Fig. 8.29 | The 22 squares eliminated by placing a queen in the upper left corner.

8.25 *(Eight Queens: Brute-Force Approaches)* In this exercise, you'll develop several brute-force approaches to solving the Eight Queens problem introduced in Exercise 8.24.

a) Use the random brute-force technique developed in Exercise 8.23 to solve the Eight Queens problem.

b) Use an exhaustive technique (i.e., try all possible combinations of eight queens on the chessboard) to solve the Eight Queens problem.

8.26 *(Knight's Tour: Closed-Tour Test)* In the Knight's Tour (Exercise 8.22), a full tour occurs when the knight makes 64 moves, touching each square of the chessboard once and only once. A closed tour occurs when the 64th move is one move away from the square in which the tour started. Modify the app you wrote in Exercise 8.22 to test for a closed tour if a full tour has occurred.

8.27 *(Sieve of Eratosthenes)* A prime number is any integer greater than 1 that's evenly divisible only by itself and 1. The Sieve of Eratosthenes finds prime numbers. It operates as follows:

a) Create a simple type `bool` array with all elements initialized to `true`. Array elements with prime indices will remain `true`. All other array elements will eventually be set to `false`.

b) Starting with array index 2, determine whether a given element is true. If so, loop through the remainder of the array and set to false every element whose index is a multiple of the index for the element with value true. Then continue the process with the next element with value true. For array index 2, all elements beyond element 2 in the array with indices that are multiples of 2 (indices 4, 6, 8, 10, etc.) will be set to false; for array index 3, all elements beyond element 3 in the array with indices that are multiples of 3 (indices 6, 9, 12, 15, etc.) will be set to false; and so on.

When this process completes, the array elements that are still true indicate that the index is a prime number. These indices can be displayed. Write an app that uses an array of 1000 elements to determine and display the prime numbers between 2 and 999. Ignore elements 0 and 1.

8.28 *(Simulation: The Tortoise and the Hare)* You'll now re-create the classic race of the tortoise and the hare. You'll use random-number generation to develop a simulation of this memorable event.

Our contenders begin the race at square 1 of 70 squares. Each square represents a possible position along the race course. The finish line is at square 70. The first contender to reach or pass square 70 is rewarded with a pail of fresh carrots and lettuce. The course weaves its way up the side of a slippery mountain, so occasionally the contenders lose ground.

A clock ticks once per second. With each tick of the clock, your app should adjust the position of the animals according to the rules in Fig. 8.30. Use variables to keep track of the positions of the animals (i.e., position numbers are 1–70). Start each animal at position 1 (the "starting gate"). If an animal slips left before square 1, move it back to square 1.

Animal	Move type	Percentage of the time	Actual move
Tortoise	Fast plod	50%	3 squares to the right
	Slip	20%	6 squares to the left
	Slow plod	30%	1 square to the right
Hare	Sleep	20%	No move at all
	Big hop	20%	9 squares to the right
	Big slip	10%	12 squares to the left
	Small hop	30%	1 square to the right
	Small slip	20%	2 squares to the left

Fig. 8.30 | Rules for adjusting the positions of the tortoise and the hare.

Generate the percentages in Fig. 8.30 by producing a random integer i in the range 1–10. For the tortoise, perform a "fast plod" when i is in the range 1–5, a "slip" when i is 6 or 7, or a "slow plod" when i is 8–10. Use a similar technique to move the hare.

Begin the race by displaying

```
ON YOUR MARK, GET SET
BANG !!!!!
AND THEY'RE OFF !!!!!
```

Then, for each tick of the clock (i.e., each iteration of a loop), display a 70-position line showing the letter T in the position of the tortoise and the letter H in the position of the hare. Occasionally, the contenders will land on the same square. In this case, the tortoise bites the hare, and your app should display OUCH!!! beginning at that position. All output positions other than the T, the H or the OUCH!!! (in case of a tie) should be blank.

After each line is displayed, test for whether either animal has reached or passed square 70. If so, display the winner and terminate the simulation. If the tortoise wins, display TORTOISE WINS!!! YAY!!! If the hare wins, display Hare wins. Yuch. If both animals win on the same tick of the clock, you may want to favor the tortoise (the "underdog"), or you may want to display It's a tie. If neither animal wins, perform the loop again to simulate the next tick of the clock. When you're ready to run your app, assemble a group of fans to watch the race. You'll be amazed at how involved your audience gets!

8.29   *(Card Shuffling and Dealing)* Modify Fig. 8.12 to deal a five-card poker hand. Then modify class DeckOfCards of Fig. 8.11 to include methods that determine whether a hand contains
   a)   a pair
   b)   two pairs
   c)   three of a kind (e.g., three jacks)
   d)   four of a kind (e.g., four aces)
   e)   a flush (i.e., all five cards of the same suit)
   f)   a straight (i.e., five cards of consecutive face values)
   g)   a full house (i.e., two cards of one face value and three cards of another face value)

8.30   *(Card Shuffling and Dealing)* Use the methods developed in Exercise 8.29 to write an app that deals two five-card poker hands, evaluates each hand and determines which is better.

Special Section: Building Your Own Computer

In the next several problems, we take a temporary diversion from the world of high-level language programming to "peel open" a computer and look at its internal structure. We introduce machine-language programming and write several machine-language programs. To make this an especially valuable experience, we then build a computer (through the technique of software-based simulation) on which you can execute your machine-language programs.

8.31   *(Machine-Language Programming)* Let's create a computer called the Simpletron. As its name implies, it's a simple machine, but powerful. The Simpletron runs programs written in the only language it directly understands: Simpletron Machine Language, or SML for short.

The Simpletron contains an *accumulator*—a special register into which information is put before the Simpletron uses it in calculations or examines it in various ways. All the information in the Simpletron is handled in terms of *words*. A word is a signed four-digit decimal number, such as +3364, -1293, +0007 and -0001. The Simpletron is equipped with a 100-word memory, and these words are referenced by their location numbers 00, 01, ..., 99.

Before running an SML program, we must *load*, or place, the code into memory. The first instruction (or statement) of every SML program is always placed in location 00. The simulator will start executing at this location.

Each instruction written in SML occupies one word of the Simpletron's memory (hence, instructions are signed four-digit decimal numbers). We shall assume that the sign of an SML instruction is always plus, but the sign of a data word may be either plus or minus. Each location in the Simpletron's memory may contain an instruction, a data value used by a program or an unused (and hence undefined) area of memory. The first two digits of each SML instruction are the *operation code* specifying the operation to be performed. SML operation codes are summarized in Fig. 8.31.

The last two digits of an SML instruction are the *operand*—the address of the memory location containing the word to which the operation applies. Let's consider several simple SML programs. The first SML program (Fig. 8.32) reads two numbers from the keyboard, then computes and displays their sum. The instruction +1007 reads the first number from the keyboard and places it into location 07 (which has been initialized to 0). Then instruction +1008 reads the next number into location 08. The *load* instruction, +2007, puts the first number into the accumulator, and the *add* instruction, +3008, adds the second number to the number in the accumulator. *All SML arith-*

Operation code	Meaning
Input/output operations:	
const int Read = 10;	Read a word from the keyboard into a specific location in memory.
const int Write = 11;	Write a word from a specific location in memory to the screen.
Load/store operations:	
const int Load = 20;	Load a word from a specific location in memory into the accumulator.
const int Store = 21;	Store a word from the accumulator into a specific location in memory.
Arithmetic operations:	
const int Add = 30;	Add a word from a specific location in memory to the word in the accumulator (leave the result in the accumulator).
const int Subtract = 31;	Subtract a word from a specific location in memory from the word in the accumulator (leave the result in the accumulator).
const int Divide = 32;	Divide a word from a specific location in memory into the word in the accumulator (leave the result in the accumulator).
const int Multiply = 33;	Multiply a word from a specific location in memory by the word in the accumulator (leave the result in the accumulator).
Transfer-of-control operations:	
const int Branch = 40;	Branch to a specific location in memory.
const int BranchNeg = 41;	Branch to a specific location in memory if the accumulator is negative.
const int BranchZero = 42;	Branch to a specific location in memory if the accumulator is zero.
const int Halt = 43;	Halt. The program has completed its task.

Fig. 8.31 | Simpletron Machine Language (SML) operation codes.

metic instructions leave their results in the accumulator. The *store* instruction, +2109, places the result in memory location 09, from which the *write* instruction, +1109, takes the number and displays it (as a signed four-digit decimal number). The *halt* instruction, +4300, terminates execution.

The second SML program (Fig. 8.33) reads two numbers from the keyboard and determines and displays the larger value. Note the use of the instruction +4107 as a conditional transfer of control, much the same as C#'s if statement.

Now write SML programs to accomplish each of the following tasks:

a) Use a sentinel-controlled loop to read positive numbers and compute and display their sum. Terminate input when a negative number is entered.

Location	Number	Instruction
00	+1007	(Read A)
01	+1008	(Read B)
02	+2007	(Load A)
03	+3008	(Add B)
04	+2109	(Store C)
05	+1109	(Write C)
06	+4300	(Halt)
07	+0000	(Variable A)
08	+0000	(Variable B)
09	+0000	(Result C)

Fig. 8.32 | SML program that reads two integers and computes their sum.

Location	Number	Instruction
00	+1009	(Read A)
01	+1010	(Read B)
02	+2009	(Load A)
03	+3110	(Subtract B)
04	+4107	(Branch negative to 07)
05	+1109	(Write A)
06	+4300	(Halt)
07	+1110	(Write B)
08	+4300	(Halt)
09	+0000	(Variable A)
10	+0000	(Variable B)

Fig. 8.33 | SML program that reads two integers and determines the larger.

b) Use a counter-controlled loop to read seven numbers, some positive and some negative, then compute and display their average.

c) Read a series of numbers, then determine and display the largest number. The first number read indicates how many numbers should be processed.

8.32 *(Computer Simulator)* In this problem, you're going to build your own computer. No, you'll not be soldering components together. Rather, you'll use the powerful technique of *software-based simulation* to create an object-oriented *software model* of the Simpletron of Exercise 8.31. Your Simpletron simulator will turn the computer you're using into a Simpletron, and you'll actually be able to run, test and debug the SML programs you wrote in Exercise 8.31.

When you run your Simpletron simulator, it should begin by displaying:

```
*** Welcome to Simpletron! ***
*** Please enter your program one instruction ***
```

```
*** (or data word) at a time into the input ***
*** text field. I will display the location   ***
*** number and a question mark (?). You then   ***
*** type the word for that location. Enter     ***
*** -99999 to stop entering your program.      ***
```

Your app should simulate the memory of the Simpletron with a one-dimensional array memory of 100 elements. Now assume that the simulator is running, and let's examine the dialog as we enter the program of Fig. 8.33 (Exercise 8.31):

```
00 ? +1009
01 ? +1010
02 ? +2009
03 ? +3110
04 ? +4107
05 ? +1109
06 ? +4300
07 ? +1110
08 ? +4300
09 ? +0000
10 ? +0000
11 ? -99999
```

Your program should display the memory location followed by a question mark. Each of the values to the right of a question mark is input by the user. When the sentinel value -99999 is input, the program should display the following:

```
*** Program loading completed ***
*** Program execution begins   ***
```

The SML program has now been placed (or loaded) in array memory. Now the Simpletron executes the SML program. Execution begins with the instruction in location 00 and, as in C#, continues sequentially, unless directed to some other part of the program by a transfer of control.

Use variable accumulator to represent the accumulator register. Use variable instruction-Counter to keep track of the location in memory that contains the instruction being performed. Use variable operationCode to indicate the operation currently being performed (i.e., the left two digits of the instruction word). Use variable operand to indicate the memory location on which the current instruction operates. Thus, operand is the rightmost two digits of the instruction currently being performed. Do not execute instructions directly from memory. Rather, transfer the next instruction to be performed from memory to a variable called instructionRegister. Then "pick off" the left two digits and place them in operationCode, and "pick off" the right two digits and place them in operand. When the Simpletron begins execution, the special registers are all initialized to zero.

Now, let's "walk through" execution of the first SML instruction, +1009 in memory location 00. This procedure is called an *instruction execution cycle.*

The instructionCounter tells us the location of the next instruction to be performed. We *fetch* the contents of that location from memory by using the C# statement

```
instructionRegister = memory[instructionCounter];
```

The operation code and the operand are extracted from the instruction register by the statements

```
operationCode = instructionRegister / 100;
operand = instructionRegister % 100;
```

Now the Simpletron must determine that the operation code is actually a *read* (versus a *write*, a *load*, or whatever). A switch differentiates among the 12 operations of SML. In the switch statement, the behavior of various SML instructions is simulated as shown in Fig. 8.34. We discuss branch instructions shortly and leave the others to you.

Instruction	Description
read:	Display the prompt "Enter an integer", then input the integer and store it in location memory[operand].
load:	accumulator = memory[operand];
add:	accumulator += memory[operand];
halt:	This instruction terminates execution of the SML and displays the message *** Simpletron execution terminated ***

Fig. 8.34 | Behavior of several SML instructions in the Simpletron.

When the SML program completes execution, the name and contents of each register, as well as the complete contents of memory, should be displayed. This is often called a memory dump. To help you program your dump method, a sample dump format is shown in Fig. 8.35. A dump after executing a Simpletron program would show the actual values of instructions and data values at the moment execution terminated.

```
REGISTERS:
accumulator          +0000
instructionCounter      00
instructionRegister  +0000
operationCode           00
operand                 00

MEMORY:
         0     1     2     3     4     5     6     7     8     9
 0   +0000 +0000 +0000 +0000 +0000 +0000 +0000 +0000 +0000 +0000
10   +0000 +0000 +0000 +0000 +0000 +0000 +0000 +0000 +0000 +0000
20   +0000 +0000 +0000 +0000 +0000 +0000 +0000 +0000 +0000 +0000
30   +0000 +0000 +0000 +0000 +0000 +0000 +0000 +0000 +0000 +0000
40   +0000 +0000 +0000 +0000 +0000 +0000 +0000 +0000 +0000 +0000
50   +0000 +0000 +0000 +0000 +0000 +0000 +0000 +0000 +0000 +0000
60   +0000 +0000 +0000 +0000 +0000 +0000 +0000 +0000 +0000 +0000
70   +0000 +0000 +0000 +0000 +0000 +0000 +0000 +0000 +0000 +0000
80   +0000 +0000 +0000 +0000 +0000 +0000 +0000 +0000 +0000 +0000
90   +0000 +0000 +0000 +0000 +0000 +0000 +0000 +0000 +0000 +0000
```

Fig. 8.35 | A sample memory dump.

Let's proceed with the execution of our program's first instruction—namely, the +1009 in location 00. As we've indicated, the switch statement simulates this task by prompting the user to enter a value, reading the value and storing it in memory location memory[operand]. The value is then read into location 09.

At this point, simulation of the first instruction is completed. All that remains is to prepare the Simpletron to execute the next instruction. Since the instruction just performed was not a transfer of control, we need merely increment the instructionCounter. This action completes the simulated execution of the first instruction. The entire process (i.e., the instruction execution cycle) begins anew with the fetch of the next instruction to execute.

Now let's consider how the branching instructions—the transfers of control—are simulated. All we need to do is adjust the value in the instruction counter appropriately. Therefore, the unconditional branch instruction (40) is simulated within the switch as

```
instructionCounter = operand;
```

The conditional "branch if accumulator is zero" instruction is simulated as

```
if (accumulator == 0)
{
    instructionCounter = operand;
}
```

At this point, you should implement your Simpletron simulator and run each of the SML programs you wrote in Exercise 8.31. If you desire, you may embellish SML with additional features and provide support for these in your simulator.

Your simulator should check for various types of errors. During the program-loading phase, for example, each number the user types into the Simpletron's memory must be in the range -9999 to +9999. Your simulator should test that each number entered is in this range and, if not, keep prompting the user to re-enter the number until the user enters a correct number.

During the execution phase, your simulator should check for various serious errors, such as attempts to divide by zero, attempts to execute invalid operation codes and accumulator overflows (i.e., arithmetic operations resulting in values larger than +9999 or smaller than -9999). Such serious errors are called *fatal errors*. When a fatal error is detected, your simulator should display an error message, such as

```
*** Attempt to divide by zero ***
*** Simpletron execution abnormally terminated ***
```

and should display a full computer dump in the format we discussed previously. This treatment will help the user locate the error in the program.

8.33 *(Project: Simpletron Simulator Modifications)* In Exercise 8.32, you wrote a software simulation of a computer that executes programs written in Simpletron Machine Language (SML). In this exercise, we propose several modifications and enhancements to the Simpletron Simulator.

a) Extend the Simpletron Simulator's memory to contain 1,000 memory locations to enable the Simpletron to handle larger programs.

b) Allow the simulator to perform remainder calculations. This modification requires an additional SML instruction.

c) Allow the simulator to perform exponentiation calculations. This modification requires an additional SML instruction.

d) Modify the simulator to use hexadecimal values rather than integer values to represent SML instructions.

e) Modify the simulator to allow output of a newline. This modification requires an additional SML instruction.

f) Modify the simulator to process floating-point values in addition to integer values.

g) Modify the simulator to handle string input. [*Hint:* Each Simpletron word can be divided into two groups, each holding a two-digit integer. Each two-digit integer represents the ASCII (see Appendix) decimal equivalent of an uppercase character. Add a machine-language instruction that will input a string and store the string beginning at a specific Simpletron memory location. The first half of the word at that location will be a count of the number of characters in the string (i.e., the length of the string). Each succeeding half-word contains one ASCII character expressed as two decimal digits. The machine-language instruction converts each character into its ASCII equivalent and assigns it to a half-word.]

h) Modify the simulator to handle output of uppercase strings stored in the format of part (g). [*Hint:* Add a machine-language instruction that will display a string beginning at a certain Simpletron memory location. The first half of the word at that location is a count of the number of characters in the string (i.e., the length of the string). Each succeeding half-word contains one ASCII character expressed as two decimal digits. The machine-language instruction checks the length and displays the string by translating each two-digit number into its equivalent character.]

Making-a-Difference Exercise

8.34 *(Polling)* The Internet and the web are enabling more people to network, join a cause, voice opinions, and so on. The presidential candidates in 2012 used the Internet intensively to get out their messages and raise money for their campaigns. In this exercise, you'll write a simple polling program that allows users to rate five social-consciousness issues from 1 (least important) to 10 (most important). Pick five causes that are important to you (for example, political issues, global environmental issues). Use a one-dimensional array topics (of type String) to store the five causes. To summarize the survey responses, use a 5-row, 10-column two-dimensional array responses (of type int), each row corresponding to an element in the topics array. When the program runs, it should ask the user to rate each issue. Have your friends and family respond to the survey. Then have the program display a summary of the results, including:

    a) A tabular report with the five topics down the left side and the 10 ratings across the top, listing in each column the number of ratings received for each topic.

    b) To the right of each row, show the average of the ratings for that issue.

    c) Which issue received the highest point total? Display both the issue and the point total.

    d) Which issue received the lowest point total? Display both the issue and the point total.

9

Introduction to LINQ and the List Collection

Objectives

In this chapter you'll:

- Learn basic LINQ concepts.

- Query an array using a range variable and the **from**, **where** and **select** clauses.

- Iterate over LINQ query results.

- Sort a LINQ query's results with the **orderby** clause.

- Learn basic interface concepts and how the **IEnumerable<T>** interface enables a **foreach** to iterate over an array or collection's elements.

- Learn basic .NET collections concepts.

- Become familiar with commonly used methods of generic class **List**.

- Create and use a generic **List** collection.

- Query a generic **List** collection using LINQ.

- Declare multiple range variables in a LINQ query with the **let** clause.

- Understand how deferred execution helps make LINQ queries reusable.

9.1 Introduction

Chapter 8 introduced arrays—simple data structures used to store items of a specific type. Although commonly used, arrays have limited capabilities. For instance, you must specify an array's size when you create it. If, at execution time, you wish to modify that size, you must do so manually by creating a new array and copying elements into it or by using class `Array`'s `Resize` method, which performs those tasks for you.

In this chapter, we introduce the .NET Framework's `List` *collection* class—which offers greater capabilities than traditional arrays. A `List` is similar to an array but provides additional functionality, such as dynamic resizing—a `List` can increase its size when items are added to it. We use the `List` collection to implement several data manipulations similar to those in the preceding chapter. `List` and the .NET Framework's other collections are reusable, reliable, powerful and efficient and have been carefully designed and tested to ensure correctness and good performance.

Large amounts of data that need to persist beyond an app's execution are typically stored in a *database*—an organized collection of data (discussed in Chapter 22). A *database management system (DBMS)* provides mechanisms for storing, organizing, retrieving and modifying data in a database. A language called SQL (Structured Query Language)—pronounced "sequel"—is the international standard used to perform queries (i.e., to request information that satisfies given criteria) and to manipulate data in *relational databases*. These organize data in tables that maintain relationships between pieces of data stored in each table—a key goal is to eliminate duplicate data. For years, programs accessing a relational database passed SQL queries to the database management system, then processed the returned results. This chapter introduces C#'s LINQ (Language Integrated Query) capabilities. LINQ allows you to write query expressions, similar to SQL queries, that retrieve information from a *variety* of data sources, not just databases. In this chapter, we use LINQ to Objects to manipulate objects in memory, such as arrays and `List`s.

LINQ Providers

The syntax of LINQ is built into C#, but LINQ queries may be used in many contexts via libraries known as *providers*. A LINQ provider is a set of classes that implement LINQ operations and enable programs to interact with *data sources* to perform tasks such as *sorting*, *grouping* and *filtering* elements. Many LINQ providers are more specialized, allowing you to interact with a specific website or data format. Figure 9.1 shows where and how we use LINQ throughout the book.

Chapter	Used to
Chapter 9, Introduction to LINQ and the List Collection	Query arrays and Lists.
Chapter 16, Strings and Characters: A Deeper Look	Select GUI controls in a Windows Forms app (located in the online section of the chapter).
Chapter 17, Files and Streams	Search a directory and manipulate text files.
Chapter 21, Generic Collections; Functional Programming with LINQ/PLINQ	Show LINQ method-call syntax with delegates and lambdas. Introduces functional-programming concepts, using LINQ to Objects to write code more concisely and with fewer bugs than programs written with previous techniques. Shows how PLINQ (Parallel LINQ) can improve LINQ to Objects performance substantially with multicore systems.
Chapter 22, Databases and LINQ	Query information from a database using *LINQ to Entities*. Like LINQ to Objects, LINQ to Entities is built into C# and the .NET Framework.
Chapter 23, Asynchronous Programming with async and await	Query an XML response from a web service using *LINQ to XML*. Like LINQ to Objects, LINQ to XML is built into C# and the .NET Framework.
Web App Development with ASP.NET online chapter	Retrieve information from a database to be used in a web-based app.
XML and LINQ to XML online chapter	Present a more in-depth discussion of querying XML documents using *LINQ to XML*.
REST Web Services online chapter	Query and update a database. Process XML returned by WCF services.

Fig. 9.1 | LINQ usage throughout the book.

LINQ Query Syntax vs. Method-Call Syntax

There are two LINQ approaches—one uses a SQL-like syntax and the other uses method-call syntax. This chapter shows the simpler SQL-like syntax. In Chapter 21, we'll show the method-call syntax, introducing the notions of delegates and lambdas—mechanisms that enable you to pass methods to other methods to help them perform their tasks.

9.2 Querying an Array of int Values Using LINQ

Figure 9.2 shows how to use *LINQ to Objects* to query an array of integers, selecting elements that satisfy a set of conditions—a process called filtering. Iteration statements that *filter* arrays focus on the process of getting the results—iterating through the elements and checking whether they satisfy the desired criteria. LINQ specifies the conditions that selected elements must satisfy. This is known as declarative programming—as opposed to imperative programming (which we've been doing so far) in which you specify the actual actions to perform a task. The query in lines 22–24 specifies that the results should consist of all the ints in the values array that are greater than 4. It *does not* specify *how* those results are obtained—the C# compiler generates all the necessary code, which is one of the great strengths of LINQ. Using LINQ to Objects requires the System.Linq namespace (line 4).

```csharp
1   // Fig. 9.2: LINQWithSimpleTypeArray.cs
2   // LINQ to Objects using an int array.
3   using System;
4   using System.Linq;
5
6   class LINQWithSimpleTypeArray
7   {
8      static void Main()
9      {
10        // create an integer array
11        var values = new[] {2, 9, 5, 0, 3, 7, 1, 4, 8, 5};
12
13        // display original values
14        Console.Write("Original array:");
15        foreach (var element in values)
16        {
17           Console.Write($" {element}");
18        }
19
20        // LINQ query that obtains values greater than 4 from the array
21        var filtered =
22           from value in values // data source is values
23           where value > 4
24           select value;
25
26        // display filtered results
27        Console.Write("\nArray values greater than 4:");
28        foreach (var element in filtered)
29        {
30           Console.Write($" {element}");
31        }
32
33        // use orderby clause to sort original values in ascending order
34        var sorted =
35           from value in values // data source is values
36           orderby value
37           select value;
38
39        // display sorted results
40        Console.Write("\nOriginal array, sorted:");
```

Fig. 9.2 | LINQ to Objects using an int array. (Part I of 2.)

```
41          foreach (var element in sorted)
42          {
43              Console.Write($" {element}");
44          }
45
46          // sort the filtered results into descending order
47          var sortFilteredResults =
48              from value in filtered    // data source is LINQ query filtered
49              orderby value descending
50              select value;
51
52          // display the sorted results
53          Console.Write(
54              "\nValues greater than 4, descending order (two queries):");
55          foreach (var element in sortFilteredResults)
56          {
57              Console.Write($" {element}");
58          }
59
60          // filter original array and sort results in descending order
61          var sortAndFilter =
62              from value in values      // data source is values
63              where value > 4
64              orderby value descending
65              select value;
66
67          // display the filtered and sorted results
68          Console.Write(
69              "\nValues greater than 4, descending order (one query):");
70          foreach (var element in sortAndFilter)
71          {
72              Console.Write($" {element}");
73          }
74
75          Console.WriteLine();
76      }
77  }
```

```
Original array: 2 9 5 0 3 7 1 4 8 5
Array values greater than 4: 9 5 7 8 5
Original array, sorted: 0 1 2 3 4 5 5 7 8 9
Values greater than 4, descending order (two queries): 9 8 7 5 5
Values greater than 4, descending order (one query): 9 8 7 5 5
```

Fig. 9.2 | LINQ to Objects using an int array. (Part 2 of 2.)

9.2.1 The from Clause

A LINQ query begins with a from clause (line 22), which specifies a range variable (value) and the data source to query (values). The range variable represents each item in the data source (one at a time), much like the control variable in a foreach statement. Since value is assigned one element at a time from the array values—an int array—the compiler *infers* that value should be of type int. You also may declare the range variable's type explicitly between the from keyword and the range-variable's name.

Introducing the range variable in the from clause allows the IDE to provide *Intelli-Sense* as you type the rest of the query. When you enter the range variable's name followed by a dot (.) in the code editor, the IDE displays the range variable's methods and properties, making it easier for you to construct queries.

Implicitly Typed Local Variables

Typically, implicitly typed local variables (declared with var) are used for the collections of data returned by LINQ queries, as we do in lines 21, 34, 47 and 61. We also use this feature to declare the control variable in the foreach statements.

9.2.2 The where Clause

If the condition in the where clause (line 23) evaluates to true, the element is *selected*—i.e., it's included in the results. Here, the ints in the array are included in the result only if they're greater than 4. An expression that takes a value and returns true or false by testing a condition on that value is known as a predicate.

9.2.3 The select Clause

For each item in the data source, the select clause (line 24) determines what value appears in the results. In this case, it's the int that the range variable currently represents, but you'll soon see that the select clause may contain an expression that transforms a value before including it in the results. Most LINQ queries end with a select clause.

9.2.4 Iterating Through the Results of the LINQ Query

Lines 28–31 use a foreach statement to display the query results. As you know, a foreach statement can iterate through the contents of an array, allowing you to process each element in the array. Actually, the foreach statement can iterate through the contents of arrays, collections and the results of LINQ queries. The foreach statement in lines 28–31 iterates over the query result filtered, displaying each of its int items.

LINQ vs. Iteration Statements

It would be simple to display the integers greater than 4 using a iteration statement that tests each value before displaying it. However, this would intertwine the code that selects elements and the code that displays them. With LINQ, these are kept separate:

- the LINQ query specifies how to locate the values and
- a loop accesses the results

making the code easier to understand and maintain.

9.2.5 The orderby Clause

The orderby clause (line 36) sorts the query results in *ascending* order. Lines 49 and 64 use the descending modifier in the orderby clause to sort the results in *descending* order. An ascending modifier also exists but isn't normally used, because it's the default. Any value that can be compared with other values of the same type may be used with the orderby clause. A value of a *simple type* (e.g., int) can always be compared to another value of the *same* type; we'll discuss how to compare values of *reference types* in Chapter 12.

The queries in lines 48–50 and 62–65 generate the same results, but in different ways. Lines 48–50 uses LINQ to sort the results of the query filtered from lines 22–24. The second query uses both the where and orderby clauses. Because queries can operate on the results of other queries, it's possible to build a query one step at a time, passing the results of queries between methods for further processing.

9.2.6 Interface IEnumerable<T>

As we mentioned, the foreach statement can iterate through the contents of *arrays, collections* and *LINQ query results*. Actually, foreach iterates over any so-called IEnumerable<T> object, which just happens to be what most LINQ queries return.

IEnumerable<T> is an interface. Interfaces define and standardize the ways in which people and systems can interact with one another. For example, the controls on a radio serve as an *interface* between radio users and the radio's internal components. The controls allow users to perform a limited set of *operations* (e.g., changing the station, adjusting the volume, and choosing between AM and FM), and different radios may implement the controls in different ways (e.g., using push buttons, dials or voice commands). The interface specifies *what* operations a radio permits users to perform but does not specify *how* the operations are implemented. Similarly, the interface between a driver and a car with a manual transmission includes the steering wheel, the gear shift, the clutch, the gas pedal and the brake pedal. This same interface is found in nearly all manual-transmission cars, enabling someone who knows how to drive one manual-transmission car to drive another.

Software objects also communicate via interfaces. A C# interface describes a set of methods and properties that can be called on an object—to tell the object, for example, to perform some task or return some piece of information. The IEnumerable<T> interface describes the functionality of any object that can be iterated over and thus offers methods and properties to access each element. A class that *implements* an interface must declare all the methods and properties described by that interface.

Most LINQ queries return an IEnumerable<T> object—some queries return a single value (e.g., the sum of an int array's elements). For queries that return an IEnumerable<T> object, you can use a foreach statement to iterate over the query results. The notation <T> indicates that the interface is a *generic* interface that can be used with any type of data (for example, ints, strings or Employees). You'll learn more about the <T> notation in Section 9.4. In Section 12.7, we'll discuss interfaces and show how to define your own interfaces. In Chapter 20, we'll cover generics in detail.

9.3 Querying an Array of Employee Objects Using LINQ

LINQ is not limited to querying arrays of simple types such as ints. It can be used with arrays of any data type, including strings and user-defined classes. It cannot be used when a query does not have a defined meaning—for example, you cannot use orderby on values that are not *comparable*. Comparable types in .NET are those that implement the IComparable interface, which is discussed in Section 20.4. All built-in types, such as string, int and double implement IComparable. Figure 9.3 presents an Employee class. Figure 9.4 uses LINQ to query an array of Employee objects.

```
 1   // Fig. 9.3: Employee.cs
 2   // Employee class with FirstName, LastName and MonthlySalary properties.
 3   class Employee
 4   {
 5      public string FirstName { get; } // read-only auto-implemented property
 6      public string LastName { get; } // read-only auto-implemented property
 7      private decimal monthlySalary; // monthly salary of employee
 8
 9      // constructor initializes first name, last name and monthly salary
10      public Employee(string firstName, string lastName,
11         decimal monthlySalary)
12      {
13         FirstName = firstName;
14         LastName = lastName;
15         MonthlySalary = monthlySalary;
16      }
17
18      // property that gets and sets the employee's monthly salary
19      public decimal MonthlySalary
20      {
21         get
22         {
23            return monthlySalary;
24         }
25         set
26         {
27            if (value >= 0M) // validate that salary is nonnegative
28            {
29               monthlySalary = value;
30            }
31         }
32      }
33
34      // return a string containing the employee's information
35      public override string ToString() =>
36         $"{FirstName,-10} {LastName,-10} {MonthlySalary,10:C}";
37   }
```

Fig. 9.3 | Employee class with FirstName, LastName and MonthlySalary properties.

```
 1   // Fig. 9.4: LINQWithArrayOfObjects.cs
 2   // LINQ to Objects querying an array of Employee objects.
 3   using System;
 4   using System.Linq;
 5
 6   class LINQWithArrayOfObjects
 7   {
 8      static void Main()
 9      {
10         // initialize array of employees
11         var employees = new[] {
12            new Employee("Jason", "Red", 5000M),
```

Fig. 9.4 | LINQ to Objects querying an array of Employee objects. (Part 1 of 3.)

```
13            new Employee("Ashley", "Green", 7600M),
14            new Employee("Matthew", "Indigo", 3587.5M),
15            new Employee("James", "Indigo", 4700.77M),
16            new Employee("Luke", "Indigo", 6200M),
17            new Employee("Jason", "Blue", 3200M),
18            new Employee("Wendy", "Brown", 4236.4M)};
19
20        // display all employees
21        Console.WriteLine("Original array:");
22        foreach (var element in employees)
23        {
24            Console.WriteLine(element);
25        }
26
27        // filter a range of salaries using && in a LINQ query
28        var between4K6K =
29            from e in employees
30            where (e.MonthlySalary >= 4000M) && (e.MonthlySalary <= 6000M)
31            select e;
32
33        // display employees making between 4000 and 6000 per month
34        Console.WriteLine("\nEmployees earning in the range" +
35            $"{4000:C}-{6000:C} per month:");
36        foreach (var element in between4K6K)
37        {
38            Console.WriteLine(element);
39        }
40
41        // order the employees by last name, then first name with LINQ
42        var nameSorted =
43            from e in employees
44            orderby e.LastName, e.FirstName
45            select e;
46
47        // header
48        Console.WriteLine("\nFirst employee when sorted by name:");
49
50        // attempt to display the first result of the above LINQ query
51        if (nameSorted.Any())
52        {
53            Console.WriteLine(nameSorted.First());
54        }
55        else
56        {
57            Console.WriteLine("not found");
58        }
59
60        // use LINQ to select employee last names
61        var lastNames =
62            from e in employees
63            select e.LastName;
64
```

Fig. 9.4 | LINQ to Objects querying an array of Employee objects. (Part 2 of 3.)

```
65              // use method Distinct to select unique last names
66              Console.WriteLine("\nUnique employee last names:");
67              foreach (var element in lastNames.Distinct())
68              {
69                  Console.WriteLine(element);
70              }
71
72              // use LINQ to select first and last names
73              var names =
74                  from e in employees
75                  select new {e.FirstName, e.LastName};
76
77              // display full names
78              Console.WriteLine("\nNames only:");
79              foreach (var element in names)
80              {
81                  Console.WriteLine(element);
82              }
83
84              Console.WriteLine();
85          }
86     }
```

```
Original array:
Jason       Red         $5,000.00
Ashley      Green       $7,600.00
Matthew     Indigo      $3,587.50
James       Indigo      $4,700.77
Luke        Indigo      $6,200.00
Jason       Blue        $3,200.00
Wendy       Brown       $4,236.40

Employees earning in the range $4,000.00-$6,000.00 per month:
Jason       Red         $5,000.00
James       Indigo      $4,700.77
Wendy       Brown       $4,236.40

First employee when sorted by name:
Jason       Blue        $3,200.00

Unique employee last names:
Red
Green
Indigo
Blue
Brown

Names only:
{ FirstName = Jason, LastName = Red }
{ FirstName = Ashley, LastName = Green }
{ FirstName = Matthew, LastName = Indigo }
{ FirstName = James, LastName = Indigo }
{ FirstName = Luke, LastName = Indigo }
{ FirstName = Jason, LastName = Blue }
{ FirstName = Wendy, LastName = Brown }
```

Fig. 9.4 | LINQ to Objects querying an array of Employee objects. (Part 3 of 3.)

9.3.1 Accessing the Properties of a LINQ Query's Range Variable

The where clause in line 30 (Fig. 9.4) accesses the range variable's properties. The compiler infers that the range variable is of type Employee, because employees was defined as an array of Employee objects (lines 11–18). Any bool expression can be used in a where clause. Line 30 uses the && (conditional AND) operator to combine conditions. Here, only employees that have a salary between $4,000 and $6,000 per month, inclusive, are included in the query result, which is displayed in lines 36–39.

9.3.2 Sorting a LINQ Query's Results by Multiple Properties

Line 44 uses orderby to sort the results according to *multiple* properties—specified in a comma-separated list. Here, the employees are sorted alphabetically by last name. Employees that have the same last name are sorted by first name.

9.3.3 Any, First and Count Extension Methods

Line 51 introduces the Any method, which returns true if the query to which it's applied has at least one element. The query result's First method (line 53) returns the first element in the result. You should check that the query result is not empty (line 51) *before* calling First, which throws an InvalidOperationException if the collection is empty.

We've not specified the class that defines methods First and Any. Your intuition probably tells you they're methods of interface IEnumerable<T>, but they aren't. They're actually extension methods that enhance a class's capabilities without modifying the class's definition. The LINQ extension methods can be used as if they were methods of IEnumerable<T>. Section 10.14 shows how to create extension methods.

LINQ defines many more extension methods, such as Count, which returns the number of elements in the results. Rather than using Any, we could have checked that Count was nonzero, but it's more efficient to determine whether there's at least one element than to count all the elements. The LINQ query syntax is actually transformed by the compiler into extension method calls, with the results of one method call used in the next. It's this design that allows queries to be run on the results of previous queries, as it simply involves passing the result of a method call to another method. For a complete list of IEnumerable<T> extension methods, visit

```
https://msdn.microsoft.com/library/9eekhta0
```

9.3.4 Selecting a Property of an Object

Line 63 uses the select clause to select the range variable's LastName property rather than the range variable itself. This causes the results of the query to consist of only the last names (as strings), instead of complete Employee objects. Lines 67–70 display the unique last names. The Distinct extension method (line 67) removes duplicate elements, causing all elements in the resulting collection to be unique.

9.3.5 Creating New Types in the select Clause of a LINQ Query

The last LINQ query in the example (lines 74–75) selects the properties FirstName and LastName. The syntax

```
new {e.FirstName, e.LastName}
```

creates a new object of an anonymous type (a type with no name), which the compiler generates for you, based on the properties listed in the curly braces ({}). In this case, each new object of the anonymous type is initialized with the FirstName and LastName values from the corresponding Employee object. These selected properties can then be accessed when iterating over the results. Implicitly typed local variables allow you to use *anonymous types* because you do not have to explicitly state the type when declaring such variables.

When the compiler creates an anonymous type, it automatically generates a ToString method that returns a string representation of the object. You can see this in the program's output—it consists of the property names and their values, enclosed in braces. Anonymous types are discussed in more detail in Chapter 22.

Projections

The query in lines 74–75 is an example of a projection, which transforms an object into a new form. In this case, the transformation creates new objects containing only the FirstName and LastName properties, but projections also can manipulate the data. For example, a projection that includes the MonthlySalary could give all employees a 10% raise by multiplying their MonthlySalary properties by 1.1 with the expression

```
e.MonthlySalary * 1.1M
```

Changing the Names of Properties in Anonymous Types

You can specify a new name for a selected property in an anonymous type. For example, if line 75 is written as

```
new {First = e.FirstName, Last = e.LastName}
```

the anonymous type would have properties named First and Last, rather than FirstName and LastName. If you don't specify a new name, the property's original name is used.

9.4 Introduction to Collections

The .NET Framework Class Library provides several classes, called *collections*, used to store groups of related objects. These classes provide efficient methods that organize, store and retrieve your data *without* requiring knowledge of how the data is being stored. This reduces app development time.

You've used arrays to store sequences of objects. Arrays do not automatically change their size at execution time to accommodate additional elements—you must do so manually by creating a new array or by using the Array class's Resize method.

9.4.1 List<T> Collection

The generic collection class List<T> (from namespace System.Collections.Generic) provides a convenient solution to this problem. The T is a placeholder—when declaring a new List, replace it with the type of elements that you want the List to hold. This is similar to specifying the type when declaring an array. For example,

```
List<int> intList;
```

declares intList as a List collection that can store only int values, and

```
List<string> stringList;
```

declares stringList as a List of references to strings. Classes with this kind of place-holder enabling them to be used with any type are called generic classes. Generic classes are discussed in Chapter 20. Additional generic collection classes are discussed in Chapter 21. Figure 21.2 provides a table of collection classes. Figure 9.5 shows some common methods and properties of class List<T>.

Method or property	Description
Add	Adds an element to the end of the List.
AddRange	Adds the elements of its collection argument to the end of the List.
Capacity	Property that *gets* or *sets* the number of elements a List can store without resizing.
Clear	Removes all the elements from the List.
Contains	Returns true if the List contains the specified element and false otherwise.
Count	Property that returns the number of elements stored in the List.
IndexOf	Returns the index of the first occurrence of the specified value in the List.
Insert	Inserts an element at the specified index.
Remove	Removes the first occurrence of the specified value.
RemoveAt	Removes the element at the specified index.
RemoveRange	Removes a specified number of elements starting at a specified index.
Sort	Sorts the List.
TrimExcess	Sets the Capacity of the List to the number of elements the List currently contains (Count).

Fig. 9.5 | Some methods and properties of class List<T>.

9.4.2 Dynamically Resizing a List<T> Collection

Figure 9.6 demonstrates dynamically resizing a List object. Line 11 creates a List of strings, then lines 14–15 display the List's initial Count and Capacity, respectively:

- The Count property returns the number of elements currently in the List.

- The Capacity property indicates how many items the List can hold without having to grow.

When the List is created, both are initially 0—though the Capacity is implementation dependent.

```
1   // Fig. 9.6: ListCollection.cs
2   // Generic List<T> collection demonstration.
3   using System;
4   using System.Collections.Generic;
5
6   class ListCollection
7   {
```

Fig. 9.6 | Generic List<T> collection demonstration. (Part 1 of 3.)

```
 8      static void Main()
 9      {
10         // create a new List of strings
11         var items = new List<string>();
12
13         // display List's Count and Capacity before adding elements
14         Console.WriteLine("Before adding to items: " +
15            $"Count = {items.Count}; Capacity = {items.Capacity}");
16
17         items.Add("red"); // append an item to the List
18         items.Insert(0, "yellow"); // insert the value at index 0
19
20         // display List's Count and Capacity after adding two elements
21         Console.WriteLine("After adding two elements to items: " +
22            $"Count = {items.Count}; Capacity = {items.Capacity}");
23
24         // display the colors in the list
25         Console.Write(
26            "\nDisplay list contents with counter-controlled loop:");
27         for (var i = 0; i < items.Count; i++)
28         {
29            Console.Write($" {items[i]}");
30         }
31
32         // display colors using foreach
33         Console.Write("\nDisplay list contents with foreach statement:");
34         foreach (var item in items)
35         {
36            Console.Write($" {item}");
37         }
38
39         items.Add("green"); // add "green" to the end of the List
40         items.Add("yellow"); // add "yellow" to the end of the List
41
42         // display List's Count and Capacity after adding two more elements
43         Console.WriteLine("\n\nAfter adding two more elements to items: " +
44            $"Count = {items.Count}; Capacity = {items.Capacity}");
45
46         // display the List
47         Console.Write("\nList with two new elements:");
48         foreach (var item in items)
49         {
50            Console.Write($" {item}");
51         }
52
53         items.Remove("yellow"); // remove the first "yellow"
54
55         // display the List
56         Console.Write("\n\nRemove first instance of yellow:");
57         foreach (var item in items)
58         {
59            Console.Write($" {item}");
60         }
```

Fig. 9.6 | Generic List<T> collection demonstration. (Part 2 of 3.)

```
61
62          items.RemoveAt(1); // remove item at index 1
63
64          // display the List
65          Console.Write("\nRemove second list element (green):");
66          foreach (var item in items)
67          {
68              Console.Write($" {item}");
69          }
70
71          // display List's Count and Capacity after removing two elements
72          Console.WriteLine("\nAfter removing two elements from items: " +
73              $"Count = {items.Count}; Capacity = {items.Capacity}");
74
75          // check if a value is in the List
76          Console.WriteLine("\n\"red\" is " +
77              $"{(items.Contains("red") ? string.Empty : "not ")}in the list");
78
79          items.Add("orange"); // add "orange" to the end of the List
80          items.Add("violet"); // add "violet" to the end of the List
81          items.Add("blue"); // add "blue" to the end of the List
82
83          // display List's Count and Capacity after adding three elements
84          Console.WriteLine("\nAfter adding three more elements to items: " +
85              $"Count = {items.Count}; Capacity = {items.Capacity}");
86
87          // display the List
88          Console.Write("List with three new elements:");
89          foreach (var item in items)
90          {
91              Console.Write($" {item}");
92          }
93          Console.WriteLine();
94      }
95  }
```

```
Before adding to items: Count = 0; Capacity = 0
After adding two elements to items: Count = 2; Capacity = 4

Display list contents with counter-controlled loop: yellow red
Display list contents with foreach statement: yellow red

After adding two more elements to items: Count = 4; Capacity = 4
List with two new elements: yellow red green yellow

Remove first instance of yellow: red green yellow
Remove second list element (green): red yellow
After removing two elements from items: Count = 2; Capacity = 4

"red" is in the list

After adding three more elements to items: Count = 5; Capacity = 8
List with three new elements: red yellow orange violet blue
```

Fig. 9.6 | Generic List<T> collection demonstration. (Part 3 of 3.)

Adding and Inserting Elements
The Add and Insert methods add elements to the List (lines 17–18):

- The Add method *appends* its argument to the end of the List.
- The Insert method inserts a new element at the specified position.

Insert's first argument is an index—as with arrays, collection indices start at zero. The second argument is the value to insert at the specified index. To make room for the new element, the indices of the elements at the specified index and above each *increase* by one—in this case, "red" initially was at index 0, but now is at index 1, so that "yellow" can be inserted at index 0.

Count and Capacity
Lines 21–22 display the List's Count (2) and Capacity (4) after the Add and Insert operations. When line 17 executes, the List grows, increasing its Capacity to 4 so that the List can accommodate *four* elements. One of these elements is immediately occupied by "red". At this point, the List's Count is 1. When line 18 executes, there's still room for three more elements, so "yellow" is inserted and the Count becomes 2.

Iterating Through a List's Contents
Lines 27–30 display the items in the List. Like array elements, List elements can be accessed by placing the index in square brackets after the List variable's name. The indexed List expression can be used to modify the element at the index. Lines 34–37 display the List using the preferred foreach statement.

Adding More Elements and Growing the List
Lines 39–51 add more elements to the List, then display its Count, Capacity and contents once again.

Removing Elements
The Remove method deletes the *first* element with a specific value (line 53), returning true if successful and false otherwise. Lines 57–60 show the List's contents after line 53 executes. A similar method, RemoveAt, removes the element at the specified index (line 62). When an element is removed through either of these methods, the indices of all elements above that index *decrease* by one—the opposite of the Insert method. Lines 66–69 show the List's contents after line 62 executes. Lines 72–73 display the List's Count (2) and Capacity (4) after the remove operations. At this point, there's room in the List for two more elements.

Determining Whether an Element Is in the List
Line 77 uses the Contains method to check whether an item is in the List. The Contains method returns true if the element is found in the List and false otherwise. The method compares its argument to each element of the List in order until the item is found, so using Contains on a large List is inefficient.

Adding More Elements and Growing the List
Lines 79–81 add three more elements to the List. Before lines 79–80 execute, Count is 2 and Capacity is 4, so there's room in the List for the two new elements added by those

statements. When Line 81 executes, however, Count and Capacity are both 4, so the List doubles its Capacity to 8 and the Count becomes 5, leaving room for three more elements.

Doubling the Capacity

When a List grows, it must (behind the scenes) create a larger internal array and copy each element to the new array. This is a time-consuming operation. It would be inefficient for the List to grow each time an element is added. To minimize the number of memory re-allocations, a List *doubles* its capacity when more memory is required.[1]

Performance Tip 9.1

Doubling a List's Capacity is an efficient way for a List to grow quickly to be "about the right size." This operation is much more efficient than growing a List by only as much space as it takes to hold the element(s) being added. A disadvantage is that the List might occupy more space than it requires. This is a classic example of the space/time trade-off.

Performance Tip 9.2

It can be wasteful to double a List's size when more space is needed. For example, a full List of 1,000,000 elements resizes to accommodate 2,000,000 elements when one new element is added. This leaves 999,999 unused elements. You can use TrimExcess (as in yourListObject.TrimExcess()) to reduce a List's Capacity to its current Count. You also can set the Capacity directly to control space usage better—for example, if you know a List will never grow beyond 100 elements, you can preallocate that space by assigning 100 to the List's Capacity or using the List constructor that receives an initial capacity.

9.5 Querying the Generic List Collection Using LINQ

As with arrays, you can use LINQ to Objects to query Lists. In Fig. 9.7, a List of strings is converted to uppercase and searched for those that begin with "R".

```
1   // Fig. 9.7: LINQWithListCollection.cs
2   // LINQ to Objects using a List<string>.
3   using System;
4   using System.Linq;
5   using System.Collections.Generic;
6
7   class LINQWithListCollection
8   {
9      static void Main()
10     {
11        // populate a List of strings
12        var items = new List<string>();
13        items.Add("aQua"); // add "aQua" to the end of the List
14        items.Add("RusT"); // add "RusT" to the end of the List
15        items.Add("yElLow"); // add "yElLow" to the end of the List
16        items.Add("rEd"); // add "rEd" to the end of the List
17
```

Fig. 9.7 | LINQ to Objects using a List<string>. (Part 1 of 2.)

---

1. This is not required and could be implementation dependent.

```
18        // display initial List
19        Console.Write("items contains:");
20        foreach (var item in items)
21        {
22            Console.Write($" {item}");
23        }
24
25        Console.WriteLine(); // output end of line
26
27        // convert to uppercase, select those starting with "R" and sort
28        var startsWithR =
29            from item in items
30            let uppercaseString = item.ToUpper()
31            where uppercaseString.StartsWith("R")
32            orderby uppercaseString
33            select uppercaseString;
34
35        // display query results
36        Console.Write("results of query startsWithR:");
37        foreach (var item in startsWithR)
38        {
39            Console.Write($" {item}");
40        }
41
42        Console.WriteLine(); // output end of line
43
44        items.Add("rUbY"); // add "rUbY" to the end of the List
45        items.Add("SaFfRon"); // add "SaFfRon" to the end of the List
46
47        // display initial List
48        Console.Write("items contains:");
49        foreach (var item in items)
50        {
51            Console.Write($" {item}");
52        }
53
54        Console.WriteLine(); // output end of line
55
56        // display updated query results
57        Console.Write("results of query startsWithR:");
58        foreach (var item in startsWithR)
59        {
60            Console.Write($" {item}");
61        }
62
63        Console.WriteLine(); // output end of line
64    }
65 }
```

```
items contains: aQua RusT yElLow rEd
results of query startsWithR: RED RUST
items contains: aQua RusT yElLow rEd rUbY SaFfRon
results of query startsWithR: RED RUBY RUST
```

Fig. 9.7 | LINQ to Objects using a List<string>. (Part 2 of 2.)

9.5.1 The let Clause

Line 30 uses LINQ's let clause to create a new range variable. This is useful if you need to store a temporary result for use later in the LINQ query. Typically, let declares a new range variable to which you assign the result of an expression that operates on the query's original range variable. In this case, we use string method ToUpper to convert each item to uppercase, then store the result in the new range variable uppercaseString. We then use uppercaseString in the where, orderby and select clauses. The where clause (line 31) uses string method StartsWith to determine whether uppercaseString starts with the character "R". Method StartsWith performs a case-sensitive comparison to determine whether a string starts with the string received as an argument. If uppercaseString starts with "R", method StartsWith returns true, and the element is included in the query results. More powerful string matching can be done using the *regular-expression* capabilities introduced in the online part of Chapter 16, Strings and Characters: A Deeper Look.

9.5.2 Deferred Execution

We create the query only once (lines 29–33), yet iterating over the results (lines 37–40 and 58–61) gives two *different* lists of colors. This demonstrates LINQ's deferred execution. A LINQ query executes *only* when you access the results—such as iterating over them or using the Count method—*not* when you define the query. This allows you to create a query once and execute it many times. Any changes to the data source are reflected in the results each time the query executes.

Performance Tip 9.3
Deferred execution can improve performance when a query's results are not immediately needed.

9.5.3 Extension Methods ToArray and ToList

There may be times when you want to retrieve a collection of the results immediately. LINQ provides extension methods ToArray and ToList for this purpose. These methods execute the query on which they're called and give you the results as an array or List<T>, respectively. We use ToArray in Section 21.12.

Performance Tip 9.4
Methods ToArray and ToList also can improve efficiency if you'll be iterating over the same results multiple times, as you execute the query only once.

9.5.4 Collection Initializers

Collection initializers provide a convenient syntax (similar to *array initializers*) for initializing a collection. For example, lines 12–16 of Fig. 9.7 could be replaced with the following statement:

```
var items = new List<string> {"aQua", "RusT", "yElLow", "rEd"};
```

In the preceding declaration, we explicitly created the List<string> with new, so the compiler knows that the initializer list contains elements for a List<string>. The following declaration would generate a compilation error, because the compiler cannot determine whether you wish to create an array or a collection

```
var items = {"aQua", "RusT", "yEllow", "rEd"};
```

9.6 Wrap-Up

This chapter introduced LINQ (Language Integrated Query), a powerful feature for querying data. We showed how to filter an array or collection using LINQ's where clause, and how to sort the query results using the orderby clause. We used the select clause to select specific properties of an object, and the let clause to introduce a new range variable to make writing queries more convenient. The StartsWith method of class string was used to filter strings starting with a specified character or series of characters. We used several LINQ extension methods to perform operations not provided by the query syntax—the Distinct method to remove duplicates from the results, the Any method to determine if the results contain any items, and the First method to retrieve the first element in the results.

We introduced the List<T> generic collection, which provides all the functionality of arrays, along with other useful capabilities such as dynamic resizing. We used method Add to append new items to the end of the List, method Insert to insert new items into specified locations in the List, method Remove to remove the first occurrence of a specified item, method RemoveAt to remove an item at a specified index and method Contains to determine if an item was in the List. We used property Count to get the number of items in the List, and property Capacity to determine the number of elements the List can hold without growing. We use more advanced features of LINQ in later chapters.

In Chapter 10 we take a deeper look at class concepts. We'll discuss the this reference, additional constructor concepts, how the runtime manages memory with garbage collection, static class members, read-only class members, object initializers and operator overloading.

9.7 Deitel LINQ Resource Center

Our LINQ Resource Center (http://www.deitel.com/LINQ/) contains many links to additional information, including blogs by Microsoft LINQ team members, books, sample chapters, FAQs, tutorials, videos, webcasts and more.

Summary

Section 9.1 Introduction

- .NET's collection classes provide reusable data structures that are reliable, powerful and efficient.

- Lists automatically increase their size to accommodate additional elements.

- Large amounts of data are often stored in a database—an organized collection of data. Today's most popular database systems are relational databases. SQL is the international standard language used almost universally with relational databases to perform queries (i.e., to request information that satisfies given criteria).

- LINQ allows you to write query expressions (similar to SQL queries) that retrieve information from a wide variety of data sources. You can query arrays and Lists, selecting elements that satisfy a set of conditions—this is known as filtering.

- A LINQ provider is a set of classes that implement LINQ operations and enable programs to interact with data sources to perform tasks such as sorting, grouping and filtering elements.

Section 9.2 Querying an Array of **int** Values Using LINQ

- Iteration statements focus on the process of iterating through elements. LINQ specifies the conditions that selected elements must satisfy, not the steps necessary to get the results.
- The System.Linq namespace contains the classes for LINQ to Objects.

Section 9.2.1 The **from** Clause

- A from clause specifies a range variable and the data source to query. The range variable represents each item in the data source (one at a time).

Section 9.2.2 The **where** Clause

- If the condition in the where clause evaluates to true for an element, it's included in the results.

Section 9.2.3 The **select** Clause

- The select clause specifies and expression that determines what value appears in the results.

Section 9.2.4 Iterating Through the Results of the LINQ Query

- A foreach statement can iterate over any object that implements the IEnumerable<T>.

Section 9.2.5 The **orderby** Clause

- The orderby clause sorts query results, based on one or more expressions, in ascending order by default. Results also can be sorted in descending order using the descending modifier.

Section 9.2.6 Interface **IEnumerable<T>**

- Most LINQ queries return an object that implements the IEnumerable<T> interface.
- A C# interface describes members that can be used to interact with an object.
- The IEnumerable<T> interface describes the functionality of any object that's capable of being iterated over and thus offers methods to access each element in sequence.
- A class that implements an interface must define each member in the interface.
- Arrays and generic collections implement the IEnumerable<T> interface.

Section 9.3 Querying an Array of **Employee** Objects Using LINQ

- LINQ can be used with collections of any data type.

Section 9.3.2 Sorting a LINQ Query's Results by Multiple Properties

- An orderby clause can sort the results according to multiple expressions specified in a comma-separated list.

Section 9.3.3 Any, **First** and **Count** Extension Methods

- Method Any returns true if there's at least one element in the query to which it's applied; otherwise, it returns false.
- The First method returns the first element of the query to which it's applied. You should check that the query result is not empty before calling First.
- The Count method returns the number of elements in the query to which it's applied.

Section 9.3.4 Selecting a Property of an Object

- The Distinct method removes duplicate values from query results.

Section 9.3.5 Creating New Types in the select Clause of a LINQ Query

- In a select clause, you can select any number of properties (a projection) and encapsulate them in objects by specifying them in a comma-separated list in braces after the new keyword. The compiler automatically creates a new class having these properties—called an anonymous type.

Section 9.4 Introduction to Collections

- The .NET collection classes provide efficient methods that organize, store and retrieve data without requiring knowledge of how the data is being stored.

Section 9.4.1 List<T> Collection

- Class List<T> is similar to an array but provides richer functionality, such as dynamic resizing.
- The Add method appends an element to the end of a List.
- The Insert method inserts a new element at a specified position in the List.
- The Count property returns the number of elements currently in a List.
- Lists can be indexed like arrays by placing the index in square brackets after the object's name.
- The Remove method is used to remove the first element with a specific value.
- The RemoveAt method removes the element at the specified index.
- The Contains method returns true if the element is found in the List, and false otherwise.
- The Capacity property indicates how many items a List can hold without growing.

Section 9.5 Querying the Generic List Collection Using LINQ

- LINQ to Objects can query Lists.

Section 9.5.1 The let Clause

- LINQ's let clause creates a new range variable. This is useful if you need to store a temporary result for use later in the LINQ query.
- The StartsWith method of the string class determines whether a string starts with the string passed to it as an argument.

Section 9.5.2 Deferred Execution

- A LINQ query uses deferred execution—it executes only when you access the results, not when you create the query.

Section 9.5.3 Extension Methods ToArray and ToList

- There may be times when you want to retrieve a collection of the results immediately. LINQ provides extension methods ToArray and ToList for this purpose.

Section 9.5.4 Collection Initializers

- Collection initializers provide a convenient syntax (similar to array initializers) for initializing a collection.

Terminology

Add method of class List<T>	collection initializer
anonymous type	Contains method of class List<T>
Any extension method for IEnumerable<T>	Count extension method for IEnumerable<T>
ascending modifier of the orderby clause	Count property of class List<T>
Capacity property of class List<T>	declarative programming

deferred execution
descending modifier of the orderby clause
Distinct extension method for IEnumerable<T>
dynamic resizing
filtering a collection with LINQ
First extension method for IEnumerable<T>
from clause of a LINQ query
IEnumerable<T> interface
imperative programming
implicitly typed local variable
Insert method of class List<T>
interface
let clause of a LINQ query
LINQ (Language Integrated Query)
LINQ provider

LINQ to Objects
List<T> collection class
orderby clause of a LINQ query
predicate
projection
query expression
query using LINQ
range variable
Remove method of class List<T>
RemoveAt method of class List<T>
select clause of a LINQ query
StartsWith method of class string
ToUpper method of class string
where clause of a LINQ query

Self-Review Exercises

9.1 Fill in the blanks in each of the following statements:
a) Use the _____ property of the List class to find the number of elements in the List.
b) The LINQ _____ clause is used for filtering.
c) _____ are classes specifically designed to store groups of objects and provide methods that organize, store and retrieve those objects.
d) To add an element to the end of a List, use the _____ method.
e) To get only unique results from a LINQ query, use the _____ method.

9.2 State whether each of the following is *true* or *false*. If *false*, explain why.
a) The orderby clause in a LINQ query can sort only in ascending order.
b) LINQ queries can be used on both arrays and collections.
c) The Remove method of the List class removes an element at a specific index.

Answers to Self-Review Exercises

9.1 a) Count. b) where. c) Collections. d) Add. e) Distinct.

9.2 a) False. The descending modifier is used to make orderby sort in descending order. b) True. c) False. Remove removes the first element equal to its argument. RemoveAt removes the element at a specific index.

Exercises

9.3 *(Querying an Array of Invoice Objects)* Use the class Invoice provided in the ex09_03 folder with this chapter's examples to create an array of Invoice objects. Use the sample data shown in Fig. 9.8. Class Invoice includes four properties—a PartNumber (type int), a PartDescription (type string), a Quantity of the item being purchased (type int) and a Price (type decimal). Perform the following queries on the array of Invoice objects and display the results:
a) Use LINQ to sort the Invoice objects by PartDescription.
b) Use LINQ to sort the Invoice objects by Price.
c) Use LINQ to select the PartDescription and Quantity and sort the results by Quantity.

d) Use LINQ to select from each Invoice the PartDescription and the value of the Invoice (i.e., Quantity * Price). Name the calculated column InvoiceTotal. Order the results by Invoice value. [*Hint:* Use let to store the result of Quantity * Price in a new range variable total.]

e) Using the results of the LINQ query in part (d), select the InvoiceTotals in the range $200 to $500.

Part number	Part description	Quantity	Price
83	Electric sander	7	57.98
24	Power saw	18	99.99
7	Sledge hammer	11	21.50
77	Hammer	76	11.99
39	Lawn mower	3	79.50
68	Screwdriver	106	6.99
56	Jig saw	21	11.00
3	Wrench	34	7.50

Fig. 9.8 | Sample data for Exercise 9.3.

9.4 *(Duplicate Word Removal)* Write a console app that inputs a sentence from the user (assume no punctuation), then determines and displays the nonduplicate words in alphabetical order. Treat uppercase and lowercase letters the same. [*Hint:* You can use string method Split with no arguments, as in sentence.Split(), to break a sentence into an array of strings containing the individual words. By default, Split uses spaces as delimiters. Use string method ToLower before calling Split.]

9.5 *(Sorting Letters and Removing Duplicates)* Write a console app that inserts 30 random letters into a List<char>. Perform the following queries on the List and display your results: [*Hint:* Strings can be indexed like arrays to access a character at a specific index.]

a) Use LINQ to sort the List in ascending order.

b) Use LINQ to sort the List in descending order.

c) Display the List in ascending order with duplicates removed.

10

Classes and Objects: A Deeper Look

10.1 Introduction

In this chapter, we take a deeper look at building classes, controlling access to members of a class and creating constructors. We discuss *composition*—a capability that allows a class to have references to objects of other classes as members. The chapter also discusses static class members and readonly instance variables and properties.

We also introduce operator overloading. In previous chapters, we declared our own classes and used methods to perform tasks on objects of those classes. Operator overloading allows us to define the behavior of the built-in operators, such as + and -, when used on objects of our own classes. This can provide a more convenient notation than calling methods for performing certain tasks (such as arithmetic) using objects.

We show how to create your own value types using struct, discuss key differences between structs and classes, and discuss when struct types should be used. Finally, we demonstrate how to create your own extension methods to add functionality to an existing type that you did not define.

10.2 Time Class Case Study; Throwing Exceptions

Our first example consists of classes Time1 (Fig. 10.1) and Time1Test (Fig. 10.2). Class Time1 represents the time of day.[1] Class Time1Test's Main method creates an object of class Time1 and invokes its methods. The output of this app appears in Fig. 10.2.

---

1. C# has the types like DateTime and DateTimeOffset for date and time manipulations. Our time examples are for demonstration purposes—you do not need to create your own types for dates and times. We use DateTime in Section 15.4.

10.2.1 Time1 Class Declaration

Class Time1 contains three public properties of type int—Hour, Minute and Second (Fig. 10.1, lines 7–9). These represent the time in universal-time format (24-hour clock format, in which hours are in the range 0–23). Class Time1 contains public methods Set-Time (lines 13–25), ToUniversalString (lines 28–29) and ToString (lines 32–34). These are the public services or the public interface that this class provides to its clients. In this example, class Time1 does not declare a constructor, so the compiler defines a default constructor. Each property receives the default value 0 for an int. Instance variables and auto-implemented properties also can be assigned values in their declarations.

```
1   // Fig. 10.1: Time1.cs
2   // Time1 class declaration maintains the time in 24-hour format.
3   using System; // namespace containing ArgumentOutOfRangeException
4
5   public class Time1
6   {
7      public int Hour { get; set; } // 0 - 23
8      public int Minute { get; set; } // 0 - 59
9      public int Second { get; set; } // 0 - 59
10
11     // set a new time value using universal time; throw an
12     // exception if the hour, minute or second is invalid
13     public void SetTime(int hour, int minute, int second)
14     {
15        // validate hour, minute and second
16        if ((hour < 0 || hour > 23) || (minute < 0 || minute > 59) ||
17           (second < 0 || second > 59))
18        {
19           throw new ArgumentOutOfRangeException();
20        }
21
22        Hour = hour;
23        Minute = minute;
24        Second = second;
25     }
26
27     // convert to string in universal-time format (HH:MM:SS)
28     public string ToUniversalString() =>
29        $"{Hour:D2}:{Minute:D2}:{Second:D2}";
30
31     // convert to string in standard-time format (H:MM:SS AM or PM)
32     public override string ToString() =>
33        $"{((Hour == 0 || Hour == 12) ? 12 : Hour % 12)}:" +
34        $"{Minute:D2}:{Second:D2} {(Hour < 12 ? "AM" : "PM")}";
35  }
```

Fig. 10.1 | Time1 class declaration maintains the time in 24-hour format.

public *Class*

In Fig. 10.1, we declared class Time1 as a public class, meaning that it potentially can be re-used in other projects. Although we use class Time1 only in this project, from this point forward, we'll declare as public any class that could potentially be reused in another project.

Method SetTime and Throwing Exceptions

Method SetTime (lines 13–25) is a public method that declares three int parameters and uses them to set the time. Lines 16–17 test each argument to determine whether the value is out of range. If all the values are in range, lines 22–24 assign the values to the Hour, Minute and Second properties. The hour (line 13) must be in the range 0 to 23, because universal-time format represents hours as integers from 0 to 23 (e.g., 1 PM is hour 13 and 11 PM is hour 23; midnight is hour 0 and noon is hour 12). Similarly, both minute and second values must be in the range 0 to 59. For values outside these ranges, line 19 throws an exception of type ArgumentOutOfRangeException (namespace System), which notifies the client code that an invalid argument was passed to the method. As you learned in Chapter 8, you can use try...catch to catch exceptions and attempt to recover from them, which we'll do in Fig. 10.2. The throw statement (line 19) creates a new object of type ArgumentOutOfRangeException. The parentheses following the class name indicate a call to the ArgumentOutOfRangeException constructor. After the exception object is created, the throw statement immediately terminates method SetTime and the exception is returned to the code that attempted to set the time, where it can be *caught* and dealt with.

Method ToUniversalString

Method ToUniversalString (lines 28–29) is an expression-bodied method—recall this is a shorthand notation for a method that contains only a return statement. The method takes no arguments and returns a string in universal-time format, consisting of six digits—two for the hour, two for the minute and two for the second. For example, if the time were 1:30:07 PM, method ToUniversalString would return 13:30:07. The method implicitly returns the value of the string-interpolation expression in line 29. The D2 format specifier formats an integer with two digits and, where needed, a leading 0 if the integer has fewer than two digits.

Method ToString

Method ToString (lines 32–34) is an expression-bodied method that takes no arguments and returns a string in which the Hour, Minute and Second values are separated by colons and followed by an AM or PM indicator (e.g., 1:27:06 PM). Like method ToUniversalString, method ToString implicitly returns the value of a string-interpolation expression. In this case, we do not format the Hour, but we format the Minute and Second as two-digit values with leading 0s, if necessary. Line 33 uses a conditional operator (?:) to determine the value for Hour in the string—if the hour is 0 or 12 (AM or PM), it appears as 12—otherwise, it appears as a value from 1 to 11. The conditional operator in line 34 determines whether AM or PM will be inserted in the string.

10.2.2 Using Class Time1

The Time1Test app class (Fig. 10.2) uses class Time1. Line 10 creates a Time1 object and assigns it to local variable time. Operator new invokes class Time1's *default constructor*, since Time1 does not declare any constructors. Lines 13–17 output the time, first in universal-time format (by invoking time's ToUniversalString method in line 14), then in standard-time format (by explicitly invoking time's ToString method in line 16) to confirm that the Time1 object was initialized properly. Line 20 invokes method SetTime of the time object to change the time. Then lines 21–24 output the time again in both formats to confirm that the time was set correctly.

```csharp
1   // Fig. 10.2: Time1Test.cs
2   // Time1 object used in an app.
3   using System;
4
5   class Time1Test
6   {
7      static void Main()
8      {
9         // create and initialize a Time1 object
10        var time = new Time1(); // invokes Time1 constructor
11
12        // output string representations of the time
13        Console.WriteLine(
14           $"The initial universal time is: {time.ToUniversalString()}");
15        Console.WriteLine(
16           $"The initial standard time is: {time.ToString()}");
17        Console.WriteLine(); // output a blank line
18
19        // change time and output updated time
20        time.SetTime(13, 27, 6);
21        Console.WriteLine(
22           $"Universal time after SetTime is: {time.ToUniversalString()}");
23        Console.WriteLine(
24           $"Standard time after SetTime is: {time.ToString()}");
25        Console.WriteLine(); // output a blank line
26
27        // attempt to set time with invalid values
28        try
29        {
30           time.SetTime(99, 99, 99);
31        }
32        catch (ArgumentOutOfRangeException ex)
33        {
34           Console.WriteLine(ex.Message + "\n");
35        }
36
37        // display time after attempt to set invalid values
38        Console.WriteLine("After attempting invalid settings:");
39        Console.WriteLine($"Universal time: {time.ToUniversalString()}");
40        Console.WriteLine($"Standard time: {time.ToString()}");
41     }
42  }
```

```
The initial universal time is: 00:00:00
The initial standard time is: 12:00:00 AM

Universal time after SetTime is: 13:27:06
Standard time after SetTime is: 1:27:06 PM

Specified argument was out of the range of valid values.

After attempting invalid settings:
Universal time: 13:27:06
Standard time: 1:27:06 PM
```

Fig. 10.2 | Time1 object used in an app.

Calling **Time** *Method* **SetTime** *with Invalid Values*

To illustrate that method SetTime validates its arguments, line 30 calls method SetTime with invalid arguments of 99 for the hour, minute and second. This statement is placed in a try block (lines 28–31) in case SetTime throws an ArgumentOutOfRangeException, which it will do since the arguments are all invalid. When this occurs, the exception is caught at lines 32–35 and the exception's Message property is displayed. Lines 38–40 output the time again in both formats to confirm that SetTime did *not* change the time when invalid arguments were supplied.

Notes on the **Time1** *Class Declaration*

Consider several class-design issues with respect to class Time1. The time is represented as three integers for the hour, minute and second. However, the actual data representation used within the class is of no concern to the class's clients. For example, it would be perfectly reasonable for Time1 to represent the time internally as the number of seconds since midnight or the number of minutes and seconds since midnight. Clients could use the same public methods and properties to get the same results without being aware of this—of course, the Hour, Minute and Second properties would need to be reimplemented to work with the new data representation. (Exercise 10.4 asks you to represent the time as the number of seconds since midnight and show that indeed no change is visible to the clients of the class.)

Software Engineering Observation 10.1

Classes simplify programming because the client can use only the public *members exposed by the class. Such members are usually client oriented rather than implementation oriented. Clients are neither aware of, nor involved in, a class's implementation. Clients generally care about* what *the class does but not* how *the class does it. Clients do, of course, care that the class operates correctly and efficiently.*

Software Engineering Observation 10.2

Interfaces change less frequently than implementations. When an implementation changes, implementation-dependent code must change accordingly. Hiding the implementation reduces the possibility that other parts of the app become dependent on class-implementation details.

Software Engineering Observation 10.3

Date and time manipulations are more complex than the simplified classes we use in this book. For applications that require date and time processing, check out .NET's DateTimeOffest, DateTime, TimeSpan *and* TimeZoneInfo *value types in namespace* System.

10.3 Controlling Access to Members

The access modifiers public and private control access to a class's variables, methods and properties. (In Chapter 11, we'll introduce the additional access modifier protected.) As we stated in Section 10.2, the primary purpose of public methods and properties is to present to the class's clients a view of the services the class provides (that is, the class's *public interface*). Clients of the class need not be concerned with how the class accomplishes its tasks. For this reason, a class's private variables, properties and methods (i.e., the class's implementation details) are not directly accessible to the class's clients.

Figure 10.3 demonstrates that private class members are not directly accessible outside the class. In this app, we use a modified version of class Time1 that declares private instance variables hour, minute and second, rather than public properties Hour, Minute and Second. Lines 9–11 attempt to directly access private instance variables hour, minute and second of Time1 object time. When this app is compiled, the compiler generates error messages stating that these private members are not accessible.

```
1   // Fig. 10.3: MemberAccessTest.cs
2   // Private members of class Time1 are not accessible outside the class.
3   class MemberAccessTest
4   {
5      static void Main()
6      {
7         var time = new Time1(); // create and initialize Time1 object
8
9         time.hour = 7; // error: hour has private access in Time1
10        time.minute = 15; // error: minute has private access in Time1
11        time.second = 30; // error: second has private access in Time1
12     }
13  }
```

Fig. 10.3 | Private members of class Time1 are not accessible outside the class.

10.4 Referring to the Current Object's Members with the this Reference

Every object can access a *reference to itself* with keyword this (also called the this reference). When a non-static method (or property) is called for a particular object, the method's body *implicitly* uses keyword this to refer to the object's instance variables and other non-static class members. As you'll see in Fig. 10.4, you also can use keyword this *explicitly* in a non-static method's body. Section 10.5 shows a more interesting use of keyword this. Section 10.9 explains why keyword this cannot be used in a static method.

```
1   // Fig. 10.4: ThisTest.cs
2   // this used implicitly and explicitly to refer to members of an object.
3   using System;
4
5   class ThisTest
6   {
```

Fig. 10.4 | this used implicitly and explicitly to refer to members of an object. (Part 1 of 2.)

```
 7        static void Main()
 8        {
 9            var time = new SimpleTime(15, 30, 19);
10            Console.WriteLine(time.BuildString());
11        }
12    }
13
14    // class SimpleTime demonstrates the "this" reference
15    public class SimpleTime
16    {
17        private int hour; // 0-23
18        private int minute; // 0-59
19        private int second; // 0-59
20
21        // if the constructor uses parameter names identical to
22        // instance-variable names, the "this" reference is
23        // required to distinguish between the names
24        public SimpleTime(int hour, int minute, int second)
25        {
26            this.hour = hour; // set "this" object's hour instance variable
27            this.minute = minute; // set "this" object's minute
28            this.second = second; // set "this" object's second
29        }
30
31        // use explicit and implicit "this" to call ToUniversalString
32        public string BuildString() =>
33            $"{"this.ToUniversalString()",24}: {this.ToUniversalString()}" +
34            $"\n{"ToUniversalString()",24}: {ToUniversalString()}";
35
36        // convert to string in universal-time format (HH:MM:SS);
37        // "this" is not required here to access instance variables,
38        // because the method does not have local variables with the same
39        // names as the instance variables
40        public string ToUniversalString() =>
41            $"{this.hour:D2}:{this.minute:D2}:{this.second:D2}";
42    }
```

```
this.ToUniversalString(): 15:30:19
    ToUniversalString(): 15:30:19
```

Fig. 10.4 | this used implicitly and explicitly to refer to members of an object. (Part 2 of 2.)

Figure 10.4 demonstrates implicit and explicit use of the this reference to enable class ThisTest's Main method to display the private data of a SimpleTime object. For the sake of brevity, we declare two classes in one file—class ThisTest is declared in lines 5–12, and class SimpleTime is declared in lines 15–42.

Class SimpleTime declares three private instance variables—hour, minute and second (lines 17–19). The constructor (lines 24–29) receives three int arguments to initialize a SimpleTime object (without validation for simplicity). Here, we used parameter names that are *identical* to the class's instance-variable names (lines 17–19). We did this intentionally to *hide* the corresponding instance variables so that we could illustrate explicit use of the this reference. If a method contains a local variable with the *same* name as an instance variable, the local variable is said to *shadow* (or hide) the instance variable in the method's body. However, you can use this to access the hidden instance variable explicitly, as shown in lines 26–28 for SimpleTime's hidden instance variables.

Software Engineering Observation 10.4

Using properties throughout a class to access the class's instance variables normally eliminates shadowing because property names use Pascal Case naming (capital first letter) and parameter names use Camel Case (lowercase first letter).

Method BuildString (lines 32–34) returns a string created by a statement that uses the this reference explicitly and implicitly. Line 33 uses the this reference *explicitly* to call method ToUniversalString. Line 34 uses the this reference *implicitly* to call the same method. Programmers typically do not use the this reference explicitly to reference other methods in the current object. Also, line 41 in method ToUniversalString explicitly uses the this reference to access each instance variable. This is not necessary here, because the method does *not* have any local variables that hide the instance variables of the class.

Class ThisTest (lines 5–12) demonstrates class SimpleTime. Line 9 creates an instance of class SimpleTime and invokes its constructor. Line 10 invokes the object's BuildString method, then displays the results.

10.5 Time Class Case Study: Overloaded Constructors

Next, we demonstrate a class with several overloaded constructors that enable objects of that class to be conveniently initialized in different ways. To overload constructors, simply provide multiple constructor declarations with different signatures.

10.5.1 Class Time2 with Overloaded Constructors

By default, the properties Hour, Minute and Second of class Time1 (Fig. 10.1) are initialized to their default values of 0—midnight in universal time. Class Time1 doesn't enable the class's clients to initialize the time with specific nonzero values, because it does not define such a constructor. Class Time2 (Fig. 10.5) contains overloaded constructors. In this app, one constructor invokes the other, which in turn calls SetTime to set the private instance variables hour, minute and second via the class's Hour, Minute and Second properties, which perform validation. The compiler invokes the appropriate Time2 constructor by matching the number and types of the arguments specified in the constructor call with the number and types of the parameters specified in each constructor declaration.

```
1   // Fig. 10.5: Time2.cs
2   // Time2 class declaration with overloaded constructors.
3   using System; // for class ArgumentOutOfRangeException
4
5   public class Time2
6   {
7      private int hour; // 0 - 23
8      private int minute; // 0 - 59
9      private int second; // 0 - 59
```

Fig. 10.5 | Time2 class declaration with overloaded constructors. (Part 1 of 3.)

```
10
11     // constructor can be called with zero, one, two or three arguments
12     public Time2(int hour = 0, int minute = 0, int second = 0)
13     {
14        SetTime(hour, minute, second); // invoke SetTime to validate time
15     }
16
17     // Time2 constructor: another Time2 object supplied as an argument
18     public Time2(Time2 time)
19        : this(time.Hour, time.Minute, time.Second) { }
20
21     // set a new time value using universal time; invalid values
22     // cause the properties' set accessors to throw exceptions
23     public void SetTime(int hour, int minute, int second)
24     {
25        Hour = hour; // set the Hour property
26        Minute = minute; // set the Minute property
27        Second = second; // set the Second property
28     }
29
30     // property that gets and sets the hour
31     public int Hour
32     {
33        get
34        {
35           return hour;
36        }
37        set
38        {
39           if (value < 0 || value > 23)
40           {
41              throw new ArgumentOutOfRangeException(nameof(value),
42                 value, $"{nameof(Hour)} must be 0-23");
43           }
44
45           hour = value;
46        }
47     }
48
49     // property that gets and sets the minute
50     public int Minute
51     {
52        get
53        {
54           return minute;
55        }
56        set
57        {
58           if (value < 0 || value > 59)
59           {
60              throw new ArgumentOutOfRangeException(nameof(value),
61                 value, $"{nameof(Minute)} must be 0-59");
62           }
```

Fig. 10.5 | Time2 class declaration with overloaded constructors. (Part 2 of 3.)

```
63
64              minute = value;
65         }
66     }
67
68     // property that gets and sets the second
69     public int Second
70     {
71         get
72         {
73             return second;
74         }
75         set
76         {
77             if (value < 0 || value > 59)
78             {
79                 throw new ArgumentOutOfRangeException(nameof(value),
80                     value, $"{nameof(Second)} must be 0-59");
81             }
82
83             second = value;
84         }
85     }
86
87     // convert to string in universal-time format (HH:MM:SS)
88     public string ToUniversalString() =>
89         $"{Hour:D2}:{Minute:D2}:{Second:D2}";
90
91     // convert to string in standard-time format (H:MM:SS AM or PM)
92     public override string ToString() =>
93         $"{((Hour == 0 || Hour == 12) ? 12 : Hour % 12)}:" +
94         $"{Minute:D2}:{Second:D2} {(Hour < 12 ? "AM" : "PM")}";
95 }
```

Fig. 10.5 | Time2 class declaration with overloaded constructors. (Part 3 of 3.)

Class *Time2*'s Three-Argument Constructor

Lines 12–15 declare a constructor with three *default parameters*. We did not define a constructor with an empty parameter list, so for class Time2 the constructor at lines 12–15 is also considered to be the class's parameterless constructor—you can call the constructor without arguments and the compiler will provide the default values. This constructor also can be called with one argument for the hour, two for the hour and minute, or three for the hour, minute and second. This constructor calls SetTime to set the time.

Common Programming Error 10.1

A constructor can call methods of its class. Be aware that the instance variables might not yet be initialized, because the constructor is in the process of initializing the object. Using instance variables before they have been initialized properly is a logic error.

Constructor Initializers

Lines 18–19 declare another Time2 constructor that receives a reference to a Time2 object. In this case, the values from the Time2 argument are passed to the three-parameter constructor at lines 12–15 to initialize the hour, minute and second. In this constructor, we use this in a manner that's allowed *only* in the constructor's header. In line 19,

```
    : this(time.Hour, time.Minute, time.Second) { }
```

: this followed by parentheses containing arguments indicates a call to one of the class's other constructors—in this case, the Time2 constructor that takes three int arguments (lines 12–15). Line 19 passes the values of the time argument's Hour, Minute and Second properties to initialize the Time2 object being constructed. Any initialization code in the body of the constructor at lines 18–19 would execute *after* the other constructor is called.

Using this as in line 19 is called a constructor initializer. It enables a class to reuse initialization code provided by a constructor, rather than defining similar code in another constructor. If we needed to change how objects of class Time2 are initialized, only the constructor at lines 12–15 would need to be modified. Even that constructor might not need modification—it simply calls the SetTime method to perform the actual initialization, so it's possible that the changes the class might require would be localized to SetTime.

Software Engineering Observation 10.5

Constructor initializers make classes easier to maintain, modify and debug, because the common initialization code can be defined in one constructor and called by others.

Line 19 could have directly accessed instance variables hour, minute and second of the constructor's time argument with the expressions time.hour, time.minute and time.second—even though they're declared as private variables of class Time2.

Software Engineering Observation 10.6

When executing a method of a class, if that method has a reference to another object of the same class (typically received via a parameter), the method can access all *of that other object's data and methods (including those that are* private).

SetTime *Method and the* Hour, Minute *and* Second *Properties*

Method SetTime (lines 23–28) invokes the set accessors of the properties Hour (lines 31–47), Minute (lines 50–66) and Second (lines 69–85), which ensure that the hour is in the range 0 to 23 and that the values for the minute and second are each in the range 0 to 59. If a value is out of range, each set accessor throws an ArgumentOutOfRangeException (lines 41–42, 60–61 and 79–80). In this example, we use the exception class's overloaded constructor that receives three arguments:

- the string name of the item that was out of range
- the value that was supplied for that item and
- a string error message.

It's common to include in an exception's error message a variable's or property's identifier. This information can help a client-code programmer understand the context in which the exception occurred. Prior to C# 6, you had to hard code these identifiers into your error-message strings. As of C# 6, you can instead use the nameof operator (lines 41–42, 60–61 and 79–80), which returns a string representation of the identifier enclosed in parentheses. For example, the expression

6

```
    nameof(value)
```

in line 41 returns the string "value" and the expression

```
nameof(Hour)
```

in line 42 returns the string "Hour".

Good Programming Practice 10.1

When you need to include an identifier in a string literal, use the nameof operator rather than hard coding the identifier's name in the string. If you right click an identifier in Visual Studio then use the **Rename...** *option to change the identifier's name throughout your code, the string that nameof returns will be updated automatically with the identifier's new name.*

Notes Regarding Class Time2's Methods, Properties and Constructors

Time2's properties are accessed throughout the class's body—SetTime assigns values to Hour, Minute and Second in lines 25–27, and ToUniversalString and ToString use properties Hour, Minute and Second in line 89 and lines 93–94, respectively. These methods could access the class's private data directly. However, consider changing the time's representation from three int values (requiring 12 bytes of memory) to one int value representing the total number of elapsed seconds since midnight (requiring only four bytes of memory). If we make this change, only code that accesses the private data *directly* would need to change—for class Time2, the bodies of properties Hour, Minute and Second. There would be no need to modify SetTime, ToUniversalString or ToString, because they access the private data *indirectly* through Hour, Minute and Second. Designing a class in this manner reduces the likelihood of programming errors when altering the class's implementation.

Similarly, each constructor could include a copy of the appropriate statements from method SetTime. Doing so may be slightly more efficient, because the extra constructor call and the call to SetTime are eliminated. However, duplicating statements in multiple methods or constructors makes changing the class's internal data representation more difficult and error-prone. Having one constructor call the other or even call SetTime directly allows any changes to SetTime's implementation to be made only once.

Software Engineering Observation 10.7

When implementing a method of a class, using the class's properties to access the class's private data simplifies code maintenance and reduces the likelihood of errors.

10.5.2 Using Class Time2's Overloaded Constructors

Class Time2Test (Fig. 10.6) creates six Time2 objects (lines 9–13 and 41) to invoke the overloaded Time2 constructors.

```
1   // Fig. 10.6: Time2Test.cs
2   // Overloaded constructors used to initialize Time2 objects.
3   using System;
4
5   public class Time2Test
6   {
```

Fig. 10.6 | Overloaded constructors used to initialize Time2 objects. (Part 1 of 3.)

```csharp
7      static void Main()
8      {
9          var t1 = new Time2(); // 00:00:00
10         var t2 = new Time2(2); // 02:00:00
11         var t3 = new Time2(21, 34); // 21:34:00
12         var t4 = new Time2(12, 25, 42); // 12:25:42
13         var t5 = new Time2(t4); // 12:25:42
14
15         Console.WriteLine("Constructed with:\n");
16         Console.WriteLine("t1: all arguments defaulted");
17         Console.WriteLine($"   {t1.ToUniversalString()}"); // 00:00:00
18         Console.WriteLine($"   {t1.ToString()}\n"); // 12:00:00 AM
19
20         Console.WriteLine(
21            "t2: hour specified; minute and second defaulted");
22         Console.WriteLine($"   {t2.ToUniversalString()}"); // 02:00:00
23         Console.WriteLine($"   {t2.ToString()}\n"); // 2:00:00 AM
24
25         Console.WriteLine(
26            "t3: hour and minute specified; second defaulted");
27         Console.WriteLine($"   {t3.ToUniversalString()}"); // 21:34:00
28         Console.WriteLine($"   {t3.ToString()}\n"); // 9:34:00 PM
29
30         Console.WriteLine("t4: hour, minute and second specified");
31         Console.WriteLine($"   {t4.ToUniversalString()}"); // 12:25:42
32         Console.WriteLine($"   {t4.ToString()}\n"); // 12:25:42 PM
33
34         Console.WriteLine("t5: Time2 object t4 specified");
35         Console.WriteLine($"   {t5.ToUniversalString()}"); // 12:25:42
36         Console.WriteLine($"   {t5.ToString()}"); // 12:25:42 PM
37
38         // attempt to initialize t6 with invalid values
39         try
40         {
41             var t6 = new Time2(27, 74, 99); // invalid values
42         }
43         catch (ArgumentOutOfRangeException ex)
44         {
45             Console.WriteLine("\nException while initializing t6:");
46             Console.WriteLine(ex.Message);
47         }
48     }
49  }
```

```
Constructed with:

t1: all arguments defaulted
   00:00:00
   12:00:00 AM

t2: hour specified; minute and second defaulted
   02:00:00
   2:00:00 AM
```

Fig. 10.6 | Overloaded constructors used to initialize Time2 objects. (Part 2 of 3.)

```
t3: hour and minute specified; second defaulted
   21:34:00
   9:34:00 PM

t4: hour, minute and second specified
   12:25:42
   12:25:42 PM

t5: Time2 object t4 specified
   12:25:42
   12:25:42 PM

Exception while initializing t6:
Hour must be 0-23
Parameter name: value
Actual value was 27.
```

Fig. 10.6 | Overloaded constructors used to initialize `Time2` objects. (Part 3 of 3.)

Lines 9–13 demonstrate passing arguments to the `Time2` constructors. C# invokes the appropriate overloaded constructor by matching the number and types of the arguments in the constructor call with the number and types of the parameters in each constructor declaration. Lines 9–12 each invoke the constructor at lines 12–15 of Fig. 10.5:

- Line 9 of Fig. 10.6 invokes the constructor with no arguments—the compiler supplies the default value 0 for each of the three parameters.

- Line 10 invokes the constructor with one argument that represents the hour— the compiler supplies the default value 0 for the minute and second.

- Line 11 invokes the constructor with two arguments that represent the hour and minute—the compiler supplies the default value 0 for the second.

- Line 12 invoke the constructor with values for the hour, minute and second.

Line 13 invokes the constructor at lines 18–19 of Fig. 10.5. Lines 15–36 (Fig. 10.6) display the `string` representation of each initialized `Time2` object to confirm that each was initialized properly.

Line 41 attempts to initialize `t6` by creating a new `Time2` object and passing three invalid values to the constructor. When the constructor attempts to use the invalid hour value to initialize the `Hour` property, an `ArgumentOutOfRangeException` occurs. We catch this exception at line 43 and display its `Message` property, which results in the last three lines of the output in Fig. 10.6. Because we used the three-argument `Argument-OutOfRangeException` constructor when the exception object was created, the exception's `Message` property also includes the *information about the out-of-range value*.

10.6 Default and Parameterless Constructors

Every class *must* have at least one constructor—if you do not provide any constructors in a class's declaration, the compiler creates a *default constructor* that takes no arguments when it's invoked. In Section 11.4.1, you'll learn that the default constructor implicitly performs a special task.

The compiler will *not* create a default constructor for a class that *explicitly* declares at least one constructor. In this case, if you want to be able to invoke the constructor with no arguments, you must declare a *parameterless constructor*—that is, one that's declared with no parameters *or* one in which all the parameters have default values (e.g., line 12 of Fig. 10.5). Like a default constructor, a parameterless constructor is invoked with *empty parentheses*. If you call class Time2's three-argument constructor with no arguments, the compiler explicitly passes 0 to each parameter. If we omit from class Time2 a constructor that can be called with no arguments, clients of this class would not be able to create a Time2 object with the expression new Time2(). If a class provides both a parameterless constructor *and* a constructor with a default arguments for all of its parameters, the compiler will use the parameterless constructor when you pass no arguments to the constructor.

10.7 Composition

A class can have objects of values types or references to objects of other classes as members. This is called composition and is sometimes referred to as a *has-a* relationship. For example, an object of class AlarmClock needs to know the current time *and* the time when it's supposed to sound its alarm, so it's reasonable to include *two* references to Time objects in an AlarmClock object.

> ### Software Engineering Observation 10.8
> *One form of software reuse is composition, in which a class contains references to other objects. Recall that classes are reference types. A class can have a property of its own type—for example, a Person class could have Mother and Father properties of type Person that reference other Person objects.*

10.7.1 Class Date

Our example of composition contains three classes—Date (Fig. 10.7), Employee (Fig. 10.8) and EmployeeTest (Fig. 10.9). Class Date (Fig. 10.7) declares int instance variables month and day (lines 7–8) and *auto-implemented property* Year (line 9) to represent a date.

```
 1   // Fig. 10.7: Date.cs
 2   // Date class declaration.
 3   using System;
 4
 5   public class Date
 6   {
 7      private int month; // 1-12
 8      private int day; // 1-31 based on month
 9      public int Year { get; private set; } // auto-implemented property Year
10
11      // constructor: use property Month to confirm proper value for month;
12      // use property Day to confirm proper value for day
13      public Date(int month, int day, int year)
14      {
15         Month = month; // validates month
```

Fig. 10.7 | Date class declaration. (Part 1 of 3.)

```
16          Year = year; // could validate year
17          Day = day; // validates day
18          Console.WriteLine($"Date object constructor for date {this}");
19       }
20
21       // property that gets and sets the month
22       public int Month
23       {
24          get
25          {
26             return month;
27          }
28          private set // make writing inaccessible outside the class
29          {
30             if (value <= 0 || value > 12) // validate month
31             {
32                throw new ArgumentOutOfRangeException(
33                   nameof(value), value, $"{nameof(Month)} must be 1-12");
34             }
35
36             month = value;
37          }
38       }
39
40       // property that gets and sets the day
41       public int Day
42       {
43          get
44          {
45             return day;
46          }
47          private set // make writing inaccessible outside the class
48          {
49             int[] daysPerMonth =
50                {0, 31, 29, 31, 30, 31, 30, 31, 31, 30, 31, 30, 31};
51
52             // check if day in range for month
53             if (value <= 0 || value > daysPerMonth[Month])
54             {
55                throw new ArgumentOutOfRangeException(nameof(value), value,
56                   $"{nameof(Day)} out of range for current month/year");
57             }
58             // check for leap year
59             if (Month == 2 && value == 29 &&
60                !(Year % 400 == 0 || (Year % 4 == 0 && Year % 100 != 0)))
61             {
62                throw new ArgumentOutOfRangeException(nameof(value), value,
63                   $"{nameof(Day)} out of range for current month/year");
64             }
65
66             day = value;
67          }
68       }
```

Fig. 10.7 | Date class declaration. (Part 2 of 3.)

```
69
70      // return a string of the form month/day/year
71      public override string ToString() => $"{Month}/{Day}/{Year}";
72  }
```

Fig. 10.7 | Date class declaration. (Part 3 of 3.)

Constructor

The constructor (lines 13–19) receives three ints. Line 15 invokes property Month's set accessor (lines 28–37) to validate the month—if the value is out-of-range the accessor throws an exception. Line 16 uses property Year to set the year. Since Year is an auto-implemented property, it provides no validation—we're assuming in this example that Year's value is correct. Line 17 uses property Day's set accessor (lines 47–67) to validate and assign the value for day based on the current Month and Year (by using properties Month and Year in turn to obtain the values of month and Year).

The *order of initialization is important*, because property Day's set accessor performs its validation assuming that Month and Year are correct. Line 53 determines whether the day is out of range, based on the number of days in the Month and, if so, throw an exception. Lines 59–60 determine whether the Month is February, the day is 29 and the Year is *not* a leap year (in which case, 29 is out of range) and, if so, throw an exception. If no exceptions are thrown, the value for day is correct and assigned to the instance variable at line 66. Line 18 in the constructor formats the this reference as a string. Since this is a reference to the current Date object, the object's ToString method (line 71) is called *implicitly* to obtain the Date's string representation.

***private set** Accessors*

Class Date uses access modifiers to ensure that *clients* of the class must use the appropriate methods and properties to access private data. In particular, the properties Year, Month and Day declare private set accessors (lines 9, 28 and 47, respectively)—these set accessors can be used only within the class. We declare these private for the same reasons that we declare instance variables private—to simplify code maintenance and control access to the class's data. Although the constructor, method and properties in class Date still have all the advantages of using the set accessors to perform validation, clients of the class must use the class's constructor to initialize the data in a Date object. The get accessors of Year, Month and Day are *implicitly* public—when there's no access modifier before a get or set accessor, the property's access modifier is used.

10.7.2 Class Employee

Class Employee (Fig. 10.8) has public auto-implemented, getter-only properties FirstName, LastName, BirthDate and HireDate. BirthDate and HireDate (lines 7–8) refer to Date objects, demonstrating that *a class can have references to objects of other classes as members*. This, of course, also is true of FirstName and LastName, which refer to String objects. The Employee constructor (lines 11–18) uses its four parameters to initialize the class's properties. When class Employee's ToString method is called, it returns a string containing the string representations of the two Date objects. Each of these strings is obtained with an *implicit* call to the Date class's ToString method.

```
1   // Fig. 10.8: Employee.cs
2   // Employee class with references to other objects.
3   public class Employee
4   {
5      public string FirstName { get; }
6      public string LastName { get; }
7      public Date BirthDate { get; }
8      public Date HireDate { get; }
9
10     // constructor to initialize name, birth date and hire date
11     public Employee(string firstName, string lastName,
12        Date birthDate, Date hireDate)
13     {
14        FirstName = firstName;
15        LastName = lastName;
16        BirthDate = birthDate;
17        HireDate = hireDate;
18     }
19
20     // convert Employee to string format
21     public override string ToString() => $"{LastName}, {FirstName} " +
22        $"Hired: {HireDate}  Birthday: {BirthDate}";
23  }
```

Fig. 10.8 | Employee class with references to other objects.

10.7.3 Class EmployeeTest

Class EmployeeTest (Fig. 10.9) creates two Date objects (lines 9–10) to represent an Employee's birthday and hire date, respectively. Line 11 creates an Employee and initializes its instance variables by passing to the constructor two strings (representing the Employee's first and last names) and two Date objects (representing the birthday and hire date). Line 13 *implicitly* invokes the Employee's ToString method to display the Employee's string representation and demonstrate that the object was initialized properly.

```
1   // Fig. 10.9: EmployeeTest.cs
2   // Composition demonstration.
3   using System;
4
5   class EmployeeTest
6   {
7      static void Main()
8      {
9         var birthday = new Date(7, 24, 1949);
10        var hireDate = new Date(3, 12, 1988);
11        var employee = new Employee("Bob", "Blue", birthday, hireDate);
12
13        Console.WriteLine(employee);
14     }
15  }
```

Fig. 10.9 | Composition demonstration. (Part 1 of 2.)

```
Date object constructor for date 7/24/1949
Date object constructor for date 3/12/1988
Blue, Bob  Hired: 3/12/1988  Birthday: 7/24/1949
```

Fig. 10.9 | Composition demonstration. (Part 2 of 2.)

10.8 Garbage Collection and Destructors

Every object you create uses various system resources, such as memory. In many programming languages, these system resources are reserved for the object's use until they're explicitly released by the programmer. If all the references to the object that manages a resource are lost before the resource is explicitly released, the app can no longer access the resource to release it. This is known as a resource leak.

To avoid resource leaks, we need a disciplined way to give resources back to the system when they're no longer needed. The Common Language Runtime (CLR) performs automatic memory management by using a garbage collector that *reclaims* the memory occupied by objects no longer in use, so the memory can be used for other objects. When there are no more references to an object, the object becomes eligible for destruction. Every object has a special member, called a destructor, that's invoked by the garbage collector to perform termination housekeeping on an object before the garbage collector reclaims the object's memory. A destructor is declared like a parameterless constructor, except that its name is the class name, preceded by a tilde (~), and it has no access modifier in its header. After the garbage collector calls the object's destructor, the object becomes eligible for garbage collection. The memory for such an object can be reclaimed by the garbage collector.

Memory leaks, which are common in other languages such as C and C++ (because memory is *not* automatically reclaimed in those languages), are less likely in C#, but some can still happen in subtle ways. Other types of resource leaks can occur. For example, an app could open a file on disk to modify its contents. If the app does not close the file, no other app can modify (or possibly even use) the file until the app that opened it terminates.

A problem with the garbage collector is it doesn't guarantee that it will perform its tasks at a specified time. Therefore, the garbage collector may call the destructor any time after the object becomes eligible for destruction, and may reclaim the memory any time after the destructor executes. In fact, it's possible that neither will happen before the app terminates. Thus, it's unclear whether, or when, the destructor will be called. For this reason, destructors are rarely used.

Software Engineering Observation 10.9

A class that uses resources, such as files on disk, should provide a method to eventually release the resources. Many Framework Class Library classes provide Close *or* Dispose *methods for this purpose. Section 13.6 introduces the* Dispose *method, which is then used in many later examples.* Close *methods are typically used with objects that are associated with files (Chapter 17) and other types of so-called streams of data.*

10.9 static Class Members

Every object has its *own* copy of its class's instance variables. In certain cases, only one copy of a particular variable should be *shared* by all objects of a class. A **static** variable (or property) is used in such cases. A static variable or property represents classwide information—all objects of the class share the same piece of data. The declaration of a static variable or property begins with the keyword static.

Let's motivate static data with an example. Suppose that we have a video game with Martians and other space creatures. Each Martian tends to be brave and willing to attack other space creatures when it's aware that there are at least four other Martians present. If fewer than five Martians are present, each Martian becomes cowardly. Thus each Martian needs to know the martianCount. We could endow class Martian with martianCount as an instance variable (or as a property, but we'll use an instance variable for discussion purposes here). If we do this, every Martian will have a separate copy of the instance variable, and every time we create a new Martian, we'll have to update the instance variable martianCount in every Martian. This wastes space on redundant copies, wastes time updating the separate copies and is error prone. Instead, we declare martianCount to be static, making martianCount classwide data. Every Martian can access the martianCount, but only one copy of the static martianCount is maintained. This saves space. We save time by having the Martian constructor increment the static martianCount—there's *only one copy*, so we do not have to increment separate copies of martianCount for each Martian object.

Software Engineering Observation 10.10

Use a static variable when all objects of a class must share the same copy of the variable.

static *Variable Scope*

The scope of a static variable is the body of its class. A class's public static members can be accessed by qualifying the member name with the class name and the member access (.) operator, as in Math.PI. A class's private static class members can be accessed *only* through the class's methods and properties. To access a private static member from outside its class, a public static method or property can be provided.

Common Programming Error 10.2

It's a compilation error to access or invoke a static member by referencing it through an instance of the class, like a non-static member.

Software Engineering Observation 10.11

static variables, methods and properties exist, and can be used, even if no objects of that class have been instantiated. static members are available as soon as the class is loaded into memory at execution time.

static *Methods and Non-static Class Members*

A static method (or property) cannot access non-static class members directly, because a static method (or property) can be called even when *no* objects of the class exist. For the same reason, this cannot be used in a static method—the this reference always refers to a *specific object* of the class. When a static method is called, it does not know which object to manipulate and there might *not* be *any* objects of its class in memory.

Class *Employee*

Our next app contains classes Employee (Fig. 10.10) and EmployeeTest (Fig. 10.11). Class Employee declares private static auto-implemented property Count to maintain a count of the number of Employee objects that have been created. We declare Count's set accessor private, because only class Employee should be able to modify Count's value. Count is a static auto-implemented property, so the compiler creates a corresponding private static variable that Count manages. When you declare a static variable and do not initialize it, the compiler initializes it to the type's default value (in this case, 0).

When Employee objects exist, Count can be used in any method or property of class Employee—this example increments Count in the constructor (line 19). Client code can access the Count with the expression Employee.Count, which evaluates to the number of Employee objects that have been created.

```csharp
 1  // Fig. 10.10: Employee.cs
 2  // static property used to maintain a count of the number of
 3  // Employee objects that have been created.
 4  using System;
 5
 6  public class Employee
 7  {
 8     public static int Count { get; private set; } // objects in memory
 9
10     public string FirstName { get; }
11     public string LastName { get; }
12
13     // initialize employee, add 1 to static Count and
14     // output string indicating that constructor was called
15     public Employee(string firstName, string lastName)
16     {
17        FirstName = firstName;
18        LastName = lastName;
19        ++Count; // increment static count of employees
20        Console.WriteLine("Employee constructor: " +
21           $"{FirstName} {LastName}; Count = {Count}");
22     }
23  }
```

Fig. 10.10 | static property used to maintain a count of the number of Employee objects that have been created.

Class *EmployeeTest*
EmployeeTest method Main (Fig. 10.11) instantiates two Employee objects (lines 14–15). When each object's constructor is invoked, lines 17–18 of Fig. 10.10 assign the Employee's first name and last name to properties FirstName and LastName. These two statements do *not* make copies of the original string arguments.

Software Engineering Observation 10.12
Actually, string objects in C# are immutable—they cannot be modified after they're created. Therefore, it's safe to have many references to one string. This is not normally the case for objects of most other classes. If string objects are immutable, you might wonder why we're able to use operators + and += to concatenate strings. String-concatenation operations actually result in a new string object containing the concatenated values. The original string objects are not modified.

```
1   // Fig. 10.11: EmployeeTest.cs
2   // static member demonstration.
3   using System;
4
5   class EmployeeTest
6   {
7      static void Main()
8      {
9         // show that Count is 0 before creating Employees
10        Console.WriteLine(
11           $"Employees before instantiation: {Employee.Count}");
12
13        // create two Employees; Count should become 2
14        var e1 = new Employee("Susan", "Baker");
15        var e2 = new Employee("Bob", "Blue");
16
17        // show that Count is 2 after creating two Employees
18        Console.WriteLine(
19           $"\nEmployees after instantiation: {Employee.Count}");
20
21        // get names of Employees
22        Console.WriteLine($"\nEmployee 1: {e1.FirstName} {e1.LastName}");
23        Console.WriteLine($"Employee 2: {e2.FirstName} {e2.LastName}");
24
25        // in this example, there is only one reference to each Employee,
26        // so the following statements cause the CLR to mark each
27        // Employee object as being eligible for garbage collection
28        e1 = null; // mark object referenced by e1 as no longer needed
29        e2 = null; // mark object referenced by e2 as no longer needed
30     }
31  }
```

```
Employees before instantiation: 0
Employee constructor: Susan Baker; Count = 1
Employee constructor: Bob Blue; Count = 2

Employees after instantiation: 2

Employee 1: Susan Baker
Employee 2: Bob Blue
```

Fig. 10.11 | static member demonstration.

Lines 18–19 of Fig. 10.11 display the updated Count. When Main has finished using the two Employee objects, references e1 and e2 are set to null at lines 28–29, so they no longer refer to the objects that were instantiated in lines 14–15. The objects become *eligible for destruction* because there are *no more references to them*. After the objects' destructors are called, the objects become *eligible* for garbage collection. (Note that we did not need to set e1 and e2 are set to null here as they're local variables—when a local variable of a reference type goes out of scope, the object's reference count is decremented automatically.)

Eventually, the garbage collector might reclaim the memory for these objects (or the operating system will reclaim it when the app terminates). C# does not guarantee when, or even whether, the garbage collector will execute. When the garbage collector does run, it's possible that no objects or only a subset of the eligible objects will be collected.

10.10 `readonly` Instance Variables

The principle of least privilege is fundamental to good software engineering. In the context of an app, the principle states that *code should be granted the amount of privilege and access needed to accomplish its designated task, but no more*. Let's see how this principle applies to instance variables.

Some instance variables need to be modifiable, and some do not. In Section 8.4, we used keyword `const` to declare a constant, which must be initialized in its declaration—all objects of the class have the same value for that constant. Suppose, however, we want a constant that can have a *different* value for each object of a class. For this purpose, C# provides keyword `readonly` to specify that an instance variable of an object is *not* modifiable and that any attempt to modify it *after* the object is constructed is an error. For example,

```
private readonly int Increment;
```

declares `readonly` instance variable `Increment` of type `int`. Like a constant, a `readonly` variable's identifier uses Pascal Case by convention. Although `readonly` instance variables can be initialized when they're declared, this isn't required. A `readonly` variable should be initialized *by each* of the class's constructors or in the variable's declaration. Each constructor can assign values to a `readonly` instance variable multiple times—the variable doesn't become unmodifiable until *after* the constructor completes execution. If a constructor does not initialize the `readonly` variable, the variable uses the same default value as any other instance variable (0 for numeric simple types, `false` for `bool` type and `null` for reference types)—these values actually are set before a constructor executes and can be overwritten by the called constructor.

Software Engineering Observation 10.13

Declaring an instance variable as `readonly` helps enforce the principle of least privilege. If an instance variable should not be modified after the object is constructed, declare it to be `readonly` to prevent modification.

`const` members must be assigned values at compile time. Therefore, `const` members can be initialized *only* with other constant values, such as integers, `string` literals, characters and other `const` members. Constant members with values that cannot be determined at compile time—such as constants that are initialized with the result of a method call—must be declared with keyword `readonly`, so they can be initialized at *execution time*. Variables that are `readonly` can be initialized with more complex expressions, such as an array initializer or a method call that returns a value or a reference to an object.

Common Programming Error 10.3

Attempting to modify a `readonly` instance variable anywhere but in its declaration or the object's constructors is a compilation error.

Error-Prevention Tip 10.1

Attempts to modify a `readonly` instance variable are caught at compilation time rather than causing execution-time errors. It's always preferable to get bugs out at compile time, if possible, rather than allowing them to slip through to execution time (where studies have found that repairing bugs is often much more costly).

Software Engineering Observation 10.14

If a readonly instance variable is initialized to a constant only in its declaration, it's not necessary to have a separate copy of the instance variable for every object of the class. The variable should be declared const instead. Constants declared with const are implicitly static, so there will only be one copy for the entire class.

C# 6 Getter-Only Auto-Implemented Properties and readonly

Section 8.6.1 introduced C# 6's getter-only auto-implemented properties. When an auto-implemented property has only a get accessor, the property can be used only to read the value, so the compiler implicitly declares the corresponding private instance variable as readonly. Getter-only auto-implemented properties can be initialized in their declarations or in constructors.

10.11 Class View and Object Browser

Now that we have introduced key concepts of object-oriented programming, we present two Visual Studio features that facilitate the design of object-oriented apps—the **Class View** and the **Object Browser**.

10.11.1 Using the **Class View** Window

The **Class View** displays the fields, methods and properties for all classes in a project. Select **View > Class View** to display the **Class View** as a tab in the same position within the IDE as the **Solution Explorer**. Figure 10.12 shows the **Class View** for the Time1 project of Fig. 10.1 (class Time1) and Fig. 10.2 (class Time1Test).

Fig. 10.12 | Class View of class Time1 (Fig. 10.1) and class Time1Test (Fig. 10.2).

The view follows a hierarchical structure, positioning the project name (Time1) as the *root* and including a series of nodes that represent the classes, variables, methods and properties in the project. If a appears to the left of a node, that node can be *expanded* to show other nodes. If a

appears to the left of a node, that node can be *collapsed*. According to the **Class View**, project Time1 contains class Time1 and class Time1Test as children. When class Time1 is selected, the class's members appear in the lower half of the window. Class Time1 contains methods SetTime, ToString and ToUniversalString, indicated by purple boxes

and public properties Hour, Minute and Second, indicated by wrench icons

If a class has any private members, those members' icons contain small padlocks. Both class Time1 and class Time1Test contain the **Base Types** node. If you expand this node, you'll see class Object in each case, because each class *inherits* from class System.Object—we discuss this concept in Chapter 11.

10.11.2 Using the Object Browser

Visual Studio's **Object Browser** lists all classes in the .NET library. You can use the **Object Browser** to learn about the functionality provided by a specific class. To open the **Object Browser**, select **View > Object Browser**. Figure 10.13 depicts the **Object Browser** when the user navigates to the Math class in namespace System. To do this, we expanded the node for mscorlib (Microsoft Core Library) in the upper-left pane of the **Object Browser**, then expanded its subnode for System. The most common classes from the System namespace, such as System.Math, are in mscorlib.

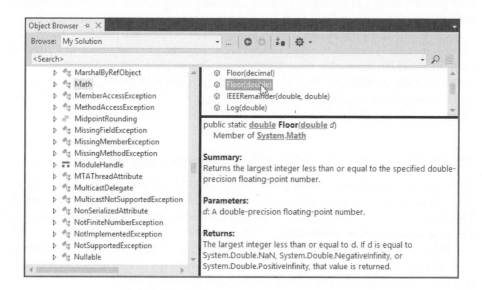

Fig. 10.13 | **Object Browser** for class Math.

The **Object Browser** lists all methods provided by class Math in the upper-right pane—this offers you "instant access" to information regarding the functionality of various objects. Clicking the name of a member in the upper-right pane displays a description of that member in the lower-right pane. The **Object Browser** can be used to quickly learn about a class or one of its methods. You also can view the complete description of a class or a method in the online documentation by selecting the type or member in the **Object Browser** and pressing *F1*.

10.12 Object Initializers

Object initializers allow you to create an object and initialize its public properties (and public instance variables, if any) in the same statement. This can be useful when a class does not provide an appropriate constructor to meet your needs, but does provide a constructor that can be called with no arguments and properties that you can use to set the class's data. The following statements demonstrate object initializers using the class Time2 from Fig. 10.5.

```
// create a Time2 object and initialize its properties
var aTime = new Time2 {Hour = 14, Minute = 30, Second = 12};

// create a Time2 object and initialize only its Minute property
var anotherTime = new Time2 {Minute = 45};
```

The first statement creates a Time2 object (aTime), initializes it with class Time2's constructor that can be called with no arguments, then uses an object initializer to set its Hour, Minute and Second properties. Notice that new Time2 is immediately followed by an object-initializer list—a comma-separated list in curly braces ({ }) of properties and their values. Each property name can appear only *once* in the object-initializer list. The object initializer executes the property initializers in the order in which they appear.

The second statement creates a new Time2 object (anotherTime), initializes it with class Time2's constructor that can be called with no arguments, then sets only its Minute property using an object initializer. When the Time2 constructor is called with no arguments, it initializes the time to midnight. The object initializer then sets each specified property to the supplied value. In this case, the Minute property is set to 45. The Hour and Second properties retain their default values, because no values are specified for them in the object initializer.

10.13 Operator Overloading; Introducing struct

Method-call notation can be cumbersome for certain kinds of operations, such as arithmetic. In these cases, it would be convenient to use C#'s rich set of built-in operators instead. This section shows how to create operators that work with objects of your own types—via a process called operator overloading.

You can overload most operators. Some are overloaded more frequently than others, especially the arithmetic operators, such as + and -, where operator notation is more natural than calling methods. For a list of overloadable operators, see

```
https://msdn.microsoft.com/library/8edha89s
```

10.13.1 Creating Value Types with struct

To demonstrate operator overloading, we'll define type ComplexNumber (Section 10.13.2). Complex numbers have the form

$$realPart + imaginaryPart * \texttt{i}$$

where i is $\sqrt{-1}$. Like integers and floating-point numbers, complex numbers are arithmetic types that are commonly used in calculations. As you know, C#'s simple numeric types are *value types*. To mimic the simple numeric types, we'll define ComplexNumber as a value type by using a struct (short for "structure") rather than a class. C#'s simple types like int and double are actually aliases for struct types—an int is defined by the struct System.Int32, a long by System.Int64, a double by System.Double and so on. The operator overloading techniques shown in Section 10.13.2 also can be applied to classes.

When to Declare a struct Type

Microsoft recommends using classes for most new types, but recommends a struct if:

- the type represents a single value—a complex number represents one number that happens to have a real part and an imaginary part.

- the size of an object is 16 bytes or smaller—we'll represent a complex number's real and imaginary parts using two doubles (a total of 16 bytes).

For the complete list of struct recommendations, see

```
https://msdn.microsoft.com/library/ms229017
```

10.13.2 Value Type ComplexNumber

Value type ComplexNumber (Fig. 10.14) overloads the plus (+), minus (-) and multiplication (*) operators to enable programs to add, subtract and multiply instances of class ComplexNumber using common mathematical notation. Lines 9–10 define getter-only auto-implemented properties for the ComplexNumber's Real and Imaginary components.

```csharp
1   // Fig. 10.14: ComplexNumber.cs
2   // Value type that overloads operators for adding, subtracting
3   // and multiplying complex numbers.
4   using System;
5
6   public struct ComplexNumber
7   {
8       // read-only properties that get the real and imaginary components
9       public double Real { get; }
10      public double Imaginary { get; }
11
12      // constructor
13      public ComplexNumber(double real, double imaginary)
14      {
```

Fig. 10.14 | Value type that overloads operators for adding, subtracting and multiplying complex numbers. (Part 1 of 2.)

```
15              Real = real;
16              Imaginary = imaginary;
17          }
18
19          // return string representation of ComplexNumber
20          public override string ToString() =>
21              $"({Real} {(Imaginary < 0 ? "-" : "+")} {Math.Abs(Imaginary)}i)";
22
23          // overload the addition operator
24          public static ComplexNumber operator+(ComplexNumber x, ComplexNumber y)
25          {
26              return new ComplexNumber(x.Real + y.Real,
27                  x.Imaginary + y.Imaginary);
28          }
29
30          // overload the subtraction operator
31          public static ComplexNumber operator-(ComplexNumber x, ComplexNumber y)
32          {
33              return new ComplexNumber(x.Real - y.Real,
34                  x.Imaginary - y.Imaginary );
35          }
36
37          // overload the multiplication operator
38          public static ComplexNumber operator*(ComplexNumber x, ComplexNumber y)
39          {
40              return new ComplexNumber(
41                  x.Real * y.Real - x.Imaginary * y.Imaginary,
42                  x.Real * y.Imaginary + y.Real * x.Imaginary);
43          }
44      }
```

Fig. 10.14 | Value type that overloads operators for adding, subtracting and multiplying complex numbers. (Part 2 of 2.)

Constructor

Lines 13–17 define a ComplexNumber constructor that receives parameters to initialize the Real and Imaginary properties. Unlike a class, you cannot define a parameterless constructor for a struct—the compiler always provides a default constructor that initializes the struct's instance variables to their default values. Also, structs cannot specify initial values in instance variable or property declarations.

Overloaded Operators

Lines 24–28 overload the plus operator (+) to add ComplexNumbers. Keyword **operator**, followed by an operator symbol (such as +), indicates that a method overloads the specified operator. Overloaded operator methods are *required* to be public and static.

Methods that overload binary operators must take two arguments—the *first* is the *left* operand and the *second* is the *right* operand. Class ComplexNumber's overloaded + operator takes two ComplexNumbers as arguments and returns a ComplexNumber that represents the sum of the arguments. The method's body adds the ComplexNumbers and returns the result as a new ComplexNumber.

We do *not* modify the contents of either of the original operands passed as arguments x and y. This matches our intuitive sense of how this operator should behave—adding two numbers does not modify either of the original values. Lines 31–43 declare similar overloaded operators to subtract and multiply ComplexNumbers.

Software Engineering Observation 10.15

Overload operators to perform the same function or similar functions on objects as the operators perform on objects of simple types. Avoid nonintuitive use of operators.

Software Engineering Observation 10.16

At least one parameter of an overloaded operator method must be of the type in which the operator is overloaded. This prevents you from changing how operators work on simple types.

Software Engineering Observation 10.17

Though you cannot overload the arithmetic assignment operators (e.g., += and -=), C# allows you to use them with any type that declares the corresponding arithmetic operator (e.g., + and -).

10.13.3 Class ComplexTest

Class ComplexTest (Fig. 10.15) demonstrates the overloaded ComplexNumber operators +, - and *. Lines 10–21 prompt the user to enter the real and imaginary parts of two complex numbers, then use this input to create two ComplexNumber objects for use in calculations.

```
1   // Fig. 10.15: ComplexTest.cs
2   // Overloading operators for complex numbers.
3   using System;
4
5   class ComplexTest
6   {
7      static void Main()
8      {
9         // prompt the user to enter the first complex number
10        Console.Write("Enter the real part of complex number x: ");
11        double realPart = double.Parse(Console.ReadLine());
12        Console.Write("Enter the imaginary part of complex number x: ");
13        double imaginaryPart = double.Parse(Console.ReadLine());
14        var x = new ComplexNumber(realPart, imaginaryPart);
15
16        // prompt the user to enter the second complex number
17        Console.Write("\nEnter the real part of complex number y: ");
18        realPart = double.Parse(Console.ReadLine());
19        Console.Write("Enter the imaginary part of complex number y: ");
20        imaginaryPart = double.Parse(Console.ReadLine());
21        var y = new ComplexNumber(realPart, imaginaryPart);
22
23        // display the results of calculations with x and y
24        Console.WriteLine();
```

Fig. 10.15 | Overloading operators for complex numbers. (Part 1 of 2.)

```
25          Console.WriteLine($"{x} + {y} = {x + y}");
26          Console.WriteLine($"{x} - {y} = {x - y}");
27          Console.WriteLine($"{x} * {y} = {x * y}");
28      }
29  }
```

```
Enter the real part of complex number x: 2
Enter the imaginary part of complex number x: 4

Enter the real part of complex number y: 4
Enter the imaginary part of complex number y: -2

(2 + 4i) + (4 - 2i) = (6 + 2i)
(2 + 4i) - (4 - 2i) = (-2 + 6i)
(2 + 4i) * (4 - 2i) = (16 + 12i)
```

Fig. 10.15 | Overloading operators for complex numbers. (Part 2 of 2.)

Lines 25–27 add, subtract and multiply x and y with the overloaded operators (in string-interpolation expressions), then output the results. In line 25, we use the + operator with ComplexNumber operands x and y. Without operator overloading, the expression x + y wouldn't make sense—the compiler wouldn't know how to add two ComplexNumber objects. This expression makes sense here because we've defined the + operator for two ComplexNumbers in lines 24–28 of Fig. 10.14. When the two ComplexNumbers are "added" in line 25 of Fig. 10.15, this invokes the operator+ declaration, passing the left operand as the first argument and the right operand as the second argument. When we use the subtraction and multiplication operators in lines 26–27, their respective overloaded operator declarations are invoked similarly.

Each calculation's result is the new ComplexNumber object returned by the corresponding overloaded operator method. When this new object is placed in a string-interpolation expression, its ToString method (Fig. 10.14, lines 20–21) is implicitly invoked. The expression x + y in line 25 of Fig. 10.15 could be rewritten to explicitly invoke the ToString method of the resulting ComplexNumber object, as in:

```
(x + y).ToString()
```

10.14 Time Class Case Study: Extension Methods

You can use extension methods to add functionality to an existing type without modifying the type's source code. You saw in Section 9.3.3 that LINQ's capabilities are implemented as extension methods. Figure 10.16 uses extension methods to add two new methods to class Time2 (Section 10.5)—DisplayTime and AddHours.

```
1   // Fig. 10.16: TimeExtensionsTest.cs
2   // Demonstrating extension methods.
3   using System;
4
5   class TimeExtensionsTest
6   {
```

Fig. 10.16 | Demonstrating extension methods. (Part 1 of 2.)

```
 7      static void Main()
 8      {
 9         var myTime = new Time2(); // call Time2 constructor
10         myTime.SetTime(11, 34, 15); // set the time to 11:34:15
11
12         // test the DisplayTime extension method
13         Console.Write("Use the DisplayTime extension method: ");
14         myTime.DisplayTime();
15
16         // test the AddHours extension method
17         Console.Write("Add 5 hours with the AddHours extension method: ");
18         var timeAdded = myTime.AddHours(5); // add five hours
19         timeAdded.DisplayTime(); // display the new Time2 object
20
21         // add hours and display the time in one statement
22         Console.Write("Add 15 hours with the AddHours extension method: ");
23         myTime.AddHours(15).DisplayTime(); // add hours and display time
24
25         // use fully qualified extension-method name to display the time
26         Console.Write("Use fully qualified extension-method name: ");
27         TimeExtensions.DisplayTime(myTime);
28      }
29   }
30
31   // extension-methods class
32   static class TimeExtensions
33   {
34      // display the Time2 object in console
35      public static void DisplayTime(this Time2 aTime)
36      {
37         Console.WriteLine(aTime.ToString());
38      }
39
40      // add the specified number of hours to the time
41      // and return a new Time2 object
42      public static Time2 AddHours(this Time2 aTime, int hours)
43      {
44         // create a new Time2 object
45         var newTime = new Time2() {
46            Minute = aTime.Minute, Second = aTime.Second};
47
48         // add the specified number of hours to the given time
49         newTime.Hour = (aTime.Hour + hours) % 24;
50
51         return newTime; // return the new Time2 object
52      }
53   }
```

```
Use the DisplayTime extension method: 11:34:15 AM
Add 5 hours with the AddHours extension method: 4:34:15 PM
Add 15 hours with the AddHours extension method: 2:34:15 AM
Use fully qualified extension-method name: 11:34:15 AM
```

Fig. 10.16 | Demonstrating extension methods. (Part 2 of 2.)

Extension Method `DisplayTime`

The extension method `DisplayTime` (lines 35–38) displays the `string` representation of the time in the console window. The key new feature of method `DisplayTime` is the `this` keyword that precedes the `Time2` parameter in the method header (line 35)—this notifies the compiler that `DisplayTime` is an extension method for an existing class (`Time2`). The type of an extension method's first parameter specifies the type of object on which you can call the method—for this reason, each extension method *must* define at least one parameter. Also, extension methods must be defined as `static` methods in a `static` class such as `TimeExtensions` (lines 32–53). A `static` class can contain only `static` members and cannot be instantiated.

Calling Extension Method `DisplayTime`

Line 14 uses `Time2` object `myTime` to call the `DisplayTime` extension method. Note that we do not provide an argument to the method call. The compiler implicitly passes the object that calls the method (`myTime`) as the extension method's first argument. This allows you to call `DisplayTime` as if it were a `Time2` instance method. In fact, *IntelliSense* displays extension methods with the class's instance methods and identifies them with a distinct icon

The down-arrow in the icon denotes an extension method. Also, when you select an extension method in the *IntelliSense* window, the tool tip that describes the method includes the text **(extension)** for each extension method.

Extension Method `AddHours`

Lines 42–52 of Fig. 10.16 declare the `AddHours` extension method. Again, the `this` keyword in the first parameter's declaration indicates that `AddHours` can be called on a `Time2` object. The second parameter is an `int` value specifying the number of hours to add to the time. The `AddHours` method returns a new `Time2` object with the specified number of hours added.

Lines 45–46 create the new `Time2` object and use an object initializer to set its `Minute` and `Second` properties to the corresponding values in the parameter `aTime`—these are not modified when we add hours to the time. Line 49 adds the second argument's number of hours to the original `Time2` object's `Hour` property, then uses the `%` operator to ensure the value remains in the range 0–23. The result is assigned to the new `Time2` object's `Hour` property. Line 51 returns the new `Time2` object to the caller.

Calling Extension Method `AddHours`

Line 18 calls the `AddHours` extension method to add five hours to the `myTime` object's hour value. Note that the method call specifies only one argument—the number of hours to add. Again, the compiler implicitly passes the object that's used to call the method (`myTime`) as the extension method's first argument. The `Time2` object returned by `AddHours` is assigned to a local variable (`timeAdded`) and displayed in the console using the `DisplayTime` extension method (line 19).

Calling Both Extension Methods in a Single Statement

Line 23 uses both extension methods (`DisplayTime` and `AddHours`) in a single statement to add 15 hours to the original `myTime` and display the result in the console. Multiple method calls in the same statement are known as cascaded method calls. When a method returns an object, you can follow the method call with a member access operator (.) then call a method on the object that was returned. The methods are called from left to right. In line 23, the `DisplayTime` method is called on the `Time2` object returned by method `AddHours`. This eliminates the need to assign the object returned by `AddHours` to a variable, then call `DisplayTime` in a separate statement.

Calling an Extension Method With Its Fully Qualified Name

Line 27 calls extension method `DisplayTime` using its fully qualified name—the name of the class in which the extension method is defined (`TimeExtensions`), followed by the member access operator (.), the method name (`DisplayTime`) and its argument list. Note in line 27 that the call to `DisplayTime` passes a `Time2` object as an argument to the method. When using the fully qualified method name, you must specify an argument for extension method's first parameter. This use of the extension method uses the syntax of a `static` method call.

Extension Method Cautions

If a type for which you declare an extension method already defines an instance method with the same name and a compatible signature, the instance method will shadow (i.e., hide) the extension method. Also, if a predefined type is later updated to include an instance method that shadows an extension method, the compiler does not report any errors and the extension method does not appear in *IntelliSense*.

10.15 Wrap-Up

In this chapter, we discussed additional class concepts. The time examples concluded with a complete class declaration consisting of `private` data, overloaded `public` constructors for initialization flexibility, properties for manipulating the class's data and methods that returned `string` representations of a time in two different formats.

We mentioned that the `this` reference is used implicitly in a class's non-`static` methods and properties to access the current object's instance variables and other non-`static` members. You saw explicit uses of the `this` reference to access the class's members (including shadowed instance variables) and how to use keyword `this` in a constructor to call another constructor of the same class.

You saw that composition enables a class to have references to objects of other classes as members. We discussed C#'s garbage-collection capability and how it reclaims the memory of objects that are no longer used. We motivated the notion of `static` class variables and demonstrated how to declare and use `static` variables and methods in your own classes. You saw how to declare and initialize `readonly` variables and we discussed that the compiler automatically marks as `readonly` the instance variable for a getter-only auto-implemented variable.

We also showed how to use Visual Studio's **Class View** and **Object Browser** windows to navigate the classes of the Framework Class Library and your own apps to discover information about those classes. You initialized an object's properties as you created it with an object initializer. We showed how to define the behavior of the built-in operators on objects of your own classes with operator overloading, and demonstrated how to create your own value types with `struct`. Finally, we showed how to use extension methods to add capabilities to existing types without modifying their source code.

In the next chapter, you'll learn about inheritance. You'll see that all classes in C# are related directly or indirectly to the `object` root class and begin to understand how inheritance enables you to build related classes faster.

Summary

Section 10.2.1 `Time1` Class Declaration

- The `public` methods of a class are part of the public services or the public interface that the class provides to its clients.
- Methods and properties that modify the values of `private` variables should verify that the intended new values are valid.
- A class's methods and properties can throw exceptions to indicate invalid data.

Section 10.2.2 Using Class `Time1`

- The actual data representation used within the class is of no concern to the class's clients. This allows you to change the implementation of the class. Clients could use the same `public` methods and properties to get the same results without being aware of this change.
- Clients are neither aware of, nor involved in, a class's implementation. Clients generally care about *what* the class does but not *how* the class does it.

Section 10.3 Controlling Access to Members

- Access modifiers `public` and `private` control access to a class's variables, methods and properties. A class's `private` variables, methods and properties are not directly accessible to the class's clients.
- If a client attempts to use the `private` members of another class, the compiler generates error messages stating that these `private` members are not accessible.

Section 10.4 Referring to the Current Object's Members with the `this` Reference

- Every object can access a reference to itself with keyword `this`. When a non-`static` method is called for a particular object, the method's body implicitly uses keyword `this` to refer to the object's instance variables, other methods and properties.
- If a method contains a local variable with the same name as a field, that method will refer to the local variable rather than the field. However, a non-`static` method can use the `this` reference to refer to a hidden instance variable explicitly.
- Avoid method-parameter names or local-variable names that conflict with field names. This helps prevent subtle, hard-to-locate bugs.

Section 10.5 `Time` Class Case Study: Overloaded Constructors

- To overload constructors, provide multiple constructor declarations with different signatures.

Section 10.5.1 Class `Time2` with Overloaded Constructors

- Following the constructor header with the constructor initializer : `this` (*args*) invokes the matching overloaded constructor in the same class.
- Constructor initializers are a popular way to reuse initialization code provided by one of the class's constructors rather than defining similar code in another constructor's body.
- When one object of a class has a reference to another object of the same class, the first object can access all the second object's data and methods (including those that are `private`).

- When implementing a method of a class, use the class's properties to access the class's `private` data. This simplifies code maintenance and reduces the likelihood of errors.
- The `ArgumentOutOfRangeException` constructor with three arguments lets you specify the name of the item that's out of range, the value that was out of range and an error message.

Section 10.6 Default and Parameterless Constructors
- Every class must have at least one constructor. If there are no constructors in a class's declaration, the compiler creates a default constructor for the class.
- The compiler will not create a default constructor for a class that explicitly declares at least one constructor. In this case, if you want to be able to invoke the constructor with no arguments, you must declare a parameterless constructor.

Section 10.7 Composition
- A class can have objects of value types or references to objects of other classes as members. Such a capability is called composition and is sometimes referred to as a *has-a* relationship.

Section 10.8 Garbage Collection and Destructors
- Every object you create uses various system resources, such as memory. The CLR performs automatic memory management by using a garbage collector to reclaim the memory occupied by objects that are no longer in use.
- The destructor is invoked by the garbage collector to perform termination housekeeping on an object before the garbage collector reclaims the object's memory.
- Memory leaks, which are common in other languages like C and C++ (because memory is not automatically reclaimed in those languages), are less likely in C#.
- A problem with the garbage collector is that it's not guaranteed to perform its tasks at a specified time. Therefore, the garbage collector may call the destructor any time after the object becomes eligible for destruction, making it unclear when, or whether, the destructor will be called.

Section 10.9 `static` Class Members
- A `static` variable represents classwide information—all objects of the class share the variable.
- The scope of a `static` variable is the body of its class. A class's `public` `static` members can be accessed by qualifying the member name with the class name and the member access (.) operator.
- Static class members exist even when no objects of the class exist—they're available as soon as the class is loaded into memory at execution time.
- String objects in C# are immutable—they cannot be modified after they're created. Therefore, it's safe to have many references to one `string` object.
- A method declared `static` cannot access non-static class members directly, because a `static` method can be called even when no objects of the class exist. For the same reason, the `this` reference cannot be used in a `static` method.

Section 10.10 `readonly` Instance Variables
- The principle of least privilege is fundamental to good software engineering. In the context of an app, the principle states that code should be granted only the amount of privilege and access needed to accomplish its designated task, but no more.
- Any attempt to modify a `readonly` instance variable after its object is constructed is an error.
- Although `readonly` instance variables can be initialized when they're declared, this is not required. A `readonly` variable can be initialized by each of the class's constructors.

- Members that are declared as const must be assigned values at compile time. Constant members with values that cannot be determined at compile time must be declared with keyword readonly, so they can be initialized at execution time.

- When an auto-implemented property has only a get accessor, the property can be used only to read the value, so the compiler implicitly declares the corresponding private instance variable as readonly.

Section 10.11.1 Using the Class View Window

- The Class View displays the fields, methods and properties for all classes in a project. The view follows a hierarchical structure, positioning the project name as the root and including a series of nodes that represent the classes, fields, methods and properties in the project.

Section 10.11.2 Using the Object Browser

- The Object Browser lists all classes of the Framework Class Library. The Object Browser can be a quick mechanism to learn about a class or method of a class.

Section 10.12 Object Initializers

- Object initializers allow you to create an object and initialize its public properties (and public instance variables, if any) in the same statement.

- An object-initializer list is a comma-separated list in curly braces ({}) of properties (and public instance variables, if any) and their values.

- Each property and instance variable name can appear only once in the object-initializer list.

- An object initializer first calls the class's constructor, then sets in the order in which they appear the value of each property and variable specified in the object-initializer list.

Section 10.13 Operator Overloading; Introducing struct

- Method-call notation is cumbersome for certain kinds of classes, especially mathematical classes. Sometimes, it's convenient to use C#'s built-in operators to specify object manipulations.

Section 10.13.1 Creating Value Types with struct

- You can define your own value types as structs.

- C#'s simple types like int and double are actually aliases for struct types.

- Microsoft recommends using classes for most new types, but recommends a struct if: the type represents a single value and the size of an object is 16 bytes or smaller.

Section 10.13.2 Value Type ComplexNumber

- Keyword operator, followed by an operator, indicates that a method overloads the specified operator. Methods that overload binary operators must be declared static and must take two arguments. The first argument is the left operand, and the second is the right operand.

- Overload operators to perform the same function or similar functions on class objects as the operators perform on objects of simple types. Avoid nonintuitive use of operators.

Section 10.14 Time Class Case Study: Extension Methods

- Extension methods add functionality to a type without modifying the types's source code.

- LINQ capabilities are implemented as extension methods.

- Preceding an object parameter that's the first parameter in the method header with the this keyword indicates that the method extends an existing type. The compiler uses this information to add code into the compiled program that enables extension methods to work with existing types.

- The type of an extension method's first parameter specifies the type that you're extending.
- Extension methods must be defined as `static` methods in a `static` class.
- The compiler implicitly passes the object that's used to call the method as the extension method's first argument. This allows you to call an extension method as if it were an instance method of the extended class.
- *IntelliSense* displays extension methods with the extended class's instance methods and identifies them with a distinct icon.
- Cascaded method calls are called from left to right.
- An extension method's fully qualified name is the name of the class in which the extension method is defined, followed by the name of the method and its argument list. When using the fully qualified method name, you must specify an argument for first parameter.
- If the type being extended defines an instance method with the same name as your extension method and a compatible signature, the instance method shadows the extension method.

Terminology

`ArgumentOutOfRangeException` class
Class View
classwide information
composition
constructor initializer
data representation
destructor
eligible for destruction
eligible for garbage collection
extension method
garbage collector
has-a relationship
immutable
memory leak
nameof operator
Object Browser
object initializer

object-initializer list
`operator` keyword
operator overloading
overloaded constructors
parameterless constructor
principle of least privilege
`public` interface
`public` service
`readonly` instance variable
resource leak
service of a class
`static` variable
termination housekeeping
`this` keyword
throw an exception
unmodifiable variable

Self-Review Exercises

10.1 Fill in the blanks in each of the following statements:
a) The `public` members of a class are also known as the class's _____ or _____.
b) If a method contains a local variable with the same name as one of its class's fields, the local variable _____ the field in that method's scope.
c) The _____ is called by the garbage collector before it reclaims an object's memory.
d) If a class declares constructors, the compiler will not create a(n) _____.
e) An object's _____ method can be called implicitly when an object appears in code where a `string` is needed.
f) Composition is sometimes referred to as a(n) _____ relationship.
g) A(n) _____ variable represents classwide information that's shared by all the objects of the class.
h) The _____ states that code should be granted only the amount of access needed to accomplish its designated task.

      i)   Declaring an instance variable with keyword _____ specifies that the variable is not modifiable.

      j)   The _____ operator returns the `string` representation of an identifier's name.

      k)   _____ enables you to define how built-in operators work with objects of your own types.

      l)   _____ enable you to add new capabilities to existing types.

10.2   Suppose class `Book` defines properties `Title`, `Author` and `Year`. Use an object initializer to create an object of class `Book` and initialize its properties.

Answers to Self-Review Exercises

10.1   a) public services, public interface. b) hides. c) destructor. d) default constructor. e) `ToString`. f) *has-a*. g) `static`. h) principle of least privilege. i) `readonly`. j) `nameof`. k) operator overloading. l) extension methods.

10.2   `new Book {Title = "Visual C# How to Program", Author = "Deitel", Year = 2017}`

Exercises

10.3   *(Rectangle Class)* Create class `Rectangle`. The class has attributes `length` and `width`, each of which defaults to 1. It has read-only properties that calculate the `Perimeter` and the `Area` of the rectangle. It has properties for both `length` and `width`. The `set` accessors should verify that `length` and `width` are each floating-point numbers greater than 0.0 and less than 20.0. Write an app to test class `Rectangle`.

10.4   *(Modifying the Internal Data Representation of a Class)* It would be perfectly reasonable for the `Time2` class of Fig. 10.5 to represent the time internally as the number of seconds since midnight rather than the three integer values `hour`, `minute` and `second`. Clients could use the same public methods and properties to get the same results. Modify the `Time2` class of Fig. 10.5 to implement the `Time2` as the number of seconds since midnight and show that no change is visible to the clients of the class by using the same test app from Fig. 10.6.

10.5   *(Savings-Account Class)* Create the class `SavingsAccount`. Use the `static` read-write property `AnnualInterestRate` to store the annual interest rate for all account holders. Each object of the class contains a property `SavingsBalance`, indicating the amount the saver currently has on deposit. Provide method `CalculateMonthlyInterest` to calculate the monthly interest by multiplying the `SavingsBalance` by `AnnualInterestRate` divided by 12—this interest should be added to `savingsBalance`. Write an app to test class `SavingsAccount`. Create two `savingsAccount` objects, `saver1` and `saver2`, with balances of $2000.00 and $3000.00, respectively. Set `AnnualInterestRate` to 4%, then calculate the monthly interest and display the new balances for both savers. Then set the `AnnualInterestRate` to 5%, calculate the next month's interest and display the new balances for both savers.

10.6   *(Enhancing Class **Date**)* Modify class `Date` of Fig. 10.7 to perform error checking on the initializer values for instance variables `month`, `day` and `year` (class `Date` currently validates only the month and day). You'll need to convert the auto-implemented property `Year` into instance variable `year` with an associated `Year` property. Provide method `NextDay` to increment the day by 1. The `Date` object should always maintain valid data and throw exceptions when attempts are made to set invalid values. Write an app that tests the `NextDay` method in a loop that displays the date during each iteration of the loop to illustrate that the `NextDay` method works correctly. Test the following cases:

      a)   incrementing to the next month and

      b)   incrementing to the next year.

10.7 *(Set of Integers)* Create class `IntegerSet`. Each `IntegerSet` object can hold integers in the range 0–100. The set is represented by an array of `bool`s. Array element `a[i]` is `true` if integer *i* is in the set. Array element `a[j]` is `false` if integer *j* is not in the set. The parameterless constructor initializes the array to the "empty set" (i.e., a set whose array representation contains all `false` values).

Provide the following methods:

a) Method `Union` creates a third set that's the set-theoretic union of two existing sets (i.e., an element of the third set's array is set to `true` if that element is `true` in either or both of the existing sets—otherwise, the element of the third set is set to `false`).

b) Method `Intersection` creates a third set which is the set-theoretic intersection of two existing sets (i.e., an element of the third set's array is set to `false` if that element is `false` in either or both of the existing sets—otherwise, the element of the third set is set to `true`).

c) Method `InsertElement` inserts a new integer *k* into a set (by setting `a[k]` to `true`).

d) Method `DeleteElement` deletes integer *m* (by setting `a[m]` to `false`).

e) Method `ToString` returns a string containing a set as a list of numbers separated by spaces. Include only those elements that are present in the set. Use `---` to represent an empty set.

f) Method `IsEqualTo` determines whether two sets are equal.

Write an app to test class `IntegerSet`. Instantiate several `IntegerSet` objects. Test that all your methods work properly.

10.8 *(Rational Numbers)* Create a class called `Rational` for performing arithmetic with fractions. Write an app to test your class. Use integer variables to represent the `private` instance variables of the class—the numerator and the denominator. Provide a constructor that enables an object of this class to be initialized when it's declared. The constructor should store the fraction in reduced form. The fraction

> 2/4

is equivalent to 1/2 and would be stored in the object as 1 in the `numerator` and 2 in the `denominator`. Provide a parameterless constructor with default values in case no initializers are provided. Provide `public` methods that perform each of the following operations (all calculation results should be stored in a reduced form):

a) Add two `Rational` numbers.

b) Subtract two `Rational` numbers.

c) Multiply two `Rational` numbers.

d) Divide two `Rational` numbers.

e) Display `Rational` numbers in the form a/b, where a is the numerator and b is the denominator.

f) Display `Rational` numbers in floating-point format. (Consider providing formatting capabilities that enable the user of the class to specify the number of digits of precision to the right of the decimal point.)

10.9 *(HugeInteger Class)* Create a class `HugeInteger` which uses a 40-element array of digits to store integers as large as 40 digits each. Provide methods `Input`, `ToString`, `Add` and `Subtract`. For comparing `HugeInteger` objects, provide the following methods: `IsEqualTo`, `IsNotEqualTo`, `IsGreaterThan`, `IsLessThan`, `IsGreaterThanOrEqualTo` and `IsLessThanOrEqualTo`. Each of these is a method that returns `true` if the relationship holds between the two `HugeInteger` objects and returns `false` if the relationship does not hold. Provide method `IsZero`. If you feel ambitious, also provide methods `Multiply`, `Divide` and `Remainder`. In the `Input` method, use the `string` method `ToCharArray` to convert the input string into an array of characters, then iterate through these characters to create your `HugeInteger`. If you feel ambitious, provide methods `Multiply`, `Divide` and `Remainder`. [*Note:* The .NET Framework Class Library includes type `BigInteger` for arbitrary sized integer values.]

10.10 *(Tic-Tac-Toe)* Create class TicTacToe that will enable you to write a complete app to play the game of Tic-Tac-Toe. The class contains a private 3-by-3 rectangular array of integers. The constructor should initialize the empty board to all 0s. Allow two human players. Wherever the first player moves, place a 1 in the specified square, and place a 2 wherever the second player moves. Each move must be to an empty square. After each move, determine whether the game has been won and whether it's a draw. If you feel ambitious, modify your app so that the computer makes the moves for one of the players. Also, allow the player to specify whether he or she wants to go first or second. If you feel exceptionally ambitious, develop an app that will play three-dimensional Tic-Tac-Toe on a 4-by-4-by-4 board.

10.11 *(Extension Methods for Class Time2)* Use an extension method to provide for class Time2 (Fig. 10.5) a Tick method that increments the time by one second. The Time2 object should always remain in a consistent state, so be sure to account for and test the following cases:
   a) incrementing into the next minute.
   b) incrementing into the next hour.
   c) incrementing into the next day (i.e., 11:59:59 PM to 12:00:00 AM).

10.12 *(Enhanced ComplexNumber Class)* Enhance class ComplexNumber (Fig. 10.14) with overloaded == and != operators that enable you to compare complex numbers for equality and inequality. Each overloaded-operator method should return a bool. Test your new overloaded operators.

10.13 *(Project: Replacing Rational Methods with Overloaded Operators)* Modify class Rational (Exercise 10.8) to declare overloaded operators +, -, * and / that replace the class's methods for adding, subtracting, multiplying and dividing fractions. Test your new overloaded operators.

10.14 *(Project: Replacing HugeInteger Methods with Overloaded Operators)* Modify class HugeInteger (Exercise 10.9) to declare overloaded operators +, -, ==, !=, >, <, >= and <= that replace the class's methods Add, Subtract, IsEqualTo, IsNotEqualTo, IsGreaterThan, IsLessThan, IsGreaterThanOrEqualTo and IsLessThanOrEqualTo. Test your new overloaded operators. If you feel ambitious, provide overloaded operators for multiplication (*), division (/) and remainder (%).

Object-Oriented Programming: Inheritance

11

Objectives

In this chapter you'll:

- Understand how inheritance promotes software reusability.

- Create a derived class that inherits attributes and behaviors from a base class.

- Override base-class methods in derived classes.

- Use access modifier **protected** to give derived-class methods access to base-class members.

- Access base-class members with **base**.

- Understand how constructors are used in inheritance hierarchies.

- See an overview of the methods of class **object**, the direct or indirect base class of all classes.

11.1 Introduction

This chapter continues our discussion of object-oriented programming (OOP) by introducing one of its primary features—*inheritance*, a form of *software reuse* in which a new class is created by absorbing an existing class's members and enhancing them with new or modified capabilities. Inheritance lets you save time during app development by reusing proven, high-performance and debugged high-quality software. This also increases the likelihood that a system will be implemented effectively.

The existing class from which a new class inherits members is called the base class, and the new class is the derived class. Each derived class can become the base class for future derived classes. A derived class normally adds its own fields, properties and methods. Therefore, it's more *specific* than its base class and represents a more *specialized* group of objects. Typically, the derived class exhibits the behaviors of its base class and additional ones that are specific to itself.

The direct base class is the base class from which a derived class explicitly inherits. An indirect base class is any class above the direct base class in the class hierarchy, which defines the inheritance relationships among classes. The class hierarchy begins with class object—a C# keyword that's an alias for System.Object in the Framework Class Library. Every class directly or indirectly extends (or "inherits from") object. Section 11.7 lists class object's methods, which every other class inherits. In single inheritance, a class is derived from *one* direct base class. C# supports only single inheritance. In Chapter 12, OOP: Polymorphism and Interfaces, we explain how you can use interfaces to realize many of the benefits of multiple inheritance (i.e., inheriting from multiple direct base classes) while avoiding the associated problems that occur in some programming languages.

Experience in building software systems indicates that significant amounts of code deal with closely related special cases. When you're preoccupied with special cases, the details can obscure the big picture. With object-oriented programming, you can, when appropriate, focus on the *commonalities* among objects in the system rather than the special cases.

We distinguish between the *is-a* relationship and the *has-a* relationship. *Is-a* represents inheritance. In an *is-a* relationship, an object of a derived class also can be treated as an object of its base class. For example, a car *is a* vehicle, and a truck *is a* vehicle. By contrast, *has-a* represents composition (see Chapter 10). In a *has-a* relationship, an object contains as members references to other objects. For example, a car *has a* steering wheel, and a car object *has a* reference to a steering-wheel object.

New classes can inherit from classes in class libraries. Organizations develop their own class libraries and can take advantage of others available worldwide. Some day, most new software likely will be constructed from standardized reusable components, just as automobiles and most computer hardware are constructed today. This will facilitate the development of more powerful, abundant and economical software.

11.2 Base Classes and Derived Classes

Often, an object of one class *is an* object of another class as well. For example, in geometry, a rectangle *is a* quadrilateral (as are squares, parallelograms and trapezoids). Thus, class Rectangle can be said to inherit from class Quadrilateral. In this context, class Quadrilateral is a *base class* and class Rectangle is a *derived class*. A rectangle *is a* specific type of quadrilateral, but it's incorrect to claim that every quadrilateral *is a* rectangle—the quadrilateral could be a parallelogram or some other shape. Figure 11.1 lists several simple examples of base classes and derived classes—base classes tend to be more *general*, and derived classes tend to be more *specific*.

Base class	Derived classes
Student	GraduateStudent, UndergraduateStudent
Shape	Circle, Triangle, Rectangle
Loan	CarLoan, HomeImprovementLoan, MortgageLoan
Employee	Faculty, Staff, HourlyWorker, CommissionWorker
SpaceObject	Star, Moon, Planet, FlyingSaucer
BankAccount	CheckingAccount, SavingsAccount

Fig. 11.1 | Inheritance examples.

Because every derived-class object *is an* object of its base class, and one base class can have *many* derived classes, the set of objects represented by a base class is typically larger than the set of objects represented by any of its derived classes. For example, the base class Vehicle represents *all* vehicles—cars, trucks, boats, bicycles and so on. By contrast, derived class Car represents a smaller, more specific subset of vehicles.

Inheritance relationships form treelike hierarchical structures (Figs. 11.2 and 11.3). A base class exists in a hierarchical relationship with its derived classes. When classes participate in inheritance relationships, they become "affiliated" with other classes. A class becomes either a base class, supplying members to other classes, or a derived class, inheriting its members from another class. Sometimes, a class is *both* a base and a derived class.

Let us develop a sample class hierarchy, also called an inheritance hierarchy (Fig. 11.2). The UML class diagram of Fig. 11.2 shows a university community that has many types of members, including employees, students and alumni. Employees are either faculty members or staff members. Faculty members are either administrators (such as deans and department chairpersons) or teachers. The hierarchy could contain many other classes. For example, students can be graduate or undergraduate students. Undergraduate students can be freshmen, sophomores, juniors or seniors.

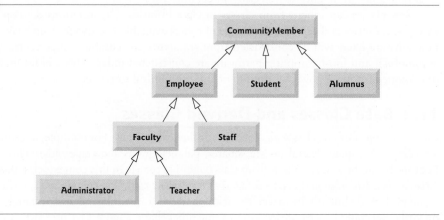

Fig. 11.2 | Inheritance hierarchy UML class diagram for university CommunityMembers.

Each arrow with a *hollow triangular arrowhead* in the hierarchy diagram represents an *is-a* relationship. As we follow the arrows, we can state, for instance, that "an Employee *is a* CommunityMember" and "a Teacher *is a* Faculty member." CommunityMember is the *direct* base class of Employee, Student and Alumnus and is an *indirect* base class of all the other classes in the diagram. Starting from the bottom, you can follow the arrows and apply the *is-a* relationship up to the topmost base class. For example, an Administrator *is a* Faculty member, *is an* Employee and *is a* CommunityMember.

Now consider the Shape hierarchy in Fig. 11.3, which begins with base class Shape. This class is extended by derived classes TwoDimensionalShape and ThreeDimensionalShape—a Shape is either a TwoDimensionalShape or a ThreeDimensionalShape. The third level of this hierarchy contains *specific* TwoDimensionalShapes and ThreeDimensionalShapes. We can follow the arrows from the bottom to the topmost base class in this hierarchy to identify the *is-a* relationships. For instance, a Triangle *is a* TwoDimensionalShape and *is a* Shape, while a Sphere *is a* ThreeDimensionalShape and *is a* Shape. This hierarchy could contain many other classes. For example, ellipses and trapezoids also are TwoDimensionalShapes.

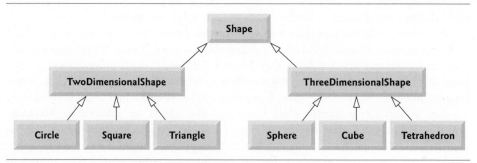

Fig. 11.3 | UML class diagram showing an inheritance hierarchy for Shapes.

Not every class relationship is an inheritance relationship. In Chapter 10 we discussed the *has-a* relationship, in which classes have members that are references to objects of other classes. Such relationships create classes by *composition* of existing classes. For example, given the classes Employee, BirthDate and TelephoneNumber, it's improper to say that an Employee *is a* BirthDate or that an Employee *is a* TelephoneNumber. However, an Employee *has a* BirthDate, and an Employee *has a* TelephoneNumber.

It's possible to treat base-class objects and derived-class objects similarly—their commonalities are expressed in the base class's members. Objects of all classes that extend a common base class can be treated as objects of that base class—such objects have an *is-a* relationship with the base class. However, *base-class objects cannot be treated as objects of their derived classes*. For example, all cars are vehicles, but not all vehicles are cars (other vehicles could be trucks, planes, bicycles, etc.). This chapter and Chapter 12 consider many examples of *is-a* relationships.

A derived class can customize methods it inherits from its base class. In such cases, the derived class can override (redefine) the base-class method with an appropriate implementation, as we'll see often in the chapter's code examples.

11.3 protected Members

Chapter 10 discussed access modifiers public and private. A class's public members are accessible wherever the app has a reference to an object of that class or one of its derived classes. A class's private members are accessible *only* within the class itself. A base class's private members *are* inherited by its derived classes, but are *not* directly accessible by derived-class methods and properties. In this section, we introduce access modifier protected. Using protected access offers an intermediate level of access between public and private. A base class's protected members can be accessed by members of that base class *and* by members of its derived classes, but not by clients of the class.

All non-private base-class members retain their original access modifier when they become members of the derived class—public members of the base class become public members of the derived class, and protected members of the base class become protected members of the derived class.

Derived-class methods can refer to public and protected members inherited from the base class simply by using the member names. When a derived-class method overrides a base-class method, the base-class version can be accessed from the derived class by preceding the base-class method name with the keyword base and the member access (.) operator. We discuss accessing overridden members of the base class in Section 11.4.

Software Engineering Observation 11.1

Properties and methods of a derived class cannot directly access private members of the base class. A derived class can change the state of private base-class fields only through non-private methods and properties provided in the base class.

Software Engineering Observation 11.2

Declaring private fields in a base class helps you test, debug and correctly modify systems. If a derived class could access its base class's private fields, classes that inherit from that derived class could access the fields as well. This would propagate access to what should be private fields, and the benefits of information hiding would be lost.

11.4 Relationship between Base Classes and Derived Classes

In this section, we use an inheritance hierarchy containing types of employees in a company's payroll app to discuss the relationship between a base class and a derived class. In this company:

- *commission employees*—who will be represented as objects of a base class—are paid a percentage of their sales, while

- *base-salaried commission employees*—who will be represented as objects of a derived class—receive a base salary *plus* a percentage of their sales.

We divide our discussion of the relationship between these employee types into an evolutionary set of five examples that was carefully designed to teach key capabilities for good software engineering with inheritance:

1. The first example creates class CommissionEmployee, which directly inherits from class object. The class declares public auto-implemented properties for the first name, last name and social security number, and private instance variables for the commission rate and gross (i.e., total) sales amount.

2. The second example declares class BasePlusCommissionEmployee, which also directly inherits from object. The class declares public auto-implemented properties for the first name, last name and social security number, and private instance variables for the commission rate, gross sales amount *and* base salary. We create the class by writing *every* line of code the class requires—we'll soon see that it's more efficient to create this class by inheriting from CommissionEmployee.

3. The third example declares a separate BasePlusCommissionEmployee class that extends class CommissionEmployee—that is, a BasePlusCommissionEmployee *is a* CommissionEmployee who also has a base salary. BasePlusCommissionEmployee attempts to access class CommissionEmployee's private members, but this results in compilation errors because a derived class *cannot* access its base class's private instance variables.

4. The fourth example shows that if base class CommissionEmployee's instance variables are declared as protected, a BasePlusCommissionEmployee class that inherits from CommissionEmployee can access that data directly.

5. The fifth and final example demonstrates *best practice* by setting the CommissionEmployee instance variables back to private in class CommissionEmployee to enforce good software engineering. Then we show how a separate BasePlusCommissionEmployee class that inherits from class CommissionEmployee can use CommissionEmployee's public methods and properties to manipulate CommissionEmployee's private instance variables in a controlled manner.

In the first four examples, we'll directly access instance variables in several cases where properties should be used. In the fifth example, we'll apply effective software engineering techniques that we've presented up to this point in the book to create classes that are easy to maintain, modify and debug.

11.4.1 Creating and Using a CommissionEmployee Class

We begin with class CommissionEmployee (Fig. 11.4). The colon (:) followed by class name object in line 5 indicates that class CommissionEmployee *extends* (i.e., *inherits from*) class object (an alias for class Object in namespace System). You use inheritance to create classes from existing classes. *Every* class (except object) extends an existing class. Because class CommissionEmployee extends object, class CommissionEmployee inherits object's methods—object has no fields. (Section 11.7 summarizes object's methods.) Every C# class directly or indirectly inherits object's methods. If a class does not specify that it inherits from another class, the new class *implicitly* inherits from object. For this reason, you typically do *not* include ": object" in your code—we do so in this example, then not again in the book.

```csharp
1   // Fig. 11.4: CommissionEmployee.cs
2   // CommissionEmployee class represents a commission employee.
3   using System;
4
5   public class CommissionEmployee : object
6   {
7      public string FirstName { get; }
8      public string LastName { get; }
9      public string SocialSecurityNumber { get; }
10     private decimal grossSales; // gross weekly sales
11     private decimal commissionRate; // commission percentage
12
13     // five-parameter constructor
14     public CommissionEmployee(string firstName, string lastName,
15        string socialSecurityNumber, decimal grossSales,
16        decimal commissionRate)
17     {
18        // implicit call to object constructor occurs here
19        FirstName = firstName;
20        LastName = lastName;
21        SocialSecurityNumber = socialSecurityNumber;
22        GrossSales = grossSales; // validates gross sales
23        CommissionRate = commissionRate; // validates commission rate
24     }
25
26     // property that gets and sets commission employee's gross sales
27     public decimal GrossSales
28     {
29        get
30        {
31           return grossSales;
32        }
33        set
34        {
35           if (value < 0) // validation
36           {
37              throw new ArgumentOutOfRangeException(nameof(value),
38                 value, $"{nameof(GrossSales)} must be >= 0");
39           }
```

Fig. 11.4 | CommissionEmployee class represents a commission employee. (Part 1 of 2.)

```
40
41          grossSales = value;
42      }
43   }
44
45   // property that gets and sets commission employee's commission rate
46   public decimal CommissionRate
47   {
48      get
49      {
50         return commissionRate;
51      }
52      set
53      {
54         if (value <= 0 || value >= 1) // validation
55         {
56            throw new ArgumentOutOfRangeException(nameof(value),
57               value, $"{nameof(CommissionRate)} must be > 0 and < 1");
58         }
59
60         commissionRate = value;
61      }
62   }
63
64   // calculate commission employee's pay
65   public decimal Earnings() => commissionRate * grossSales;
66
67   // return string representation of CommissionEmployee object
68   public override string ToString() =>
69      $"commission employee: {FirstName} {LastName}\n" +
70      $"social security number: {SocialSecurityNumber}\n" +
71      $"gross sales: {grossSales:C}\n" +
72      $"commission rate: {commissionRate:F2}";
73 }
```

Fig. 11.4 | CommissionEmployee class represents a commission employee. (Part 2 of 2.)

CommissionEmployee *Class Overview*

CommissionEmployee's attributes include public, getter-only, auto-implemented properties FirstName, LastName and SocialSecurityNumber, and private instance variables grossSales and commissionRate. The class provides

- a constructor (lines 14–24)
- public properties (lines 27–62) to *set* and *get* grossSales and commissionRate, and
- expression-bodied methods Earnings (line 65) and ToString (lines 68–72).

Because instance variables grossSales and commissionRate are private, other classes cannot directly access these variables. Declaring instance variables as private and providing public properties to manipulate and validate them helps enforce good software engineering. The set accessors of properties GrossSales and CommissionRate *validate* their arguments before assigning the values to instance variables grossSales and commissionRate, respectively.

CommissionEmployee *Constructor*

Constructors are *not* inherited, so class CommissionEmployee does not inherit class object's constructor. However, class CommissionEmployee's constructor calls object's constructor *implicitly*. In fact, before executing the code in its own body, every derived class's constructor calls a constructor in its direct base class, either explicitly or implicitly (if no constructor call is specified), to ensure that the instance variables inherited from the base class are initialized properly.

Calling a base-class constructor *explicitly* is discussed in Section 11.4.3. If the code does not *explicitly* call the base-class constructor, the compiler generates an *implicit* call to the base class's *default* or *parameterless* constructor, or a constructor with all default arguments. The comment in line 18 indicates where the implicit call to the base class object's constructor is made (you do not write the code for this call). Even if a class does not have constructors, the default constructor that the compiler implicitly declares for the class will call the base class's default or parameterless constructor. Class object is the *only* class that does not have a base class.

After the implicit call to object's constructor occurs, lines 19–23 in the constructor assign values to the class's properties. We do *not* validate the values of arguments first-Name, lastName and socialSecurityNumber. We certainly could validate the first and last names—perhaps by ensuring that they're of a reasonable length. Similarly, a social security number could be validated to ensure that it contains nine digits, with or without dashes (e.g., 123-45-6789 or 123456789).

CommissionEmployee *Method* Earnings

Method Earnings (line 65) calculates a CommissionEmployee's earnings by multiplying the commissionRate and the grossSales, then returns the result. As a best practice, we should use the properties CommissionRate and GrossSales to access the instance variables in line 65. We access them directly here and in the next few examples to help motivate then demonstrate the protected access modifier. In this chapter's final example, we'll follow best practice.

CommissionEmployee *Method* ToString

Method ToString (lines 68–72) is special—it's one of the methods that *every* class inherits directly or indirectly from class object. Method ToString returns a string representing an object. It can be called explicitly, but it's called *implicitly* by an app whenever an object must be converted to a string representation, such as when displaying an object with Console's Write or WriteLine methods or inserting an object in a string-interpolation expression. By default, class object's ToString method returns the object's fully qualified class name. For object, ToString returns

```
System.Object
```

because object is an alias for class Object in the System namespace. ToString is primarily a placeholder that can be (and typically should be) *overridden* by a derived class to specify an appropriate string representation of the data in a derived class object.

Method ToString of class CommissionEmployee overrides (redefines) class object's ToString method. When invoked, CommissionEmployee's ToString method returns a string containing information about the CommissionEmployee. Line 71 uses the format specifier C (in "{grossSales:C}") to format grossSales as currency and line 72 uses the format specifier F2 (in "{commissionRate:F2}") to format the commissionRate with two digits to the right of the decimal point.

To override a base-class method, a derived class must declare a method with keyword **override** and with the *same signature* (method name, number of parameters and parameter types) *and* return type as the base-class method—object's ToString method takes *no* parameters and returns type string, so CommissionEmployee declares ToString with the same parameter list and return type. As you'll soon see, the base-class method also must be declared virtual, which is the case for object method ToString.

Common Programming Error 11.1

It's a compilation error to override a method with one that has a different *access modifier. Overriding a method with a* more restrictive *access modifier would break the* is-a *relationship. If a* public *method could be overridden as a* protected *or* private *method, the derived-class objects would not be able to respond to the same method calls as base-class objects. In particular, once a method is declared in a base class, the method* must *have the same* access modifier *for all that class's direct and indirect derived classes.*

Class CommissionEmployeeTest

Figure 11.5 tests class CommissionEmployee. Lines 10–11 create a CommissionEmployee object and invoke its constructor (lines 14–24 of Fig. 11.4) to initialize it. Again, we append the M suffix to the gross sales amount and the commission rate to indicate these are decimal literals. Lines 16–22 in Fig. 11.5 use CommissionEmployee's properties to retrieve the object's instance-variable values for output. Line 23 outputs the amount calculated by the Earnings method. Lines 25–26 invoke the set accessors of the object's GrossSales and CommissionRate properties to change the values of instance variables grossSales and commissionRate. Line 30 outputs the string representation of the updated CommissionEmployee. When an object is output by Console's WriteLine method, which displays the object's string representation, the ToString method is invoked *implicitly*. Line 31 outputs the updated earnings.

```
1   // Fig. 11.5: CommissionEmployeeTest.cs
2   // Testing class CommissionEmployee.
3   using System;
4
5   class CommissionEmployeeTest
6   {
7      static void Main()
8      {
9         // instantiate CommissionEmployee object
10        var employee = new CommissionEmployee("Sue", "Jones",
11           "222-22-2222", 10000.00M, .06M);
12
13        // display CommissionEmployee data
14        Console.WriteLine(
15           "Employee information obtained by properties and methods: \n");
16        Console.WriteLine($"First name is {employee.FirstName}");
```

Fig. 11.5 | Testing class CommissionEmployee. (Part 1 of 2.)

```
17        Console.WriteLine($"Last name is {employee.LastName}");
18        Console.WriteLine(
19            $"Social security number is {employee.SocialSecurityNumber}");
20        Console.WriteLine($"Gross sales are {employee.GrossSales:C}");
21        Console.WriteLine(
22            $"Commission rate is {employee.CommissionRate:F2}");
23        Console.WriteLine($"Earnings are {employee.Earnings():C}");
24
25        employee.GrossSales = 5000.00M; // set gross sales
26        employee.CommissionRate = .1M; // set commission rate
27
28        Console.WriteLine(
29            "\nUpdated employee information obtained by ToString:\n");
30        Console.WriteLine(employee);
31        Console.WriteLine($"earnings: {employee.Earnings():C}");
32    }
33 }
```

```
Employee information obtained by properties and methods:

First name is Sue
Last name is Jones
Social security number is 222-22-2222
Gross sales are $10,000.00
Commission rate is 0.06
Earnings are $600.00

Updated employee information obtained by ToString:

commission employee: Sue Jones
social security number: 222-22-2222
gross sales: $5,000.00
commission rate: 0.10
earnings: $500.00
```

Fig. 11.5 | Testing class CommissionEmployee. (Part 2 of 2.)

11.4.2 Creating a BasePlusCommissionEmployee Class without Using Inheritance

We now discuss the second part of our introduction to inheritance by declaring and testing the completely new and independent class BasePlusCommissionEmployee (Fig. 11.6), which contains a first name, last name, social security number, gross sales amount, commission rate *and* base salary—"Base" in the class name stands for "base salary" not base class.

```
1   // Fig. 11.6: BasePlusCommissionEmployee.cs
2   // BasePlusCommissionEmployee class represents an employee that receives
3   // a base salary in addition to a commission.
4   using System;
5
```

Fig. 11.6 | BasePlusCommissionEmployee class represents an employee that receives a base salary in addition to a commission. (Part 1 of 3.)

```csharp
 6   public class BasePlusCommissionEmployee
 7   {
 8      public string FirstName { get; }
 9      public string LastName { get; }
10      public string SocialSecurityNumber { get; }
11      private decimal grossSales; // gross weekly sales
12      private decimal commissionRate; // commission percentage
13      private decimal baseSalary; // base salary per week
14
15      // six-parameter constructor
16      public BasePlusCommissionEmployee(string firstName, string lastName,
17         string socialSecurityNumber, decimal grossSales,
18         decimal commissionRate, decimal baseSalary)
19      {
20         // implicit call to object constructor occurs here
21         FirstName = firstName;
22         LastName = lastName;
23         SocialSecurityNumber = socialSecurityNumber;
24         GrossSales = grossSales; // validates gross sales
25         CommissionRate = commissionRate; // validates commission rate
26         BaseSalary = baseSalary; // validates base salary
27      }
28
29      // property that gets and sets gross sales
30      public decimal GrossSales
31      {
32         get
33         {
34            return grossSales;
35         }
36         set
37         {
38            if (value < 0) // validation
39            {
40               throw new ArgumentOutOfRangeException(nameof(value),
41                  value, $"{nameof(GrossSales)} must be >= 0");
42            }
43
44            grossSales = value;
45         }
46      }
47
48      // property that gets and sets commission rate
49      public decimal CommissionRate
50      {
51         get
52         {
53            return commissionRate;
54         }
55         set
56         {
```

Fig. 11.6 | BasePlusCommissionEmployee class represents an employee that receives a base salary in addition to a commission. (Part 2 of 3.)

```
57                if (value <= 0 || value >= 1) // validation
58                {
59                    throw new ArgumentOutOfRangeException(nameof(value),
60                        value, $"{nameof(CommissionRate)} must be > 0 and < 1");
61                }
62
63                commissionRate = value;
64            }
65        }
66
67        // property that gets and sets BasePlusCommissionEmployee's base salary
68        public decimal BaseSalary
69        {
70            get
71            {
72                return baseSalary;
73            }
74            set
75            {
76                if (value < 0) // validation
77                {
78                    throw new ArgumentOutOfRangeException(nameof(value),
79                        value, $"{nameof(BaseSalary)} must be >= 0");
80                }
81
82                baseSalary = value;
83            }
84        }
85
86        // calculate earnings
87        public decimal Earnings() =>
88            baseSalary + (commissionRate * grossSales);
89
90        // return string representation of BasePlusCommissionEmployee
91        public override string ToString() =>
92            $"base-salaried commission employee: {FirstName} {LastName}\n" +
93            $"social security number: {SocialSecurityNumber}\n" +
94            $"gross sales: {grossSales:C}\n" +
95            $"commission rate: {commissionRate:F2}\n" +
96            $"base salary: {baseSalary:C}";
97    }
```

Fig. 11.6 | BasePlusCommissionEmployee class represents an employee that receives a base salary in addition to a commission. (Part 3 of 3.)

BasePlusCommissionEmployee's attributes include public, getter-only, auto-implemented properties for the FirstName, LastName and SocialSecurityNumber, and private instance variables for the grossSales, commissionRate *and* baseSalary. The class provides

- a constructor (lines 16–27)
- public properties (lines 30–84) for manipulating the grossSales, commissionRate and baseSalary, and
- expression-bodied methods Earnings (lines 87–88) and ToString (lines 91–96).

Instance variables grossSales, commissionRate and baseSalary are private, so objects of other classes cannot directly access these variables. The set accessors of properties Gross-Sales, CommissionRate and BaseSalary *validate* their arguments before assigning the values to instance variables grossSales, commissionRate and baseSalary, respectively.

BasePlusCommissionEmployee's variables, properties and methods *encapsulate* all the necessary features of a base-salaried commission employee. Note the similarity between this class and class CommissionEmployee (Fig. 11.4)—in this example, *we do not yet exploit that similarity*.

Class BasePlusCommissionEmployee does *not* specify that it extends object with the syntax ": object" in line 6, so the class *implicitly* extends object. Also, like class CommissionEmployee's constructor (lines 14–24 of Fig. 11.4), class BasePlusCommissionEmployee's constructor invokes class object's default constructor *implicitly*, as noted in the comment in line 20 of Fig. 11.6.

Class BasePlusCommissionEmployee's Earnings method (lines 87–88) computes the earnings of a base-salaried commission employee. Line 88 adds the employee's base salary to the product of the commission rate and the gross sales, and returns the result.

Class BasePlusCommissionEmployee overrides object method ToString (lines 91–96) to return a string containing the BasePlusCommissionEmployee's information. Once again, we use format specifier C to format the gross sales and base salary as currency and format specifier F2 to format the commission rate with two digits of precision to the right of the decimal point.

Class *BasePlusCommissionEmployeeTest*

Figure 11.7 tests class BasePlusCommissionEmployee. Lines 10–11 instantiate a BasePlusCommissionEmployee object and pass "Bob", "Lewis", "333-33-3333", 5000.00M, .04M and 300.00M to the constructor as the first name, last name, social security number, gross sales, commission rate and base salary, respectively. Lines 16–24 use BasePlusCommissionEmployee's properties and methods to retrieve the values of the object's instance variables and calculate the earnings for output. Line 26 invokes the object's BaseSalary property to *change* the base salary. Property BaseSalary's set accessor (Fig. 11.6, lines 68–84) ensures that instance variable baseSalary is not assigned a negative value, because an employee's base salary cannot be negative. Lines 30–31 of Fig. 11.7 invoke the object's ToString method *implicitly* and invoke the object's Earnings method.

```
1   // Fig. 11.7: BasePlusCommissionEmployeeTest.cs
2   // Testing class BasePlusCommissionEmployee.
3   using System;
4
5   class BasePlusCommissionEmployeeTest
6   {
7      static void Main()
8      {
9         // instantiate BasePlusCommissionEmployee object
10        var employee = new BasePlusCommissionEmployee("Bob", "Lewis",
11           "333-33-3333", 5000.00M, .04M, 300.00M);
12
```

Fig. 11.7 | Testing class BasePlusCommissionEmployee. (Part 1 of 2.)

```
13          // display BasePlusCommissionEmployee's data
14          Console.WriteLine(
15             "Employee information obtained by properties and methods: \n");
16          Console.WriteLine($"First name is {employee.FirstName}");
17          Console.WriteLine($"Last name is {employee.LastName}");
18          Console.WriteLine(
19             $"Social security number is {employee.SocialSecurityNumber}");
20          Console.WriteLine($"Gross sales are {employee.GrossSales:C}");
21          Console.WriteLine(
22             $"Commission rate is {employee.CommissionRate:F2}");
23          Console.WriteLine($"Earnings are {employee.Earnings():C}");
24          Console.WriteLine($"Base salary is {employee.BaseSalary:C}");
25
26          employee.BaseSalary = 1000.00M; // set base salary
27
28          Console.WriteLine(
29             "\nUpdated employee information obtained by ToString:\n");
30          Console.WriteLine(employee);
31          Console.WriteLine($"earnings: {employee.Earnings():C}");
32       }
33    }
```

```
Employee information obtained by properties and methods:

First name is Bob
Last name is Lewis
Social security number is 333-33-3333
Gross sales are $5,000.00
Commission rate is 0.04
Earnings are $500.00
Base salary is $300.00

Updated employee information obtained by ToString:

base-salaried commission employee: Bob Lewis
social security number: 333-33-3333
gross sales: $5,000.00
commission rate: 0.04
base salary: $1,000.00
earnings: $1,200.00
```

Fig. 11.7 | Testing class BasePlusCommissionEmployee. (Part 2 of 2.)

Code Duplication

Much of the code for class BasePlusCommissionEmployee (Fig. 11.6) is similar, or identical, to that of class CommissionEmployee (Fig. 11.4). For example, in class BasePlusCommissionEmployee, properties FirstName, LastName and SocialSecurityNumber are identical to those of class CommissionEmployee. Classes CommissionEmployee and BasePlusCommissionEmployee also both contain private instance variables commissionRate and grossSales, as well as identical properties to manipulate these variables. In addition, the BasePlusCommissionEmployee constructor is almost identical to that of class CommissionEmployee, except that BasePlusCommissionEmployee's constructor also sets the BaseSalary.

The other additions to class BasePlusCommissionEmployee are private instance variable baseSalary and public property BaseSalary. Class BasePlusCommissionEmployee's Earnings method is nearly identical to that of class CommissionEmployee, except that BasePlusCommissionEmployee's Earnings also adds the baseSalary. Similarly, class BasePlusCommissionEmployee's ToString method is nearly identical to that of class CommissionEmployee, except that BasePlusCommissionEmployee's ToString also formats the value of instance variable baseSalary as currency.

We literally *copied* the code from class CommissionEmployee and *pasted* it into class BasePlusCommissionEmployee, then modified class BasePlusCommissionEmployee to include a base salary and methods and properties that manipulate the base salary. This "copy-and-paste" approach is error prone and time consuming. Worse yet, it can spread many physical copies of the same code throughout a system, creating a code-maintenance nightmare. Is there a way to "absorb" the members of one class in a way that makes them part of other classes without copying code? In the next several examples we answer this question, using a more elegant approach to building classes—namely, *inheritance*.

Error-Prevention Tip 11.1

Copying and pasting code from one class to another can spread errors across multiple source-code files. To avoid duplicating code (and possibly errors) in situations where you want one class to "absorb" the members of another class, use inheritance rather than the "copy-and-paste" approach.

Software Engineering Observation 11.3

With inheritance, the common members of all the classes in the hierarchy are declared in a base class. When changes are required for these common features, you need to make the changes only in the base class—derived classes then inherit the changes. Without inheritance, changes would need to be made to all the source-code files that contain a copy of the code in question.

11.4.3 Creating a CommissionEmployee–BasePlusCommissionEmployee Inheritance Hierarchy

Now we declare class BasePlusCommissionEmployee (Fig. 11.8), which extends (inherits from) class CommissionEmployee (Fig. 11.4).[1] A BasePlusCommissionEmployee object *is a* CommissionEmployee (because inheritance passes on the capabilities of class CommissionEmployee), but class BasePlusCommissionEmployee also has instance variable baseSalary (Fig. 11.8, line 7). The colon (:) in line 5 of the class declaration indicates inheritance. As a derived class, BasePlusCommissionEmployee inherits CommissionEmployee's members and can access only those that are non-private. CommissionEmployee's constructor is *not* inherited. Thus, the public services of BasePlusCommissionEmployee include its constructor (lines 11–18), public methods and properties inherited from class CommissionEmployee, property BaseSalary (lines 22–38), method Earnings (lines 41–42) and method ToString (lines 45–51). We'll explain the errors in Fig. 11.8 momentarily.

---

1. For this purpose, we created a project containing a copy of CommissionEmployee.cs from Fig. 11.4.

```
 1   // Fig. 11.8: BasePlusCommissionEmployee.cs
 2   // BasePlusCommissionEmployee inherits from CommissionEmployee.
 3   using System;
 4
 5   public class BasePlusCommissionEmployee : CommissionEmployee
 6   {
 7      private decimal baseSalary; // base salary per week
 8
 9      // six-parameter derived-class constructor
10      // with call to base class CommissionEmployee constructor
11      public BasePlusCommissionEmployee(string firstName, string lastName,
12         string socialSecurityNumber, decimal grossSales,
13         decimal commissionRate, decimal baseSalary)
14         : base(firstName, lastName, socialSecurityNumber,
15            grossSales, commissionRate)
16      {
17         BaseSalary = baseSalary; // validates base salary
18      }
19
20      // property that gets and sets
21      // BasePlusCommissionEmployee's base salary
22      public decimal BaseSalary
23      {
24         get
25         {
26            return baseSalary;
27         }
28         set
29         {
30            if (value < 0) // validation
31            {
32               throw new ArgumentOutOfRangeException(nameof(value),
33                  value, $"{nameof(BaseSalary)} must be >= 0");
34            }
35
36            baseSalary = value;
37         }
38      }
39
40      // calculate earnings
41      public override decimal Earnings() =>
42         baseSalary + (commissionRate * grossSales);
43
44      // return string representation of BasePlusCommissionEmployee
45      public override string ToString() =>
46         // not allowed: attempts to access private base-class members
47         $"base-salaried commission employee: {FirstName} {LastName}\n" +
48         $"social security number: {SocialSecurityNumber}\n" +
49         $"gross sales: {grossSales:C}\n" +
50         $"commission rate: {commissionRate:F2}\n" +
51         $"base salary: {baseSalary}";
52   }
```

Fig. 11.8 | BasePlusCommissionEmployee inherits from CommissionEmployee. (Part 1 of 2.)

	Code	Description ▲	File	Line
⊗	CS0506	'BasePlusCommissionEmployee.Earnings()': cannot override inherited member 'CommissionEmployee.Earnings()' because it is not marked virtual, abstract, or override	BasePlusCommissionEmployee.cs	41
⊗	CS0122	'CommissionEmployee.commissionRate' is inaccessible due to its protection level	BasePlusCommissionEmployee.cs	42
⊗	CS0122	'CommissionEmployee.commissionRate' is inaccessible due to its protection level	BasePlusCommissionEmployee.cs	50
⊗	CS0122	'CommissionEmployee.grossSales' is inaccessible due to its protection level	BasePlusCommissionEmployee.cs	42
⊗	CS0122	'CommissionEmployee.grossSales' is inaccessible due to its protection level	BasePlusCommissionEmployee.cs	49
⊗	CS1022	Type or namespace definition, or end-of-file expected	BasePlusCommissionEmployee.cs	53

Error List — Entire Solution — ⊗ 6 Errors — ⚠ 0 Warnings — ⓘ 0 Messages — Build + IntelliSense — Search Error List

Fig. 11.8 | `BasePlusCommissionEmployee` inherits from `CommissionEmployee`. (Part 2 of 2.)

A Derived Class's Constructor Must Call Its Base Class's Constructor

Each derived-class constructor *must* implicitly or explicitly call its base-class constructor to ensure that the instance variables inherited from the base class are initialized properly. `BasePlusCommissionEmployee`'s six-parameter constructor explicitly calls class `CommissionEmployee`'s five-parameter constructor to initialize the `CommissionEmployee` portion of a `BasePlusCommissionEmployee` object—that is, the `FirstName`, `LastName`, `SocialSecurityNumber`, `GrossSales` and `CommissionRate`.

Lines 14–15 in `BasePlusCommissionEmployee`'s constructor invoke `CommissionEmployee`'s constructor (declared at lines 14–24 of Fig. 11.4) via a *constructor initializer*. In Section 10.5, we used a constructor initializer with keyword `this` to call an overloaded constructor in the *same* class. Line 14 of Fig. 11.8 uses a constructor initializer with keyword **base** to invoke the *base-class constructor*, passing arguments to initialize the base class's corresponding properties that were inherited into the derived-class object. If `BasePlusCommissionEmployee`'s constructor did not invoke `CommissionEmployee`'s constructor explicitly, C# would attempt to invoke class `CommissionEmployee`'s parameterless or default constructor *implicitly*. `CommissionEmployee` does *not* have such a constructor, so the compiler would issue an error.

Common Programming Error 11.2

A compilation error occurs if a derived-class constructor calls one of its base-class constructors with arguments that do not match the number and types of parameters specified in one of the base-class constructor declarations.

BasePlusCommissionEmployee Method Earnings

Lines 41–42 of Fig. 11.8 declare method `Earnings` using keyword `override` to override the `CommissionEmployee`'s `Earnings` method, as we did with method `ToString` in previous examples. Line 41 causes the first compilation error shown in Fig. 11.8, indicating that we cannot override the base class's `Earnings` method because it was not explicitly "marked virtual, abstract, or override." The **virtual** and **abstract** keywords indicate that a base-class method can be overridden in derived classes.[2] The override modifier declares

---

2.   As you'll learn in Section 12.4, abstract methods are *implicitly* `virtual`.

that a derived-class method overrides a `virtual` or `abstract` base-class method. This modifier also *implicitly* declares the derived-class method `virtual` and allows it to be over-ridden in derived classes further down the inheritance hierarchy. Adding the keyword `virtual` to method Earnings' declaration in Fig. 11.4, as in

```
public virtual decimal Earnings()
```

eliminates the first compilation error in Fig. 11.8.

The compiler generates additional errors for line 42 of Fig. 11.8, because base class CommissionEmployee's instance variables commissionRate and grossSales are private—derived class BasePlusCommissionEmployee's methods are not allowed to access the base class's `private` members. The compiler also issues errors at lines 49–50 in method ToString for the same reason. The errors in BasePlusCommissionEmployee could have been prevented by using the `public` properties inherited from class CommissionEmployee. For example, line 42, 49 and 50 could have invoked the `get` accessors of properties CommissionRate and GrossSales to access CommissionEmployee's `private` instance variables commissionRate and grossSales, respectively.

11.4.4 CommissionEmployee–BasePlusCommissionEmployee Inheritance Hierarchy Using protected Instance Variables

To enable class BasePlusCommissionEmployee to directly access base-class instance variables grossSales and commissionRate, we can declare those members as protected in the base class. As we discussed in Section 11.3, a base class's `protected` members *are* accessible to all derived classes of that base class. Class CommissionEmployee in this example is a modification of the version from Fig. 11.4 that declares its instance variables gross-Sales and commissionRate as

```
protected decimal grossSales; // gross weekly sales
protected decimal commissionRate; // commission percentage
```

rather than `private`. We also declare the Earnings method `virtual` so that BasePlusCommissionEmployee can override the method. The rest of class CommissionEmployee in this example is identical to Fig. 11.4. The complete source code for class CommissionEmployee is included in this example's project.

Class BasePlusCommissionEmployee

Class BasePlusCommissionEmployee (Fig. 11.9) in this example extends the version of class CommissionEmployee with protected instance variables grossSales and commissionRate. Each BasePlusCommissionEmployee object contains these CommissionEmployee instance variables, which are inherited into BasePlusCommissionEmployee as protected members. As a result, directly accessing instance variables grossSales and commissionRate no longer generates compilation errors in methods Earnings and ToString. If another class extends BasePlusCommissionEmployee, the new derived class also inherits grossSales and commissionRate as protected members.

Class BasePlusCommissionEmployee does *not* inherit class CommissionEmployee's constructor. However, class BasePlusCommissionEmployee's constructor (lines 12–19) calls class CommissionEmployee's constructor with a constructor initializer. Again, Base-PlusCommissionEmployee's constructor must *explicitly* call CommissionEmployee's constructor, because CommissionEmployee does *not* provide a parameterless constructor that could be invoked implicitly.

```csharp
1   // Fig. 11.9: BasePlusCommissionEmployee.cs
2   // BasePlusCommissionEmployee inherits from CommissionEmployee and has
3   // access to CommissionEmployee's protected members.
4   using System;
5
6   public class BasePlusCommissionEmployee : CommissionEmployee
7   {
8      private decimal baseSalary; // base salary per week
9
10     // six-parameter derived-class constructor
11     // with call to base class CommissionEmployee constructor
12     public BasePlusCommissionEmployee(string firstName, string lastName,
13        string socialSecurityNumber, decimal grossSales,
14        decimal commissionRate, decimal baseSalary)
15        : base(firstName, lastName, socialSecurityNumber,
16           grossSales, commissionRate)
17     {
18        BaseSalary = baseSalary; // validates base salary
19     }
20
21     // property that gets and sets
22     // BasePlusCommissionEmployee's base salary
23     public decimal BaseSalary
24     {
25        get
26        {
27           return baseSalary;
28        }
29        set
30        {
31           if (value < 0) // validation
32           {
33              throw new ArgumentOutOfRangeException(nameof(value),
34                 value, $"{nameof(BaseSalary)} must be >= 0");
35           }
36
37           baseSalary = value;
38        }
39     }
40
41     // calculate earnings
42     public override decimal Earnings() =>
43        baseSalary + (commissionRate * grossSales);
44
45     // return string representation of BasePlusCommissionEmployee
46     public override string ToString() =>
47        $"base-salaried commission employee: {FirstName} {LastName}\n" +
48        $"social security number: {SocialSecurityNumber}\n" +
```

Fig. 11.9 | BasePlusCommissionEmployee inherits from CommissionEmployee and has access to CommissionEmployee's protected members. (Part 1 of 2.)

```
49          $"gross sales: {grossSales:C}\n" +
50          $"commission rate: {commissionRate:F2}\n" +
51          $"base salary: {baseSalary}";
52    }
```

Fig. 11.9 | BasePlusCommissionEmployee inherits from CommissionEmployee and has access to CommissionEmployee's protected members. (Part 2 of 2.)

Testing Class *BasePlusCommissionEmployee*

The BasePlusCommissionEmployeeTest class in this example's project is identical to that of Fig. 11.7 and produces the same output, so we do not show the code here. Although the version of class BasePlusCommissionEmployee in Fig. 11.6 does not use inheritance and the version in Fig. 11.9 does, both classes provide the *same* functionality. The source code in Fig. 11.9 (52 lines) is considerably shorter than that in Fig. 11.6 (97 lines), because a large portion of the class's functionality is now inherited from CommissionEmployee—there's now only one copy of the CommissionEmployee functionality. This makes the code easier to maintain, modify and debug, because the code related to a CommissionEmployee exists *only* in that class.

public vs. protected Data

We could have declared base class CommissionEmployee's instance variables grossSales and commissionRate as public to enable derived class BasePlusCommissionEmployee to access the base-class instance variables. However, declaring public instance variables is poor software engineering, because it allows unrestricted access to the instance variables by *any* of the class's clients, greatly increasing the chance of errors and inconsistencies. With protected instance variables, the derived class gets access to the instance variables, but classes that are not derived from the base class cannot access its variables directly.

Problems with *protected* Instance Variables

In this example, we declared base-class instance variables as protected so that derived classes could access them. Inheriting protected instance variables enables you to directly access the variables in the derived class *without* invoking the set or get accessors of the corresponding property, thus violating encapsulation. In most cases, it's better to use private instance variables and access them via properties to encourage proper software engineering. Your code will be easier to maintain, modify and debug.

Using protected instance variables creates several potential problems. First, since the derived-class object can set an inherited variable's value directly *without* using a property's set accessor, a derived-class object can assign an *invalid* value to the variable. For example, if we were to declare CommissionEmployee's instance variable grossSales as protected, a derived-class object (e.g., BasePlusCommissionEmployee) could then directly assign a *negative* value to grossSales, making it invalid.

The second problem with protected instance variables is that derived-class methods are more likely to be written to *depend* on the base class's data implementation. In practice, derived classes should depend only on the base-class *services* (i.e., non-private methods and properties) and *not* on the base-class data implementation. With protected instance variables in the base class, we may need to modify all the derived classes of the base class if the base-class implementation changes. For example, if for some reason we were to change the names of instance variables grossSales and commissionRate, then we'd have to do so for all occurrences in which a derived class directly references base-class instance variables grossSales and commissionRate. In such a case, the software is said to be fragile or brittle, because a small change in the base class can "break" derived-class implementation. You should be able to *change* the base-class *implementation* while still providing the *same services* to the derived classes. Of course, if the base-class services change, we must reimplement our derived classes.

Software Engineering Observation 11.4

Declaring base-class instance variables private *(as opposed to* protected*) enables the base-class implementation of these instance variables to change without affecting derived-class implementations.*

11.4.5 CommissionEmployee–BasePlusCommissionEmployee Inheritance Hierarchy Using private Instance Variables

We now reexamine our hierarchy, this time using the best software engineering practices.

Base Class CommissionEmployee

Class CommissionEmployee (Fig. 11.10) once again declares instance variables grossSales and commissionRate as private (lines 10–11). Methods Earnings (line 65) and ToString (lines 68–72) no longer directly access these instance variables—rather they use properties GrossSales and CommissionRate to access the data. If we decide to change the instance-variable names, the Earnings and ToString declarations will *not* require modification—only the bodies of the properties GrossSales and CommissionRate that directly manipulate the instance variables will need to change. These changes occur solely within the base class—no changes to the derived class are needed. Localizing the effects of changes like this is a good software engineering practice. Derived class BasePlusCommissionEmployee (Fig. 11.11) inherits from CommissionEmployee and can access the private base-class members via the inherited public properties.

```
 1    // Fig. 11.10: CommissionEmployee.cs
 2    // CommissionEmployee class represents a commission employee.
 3    using System;
 4
 5    public class CommissionEmployee
 6    {
 7       public string FirstName { get; }
 8       public string LastName { get; }
 9       public string SocialSecurityNumber { get; }
10       private decimal grossSales; // gross weekly sales
11       private decimal commissionRate; // commission percentage
12
13       // five-parameter constructor
14       public CommissionEmployee(string firstName, string lastName,
15          string socialSecurityNumber, decimal grossSales,
16          decimal commissionRate)
17       {
```

Fig. 11.10 | CommissionEmployee class represents a commission employee. (Part 1 of 3.)

```
18          // implicit call to object constructor occurs here
19          FirstName = firstName;
20          LastName = lastName;
21          SocialSecurityNumber = socialSecurityNumber;
22          GrossSales = grossSales; // validates gross sales
23          CommissionRate = commissionRate; // validates commission rate
24       }
25
26       // property that gets and sets commission employee's gross sales
27       public decimal GrossSales
28       {
29          get
30          {
31             return grossSales;
32          }
33          set
34          {
35             if (value < 0) // validation
36             {
37                throw new ArgumentOutOfRangeException(nameof(value),
38                   value, $"{nameof(GrossSales)} must be >= 0");
39             }
40
41             grossSales = value;
42          }
43       }
44
45       // property that gets and sets commission employee's commission rate
46       public decimal CommissionRate
47       {
48          get
49          {
50             return commissionRate;
51          }
52          set
53          {
54             if (value <= 0 || value >= 1) // validation
55             {
56                throw new ArgumentOutOfRangeException(nameof(value),
57                   value, $"{nameof(CommissionRate)} must be > 0 and < 1");
58             }
59
60             commissionRate = value;
61          }
62       }
63
64       // calculate commission employee's pay
65       public virtual decimal Earnings() => CommissionRate * GrossSales;
66
67       // return string representation of CommissionEmployee object
68       public override string ToString() =>
69          $"commission employee: {FirstName} {LastName}\n" +
70          $"social security number: {SocialSecurityNumber}\n" +
```

Fig. 11.10 | CommissionEmployee class represents a commission employee. (Part 2 of 3.)

```
71        $"gross sales: {GrossSales:C}\n" +
72        $"commission rate: {CommissionRate:F2}";
73   }
```

Fig. 11.10 | CommissionEmployee class represents a commission employee. (Part 3 of 3.)

Derived Class BasePlusCommissionEmployee

Class BasePlusCommissionEmployee (Fig. 11.11) has several changes to its method implementations that distinguish it from the version in Fig. 11.9. Methods Earnings (Fig. 11.11, line 43) and ToString (lines 46–47) each invoke property BaseSalary's get accessor to obtain the base-salary value, rather than accessing baseSalary directly. If we decide to rename instance variable baseSalary, only the body of property BaseSalary will need to change.

```
1    // Fig. 11.11: BasePlusCommissionEmployee.cs
2    // BasePlusCommissionEmployee inherits from CommissionEmployee and has
3    // controlled access to CommissionEmployee's private data via
4    // its public properties.
5    using System;
6
7    public class BasePlusCommissionEmployee : CommissionEmployee
8    {
9       private decimal baseSalary; // base salary per week
10
11      // six-parameter derived-class constructor
12      // with call to base class CommissionEmployee constructor
13      public BasePlusCommissionEmployee(string firstName, string lastName,
14         string socialSecurityNumber, decimal grossSales,
15         decimal commissionRate, decimal baseSalary)
16         : base(firstName, lastName, socialSecurityNumber,
17              grossSales, commissionRate)
18      {
19         BaseSalary = baseSalary; // validates base salary
20      }
21
22      // property that gets and sets
23      // BasePlusCommissionEmployee's base salary
24      public decimal BaseSalary
25      {
26         get
27         {
28            return baseSalary;
29         }
30         set
31         {
32            if (value < 0) // validation
33            {
```

Fig. 11.11 | BasePlusCommissionEmployee inherits from CommissionEmployee and has access to CommissionEmployee's private data via its public properties. (Part 1 of 2.)

```
34                  throw new ArgumentOutOfRangeException(nameof(value),
35                     value, $"{nameof(BaseSalary)} must be >= 0");
36             }
37
38             baseSalary = value;
39          }
40       }
41
42       // calculate earnings
43       public override decimal Earnings() => BaseSalary + base.Earnings();
44
45       // return string representation of BasePlusCommissionEmployee
46       public override string ToString() =>
47          $"base-salaried {base.ToString()}\nbase salary: {BaseSalary:C}";
48    }
```

Fig. 11.11 | BasePlusCommissionEmployee inherits from CommissionEmployee and has access to CommissionEmployee's private data via its public properties. (Part 2 of 2.)

BasePlusCommissionEmployee *Method* Earnings

Class BasePlusCommissionEmployee's Earnings method (Fig. 11.11, line 43) overrides class CommissionEmployee's Earnings method (Fig. 11.10, line 65) to calculate the earnings of a BasePlusCommissionEmployee. The new version obtains the portion of the employee's earnings based on commission alone by calling CommissionEmployee's Earnings method with the expression base.Earnings() (Fig. 11.11, line 43), then adds the base salary to this value to calculate the total earnings of the employee. Note the syntax used to invoke an overridden base-class method from a derived class—place the keyword base and the member access operator (.) before the base-class method name. This method invocation is a good software engineering practice—by having BasePlusCommissionEmployee's Earnings method invoke CommissionEmployee's Earnings method to calculate part of a BasePlusCommissionEmployee object's earnings, we avoid duplicating the code and reduce code-maintenance problems.

Common Programming Error 11.3

When a base-class method is overridden in a derived class, the derived-class version often calls the base-class version to do a portion of the work. Failure to prefix the base-class method name with the keyword base and the member access (.) operator when referencing the base class's method from the derived-class version causes the derived-class method to call itself, creating infinite recursion.

BasePlusCommissionEmployee *Method* ToString

Similarly, BasePlusCommissionEmployee's ToString method (Fig. 11.11, lines 46–47) overrides CommissionEmployee's (Fig. 11.10, lines 68–72) to return a string representation that's appropriate for a base-salaried commission employee. The new version creates part of BasePlusCommissionEmployee string representation (i.e., the string "commission employee" and the values of CommissionEmployee's data) by calling CommissionEmployee's ToString method with the expression base.ToString() (Fig. 11.11, line 47) and incorporating the result into the string returned by the derived class's ToString method, which includes the base salary.

*Testing Class **BasePlusCommissionEmployee***

Class BasePlusCommissionEmployeeTest performs the same manipulations on a Base-PlusCommissionEmployee object as in Figs. 11.7 and produces the same output, so we do not show it here. Although each BasePlusCommissionEmployee class you've seen behaves identically, the version in Fig. 11.11 is the best engineered. *By using inheritance and by using properties that hide the data and ensure consistency, we have efficiently and effectively constructed a well-engineered class.*

11.5 Constructors in Derived Classes

As we explained in the preceding section, instantiating a derived-class object begins a chain of constructor calls. The derived-class constructor, before performing its own tasks, invokes its direct base class's constructor either explicitly (via a constructor initializer with the base reference) or implicitly (calling the base class's default constructor or parameterless constructor). Similarly, if the base class is derived from another class, the base-class constructor invokes the constructor of the next class up in the hierarchy, and so on. The *last* constructor called in the chain is always the constructor for class object. The original derived-class constructor's body finishes executing last. Each base class's constructor manipulates the base-class data that the derived-class object inherits.

For example, consider again the CommissionEmployee–BasePlusCommissionEmployee hierarchy from Figs. 11.10 and 11.11. When an app creates a BasePlusCommissionEmployee object, the BasePlusCommissionEmployee constructor is called. That constructor *immediately* calls CommissionEmployee's constructor, which in turn *immediately* calls object's constructor implicitly. Class object's constructor performs its task, then immediately returns control to CommissionEmployee's constructor, which then initializes the CommissionEmployee data that's part of the BasePlusCommissionEmployee object. When CommissionEmployee's constructor completes execution, it returns control to BasePlusCommissionEmployee's constructor, which then initializes the BasePlusCommissionEmployee object's BaseSalary.

11.6 Software Engineering with Inheritance

This section discusses customizing existing software with inheritance. When a new class extends an existing class, the new class inherits the members of the existing class. We can customize the new class to meet our needs by including additional members and by overriding base-class members. C# simply requires access to the compiled base-class code, so it can compile and execute any app that uses or extends the base class. This powerful capability is attractive to independent software vendors (ISVs), who can develop proprietary classes for sale or license and make them available to users in class libraries. Users then can derive new classes from these library classes rapidly, without accessing the ISVs' proprietary source code.

Software Engineering Observation 11.5

Although inheriting from a class does not require access to the class's source code, developers often insist on seeing the source code to understand how the class is implemented. They may, for example, want to ensure that they're extending a class that performs well and is implemented securely.

Students sometimes have difficulty appreciating the scope of the problems faced by designers who work on large-scale software projects in industry. People experienced with such projects say that effective software reuse improves the software-development process. Object-oriented programming facilitates software reuse, potentially shortening development times. The availability of substantial and useful class libraries helps deliver the maximum benefits of software reuse through inheritance.

Software Engineering Observation 11.6

At the design stage in an object-oriented system, the designer often finds that certain classes are closely related. The designer should "factor out" common members and place them in a base class. Then the designer should use inheritance to develop derived classes, specializing them with capabilities beyond those inherited from the base class.

Software Engineering Observation 11.7

Declaring a derived class does not affect its base class's source code. Inheritance preserves the integrity of the base class.

Reading derived-class declarations can be confusing, because inherited members are not declared explicitly in the derived classes but are nevertheless present in them. A similar problem exists in documenting derived-class members.

11.7 Class object

As we discussed earlier in this chapter, all classes inherit directly or indirectly from class object—an alias for System.Object in the Framework Class Library—so its non-static methods are inherited by *all* classes. Figure 11.12 summarizes object's methods. You can learn more about object's methods at

> http://msdn.microsoft.com/library/system.object

Method	Description
Equals	This method compares the current object to another object for equality and returns true if they're equal and false otherwise. It takes any object as an argument. When objects of a particular class must be compared for equality, the class should override method Equals to compare the *contents* of the two objects. The website http://bit.ly/OverridingEqualsCSharp explains the requirements for a properly overridden Equals method.
Finalize	This method cannot be explicitly declared or called. When a class contains a destructor, the compiler implicitly renames it to override the protected method Finalize, which is called *only* by the garbage collector before it reclaims an object's memory. The garbage collector is not guaranteed to reclaim an object, thus it's *not* guaranteed that an object's Finalize method will execute. When a derived class's Finalize method executes, it performs its task, then invokes the base class's Finalize method. In general, you should avoid using Finalize.

Fig. 11.12 | object methods that are inherited directly or indirectly by all classes. (Part 1 of 2.)

Method	Description
GetHashCode	A hashtable data structure relates objects, called *keys*, to corresponding objects, called *values*. We discuss Hashtable in Chapter 21. When a value is initially inserted in a hashtable, the key's GetHashCode method is called. The value returned is used by the hashtable to determine the location at which to insert the corresponding value. The key's hashcode is also used by the hashtable to locate the key's corresponding value.
GetType	Every object knows its own type at execution time. Method GetType (used in Section 12.5) returns an object of class Type (namespace System) that contains information about the object's type, such as its class name (obtained from Type property FullName).
MemberwiseClone	This protected method, which takes no arguments and returns an object reference, makes a copy of the object on which it's called. The implementation of this method performs a shallow copy—instance-variable values in one object are copied into another object of the same type. For reference types, only the references are copied.
ReferenceEquals	This static method receives two object references and returns true if they're the same instance or if they're null references. Otherwise, it returns false.
ToString	This method (introduced in Section 7.4) returns a string representation of the current object. The default implementation of this method returns the namespace followed by a dot and the class name of the object's class.

Fig. 11.12 | object methods that are inherited directly or indirectly by all classes. (Part 2 of 2.)

11.8 Wrap-Up

This chapter introduced inheritance—the ability to create classes by absorbing an existing class's members and enhancing them with new capabilities. You learned the notions of base classes and derived classes and created a derived class that inherits members from a base class and overrides inherited virtual methods. We introduced access modifier protected; derived-class members can access protected base-class members. You learned how to access base-class members with base. You also saw how constructors are used in inheritance hierarchies. Finally, you learned about the methods of class object, the direct or indirect base class of *all* classes.

In Chapter 12, we build on our discussion of inheritance by introducing polymorphism—an object-oriented concept that enables us to write apps that handle, in a more general manner, objects of a wide variety of classes related by inheritance. After studying Chapter 12, you'll be familiar with classes, objects, encapsulation, inheritance and polymorphism—the most essential aspects of object-oriented programming.

Summary

Section 11.1 Introduction
- Inheritance is a form of software reuse in which a new class is created by absorbing an existing class's members and enhancing them with new or modified capabilities. With inheritance, you save time during app development by reusing proven and debugged high-quality software.

- A derived class is more specific than its base class and represents a more specialized group of objects.

- The *is-a* relationship represents inheritance. In an *is-a* relationship, an object of a derived class also can be treated as an object of its base class.

Section 11.2 Base Classes and Derived Classes

- Inheritance relationships form treelike hierarchical structures. A base class exists in a hierarchical relationship with its derived classes.

- Objects of all classes that extend a common base class can be treated as objects of that base class. However, base-class objects cannot be treated as objects of their derived classes.

- When a base-class method is inherited by a derived class, that derived class often needs a customized version of the method. In such cases, the derived class can override the base-class method with an appropriate implementation.

Section 11.3 `protected` Members

- Using `protected` access offers an intermediate level of access between `public` and `private`. A base class's `protected` members can be accessed by members of that base class *and* by members of its derived classes.

- Base-class members retain their original access modifier when they become members of the derived class.

- Methods of a derived class cannot directly access `private` members of the base class.

Section 11.4.1 Creating and Using a `CommissionEmployee` Class

- A colon (:) followed by a base-class name at the end of a class declaration header indicates that the declared class extends the base class.

- If a class does not specify that it inherits from another class, the class implicitly inherits from `object`.

- The first task of any derived class's constructor is to call its direct base class's constructor, either explicitly or implicitly (if no constructor call is specified).

- Constructors are not inherited. Even if a class does not have constructors, the default constructor that the compiler implicitly declares for the class will call the base class's default or parameterless constructor.

- Method `ToString` is one of the methods that every class inherits directly or indirectly from class `object`, which is the root of the C# class hierarchy.

- To override a base-class method, a derived class must declare a method with keyword `override` and with the same signature (method name, number of parameters and parameter types) and return type as the base-class method. Also, the base-class method must be declared `virtual`.

- It's a compilation error to override a method with a different access modifier.

Section 11.4.2 Creating a `BasePlusCommissionEmployee` Class without Using Inheritance

- Copying and pasting code from one class to another can spread errors across multiple source-code files. To avoid duplicating code (and possibly errors) in situations where you want one class to "absorb" the members of another class, use inheritance.

Section 11.4.3 Creating a `CommissionEmployee`–`BasePlusCommissionEmployee` Inheritance Hierarchy

- The `virtual` and `abstract` keywords indicate that a base-class property or method can be overridden in derived classes.

- The override modifier declares that a derived-class method overrides a virtual or abstract base-class method. This modifier also implicitly declares the derived-class method virtual.

- When a base class's members are private, a derived class's members are not allowed to access them.

Section 11.4.4 *CommissionEmployee–BasePlusCommissionEmployee Inheritance Hierarchy Using* **protected** *Instance Variables*

- Inheriting protected instance variables enables you to directly access the variables in the derived class without invoking the set or get accessors of the corresponding property.

- Software is said to be fragile or brittle when a small change in the base class can "break" derived-class implementation. You should be able to change the base-class implementation while still providing the same services to the derived classes.

- Declaring base-class instance variables private enables the base-class implementation of these instance variables to change without affecting derived-class implementations.

Section 11.4.5 *CommissionEmployee–BasePlusCommissionEmployee Inheritance Hierarchy Using* **private** *Instance Variables*

- Place the keyword base and the member access (.) operator before the base-class method name to invoke an overridden base-class method from a derived class.

- Failure to prefix the base-class method name with the keyword base and the member access (.) operator when referencing the base class's method causes the derived-class method to call itself, creating infinite recursion.

Section 11.5 Constructors in Derived Classes

- Instantiating a derived-class object begins a chain of constructor calls. The last constructor called in the chain is always the constructor for class object. The original derived class constructor's body finishes executing last.

Section 11.6 Software Engineering with Inheritance

- We can customize new classes to meet our needs by including additional members and by overriding base-class members.

Section 11.7 Class **object**

- All classes in C# inherit directly or indirectly from the object class, so its seven methods are inherited by all other classes. These methods are Equals, Finalize, GetHashCode, GetType, MemberwiseClone, ReferenceEquals and ToString.

Terminology

base class	direct base class
base-class constructor	Equals method of class object
base-class constructor call syntax	extend a base class
base-class parameterless constructor	Finalize method of class object
base keyword	fragile software
brittle software	GetHashCode method of class object
class hierarchy	GetType method of class object
class library	*has-a* relationship
composition	hierarchical relationship
derived class	hierarchy diagram
derived-class constructor	indirect base class

inheritance	override (redefine) a base-class method
inheritance hierarchy	`private` base-class member
inherited member	`protected` base-class member
inherited method	`protected` access modifier
invoke a base-class constructor	`public` base-class member
invoke a base-class method	`ReferenceEquals` method of class `object`
is-a relationship	single inheritance
`MemberwiseClone` method of class `object`	shallow copy
`object` class	software reuse
object of a derived class	standardized reusable components
object of a base class	`ToString` method of class `object`
`override` keyword	`virtual` keyword

Self-Review Exercises

11.1 Fill in the blanks in each of the following statements:

a) _____ is a form of software reusability in which new classes acquire the members of existing classes and enhance those classes with new capabilities.

b) A base class's _____ members can be accessed only in the base-class declaration and in derived-class declarations.

c) In a(n) _____ relationship, an object of a derived class also can be treated as an object of its base class.

d) In a(n) _____ relationship, a class object has references to objects of other classes as members.

e) In single inheritance, a base class exists in a(n) _____ relationship with its derived classes.

f) A base class's _____ members are accessible anywhere that the app has a reference to an object of that base class or to an object of any of its derived classes.

g) When an object of a derived class is instantiated, a base class _____ is called implicitly or explicitly.

h) Derived-class constructors can call base class constructors via the _____ keyword.

11.2 State whether each of the following is *true* or *false*. If a statement is *false*, explain why.

a) Base-class constructors are not inherited by derived classes.

b) A *has-a* relationship is implemented via inheritance.

c) A `Car` class has *is-a* relationships with the `SteeringWheel` and `Brakes` classes.

d) Inheritance encourages the reuse of proven high-quality software.

e) When a derived class redefines a base-class method by using the same signature and return type, the derived class is said to overload that base-class method.

Answers to Self-Review Exercises

11.1 a) Inheritance. b) `protected`. c) *is-a* or inheritance. d) *has-a* or composition. e) hierarchical. f) `public`. g) constructor. h) `base`.

11.2 a) True. b) False. A *has-a* relationship is implemented via composition. An *is-a* relationship is implemented via inheritance. c) False. These are examples of *has-a* relationships. Class `Car` has an *is-a* relationship with class `Vehicle`. d) True. e) False. This is known as overriding, not overloading.

Exercises

11.3 *(Composition vs. Inheritance)* Many apps written with inheritance could be written with composition instead, and vice versa. Rewrite class `BasePlusCommissionEmployee` (Fig. 11.11) of the

CommissionEmployee–BasePlusCommissionEmployee hierarchy to use composition rather than inheritance.

11.4   *(Inheritance and Software Reuse)* Discuss the ways in which inheritance promotes software reuse, saves time during app development and helps prevent errors.

11.5   *(Student Inheritance Hierarchy)* Draw a UML class diagram for an inheritance hierarchy for students at a university similar to the hierarchy shown in Fig. 11.2. Use Student as the base class of the hierarchy, then extend Student with classes UndergraduateStudent and GraduateStudent. Continue to extend the hierarchy as deeply (i.e., as many levels) as possible. For example, Freshman, Sophomore, Junior and Senior might extend UndergraduateStudent, and DoctoralStudent and MastersStudent might be derived classes of GraduateStudent. After drawing the hierarchy, discuss the relationships that exist between the classes. [*Note:* You do not need to write any code for this exercise.]

11.6   *(Shape Inheritance Hierarchy)* The world of shapes is much richer than the shapes included in the inheritance hierarchy of Fig. 11.3. Write down all the shapes you can think of—both two-dimensional and three-dimensional—and form them into a more complete Shape hierarchy with as many levels as possible. Your hierarchy should have class Shape at the top. Class TwoDimensionalShape and class ThreeDimensionalShape should extend Shape. Add additional derived classes, such as Quadrilateral and Sphere, at their correct locations in the hierarchy as necessary.

11.7   *(Protected vs. Private Access)* Some programmers prefer not to use protected access, because they believe it breaks the encapsulation of the base class. Discuss the relative merits of using protected access vs. using private access in base classes.

11.8   *(Quadrilateral Inheritance Hierarchy)* Write an inheritance hierarchy for classes Quadrilateral, Trapezoid, Parallelogram, Rectangle and Square. Use Quadrilateral as the base class of the hierarchy. Make the hierarchy as deep (i.e., as many levels) as possible. Specify the instance variables, properties and methods for each class. The private instance variables of Quadrilateral should be the *x–y* coordinate pairs for the four endpoints of the Quadrilateral. Write an app that instantiates objects of your classes and outputs each object's area (except Quadrilateral).

11.9   *(Account Inheritance Hierarchy)* Create an inheritance hierarchy that a bank might use to represent customers' bank accounts. All customers at this bank can deposit (i.e., credit) money into their accounts and withdraw (i.e., debit) money from their accounts. More specific types of accounts also exist. Savings accounts, for instance, earn interest on the money they hold. Checking accounts, on the other hand, charge a fee per transaction.

Create base class Account and derived classes SavingsAccount and CheckingAccount that inherit from class Account. Base class Account should include one private instance variable of type decimal to represent the account balance. The class should provide a constructor that receives an initial balance and uses it to initialize the instance variable with a public property. The property should validate the initial balance to ensure that it's greater than or equal to 0.0; if not, throw an exception. The class should provide two public methods. Method Credit should add an amount to the current balance. Method Debit should withdraw money from the Account and ensure that the debit amount does not exceed the Account's balance. If it does, the balance should be left unchanged, and the method should display the message "Debit amount exceeded account balance." The class should also provide a get accessor in property Balance that returns the current balance.

Derived class SavingsAccount should inherit the functionality of an Account, but also include a decimal instance variable indicating the interest rate (percentage) assigned to the Account. SavingsAccount's constructor should receive the initial balance, as well as an initial value for the interest rate. SavingsAccount should provide public method CalculateInterest that returns a decimal indicating the amount of interest earned by an account. Method CalculateInterest should determine this amount by multiplying the interest rate by the account balance. [*Note:* SavingsAccount should inherit methods Credit and Debit without redefining them.]

Derived class CheckingAccount should inherit from base class Account and include a decimal instance variable that represents the fee charged per transaction. CheckingAccount's constructor should receive the initial balance, as well as a parameter indicating a fee amount. Class Checking-Account should redefine methods Credit and Debit so that they subtract the fee from the account balance whenever either transaction is performed successfully. CheckingAccount's versions of these methods should invoke the base-class Account version to perform the updates to an account balance. CheckingAccount's Debit method should charge a fee only if money is actually withdrawn (i.e., the debit amount does not exceed the account balance). [*Hint:* Define Account's Debit method so that it returns a bool indicating whether money was withdrawn. Then use the return value to determine whether a fee should be charged.]

After defining the classes in this hierarchy, write an app that creates objects of each class and tests their methods. Add interest to the SavingsAccount object by first invoking its CalculateInterest method, then passing the returned interest amount to the object's Credit method.

12

OOP: Polymorphism and Interfaces

Objectives

In this chapter you'll:

- Understand how polymorphism enables you to "program in the general" and make systems extensible.

- Use overridden methods to effect polymorphism.

- Create abstract classes and methods.

- Determine an object's type at execution time with operator `is`, then use downcasting to perform type-specific processing.

- Create `sealed` methods and classes.

- Declare and implement interfaces.

- Be introduced to interfaces `IComparable`, `IComponent`, `IDisposable` and `IEnumerator` of the .NET Framework Class Library.

12.1 Introduction

We now continue our study of object-oriented programming by explaining and demonstrating **polymorphism** with inheritance hierarchies. Polymorphism enables us to *program in the general* rather than *program in the specific*. In particular, polymorphism enables us to write apps that process objects that share the *same* base class in a class hierarchy as if they were all objects of the base class.

Let's consider a polymorphism example. Suppose we create an app that simulates moving several types of animals for a biological study. Classes Fish, Frog and Bird represent the types of animals under investigation. Imagine that each class extends base class Animal, which contains a method Move and maintains an animal's current location as *x*–*y*–*z* coordinates. Each derived class implements method Move differently. Our app maintains a collection of references to objects of the various Animal-derived classes. To simulate an animal's movements, the app sends each object the *same* message once per second—namely, Move. Each specific type of Animal responds to a Move message in a unique way—a Fish might swim three feet, a Frog might jump five feet and a Bird might fly 10 feet. The app issues the Move message to each animal object *generically*, but each object modifies its *x*–*y*–*z* coordinates appropriately for its *specific* type of movement. Relying on each object to "do the right thing" in response to the *same* method call is the key concept of polymorphism. The *same* message (in this case, Move) sent to a *variety* of objects has *many forms* of results—hence the term polymorphism.

Systems Are Easy to Extend

With polymorphism, we can design and implement systems that are easily *extensible*—new classes can be added with little or no modification to the polymorphic portions of the app, as long as the new classes are part of the inheritance hierarchy that the app processes generically. The only parts of an app that must be altered to accommodate new classes are those that require direct knowledge of the new classes that you add to the hierarchy. For example, if we extend class `Animal` to create class `Tortoise` (which might respond to a `Move` message by crawling one inch), we need to write only the `Tortoise` class and the part of the simulation that instantiates a `Tortoise` object. The portions of the simulation that process each `Animal` generically can remain the *same*.

This chapter has several parts. First, we discuss common examples of polymorphism. We then provide an example demonstrating polymorphic behavior. As you'll soon see, you'll use base-class references to manipulate both base-class objects *and* derived-class objects polymorphically.

Polymorphic Employee Inheritance Hierarchy

We then present a case study that revisits the `Employee` hierarchy of Section 11.4.5. We develop a simple payroll app that polymorphically calculates the weekly pay of several different types of employees using each employee's `Earnings` method. Though the earnings of each type of employee are calculated in a *specific* way, polymorphism allows us to process the employees "in the *general*." In the case study, we enlarge the hierarchy to include two new classes—`SalariedEmployee` (for people paid a fixed weekly salary) and `HourlyEmployee` (for people paid an hourly salary and "time-and-a-half" for overtime). We declare a *common set of functionality* for all the classes in the updated hierarchy in a base class `Employee` (Section 12.5.1) from which classes `SalariedEmployee`, `HourlyEmployee` and `CommissionEmployee` *inherit directly* and class `BasePlusCommissionEmployee` *inherits indirectly*. As you'll soon see, when we invoke each employee's `Earnings` method via a base-class `Employee` reference, the correct earnings calculation is performed due to C#'s polymorphic capabilities.

Determining the Type of an Object at Execution Time

Occasionally, when performing polymorphic processing, we need to program "in the *specific*." Our `Employee` case study demonstrates that an app can determine the type of an object at *execution* time and act on that object accordingly. In the case study, we use these capabilities to determine whether a particular employee object *is a* `BasePlusCommissionEmployee`. If so, we increase that employee's base salary by 10%.

Interfaces

The chapter continues with an introduction to C# interfaces. An interface describes a set of methods and properties that can be called on an object, but does *not* provide *concrete* implementations for them. You can declare classes that **implement** (i.e., provide *concrete* implementations for the methods and properties of) one or more interfaces. Each interface member must be defined for *all* the classes that implement the interface. Once a class implements an interface, all objects of that class have an *is-a* relationship with the interface type, and all objects of the class are *guaranteed* to provide the functionality described by the interface. This is true of all *derived* classes of that class as well.

Interfaces are particularly useful for assigning common functionality to possibly *unrelated* classes. This allows objects of unrelated classes to be processed polymorphically—objects of classes that implement the *same* interface can respond to the *same* method calls. To demonstrate creating and using interfaces, we modify our payroll app to create a general accounts-payable app that can calculate payments due for the earnings of company employees and for invoice amounts to be billed for purchased goods. As you'll see, interfaces enable polymorphic capabilities similar to those enabled by inheritance.

12.2 Polymorphism Examples

Let's consider several additional examples of polymorphism.

Quadrilateral *Inheritance Hierarchy*

If class `Rectangle` is derived from class `Quadrilateral` (a four-sided shape), then a `Rectangle` *is a* more specific version of a `Quadrilateral`. Any operation (e.g., calculating the perimeter or the area) that can be performed on a `Quadrilateral` object also can be performed on a `Rectangle` object. These operations also can be performed on other `Quadrilaterals`, such as Squares, `Parallelograms` and `Trapezoids`. The polymorphism occurs when an app invokes a method through a base-class variable—at execution time, the correct derived-class version of the method is called, based on the type of the referenced object. You'll see a simple code example that illustrates this process in Section 12.3.

Video Game `SpaceObject` *Inheritance Hierarchy*

As another example, suppose we design a video game that manipulates objects of many different types, including objects of classes `Martian`, `Venusian`, `Plutonian`, `SpaceShip` and `LaserBeam`. Imagine that each class inherits from the common base class `SpaceObject`, which contains method `Draw`. Each derived class implements this method. A screen-manager app maintains a collection (e.g., a `SpaceObject` array) of references to objects of the various classes. To refresh the screen, the screen manager periodically sends each object the *same message*—namely, `Draw`. However, each object responds in a unique way. For example, a `Martian` object might *draw itself* in red with the appropriate number of antennae. A `SpaceShip` object might *draw itself* as a bright silver flying saucer. A `LaserBeam` object might *draw itself* as a bright red beam across the screen. Again, the *same message* (in this case, `Draw`) sent to a variety of objects has *many forms* of results.

A screen manager might use polymorphism to facilitate adding new classes to a system with minimal modifications to the system's code. Suppose we want to add `Mercurian` objects to our video game. To do so, we must build a `Mercurian` class that extends `SpaceObject` and provides its own `Draw` method implementation. When objects of class `Mercurian` appear in the `SpaceObject` collection, the screen-manager code invokes method `Draw`, exactly as it does for every other object in the collection, *regardless of its type*, so the new `Mercurian` objects simply "plug right in" without any modification of the screen-manager code by the programmer. Thus, without modifying the system (other than to build new classes and modify the code that creates new objects), you can use polymorphism to include additional types that might not have been envisioned when the system was created.

Software Engineering Observation 12.1

Polymorphism promotes extensibility: Software that invokes polymorphic behavior is independent of the object types to which messages are sent. New object types that can respond to existing method calls can be incorporated into a system without requiring modification of the polymorphic system logic. Only client code that instantiates new objects must be modified to accommodate new types.

12.3 Demonstrating Polymorphic Behavior

Section 11.4 created a commission-employee class hierarchy, in which class `BasePlusCommissionEmployee` inherited from class `CommissionEmployee`. The examples in that section manipulated `CommissionEmployee` and `BasePlusCommissionEmployee` objects by using references to them to invoke their methods. We aimed base-class references at base-class objects and derived-class references at derived-class objects. These assignments are natural and straightforward—base-class references are intended to refer to base-class objects, and derived-class references are intended to refer to derived-class objects. However, other assignments are possible.

The next example aims a base-class reference at a derived-class object, then shows how invoking a method on a derived-class object via a base-class reference invokes the derived-class functionality—*the type of the actual referenced object, not the type of the reference, determines which method is called.* This demonstrates the key concept that a derived-class object can be treated as an object of its base class, which enables various interesting manipulations. An app can create a collection of base-class references that refer to objects of many derived-class types, because each derived-class object *is an* object of its base class. For instance, we can assign the reference of a `BasePlusCommissionEmployee` object to a base-class `CommissionEmployee` variable because a `BasePlusCommissionEmployee` *is a* `CommissionEmployee`—so we can treat a `BasePlusCommissionEmployee` as a `CommissionEmployee`.

A base-class object is not an object of any of its derived classes. For example, we cannot directly assign the reference of a `CommissionEmployee` object to a derived-class `BasePlusCommissionEmployee` variable, because a `CommissionEmployee` *is not* a `BasePlusCommissionEmployee`—a `CommissionEmployee` does not, for example, have a `baseSalary` instance variable and does not have a `BaseSalary` property. The compiler allows the assignment of a base-class reference to a derived-class variable *if* we explicitly cast the base-class reference to the derived-class type—a technique we discuss in greater detail in Section 12.5.6.

> **Software Engineering Observation 12.2**
> *The* is-a *relationship applies from a derived class to its direct and indirect base classes, but not vice versa.*

Figure 12.1 demonstrates three ways to use base-class and derived-class variables to store references to base-class and derived-class objects. The first two are straightforward— as in Section 11.4, we assign a base-class reference to a base-class variable, and we assign a derived-class reference to a derived-class variable. Then we demonstrate the relationship between derived classes and base classes (i.e., the *is-a* relationship) by assigning a derived-class reference to a base-class variable. [*Note:* This app uses classes `CommissionEmployee` and `BasePlusCommissionEmployee` from Fig. 11.10 and Fig. 11.11, respectively.]

```
1   // Fig. 12.1: PolymorphismTest.cs
2   // Assigning base-class and derived-class references to base-class and
3   // derived-class variables.
4   using System;
5
```

Fig. 12.1 | Assigning base-class and derived-class references to base-class and derived-class variables. (Part 1 of 3.)

```csharp
 6   class PolymorphismTest
 7   {
 8      static void Main()
 9      {
10         // assign base-class reference to base-class variable
11         var commissionEmployee = new CommissionEmployee(
12            "Sue", "Jones", "222-22-2222", 10000.00M, .06M);
13
14         // assign derived-class reference to derived-class variable
15         var basePlusCommissionEmployee = new BasePlusCommissionEmployee(
16            "Bob", "Lewis", "333-33-3333", 5000.00M, .04M, 300.00M);
17
18         // invoke ToString and Earnings on base-class object
19         // using base-class variable
20         Console.WriteLine(
21            "Call CommissionEmployee's ToString and Earnings methods " +
22            "with base-class reference to base class object\n");
23         Console.WriteLine(commissionEmployee.ToString());
24         Console.WriteLine($"earnings: {commissionEmployee.Earnings()}\n");
25
26         // invoke ToString and Earnings on derived-class object
27         // using derived-class variable
28         Console.WriteLine("Call BasePlusCommissionEmployee's ToString and" +
29            " Earnings methods with derived class reference to" +
30            " derived-class object\n");
31         Console.WriteLine(basePlusCommissionEmployee.ToString());
32         Console.WriteLine(
33            $"earnings: {basePlusCommissionEmployee.Earnings()}\n");
34
35         // invoke ToString and Earnings on derived-class object
36         // using base-class variable
37         CommissionEmployee commissionEmployee2 = basePlusCommissionEmployee;
38         Console.WriteLine(
39            "Call BasePlusCommissionEmployee's ToString and Earnings " +
40            "methods with base class reference to derived-class object");
41         Console.WriteLine(commissionEmployee2.ToString());
42         Console.WriteLine(
43            $"earnings: {basePlusCommissionEmployee.Earnings()}\n");
44      }
45   }
```

```
Call CommissionEmployee's ToString and Earnings methods with base class
reference to base class object:

commission employee: Sue Jones
social security number: 222-22-2222
gross sales: $10,000.00
commission rate: 0.06
earnings: $600.00
```

Fig. 12.1 | Assigning base-class and derived-class references to base-class and derived-class variables. (Part 2 of 3.)

```
Call BasePlusCommissionEmployee's ToString and Earnings methods with derived
class reference to derived class object:

base-salaried commission employee: Bob Lewis
social security number: 333-33-3333
gross sales: $5,000.00
commission rate: 0.04
base salary: $300.00
earnings: $500.00

Call BasePlusCommissionEmployee's ToString and Earnings methods with base
class reference to derived class object:

base-salaried commission employee: Bob Lewis
social security number: 333-33-3333
gross sales: $5,000.00
commission rate: 0.04
base salary: $300.00
earnings: $500.00
```

Fig. 12.1 | Assigning base-class and derived-class references to base-class and derived-class variables. (Part 3 of 3.)

In Fig. 12.1, lines 11–12 create a new CommissionEmployee object and assign its reference to a CommissionEmployee variable and lines 15–16 create a new BasePlusCommissionEmployee object and assign its reference to a BasePlusCommissionEmployee variable. These assignments are *natural*—a CommissionEmployee variable's primary purpose is to hold a reference to a CommissionEmployee object. Lines 23–24 use the reference commissionEmployee to invoke methods ToString and Earnings. Because commissionEmployee refers to a CommissionEmployee object, *base class* CommissionEmployee's version of the methods are called. Similarly, lines 31–33 use the reference basePlusCommissionEmployee to invoke the methods ToString and Earnings on the BasePlusCommissionEmployee object. This invokes *derived class* BasePlusCommissionEmployee's version of the methods.

Line 37 then assigns the reference to derived-class object basePlusCommissionEmployee to a *base-class* CommissionEmployee variable, which lines 41–43 use to invoke methods ToString and Earnings. Note that the call commissionEmployee2.ToString() in line 41 actually calls *derived* class BasePlusCommissionEmployee's ToString method. The compiler allows this "crossover" because an object of a derived class *is an* object of its base class (but not vice versa). When the compiler encounters a virtual method call made through a variable, the compiler checks the *variable's* class type to determine if the method can be called. If that class contains the proper method declaration (or inherits one), the call compiles. At execution time, *the type of the object to which the variable refers* determines the actual method to use.

 Software Engineering Observation 12.3

A base-class variable that contains a reference to a derived-class object and is used to call a virtual method actually calls the overriding derived-class version of the method.

12.4 Abstract Classes and Methods

When we think of a class type, we assume that apps will create objects of that type. In some cases, however, it's useful to declare *classes for which you never intend to instantiate objects*. Such classes are called abstract classes. Because they're used only as base classes in inheritance hierarchies, we refer to them as abstract base classes. These classes *cannot* be used to instantiate objects, because, as you'll soon see, abstract classes are *incomplete*—derived classes must define the "missing pieces." Section 12.5.1 demonstrates abstract classes.

Purpose of an Abstract Class
The purpose of an abstract class is primarily to provide an appropriate base class from which other classes can inherit, and thus *share a common design*. In the Shape hierarchy of Fig. 11.3, for example, derived classes inherit the notion of what it means to be a Shape—common attributes such as Location, Color and BorderThickness, and behaviors such as Draw, Move, Resize and ChangeColor. Classes that can be used to instantiate objects are called concrete classes. Such classes provide implementations of *every* method they declare (some of the implementations can be inherited). For example, we could derive concrete classes Circle, Square and Triangle from abstract base class TwoDimensionalShape. Similarly, we could derive concrete classes Sphere, Cube and Tetrahedron from abstract base class ThreeDimensionalShape. Abstract classes are too *general* to create real objects—they specify only what is common among derived classes. We need to be more *specific* before we can create objects. For example, if you send the Draw message to abstract class TwoDimensionalShape, the class knows that two-dimensional shapes should be drawable, but it does *not* know what *specific* shape to draw, so it cannot implement a real Draw method. *Concrete* classes provide the *specifics* needed to instantiate objects.

Client Code That Uses Only Abstract Base-Class Types
Not all inheritance hierarchies contain abstract classes. However, you'll often write client code that uses only abstract base-class types to reduce client code's dependencies on a range of specific derived-class types. For example, you can write a method with a parameter of an abstract base-class type. When called, such a method can be passed an object of any concrete class that directly or indirectly extends the abstract base class specified as the parameter's type.

Multiple Levels of Abstract Base-Class Types in a Hierarchy
Abstract classes sometimes constitute several levels of the hierarchy. For example, the Shape hierarchy of Fig. 11.3 begins with *abstract* class Shape. On the next level of the hierarchy are two more *abstract* classes, TwoDimensionalShape and ThreeDimensionalShape. The next level of the hierarchy declares *concrete* classes for TwoDimensionalShapes (Circle, Square and Triangle) and for ThreeDimensionalShapes (Sphere, Cube and Tetrahedron).

Creating an Abstract Class
You make a class abstract by declaring it with the keyword abstract. An abstract class normally contains one or more abstract methods. An abstract method is one with keyword abstract in its declaration, as in

```
public abstract void Draw(); // abstract method
```

Abstract methods are implicitly virtual and do not provide implementations. A class that contains abstract methods must be declared as an abstract class *even if* it contains some concrete (non-abstract) methods. Each *concrete* derived class of an abstract base class also must provide concrete implementations of the base class's abstract methods. We show an example of an abstract class with an abstract method in Fig. 12.4.

Abstract Properties

Properties also can be declared abstract or virtual, then overridden in derived classes with the override keyword, just like methods. This allows an abstract base class to specify common properties of its derived classes. Abstract property declarations have the form:

```
public abstract PropertyType MyProperty { get; set; }
```

The semicolons after the get and set keywords indicate that we provide *no implementation* for these accessors. An abstract property omits implementations for the get accessor and/or the set accessor. Concrete derived classes *must* provide implementations for *every* accessor declared in the abstract property. When both get and set accessors are specified, every concrete derived class must implement both. If one accessor is omitted, the derived class is *not* allowed to implement that accessor. Doing so causes a compilation error.

*Constructors and **static** Methods Cannot be **abstract** or **virtual***

Constructors and static methods *cannot* be declared abstract or virtual. Constructors are not inherited, so such a constructor could never be implemented. Similarly, derived classes cannot override static methods, so such as static method could never be implemented.

Software Engineering Observation 12.4

An abstract class declares common attributes and behaviors of the various classes that inherit from it, either directly or indirectly, in a class hierarchy. An abstract class typically contains one or more abstract methods or properties that concrete derived classes must override. The instance variables, concrete methods and concrete properties of an abstract class are subject to the normal rules of inheritance.

Common Programming Error 12.1

Attempting to instantiate an object of an abstract class is a compilation error.

Common Programming Error 12.2

Failure to implement a base class's abstract methods and properties in a derived class is a compilation error unless the derived class is also declared abstract.

Declaring Variables of Abstract Base-Class Types

Although we cannot instantiate objects of abstract base classes, you'll soon see that we *can* use abstract base classes to declare variables that can hold references to objects of *any* concrete classes *derived* from those abstract classes. Apps typically use such variables to manipulate derived-class objects polymorphically. Also, you can use abstract base-class names to invoke static methods declared in those abstract base classes.

Polymorphism and Device Drivers

Polymorphism is particularly effective for implementing so-called *layered software systems*. In operating systems, for example, each different type of physical device could operate quite differently from the others. Even so, common commands can read or write data from and to the devices. For each device, the operating system uses a piece of software called a *device driver* to control all communication between the system and the device. The write message sent to a device-driver object needs to be interpreted *specifically* in the context of that driver and how it manipulates a specific device. However, the write call itself really is no different from the write to any other device in the system: Place some number of bytes from memory onto that device. An object-oriented operating system might use an abstract base class to provide an "interface" appropriate for all device drivers. Then, through inheritance from that abstract base class, derived classes are formed that all behave similarly. The device-driver methods are declared as abstract methods in the abstract base class. The implementations of these abstract methods are provided in the derived classes that correspond to the specific types of device drivers. New devices are always being developed, often long after the operating system has been released. When you buy a new device, it comes with a device driver provided by the device vendor. The device is immediately operational after you connect it to your computer and install the device driver. This is another elegant example of how polymorphism makes systems *extensible*.

12.5 Case Study: Payroll System Using Polymorphism

This section reexamines the CommissionEmployee-BasePlusCommissionEmployee hierarchy that we explored in Section 11.4. Now we use an abstract method and polymorphism to perform payroll calculations based on the type of employee. We create an enhanced employee hierarchy to solve the following problem:

> A company pays its employees on a weekly basis. The employees are of four types:
>
> 1. Salaried employees are paid a fixed weekly salary regardless of the number of hours worked.
> 2. Hourly employees are paid by the hour and receive "time-and-a-half" overtime pay for all hours worked in excess of 40 hours
> 3. Commission employees are paid a percentage of their sales.
> 4. Salaried-commission employees receive a base salary plus a percentage of their sales.
>
> For the current pay period, the company has decided to reward salaried-commission employees by adding 10% to their base salaries. The company wants to implement an app that performs its payroll calculations polymorphically.

We use abstract class Employee to represent the general concept of an employee. The classes that extend Employee are SalariedEmployee, CommissionEmployee and HourlyEmployee. Class BasePlusCommissionEmployee—which extends CommissionEmployee—represents the last employee type. The UML class diagram in Fig. 12.2 shows the inheritance hierarchy for our polymorphic employee payroll app. Abstract class Employee is *italicized*, as per the convention of the UML.

Abstract base class Employee declares the "interface" to the hierarchy—that is, the set of members that an app can invoke on all Employee objects. We use the term "interface" here in a general sense to refer to the various ways apps can communicate with objects of any Employee derived class. Be careful not to confuse the general notion of an "interface" with the formal notion of a C# interface, the subject of Section 12.7. Each employee, regardless of the way his or her earnings are calculated, has a first name, a last name and a social security number, so those pieces of data appear in abstract base class Employee.

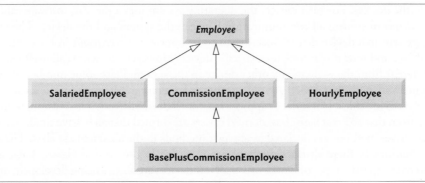

Fig. 12.2 | `Employee` hierarchy UML class diagram.

The following subsections implement the `Employee` class hierarchy. Section 12.5.1 implements `abstract` base class `Employee`. Sections 12.5.2–12.5.5 each implement one of the concrete classes. Section 12.5.6 implements a test app that builds objects of all these classes and processes those objects polymorphically.

12.5.1 Creating Abstract Base Class `Employee`

Class `Employee` (Fig. 12.4) provides methods `Earnings` and `ToString`, in addition to the auto-implemented properties that manipulate `Employee`'s data. An `Earnings` method certainly applies generically to all employees. But each earnings calculation depends on the employee's class. So we declare `Earnings` as `abstract` in base class `Employee`, because a default implementation does not make sense for that method—there's not enough information to determine what amount `Earnings` should return. Each derived class overrides `Earnings` with a specific implementation. To calculate an employee's earnings, the app assigns a reference to the employee's object to a base class `Employee` variable, then invokes the `Earnings` method on that variable. We maintain a `List` of `Employee` variables, each of which holds a reference to an `Employee` object (of course, there *cannot* be `Employee` objects because `Employee` is an *abstract* class—because of inheritance, however, all objects of all derived classes of `Employee` may nevertheless be thought of as `Employee` objects). The app iterates through the `List` and calls method `Earnings` for each `Employee` object. These method calls are processed polymorphically. Including `Earnings` as an abstract method in `Employee` *forces* every directly derived *concrete* class of `Employee` to override `Earnings` with a method that performs an appropriate pay calculation.

Method `ToString` in class `Employee` returns a `string` containing the employee's first name, last name and social security number. Each derived class of `Employee` overrides method `ToString` to create a `string` representation of an object of that class containing the employee's type (e.g., `"salaried employee:"`), followed by the rest of the employee's information.

The diagram in Fig. 12.3 shows each of the five classes in the hierarchy down the left side and methods `Earnings` and `ToString` across the top. For each class, the diagram shows the desired results of each method. [*Note:* We do not list base class `Employee`'s properties because they're not overridden in any of the derived classes—each of these properties is inherited and used "as is" by each of the derived classes.]

	Earnings	ToString
Employee	abstract	*firstName lastName* social security number: *SSN*
Salaried-Employee	weeklySalary	salaried employee: *firstName lastName* social security number: *SSN* weekly salary: *weeklysalary*

Hourly-Employee	*If hours <= 40*
	    wage * hours
	 If hours > 40
	    40 * wage +
	    (hours - 40) *
	    wage * 1.5
		hourly employee: *firstName lastName*
		 social security number: *SSN*
		 hourly wage: *wage*
		 hours worked: *hours*

Commission-Employee	commissionRate * grossSales	commission employee: *firstName lastName* social security number: *SSN* gross sales: *grossSales* commission rate: *commissionRate*
BasePlus-Commission-Employee	baseSalary + (commissionRate * grossSales)	base salaried commission employee: *firstName lastName* social security number: *SSN* gross sales: *grossSales* commission rate: *commissionRate* base salary: *baseSalary*

Fig. 12.3 | Polymorphic interface for the `Employee` hierarchy classes.

Class *Employee*

Let's consider class `Employee`'s declaration (Fig. 12.4). The class includes auto-implemented, getter-only properties for the first name, last name and social security number (lines 5–7); a constructor that initializes the first name, last name and social security number (lines 10–16); expression-bodied method `ToString` (lines 19–20), which uses properties to return an `Employee`'s `string` representation; and abstract method `Earnings` (line 23), which *must* be implemented by *concrete* derived classes. The `Employee` constructor does not validate the social security number in this example. Normally, such validation should be provided.

```
1   // Fig. 12.4: Employee.cs
2   // Employee abstract base class.
3   public abstract class Employee
4   {
5       public string FirstName { get; }
6       public string LastName { get; }
7       public string SocialSecurityNumber { get; }
```

Fig. 12.4 | `Employee` abstract base class. (Part 1 of 2.)

```
 8
 9     // three-parameter constructor
10     public Employee(string firstName, string lastName,
11        string socialSecurityNumber)
12     {
13        FirstName = firstName;
14        LastName = lastName;
15        SocialSecurityNumber = socialSecurityNumber;
16     }
17
18     // return string representation of Employee object, using properties
19     public override string ToString() => $"{FirstName} {LastName}\n" +
20        $"social security number: {SocialSecurityNumber}";
21
22     // abstract method overridden by derived classes
23     public abstract decimal Earnings(); // no implementation here
24  }
```

Fig. 12.4 | Employee abstract base class. (Part 2 of 2.)

Why did we declare Earnings as an abstract method? As explained earlier, it simply does not make sense to provide an implementation of this method in class Employee. We cannot calculate the earnings for a *general* Employee—we first must know the *specific* Employee type to determine the appropriate earnings calculation. By declaring this method abstract, we indicate that each *concrete* derived class *must* provide an appropriate Earnings implementation and that an app will be able to use base-class Employee variables to invoke method Earnings polymorphically for *any* type of Employee.

12.5.2 Creating Concrete Derived Class SalariedEmployee

Class SalariedEmployee (Fig. 12.5) extends class Employee (line 5) and overrides Earnings (line 37), which makes SalariedEmployee a concrete class. The class includes a constructor (lines 10–15) that takes a first name, a last name, a social security number and a weekly salary as arguments; property WeeklySalary (lines 18–34) to manipulate instance variable weeklySalary, including a set accessor that ensures we assign only nonnegative values to weeklySalary; method Earnings (line 37) to calculate a SalariedEmployee's earnings; and method ToString (lines 40–42), which returns a string including the employee's type, namely, "salaried employee: ", followed by employee-specific information produced by base class Employee's ToString method and SalariedEmployee's WeeklySalary property. Class SalariedEmployee's constructor passes the first name, last name and social security number to the Employee constructor (line 12) via a constructor initializer to initialize the base class's data. Method Earnings overrides Employee's abstract method Earnings to provide a concrete implementation that returns the SalariedEmployee's weekly salary. If we do not implement Earnings, class Salaried-Employee must be declared abstract—otherwise, a compilation error occurs (and, of course, we want SalariedEmployee to be a concrete class).

```
1    // Fig. 12.5: SalariedEmployee.cs
2    // SalariedEmployee class that extends Employee.
3    using System;
4
5    public class SalariedEmployee : Employee
6    {
7       private decimal weeklySalary;
8
9       // four-parameter constructor
10      public SalariedEmployee(string firstName, string lastName,
11         string socialSecurityNumber, decimal weeklySalary)
12         : base(firstName, lastName, socialSecurityNumber)
13      {
14         WeeklySalary = weeklySalary; // validate salary
15      }
16
17      // property that gets and sets salaried employee's salary
18      public decimal WeeklySalary
19      {
20         get
21         {
22            return weeklySalary;
23         }
24         set
25         {
26            if (value < 0) // validation
27            {
28               throw new ArgumentOutOfRangeException(nameof(value),
29                  value, $"{nameof(WeeklySalary)} must be >= 0");
30            }
31
32            weeklySalary = value;
33         }
34      }
35
36      // calculate earnings; override abstract method Earnings in Employee
37      public override decimal Earnings() => WeeklySalary;
38
39      // return string representation of SalariedEmployee object
40      public override string ToString() =>
41         $"salaried employee: {base.ToString()}\n" +
42         $"weekly salary: {WeeklySalary:C}";
43   }
```

Fig. 12.5 | SalariedEmployee class that extends Employee.

SalariedEmployee method ToString (lines 40–42) overrides Employee's version. If class SalariedEmployee did *not* override ToString, SalariedEmployee would have inherited the Employee version. In that case, SalariedEmployee's ToString method would simply return the employee's full name and social security number, which does not adequately represent a SalariedEmployee.

To produce a complete SalariedEmployee string representation, the derived class's ToString method returns "salaried employee: ", followed by the base-class Employee-specific information (i.e., first name, last name and social security number) obtained by invoking the base class's ToString via keyword base (line 41)—this is a nice example of code reuse. The string representation also contains the employee's weekly salary, obtained via property WeeklySalary.

12.5.3 Creating Concrete Derived Class HourlyEmployee

Class HourlyEmployee (Fig. 12.6) also extends class Employee (line 5). The class includes a constructor (lines 11–18) that takes as arguments a first name, a last name, a social security number, an hourly wage and the number of hours worked. Lines 21–37 and 40–56 declare properties Wage and Hours for instance variables wage and hours (lines 7–8), respectively. Wage's set accessor ensures that wage is nonnegative, and Hours' set accessor ensures that hours is in the range 0–168 (the total number of hours in a week) inclusive. The class overrides method Earnings (lines 59–69) to calculate an HourlyEmployee's earnings and method ToString (lines 72–74) to return an HourlyEmployee's string representation. The HourlyEmployee constructor passes the first name, last name and social security number to the base-class Employee constructor (line 14) to initialize the base class's data. Also, method ToString calls base-class method ToString (line 73) to get the string representation of the Employee-specific information (i.e., first name, last name and social security number).

```
1   // Fig. 12.6: HourlyEmployee.cs
2   // HourlyEmployee class that extends Employee.
3   using System;
4
5   public class HourlyEmployee : Employee
6   {
7      private decimal wage; // wage per hour
8      private decimal hours; // hours worked for the week
9
10     // five-parameter constructor
11     public HourlyEmployee(string firstName, string lastName,
12        string socialSecurityNumber, decimal hourlyWage,
13        decimal hoursWorked)
14        : base(firstName, lastName, socialSecurityNumber)
15     {
16        Wage = hourlyWage; // validate hourly wage
17        Hours = hoursWorked; // validate hours worked
18     }
19
20     // property that gets and sets hourly employee's wage
21     public decimal Wage
22     {
23        get
24        {
25           return wage;
26        }
27        set
28        {
```

Fig. 12.6 | HourlyEmployee class that extends Employee. (Part 1 of 2.)

```
29              if (value < 0) // validation
30              {
31                  throw new ArgumentOutOfRangeException(nameof(value),
32                      value, $"{nameof(Wage)} must be >= 0");
33              }
34
35              wage = value;
36          }
37      }
38
39      // property that gets and sets hourly employee's hours
40      public decimal Hours
41      {
42          get
43          {
44              return hours;
45          }
46          set
47          {
48              if (value < 0 || value > 168) // validation
49              {
50                  throw new ArgumentOutOfRangeException(nameof(value),
51                      value, $"{nameof(Hours)} must be >= 0 and <= 168");
52              }
53
54              hours = value;
55          }
56      }
57
58      // calculate earnings; override Employee's abstract method Earnings
59      public override decimal Earnings()
60      {
61          if (Hours <= 40) // no overtime
62          {
63              return Wage * Hours;
64          }
65          else
66          {
67              return (40 * Wage) + ((Hours - 40) * Wage * 1.5M);
68          }
69      }
70
71      // return string representation of HourlyEmployee object
72      public override string ToString() =>
73          $"hourly employee: {base.ToString()}\n" +
74          $"hourly wage: {Wage:C}\nhours worked: {Hours:F2}";
75  }
```

Fig. 12.6 | HourlyEmployee class that extends Employee. (Part 2 of 2.)

12.5.4 Creating Concrete Derived Class CommissionEmployee

Class CommissionEmployee (Fig. 12.7) extends class Employee (line 5). The class includes a constructor (lines 11–18) that takes a first name, a last name, a social security number, a sales amount and a commission rate; properties GrossSales and CommissionRate (lines 21–37 and 40–56) to manipulate instance variables grossSales and commissionRate, respectively; overridden method Earnings (line 59) to calculate a CommissionEmployee's earnings; and overridden method ToString (lines 62–65), which returns a Commission-Employee's string representation. The constructor also passes the first name, last name and social security number to the Employee constructor (line 14) to initialize Employee's data. Method ToString calls base-class method ToString (line 63) to get the string representation of the Employee-specific information (i.e., first name, last name and social security number).

```
 1   // Fig. 12.7: CommissionEmployee.cs
 2   // CommissionEmployee class that extends Employee.
 3   using System;
 4
 5   public class CommissionEmployee : Employee
 6   {
 7      private decimal grossSales; // gross weekly sales
 8      private decimal commissionRate; // commission percentage
 9
10      // five-parameter constructor
11      public CommissionEmployee(string firstName, string lastName,
12         string socialSecurityNumber, decimal grossSales,
13         decimal commissionRate)
14         : base(firstName, lastName, socialSecurityNumber)
15      {
16         GrossSales = grossSales; // validates gross sales
17         CommissionRate = commissionRate; // validates commission rate
18      }
19
20      // property that gets and sets commission employee's gross sales
21      public decimal GrossSales
22      {
23         get
24         {
25            return grossSales;
26         }
27         set
28         {
29            if (value < 0) // validation
30            {
31               throw new ArgumentOutOfRangeException(nameof(value),
32                  value, $"{nameof(GrossSales)} must be >= 0");
33            }
34
35            grossSales = value;
36         }
37      }
38
39      // property that gets and sets commission employee's commission rate
40      public decimal CommissionRate
41      {
```

Fig. 12.7 | CommissionEmployee class that extends Employee. (Part 1 of 2.)

```
42          get
43          {
44              return commissionRate;
45          }
46          set
47          {
48              if (value <= 0 || value >= 1) // validation
49              {
50                  throw new ArgumentOutOfRangeException(nameof(value),
51                      value, $"{nameof(CommissionRate)} must be > 0 and < 1");
52              }
53
54              commissionRate = value;
55          }
56      }
57
58      // calculate earnings; override abstract method Earnings in Employee
59      public override decimal Earnings() => CommissionRate * GrossSales;
60
61      // return string representation of CommissionEmployee object
62      public override string ToString() =>
63          $"commission employee: {base.ToString()}\n" +
64          $"gross sales: {GrossSales:C}\n" +
65          $"commission rate: {CommissionRate:F2}";
66  }
```

Fig. 12.7 | CommissionEmployee class that extends Employee. (Part 2 of 2.)

12.5.5 Creating Indirect Concrete Derived Class BasePlusCommissionEmployee

Class BasePlusCommissionEmployee (Fig. 12.8) extends class CommissionEmployee (line 5) and therefore is an *indirect* derived class of class Employee. BasePlusCommissionEmployee has a constructor (lines 10–17) that takes as arguments a first name, a last name, a social security number, a sales amount, a commission rate and a base salary. It then passes the first name, last name, social security number, sales amount and commission rate to the CommissionEmployee constructor (lines 13–14) to initialize the base class's data. BasePlusCommissionEmployee also contains property BaseSalary (lines 21–37) to manipulate instance variable baseSalary. Overridden method Earnings (line 40) calculates a BasePlusCommissionEmployee's earnings, calling base class CommissionEmployee's Earnings to calculate the commission-based portion of the BasePlusCommissionEmployee's earnings. Again, this shows the benefits of code reuse. The overridden ToString method (lines 43–44) creates a string representation of a BasePlusCommissionEmployee that contains "base-salaried", followed by the string returned by base class CommissionEmployee's ToString method (another example of code reuse), then the base salary. The result is a string beginning with "base-salaried commission employee", followed by the rest of the BasePlusCommissionEmployee's information. Recall that CommissionEmployee's ToString method obtains the employee's first name, last name and social security number by invoking the ToString method of *its* base class (i.e., Employee)—a further demonstration of code reuse. BasePlusCommissionEmployee's ToString initiates a *chain of method calls* that spans all three levels of the Employee hierarchy.

```
 1   // Fig. 12.8: BasePlusCommissionEmployee.cs
 2   // BasePlusCommissionEmployee class that extends CommissionEmployee.
 3   using System;
 4
 5   public class BasePlusCommissionEmployee : CommissionEmployee
 6   {
 7      private decimal baseSalary; // base salary per week
 8
 9      // six-parameter constructor
10      public BasePlusCommissionEmployee(string firstName, string lastName,
11         string socialSecurityNumber, decimal grossSales,
12         decimal commissionRate, decimal baseSalary)
13         : base(firstName, lastName, socialSecurityNumber,
14             grossSales, commissionRate)
15      {
16         BaseSalary = baseSalary; // validates base salary
17      }
18
19      // property that gets and sets
20      // BasePlusCommissionEmployee's base salary
21      public decimal BaseSalary
22      {
23         get
24         {
25            return baseSalary;
26         }
27         set
28         {
29            if (value < 0) // validation
30            {
31               throw new ArgumentOutOfRangeException(nameof(value),
32                  value, $"{nameof(BaseSalary)} must be >= 0");
33            }
34
35            baseSalary = value;
36         }
37      }
38
39      // calculate earnings
40      public override decimal Earnings() => BaseSalary + base.Earnings();
41
42      // return string representation of BasePlusCommissionEmployee
43      public override string ToString() =>
44         $"base-salaried {base.ToString()}\nbase salary: {BaseSalary:C}";
45   }
```

Fig. 12.8 | BasePlusCommissionEmployee class that extends CommissionEmployee.

12.5.6 Polymorphic Processing, Operator is and Downcasting

To test our Employee hierarchy, the app in Fig. 12.9 creates an object of each of the four concrete classes SalariedEmployee, HourlyEmployee, CommissionEmployee and Base-PlusCommissionEmployee (lines 11–19). The app manipulates these objects, first via variables of each object's own type (lines 23–30), then polymorphically, using a List of

Employee variables (lines 33–56)—each object's ToString method is called *implicitly* by WriteLine when the object is output as a string. While processing the objects polymorphically, the app increases the base salary of each BasePlusCommissionEmployee by 10% (this, of course, requires determining the object's type at *execution* time). Finally, lines 59–63 polymorphically determine and output the type of each object in the Employee List.

```csharp
1   // Fig. 12.9: PayrollSystemTest.cs
2   // Employee hierarchy test app.
3   using System;
4   using System.Collections.Generic;
5
6   class PayrollSystemTest
7   {
8      static void Main()
9      {
10        // create derived-class objects
11        var salariedEmployee = new SalariedEmployee("John", "Smith",
12           "111-11-1111", 800.00M);
13        var hourlyEmployee = new HourlyEmployee("Karen", "Price",
14           "222-22-2222", 16.75M, 40.0M);
15        var commissionEmployee = new CommissionEmployee("Sue", "Jones",
16           "333-33-3333", 10000.00M, .06M);
17        var basePlusCommissionEmployee =
18           new BasePlusCommissionEmployee("Bob", "Lewis",
19           "444-44-4444", 5000.00M, .04M, 300.00M);
20
21        Console.WriteLine("Employees processed individually:\n");
22
23        Console.WriteLine($"{salariedEmployee}\nearned: " +
24           $"{salariedEmployee.Earnings():C}\n");
25        Console.WriteLine(
26           $"{hourlyEmployee}\nearned: {hourlyEmployee.Earnings():C}\n");
27        Console.WriteLine($"{commissionEmployee}\nearned: " +
28           $"{commissionEmployee.Earnings():C}\n");
29        Console.WriteLine($"{basePlusCommissionEmployee}\nearned: " +
30           $"{basePlusCommissionEmployee.Earnings():C}\n");
31
32        // create List<Employee> and initialize with employee objects
33        var employees = new List<Employee>() {salariedEmployee,
34           hourlyEmployee, commissionEmployee, basePlusCommissionEmployee};
35
36        Console.WriteLine("Employees processed polymorphically:\n");
37
38        // generically process each element in employees
39        foreach (var currentEmployee in employees)
40        {
41           Console.WriteLine(currentEmployee); // invokes ToString
42
43           // determine whether element is a BasePlusCommissionEmployee
44           if (currentEmployee is BasePlusCommissionEmployee)
45           {
```

Fig. 12.9 | Employee hierarchy test app. (Part I of 3.)

```
46                // downcast Employee reference to
47                // BasePlusCommissionEmployee reference
48                var employee = (BasePlusCommissionEmployee) currentEmployee;
49
50                employee.BaseSalary *= 1.10M;
51                Console.WriteLine("new base salary with 10% increase is: " +
52                    $"{employee.BaseSalary:C}");
53            }
54
55            Console.WriteLine($"earned: {currentEmployee.Earnings():C}\n");
56        }
57
58        // get type name of each object in employees
59        for (int j = 0; j < employees.Count; j++)
60        {
61            Console.WriteLine(
62                $"Employee {j} is a {employees[j].GetType()}");
63        }
64    }
65 }
```

```
Employees processed individually:

salaried employee: John Smith
social security number: 111-11-1111
weekly salary: $800.00
earned: $800.00

hourly employee: Karen Price
social security number: 222-22-2222
hourly wage: $16.75
hours worked: 40.00
earned: $670.00

commission employee: Sue Jones
social security number: 333-33-3333
gross sales: $10,000.00
commission rate: 0.06
earned: $600.00

base-salaried commission employee: Bob Lewis
social security number: 444-44-4444
gross sales: $5,000.00
commission rate: 0.04
base salary: $300.00
earned: $500.00


Employees processed polymorphically:

salaried employee: John Smith
social security number: 111-11-1111
weekly salary: $800.00
earned: $800.00
```

Fig. 12.9 | Employee hierarchy test app. (Part 2 of 3.)

```
hourly employee: Karen Price
social security number: 222-22-2222
hourly wage: $16.75
hours worked: 40.00
earned: $670.00

commission employee: Sue Jones
social security number: 333-33-3333
gross sales: $10,000.00
commission rate: 0.06
earned: $600.00

base-salaried commission employee: Bob Lewis
social security number: 444-44-4444
gross sales: $5,000.00
commission rate: 0.04
base salary: $300.00
new base salary with 10% increase is: $330.00
earned: $530.00

Employee 0 is a SalariedEmployee
Employee 1 is a HourlyEmployee
Employee 2 is a CommissionEmployee
Employee 3 is a BasePlusCommissionEmployee
```

Fig. 12.9 | Employee hierarchy test app. (Part 3 of 3.)

Assigning Derived-Class Objects to Base-Class References

Lines 33–34 create the List<Employee> named employees and initialize it with the SalariedEmployee, HourlyEmployee, CommissionEmployee and BasePlusCommissionEmployee created in lines 11–19. Each element of the List is an Employee variable. The derived-class objects can each be assigned to an element of employees, because a SalariedEmployee *is an* Employee, an HourlyEmployee *is an* Employee, a CommissionEmployee *is an* Employee and a BasePlusCommissionEmployee *is an* Employee. This is allowed even though Employee is an *abstract* class.

Polymorphic Processing of Employees

Lines 39–56 iterate through employees and invoke methods ToString and Earnings with Employee variable currentEmployee, which is assigned the reference of a different Employee during each iteration. The output illustrates that the appropriate methods for each class are indeed invoked. All calls to virtual methods ToString and Earnings are resolved at *execution* time, based on the type of the object to which currentEmployee refers. This process is known as dynamic binding or late binding. For example, line 41 *implicitly* invokes method ToString of the object to which currentEmployee refers. Only the methods of class Employee can be called via an Employee variable—and Employee includes class object's methods, such as ToString. (Section 11.7 discussed the methods that all classes inherit from class object.) A base-class reference can be used to invoke only methods that were originally declared in the base class or higher in the class hierarchy.

Giving BasePlusCommissionEmployees 10% Raises

We perform special processing on BasePlusCommissionEmployee objects—as we encounter them, we increase their base salary by 10%. When processing objects polymorphically, we typically do not need to worry about the *specifics*, but to adjust the base salary, we do have to determine the specific type of each `Employee` object at execution time. Line 44 uses the `is` operator to determine whether a particular `Employee` object's type is `BasePlusCommissionEmployee`. The condition in line 44 is true only if the object referenced by `currentEmployee` *is a* `BasePlusCommissionEmployee`. This would also be true for any object of a `BasePlusCommissionEmployee` derived class (if there were any), because an object of any `BasePlusCommissionEmployee` derived class *is a* `BasePlusCommissionEmployee`.

Line 48 casts `currentEmployee` from type `Employee` to type `BasePlusCommissionEmployee` and assigns the result to `BasePlusCommissionEmployee` variable `employee`. This is known as a **downcast**, because the cast is to a type lower down in the class hierarchy. This downcast is allowed only if the object to which `currentEmployee` refers has an *is-a* relationship with `BasePlusCommissionEmployee`—the condition at line 44 ensures this is the case. Why would we ever want to perform such a downcast? *A base-class reference can be used to invoke only the methods declared in the base class*—attempting to invoke a derived-class-only method through a base-class reference results in a compilation error. If an app needs to perform a derived-class-specific operation on a derived-class object referenced by a base-class variable, the app must first cast the base-class reference to a derived-class reference. So, this cast is *required* in this program for us to use derived class `BasePlusCommissionEmployee`'s `BaseSalary` property on the `currentEmployee`.

Common Programming Error 12.3

Assigning a base-class variable to a derived-class variable (without an explicit downcast) is a compilation error.

Software Engineering Observation 12.5

If at execution time the reference to a derived-class object has been assigned to a variable of one of its direct or indirect base classes, it's acceptable to cast the reference stored in that base-class variable back to a reference of the derived-class type. Before performing such a cast, use the `is` operator to ensure that the object is indeed an object of an appropriate derived-class type.

When *downcasting* an object, an `InvalidCastException` (of namespace `System`) occurs if at execution time the object does not have an *is a* relationship with the type specified in the cast operator. An object can be cast only to its own type or to the type of one of its base classes. You can avoid a potential `InvalidCastException` by using the **as** operator to perform a downcast rather than a cast operator. For example, in the statement

```
var employee = currentEmployee as BasePlusCommissionEmployee;
```

`employee` is assigned a reference to an object that *is a* `BasePlusCommissionEmployee`, or the value `null` if `currentEmployee` is not a `BasePlusCommissionEmployee`. You can then compare `employee` with `null` to determine whether the cast succeeded.

If the `is` expression in line 44 is true, the `if` statement (lines 44–53) performs the special processing required for the `BasePlusCommissionEmployee` object. Using `BasePlusCommissionEmployee` variable `employee`, line 50 accesses the derived-class-only property `BaseSalary` to retrieve and update the employee's base salary with the 10% raise.

Line 55 invokes method `Earnings` on `currentEmployee`, which calls the appropriate derived-class object's `Earnings` method polymorphically. Obtaining the earnings of the `Sal-`

ariedEmployee, HourlyEmployee and CommissionEmployee polymorphically in line 55 produces the same result as obtaining these employees' earnings individually in lines 24, 26 and 28. However, the earnings amount obtained for the BasePlusCommissionEmployee in lines 55 is higher than that obtained in line 30, due to the 10% increase in its base salary.

Every Object Knows Its Own Type

Lines 59–63 display each employee's *type* as a string. Every object knows its own type and can access this information through method **GetType**, which all classes inherit from class object. This method returns an object of class Type (of namespace System), which contains information about the object's type, including its class name, the names of its methods and the name of its base class. Line 62 invokes method GetType on the object to get its runtime class (i.e., a Type object that represents the object's type). Then method ToString is *implicitly* invoked on the object returned by GetType. The Type class's ToString method returns the class name.

Avoiding Compilation Errors with Downcasting

In the previous example, we avoid compilation errors by *downcasting* an Employee variable to a BasePlusCommissionEmployee variable in line 48—the type BasePlusCommissionEmployee is inferred from the cast operation. If we remove the cast operator and attempt to assign Employee variable currentEmployee directly to a BasePlusCommissionEmployee variable named employee (with its type explicitly declared, rather than using var), we'd receive a "Cannot implicitly convert type" compilation error. This error indicates that the attempt to assign the reference of base-class object currentEmployee to derived-class variable employee is *not* allowed without an appropriate cast operator. The compiler prevents this assignment, because a CommissionEmployee is *not* a BasePlusCommissionEmployee—again, the *is-a* relationship applies only between the derived class and its base classes, not vice versa.

Similarly, if lines 50 and 52 use base-class variable currentEmployee, rather than derived-class variable employee, when accessing derived-class-only property BaseSalary, we receive an "'Employee' does not contain a definition for 'BaseSalary'" compilation error on each of these lines. *Attempting to invoke derived-class-only methods or properties on a base-class reference is not allowed.* While lines 50 and 52 execute only if is in line 44 returns true to indicate that currentEmployee refers to a BasePlusCommissionEmployee object, we *cannot* attempt to use derived-class BasePlusCommissionEmployee property BaseSalary with base-class Employee reference currentEmployee. The compiler would generate errors in lines 50 and 52, because BaseSalary is not a base-class member and cannot be used with a base-class variable. Although the actual method that's called depends on the object's type at execution time, *a variable can be used to invoke only those methods that are members of that variable's type*, which the compiler verifies. Using a base-class Employee variable, we can invoke only methods and properties found in class Employee—methods Earnings and ToString, and properties FirstName, LastName and SocialSecurityNumber—and methods inherited from class object.

12.5.7 Summary of the Allowed Assignments Between Base-Class and Derived-Class Variables

Now that you've seen a complete app that processes diverse derived-class objects polymorphically, we summarize what you can and cannot do with base-class and derived-class objects and variables. Although a derived-class object also *is a* base-class object, the two are nevertheless different. As discussed previously, derived-class objects can be treated as if they were base-class objects. However, the derived class can have additional derived-class-only members. For this reason, assigning a base-class reference to a derived-class variable is *not* allowed without an *explicit* cast—such an assignment would leave the derived-class members *undefined* for a base-class object.

We've discussed four ways to assign base-class and derived-class references to variables of base-class and derived-class types:

1. *Assigning a base-class reference to a base-class variable* is straightforward.

2. *Assigning a derived-class reference to a derived-class variable* is straightforward.

3. *Assigning a derived-class reference to a base-class variable* is safe, because the derived-class object *is an* object of its base class. However, this reference can be used to refer *only* to base-class members. If this code refers to derived-class-only members through the base-class variable, the compiler reports errors.

4. *Attempting to assign a base-class reference to a derived-class variable* is a compilation error. To avoid this error, the base-class reference must be cast to a derived-class type explicitly or must be converted using the as operator. At execution time, if the object to which the reference refers is *not* a derived-class object, an exception will occur (unless you use the as operator, in which case you'll have to check the expression's result for null). The is operator can be used to ensure that such a cast is performed *only* if the object is a derived-class object.

12.6 sealed Methods and Classes

Only methods declared virtual, override or abstract can be *overridden* in derived classes. A method declared sealed in a base class *cannot* be overridden in a derived class. Methods that are declared private are implicitly sealed, because it's impossible to override them in a derived class (though the derived class can declare a new method with the same signature as the private method in the base class). Methods that are declared static also are implicitly sealed, because static methods cannot be overridden either. A derived-class method declared both override and sealed can override a base-class method, but cannot be overridden in derived classes further down the inheritance hierarchy.

A sealed method's declaration can never change, so all derived classes use the same method implementation, and calls to sealed methods (and non-virtual methods) are resolved at *compile time*—this is known as static binding. Since the compiler knows that sealed methods cannot be overridden, it can often *optimize* code by removing calls to sealed methods and replacing them with the expanded code of their declarations at each method-call location—a technique known as inlining the code.

Performance Tip 12.1
The compiler can decide to inline a sealed method call and will do so for small, simple sealed methods. Inlining does not violate encapsulation or information hiding, but does improve performance, because it eliminates the overhead of making a method call.

A class that's declared sealed *cannot* be a base class (i.e., a class cannot extend a sealed class). All methods in a sealed class are implicitly sealed. Class string is a sealed class. This class cannot be extended, so apps that use `strings` can rely on the functionality of `string` objects as specified in the Framework Class Library.

Common Programming Error 12.4

Attempting to declare a derived class of a `sealed` class is a compilation error.

12.7 Case Study: Creating and Using Interfaces

Our next example (Figs. 12.11–12.14) reexamines the payroll system of Section 12.5. Suppose that the company involved wishes to perform several accounting operations in a single accounts-payable app—in addition to calculating the payroll earnings that must be paid to each employee, the company must also calculate the payment due on each of several invoices (i.e., bills for goods purchased). Though applied to unrelated things (i.e., employees and invoices), both operations have to do with calculating some kind of payment amount. For an employee, the payment refers to the employee's earnings. For an invoice, the payment refers to the total cost of the goods listed on the invoice. Can we calculate such different things as the payments due for employees and invoices polymorphically in a single app? Is there a capability that can require *unrelated* classes to implement a set of common methods (e.g., a method that calculates a payment amount)? *Interfaces* offer exactly this capability.

Standardized Interactions

Interfaces define and standardize the ways in which people and systems can interact with one another. For example, the controls on a radio serve as an interface between a radio's users and its internal components. The controls allow users to perform a limited set of operations (e.g., changing the station, adjusting the volume, choosing between AM and FM), and different radios may implement the controls in different ways (e.g., using push buttons, dials, voice commands). The interface specifies *what* operations a radio must permit users to perform but does not specify *how* they're performed. Similarly, the interface between a driver and a car with a manual transmission includes the steering wheel, the gear shift, the clutch pedal, the gas pedal and the brake pedal. This same interface is found in nearly all manual-transmission cars, enabling someone who knows how to drive one particular manual-transmission car to drive just about any other. The components of each car may look a bit different, but the *general* purpose is the same—to allow people to drive the car.

Interfaces in Software

Software objects also communicate via interfaces. A C# interface describes a set of methods and properties that can be called on an object—to tell it, for example, to perform some task or return some piece of information. The next example introduces an interface named `IPayable` that describes the functionality of any object that must be capable of being paid and thus must offer a method to determine the proper payment amount due. An interface declaration begins with the keyword `interface` and can contain only

- abstract methods,
- abstract properties,
- abstract indexers (not covered in this book) and
- abstract events (events are discussed in Chapter 14, Graphical User Interfaces with Windows Forms: Part 1).

All interface members are *implicitly* declared both `public` and `abstract`. In addition, each interface can extend one or more other interfaces to create a more elaborate interface that other classes can implement.

Common Programming Error 12.5

It's a compilation error to explicitly declare an interface member `public` or `abstract`, because they're redundant in interface-member declarations. It's also a compilation error to specify in an interface any implementation details, such as concrete method declarations.

Implementing an Interface

A class must specify that it **implements** the interface by listing the interface name after the colon (`:`) in the class declaration. This is the *same* syntax used to indicate inheritance from a base class. A concrete class implementing the interface must declare each member of the interface with the signature specified in the interface declaration. A class that implements an interface but does *not* implement all its members is an abstract class—it must be declared `abstract` and must contain an `abstract` declaration for each unimplemented member of the interface. Implementing an interface is like signing a contract with the compiler that states, "I will provide an implementation for all the members specified by the interface, or I will declare them `abstract`."

Common Programming Error 12.6

Failing to define or declare any member of an interface in a class that implements the interface results in a compilation error.

Common Methods for Unrelated Classes

An interface is typically used when *unrelated* classes need to *share* common methods. This allows objects of unrelated classes to be processed polymorphically—objects of classes that implement the same interface can respond to the *same* method calls. You can create an interface that describes the desired functionality, then implement this interface in any classes requiring that functionality. For example, in the accounts-payable app developed in this section, we implement interface `IPayable` in each class (e.g., `Employee`, `Invoice`) that must be able to calculate a payment amount.

Interfaces vs. Abstract Classes

An interface often is used in place of an `abstract` class when there's no default implementation to inherit—that is, no fields and no default method implementations. Like `abstract` classes, interfaces are typically `public` types, so they're normally declared in files by themselves with the same name as the interface and the `.cs` filename extension.

12.7.1 Developing an `IPayable` Hierarchy

To build an app that can determine payments for employees and invoices alike, we first create an interface named `IPayable`. Interface `IPayable` contains method `GetPaymentAmount` that returns a `decimal` amount to be paid for an object of any class that implements the interface. Method `GetPaymentAmount` is a general-purpose version of method `Earnings` of the `Employee` hierarchy—method `Earnings` calculates a payment amount specifically for an `Employee`, while `GetPaymentAmount` can be applied to a broad range of *unrelated* objects. After declaring interface `IPayable`, we introduce class `Invoice`, which implements interface `IPayable`. We then modify class `Employee` such that it also implements interface `IPayable`.

Classes `Invoice` and `Employee` both represent things for which the company must be able to calculate a payment amount. Both classes implement `IPayable`, so an app can invoke method `GetPaymentAmount` on `Invoice` objects and `Employee` objects alike. This enables the polymorphic processing of `Invoice`s and `Employee`s required for our company's accounts-payable app.

Good Programming Practice 12.1
By convention, the name of an interface begins with I (e.g., IPayable). This helps distinguish interfaces from classes, improving code readability.

Good Programming Practice 12.2
When declaring a method in an interface, choose a name that describes the method's purpose in a general manner, because the method may be implemented by a broad range of unrelated classes.

UML Diagram Containing an Interface
The UML class diagram in Fig. 12.10 shows the interface and class hierarchy used in our accounts-payable app. The hierarchy begins with interface `IPayable`. The UML distinguishes an interface from a class by placing the word "interface" in guillemets (« and ») above the interface name. The UML expresses the relationship between a class and an interface through a realization. A class is said to "realize," or implement, an interface. A class diagram models a realization as a dashed arrow with a *hollow arrowhead* pointing from the implementing class to the interface. The diagram in Fig. 12.10 indicates that classes `Invoice` and `Employee` each realize (i.e., implement) interface `IPayable`. As in the class diagram of Fig. 12.2, class `Employee` appears in italics, indicating that it's an abstract class. Concrete class `SalariedEmployee` extends `Employee` and inherits its base class's realization relationship with interface `IPayable`. Figure 12.10 could include Section 12.5's entire `Employee` class hierarchy—to keep the forthcoming example small, we did not include classes `HourlyEmployee`, `CommissionEmployee` and `BasePlusCommissionEmployee`.

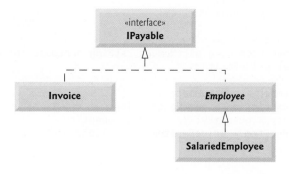

Fig. 12.10 | `IPayable` interface and class hierarchy UML class diagram.

12.7.2 Declaring Interface `IPayable`

The declaration of interface `IPayable` begins in Fig. 12.11 at line 3. Interface `IPayable` contains `public abstract` method `GetPaymentAmount` (line 5). The method cannot be *explicitly* declared `public` or `abstract`. Interfaces can have *any* number of members and interface methods can have parameters.

```
1   // Fig. 12.11: IPayable.cs
2   // IPayable interface declaration.
3   public interface IPayable
4   {
5      decimal GetPaymentAmount(); // calculate payment; no implementation
6   }
```

Fig. 12.11 | `IPayable` interface declaration.

12.7.3 Creating Class `Invoice`

We now create class `Invoice` (Fig. 12.12) to represent a simple invoice that contains billing information for one kind of part. The class contains properties `PartNumber` (line 7), `PartDescription` (line 8), `Quantity` (lines 23–39) and `PricePerItem` (lines 42–58) that indicate the part number, the description of the part, the quantity of the part ordered and the price per item. Class `Invoice` also contains a constructor (lines 13–20) and a `ToString` method (lines 61–63) that returns a string representation of an `Invoice` object. The set accessors of properties `Quantity` and `PricePerItem` ensure that `quantity` and `pricePerItem` are assigned only nonnegative values.

```
1   // Fig. 12.12: Invoice.cs
2   // Invoice class implements IPayable.
3   using System;
4
5   public class Invoice : IPayable
6   {
7      public string PartNumber { get; }
8      public string PartDescription { get; }
9      private int quantity;
10     private decimal pricePerItem;
11
12     // four-parameter constructor
13     public Invoice(string partNumber, string partDescription, int quantity,
14        decimal pricePerItem)
15     {
16        PartNumber = partNumber;
17        PartDescription = partDescription;
18        Quantity = quantity; // validate quantity
19        PricePerItem = pricePerItem; // validate price per item
20     }
21
```

Fig. 12.12 | `Invoice` class implements `IPayable`. (Part 1 of 2.)

```
22     // property that gets and sets the quantity on the invoice
23     public int Quantity
24     {
25        get
26        {
27           return quantity;
28        }
29        set
30        {
31           if (value < 0) // validation
32           {
33              throw new ArgumentOutOfRangeException(nameof(value),
34                 value, $"{nameof(Quantity)} must be >= 0");
35           }
36
37           quantity = value;
38        }
39     }
40
41     // property that gets and sets the price per item
42     public decimal PricePerItem
43     {
44        get
45        {
46           return pricePerItem;
47        }
48        set
49        {
50           if (value < 0) // validation
51           {
52              throw new ArgumentOutOfRangeException(nameof(value),
53                 value, $"{nameof(PricePerItem)} must be >= 0");
54           }
55
56           pricePerItem = value;
57        }
58     }
59
60     // return string representation of Invoice object
61     public override string ToString() =>
62        $"invoice:\npart number: {PartNumber} ({PartDescription})\n" +
63        $"quantity: {Quantity}\nprice per item: {PricePerItem:C}";
64
65     // method required to carry out contract with interface IPayable
66     public decimal GetPaymentAmount() => Quantity * PricePerItem;
67  }
```

Fig. 12.12 | Invoice class implements IPayable. (Part 2 of 2.)

Line 5 indicates that class Invoice implements interface IPayable. Like all classes, class Invoice also implicitly inherits from class object. All objects of a class can implement multiple interfaces, in which case they have the *is-a* relationship with each implemented interface type.

To implement more than one interface, use a comma-separated list of interface names after the colon (:) in the class declaration, as in

> **public class** *ClassName* : *BaseClassName*, *FirstInterface*, *SecondInterface*, ...

When a class inherits from a base class and implements one or more interfaces, the class declaration *must* list the base-class name *before* any interface names.

Software Engineering Observation 12.6

C# does not allow derived classes to inherit from more than one base class, but it does allow a class to inherit from a base class and implement any number of interfaces.

Class `Invoice` implements the one method in interface `IPayable`—method `Get-PaymentAmount` is declared in line 66. The method calculates the amount required to pay the invoice. The method multiplies the values of `quantity` and `pricePerItem` (obtained through the appropriate properties) and returns the result. This method satisfies the implementation requirement for the method in interface `IPayable`—we've *fulfilled the interface contract* with the compiler.

12.7.4 Modifying Class `Employee` to Implement Interface `IPayable`

We now modify class `Employee` to implement interface `IPayable` (Fig. 12.13). This class declaration is identical to that of Fig. 12.4 with two exceptions:

- Line 3 of Fig. 12.13 indicates that class `Employee` now implements interface `IPayable`.

- Line 27 implements interface `IPayable`'s `GetPaymentAmount` method.

Notice that `GetPaymentAmount` simply calls `Employee`'s abstract method `Earnings`. At execution time, when `GetPaymentAmount` is called on an object of an `Employee` derived class, `GetPaymentAmount` calls that class's concrete `Earnings` method, which knows how to calculate earnings for objects of that derived-class type.

```
1   // Fig. 12.13: Employee.cs
2   // Employee abstract base class that implements interface IPayable.
3   public abstract class Employee : IPayable
4   {
5      public string FirstName { get; }
6      public string LastName { get; }
7      public string SocialSecurityNumber { get; }
8
9      // three-parameter constructor
10     public Employee(string firstName, string lastName,
11        string socialSecurityNumber)
12     {
13        FirstName = firstName;
14        LastName = lastName;
15        SocialSecurityNumber = socialSecurityNumber;
16     }
17
```

Fig. 12.13 | Employee abstract base class that implements interface `IPayable`. (Part 1 of 2.)

```
18      // return string representation of Employee object, using properties
19      public override string ToString() => $"{FirstName} {LastName}\n" +
20         $"social security number: {SocialSecurityNumber}";
21
22      // abstract method overridden by derived classes
23      public abstract decimal Earnings(); // no implementation here
24
25      // implementing GetPaymentAmount here enables the entire Employee
26      // class hierarchy to be used in an app that processes IPayables
27      public decimal GetPaymentAmount() => Earnings();
28   }
```

Fig. 12.13 | Employee abstract base class that implements interface IPayable. (Part 2 of 2.)

Derived Classes of *Employee* and Interface *IPayable*

When a class implements an interface, the same *is-a* relationship as inheritance applies. Class Employee implements IPayable, so we can say that an Employee *is an* IPayable, and thus any object of an Employee derived class also *is an* IPayable. So, if we update the class hierarchy in Section 12.5 with the new Employee class in Fig. 12.13, then SalariedEmployees, HourlyEmployees, CommissionEmployees and BasePlusCommissionEmployees are all IPayable objects. Just as we can assign the reference of a SalariedEmployee derived-class object to a base-class Employee variable, we can assign the reference of a SalariedEmployee object (or any other Employee derived-class object) to an IPayable variable. Invoice implements IPayable, so an Invoice object also *is an* IPayable object, and we can assign the reference of an Invoice object to an IPayable variable.

Software Engineering Observation 12.7

Inheritance and interfaces are similar in their implementation of the is-a *relationship. An object of a class that implements an interface may be thought of as an object of that interface type. An object of any derived classes of a class that implements an interface also can be thought of as an object of the interface type.*

Software Engineering Observation 12.8

The is-a *relationship that exists between base classes and derived classes, and between interfaces and the classes that implement them, holds when passing an object to a method. When a method parameter receives an argument of a base class or interface type, the method polymorphically processes the object received as an argument.*

12.7.5 Using Interface IPayable to Process Invoices and Employees Polymorphically

PayableInterfaceTest (Fig. 12.14) illustrates that interface IPayable can be used to process a set of Invoices and Employees polymorphically in a single app. Lines 12–16 create a List<IPayable> named payableObjects and initialize it with four new objects—two Invoice objects (lines 13–14) and two SalariedEmployee objects (lines 15–16). These assignments are allowed because an Invoice *is an* IPayable, a SalariedEmployee *is an* Employee and an Employee *is an* IPayable. Lines 22–28 use a foreach statement to process each IPayable object in payableObjects polymorphically, displaying the object as a string, along with the payment due. Line 25 implicitly invokes method ToString using the IPayable interface reference payable, even though ToString is not declared in interface IPayable—all references (including those of interface types) refer to objects of classes that extend object and therefore have a ToString method. Line 27 invokes IPayable method GetPaymentAmount to obtain the payment amount for each object in payableObjects, regardless of the actual type of the object. The output reveals that the method calls in lines 25 and 27 invoke the appropriate class's implementation of methods ToString and GetPaymentAmount.

Software Engineering Observation 12.9

All methods of class object *can be called by using a reference of an interface type—the reference refers to an object, and all objects inherit the methods of class* object.

```
1   // Fig. 12.14: PayableInterfaceTest.cs
2   // Tests interface IPayable with disparate classes.
3   using System;
4   using System.Collections.Generic;
5
6   class PayableInterfaceTest
7   {
8      static void Main()
9      {
10        // create a List<IPayable> and initialize it with four
11        // objects of classes that implement interface IPayable
12        var payableObjects = new List<IPayable>() {
13           new Invoice("01234", "seat", 2, 375.00M),
14           new Invoice("56789", "tire", 4, 79.95M),
15           new SalariedEmployee("John", "Smith", "111-11-1111", 800.00M),
16           new SalariedEmployee("Lisa", "Barnes", "888-88-8888", 1200.00M)};
17
18        Console.WriteLine(
19           "Invoices and Employees processed polymorphically:\n");
20
21        // generically process each element in payableObjects
22        foreach (var payable in payableObjects)
23        {
24           // output payable and its appropriate payment amount
25           Console.WriteLine($"{payable}");
26           Console.WriteLine(
27              $"payment due: {payable.GetPaymentAmount():C}\n");
28        }
29     }
30  }
```

```
Invoices and Employees processed polymorphically:

invoice:
part number: 01234 (seat)
quantity: 2
price per item: $375.00
payment due: $750.00
```

Fig. 12.14 | Tests interface IPayable with disparate classes. (Part 1 of 2.)

```
invoice:
part number: 56789 (tire)
quantity: 4
price per item: $79.95
payment due: $319.80

salaried employee: John Smith
social security number: 111-11-1111
weekly salary: $800.00
payment due: $800.00

salaried employee: Lisa Barnes
social security number: 888-88-8888
weekly salary: $1,200.00
payment due: $1,200.00
```

Fig. 12.14 | Tests interface IPayable with disparate classes. (Part 2 of 2.)

12.7.6 Common Interfaces of the .NET Framework Class Library

In this section, we overview several common interfaces defined in the .NET Framework Class Library. These interfaces are implemented and used in the same manner as those you create (e.g., interface IPayable in Section 12.7.2). Implementing these interfaces enables you to incorporate objects of your own types into many important aspects of the Framework Class Library. Figure 12.15 overviews several commonly used Framework Class Library interfaces and why you might implement them in your own types.

Interface	Description
IComparable	C# contains several comparison operators (e.g., <, <=, >, >=, ==, !=) that allow you to compare simple-type values. Section 10.13 showed that you can overload these operators for your own types. Interface IComparable can be used to allow objects of a class that implements the interface to be compared to one another. The interface contains one method, CompareTo, which compares the object that calls the method to the object passed as an argument. Classes must implement CompareTo to return a value indicating whether the object on which it's invoked is less than (negative integer return value), equal to (0 return value) or greater than (positive integer return value) the object passed as an argument, using any criteria you specify. For example, if class Employee implements IComparable, its CompareTo method could compare Employee objects by their earnings amounts. Interface IComparable is commonly used for ordering objects in a collection such as an array. We use IComparable in Chapter 20, Generics, and Chapter 21, Generic Collections; Functional Programming with LINQ/PLINQ.
IComponent	Implemented by any class that represents a component, including Graphical User Interface (GUI) controls (such as buttons or labels). Interface IComponent defines the behaviors that components must implement. We discuss IComponent and many GUI controls that implement this interface in Chapter 14, Graphical User Interfaces with Windows Forms: Part 1, and Chapter 15, Graphical User Interfaces with Windows Forms: Part 2.

Fig. 12.15 | Common interfaces of the .NET Framework Class Library. (Part 1 of 2.)

Interface	Description
IDisposable	Implemented by classes that must provide an explicit mechanism for *releasing* resources. Some resources can be used by only one program at a time. In addition, some resources, such as files on disk, are unmanaged resources that, unlike memory, cannot be released by the garbage collector. Classes that implement interface IDisposable provide a Dispose method that can be called to explicitly release resources that are explicitly associated with an object. We discuss IDisposable briefly in Chapter 13, Exception Handling: A Deeper Look. You can learn more about this interface at http://msdn.microsoft.com/library/system.idisposable. The MSDN article *Implementing a Dispose Method* at http://msdn.microsoft.com/library/fs2xkftw discusses the proper implementation of this interface in your classes.
IEnumerator	Used for iterating through the elements of a *collection* (such as an array or a List) one element at a time—the foreach statement uses an IEnumerator object to iterate through elements. Interface IEnumerator contains method MoveNext to move to the next element in a collection, method Reset to move to the position before the first element and property Current to return the object at the current location. We use IEnumerator in Chapter 21. All IEnumberable objects (Chapter 9) provide a GetEnumerator method that returns an IEnumerator object.

Fig. 12.15 | Common interfaces of the .NET Framework Class Library. (Part 2 of 2.)

12.8 Wrap-Up

This chapter introduced polymorphism—the ability to process objects that share the same base class in a class hierarchy as if they were all objects of the base class. The chapter discussed how polymorphism makes systems extensible and maintainable, then demonstrated how to use overridden methods to effect polymorphic behavior. We introduced the notion of an abstract class, which allows you to provide an appropriate base class from which other classes can inherit. You learned that an abstract class can declare abstract methods that each derived class must implement to become a concrete class. We also discussed that an app can use variables of an abstract class to invoke concrete derived-class implementations of abstract methods polymorphically. You also learned how to determine an object's type at execution time. We showed how to create sealed methods and classes. Finally, the chapter discussed declaring and implementing an interface as another way to achieve polymorphic behavior, often among objects of different, unrelated classes.

You should now be familiar with classes, objects, encapsulation, inheritance, interfaces and polymorphism—the most essential aspects of object-oriented programming. Next, we take a deeper look at using exception handling to deal with runtime errors.

Summary

Section 12.1 Introduction
- With polymorphism, we can design and implement systems that are easily extensible—new classes can be added with little or no modification to the general portions of the app.

Section 12.2 Polymorphism Examples

- With polymorphism, the same method name and signature can be used to cause different actions to occur, depending on the type of object on which the method is invoked.

- Polymorphism promotes extensibility: Software that invokes polymorphic behavior is independent of the object types to which messages are sent. New object types that can respond to existing method calls can be incorporated in a system without requiring modification of the base system.

Section 12.3 Demonstrating Polymorphic Behavior

- Invoking a method on a derived-class object via a base-class reference invokes the derived-class functionality—the type of the referenced object determines which method is called.

Section 12.4 Abstract Classes and Methods

- Abstract classes are incomplete classes for which you never intend to instantiate objects.

- The purpose of an abstract class is primarily to provide an appropriate base class from which other classes can inherit, and thus share a common design.

- Classes that can be used to instantiate objects are called concrete classes.

- You make a class abstract by declaring it with keyword abstract.

- Each concrete derived class of an abstract base class must provide concrete implementations of the base class's abstract methods and properties.

- Failure to implement a base class's abstract methods and properties in a derived class is a compilation error unless the derived class is also declared abstract.

- Although we cannot instantiate objects of abstract base classes, we can use them to declare variables that can hold references to objects of any concrete class derived from those abstract classes.

Section 12.5 Case Study: Payroll System Using Polymorphism

- By declaring a method abstract, we indicate that each concrete derived class must provide an appropriate implementation.

- All virtual method calls are resolved at execution time, based on the type of the object to which the reference-type variable refers. This process is known as dynamic binding or late binding.

- The is operator determines whether the type of the object in the left operand matches the type specified by the right operand and returns true if the two have an *is-a* relationship.

- The as operator performs a downcast that returns a reference to the appropriate object if the downcast is successful and returns null if the downcast fails.

- A base-class reference can be used to invoke only the methods declared in the base class. If an app needs to perform a derived-class-specific operation on a derived-class object referenced by a base-class variable, the app must first downcast the base-class reference to a derived-class reference.

- Every object knows its own type and can access this information through method GetType, which all classes inherit from class object.

- Assigning a base-class reference to a derived-class variable is not allowed without an explicit cast or without using the as operator. The is operator can be used to ensure that such a cast is performed only if the object is a derived-class object.

Section 12.6 sealed Methods and Classes

- A method that's declared sealed in a base class cannot be overridden in a derived class.

- A class that's declared sealed cannot be a base class (i.e., a class cannot extend a sealed class). All methods in a sealed class are implicitly sealed.

Section 12.7 Case Study: Creating and Using Interfaces

- Interfaces define and standardize the ways in which things such as people and systems can interact with one another.

- An interface declaration begins with keyword `interface` and can contain only abstract methods, properties, indexers and events.

- All interface members are implicitly declared both `public` and `abstract`. They do not specify any implementation details, such as concrete method declarations.

- Each interface can extend one or more other interfaces to create a more elaborate interface that other classes can implement.

- A class must specify that it implements the interface by listing it after the colon (:) in the class declaration.

- A class that implements an interface but doesn't implement all the interface's members must be declared `abstract` and contain an abstract declaration of each unimplemented interface member.

- The UML expresses the relationship between a class and an interface through a realization. A class is said to "realize," or implement, an interface.

- To implement more than one interface, use a comma-separated list of interface names after the colon (:) in the class declaration.

- Inheritance and interfaces are similar in their implementation of the *is-a* relationship. An object of a class that implements an interface may be thought of as an object of that interface type.

- All methods of class `object` can be called by using a reference of an interface type—the reference refers to an object, and all objects inherit the methods of class `object`.

Terminology

abstract class	interface declaration
abstract keyword	interface inheritance
abstract method	`interface` keyword
abstract operation	*is-a* relationship
as operator	`is` operator
base-class reference	late binding
concrete class	polymorphism
derived-class reference	realization
downcasting	`sealed` class
dynamic binding	`sealed` method
`GetType` method of class `object`	static binding
implement an interface	`Type` class
inlining code	

Self-Review Exercises

12.1   Fill in the blanks in each of the following statements:

a) If a class contains at least one abstract method, it must be declared as a(n) _____ class.

b) Classes from which objects can be instantiated are called _____ classes.

c) _____ involves using a base-class variable to invoke methods on base-class and derived-class objects, enabling you to "program in the general."

d) Methods in a class that do not provide implementations must be declared using keyword _____.

e) Casting a reference stored in a base-class variable to a derived-class type is called _____.

12.2   State whether each of the statements that follows is *true* or *false*. If *false*, explain why.
a)   It's possible to treat base-class objects and derived-class objects similarly.
b)   All methods in an abstract class must be declared as abstract methods.
c)   Attempting to invoke a derived-class-only method through a base-class variable is an error.
d)   If a base class declares an abstract method, a derived class must implement that method.
e)   An object of a class that implements an interface may be thought of as an object of that interface type.

Answers to Self-Review Exercises

12.1   a) abstract. b) concrete. c) Polymorphism. d) abstract. e) downcasting.

12.2   a) True. b) False. An abstract class can include methods with implementations and abstract methods. c) True. d) False. Only a concrete derived class must implement the method. e) True.

Exercises

12.3   *(Programming in the General)* How does polymorphism enable you to program "in the general" rather than "in the specific"? Discuss the key advantages of programming "in the general."

12.4   *(Inheriting Interface vs. Inheriting Implementation)* A derived class can inherit "interface" or "implementation" from a base class. How do inheritance hierarchies designed for inheriting interface differ from those designed for inheriting implementation?

12.5   *(Abstract Methods)* What are abstract methods? Describe the circumstances in which an abstract method would be appropriate.

12.6   *(Polymorphism and Extensibility)* How does polymorphism promote extensibility?

12.7   *(Assigning Base-Class and Derived-Class References)* Discuss four ways in which you can assign base-class and derived-class references to variables of base-class and derived-class types.

12.8   *(Abstract Classes vs. Interfaces)* Compare and contrast abstract classes and interfaces. Why would you use an abstract class? Why would you use an interface?

12.9   *(Payroll System Modification)* Modify the payroll system of Figs. 12.4–12.9 to include private instance variable birthDate in class Employee. Use class Date of Fig. 10.7 to represent an employee's birthday. Assume that payroll is processed once per month. Create an array of Employee variables to store references to the various employee objects. In a loop, calculate the payroll for each Employee (polymorphically), and add a $100.00 bonus to the person's payroll amount if the current month is the month in which the Employee's birthday occurs.

12.10   *(Shape Hierarchy)* Implement the Shape hierarchy of Fig. 11.3. Omit the Triangle and Tetrahedron classes. Each TwoDimensionalShape should contain read-only abstract property Area to calculate the area of the two-dimensional shape. Each ThreeDimensionalShape should have read-only abstract properties Area and Volume to calculate the surface area and volume, respectively, of the three-dimensional shape. Create an app that uses an array of Shape references to objects of each concrete class in the hierarchy. Display a text description of the object to which each array element refers. Also, in the loop that processes all the shapes in the array, determine whether each shape is a TwoDimensionalShape or a ThreeDimensionalShape. If a shape is a TwoDimensionalShape, display its area. If a shape is a ThreeDimensionalShape, display its area and volume.

12.11   *(Payroll System Modification)* Modify the payroll system of Figs. 12.4–12.9 to include an additional Employee derived class, PieceWorker, that represents an employee whose pay is based on the number of pieces of merchandise produced. Class PieceWorker should contain private instance variables wage (to store the employee's wage per piece) and pieces (to store the number of pieces produced). Provide a concrete implementation of method Earnings in class PieceWorker that calculates the employee's earnings by multiplying the number of pieces produced by the wage per piece. Create an array of Employee variables to store references to objects of each concrete class in the new Employee hierarchy. Display each Employee's string representation and earnings.

12.12 *(Accounts Payable System Modification)* Modify the accounts payable app of Figs. 12.11–12.14 to include the complete functionality of the payroll app of Figs. 12.4–12.9. The app should still process two Invoice objects, but now should process one object of each of the four Employee derived classes. If the object currently being processed is a BasePlusCommissionEmployee, the app should increase the BasePlusCommissionEmployee's base salary by 10%. Finally, the app should output the payment amount for each object. Modify PayableInterfaceTest (Fig. 12.14) to polymorphically process two Invoices, one SalariedEmployee, one HourlyEmployee, one Commission-Employee and one BasePlusCommissionEmployee. First, output a string representation of each IPayable object. Next, if an object is a BasePlusCommissionEmployee, increase its base salary by 10%. Finally, output the payment amount for each IPayable object.

12.13 *(Polymorphic Banking Program Using Account Hierarchy)* Develop a polymorphic banking app using the Account hierarchy created in Exercise 11.9. Create an array of Account references to SavingsAccount and CheckingAccount objects. For each Account in the array, allow the user to specify an amount of money to withdraw from the Account using method Debit and an amount of money to deposit into the Account using method Credit. As you process each Account, determine its type. If an Account is a SavingsAccount, calculate the amount of interest owed to the Account using method CalculateInterest, then add the interest to the account balance using method Credit. After processing an Account, display the updated account balance obtained by using base-class property Balance.

Making-a-Difference Exercise

12.14 *(CarbonFootprint Interface: Polymorphism)* Using interfaces, as you learned in this chapter, you can specify similar behaviors for possibly disparate classes. Governments and companies worldwide are becoming increasingly concerned with carbon footprints (annual releases of carbon dioxide into the atmosphere) from buildings burning various types of fuels for heat, vehicles burning fuels for power, and the like. Many scientists blame these greenhouse gases for the phenomenon called global warming. Create three small classes unrelated by inheritance—classes Building, Car and Bicycle. Write an interface ICarbonFootprint with a GetCarbonFootprint method. Have each of your classes implement that interface, so that its GetCarbonFootprint method calculates an appropriate carbon footprint for that class (check out a few websites that explain how to calculate carbon footprints). Write an app that creates objects of each of the three classes, places references to those objects in List<ICarbonFootprint>, then iterates through the List, polymorphically invoking each object's GetCarbonFootprint method.

Exception Handling: A Deeper Look

13

13.1 Introduction

In this chapter, we take a deeper look at exception handling. As you know from Section 8.5, an exception indicates that a problem occurred during a program's execution. The name "exception" comes from the fact that, although the problem can occur, it occurs infrequently. As we showed in Section 8.5 and in Chapter 10, exception handling enables you to create apps that can *handle* exceptions—in many cases allowing a program to continue executing as if no problems had been encountered. More severe problems may prevent a program from continuing normal execution, instead requiring it to notify the user of the problem, then terminate in a controlled manner. The features presented in this chapter enable you to write clear, robust and more fault-tolerant programs (i.e., programs that are able to deal with problems that may arise and continue executing). "Best practices" for exception handling in Visual C# are specified in the Visual Studio documentation.[1]

After reviewing exception-handling concepts and basic exception-handling techniques, we overview .NET's exception-handling class hierarchy. Programs typically *request* and *release* resources (such as files on disk) during program execution. Often, the supply

---

1. "Best Practices for Handling Exceptions [C#]," *.NET Framework Developer's Guide*, Visual Studio .NET Online Help. Available at `https://msdn.microsoft.com/library/seyhszts`.

of these resources is limited, or the resources can be used by only one program at a time. We demonstrate a part of the exception-handling mechanism that enables a program to use a resource, then *guarantee* that it will be released for use by other programs, even if an exception occurs. We show several properties of class System.Exception (the base class of all exception classes) and discuss how you can create and use your own exception classes.

You'll see various C# features for working with values that can be null, including:

- C# 6's null-conditional operator (?.), which determines whether a reference is null before using it to call a method or access a property.

- The null-coalescing operator (??), which returns its left operand's value if it's not null and returns its right operand's value, otherwise.

- Nullable types, which specify that a value-type variable may contain a value or null.

Finally, we'll present C# 6's exception filters that specify a condition for catching an exception.

13.2 Example: Divide by Zero without Exception Handling

Let's revisit what happens when errors arise in a console app that does not use exception handling. Figure 13.1 inputs two integers from the user, then divides the first integer by the second, using integer division to obtain an int result. In this example, an exception is thrown (i.e., an exception occurs) when a method detects a problem and is unable to handle it.

```
1   // Fig. 13.1: DivideByZeroNoExceptionHandling.cs
2   // Integer division without exception handling.
3   using System;
4
5   class DivideByZeroNoExceptionHandling
6   {
7      static void Main()
8      {
9         // get numerator
10        Console.Write("Please enter an integer numerator: ");
11        var numerator = int.Parse(Console.ReadLine());
12
13        // get denominator
14        Console.Write("Please enter an integer denominator: ");
15        var denominator = int.Parse(Console.ReadLine());
16
17        // divide the two integers, then display the result
18        var result = numerator / denominator;
19        Console.WriteLine(
20           $"\nResult: {numerator} / {denominator} = {result}");
21     }
22  }
```

Fig. 13.1 | Integer division without exception handling. (Part 1 of 2.)

```
Please enter an integer numerator: 100
Please enter an integer denominator: 7

Result: 100 / 7 = 14
```

```
Please enter an integer numerator: 100
Please enter an integer denominator: 0

Unhandled Exception: System.DivideByZeroException:
   Attempted to divide by zero.
   at DivideByZeroNoExceptionHandling.Main()
     in C:\Users\PaulDeitel\Documents\examples\ch13\Fig13_01\
     DivideByZeroNoExceptionHandling\DivideByZeroNoExceptionHandling\
     DivideByZeroNoExceptionHandling.cs:line 18
```

```
Please enter an integer numerator: 100
Please enter an integer denominator: hello

Unhandled Exception: System.FormatException:
   Input string was not in a correct format.
   at System.Number.StringToNumber(String str, NumberStyles options,
     NumberBuffer& number, NumberFormatInfo info, Boolean parseDecimal)
   at System.Number.ParseInt32(String s, NumberStyles style,
     NumberFormatInfo info)
   at System.Int32.Parse(String s)
   at DivideByZeroNoExceptionHandling.Main()
     in C:\Users\PaulDeitel\Documents\examples\ch13\Fig13_01\
     DivideByZeroNoExceptionHandling\DivideByZeroNoExceptionHandling\
     DivideByZeroNoExceptionHandling.cs:line 15
```

Fig. 13.1 | Integer division without exception handling. (Part 2 of 2.)

Running the App

In most of our examples, an app appears to run the same regardless of whether you run it by choosing **Start Debugging** or **Start Without Debugging** from the **Debug** menu. As we'll discuss shortly, the example in Fig. 13.1 might cause exceptions, depending on the user's input. For this example, we do not wish to debug the app; we simply want to see what happens when errors arise. For this reason, we executed this app with **Debug > Start Without Debugging**. If an exception occurs during execution, a dialog appears indicating that the app "has stopped working." You can simply click **Cancel** or **Close Program** to terminate the app. An error message describing the exception that occurred is displayed in the program's output. We formatted the error messages in Fig. 13.1 for readability. In the first sample execution, the program performs a successful division and runs to completion with no exceptions.

13.2.1 Dividing By Zero

In the second sample execution, the user enters 0 as the denominator. Several lines of information are displayed in response to the invalid input. This information—known as a stack trace—includes the exception class's name (System.DivideByZeroException) in a message indicating the problem that occurred and the path of execution that led to the exception, method by method. Stack traces help you debug a program. The first line of the error message specifies that a DivideByZeroException occurred. When a program divides an integer by 0, the CLR throws a **DivideByZeroException** (namespace System). The text after the exception name, "Attempted to divide by zero," is an error message that indicates why this exception occurred. Division by zero is not allowed in integer arithmetic.[2]

Each "at" line in a stack trace indicates a line of code in a particular method that was executing when the exception occurred. The "at" line contains the namespace, class and method in which the exception occurred

```
DivideByZeroNoExceptionHandling.Main
```

the location and name of the file containing the code

```
C:\Users\PaulDeitel\Documents\examples\ch13\Fig13_01\
    DivideByZeroNoExceptionHandling\
    DivideByZeroNoExceptionHandling\
    DivideByZeroNoExceptionHandling.cs
```

and the line number

```
:line 18
```

where the exception occurred. (Class DivideByZeroNoExceptionHandling is not declared in a namespace, so no namespace is displayed before the class name in this example's stack traces.)

In this case, the stack trace indicates that the DivideByZeroException occurred when the program was executing line 18 of method Main. The first "at" line in the stack trace indicates the exception's **throw point**—the initial point at which the exception occurred (i.e., line 18 in Main). This information makes it easy for you to see which method call caused the exception. Subsequent "at" lines in the stack trace specify what method calls were made to get to the throw point in the program.

13.2.2 Enter a Non-Numeric Denominator

In the third sample execution, the user enters the string "hello" as the denominator. This causes a FormatException, and another stack trace is displayed. Our earlier examples that read numeric values from the user assumed that the user would input an integer value, but a noninteger value could be entered. A **FormatException** (namespace System) occurs, for example, when int.Parse receives a string that does not represent a valid integer. Starting from the last "at" line in the stack trace, we see that the exception was detected in line 15 of method Main. The stack trace also shows the other methods that led to the exception being thrown:

- Main called Int32.Parse—recall that int is just an alias for Int32,
- Int32.Parse called method Number.ParseInt32, and
- Number.ParseInt32 called Number.StringToNumber.

---

2. Division by zero with floating-point values *is* allowed and results in the value infinity—represented by either constant **Double.PositiveInfinity** or constant **Double.NegativeInfinity**, depending on whether the numerator is positive or negative. These values are displayed as Infinity or -Infinity. If *both* the numerator and denominator are *zero*, the result of the calculation is the constant **Double.NaN** ("not a number"), which is returned when a calculation's result is *undefined*.

The throw point occurred in Number.StringToNumber, as indicated by the first "at" line in the stack trace. Note that the stack trace's actual text depends on your locale.

13.2.3 Unhandled Exceptions Terminate the App

In the sample executions in Fig. 13.1, the program terminates when an *unhandled* exception occurs and a stack trace is displayed. This does not always happen—sometimes a program may continue executing even though an exception has occurred and a stack trace has been displayed. In such cases, the app may produce incorrect results. The next section demonstrates how to handle exceptions to enable the program to run to completion.

13.3 Example: Handling DivideByZeroExceptions and FormatExceptions

Now, let's consider a simple example of exception handling. The app in Fig. 13.2 uses exception handling to process any DivideByZeroExceptions and FormatExceptions that might arise. The app reads two integers from the user (lines 18–21). Assuming that the user provides integers as input and does not specify 0 as the denominator for the division, line 25 performs the division and lines 28–29 display the result. However, if the user inputs a noninteger value or supplies 0 as the denominator, an exception occurs. This program demonstrates how to catch and handle such exceptions—in this case, displaying an error message and allowing the user to enter another set of values.

```
1   // Fig. 13.2: DivideByZeroExceptionHandling.cs
2   // FormatException and DivideByZeroException handlers.
3   using System;
4
5   class DivideByZeroExceptionHandling
6   {
7       static void Main(string[] args)
8       {
9           var continueLoop = true; // determines whether to keep looping
10
11          do
12          {
13              // retrieve user input and calculate quotient
14              try
15              {
16                  // int.Parse generates FormatException
17                  // if argument cannot be converted to an integer
18                  Console.Write("Enter an integer numerator: ");
19                  var numerator = int.Parse(Console.ReadLine());
20                  Console.Write("Enter an integer denominator: ");
21                  var denominator = int.Parse(Console.ReadLine());
22
23                  // division generates DivideByZeroException
24                  // if denominator is 0
25                  var result = numerator / denominator;
26
```

Fig. 13.2 | FormatException and DivideByZeroException handlers. (Part 1 of 2.)

```
27              // display result
28              Console.WriteLine(
29                  $"\nResult: {numerator} / {denominator} = {result}" );
30              continueLoop = false;
31          }
32          catch (FormatException formatException)
33          {
34              Console.WriteLine($"\n{formatException.Message}" );
35              Console.WriteLine(
36                  "You must enter two integers. Please try again.\n");
37          }
38          catch (DivideByZeroException divideByZeroException)
39          {
40              Console.WriteLine($"\n{divideByZeroException.Message}" );
41              Console.WriteLine(
42                  "Zero is an invalid denominator. Please try again.\n");
43          }
44      } while (continueLoop);
45   }
46 }
```

```
Please enter an integer numerator: 100
Please enter an integer denominator: 7

Result: 100 / 7 = 14
```

```
Enter an integer numerator: 100
Enter an integer denominator: 0

Attempted to divide by zero.
Zero is an invalid denominator. Please try again.

Enter an integer numerator: 100
Enter an integer denominator: 7

Result: 100 / 7 = 14
```

```
Enter an integer numerator: 100
Enter an integer denominator: hello

Input string was not in a correct format.
You must enter two integers. Please try again.

Enter an integer numerator: 100
Enter an integer denominator: 7

Result: 100 / 7 = 14
```

Fig. 13.2 | FormatException and DivideByZeroException handlers. (Part 2 of 2.)

Sample Outputs

Before we discuss the details of the program, let's consider the sample outputs in Fig. 13.2. The first sample output shows a successful calculation in which the user enters the numerator 100 and the denominator 7. The result (14) is an int, because integer division always yields an int result. The second sample output demonstrates the result of an attempt to divide by zero. In integer arithmetic, the CLR tests for division by zero and generates a

DivideByZeroException if the denominator is zero. The program detects the exception and displays an error message indicating the attempt to divide by zero. The last sample output depicts the result of inputting a non-int value—in this case, the user enters the string "hello" as the denominator. The program attempts to convert the input strings to ints using method int.Parse (lines 19 and 21). If an argument cannot be converted to an int, the method throws a FormatException. The program catches the exception and displays an error message indicating that the user must enter two ints.

Another Way to Convert Strings to Integers
Another way to validate the input is to use the int.TryParse method, which converts a string to an int value *if possible*. Like int.Parse, each of the numeric simple types has a TryParse method. TryParse requires two arguments—one is the string to parse and the other is the variable in which the converted value is to be stored. The method returns a bool value that's true only if the string was converted successfully to an int. If not, TryParse assigns the value 0 to the second argument—that argument is passed by reference so TryParse can modify its value.

> **Error-Prevention Tip 13.1**
>
> *Method TryParse can be used to validate input in code rather than allowing the code to throw an exception—this technique is generally preferred.*

13.3.1 Enclosing Code in a try Block
Now we consider the user interactions and flow of control that yield the results shown in the sample output windows. Lines 14–31 define a try block enclosing the code that might throw exceptions, as well as some code that will be skipped when an exception occurs. For example, the program should not display a new result (lines 28–29) unless the calculation in line 25 completes successfully.

The user inputs values that represent the numerator and denominator. The two statements that read the ints (lines 19 and 21) call method int.Parse to convert strings to int values. This method throws a FormatException if it cannot convert its string argument to an int. If lines 19 and 21 convert the values properly (i.e., no exceptions occur), then line 25 divides the numerator by the denominator and assigns the result to variable result. If denominator is 0, line 25 causes the CLR to throw a DivideByZeroException. If line 25 does not cause an exception to be thrown, then lines 28–29 display the result of the division.

13.3.2 Catching Exceptions
Exception-handling code appears in a catch block. In general, when an exception occurs in a try block, a corresponding catch block *catches* the exception and *handles* it. The try block in this example is followed by two catch blocks—one that handles a FormatException (lines 32–37) and one that handles a DivideByZeroException (lines 38–43). A catch block specifies an exception parameter representing the exception that the catch block can handle. The catch block can use the parameter's identifier (which you choose) to interact with a caught exception object. If there's no need to use the exception object in the catch block, the exception parameter's identifier can be omitted. The type of the catch's parameter is the type of the exception that the catch block handles. Optionally,

you can include a `catch` block that does *not* specify an exception type—such a `catch` block (known as a **general `catch` clause**) catches all exception types. At least one `catch` block and/or a **`finally` block** (discussed in Section 13.5) must immediately follow a `try` block.

In Fig. 13.2, the first `catch` block catches `FormatExceptions` (thrown by method `int.Parse`), and the second `catch` block catches `DivideByZeroExceptions` (thrown by the CLR). If an exception occurs, the program executes only the first matching `catch` block. Both exception handlers in this example display an error-message dialog. After either `catch` block terminates, program control continues with the first statement after the last `catch` block (the end of the method, in this example). We'll soon take a deeper look at how this flow of control works in exception handling.

13.3.3 Uncaught Exceptions

An **uncaught exception** (or **unhandled exception**) is one for which there's no matching `catch` block. You saw the results of uncaught exceptions in the second and third outputs of Fig. 13.1. Recall that when exceptions occur in that example, the app terminates early (after displaying the exception's stack trace). The result of an uncaught exception depends on how you execute the program—Fig. 13.1 demonstrated the results of an uncaught exception when an app is executed using **Debug > Start Without Debugging**. If you run the app by using **Debug > Start Debugging** and the runtime environment detects an uncaught exception, the app pauses, and the **Exception Assistant** window (Fig. 13.3) appears.

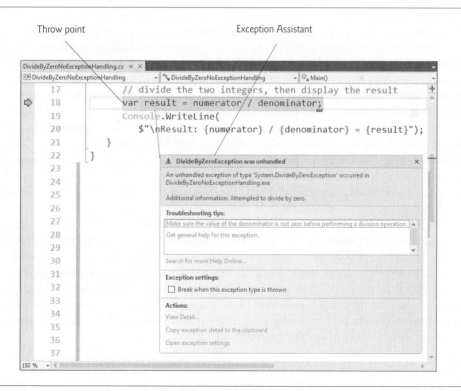

Fig. 13.3 | Exception Assistant.

The Exception Assistant window contains

- a line pointing from the Exception Assistant to the line of code that caused the exception,
- the type of the exception,
- **Troubleshooting tips** with links to helpful information on what might have caused the exception and how to handle it, and
- links to view or copy the complete exception details

Figure 13.3 shows the Exception Assistant that's displayed if the user attempts to divide by zero in the app of Fig. 13.1.

13.3.4 Termination Model of Exception Handling

Recall that the point in the program at which an exception occurs is called the *throw point*—this is an important location for debugging purposes (as we demonstrate in Section 13.7). If an exception occurs in a try block (such as a FormatException being thrown as a result of the code in lines 19 and 21 in Fig. 13.2), the try block terminates immediately, and program control transfers to the first of the following catch blocks in which the exception parameter's type matches that of the thrown exception. After the exception is handled, program control does *not* return to the throw point because the try block has *exited* (which also causes any of its local variables to go out of scope). Rather, control resumes after the last catch block. This is known as the termination model of exception handling. [*Note:* Some languages use the resumption model of exception handling, in which, after an exception is handled, control resumes just after the throw point.]

If no exceptions occur in the try block, the program successfully completes the try block (setting continueLoop to false) and ignores the catch blocks in lines 32–37 and 38–43. Then the program executes the first statement following the try and catch blocks. In this example, the program reaches the end of the do...while loop (line 44) in which the condition is now false, so the program terminates because the end of Main is reached.

The try block and its corresponding catch and finally blocks together form a try statement. It's important not to confuse the terms "try block" and "try statement"—the term "try block" refers to the block of code following the keyword try (but before any catch or finally blocks), while the term "try statement" includes all the code from the opening try keyword to the end of the last catch or finally block. This includes the try block, as well as any associated catch blocks and finally block.

When a try block terminates, its local variables go out of scope. If a try block terminates due to an exception, the CLR searches for the first catch block that can process the type of exception that occurred—in an outer block in the same method or in a previous method in the method-call stack. The CLR locates the matching catch by comparing the type of the thrown exception to each catch's parameter type. A match occurs if the types are identical or if the thrown exception's type is a derived class of the catch's parameter type. Once an exception is matched to a catch block, the code in that block executes and the other catch blocks in the try statement are ignored.

13.3.5 Flow of Control When Exceptions Occur

In the third sample output of Fig. 13.2, the user inputs hello as the denominator. When line 21 executes, int.Parse cannot convert this string to an int, so the method throws a FormatException object to indicate that the method was unable to convert the string to an int. When the exception occurs, the try block exits (terminates). Next, the CLR attempts to locate a matching catch block. A match occurs with the catch block in line 32, so the exception handler displays the exception's Message property (to retrieve the error message associated with the exception) and the program ignores all other exception handlers following the try block. Program control continues with line 44 once the catch block completes execution.

> **Common Programming Error 13.1**
>
> *Specifying a comma-separated list of parameters in a catch block is a syntax error. A catch block can have at most one parameter. Section 13.10 shows how you can use exception filters to specify additional conditions for which an exception can be caught.*

In the second sample output of Fig. 13.2, the user inputs 0 as the denominator. When the division in line 25 executes, a DivideByZeroException occurs. Once again, the try block terminates, and the program attempts to locate a matching catch block. In this case, the first catch block does not match—the exception type in the catch-handler declaration is not the same as the type of the thrown exception, and FormatException is not a base class of DivideByZeroException. Therefore the program continues to search for a matching catch block, which it finds in line 38. Line 40 displays the exception's Message property. Again, program control continues with line 44 once the catch block completes execution.

13.4 .NET Exception Hierarchy

In C#, the exception-handling mechanism allows only objects of class Exception (namespace System) and its derived classes to be thrown and caught. Note, however, that C# programs may interact with software components written in other .NET languages (such as C++) that do not restrict exception types. The general catch clause can be used to catch such exceptions.

This section overviews several of the .NET Framework's exception classes and focuses exclusively on exceptions that derive from class Exception. In addition, we discuss how to determine whether a particular method throws exceptions.

13.4.1 Class SystemException

Class Exception (namespace System) is the base class of .NET's exception class hierarchy. An important derived class is SystemException. The CLR generates SystemExceptions. Many of these can be avoided if apps are coded properly. For example, if a program attempts to access an out-of-range array index, the CLR throws an exception of type Index-OutOfRangeException (a derived class of SystemException). Similarly, an exception occurs when a program uses a reference-type variable to call a method when the reference has a value of null. This causes a NullReferenceException (another derived class of SystemException). You saw earlier in this chapter that a DivideByZeroException occurs in integer division when a program attempts to divide by zero.

Other exceptions thrown by the CLR include OutOfMemoryException, StackOverflowException and ExecutionEngineException, which are thrown when something goes wrong that causes the CLR to become unstable. Sometimes such exceptions cannot even be caught. It's best to simply log such exceptions (using a tool such as Apache's *log4net*—`http://logging.apache.org/log4net/`), then terminate your app.

A benefit of the exception class hierarchy is that a `catch` block can catch exceptions of a particular type or—because of the *is-a* relationship of inheritance—can use a base-class type to catch exceptions in a hierarchy of related exception types. For example, Section 13.3.2 discussed the `catch` block with no parameter, which catches exceptions of all types (including those that are not derived from `Exception`). A `catch` block that specifies a parameter of type `Exception` can catch all exceptions that derive from `Exception`, because `Exception` is the base class of all exception classes in the .NET Framework. The advantage of this approach is that the exception handler can access the caught exception's information via the parameter in the `catch`. We'll say more about accessing exception information in Section 13.7.

Using inheritance with exceptions enables a `catch` block to catch related exceptions using a concise notation. A set of exception handlers could catch each derived-class exception type individually, but catching the base-class exception type is more concise. However, this technique makes sense *only* if the handling behavior is the same for a base class and all derived classes. Otherwise, catch each derived-class exception individually.

Common Programming Error 13.2

The compiler issues an error if a catch block that catches a base-class exception is placed before a catch block for any of that class's derived-class types. In this case, the base-class catch block would catch all base-class and derived-class exceptions, so the derived-class exception handler would never execute.

13.4.2 Which Exceptions Might a Method Throw?

How do we determine that an exception might occur in a program? For methods contained in the .NET Framework classes, read the detailed descriptions of the methods in the online documentation. If a method may throw an exception, its description contains a section called **Exceptions** that specifies the types of exceptions the method may throw and briefly describes what causes them. For an example, search for "`int.Parse` method" in the Visual Studio online documentation. The **Exceptions** section of this method's web page indicates that method `int.Parse` throws three exception types:

- `ArgumentNullException`,
- `FormatException`, and
- `OverflowException`

and describes the reasons for each. [*Note:* You also can find this information in the **Object Browser** described in Section 10.11.]

Software Engineering Observation 13.1

If a method may throw exceptions, statements that invoke the method directly or indirectly should be placed in try blocks, and those exceptions should be caught and handled.

It's more difficult to determine when the CLR may throw exceptions. Such information appears in the *C# Language Specification*, which specifies cases in which exceptions are thrown. At time of writing, the C# specification has not yet been officially released by Microsoft. You can view an unofficial copy at:

https://github.com/ljw1004/csharpspec/blob/gh-pages/README.md

13.5 finally Block

Programs frequently request and release resources dynamically (i.e., at execution time). For example, a program that reads a file from disk first makes a file-open request (as we'll see in Chapter 17, Files and Streams). If that request succeeds, the program reads the contents of the file. Operating systems typically prevent more than one program from manipulating a file at once. Therefore, when a program finishes processing a file, the program should close the file (i.e., release the resource) so other programs can use it. If the file is not closed, a resource leak occurs. In such a case, the file resource is not available to other programs.

In programming languages such as C and C++, in which the programmer is responsible for dynamic memory management, the most common type of resource leak is a memory leak. A memory leak occurs when a program allocates memory (as C# programmers do via keyword new), but does not deallocate the memory when it's no longer needed. Normally, this is *not* an issue in C#, because the CLR performs *garbage collection* of memory that's no longer needed by an executing program (Section 10.8). However, other kinds of resource leaks (such as unclosed files) can occur.

Error-Prevention Tip 13.2

The CLR does not completely eliminate memory leaks. It will not garbage-collect an object until the program contains no more references to that object, and even then there may be a delay until the memory is required. Thus, memory leaks can occur if you inadvertently keep references to unwanted objects.

13.5.1 Moving Resource-Release Code to a finally Block

Exceptions often occur when an app uses resources that require explicit release. For example, a program that processes a file might receive IOExceptions during the processing. For this reason, file-processing code normally appears in a try block. Regardless of whether a program experiences exceptions while processing a file, the program should close the file when it's no longer needed. Suppose a program places all resource-request and resource-release code in a try block. If no exceptions occur, the try block executes normally and releases the resources after using them. However, if an exception occurs, the try block may exit *before* the resource-release code can execute. We could duplicate all the resource-release code in each of the catch blocks, but this would make the code more difficult to modify and maintain. We could also place the resource-release code after the try statement; however, if the try block terminated due to a return statement or an exception occurred, code following the try statement would never execute.

To address these problems, C#'s exception-handling mechanism provides the finally block, which is *guaranteed* to execute regardless of whether the try block executes successfully or an exception occurs. This makes the finally block an ideal location in which to place resource-release code for resources that are acquired and manipulated in the corresponding try block:

- If the try block executes successfully, the finally block executes immediately after the try block terminates—either by reaching the block's closing brace or if a return statement executes in the block.

- If an exception occurs in the try block, the finally block executes immediately after a catch block completes—either by reaching the block's closing brace or if a return statement executes in the block.

- If there is no catch block, if the exception is not caught by a catch block associated with the try block, or if a catch block associated with the try block throws an exception itself, the finally block executes before the exception is processed by the next enclosing try block, which could be in the calling method.

By placing the resource-release code in a finally block, we ensure that even if the program terminates due to an uncaught exception, the resource will be deallocated. Local variables in a try block cannot be accessed in the corresponding finally block. For this reason, variables that must be accessed in both a try block and its corresponding finally block should be declared before the try block.

Error-Prevention Tip 13.3
A finally block typically contains code to release resources acquired in the corresponding try block, which makes the finally block an effective mechanism for eliminating resource leaks.

Performance Tip 13.1
As a rule, resources should be released as soon as they're no longer needed in a program. This makes them available for reuse promptly.

If one or more catch blocks follow a try block, the finally block is optional. However, if no catch blocks follow a try block, a finally block must appear immediately after the try block. If any catch blocks follow a try block, the finally block (if there is one) appears *after* the last catch block. Only whitespace and comments can separate the blocks in a try statement.

13.5.2 Demonstrating the finally Block

The app in Fig. 13.4 demonstrates that the finally block *always* executes, regardless of whether an exception occurs in the corresponding try block. The app consists of method Main (lines 8–47) and four other methods that Main invokes to demonstrate finally. These methods are DoesNotThrowException (lines 50–67), ThrowExceptionWithCatch (lines 70–89), ThrowExceptionWithoutCatch (lines 92–108) and ThrowException-CatchRethrow (lines 111–136).

```
1   // Fig. 13.4: UsingExceptions.cs
2   // finally blocks always execute, even when no exception occurs.
3
4   using System;
5
```

Fig. 13.4 | finally blocks always execute, even when no exception occurs. (Part 1 of 4.)

```
 6    class UsingExceptions
 7    {
 8       static void Main()
 9       {
10          // Case 1: No exceptions occur in called method
11          Console.WriteLine("Calling DoesNotThrowException");
12          DoesNotThrowException();
13
14          // Case 2: Exception occurs and is caught in called method
15          Console.WriteLine("\nCalling ThrowExceptionWithCatch");
16          ThrowExceptionWithCatch();
17
18          // Case 3: Exception occurs, but is not caught in called method
19          // because there is no catch block.
20          Console.WriteLine("\nCalling ThrowExceptionWithoutCatch");
21
22          // call ThrowExceptionWithoutCatch
23          try
24          {
25             ThrowExceptionWithoutCatch();
26          }
27          catch
28          {
29             Console.WriteLine(
30                "Caught exception from ThrowExceptionWithoutCatch in Main");
31          }
32
33          // Case 4: Exception occurs and is caught in called method,
34          // then rethrown to caller.
35          Console.WriteLine("\nCalling ThrowExceptionCatchRethrow");
36
37          // call ThrowExceptionCatchRethrow
38          try
39          {
40             ThrowExceptionCatchRethrow();
41          }
42          catch
43          {
44             Console.WriteLine(
45                "Caught exception from ThrowExceptionCatchRethrow in Main");
46          }
47       }
48
49       // no exceptions thrown
50       static void DoesNotThrowException()
51       {
52          // try block does not throw any exceptions
53          try
54          {
55             Console.WriteLine("In DoesNotThrowException");
56          }
57          catch
58          {
```

Fig. 13.4 | finally blocks always execute, even when no exception occurs. (Part 2 of 4.)

```
59              Console.WriteLine("This catch never executes");
60          }
61          finally
62          {
63              Console.WriteLine("finally executed in DoesNotThrowException");
64          }
65
66          Console.WriteLine("End of DoesNotThrowException");
67      }
68
69      // throws exception and catches it locally
70      static void ThrowExceptionWithCatch()
71      {
72          // try block throws exception
73          try
74          {
75              Console.WriteLine("In ThrowExceptionWithCatch");
76              throw new Exception("Exception in ThrowExceptionWithCatch");
77          }
78          catch (Exception exceptionParameter)
79          {
80              Console.WriteLine($"Message: {exceptionParameter.Message}");
81          }
82          finally
83          {
84              Console.WriteLine(
85                  "finally executed in ThrowExceptionWithCatch");
86          }
87
88          Console.WriteLine("End of ThrowExceptionWithCatch");
89      }
90
91      // throws exception and does not catch it locally
92      static void ThrowExceptionWithoutCatch()
93      {
94          // throw exception, but do not catch it
95          try
96          {
97              Console.WriteLine("In ThrowExceptionWithoutCatch");
98              throw new Exception("Exception in ThrowExceptionWithoutCatch");
99          }
100         finally
101         {
102             Console.WriteLine(
103                 "finally executed in ThrowExceptionWithoutCatch");
104         }
105
106         // unreachable code; logic error
107         Console.WriteLine("End of ThrowExceptionWithoutCatch");
108     }
109
```

Fig. 13.4 | `finally` blocks always execute, even when no exception occurs. (Part 3 of 4.)

```
110     // throws exception, catches it and rethrows it
111     static void ThrowExceptionCatchRethrow()
112     {
113         // try block throws exception
114         try
115         {
116             Console.WriteLine("In ThrowExceptionCatchRethrow");
117             throw new Exception("Exception in ThrowExceptionCatchRethrow");
118         }
119         catch (Exception exceptionParameter)
120         {
121             Console.WriteLine("Message: " + exceptionParameter.Message);
122
123             // rethrow exception for further processing
124             throw;
125
126             // unreachable code; logic error
127         }
128         finally
129         {
130             Console.WriteLine(
131                 "finally executed in ThrowExceptionCatchRethrow");
132         }
133
134         // any code placed here is never reached
135         Console.WriteLine("End of ThrowExceptionCatchRethrow");
136     }
137 }
```

```
Calling DoesNotThrowException
In DoesNotThrowException
finally executed in DoesNotThrowException
End of DoesNotThrowException

Calling ThrowExceptionWithCatch
In ThrowExceptionWithCatch
Message: Exception in ThrowExceptionWithCatch
finally executed in ThrowExceptionWithCatch
End of ThrowExceptionWithCatch

Calling ThrowExceptionWithoutCatch
In ThrowExceptionWithoutCatch
finally executed in ThrowExceptionWithoutCatch
Caught exception from ThrowExceptionWithoutCatch in Main

Calling ThrowExceptionCatchRethrow
In ThrowExceptionCatchRethrow
Message: Exception in ThrowExceptionCatchRethrow
finally executed in ThrowExceptionCatchRethrow
Caught exception from ThrowExceptionCatchRethrow in Main
```

Fig. 13.4 | finally blocks always execute, even when no exception occurs. (Part 4 of 4.)

Line 12 of Main invokes method DoesNotThrowException. This method's try block outputs a message (line 55). Because the try block does *not* throw any exceptions, program control ignores the catch block (lines 57–60) and executes the finally block (lines 61–64), which outputs a message. At this point, program control continues with the first statement after the close of the finally block (line 66), which outputs a message indicating that the end of the method has been reached. Then program control returns to Main.

13.5.3 Throwing Exceptions Using the throw Statement

Line 16 of Main invokes method ThrowExceptionWithCatch (lines 70–89), which begins in its try block (lines 73–77) by outputting a message. Next, the try block creates an Exception object and uses a **throw statement** to throw it (line 76). Executing the throw statement indicates that a problem has occurred in the code. As you've seen in earlier chapters, you can throw exceptions by using the throw statement. Just as with exceptions thrown by the Framework Class Library's methods and the CLR, this indicates to client apps that an error has occurred. A throw statement specifies an object to be thrown. The operand of a throw statement can be of type Exception or of any type derived from it.

The string passed to the constructor becomes the exception object's error message. When a throw statement in a try block executes, the try block *exits immediately*, and program control continues with the first matching catch block (lines 78–81) following the try block. In this example, the type thrown (Exception) matches the type specified in the catch, so line 80 outputs a message indicating the exception that occurred. Then, the finally block (lines 82–86) executes and outputs a message. At this point, program control continues with the first statement after the close of the finally block (line 88), which outputs a message indicating that the end of the method has been reached. Program control then returns to Main. In line 80, we use the exception object's Message property to retrieve the error message associated with the exception (i.e., the message passed to the Exception constructor). Section 13.7 discusses several properties of class Exception.

Lines 23–31 of Main define a try statement in which Main invokes method ThrowExceptionWithoutCatch (lines 92–108). The try block enables Main to catch any exceptions thrown by ThrowExceptionWithoutCatch. The try block in lines 95–99 of ThrowExceptionWithoutCatch begins by outputting a message. Next, the try block throws an Exception (line 98) and exits immediately.

Normally, program control would continue at the first catch following this try block. However, this try block does not have any catch blocks. Therefore, the exception is not caught in method ThrowExceptionWithoutCatch. Program control proceeds to the finally block (lines 100–104), which outputs a message. At this point, program control returns to Main in search of an appropriate catch block—any statements appearing after the finally block (e.g., line 107) do not execute. (In fact, the compiler issues a warning about this.) In this example, such statements could cause logic errors, because the exception thrown in line 98 is not caught. In Main, the catch block in lines 27–31 catches the exception and displays a message indicating that the exception was caught in Main.

13.5.4 Rethrowing Exceptions

Lines 38–46 of Main define a try statement in which Main invokes method ThrowExceptionCatchRethrow (lines 111–136). The try statement enables Main to catch any exceptions thrown by ThrowExceptionCatchRethrow. The try statement in lines 114–132 of ThrowExceptionCatchRethrow begins by outputting a message. Next, the try block throws an Exception (line 117). The try block *exits immediately*, and program control continues at the first catch (lines 119–127) following the try block. In this example, the type thrown (Exception) matches the type specified in the catch, so line 121 outputs a message indicating where the exception occurred. Line 124 uses the throw statement to rethrow the exception. This indicates that the catch block performed partial processing of the exception and now is throwing the exception again (in this case, back to the method Main) for further processing.

You also can rethrow an exception with a version of the throw statement which takes an operand that's the reference to the exception that was caught. It's important to note, however, that this form of throw statement *resets the throw point*, so the original throw point's stack-trace information is *lost*. Section 13.7 demonstrates using a throw statement with an operand from a catch block. In that section, you'll see that after an exception is caught, you can create and throw a different type of exception object from the catch block and you can include the original exception as part of the new exception object. Class library designers often do this to *customize* the exception types thrown from methods in their class libraries or to provide additional debugging information.

Software Engineering Observation 13.2

In general, it's considered better practice to throw a new exception and pass the original one to the new exception's constructor, rather than rethrowing the original exception. This maintains all of the stack-trace information from the original exception. We demonstrate passing an existing exception to a new exception's constructor in Section 13.7.3.

The exception handling in method ThrowExceptionCatchRethrow does not complete, because the throw statement in line 124 immediately terminates the catch block—if there were any code between line 124 and the end of the block, it would not execute. When line 124 executes, method ThrowExceptionCatchRethrow terminates and returns control to Main in search of an appropriate catch. Once again, the finally block (lines 128–132) executes and outputs a message before control returns to Main. When control returns to Main, the catch block in lines 42–46 catches the exception and displays a message indicating that the exception was caught. Then the program terminates.

13.5.5 Returning After a finally Block

The next statement to execute after a finally block terminates depends on the exception-handling state. If the try block successfully completes, or if a catch block catches and handles an exception, the program continues its execution with the next statement after the finally block. However, if an exception is not caught, or if a catch block rethrows an exception, program control continues in the next enclosing try block. The enclosing try could be in the calling method or in one of its callers. It also is possible to nest a try statement in a try block; in such a case, the outer try statement's catch blocks would process any exceptions that were not caught in the inner try statement. If a try block executes and has a corresponding finally block, the finally block executes even if the try block terminates due to a return statement. The return occurs after the execution of the finally block.

Common Programming Error 13.3

If an uncaught exception is awaiting processing when the finally block executes, and the finally block throws a new exception that's not caught in the finally block, the first exception is lost, and the new exception is passed to the next enclosing try block.

Error-Prevention Tip 13.4

When placing code that can throw an exception in a `finally` *block, always enclose the code in a* `try` *statement that catches the appropriate exception types. This prevents the loss of any uncaught and rethrown exceptions that occur before the* `finally` *block executes.*

Software Engineering Observation 13.3

Do not place `try` *blocks around every statement that might throw an exception—this can make programs difficult to read. Instead, place one* `try` *block around a significant portion of code, and follow this* `try` *block with* `catch` *blocks that handle each possible exception. Then follow the* `catch` *blocks with a single* `finally` *block. Use separate* `try` *blocks to distinguish between multiple statements that can throw the same exception type.*

13.6 The `using` Statement

Typically resource-release code should be placed in a `finally` block to ensure that a resource is released, *regardless* of whether there were exceptions when the resource was used in the corresponding `try` block. An alternative notation—the `using` statement (not to be confused with the `using` directive for using namespaces)—simplifies writing code in which you obtain a resource, use the resource in a `try` block and release the resource in a corresponding `finally` block. For example, a file-processing app (Chapter 17) could process a file with a `using` statement to ensure that the file is closed properly when it's no longer needed. The resource must be an object that implements the `IDisposable` interface and therefore has a `Dispose` method. The general form of a `using` statement is

```
using (var exampleObject = new ExampleClass())
{
    exampleObject.SomeMethod(); // do something with exampleObject
}
```

where `ExampleClass` is a class that implements the `IDisposable` interface. This code creates an object of type `ExampleClass` and uses it in a statement, then calls its `Dispose` method to release any resources used by the object. The `using` statement implicitly places the code in its body in a `try` block with a corresponding `finally` block that calls the object's `Dispose` method. For instance, the preceding brief code segment is equivalent to

```
{
    var exampleObject = new ExampleClass();
    try
    {
        exampleObject.SomeMethod();
    }
    finally
    {
        if (exampleObject != null)
        {
            exampleObject.Dispose();
        }
    }
}
```

The `if` statement in the `finally` block ensures that `exampleObject` is not null—that is, it references an object—otherwise, a `NullReferenceException` would occur when attempting to call `Dispose`. Section 13.9 introduces C# 6's new `?.` operator, which can be used to express the above `if` statement more elegantly as a single line of code.

13.7 Exception Properties

As we discussed in Section 13.4, exception types derive from class `Exception`, which has several properties. These frequently are used to formulate error messages indicating a caught exception. Two important properties are `Message` and **`StackTrace`**. Property `Message` stores the `string` error message associated with an `Exception` object. This message can be a default message defined in the exception type or a customized message passed to an `Exception` object's constructor when the `Exception` object is thrown. Property `StackTrace` contains a `string` that represents the method-call stack. Recall that the runtime environment at all times keeps a list of open method calls that have been made but have not yet returned. The `StackTrace` represents the series of methods that have not finished processing at the time the exception occurs. If the debugging information that's generated by the compiler for the method is accessible to the IDE (e.g., the code is part of your project, rather than some third party library), the stack trace also includes line numbers; the first line number indicates the *throw point*, and subsequent line numbers indicate the locations from which the methods in the stack trace were called.

13.7.1 Property `InnerException`

Another frequently used property is `InnerException`. When an exception occurs in a class library, it's common for the library to catch that exception, then `throw` a new one containing information that helps the client code programmer determine the exception's cause. Class library programmers typically "wrap" the original exception object in the new exception object—this gives the client code programmer complete details of what led to the exception.

For example, a programmer implementing libraries used in an accounting system might have account-number processing code in which account numbers are input as `string`s but represented as `int`s in the code. Recall that a program can convert `string`s to `int` values with `int.Parse`, which throws a `FormatException` if it encounters an invalid number format. When this happens, the library programmer might wish to employ a different error message than the default message supplied by `FormatException` or might wish to indicate a new exception type, such as `InvalidAccountNumberException`.

In such cases, the library programmer would provide code to catch the `FormatException`, then create an `InvalidAccountNumberException` object in the `catch` block, passing the original exception as a constructor argument. The original exception object becomes the `InvalidAccountNumberException` object's `InnerException`. Section 13.8 shows how to create a custom exception class.

When an `InvalidAccountNumberException` occurs in code that uses the accounting-system library, the `catch` handler can reference the original exception via property `InnerException`. So the `InvalidAccountNumberException` can indicate *both* that the user specified an invalid account number and that the number format was invalid. If the `InnerException` property is `null`, this indicates that the exception was not caused by another exception.

13.7.2 Other Exception Properties

Class Exception provides other properties, including HelpLink, Source and TargetSite:

- Property HelpLink specifies a link to the help file that describes the problem that occurred. This property is null if no such file exists.

- Property Source specifies the name of the assembly (i.e., app or library) that caused the exception.

- Property TargetSite specifies the method where the exception originated.

13.7.3 Demonstrating Exception Properties and Stack Unwinding

Our next example (Fig. 13.5) demonstrates properties Message, StackTrace and InnerException of class Exception. In addition, the example formally introduces stack unwinding—when an exception is thrown but not caught in a particular scope, the method-call stack is "unwound," and an attempt is made to catch the exception in the next outer try block. We keep track of the methods on the call stack as we discuss property StackTrace and the stack-unwinding mechanism. To see the proper stack trace, you should execute this program using steps similar to those presented in Section 13.2.

```
1   // Fig. 13.5: Properties.cs
2   // Stack unwinding and Exception class properties.
3   // Demonstrates using properties Message, StackTrace and InnerException.
4   using System;
5
6   class Properties
7   {
8      static void Main()
9      {
10        // call Method1; any Exception generated is caught
11        // in the catch block that follows
12        try
13        {
14           Method1();
15        }
16        catch (Exception exceptionParameter)
17        {
18           // output the string representation of the Exception, then output
19           // properties Message, StackTrace and InnerException
20           Console.WriteLine("exceptionParameter.ToString: \n" +
21              exceptionParameter);
22           Console.WriteLine("\nexceptionParameter.Message: \n" +
23              exceptionParameter.Message);
24           Console.WriteLine("\nexceptionParameter.StackTrace: \n" +
25              exceptionParameter.StackTrace);
26           Console.WriteLine("\nexceptionParameter.InnerException: \n" +
27              exceptionParameter.InnerException);
28        }
29     }
30
```

Fig. 13.5 | Stack unwinding and Exception class properties. (Part 1 of 3.)

```
31      // calls Method2
32      static void Method1()
33      {
34          Method2();
35      }
36
37      // calls Method3
38      static void Method2()
39      {
40          Method3();
41      }
42
43      // throws an Exception containing an InnerException
44      static void Method3()
45      {
46          // attempt to convert string to int
47          try
48          {
49              int.Parse("Not an integer");
50          }
51          catch (FormatException formatExceptionParameter)
52          {
53              // wrap FormatException in new Exception
54              throw new Exception("Exception occurred in Method3",
55                  formatExceptionParameter);
56          }
57      }
58  }
```

```
exceptionParameter.ToString:
System.Exception: Exception occurred in Method3 --->
   System.FormatException: Input string was not in a correct format.
   at System.Number.StringToNumber(String str, NumberStyles options,
      NumberBuffer& number, NumberFormatInfo info, Boolean parseDecimal)
   at System.Number.ParseInt32(String s, NumberStyles style,
      NumberFormatInfo info)
   at System.Int32.Parse(String s)
   at Properties.Method3() in C:\Users\PaulDeitel\Documents\examples\
      ch13\Fig13_05\Properties\Properties\Properties.cs:line 49
   --- End of inner exception stack trace ---
   at Properties.Method3() in C:\Users\PaulDeitel\Documents\examples\
      ch13\Fig13_05\Properties\Properties\Properties.cs:line 54
   at Properties.Method2() in C:\Users\PaulDeitel\Documents\examples\
      ch13\Fig13_05\Properties\Properties\Properties.cs:line 40
   at Properties.Method1() in C:\Users\PaulDeitel\Documents\examples\
      ch13\Fig13_05\Properties\Properties\Properties.cs:line 34
   at Properties.Main() in C:\Users\PaulDeitel\Documents\examples\
      ch13\Fig13_05\Properties\Properties\Properties.cs:line 14

exceptionParameter.Message:
Exception occurred in Method3
```

Fig. 13.5 | Stack unwinding and Exception class properties. (Part 2 of 3.)

```
exceptionParameter.StackTrace:
   at Properties.Method3() in C:\Users\PaulDeitel\Documents\examples\
      ch13\Fig13_05\Properties\Properties\Properties.cs:line 54
   at Properties.Method2() in C:\Users\PaulDeitel\Documents\examples\
      ch13\Fig13_05\Properties\Properties\Properties.cs:line 40
   at Properties.Method1() in C:\Users\PaulDeitel\Documents\examples\
      ch13\Fig13_05\Properties\Properties\Properties.cs:line 34
   at Properties.Main() in C:\Users\PaulDeitel\Documents\examples\
      ch13\Fig13_05\Properties\Properties\Properties.cs:line 14

exceptionParameter.InnerException:
System.FormatException: Input string was not in a correct format.
   at System.Number.StringToNumber(String str, NumberStyles options,
        NumberBuffer& number, NumberFormatInfo info, Boolean parseDecimal)
   at System.Number.ParseInt32(String s, NumberStyles style,
      NumberFormatInfo info)
   at System.Int32.Parse(String s)
   at Properties.Method3() in C:\Users\PaulDeitel\Documents\examples\
      ch13\Fig13_05\Properties\Properties\Properties.cs:line 49
```

Fig. 13.5 | Stack unwinding and Exception class properties. (Part 3 of 3.)

Program execution begins with Main, which becomes the first method on the method-call stack. Line 14 of the try block in Main invokes Method1 (declared in lines 32–35), which becomes the second method on the stack. If Method1 throws an exception, the catch block in lines 16–28 handles the exception and outputs information about the exception that occurred. Line 34 of Method1 invokes Method2 (lines 38–41), which becomes the third method on the stack. Then line 40 of Method2 invokes Method3 (lines 44–57), which becomes the fourth method on the stack.

At this point, the method-call stack (from top to bottom) for the program is

```
Method3
Method2
Method1
Main
```

The method called *most recently* (Method3) appears at the *top* of the stack; the *first* method called (Main) appears at the *bottom*. The try statement (lines 47–56) in Method3 invokes method int.Parse (line 49), which attempts to convert a string to an int. At this point, int.Parse becomes the fifth and final method on the call stack.

13.7.4 Throwing an Exception with an InnerException

Because the argument to int.Parse is not in int format, line 49 throws a Format-Exception that's caught in line 51 of Method3. The exception terminates the call to int.Parse, so the method is *unwound* (i.e., removed) from the method-call stack. The catch block in Method3 then creates and throws an Exception object. The first argument to the Exception constructor is the custom error message for our example, "Exception occurred in Method3." The second argument is the InnerException—the Format-Exception that was caught. The StackTrace for this new exception object reflects the point at which the exception was thrown (lines 54–55). Now Method3 terminates, because the exception thrown in the catch block is not caught in the method body. Thus, control returns to the statement that invoked `Method3` in the prior method in the call stack (`Method2`). This *unwinds* `Method3` from the method-call stack.

When control returns to line 40 in `Method2`, the CLR determines that line 40 is not in a `try` block. Therefore the exception cannot be caught in `Method2`, and `Method2` terminates. This *unwinds* `Method2` from the call stack and returns control to line 34 in `Method1`.

Here again, line 34 is not in a `try` block, so `Method1` cannot catch the exception. The method terminates and is *unwound* from the call stack, returning control to line 14 in `Main`, which *is* located in a `try` block. The `try` block in `Main` exits and the `catch` block (lines 16–28) catches the exception. The `catch` block uses properties `Message`, `Stack-Trace` and `InnerException` to create the output. Stack unwinding continues until a `catch` block catches the exception or the program terminates.

13.7.5 Displaying Information About the `Exception`

The first block of output (which we reformatted for readability) in Fig. 13.5 contains the exception's `string` representation, which is returned from an *implicit* call to method `To-String`. The `string` begins with the name of the exception class followed by the `Message` property value. The next four items present the stack trace of the `InnerException` object. The remainder of the block of output shows the `StackTrace` for the exception thrown in lines 54–55 of `Method3`. The `StackTrace` represents the state of the method-call stack at the throw point of the exception, rather than at the point where the exception eventually is caught. Each `StackTrace` line that begins with "at" represents a method on the call stack. These lines indicate the method in which the exception occurred, the file in which the method resides and the line number of the throw point in the file. The inner-exception information includes the *inner-exception stack trace*.

> **Error-Prevention Tip 13.5**
>
> *When catching and rethrowing an exception, provide additional debugging information in the rethrown exception. To do so, create an object of an `Exception` subclass containing more specific debugging information, then pass the original caught exception to the new exception object's constructor to initialize the `InnerException` property.*

The next block of output (two lines) simply displays the `Message` property's value (`Exception occurred in Method3`) of the exception thrown in `Method3`.

The third block of output displays the `StackTrace` property of the exception thrown in `Method3`. This `StackTrace` property contains the stack trace starting from line 54 in `Method3`, because that's the point at which the `Exception` object was created and thrown. The stack trace *always* begins from the exception's throw point.

Finally, the last block of output displays the `string` representation of the `Inner-Exception` property, which includes the namespace and class name of the exception object, as well as its `Message` and `StackTrace` properties.

13.8 User-Defined Exception Classes

In many cases, you can use existing exception classes from the .NET Framework Class Library to indicate exceptions that occur in your programs. In some cases, however, you might wish to create new exception classes specific to the problems that occur in your programs. User-defined exception classes should derive directly or indirectly from class Exception of namespace System. When you create code that throws exceptions, they should be well documented, so that other developers who use your code will know how to handle them.

Good Programming Practice 13.1
Associating each type of malfunction with an appropriately named exception class improves program clarity.

Software Engineering Observation 13.4
Before creating a user-defined exception class, investigate the existing exceptions in the .NET Framework Class Library to determine whether an appropriate exception type already exists.

Class *NegativeNumberException*

Figures 13.6–13.7 demonstrate a user-defined exception class. NegativeNumber-Exception (Fig. 13.6) represents exceptions that occur when a program performs an illegal operation on a negative number, such as attempting to calculate its square root. According to Microsoft's "Best Practices for Handling Exceptions" (bit.ly/Exceptions-BestPractices), user-defined exceptions should typically extend class Exception, have a class name that ends with Exception and define three constructors:

- a *parameterless constructor,*

- a *constructor that receives a string argument* (the error message), and

- a *constructor that receives a string argument and an Exception argument* (the error message and the inner-exception object).

Defining these three constructors makes your exception class more flexible, allowing other programmers to easily use and extend it.

```
1   // Fig. 13.6: NegativeNumberException.cs
2   // NegativeNumberException represents exceptions caused by
3   // illegal operations performed on negative numbers.
4   using System;
5
6   public class NegativeNumberException : Exception
7   {
8      // default constructor
9      public NegativeNumberException()
10        : base("Illegal operation for a negative number")
11     {
12        // empty body
13     }
14
15     // constructor for customizing error message
16     public NegativeNumberException(string messageValue)
17        : base(messageValue)
18     {
```

Fig. 13.6 | NegativeNumberException represents exceptions caused by illegal operations performed on negative numbers. (Part 1 of 2.)

```
19          // empty body
20      }
21
22      // constructor for customizing the exception's error
23      // message and specifying the InnerException object
24      public NegativeNumberException(string messageValue, Exception inner)
25          : base(messageValue, inner)
26      {
27          // empty body
28      }
29  }
```

Fig. 13.6 | NegativeNumberException represents exceptions caused by illegal operations performed on negative numbers. (Part 2 of 2.)

NegativeNumberExceptions most frequently occur during arithmetic operations, so it seems logical to derive class NegativeNumberException from class ArithmeticException. However, class ArithmeticException derives from class SystemException—the category of exceptions thrown by the CLR. Per Microsoft's best practices for exception handling, *user-defined exception classes should inherit from Exception* rather than SystemException. In this case, we could have used the built-in ArgumentOutOfRangeException class (introduced in Chapter 10), which is recommended in the best practices for invalid argument values. We create our own exception type here simply for demonstration purposes.

Using Class *NegativeNumberException*

Class SquareRootTest (Fig. 13.7) demonstrates our user-defined exception class. The app enables the user to input a numeric value, then invokes method SquareRoot (lines 40–52) to calculate the square root of that value. To perform this calculation, SquareRoot invokes class Math's Sqrt method, which receives a double value as its argument. Normally, if the argument is *negative*, method Sqrt returns NaN. In this program, we'd like to *prevent* the user from calculating the square root of a negative number. If the numeric value that the user enters is negative, method SquareRoot throws a NegativeNumberException (lines 45–46). Otherwise, SquareRoot invokes class Math's method Sqrt to compute the square root (line 50).

```
1   // Fig. 13.7: SquareRootTest.cs
2   // Demonstrating a user-defined exception class.
3   using System;
4
5   class SquareRootTest
6   {
7       static void Main(string[] args)
8       {
9           var continueLoop = true;
10
11          do
12          {
```

Fig. 13.7 | Demonstrating a user-defined exception class. (Part 1 of 3.)

```
13              // catch any NegativeNumberException thrown
14              try
15              {
16                  Console.Write(
17                      "Enter a value to calculate the square root of: ");
18                  double inputValue = double.Parse(Console.ReadLine());
19                  double result = SquareRoot(inputValue);
20
21                  Console.WriteLine(
22                      $"The square root of {inputValue} is {result:F6}\n");
23                  continueLoop = false;
24              }
25              catch (FormatException formatException)
26              {
27                  Console.WriteLine("\n" + formatException.Message);
28                  Console.WriteLine("Please enter a double value.\n");
29              }
30              catch (NegativeNumberException negativeNumberException)
31              {
32                  Console.WriteLine("\n" + negativeNumberException.Message);
33                  Console.WriteLine("Please enter a non-negative value.\n");
34              }
35          } while (continueLoop);
36      }
37
38      // computes square root of parameter; throws
39      // NegativeNumberException if parameter is negative
40      public static double SquareRoot(double value)
41      {
42          // if negative operand, throw NegativeNumberException
43          if (value < 0)
44          {
45              throw new NegativeNumberException(
46                  "Square root of negative number not permitted");
47          }
48          else
49          {
50              return Math.Sqrt(value); // compute square root
51          }
52      }
53  }
```

```
Enter a value to calculate the square root of: 30
The square root of 30 is 5.477226
```

```
Enter a value to calculate the square root of: hello

Input string was not in a correct format.
Please enter a double value.

Enter a value to calculate the square root of: 25
The square root of 25 is 5.000000
```

Fig. 13.7 | Demonstrating a user-defined exception class. (Part 2 of 3.)

```
Enter a value to calculate the square root of: -2

Square root of negative number not permitted
Please enter a non-negative value.

Enter a value to calculate the square root of: 2
The square root of 2 is 1.414214
```

Fig. 13.7 | Demonstrating a user-defined exception class. (Part 3 of 3.)

When the user inputs a value, the try statement (lines 14–34) attempts to invoke SquareRoot using the value input by the user. If the user input is not a number, a Format-Exception occurs, and the catch block in lines 25–29 processes the exception. If the user inputs a negative number, method SquareRoot throws a NegativeNumberException (lines 45–46); the catch block in lines 30–34 catches and handles this type of exception.

13.9 Checking for null References; Introducing C# 6's ?. Operator

In Section 13.6, we showed the following code snippet:

```
{
    var exampleObject = new ExampleClass();
    try
    {
        exampleObject.SomeMethod();
    }
    finally
    {
        if (exampleObject != null)
        {
            exampleObject.Dispose();
        }
    }
}
```

The if statement in the preceding finally block ensures that if exampleObject is null, the call to Dispose is skipped, thus preventing a NullReferenceException.

Error-Prevention Tip 13.6
Always ensure that a reference is not null before using it to call a method or access a property of an object.

13.9.1 Null-Conditional Operator (?.)

C# 6's new **null-conditional operator (?.)** provides a more elegant way to check for null. The following statement replaces the four-line if statement above:

```
exampleObject?.Dispose();
```

In this statement, Dispose is called *only* if exampleObject is not null—exactly as in the preceding if statement.

13.9.2 Revisiting Operators `is` and `as`

In Section 12.5.6, we introduced downcasting with the `is` operator and mentioned that downcasting can cause `InvalidCastExceptions`. We then mentioned that you can avoid the `InvalidCastException` by using the as operator as follows:

```
var employee = currentEmployee as BasePlusCommissionEmployee;
```

If `currentEmployee` *is a* `BasePlusCommissionEmployee`, `employee` is assigned the `BasePlusCommissionEmployee`; otherwise, it's assigned `null`. Since `employee` could be `null`, you must ensure that it's not `null` before using it. For example, to give the `BasePlusCommissionEmployee` a 10% raise, we could use the statement

```
employee?.BaseSalary *= 1.10M;
```

which accesses and modifies the `BaseSalary` property *only* if `employee` is not `null`.

13.9.3 Nullable Types

Suppose you'd like to capture the value of the expression `employee?.BaseSalary`, as in

```
decimal salary = employee?.BaseSalary;
```

This statement actually results in a compilation error indicating that you cannot implicitly convert type `decimal?` to type `decimal`.

Normally a value-type variable cannot be assigned `null`. Because the `employee` reference might be `null`, the expression

```
employee?.BaseSalary
```

returns a **nullable type**—a value type that also can be `null`. You specify a nullable type by following a value type's name with a question mark (?)—so `decimal?` represents a nullable `decimal`. The statement

```
decimal? salary = employee?.BaseSalary;
```

indicates that `salary` either will be `null` or the `employee`'s `BaseSalary`.

Nullable types have the following capabilities for accessing their underlying values:

- The `GetValueOrDefault` method checks whether a nullable-type variable contains a value. If so, the method returns that value; otherwise, it returns the value type's default value. An overload of this method receives one argument that enables you to specify a custom default value.

- The `HasValue` property returns `true` if a nullable-type variable contains a value; otherwise, it returns `false`.

- The `Value` property returns the nullable-type variable's underlying value or throws an `InvalidOperationException` if the underlying value is `null`.

Variables of nullable types also may be used as the left operand of the null-conditional operator (`?.`) or the null coalescing operator (`??`—discussed in the next section).

 Error-Prevention Tip 13.7
Before using a nullable-type variable's `Value` property, use the `HasValue` property to check whether the variable has a value. If the nullable-type variable is `null`, accessing `Value` results in an `InvalidOperationException`.

13.9.4 Null Coalescing Operator (??)

C# also offers the null coalescing operator (??) for working with values that can be null. The operator has two operands. If the left operand is not null, the entire ?? expression evaluates to the left operand's value; otherwise, it evaluates to the right operand's value. For example, in the statement

```
decimal salary = employee?.BaseSalary ?? 0M;
```

if employee is not null, salary is assigned the employee's BaseSalary; otherwise, salary is assigned 0M. The preceding statement is equivalent to

```
decimal salary = (employee?.BaseSalary).GetValueOrDefault();
```

As you can see, the preceding statements are more elegant and more compact than writing the following equivalent code, which must explicitly test for null:

```
decimal salary = 0M;

if (employee != null)
{
    salary = employee.BaseSalary
}
```

13.10 Exception Filters and the C# 6 when Clause

Prior to C# 6, you could catch an exception based only on its type. C# 6 introduces exception filters that enable you to catch an exception based on a catch's exception type and a condition that's specified with a when clause, as in

```
catch(ExceptionType  name) when (condition)
```

You also can specify an exception filter for a general catch clause that does not provide an exception type. This allows you to catch an exception based only on a condition, as in

```
catch when (condition)
```

In each case, the exception is caught only if the when clause's condition is true; otherwise, the exception is not caught and the search for an appropriate catch continues.

A typical use of an exception filter is to determine whether a property of an exception object has a specific value. Consider an app that connects to a web server to download videos. Such an app would call methods that may throw HttpExceptions—for example, the web server might not be found, you might not have permission to access the web server, etc. Class HttpException has an ErrorCode property that contains a numeric code, which apps can use to determine what went wrong and handle the exception accordingly. The following catch handler catches an HttpException *only* if the exception object's ErrorCode property contains 401, indicating your app does not have permission to access the web server:

```
catch (HttpException ex) when (exception.ErrorCode == 401)
```

You might provide several similar catch handlers with exception filters that test for various other ErrorCodes.

Common Programming Error 13.4

Following a try block with multiple catch clauses for the same type results in a compilation error, unless they provide different when clauses. If there are multiple such catches and one does not have a when clause, it must appear last; otherwise, a compilation error occurs.

13.11 Wrap-Up

In this chapter, you learned how to use exception handling to deal with errors in an app. You saw exception handling in the context of a divide-by-zero example. You learned how to use try blocks to enclose code that may throw an exception, and how to use catch blocks to deal with exceptions that may arise. We explained the termination model of exception handling, in which, after an exception is handled, program control does not return to the throw point.

We discussed several important classes of the .NET Exception hierarchy, including Exception (from which user-defined exception classes are derived) and SystemException. Next you learned how to use the finally block to release resources whether or not an exception occurs, and how to throw and rethrow exceptions with the throw statement. We showed how the using statement can be used to automate the process of releasing a resource. You then saw how to obtain information about an exception using Exception properties Message, StackTrace and InnerException, and method ToString. We demonstrated how to create your own exception classes.

We introduced C# 6's new ?. null-conditional operator for testing whether a reference is null before accessing the referenced object. We also introduced nullable value types and the ?? null coalescing operator. Finally, we showed how to use C# 6's new when clause for adding exception filters to catch clauses.

In the next two chapters, we present an in-depth treatment of graphical user interfaces. In these chapters and throughout the rest of the book, we use exception handling to make our examples more robust, while demonstrating new features of the language.

Summary

Section 13.1 Introduction
- An exception is an indication of a problem that occurs during a program's execution.
- Exception handling enables you to create apps that can resolve (or handle) exceptions.

Section 13.2 Example: Divide by Zero without Exception Handling
- An exception is thrown when a method or the CLR detects a problem and is unable to handle it.

Section 13.2.1 Dividing By Zero
- A stack trace includes the name of the exception in a descriptive message that indicates the problem that occurred and the complete method-call stack at the time the exception occurred.
- Division by zero is not allowed in integer arithmetic.
- Division by zero is allowed with floating-point values. Such a calculation results in the value infinity, which is represented by Double.PositiveInfinity or Double.NegativeInfinity, depend-

ing on whether the numerator is positive or negative. If both the numerator and denominator are zero, the result of the calculation is `Double.NaN`.

- When division by zero occurs in integer arithmetic, a `DivideByZeroException` is thrown.

Section 13.2.2 Enter a Non-Numeric Denominator
- A `FormatException` occurs when `int.Parse` receives a `string` that does not contain a valid integer.

Section 13.3.1 Enclosing Code in a **try** Block
- A `try` block encloses the code that might throw exceptions, as well as the code that should not execute if an exception occurs.

Section 13.3.2 Catching Exceptions
- A `catch` block can specify an identifier representing the exception that the `catch` block can handle. A general `catch` clause catches all exception types, but cannot access exception information.
- At least one `catch` block and/or a `finally` block must immediately follow the `try` block.

Section 13.3.3 Uncaught Exceptions
- An uncaught exception is an exception that occurs for which there's no matching `catch` block.

Section 13.3.4 Termination Model of Exception Handling
- After an exception is handled, program control does not return to the throw point, because the `try` block has exited. Instead, control resumes after the `try` statement's last `catch` block. This is known as the termination model of exception handling.

Section 13.3.5 Flow of Control When Exceptions Occur
- When a method called in a program detects an exception, or when the CLR detects a problem, the method or the CLR throws an exception.
- The point in the program at which an exception occurs is called the throw point.
- If an exception occurs in a `try` block, the `try` block terminates immediately, and program control transfers to the first of the following `catch` blocks in which the exception parameter's type matches the type of the thrown exception.
- The `try` block and its corresponding `catch` and `finally` blocks together form a `try` statement.
- The CLR locates the matching `catch` by comparing the thrown exception's type to each `catch`'s exception-parameter type. A match occurs if the types are identical or if the thrown exception's type is a derived class of the exception-parameter type.
- Once an exception is matched to a `catch` block, the other `catch` blocks are ignored.

Section 13.4 .NET **Exception** Hierarchy
- The C# exception-handling mechanism allows objects only of class `Exception` and its derived classes to be thrown and caught.
- Class `Exception` of namespace `System` is the base class of the .NET Framework Class Library exception class hierarchy.

Section 13.4.1 Class **SystemException**
- The CLR generates `SystemExceptions`, which can occur at any point during the execution of the program. Many of these exceptions can be avoided if apps are coded properly.
- A benefit of using the exception class hierarchy is that a `catch` block can catch exceptions of a particular type or—because of the *is-a* relationship of inheritance—can use a base-class type to catch exceptions in a hierarchy of related exception types.

- A catch block that specifies an exception parameter of type Exception can catch all exceptions that derive from Exception, because Exception is the base class of all exception classes.

Section 13.5 **finally** *Block*

- The most common type of resource leak is a memory leak.
- A memory leak occurs when a program allocates memory but does not deallocate it when it's no longer needed. Normally, this is not an issue in C#, because the CLR performs garbage collection of memory that's no longer needed by an executing program.

Section 13.5.1 *Moving Resource-Release Code to a* **finally** *Block*

- C#'s exception-handling mechanism provides the finally block, which is guaranteed to execute if program control enters the corresponding try block.
- The finally block executes regardless of whether the corresponding try block executes successfully or an exception occurs. This makes the finally block an ideal location in which to place resource-release code for resources acquired and manipulated in the corresponding try block.
- If a try block executes successfully, the finally block executes immediately after the try block terminates. If an exception occurs in the try block, the finally block executes immediately after the matching catch block (if any) completes.
- If the exception is not caught by a catch block associated with the try block, or if a catch block associated with the try block throws an exception, the finally block executes before the exception is processed by the next enclosing try block (if there is one).
- A throw statement can rethrow an exception, indicating that a catch block performed partial processing of the exception and now is throwing the exception again for further processing.

Section 13.6 *The* **using** *Statement*

- The using statement simplifies writing code in which you obtain an IDisposable resource, use the resource in a try block and release the resource in a corresponding finally block.

Section 13.7 **Exception** *Properties*

- Property Message of class Exception stores the error message associated with an Exception object.
- Property StackTrace of class Exception contains a string that represents the method-call stack.

Section 13.7.1 *Property* **InnerException**

- Another Exception property used frequently by class library programmers is InnerException. Typically, you use this property to "wrap" exception objects caught in your code, so that you then can throw new exception types specific to your libraries.

Section 13.7.3 *Demonstrating* **Exception** *Properties and Stack Unwinding*

- When an exception is thrown but not caught in a particular scope, stack unwinding occurs and an attempt is made to catch the exception in the next outer try block.

Section 13.8 *User-Defined Exception Classes*

- User-defined exception classes should derive directly or indirectly from class Exception of namespace System.
- User-defined exceptions should typically extend Exception, have a class name that ends with "Exception" and define a parameterless constructor, a constructor that receives a string argument (the error message), and a constructor that receives a string argument and an Exception argument (the error message and the inner-exception object).

Section 13.9.1 Null-Conditional Operator (?.)
- C# 6's new null-conditional operator (?.) accesses a property or calls a method only if its left operand is not null; otherwise, evaluation of the expression terminates and the value of the entire expression is null.

Section 13.9.3 Nullable Types
- A nullable type is a value type that also can be null.
- You specify a nullable type by following a value type's name with a question mark (?).
- The GetValueOrDefault method checks whether a nullable-type variable contains a value. If so, the method returns that value; otherwise, it returns the value type's default value.
- The HasValue property returns true if a nullable-type variable contains a value; otherwise, it returns false.
- The Value property returns the nullable-type variable's underlying value.

Section 13.9.4 Null Coalescing Operator (??)
- The null coalescing operator (??) has two operands. If the left operand is not null, the entire ?? expression evaluates to the left operand's value; otherwise, it evaluates to the right operand's value.

Section 13.10 Exception Filters and the C# 6 *when* Clause
- Prior to C# 6, you could catch an exception based only on its type.
- C# 6 introduces exception filters that enable you to catch an exception based on a catch's exception type and a condition that's specified with a when clause.
- You also can specify an exception filter for a general catch clause that does not provide an exception type.
- A catch class with an exception filter catches an exception only if the when clause's condition is true.
- If an exception filter's condition is false, the exception will not be caught and the original exception's stack-trace information will be preserved until the exception is caught.

Terminology

catch an exception
catch block
divide by zero
DivideByZeroException class
error-processing code
exception
Exception Assistant
Exception class
exception filter
exception handling
fault-tolerant program
finally block
FormatException class
general catch clause
GetValueOrDefault method of a nullable type
handle an exception

HasValue property of a nullable type
HelpLink property of class Exception
IndexOutOfRangeException class
InnerException property of class Exception
memory leak
method-call stack
null coalescing operator (??)
null conditional operator (?.)
nullable type
NullReferenceException class
out-of-range array index
resource leak
resumption model of exception handling
rethrow an exception
robust program
Source property of class Exception

stack trace

stack unwinding

StackTrace property of class Exception

SystemException class

TargetSite property of class Exception

termination model of exception handling

throw an exception

throw point

throw statement

try block

try statement

TryParse method of structure Int32

uncaught exception

unhandled exception

user-defined exception class

using statement

Value property of a nullable type

when clause

Self-Review Exercises

13.1 Fill in the blanks in each of the following statements:

a) A method is said to _____ an exception when it detects that a problem has occurred.

b) When present, the _____ block associated with a try block always executes.

c) Exception classes are derived from class _____.

d) The statement that throws an exception is called the _____ of the exception.

e) C# uses the _____ model of exception handling as opposed to the _____ model of exception handling.

f) An uncaught exception in a method causes the method to _____ from the method-call stack.

g) Method int.Parse can throw a(n) _____ exception if its argument is not a valid integer value.

h) The _____ operator accesses a property or calls a method only if the operator's left operand is not null.

i) An expression using the _____ operator evaluates to the operator's left operand if it's not null; otherwise, the expression evaluates to the operator's right operand.

13.2 State whether each of the following is *true* or *false*. If *false*, explain why.

a) Exceptions always are handled in the method that initially detects the exception.

b) User-defined exception classes should extend class SystemException.

c) Accessing an out-of-bounds array index causes the CLR to throw an exception.

d) A finally block is optional after a try block that does not have any corresponding catch blocks.

e) A finally block is guaranteed to execute.

f) It's possible to return to the throw point of an exception using keyword return.

g) Exceptions can be rethrown.

h) Property Message of class Exception returns a string indicating the method from which the exception was thrown.

i) A when clause adds an exception filter to a catch clause.

j) A nullable-type variable's Value property always returns the underlying value.

Answers to Self-Review Exercises

13.1 a) throw. b) finally. c) Exception. d) throw point. e) termination, resumption. f) unwind. g) FormatException. h) ?. null conditional operator. i) ?? null coalescing operator.

13.2 a) False. Exceptions can be handled by other methods on the method-call stack. b) False. User-defined exception classes should typically extend class Exception. c) True. d) False. A try block that does not have any catch blocks requires a finally block. e) False. The finally block executes only if program control enters the corresponding try block. f) False. return causes control to return to the caller. g) True. h) False. Property Message of class Exception returns a string representing the error message. i) True. j) False. If the nullable-type variable is `null` and you access the `Value` property, an `InvalidOperationException` occurs.

Exercises

13.3   *(Exception Base Classes and Derived Classes)* Use inheritance to create an exception base class and various exception-derived classes. Write a program to demonstrate that the `catch` specifying the base class catches derived-class exceptions.

13.4   *(Catching Exceptions)* Write a program that demonstrates how various exceptions are caught with

```
catch (Exception ex)
```

13.5   *(Order of Exception Handlers)* To demonstrate the importance of the order of exception handlers, write two programs, one with correct ordering of `catch` blocks (i.e., place the base-class exception handler after all derived-class exception handlers) and another with improper ordering (i.e., place the base-class exception handler before the derived-class exception handlers). What happens when you attempt to compile the second program?

13.6   *(Constructor Failure)* Exceptions can be used to indicate problems that occur when an object is being constructed. Write a program that shows a constructor passing information about constructor failure to an exception handler. The exception thrown also should contain the arguments sent to the constructor.

13.7   *(Rethrowing and Exception)* Write a program that demonstrates rethrowing an exception.

13.8   *(Not Catching Every Exception)* Write a program demonstrating that a method with its own `try` block does not have to catch every possible exception that occurs within the `try` block—some exceptions can slip through to, and be handled in, other scopes.

13.9   *(Exception from a Deeply Nested Method)* Write a program that `throws` an exception from a deeply nested method. The `catch` block should follow the `try` block that encloses the call chain. The exception caught should be one you defined yourself. In catching the exception, display the exception's message and stack trace.

13.10   *(FormatExceptions)* Create an app that inputs miles driven and gallons used, and calculates miles per gallon. The example should use exception handling to process the `FormatExceptions` that occur when converting the input strings to `doubles`. If invalid data is entered, display a message informing the user.

14

Graphical User Interfaces with Windows Forms: Part 1

Objectives

In this chapter you'll learn:

- Design principles of graphical user interfaces (GUIs).

- How to create graphical user interfaces.

- How to process events in response to user interactions with GUI controls.

- The namespaces that contain the classes for GUI controls and event handling.

- How to create and manipulate various controls.

- How to add descriptive ToolTips to GUI controls.

- How to process mouse and keyboard events.

14.1 Introduction

A graphical user interface (GUI) allows a user to interact *visually* with a program. A GUI (pronounced "GOO-ee") gives a program a distinctive "look" and "feel."

 Look-and-Feel Observation 14.1
Consistent user interfaces enable a user to learn new apps more quickly because the apps have the same "look" and "feel."

As an example of a GUI, consider Fig. 14.1, which shows a Visual Studio window containing various GUI controls. Near the top, there's a *menu bar* containing the menus **File**, **Edit**, **View**, etc. Below that is a *tool bar* of buttons, each with a defined task, such as creating a new project or opening a file. Below that is a *tab* representing a currently open file—this *tabbed view* allows users to switch between the open files. These controls form a user-friendly interface through which you have been interacting with the IDE.

GUIs are built from *GUI controls* (which are sometimes called components or widgets—short for window gadgets). GUI controls are *objects* that can display information on the screen or enable users to interact with an app via the mouse, keyboard or some other form of input (such as voice commands). Several common GUI controls are listed in Fig. 14.2—in the sections that follow and in Chapter 15, we discuss each of these in detail. Chapter 15 explores the features and properties of additional GUI controls.

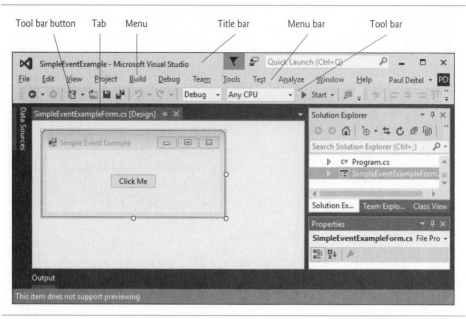

Fig. 14.1 | GUI controls in Visual Studio.

Control	Description
Label	Displays *images* or *uneditable text*.
TextBox	Enables the user to *enter data via the keyboard*. It also can be used to *display editable or uneditable text*.
Button	Triggers an *event* when clicked with the mouse.
CheckBox	Specifies an option that can be *selected* (checked) or *unselected* (not checked).
ComboBox	Provides a *drop-down list* of items from which the user can make a *selection* either by clicking an item in the list or by typing in a box.
ListBox	Provides a *list* of items from which the user can make a *selection* by clicking one or more items.
Panel	A *container* in which controls can be placed and organized.
NumericUpDown	Enables the user to select from a *range* of numeric input values.

Fig. 14.2 | Some basic GUI controls.

14.2 Windows Forms

Windows Forms is one library that can be used to create GUIs—you'll also learn about *Universal Windows Platform (UWP)* and *Windows Presentation Foundation (WPF)* in on-line chapters. A Form is a graphical element that appears on your computer's desktop; it can be a dialog, a window or an MDI window (multiple document interface window)—

discussed in Chapter 15. A *component* is an instance of a class that implements the ICom-ponent interface, which defines the behaviors that components must implement. A *control*, such as a Button or Label, is a component that has a graphical representation at runtime. Some components lack graphical representations (e.g., class Timer of namespace System.Windows.Forms—see Chapter 15). Such components are not visible at run time.

Figure 14.3 displays the Windows Forms controls and components from the C# **Toolbox**. The controls and components are organized into categories by functionality. Selecting the category **All Windows Forms** at the top of the **Toolbox** allows you to view all the controls and components from the other tabs in one list (as shown in Fig. 14.3). In this chapter and the next, we discuss many of these controls and components. To add a control or component to a Form, select that control or component from the **Toolbox** and drag it onto the Form. To *deselect* a control or component, select the **Pointer** item in the **Toolbox** (the icon at the top of the list).

Fig. 14.3 | Components and controls for Windows Forms.

Active Window and Focus

When there are several windows on the screen, the active window is the *frontmost* and has a *highlighted title bar*. A window becomes the active window when the user clicks somewhere inside it. The active window is said to "have the focus." For example, in Visual Studio the active window is the **Toolbox** when you're selecting an item from it, or the **Properties** window when you're editing a control's properties.

Auto-Generated Code Stored in Separate File

A Form is a container for controls and components. When you drag an item from the **Tool-box** onto the Form, Visual Studio generates code that creates the object and sets its basic properties. This code is updated when the control or component's properties are modified in the IDE. Removing a control or component from the Form *deletes* the corresponding generated code. The IDE maintains the generated code in a separate file using partial classes—classes that are split among multiple files and assembled into a single class by the compiler. You could write this code yourself, but it's much easier to allow Visual Studio to handle the details. We introduced visual programming concepts in Section 2.6. In this chapter and the next, we use visual programming to build more substantial GUIs.

Common Form Properties, Methods and an Event

Each control or component we present in this chapter is located in namespace System.Windows.Forms. To create a Windows Forms app, you generally create a Windows Form, set its properties, add controls to the Form, set their properties and implement *event handlers* (methods) that respond to *events* generated when a user interacts with the controls. Figure 14.4 lists common Form properties, common methods and a common event.

Form properties, methods and an event	Description
Common Properties	
AcceptButton	Default Button that's clicked when you press *Enter*.
AutoScroll	bool value (false by default) that allows or disallows *scrollbars* when needed.
CancelButton	Button that's clicked when the *Escape* key is pressed.
FormBorderStyle	*Border style* for the Form (Sizable by default).
Font	Font of text displayed on the Form, and the *default font* for controls added to the Form.
Text	Text in the Form's title bar.
Common Methods	
Close	Closes a Form and *releases all resources*, such as the memory used for the Form's contents. A closed Form cannot be reopened.
Hide	Hides a Form, but does *not* destroy the Form or release its resources.
Show	Displays a *hidden* Form.
Common Event	
Load	Occurs before a Form is displayed to the user. You'll learn about events and event-handling in the next section.

Fig. 14.4 | Common Form properties, methods and an event.

14.3 Event Handling

Normally, a user interacts with an app's GUI to indicate the tasks that the app should perform. For example, when you write an e-mail in an e-mail app, clicking the **Send** button tells the app to send the e-mail to the specified e-mail addresses. GUIs are event driven. When the user interacts with a GUI component, the interaction—known as an event—drives the program to perform a task. Before GUIs, the program told the user what to do next. With GUIs, the user tells the program what to do. Common events (user interactions) that might cause an app to perform a task include

- *clicking* a Button,
- *typing* in a TextBox,
- *selecting* an item from a menu,
- *closing* a window and
- *moving* the mouse.

All GUI controls have events associated with them. Objects of other types also can have associated events as well. A method that performs a task in response to an event is called an event handler, and the overall process of responding to events is known as event handling.

14.3.1 A Simple Event-Driven GUI

The Form in the app of Fig. 14.5 contains a Button that a user can click to display a MessageBox. In line 6, notice the namespace declaration, which is inserted for every class you create—we've been removing these from earlier simple examples. Namespaces organize groups of related classes. Recall from Section 7.4.3 that each class's name is actually a combination of its namespace name, a dot (.) and the class name—again, this is known as the class's fully qualified name. We'll use namespaces like this in Chapters 15 and 19. If another namespace also contains a class with the same name, the fully qualified class names must be used to distinguish between the classes in the app and prevent a name conflict (also called a name collision).

```
1   // Fig. 14.5: SimpleEventExampleForm.cs
2   // Simple event handling example.
3   using System;
4   using System.Windows.Forms;
5
6   namespace SimpleEventExample
7   {
8      // Form that shows a simple event handler
9      public partial class SimpleEventExampleForm : Form
10     {
11        // default constructor
12        public SimpleEventExampleForm()
13        {
14           InitializeComponent();
15        }
16
17        // handles click event of Button clickButton
18        private void clickButton_Click(object sender, EventArgs e)
19        {
```

Fig. 14.5 | Simple event-handling example. (Part 1 of 2.)

```
20                MessageBox.Show("Button was clicked.");
21           }
22       }
23   }
```

Fig. 14.5 | Simple event-handling example. (Part 2 of 2.)

Renaming the `Form1.cs` File

Using the techniques presented in Section 2.6, create a Form containing a Button. First, create a new Windows Forms app names SimpleEventExample. Then:

1. Rename the Form1.cs file to SimpleEventExampleForm.cs in the **Solution Explorer**.

2. Click the Form in the designer, then use the **Properties** window to set the Form's Text property to "Simple Event Example".

3. Set the Form's Font property to Segoe UI, 9pt. To do so, select the Font property in the **Properties** window, then click the *ellipsis (...) button* in the property's value field to display a font dialog.

*Adding a **Button** to the **Form***

Drag a Button from the **Toolbox** onto the Form. In the **Properties** window, set the (Name) property (which specifies the Button's variable name) to clickButton and the Text property to Click Me. By convention, a control's variable name ends with the control's type. For example, in the variable name clickButton, "Button" is the control's type.

*Adding an Event Handler for the **Button's** `Click` Event*

When the user clicks the Button in this example, we want the app to respond by displaying a MessageBox. To do this, you must create an *event handler* for the Button's *Click event*, which you can do by *double clicking* the Button on the Form. This opens the file containing the following *empty* event handler in the program code:

```
    private void clickButton_Click(object sender, EventArgs e)
    {
    }
```

By convention, the IDE names the event-handler method as *objectName_eventName* (e.g., clickButton_Click). The clickButton_Click event handler *executes* when the user *clicks* the clickButton control.

Event Handler Parameters

Each event handler receives two parameters when it's called. The first—an object reference named sender by default—is a reference to the *object that the user interacted with to generate the event.* The second is a reference to an `EventArgs` object (or an object of an `EventArgs` derived class), which is typically named e. This object contains additional information about the event that occurred. `EventArgs` is the *base class* of all classes that represent event information.

Displaying a *MessageBox*

To display a `MessageBox` in response to the event, insert the statement

```
MessageBox.Show("Button was clicked.");
```

in the event handler's body. The resulting event handler appears in lines 18–21 of Fig. 14.5. When you execute the app and click the `Button`, a `MessageBox` appears displaying the text "Button was clicked.".

14.3.2 Auto-Generated GUI Code

Visual Studio places the *auto-generated* GUI code in the `Form` class's `Designer.cs` file—in this example, the file `SimpleEventExampleForm.Designer.cs`. You can open this file by expanding the `Form` class's node in the **Solution Explorer** window and double clicking the file name that ends with `Designer.cs`. Figs. 14.6 and 14.7 show this file's contents. The IDE collapses the code in lines 23–57 of Fig. 14.7 by default—you can click the

icon next to line 23 to *expand* the code, then click the

icon next to that line to *collapse* it.

```
SimpleEventExampleForm.Designer.cs
[C#] SimpleEventExample                    SimpleEventExample.SimpleEventExampleForm   components
 1   namespace SimpleEventExample
 2   {
 3       partial class SimpleEventExampleForm
 4       {
 5           /// <summary>
 6           /// Required designer variable.
 7           /// </summary>
 8           private System.ComponentModel.IContainer components = null;
 9
10           /// <summary>
11           /// Clean up any resources being used.
12           /// </summary>
13           /// <param name="disposing">true if managed resources should be disposed; oth
14           protected override void Dispose(bool disposing)
15           {
16               if (disposing && (components != null))
17               {
18                   components.Dispose();
19               }
20               base.Dispose(disposing);
21           }
22
123 %
```

Fig. 14.6 | First half of the Visual Studio generated code file.

```
SimpleEventExampleForm.Designer.cs    ⧉ ×
C# SimpleEventExample                          ▾  ⚙ SimpleEventExample.SimpleEventExampleForm ▾  ⚙ components                        ▾
    23        ⊟        #region Windows Form Designer generated code                                                              ✛
    24        ⋮                                                                                                                   ▴
    25        ⊟        /// <summary>
    26                 /// Required method for Designer support - do not modify
    27                 /// the contents of this method with the code editor.
    28                 /// </summary>
    29        ⊟        private void InitializeComponent()
    30                 {
    31                     this.clickButton = new System.Windows.Forms.Button();
    32                     this.SuspendLayout();
    33                     //
    34                     // clickButton
    35                     //
    36                     this.clickButton.Location = new System.Drawing.Point(120, 37);
    37                     this.clickButton.Name = "clickButton";
    38                     this.clickButton.Size = new System.Drawing.Size(75, 23);
    39                     this.clickButton.TabIndex = 0;
    40                     this.clickButton.Text = "Click Me";
    41                     this.clickButton.UseVisualStyleBackColor = true;
    42                     this.clickButton.Click += new System.EventHandler(this.clickButton_Click);
    43                     //
    44                     // SimpleEventExampleForm
    45                     //
    46                     this.AutoScaleDimensions = new System.Drawing.SizeF(7F, 15F);
    47                     this.AutoScaleMode = System.Windows.Forms.AutoScaleMode.Font;
    48                     this.ClientSize = new System.Drawing.Size(314, 97);
    49                     this.Controls.Add(this.clickButton);
    50                     this.Font = new System.Drawing.Font("Segoe UI", 9F, System.Drawing.FontSty
    51                     this.Name = "SimpleEventExampleForm";
    52                     this.Text = "Simple Event Example";
    53                     this.ResumeLayout(false);
    54
    55                 }
    56
    57                 #endregion
    58
    59                 private System.Windows.Forms.Button clickButton;
    60             }
    61         }
123 %  ▾ ◀                                                                                          ▶
```

Fig. 14.7 | Second half of the Visual Studio generated code file.

Now that you have studied classes and objects in detail, this code will be easier to understand. Since this code is created and maintained by Visual Studio, you generally do not need to look at it. In fact, you do not need to understand most of the code shown here to build GUI apps. However, we now take a closer look to help you understand how GUI apps work.

The auto-generated code that defines the GUI is actually part of the Form's *class*—in this case, SimpleEventExampleForm. Line 3 of Fig. 14.6 (and line 9 of Fig. 14.5) uses the partial modifier, which allows this class to be split among multiple files, including the files that contain auto-generated code and those in which you write your own code. Line 59 of Fig. 14.7 declares the clickButton that we created in **Design** mode. It's declared as an instance variable of class SimpleEventExampleForm. By default, all variable declarations for controls created through C#'s *design window* have a private access modifier. The code also includes the *Dispose method* for *releasing resources* (Fig. 14.6, lines 14–21) and method InitializeComponent (Fig. 14.7, lines 29–55), which contains the code that creates the Button, then sets some of the Button's and the Form's properties. The property values correspond to the values set in the **Properties** window for each control. Visual Studio adds comments to the code that it generates, as in lines 33–35. Line 42 was generated when we created the event handler for the Button's Click event.

Method InitializeComponent is called when the Form is created, and establishes such properties as the Form title, the Form size, control sizes and text. Visual Studio also uses the code in this method to create the GUI you see in design view. Changing the code in InitializeComponent may prevent Visual Studio from displaying the GUI properly.

Error-Prevention Tip 14.1

*The code in the Designer.cs file that's generated by building a GUI in **Design** mode is not meant to be modified directly, which is why this code is placed in a separate file. Modifying this code can prevent the GUI from being displayed correctly in **Design** mode and might cause an app to function incorrectly. In **Design** mode, it's recommended that you modify control properties only in the **Properties** window, not in the Designer.cs file.*

14.3.3 Delegates and the Event-Handling Mechanism

The control that generates an event is known as the event sender. An event-handling method—known as the *event handler*—responds to a particular event that a control generates. When the event occurs, the event sender calls its event handler to perform a task (i.e., to "handle the event").

The .NET event-handling mechanism allows you to choose your own names for event-handling methods. However, each event-handling method must declare the proper parameters to receive information about the event that it handles. Since you can choose your own method names, an event sender such as a Button cannot know in advance which method will respond to its events. So, we need a mechanism to indicate which method is the event handler for an event.

Delegates

Event handlers are connected to a control's events via special objects called delegates. A delegate type declaration specifies the return type and signature of a method—in event handling, the delegate specifies the return type and arguments for an event handler. GUI controls have predefined delegates that correspond to every event they can generate. For example, the delegate for a Button's Click event is of type EventHandler (namespace System). The online help documentation declares this type as follows:

```
public delegate void EventHandler(object sender, EventArgs e);
```

This uses the **delegate** keyword to declare a delegate type named EventHandler, which can hold references to methods that return void and receive two parameters—one of type object (the *event sender*) and one of type EventArgs. If you compare the delegate declaration with clickButton_Click's first line (Fig. 14.5, line 18), you'll see that this event handler returns the same type and receives the same parameters specified by the EventHandler delegate—the parameters' names need not match. The preceding declaration actually creates an entire class for you. The details of this special class's declaration are handled by the compiler.

Indicating the Method that a Delegate Should Call

Since each event handler is declared as a delegate, the *event sender* can simply call the appropriate delegate when an event occurs—a Button calls the EventHandler delegate that corresponds to its Click event in response to a click. The delegate's job is to invoke the appropriate method. To enable the clickButton_Click method to be called, Visual Studio assigns clickButton_Click to the click Button's Click EventHandler delegate, as shown in line 42 of Fig. 14.7. This code is added by Visual Studio when you double click the Button control in **Design** mode. The expression

```
new System.EventHandler(this.clickButton_Click);
```

creates an EventHandler delegate object and initializes it with the clickButton_Click method. Line 42 uses the += operator to *add* the delegate to the Button's Click EventHandler delegate. This enables clickButton_Click to respond when a user clicks the Button. The += operator is overloaded by the delegate class that's created by the compiler.

(Optional) Multicast Delegates

You can actually specify that several methods should be invoked in response to one event by adding other delegates to the Button's Click event with statements similar to line 42 of Fig. 14.7. Event delegates are multicast—they represent a *set of delegate objects* that all have the *same signature*. When an event occurs, the event sender calls *every* method referenced by the multicast delegate. This is known as event multicasting. Event delegates derive from class MulticastDelegate, which derives from class Delegate (both from namespace System). For most cases, you'll specify only one event handler for a particular event on a control.

14.3.4 Another Way to Create Event Handlers

For the GUI app in Fig. 14.5, you double clicked the Button control on the Form to create its event handler. This technique creates an event handler for a control's default event—the event that's most frequently used with that control. Controls can generate many different events, and each one can have its own event handler. For instance, your app also can provide an event handler for a Button's MouseHover event, which occurs when the mouse pointer remains positioned over the Button for a short period of time. We now discuss how to create an event handler for an event that's not a control's default event.

Using the Properties Window to Create Event Handlers

You can create event handlers through the **Properties** window. If you select a control on the Form, then click the **Events** icon (the lightning bolt icon in Fig. 14.8) in the **Properties** window, that control's events are listed in the window. You can double click an event's name to display in the editor an existing event handler for that event, or to create the event handler if it does not yet exist in your code. You also can select an event, then use the drop-down list to its right to choose an existing method that should be used as the event handler for that event. The methods that appear in this drop-down list are the Form class's methods that have the proper signature to be an event handler for the selected event. You can return to viewing the properties of a control by selecting the **Properties** icon (Fig. 14.8).

A single method can handle events from multiple controls. For example, consider an app that displays CheckBoxes that represent bold and italic fonts. The user could select bold, italic or both. In this case, the font's style depends on both CheckBoxes, so their

Fig. 14.8 | Viewing events for a `Button` control in the **Properties** window.

events could be handled by the same method, which would determine each `CheckBox`'s state to determine the user's selected font style.

You can specify an event handler for multiple events by selecting multiple controls (drag over them, hold *Shift* and click each or hold *Ctrl* and click each) and selecting a single method in the **Properties** window's **Events** tab. If you create a new event handler this way, you should rename it appropriately so that it does not contain one control's name. You could also select each control individually and specify the same method for each one's event.

14.3.5 Locating Event Information

Read the Visual Studio documentation to learn about the different events raised by each control. To do this, select a control in the IDE (either in your `Form`'s design or in the **Tool-box** and press the *F1* key to display that control's online help (Fig. 14.9).

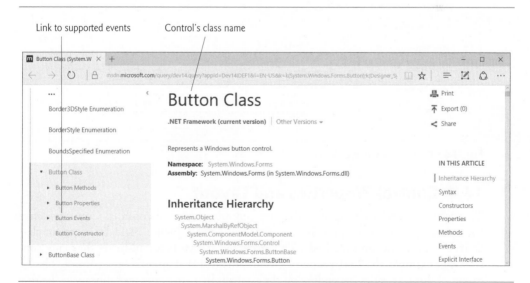

Fig. 14.9 | Link to list of `Button` events.

The web page that's displayed contains basic information about the control's class. In the left column of the page are several links to more information about the class—**Button Methods, Button Properties, Button Events** and **Button Constructor**. Each link displays a subset of the class's members. Click the link to the list of events for that control (**Button Events** in this case) to display the supported events for that control.

Next, click the name of an event to view its description and examples of its use. We selected the Click event to display the information in Fig. 14.10. The Click event is a member of class Control, an indirect base class of class Button. The **Remarks** section of the page discusses the details of the selected event. Alternatively, you could use the **Object Browser** to look up this information in the System.Windows.Forms namespace. The **Object Browser** shows only the members *originally* defined in a given class. The Click event is originally defined in class Control and inherited into Button. For this reason, you must look at class Control in the **Object Browser** to see the documentation for the Click event. See Section 10.11 for more information regarding the **Object Browser**.

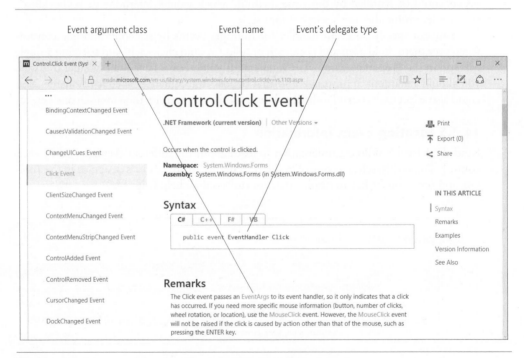

Fig. 14.10 | Click event details.

14.4 Control Properties and Layout

This section overviews properties that are common to many controls. Controls derive from class Control (namespace System.Windows.Forms). Figure 14.11 lists some of class Control's properties and methods. The properties shown here can be set for many controls. For example, the Text property specifies the text that appears on a control. The location of this text varies depending on the control. In a Form, the text appears in the title bar, but the text of a Button appears on its face.

Class `Control` properties and methods	Description
Common Properties	
`BackColor`	The control's background color.
`BackgroundImage`	The control's background image.
`Enabled`	Specifies whether the control is *enabled* (i.e., if the user can interact with it). Typically, portions of a *disabled* control appear "grayed out" as a visual indication to the user that the control is disabled.
`Focused`	Indicates whether the control *has the focus* (only available at runtime).
`Font`	The `Font` used to display the control's text.
`ForeColor`	The control's foreground color. This usually determines the color of the text in the `Text` property.
`TabIndex`	The *tab order* of the control. When the *Tab* key is pressed, the focus transfers between controls based on the tab order. You can set this order.
`TabStop`	If `true`, then a user can give focus to this control via the *Tab* key.
`Text`	The text associated with the control. The location and appearance of the text vary depending on the type of control.
`Visible`	Indicates whether the control is visible.
Common Methods	
`Hide`	Hides the control (sets the `Visible` property to `false`).
`Select`	*Acquires the focus.*
`Show`	Shows the control (sets the `Visible` property to `true`).

Fig. 14.11 | Class `Control` properties and methods.

Method `Select` transfers the focus to a control and makes it the active control. When you press the *Tab* key in an executing Windows Forms app, controls *receive the focus* in the order specified by their `TabIndex` property. This property is set by Visual Studio based on the order in which controls are added to a `Form`, but you can change the *tabbing order* using **View > Tab Order**. `TabIndex` is helpful for users who enter information in many controls, such as a set of `TextBox`es that represent a user's name, address and telephone number. The user can enter information, then quickly select the next control by pressing the *Tab* key.

Property `Enabled` indicates whether the user can interact with a control to generate an event. Often, if a control is *disabled*, it's because an option is unavailable to the user at that time. For example, text editor apps often disable the "paste" command until the user cuts or copies some text. In most cases, a disabled control's text appears in gray (rather than in black). You also can hide a control from the user without disabling the control by setting the `Visible` property to `false` or by calling method `Hide`. In each case, the control still exists but is not visible on the `Form`.

14.4.1 Anchoring and Docking

You can use anchoring and docking to specify the layout of controls inside a container— such as a `Form` or, within a `Form`, a control that groups other controls (such as a `Panel`, discussed in Section 14.6). Anchoring places controls a fixed distance from the sides of the container. Anchoring enhances the user experience. For example, if the user expects a control to appear in a particular corner of the app, anchoring ensures that the control will always be in that corner—even if the user *resizes* the Form. Docking attaches a control to a container such that the control stretches across an entire side or fills an entire area. For example, a control such as a status bar typically should remain at the bottom of the Form and stretch across the entire bottom of that Form, regardless of the Form's width. When the parent control is resized, the docked control resizes as well.

Anchoring Demonstration

When a window (or other type of *container* like a Panel) is resized, anchored controls are moved (and possibly resized) so that the distance from the sides to which they're anchored does not vary. By default, most controls are anchored to the top-left corner of the Form. To see the effects of anchoring a control, create a simple Windows Forms app that contains two Buttons. Anchor one control to the right and bottom sides by setting the **Anchor** property as shown in Fig. 14.12. Leave the other control with its default anchoring (top, left). Execute the app and enlarge the Form. The Button anchored to the bottom-right corner is always the same distance from the bottom right (Fig. 14.13). The other control stays its original distance from the top left.

Fig. 14.12 | Manipulating the **Anchor** property of a control.

Fig. 14.13 | Anchoring demonstration.

In Fig. 14.14, a `Button` is docked at the top of the `Form` (spanning the top portion). When the `Form` is resized, the `Button` is resized to the `Form`'s new width. `Form`s have a `Padding` property that specifies the distance between the docked controls and the `Form` edges. This property specifies four values (one for each side), and each value is set to 0 by default. Some common control layout properties are summarized in Fig. 14.15.

Fig. 14.14 | Docking a `Button` to the top of a `Form`.

Control layout properties	Description
Anchor	Causes a control to remain at a fixed distance from the side(s) of the container even when the container is resized.
Dock	Allows a control to span one side of its container or to fill the remaining space in the container.
Padding	Sets the space between a container's edges and docked controls. The default is 0, causing the control to appear flush with the container's sides.
Location	Specifies the location (as a set of coordinates) of the upper-left corner of the control, in relation to its container's upper-left corner.
Size	Specifies the size of the control in pixels as a `Size` object, which has properties `Width` and `Height`.
MinimumSize, MaximumSize	Indicates the minimum and maximum size of a `Control`, respectively.

Fig. 14.15 | `Control` layout properties.

A `Control`'s `Anchor` and `Dock` properties are set with respect to the container in which the `Control` resides—known as the *parent container*—which could be a `Form` or another container (such as a `Panel`). The minimum and maximum `Form` (or other `Control`) sizes can be set via properties `MinimumSize` and `MaximumSize`, respectively. Both are of type `Size`, which has properties `Width` and `Height`. Properties `MinimumSize` and `MaximumSize` allow you to design the GUI layout for a given size range. The user cannot make a `Form` smaller than the size specified by property `MinimumSize` and cannot make a `Form` larger than the size specified by property `MaximumSize`. To set a `Form` to a *fixed* size (where the `Form` cannot be resized by the user), set its minimum and maximum size to the same value.

14.4.2 Using Visual Studio To Edit a GUI's Layout

Visual Studio helps you with GUI layout. When you drag a control across a `Form`, blue *snap lines* appear to help you position the control with respect to others (Fig. 14.16) and the Form's edges. This feature makes the control you're dragging appear to "snap into place" alongside other controls. Visual Studio also provides the **Format** menu, which contains options for modifying your GUI's layout. The **Format** menu does not appear in the IDE unless you select one or more controls in design view. When you select multiple controls, you can align them with the **Format** menu's **Align** submenu. The **Format** menu also enables you to modify the space between controls or to center a control on the Form.

Fig. 14.16 | Snap lines for aligning controls.

14.5 Labels, TextBoxes and Buttons

Labels provide text information (as well as optional images) and are defined with class Label (a derived class of Control). A Label displays text that the *user cannot directly modify*. A Label's text can be changed programmatically by modifying the Label's Text property. Figure 14.17 lists common Label properties.

Common Label properties	Description
Font	The font of the text on the Label.
Text	The text on the Label.
TextAlign	The alignment of the Label's text on the control—horizontally (left, center or right) and vertically (top, middle or bottom). The default is top, left.

Fig. 14.17 | Common Label properties.

A textbox (class TextBox) is an area in which either text can be displayed by a program or the user can type text via the keyboard. A password TextBox is a TextBox that hides the information entered by the user. As the user types characters, the password TextBox masks the user input by displaying a password character. If you set the property UseSystemPasswordChar to true, the TextBox becomes a password TextBox. Users often encounter both types of TextBoxes, when logging into a computer or website—the username TextBox allows users to input their usernames; the password TextBox allows users to enter their passwords. Figure 14.18 lists the common properties and a common event of TextBoxes.

TextBox properties and an event	Description
Common Properties	
AcceptsReturn	If true in a multiline TextBox, pressing *Enter* in the TextBox creates a new line. If false (the default), pressing *Enter* is the same as pressing the default Button on the Form. The default Button is the one assigned to a Form's AcceptButton property.
Multiline	If true, the TextBox can span multiple lines. The default value is false.
ReadOnly	If true, the TextBox has a gray background, and its text cannot be edited. The default value is false.
ScrollBars	For multiline textboxes, this property indicates which scrollbars appear (None—the default, Horizontal, Vertical or Both).
Text	The TextBox's text content.
UseSystemPasswordChar	When true, the TextBox becomes a password TextBox, and the system-specified character masks each character the user types.
Common Event	
TextChanged	Generated when the text changes in a TextBox (i.e., when the user adds or deletes characters). When you double click the TextBox control in **Design** mode, an empty event handler for this event is generated.

Fig. 14.18 | TextBox properties and an event.

A button is a control that the user clicks to trigger a specific action or to select an option in a program. As you'll see, a program can use several types of buttons, such as checkboxes and radio buttons. All the button classes derive from class **ButtonBase** (namespace System.Windows.Forms), which defines common button features. In this section, we discuss class Button, which typically enables a user to issue a command to an app. Figure 14.19 lists common properties and a common event of class Button.

Button properties and an event	Description
Common Properties	
Text	Specifies the text displayed on the Button face.
FlatStyle	Modifies a Button's appearance—Flat (for the Button to display without a three-dimensional appearance), Popup (for the Button to appear flat until the user moves the mouse pointer over the Button), Standard (three-dimensional) and System, where the Button's appearance is controlled by the operating system. The default value is Standard.
Common Event	
Click	Generated when the user clicks the Button. When you double click a Button in design view, an empty event handler for this event is created.

Fig. 14.19 | Button properties and an event.

Figure 14.20 uses a TextBox, a Button and a Label. The user enters text into a password box and clicks the Button, causing the text input to be displayed in the Label. Normally, we would not display this text—the purpose of password TextBoxes is to hide the text being entered by the user. When the user clicks the **Show Me** Button, this app retrieves the text that the user typed in the password TextBox and displays it in a Label.

```
1   // Fig. 14.20: LabelTextBoxButtonTestForm.cs
2   // Using a TextBox, Label and Button to display
3   // the hidden text in a password TextBox.
4   using System;
5   using System.Windows.Forms;
6
7   namespace LabelTextBoxButtonTest
8   {
9      // Form that creates a password TextBox and
10     // a Label to display TextBox contents
11     public partial class LabelTextBoxButtonTestForm : Form
12     {
13        // default constructor
14        public LabelTextBoxButtonTestForm()
15        {
16           InitializeComponent();
17        }
18
19        // display user input in Label
20        private void displayPasswordButton_Click(object sender, EventArgs e)
21        {
22           // display the text that the user typed
23           displayPasswordLabel.Text = inputPasswordTextBox.Text;
24        }
25     }
26  }
```

Fig. 14.20 | Using a TextBox, Label and Button to display the hidden text in a password TextBox.

First, create the GUI by dragging the controls (a TextBox, a Button and a Label) onto the Form. Once the controls are positioned, change their names in the **Properties** window from the default values—textBox1, button1 and label1—to the more descriptive displayPasswordLabel, displayPasswordButton and inputPasswordTextBox. The (Name) property in the **Properties** window enables us to change the variable name for a control. Visual Studio creates the necessary code and places it in method InitializeComponent of the partial class in the file LabelTextBoxButtonTestForm.Designer.cs.

We set displayPasswordButton's Text property to "Show Me" and clear the Text of displayPasswordLabel so that it's blank when the program begins executing. The BorderStyle property of displayPasswordLabel is set to Fixed3D, giving our Label a three-dimensional appearance. We also changed its TextAlign property to MiddleLeft so that the Label's text is displayed centered between its top and bottom. The password character for inputPasswordTextBox is determined by the user's system settings when you set UseSystemPasswordChar to true.

We create an event handler for displayPasswordButton by double clicking this control in **Design** mode. We added line 23 to the event handler's body. When the user clicks the **Show Me** Button in the executing app, line 23 obtains the text entered by the user in inputPasswordTextBox and displays the text in displayPasswordLabel.

14.6 GroupBoxes and Panels

GroupBoxes and Panels arrange controls on a GUI. GroupBoxes and Panels are typically used to group several controls of similar functionality or several controls that are related in a GUI. All of the controls in a GroupBox or Panel move together when the GroupBox or Panel is moved. Furthermore, a GroupBoxes and Panels also can be used to show or hide a set of controls at once. When you modify a container's Visible property, it toggles the visibility of all the controls within it.

The primary difference between these two controls is that GroupBoxes can display a caption (i.e., text) and do *not* include scrollbars, whereas Panels can include scrollbars and do not include a caption. GroupBoxes have thin borders by default; Panels can be set so that they also have borders by changing their BorderStyle property. Figures 14.21–14.22 list the common properties of GroupBoxes and Panels, respectively.

 Look-and-Feel Observation 14.2
Panels and GroupBoxes can contain other Panels and GroupBoxes for more complex layouts.

GroupBox properties	Description
Controls	The set of controls that the GroupBox contains.
Text	Specifies the caption text displayed at the top of the GroupBox.

Fig. 14.21 | GroupBox properties.

Panel properties	Description
AutoScroll	Indicates whether scrollbars appear when the Panel is too small to display all of its controls. The default value is false.
BorderStyle	Sets the border of the Panel. The default value is None; other options are Fixed3D and FixedSingle.
Controls	The set of controls that the Panel contains.

Fig. 14.22 | Panel properties.

Look-and-Feel Observation 14.3

You can organize a GUI by anchoring and docking controls inside a GroupBox or Panel. The GroupBox or Panel then can be anchored or docked inside a Form. This divides controls into functional "groups" that can be arranged easily.

To create a GroupBox, drag its icon from the **Toolbox** onto a Form. Then, drag new controls from the **Toolbox** into the GroupBox. These controls are added to the GroupBox's Controls property and become part of the GroupBox. The GroupBox's Text property specifies the caption at the top of the GroupBox.

To create a Panel, drag its icon from the **Toolbox** onto the Form. You can then add controls directly to the Panel by dragging them from the **Toolbox** onto the Panel. To enable the scrollbars, set the Panel's AutoScroll property to true. If the Panel is resized and cannot display all of its controls, scrollbars appear (Fig. 14.23). The scrollbars can be used to view *all* the controls in the Panel—at design time *and* at execution time. In Fig. 14.23, we set the Panel's BorderStyle property to FixedSingle so that you can see the Panel in the Form.

Fig. 14.23 | Creating a Panel with scrollbars.

The program in Fig. 14.24 uses a GroupBox and a Panel to arrange Buttons. When these Buttons are clicked, their event handlers change the text on a Label.

```
1   // Fig. 14.24: GroupBoxPanelExampleForm.cs
2   // Using GroupBoxes and Panels to arrange Buttons.
3   using System;
4   using System.Windows.Forms;
5
6   namespace GroupBoxPanelExample
7   {
8      // Form that displays a GroupBox and a Panel
9      public partial class GroupBoxPanelExampleForm : Form
10     {
```

Fig. 14.24 | Using GroupBoxes and Panels to arrange Buttons. (Part 1 of 2.)

```
11          // default constructor
12          public GroupBoxPanelExampleForm()
13          {
14              InitializeComponent();
15          }
16
17          // event handler for Hi Button
18          private void hiButton_Click(object sender, EventArgs e)
19          {
20              messageLabel.Text = "Hi pressed"; // change text in Label
21          }
22
23          // event handler for Bye Button
24          private void byeButton_Click(object sender, EventArgs e)
25          {
26              messageLabel.Text = "Bye pressed"; // change text in Label
27          }
28
29          // event handler for Far Left Button
30          private void leftButton_Click(object sender, EventArgs e)
31          {
32              messageLabel.Text = "Far Left pressed"; // change text in Label
33          }
34
35          // event handler for Far Right Button
36          private void rightButton_Click(object sender, EventArgs e)
37          {
38              messageLabel.Text = "Far Right pressed"; // change text in Label
39          }
40      }
41  }
```

Fig. 14.24 | Using GroupBoxes and Panels to arrange Buttons. (Part 2 of 2.)

The mainGroupBox has two Buttons—hiButton (which displays the text **Hi**) and bye-Button (which displays the text **Bye**). The Panel (named mainPanel) also has two Buttons, leftButton (which displays the text **Far Left**) and rightButton (which displays the text **Far Right**). The mainPanel has its AutoScroll property set to true, allowing scrollbars to appear when the contents of the Panel require more space than the Panel's visible area. The Label (named messageLabel) is initially blank. To add controls to mainGroupBox or main-Panel, Visual Studio calls method Add of each container's Controls property. This code is placed in the partial class located in the file GroupBoxPanelExampleForm.Designer.cs.

The event handlers for the four Buttons are located in lines 18–39. Lines 20, 26, 32 and 38 change the text of messageLabel to indicate which Button the user pressed.

14.7 CheckBoxes and RadioButtons

C# has two types of state buttons that can be in the on/off or true/false states—**CheckBoxes** and **RadioButtons**. Like class Button, classes CheckBox and RadioButton are derived from class ButtonBase.

14.7.1 CheckBoxes

A CheckBox is a small square that either is blank or contains a check mark. When the user clicks a CheckBox to select it, a check mark appears in the box. If the user clicks the CheckBox again to deselect it, the check mark is removed. You also can configure a CheckBox to toggle between three states (*checked*, *unchecked* and *indeterminate*) by setting its **ThreeState** property to true. Any number of CheckBoxes can be selected at a time. A list of common CheckBox properties and a common event appears in Fig. 14.25.

CheckBox properties and an event	Description
Common Properties	
Appearance	By default, this property is set to Normal, and the CheckBox displays as a traditional checkbox. If it's set to Button, the CheckBox displays as a Button that looks pressed when the CheckBox is checked.
Checked	Indicates whether the CheckBox is *checked* (contains a check mark) or unchecked (blank). This property returns a bool value. The default is false (*unchecked*).
CheckState	Indicates whether the CheckBox is *checked* or *unchecked* with a value from the CheckState enumeration (Checked, Unchecked or Indeterminate). Indeterminate is used when it's unclear whether the state should be Checked or Unchecked. When CheckState is set to Indeterminate, the CheckBox is usually shaded.
Text	Specifies the text displayed to the right of the CheckBox.
ThreeState	When this property is true, the CheckBox has three states—*checked, unchecked* and *indeterminate*. By default, this property is false and the CheckBox has only two states—*checked* and *unchecked*. When true, Checked returns true for both the *checked* and *indeterminate* states.
Common Event	
CheckedChanged	Generated *any* time the Checked or CheckState property changes. This is a CheckBox's default event. When a user double clicks the CheckBox control in design view, an empty event handler for this event is generated.

Fig. 14.25 | CheckBox properties and an event.

The program in Fig. 14.26 allows the user to select CheckBoxes to change a Label's font style. The event handler for one CheckBox applies bold and the event handler for the other applies italic. If both CheckBoxes are selected, the font style is set to bold and italic. Initially, neither CheckBox is checked.

```
 1   // Fig. 14.26: CheckBoxTestForm.cs
 2   // Using CheckBoxes to toggle italic and bold styles.
 3   using System;
 4   using System.Drawing;
 5   using System.Windows.Forms;
 6
 7   namespace CheckBoxTest
 8   {
 9      // Form contains CheckBoxes to allow the user to modify sample text
10      public partial class CheckBoxTestForm : Form
11      {
12         // default constructor
13         public CheckBoxTestForm()
14         {
15            InitializeComponent();
16         }
17
18         // toggle the font style between bold and
19         // not bold based on the current setting
20         private void boldCheckBox_CheckedChanged(object sender, EventArgs e)
21         {
22            outputLabel.Font = new Font(outputLabel.Font,
23               outputLabel.Font.Style ^ FontStyle.Bold);
24         }
25
26         // toggle the font style between italic and
27         // not italic based on the current setting
28         private void italicCheckBox_CheckedChanged(
29            object sender, EventArgs e)
30         {
31            outputLabel.Font = new Font(outputLabel.Font,
32               outputLabel.Font.Style ^ FontStyle.Italic);
33         }
34      }
35   }
```

Fig. 14.26 | Using CheckBoxes to toggle italic and bold styles.

The `boldCheckBox` has its `Text` property set to `Bold`. The `italicCheckBox` has its `Text` property set to `Italic`. The `Text` property of `outputLabel` is set to `Watch the font style change`. After creating the controls, we define their event handlers. Double clicking the `CheckBox`es at design time creates empty `CheckedChanged` event handlers.

To change a `Label`'s font style, set its `Font` property to a new `Font object` (lines 22–23 and 31–32). Class `Font` is in the `System.Drawing` namespace. The `Font` constructor used here takes a `Font` and new style as arguments. The argument `outputLabel.Font` uses `outputLabel`'s original font name and size. The style is specified with a member of the `FontStyle enumeration`, which contains `Regular`, `Bold`, `Italic`, `Strikeout` and `Underline`. (The `Strikeout` style displays text with a line through it.) A `Font` object's `Style` property is read-only, so it can be set only when the `Font` object is created.

14.7.2 Combining Font Styles with Bitwise Operators

Styles can be combined via bitwise operators—operators that perform manipulation on bits of information. Recall from Chapter 1 that all data is represented in the computer as combinations of 0s and 1s. Each 0 or 1 represents a bit. The `FontStyle` (namespace `System.Drawing`) is represented as a set of bits that are selected in a way that allows us to combine different `FontStyle` elements to create compound styles, using bitwise operators. These styles are *not mutually exclusive*, so we can combine different styles and remove them without affecting the combination of previous `FontStyle` elements.

We can combine the various font styles, using either the *logical OR (|) operator* or the *logical exclusive OR (∧) operator* (also called XOR). When the *logical OR operator* is applied to two bits, if at least one bit of the two has the value 1, then the result is 1. Combining styles using the *logical OR operator* works as follows. Assume that `FontStyle.Bold` is represented by bits 01 and that `FontStyle.Italic` is represented by bits 10. When we use the *logical OR (|)* to combine the styles, we obtain the bits 11.

```
01   =   Bold
10   =   Italic
--
11   =   Bold and Italic
```

The *logical OR operator* helps create style combinations. However, what happens if we want to *undo* a style combination, as we did in Fig. 14.26?

The *logical exclusive OR operator* enables us to combine styles and to *undo* existing style settings. When *logical exclusive OR* is applied to two bits, if both bits have the same value, then the result is 0. If both bits are different, then the result is 1.

Combining styles using *logical exclusive OR* works as follows. Assume, again, that `FontStyle.Bold` is represented by bits 01 and that `FontStyle.Italic` is represented by bits 10. When we use *logical exclusive OR (∧)* on both styles, we obtain the bits 11.

```
01   =   Bold
10   =   Italic
--
11   =   Bold and Italic
```

Now, suppose that we'd like to *remove* the `FontStyle.Bold` style from the previous combination of `FontStyle.Bold` and `FontStyle.Italic`. The easiest way to do so is to reapply the *logical exclusive OR (∧) operator* to the compound style and `FontStyle.Bold`.

```
11  =   Bold and Italic
01  =   Bold
--
10  =   Italic
```

This is a simple example. The advantages of using bitwise operators to combine FontStyle values become more evident when we consider that there are five FontStyle values (Bold, Italic, Regular, Strikeout and Underline), resulting in 16 FontStyle combinations. Using bitwise operators to combine font styles greatly reduces the amount of code required to check all possible font combinations.

In Fig. 14.26, we need to set the FontStyle so that the text appears in bold if it was not bold originally, and vice versa. Line 23 uses the *bitwise logical exclusive OR operator* to do this. If outputLabel.Font.Style is bold, then the resulting style is not bold. If the text is originally italic, the resulting style is bold and italic, rather than just bold. The same applies for FontStyle.Italic in line 32.

If we didn't use bitwise operators to compound FontStyle elements, we'd have to test for the current style and change it accordingly. In boldCheckBox_CheckedChanged, we could test for the regular style and make it bold, test for the bold style and make it regular, test for the italic style and make it bold italic and test for the italic bold style and make it italic. This is cumbersome because, for every new style we add, we double the number of combinations. Adding a CheckBox for underline would require testing eight additional styles. Adding a CheckBox for strikeout would require testing 16 additional styles.

14.7.3 RadioButtons

Radio buttons (defined with class RadioButton) are similar to CheckBoxes in that they also have two states—selected and not selected (also called deselected). However, RadioButtons normally appear as a group, in which only one RadioButton can be selected at a time. Selecting one RadioButton in the group forces all the others to be deselected. Therefore, RadioButtons are used to represent a set of mutually exclusive options (i.e., a set in which multiple options *cannot* be selected at the same time).

Look-and-Feel Observation 14.4
Use RadioButtons when the user should choose only one option in a group. Use Check-Boxes when the user should be able to choose multiple options in a group.

All RadioButtons added in a container are in the same group. To divide RadioButtons into several groups, they must be added to *separate* containers, such as GroupBoxes or Panels. RadioButton's common properties and a common event are listed in Fig. 14.27.

RadioButton properties and an event	Description
Common Properties	
Checked	Indicates whether the RadioButton is checked.
Text	Specifies the RadioButton's text.

Fig. 14.27 | RadioButton properties and an event. (Part 1 of 2.)

RadioButton properties and an event	Description
Common Event	
CheckedChanged	Generated every time the RadioButton is checked or unchecked. When you double click a RadioButton control in design view, an empty event handler for this event is generated.

Fig. 14.27 | RadioButton properties and an event. (Part 2 of 2.)

 Software Engineering Observation 14.1
Forms, GroupBoxes, and Panels can act as logical groups for RadioButtons. The RadioButtons within each group are mutually exclusive to each other, but not to RadioButtons in different logical groups.

The program in Fig. 14.28 uses RadioButtons to enable users to select options for a MessageBox. After selecting the desired attributes, the user presses the **Display** Button to display the MessageBox. A Label in the lower-left corner shows the result of the MessageBox (i.e., which Button the user clicked—**Yes**, **No**, **Cancel**, etc.).

```
1   // Fig. 14.28: RadioButtonsTestForm.cs
2   // Using RadioButtons to set message window options.
3   using System;
4   using System.Windows.Forms;
5
6   namespace RadioButtonsTest
7   {
8      // Form contains several RadioButtons--user chooses one
9      // from each group to create a custom MessageBox
10     public partial class RadioButtonsTestForm : Form
11     {
12        // create variables that store the user's choice of options
13        private MessageBoxIcon IconType { get; set; }
14        private MessageBoxButtons ButtonType { get; set; }
15
16        // default constructor
17        public RadioButtonsTestForm()
18        {
19           InitializeComponent();
20        }
21
22        // change Buttons based on option chosen by sender
23        private void buttonType_CheckedChanged(object sender, EventArgs e)
24        {
25           if (sender == okRadioButton) // display OK Button
26           {
```

Fig. 14.28 | Using RadioButtons to set message-window options. (Part 1 of 4.)

```
27                  ButtonType = MessageBoxButtons.OK;
28              }
29              // display OK and Cancel Buttons
30              else if (sender == okCancelRadioButton)
31              {
32                  ButtonType = MessageBoxButtons.OKCancel;
33              }
34              // display Abort, Retry and Ignore Buttons
35              else if (sender == abortRetryIgnoreRadioButton)
36              {
37                  ButtonType = MessageBoxButtons.AbortRetryIgnore;
38              }
39              // display Yes, No and Cancel Buttons
40              else if (sender == yesNoCancelRadioButton)
41              {
42                  ButtonType = MessageBoxButtons.YesNoCancel;
43              }
44              // display Yes and No Buttons
45              else if (sender == yesNoRadioButton)
46              {
47                  ButtonType = MessageBoxButtons.YesNo;
48              }
49              // only one option left--display Retry and Cancel Buttons
50              else
51              {
52                  ButtonType = MessageBoxButtons.RetryCancel;
53              }
54          }
55
56          // change Icon based on option chosen by sender
57          private void iconType_CheckedChanged(object sender, EventArgs e)
58          {
59              if (sender == asteriskRadioButton) // display asterisk Icon
60              {
61                  IconType = MessageBoxIcon.Asterisk;
62              }
63              // display error Icon
64              else if (sender == errorRadioButton)
65              {
66                  IconType = MessageBoxIcon.Error;
67              }
68              // display exclamation point Icon
69              else if (sender == exclamationRadioButton)
70              {
71                  IconType = MessageBoxIcon.Exclamation;
72              }
73              // display hand Icon
74              else if (sender == handRadioButton)
75              {
76                  IconType = MessageBoxIcon.Hand;
77              }
```

Fig. 14.28 | Using RadioButtons to set message-window options. (Part 2 of 4.)

```
78              // display information Icon
79              else if (sender == informationRadioButton)
80              {
81                  IconType = MessageBoxIcon.Information;
82              }
83              // display question mark Icon
84              else if (sender == questionRadioButton)
85              {
86                  IconType = MessageBoxIcon.Question;
87              }
88              // display stop Icon
89              else if (sender == stopRadioButton)
90              {
91                  IconType = MessageBoxIcon.Stop;
92              }
93              // only one option left--display warning Icon
94              else
95              {
96                  IconType = MessageBoxIcon.Warning;
97              }
98          }
99
100         // display MessageBox and Button user pressed
101         private void displayButton_Click(object sender, EventArgs e)
102         {
103             // display MessageBox and store
104             // the value of the Button that was pressed
105             DialogResult result = MessageBox.Show(
106                 "This is your Custom MessageBox.", "Custom MessageBox",
107                 ButtonType, IconType);
108
109             // check to see which Button was pressed in the MessageBox
110             // change text displayed accordingly
111             switch (result)
112             {
113                 case DialogResult.OK:
114                     displayLabel.Text = "OK was pressed.";
115                     break;
116                 case DialogResult.Cancel:
117                     displayLabel.Text = "Cancel was pressed.";
118                     break;
119                 case DialogResult.Abort:
120                     displayLabel.Text = "Abort was pressed.";
121                     break;
122                 case DialogResult.Retry:
123                     displayLabel.Text = "Retry was pressed.";
124                     break;
125                 case DialogResult.Ignore:
126                     displayLabel.Text = "Ignore was pressed.";
127                     break;
128                 case DialogResult.Yes:
129                     displayLabel.Text = "Yes was pressed.";
130                     break;
```

Fig. 14.28 | Using RadioButtons to set message-window options. (Part 3 of 4.)

```
131                    case DialogResult.No:
132                        displayLabel.Text = "No was pressed.";
133                        break;
134               }
135          }
136      }
137  }
```

a) GUI for testing **RadioButton**s

b) **AbortRetryIgnore** button type

c) **OKCancel** button type

d) **OK** button type

e) **AbortRetryIgnore** button type

f) **YesNoCancel** button type

g) **YesNo** button type

h) **RetryCancel** button type

Fig. 14.28 | Using RadioButtons to set message-window options. (Part 4 of 4.)

We store the user's choices in properties IconType and ButtonType (declared in lines 13–14). IconType is of type MessageBoxIcon, and can have values Asterisk, Error, Exclamation, Hand, Information, None, Question, Stop and Warning. The sample output shows only Error, Exclamation, Information and Question icons.

ButtonType is of type MessageBoxButtons, and can have values AbortRetryIgnore, OK, OKCancel, RetryCancel, YesNo and YesNoCancel. The name indicates the options that are presented to the user in the MessageBox. The sample output windows show Message-Boxes for all of the MessageBoxButtons enumeration values.

We created separate GroupBoxes—**Button Type** and **Icon**—containing RadioButtons for the corresponding enumeration options. Only one RadioButton can be selected from each GroupBox. When a user clicks the **Display** Button, a customized MessageBox is displayed. A Label (displayLabel) shows which Button the user pressed in the MessageBox.

The RadioButtons' event handler responds to each RadioButton's CheckedChanged event. When a RadioButton in the **Button Type** GroupBox is selected, the event handler (lines 23–54)—which we set for all RadioButtons in that group—sets the ButtonType. Similarly, a RadioButton in the **Icon** GroupBox is selected, the event handler (lines 57–98)—which we set for all RadioButtons in that group—sets the IconType.

The Click event handler for displayButton (lines 101–135) creates a MessageBox (lines 105–107). The MessageBox options are specified with the values stored in IconType and ButtonType. When the user clicks one of the MessageBox's buttons, the result of the message box is returned to the app. This result is a value from the DialogResult enumeration that contains Abort, Cancel, Ignore, No, None, OK, Retry or Yes. The switch statement in lines 111–134 tests for the result and sets displayLabel.Text appropriately.

14.8 PictureBoxes

A PictureBox displays an image. The image can be one of several formats, such as bitmap, PNG (Portable Network Graphics), GIF (Graphics Interchange Format) and JPEG (Joint Photographic Experts Group). A PictureBox's Image property specifies the image that's displayed, and the SizeMode property indicates how the image is displayed (Normal, StretchImage, Autosize, CenterImage or Zoom). Figure 14.29 describes common PictureBox properties and a common event.

PictureBox properties and an event	Description
Common Properties	
Image	Sets the image to display in the PictureBox.
SizeMode	Controls image sizing and positioning. Values are Normal (default), StretchImage, AutoSize, CenterImage and Zoom. Normal places the image in the PictureBox's top-left corner, and CenterImage puts the image in the middle. Both truncate the image if it's too large. StretchImage fits the image in the PictureBox. AutoSize resizes the PictureBox to fit the image. Zoom resizes the image to to fit the PictureBox but maintains the original aspect ratio.

Fig. 14.29 | PictureBox properties and an event. (Part 1 of 2.)

PictureBox properties and an event	Description
Common Event	
Click	Occurs when the user clicks a control. When you double click this control in the designer, an event handler is generated for this event.

Fig. 14.29 | PictureBox properties and an event. (Part 2 of 2.)

Figure 14.30 uses a PictureBox named imagePictureBox to display one of three bitmap images—image0.bmp, image1.bmp or image2.bmp. These images are provided in the Images subdirectory of this chapter's examples directory. Whenever a user clicks the **Next Image** Button, the image changes to the next image in sequence. When the last image is displayed and the user clicks the **Next Image** Button, the first image is displayed again.

```csharp
1   // Fig. 14.30: PictureBoxTestForm.cs
2   // Using a PictureBox to display images.
3   using System;
4   using System.Drawing;
5   using System.Windows.Forms;
6
7   namespace PictureBoxTest
8   {
9      // Form to display different images when Button is clicked
10     public partial class PictureBoxTestForm : Form
11     {
12        private int ImageNumber { get; set; } = -1; // image to display
13
14        // default constructor
15        public PictureBoxTestForm()
16        {
17           InitializeComponent();
18        }
19
20        // change image whenever Next Button is clicked
21        private void nextButton_Click(object sender, EventArgs e)
22        {
23           ImageNumber = (ImageNumber + 1) % 3; // cycles from 0 to 2
24
25           // retrieve image from resources and load into PictureBox
26           imagePictureBox.Image =
27              (Image) (Properties.Resources.ResourceManager.GetObject(
28              $"image{ImageNumber}"));
29        }
30     }
31  }
```

Fig. 14.30 | Using a PictureBox to display images. (Part 1 of 2.)

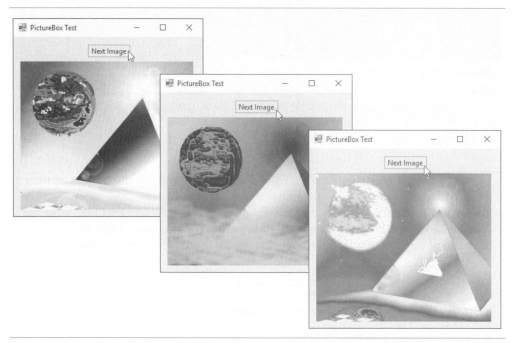

Fig. 14.30 | Using a `PictureBox` to display images. (Part 2 of 2.)

Using Resources Programmatically

In this example, we added the images to the project as resources. This causes the IDE to to copy the images into the app's executable file and enables the app to access the images through the project's `Properties` namespace. When you do this, you don't need to worry about wrapping the images with the app when you move it to another location or computer.

If you're creating a new project, use the following steps to add images to the project as resources:

1. After creating your project, right click the project's **Properties** node in the **Solution Explorer** and select **Open** to display the project's properties.

2. From the tabs on the left, click the **Resources** tab.

3. At the top of the **Resources** tab, click the down arrow next to **Add Resource** and select **Add Existing File...** to display the **Add existing file to resources** dialog.

4. Locate the image files you wish to add as resources and click the **Open** button. We provided three sample images in the `Images` folder with this chapter's examples.

5. Save your project.

The files now appear in a folder named **Resources** in the **Solution Explorer**. We'll use this technique in most examples that use images going forward.

A project's resources are accessible to the app via its `Resources` class (of the project's `Properties` namespace). The `Resources` class contains a `ResourceManager` object for interacting with the resources programmatically. To access an image, you can use the method `GetObject`, which takes as an argument the resource name as it appears in the **Resources** tab (e.g., `"image0"`) and returns the resource as an `Object`. Lines 27–28 invoke `GetObject` with the result of the string-interpolation expression

```
$"image{ImageNumber}"
```

which builds the name of the resource by placing the index of the next picture (`ImageNumber`, which was obtained earlier in line 23) at the end of the word `"image"`. You must convert this `Object` to type `Image` (namespace `System.Drawing`) to assign it to the `PictureBox`'s `Image` property (lines 26–28).

The `Resources` class also provides direct access to the resources you define with expressions of the form `Resources.resourceName`, where *resourceName* is the name you provided to the resource when you created it. When using such an expression, the resource returned already has the appropriate type. For example, `Properties.Resources.image0` is an `Image` object representing the first image.

14.9 ToolTips

In Chapter 2, we demonstrated *tool tips*—the helpful text that appears when the mouse hovers over an item in a GUI. Recall that the tool tips in Visual Studio (and most apps with GUIs) help you become familiar with the IDE's features and serve as useful reminders for each toolbar icon's functionality. This section demonstrates how to use the `ToolTip` component to add tool tips to your apps. Figure 14.31 describes common properties and a common event of class `ToolTip`.

ToolTip properties and an event	Description
Common Properties	
AutoPopDelay	The amount of time (in milliseconds) that the tool tip appears while the mouse is over a control.
InitialDelay	The amount of time (in milliseconds) that a mouse must hover over a control before a tool tip appears.
ReshowDelay	The amount of time (in milliseconds) between which two different tool tips appear (when the mouse is moved from one control to another).
Common Event	
Draw	Raised when the tool tip is about to be displayed. This event allows programmers to modify the appearance of the tool tip.

Fig. 14.31 | `ToolTip` properties and an event.

When you add a `ToolTip` component from the **Toolbox**, it appears in the component tray—at the bottom of the window when the `Form` is in **Design** mode. Once a `ToolTip` is added to a `Form`, a new property appears in the **Properties** window for the `Form`'s other controls. This property appears in the **Properties** window as **ToolTip on**, followed by the name of the `ToolTip` component. For instance, if our `Form`'s `ToolTip` were named `helpful-ToolTip`, you would set a control's **ToolTip on helpfulToolTip** property value to specify the control's tool tip text. Figure 14.32 demonstrates the ToolTip component. For this example, we create a GUI containing two Labels, so we can demonstrate different tool tip text for each Label. Since there's no event-handling code in this example, we do not show you the code for the Form class.

Fig. 14.32 | Demonstrating the ToolTip component.

In this example, the IDE named the ToolTip component toolTip1. Figure 14.33 shows the ToolTip in the component tray. We set the tool tip text for the first Label to "First Label" and the tool tip text for the second Label to "Second Label". Figure 14.34 demonstrates setting the tool tip text for the first Label.

Fig. 14.33 | Demonstrating the component tray.

Fig. 14.34 | Setting a control's tool tip text.

14.10 NumericUpDown Control

At times, you'll want to restrict a user's input choices to a specific *range of numeric values*. This is the purpose of the **NumericUpDown control**. This control appears as a TextBox, with two small Buttons on the right side—one with an up arrow and one with a down arrow.

By default, a user can type numeric values into this control as if it were a `TextBox` or click the up and down arrows to increase or decrease the value in the control, respectively. The largest and smallest values in the range are specified with the `Maximum` and `Minimum` properties, respectively (both of type `decimal`). The `Increment` property (also of type `decimal`) specifies by how much the current value changes when the user clicks the arrows. Property `DecimalPlaces` specifies the number of decimal places that the control should display. Figure 14.35 describes common `NumericUpDown` properties and an event.

NumericUpDown properties and an event	Description
Common Properties	
DecimalPlaces	Specifies how many decimal places to display in the control.
Increment	Specifies by how much the current number in the control changes when the user clicks the control's up and down arrows.
Maximum	Largest value in the control's range.
Minimum	Smallest value in the control's range.
UpDownAlign	Modifies the alignment of the up and down `Buttons` on the `NumericUpDown` control. This property can be used to display these `Buttons` either to the left or to the right of the control.
Value	The numeric value currently displayed in the control.
Common Event	
ValueChanged	This event is raised when the value in the control is changed. This is the default event for the `NumericUpDown` control.

Fig. 14.35 | NumericUpDown properties and an event.

Figure 14.36 demonstrates a `NumericUpDown` control in a GUI that calculates interest rate. The calculations performed in this app are similar to those in Fig. 6.6. `TextBoxes` are used to input the principal and interest rate amounts, and a `NumericUpDown` control is used to input the number of years for which we want to calculate interest.

```
1   // Fig. 14.36: InterestCalculatorForm.cs
2   // Demonstrating the NumericUpDown control.
3   using System;
4   using System.Windows.Forms;
5
6   namespace NumericUpDownTest
7   {
8      public partial class InterestCalculatorForm : Form
9      {
10        // default constructor
11        public InterestCalculatorForm()
12        {
```

Fig. 14.36 | Demonstrating the NumericUpDown control. (Part 1 of 2.)

```
13                InitializeComponent();
14          }
15
16          private void calculateButton_Click(object sender, EventArgs e)
17          {
18              // retrieve user input
19              decimal principal = decimal.Parse(principalTextBox.Text);
20              double rate = double.Parse(interestTextBox.Text);
21              int year = (int) yearUpDown.Value;
22
23              // set output header
24              string output = "Year\tAmount on Deposit\r\n";
25
26              // calculate amount after each year and append to output
27              for (int yearCounter = 1; yearCounter <= year; ++yearCounter)
28              {
29                  decimal amount =  principal *
30                    ((decimal) Math.Pow((1 + rate / 100), yearCounter));
31                  output += $"{yearCounter}\t{amount:C}\r\n";
32              }
33
34              displayTextBox.Text = output; // display result
35          }
36      }
37  }
```

Fig. 14.36 | Demonstrating the NumericUpDown control. (Part 2 of 2.)

For the NumericUpDown control named yearUpDown, we set the Minimum property to 1 and the Maximum property to 10. We left the Increment property set to 1, its default value. These settings specify that users can enter a number of years in the range 1 to 10 in increments of 1. If we had set the Increment to 0.5, we could also input values such as 1.5 or 2.5. If you don't modify the DecimalPlaces property (0 by default), 1.5 and 2.5 display as 2 and 3, respectively. We set the NumericUpDown's **ReadOnly property** to true to indicate that the user cannot type a number into the control to make a selection. Thus, the user must click the up and down arrows to modify the value in the control. By default, the ReadOnly property is set to false. The output for this app is displayed in a multiline readonly TextBox with a vertical scrollbar, so the user can scroll through the entire output. Notice that \r\n is required (lines 24 and 31) to move to the next line in the TextBox.

14.11 Mouse-Event Handling

This section explains how to handle mouse events, such as clicks and moves, which are generated when the user interacts with a control via the mouse. Mouse events can be handled for any control that derives from class System.Windows.Forms.Control. For most mouse events, information about the event is passed to the event-handling method through an object of class MouseEventArgs, and the delegate used to create the mouse-event handlers is MouseEventHandler. Each mouse-event-handling method for these events requires an object and a MouseEventArgs object as arguments.

Class MouseEventArgs contains information related to the mouse event, such as the mouse pointer's *x*- and *y*-coordinates, the mouse button pressed (Right, Left or Middle) and the number of times the mouse was clicked. The *x*- and *y*-coordinates of the MouseEventArgs object are relative to the control that generated the event—i.e., point (0,0) represents the upper-left corner of the control where the mouse event occurred. Several common mouse events and event arguments are described in Fig. 14.37.

Mouse events and event arguments

Mouse Events with Event Argument of Type **EventArgs**	
MouseEnter	Mouse cursor enters the control's boundaries.
MouseHover	Mouse cursor hovers within the control's boundaries.
MouseLeave	Mouse cursor leaves the control's boundaries.

Mouse Events with Event Argument of Type **MouseEventArgs**	
MouseDown	Mouse button is pressed while the mouse cursor is within a control's boundaries.
MouseMove	Mouse cursor is moved while in the control's boundaries.
MouseUp	Mouse button is released when the cursor is over the control's boundaries.
MouseWheel	Mouse wheel is moved while the control has the focus.

Class **MouseEventArgs** *Properties*	
Button	Specifies which mouse button was pressed (Left, Right, Middle or None).
Clicks	The number of times that the mouse button was clicked.
X	The *x*-coordinate within the control where the event occurred.
Y	The *y*-coordinate within the control where the event occurred.

Fig. 14.37 | Mouse events and event arguments.

Figure 14.38 uses mouse events to draw on a Form. Whenever the user *drags* the mouse (i.e., moves the mouse while a mouse button is pressed), small circles appear on the Form at the position where each mouse event occurs during the drag operation. In line 12, the program declares property ShouldPaint, which determines whether to draw on the Form. We want the program to draw only while the mouse button is pressed (i.e., held down). Thus, when the user clicks or holds down a mouse button, the system generates a Mouse-Down event, and the event handler (lines 21–25) sets ShouldPaint to true. When the user releases the mouse button, the system generates a MouseUp event, ShouldPaint is set to false in the PainterForm_MouseUp event handler (lines 28–32) and the program stops drawing. Unlike MouseMove events, which occur continuously as the user moves the mouse, the system generates a MouseDown event only when a mouse button is first *pressed* and generates a MouseUp event only when a mouse button is *released*.

```csharp
1   // Fig. 14.38: PainterForm.cs
2   // Using the mouse to draw on a Form.
3   using System;
4   using System.Drawing;
5   using System.Windows.Forms;
6
7   namespace Painter
8   {
9      // creates a Form that's a drawing surface
10     public partial class PainterForm : Form
11     {
12        bool ShouldPaint { get; set; } = false; // whether to paint
13
14        // default constructor
15        public PainterForm()
16        {
17           InitializeComponent();
18        }
19
20        // should paint when mouse button is pressed down
21        private void PainterForm_MouseDown(object sender, MouseEventArgs e)
22        {
23           // indicate that user is dragging the mouse
24           ShouldPaint = true;
25        }
26
27        // stop painting when mouse button is released
28        private void PainterForm_MouseUp(object sender, MouseEventArgs e)
29        {
30           // indicate that user released the mouse button
31           ShouldPaint = false;
32        }
33
34        // draw circle whenever mouse moves with its button held down
35        private void PainterForm_MouseMove(object sender, MouseEventArgs e)
36        {
37           if (ShouldPaint) // check if mouse button is being pressed
38           {
39              // draw a circle where the mouse pointer is present
40              using (Graphics graphics = CreateGraphics())
41              {
42                 graphics.FillEllipse(
43                    new SolidBrush(Color.BlueViolet), e.X, e.Y, 4, 4);
44              }
45           }
46        }
47     }
48  }
```

Fig. 14.38 | Using the mouse to draw on a Form. (Part 1 of 2.)

Fig. 14.38 | Using the mouse to draw on a `Form`. (Part 2 of 2.)

Whenever the mouse moves over a control, the `MouseMove` event for that control occurs. Inside the `PainterForm_MouseMove` event handler (lines 35–46), the program draws only if `ShouldPaint` is `true` (i.e., a mouse button is pressed). In the `using` statement, line 40 calls inherited `Form` method `CreateGraphics` to create a `Graphics` object that allows the program to draw on the `Form`. Class `Graphics` provides methods that draw various shapes. For example, lines 42–43 use method `FillEllipse` to draw a circle. The first parameter to method `FillEllipse` in this case is an object of class `SolidBrush`, which specifies the solid color that will fill the shape. The color is provided as an argument to class `SolidBrush`'s constructor. Type `Color` contains numerous predefined color constants—we selected `Color.BlueViolet`. `FillEllipse` draws an oval in a bounding rectangle that's specified by the x- and y-coordinates of its upper-left corner, its width and its height—the final four arguments to the method. The x- and y-coordinates represent the location of the mouse event and can be taken from the mouse-event arguments (`e.X` and `e.Y`). To draw a circle, we set the width and height of the bounding rectangle so that they're equal—in this example, both are 4 pixels. `Graphics`, `SolidBrush` and `Color` are all part of the namespace `System.Drawing`. Recall from Chapter 13 that the `using` statement automatically calls `Dispose` on the object that was created in the parentheses following keyword `using`. This is important because `Graphics` objects are a limited resource. Calling `Dispose` on a `Graphics` object ensures that its resources are returned to the system for reuse.

14.12 Keyboard-Event Handling

Key events occur when keyboard keys are pressed and released. Such events can be handled for any control that inherits from `System.Windows.Forms.Control`. There are three key events—KeyPress, KeyUp and KeyDown. The `KeyPress` event occurs when the user presses a character key or the space or backspace keys. The specific key can be determined with property `KeyChar` of the event handler's `KeyPressEventArgs` argument.

The KeyPress event does *not* indicate whether modifier keys (e.g., *Shift*, *Alt* and *Ctrl*) were pressed when a key event occurred. If this information is important, the `KeyUp` or `Key-Down` events can be used. The `KeyEventArgs` argument for each of these events contains information about modifier keys. Figure 14.39 lists important key event information. Several properties return values from the Keys enumeration, which provides constants that specify the various keys on a keyboard. Like the FontStyle enumeration (Section 14.7), the Keys enumeration is represented with a set of bits, so the enumeration's constants can be combined with the bitwise operators to indicate *multiple keys* pressed at the same time.

Keyboard events and event arguments

Key Events with Event Arguments of Type KeyEventArgs

KeyDown	Generated when a key is initially pressed.
KeyUp	Generated when a key is released.

Key Event with Event Argument of Type KeyPressEventArgs

KeyPress	Generated when a key is pressed. Raised after KeyDown and before KeyUp.

Class KeyPressEventArgs Properties

KeyChar	Returns the ASCII character for the key pressed.

Class KeyEventArgs Properties

Alt	Indicates whether the *Alt* key was pressed.
Control	Indicates whether the *Ctrl* key was pressed.
Shift	Indicates whether the *Shift* key was pressed.
KeyCode	Returns the key code for the key as a value from the Keys enumeration. This does not include modifier-key information. It's used to test for a specific key.
KeyData	Returns the key code for a key combined with modifier information as a Keys value. This property contains all information about the pressed key.
KeyValue	Returns the key code as an int, rather than as a value from the Keys enumeration. This property is used to obtain a numeric representation of the pressed key. The int value is known as a Windows virtual key code.
Modifiers	Returns a Keys value indicating any pressed modifier keys (*Alt*, *Ctrl* and *Shift*). This property is used to determine modifier-key information only.

Fig. 14.39 | Keyboard events and event arguments.

Figure 14.40 demonstrates the use of the key-event handlers to display a key pressed by a user. The program is a Form with two Labels that displays the pressed key on one Label and modifier key information on the other.

```
1   // Fig. 14.40: KeyDemo.cs
2   // Displaying information about the key the user pressed.
3   using System;
4   using System.Windows.Forms;
5
6   namespace KeyDemo
7   {
```

Fig. 14.40 | Displaying information about the key the user pressed. (Part 1 of 3.)

```
8    // Form to display key information when key is pressed
9    public partial class KeyDemo : Form
10   {
11       // default constructor
12       public KeyDemo()
13       {
14           InitializeComponent();
15       }
16
17       // display the character pressed using KeyChar
18       private void KeyDemo_KeyPress(object sender, KeyPressEventArgs e)
19       {
20           charLabel.Text = $"Key pressed: {e.KeyChar}";
21       }
22
23       // display modifier keys, key code, key data and key value
24       private void KeyDemo_KeyDown(object sender, KeyEventArgs e)
25       {
26           keyInfoLabel.Text =
27               $"Alt: {(e.Alt ? "Yes" : "No")}\n" +
28               $"Shift: {(e.Shift ? "Yes" : "No")}\n"  +
29               $"Ctrl: {(e.Control ? "Yes" : "No")}\n" +
30               $"KeyCode: {e.KeyCode}\n" +
31               $"KeyData: {e.KeyData}\n" +
32               $"KeyValue: {e.KeyValue}";
33       }
34
35       // clear Labels when key released
36       private void KeyDemo_KeyUp(object sender, KeyEventArgs e)
37       {
38           charLabel.Text = "";
39           keyInfoLabel.Text = "";
40       }
41   }
42 }
```

a) *H* pressed

b) *F7* pressed

Key Demo — □ ×

Key pressed: H

Alt: No
Shift: Yes
Ctrl: No
KeyCode: H
KeyData: H, Shift
KeyValue: 72

Key Demo — □ ×

Alt: No
Shift: No
Ctrl: No
KeyCode: F7
KeyData: F7
KeyValue: 118

Fig. 14.40 | Displaying information about the key the user pressed. (Part 2 of 3.)

Fig. 14.40 | Displaying information about the key the user pressed. (Part 3 of 3.)

Control charLabel displays the character value of the key pressed, whereas keyInfo-Label displays information relating to the pressed key. Because the KeyDown and KeyPress events convey different information, the Form (KeyDemo) handles both.

The KeyPress event handler (lines 18–21) accesses the KeyChar property of the Key-PressEventArgs object. This returns the pressed key as a char, which we then display in charLabel (line 20). If the pressed key is not an ASCII character, then the KeyPress event will not occur, and charLabel will not display any text. ASCII is a common encoding format for letters, numbers, punctuation marks and other characters. It does not support keys such as the function keys (like *F1*) or the modifier keys (*Alt, Ctrl* and *Shift*).

The KeyDown event handler (lines 24–33) displays information from its KeyEventArgs object. The handler tests for the *Alt, Shift* and *Ctrl* keys using the Alt, Shift and Control properties that each return a bool—true if the corresponding key is pressed and false otherwise. The handler then displays the KeyCode, KeyData and KeyValue properties.

The KeyCode property returns a Keys enumeration value (line 30). The KeyCode property returns the pressed key, but does not provide any information about modifier keys. Thus, both a capital and a lowercase "a" are represented as the *A* key.

The KeyData property (line 31) also returns a Keys enumeration value, but also includes modifier-key data. Thus, if "A" is input, the KeyData shows that both *A* and *Shift* were pressed. Lastly, KeyValue (line 32) returns an int representing a pressed key. This int is the key code. The key code is useful when testing for non-ASCII keys like *F12*.

The KeyUp event handler (lines 36–40) clears both Labels when the key is released. As we can see from the output, non-ASCII keys are not displayed in charLabel, because the KeyPress event is not generated. For example, charLabel does not display any text when you press the *F7* key, as shown in Fig. 14.40(b). However, the KeyDown event still is generated, and keyInfoLabel displays information about the key that's pressed. The Keys enumeration can be used to test for specific keys by comparing the KeyCode of the pressed key to values in the Keys enumeration.

Software Engineering Observation 14.2

To cause a control to react when a particular key is pressed (such as Enter*), handle a key event and test for the pressed key. To cause a* Button *to be clicked when the* Enter *key is pressed on a* Form*, set the* Form's *AcceptButton property.*

By default, a keyboard event is handled by the control that currently has the focus. Sometimes it's appropriate to have the Form handle these events. This can be accomplished by setting the Form's KeyPreview property to true, which makes the Form receive keyboard events before they're passed to another control—for example, a key press would raise the Form's KeyPress, even if a control within the Form has the focus instead of the Form itself.

14.13 Wrap-Up

This chapter introduced several common GUI controls. We discussed event handling in detail, and showed how to create event handlers. We showed how delegates are used to connect event handlers to the events of specific controls. You learned how to use a control's properties and Visual Studio to specify the layout of your GUI. We then demonstrated several controls, beginning with Labels, Buttons and TextBoxes. You learned how to use GroupBoxes and Panels to organize other controls. We then demonstrated CheckBoxes and RadioButtons, which are state buttons that allow users to select among several options. We displayed images in PictureBox controls, displayed helpful text on a GUI with ToolTip components and specified a range of numeric input values for users with a NumericUpDown control. We then demonstrated how to handle mouse and keyboard events. The next chapter introduces additional GUI controls. You'll learn how to add menus to your GUIs and create Windows Forms apps that display multiple Forms.

Summary

Section 14.1 Introduction
- A graphical user interface (GUI) allows a user to interact visually with a program.
- GUIs are built from GUI controls.
- GUI controls are objects that can display information on the screen or enable users to interact with an app via the mouse, keyboard or some other form of input.

Section 14.2 Windows Forms
- Windows Forms are used to create the GUIs for programs.
- A Form is a graphical element that appears on the desktop; it can be a dialog, a window or an MDI (multiple document interface) window.
- A component is an instance of a class that implements the IComponent interface, which defines the behaviors that components must implement, such as how the component is loaded.
- A control is a component that has a graphical representation at runtime.
- Some components lack graphical representations (e.g., class Timer of namespace System.Windows.Forms). Such components are not visible at runtime.
- When there are several windows on the screen, the active window is the frontmost and has a highlighted title bar. A window becomes the active window when the user clicks somewhere inside it.
- The active window is said to "have the focus."
- A Form is a container for controls and components.

Section 14.3 Event Handling
- Normally, a user interacts with an app's GUI to indicate the tasks that the app should perform.

- GUIs are event driven.
- When the user interacts with a GUI component, the interaction—known as an event—drives the program to perform a task. Common events include clicking a Button, typing in a TextBox, selecting an item from a menu, closing a window and moving the mouse.
- A method that performs a task in response to an event is called an event handler, and the overall process of responding to events is known as event handling.

Section 14.3.1 A Simple Event-Driven GUI
- An event handler executes only when the user performs the specific event.
- Each event handler receives two parameters when it's called. The first—an object reference typically named sender—is a reference to the object that generated the event. The second is a reference to an event arguments object of type EventArgs (or one of its derived classes), which is typically named e. This object contains additional information about the event that occurred.
- EventArgs is the base class of all classes that represent event information.

Section 14.3.2 Auto-Generated GUI Code
- Visual Studio generates the code that creates and initializes the GUI that you build in the GUI design window. This auto-generated code is placed in the Designer.cs file of the Form.
- The auto-generated code that defines the GUI is part of the Form's class. The use of the partial modifier in the class declaration allows the class to be split among multiple files.
- The Designer.cs file declares the controls you create in **Design** mode.
- The Designer.cs file includes the Dispose method for releasing resources and method InitializeComponent, which sets the properties of the Form and its controls.
- Visual Studio uses the code in InitializeComponent to create the GUI you see in design view. Changing the code in this method may prevent Visual Studio from displaying the GUI properly.

Section 14.3.3 Delegates and the Event-Handling Mechanism
- The control that generates an event is known as the event sender.
- An event-handling method—known as the event handler—responds to a particular event that a control generates.
- When an event occurs, the event sender calls its event handler to perform a task.
- The .NET event-handling mechanism allows you to choose your own names for event-handling methods. However, each event-handling method must declare the proper parameters to receive information about the event that it handles.
- Event handlers are connected to a control's events via special objects called delegates.
- A delegate object holds a reference to a method with a signature specified by the delegate type's declaration.
- GUI controls have predefined delegates that correspond to every event they can generate.
- Since each event handler is declared as a delegate, the event sender can simply call the appropriate delegate when an event occurs. The delegate's job is to invoke the appropriate method.
- Event delegates represent a set of delegate objects that all have the same signature.
- When an event occurs, its sender calls every method referenced by a multicast delegate. Multicast delegates enable several methods to be called in response to a single event.
- Event delegates derive from class MulticastDelegate, which derives from class Delegate (both from namespace System).

Section 14.3.4 Another Way to Create Event Handlers

- Double-clicking a control in the designer creates an event handler for a control's default event.
- Typically, controls can generate many different events, and each can have its own event handler.
- You can create additional event handlers through the **Properties** window.
- If you select a control on the Form, then click the **Events** icon (the lightning bolt icon) in the **Properties** window, all the events for that control are listed in the window. You can double click an event's name to display the event handler in the editor, if the event handler already exists, or to create the corresponding event handler.
- You can select an event, then use the drop-down list to its right to choose an existing method that should handle that event. The methods that appear in this drop-down list are the Form class's methods that have the proper signature to be an event handler for the selected event.
- A single event handler can handle multiple events from multiple controls.

Section 14.3.5 Locating Event Information

- Read the Visual Studio documentation to learn about the different events raised by each control. To do this, select a control in the IDE and press the *F1* key to display that control's online help. The web page that's displayed contains basic information about the control's class. Click the link to the list of events for that control to display the supported events for that control.

Section 14.4 Control Properties and Layout

- Controls derive from class Control (of namespace System.Windows.Forms).
- The Select method transfers the focus to a control and makes it the active control.
- The Enabled property indicates whether the user can interact with a control to generate an event.
- A programmer can hide a control from the user without disabling the control by setting the Visible property to false or by calling method Hide.
- Anchoring causes controls to remain at a fixed distance from the sides of the container even when the control is resized.
- Docking attaches a control to a container such that the control stretches across an entire side or fills all the remaining space.
- The Padding property specifies the distance between the docked controls and the Form edges.
- The Anchor and Dock properties of a Control are set with respect to the Control's parent container, which could be a Form or other parent container (such as a Panel).
- The minimum and maximum Form (or other Control) sizes can be set via properties MinimumSize and MaximumSize, respectively.
- When dragging a control across a Form, blue lines (known as snap lines) appear to help you position the control with respect to other controls and the Form's edges.
- Visual Studio also provides the **Format** menu, which contains several options for modifying your GUI's layout.

Section 14.5 Labels, TextBoxes and Buttons

- Labels provide text information (as well as optional images) that the user cannot directly modify.
- A textbox (class TextBox) is an area in which text either can be displayed by a program or in which the user can type text via the keyboard.
- A password TextBox is a TextBox that hides the information entered by the user. As the user types, the password TextBox masks the user input by displaying a password character (usually *). If you set the UseSystemPasswordChar property to true, the TextBox becomes a password TextBox.

- A button is a control that the user clicks to trigger an action in a program or to select an option.
- All the button classes derive from class ButtonBase (namespace System.Windows.Forms), which defines common button features.

Section 14.6 *GroupBoxes and Panels*

- GroupBoxes and Panels arrange controls on a GUI.
- GroupBoxes and Panels are typically used to group several controls of similar functionality or several controls that are related in a GUI.
- GroupBoxes can display a caption (i.e., text) and do not include scrollbars, whereas Panels can include scrollbars and do not include a caption.
- GroupBoxes have thin borders by default; Panels can be set so that they also have borders, by changing their BorderStyle property.
- The controls of a GroupBox or Panel are added to their Controls properties.
- To enable a Panel's scrollbars, set the Panel's AutoScroll property to true. If the Panel is resized and cannot display all of its controls, scrollbars appear.

Section 14.7 *CheckBoxes and RadioButtons*

- CheckBoxes and RadioButtons can be in the on/off or true/false states.
- Classes CheckBox and RadioButton are derived from class ButtonBase.
- A CheckBox is a small square that either is blank or contains a check mark. When a CheckBox is selected, a check mark appears in the box. Any number of CheckBoxes can be selected at a time.
- A CheckBox can be configured to have three states—checked, unchecked, and indeterminate— by setting its ThreeState property to true.
- Font styles can be combined via bitwise operators, such as the logical OR (|) operator or the logical exclusive OR (∧) operator.
- RadioButtons (defined with class RadioButton) are similar to CheckBoxes in that they also have two states: selected and not selected (also called deselected).
- RadioButtons normally appear as a group, in which only one RadioButton can be selected at a time. The selection of one RadioButton in the group forces all the others to be deselected. Therefore, RadioButtons are used to represent a set of mutually exclusive options.
- All RadioButtons added to a container become part of the same group.

Section 14.8 *PictureBoxes*

- A PictureBox displays an image.
- The Image property specifies the image that's displayed
- The SizeMode property indicates how the image is displayed (Normal, StretchImage, Autosize, CenterImage, or Zoom).
- You can embed images into a project as resources.
- Embedded image files appear in a folder named **Resources** in the **Solution Explorer**.
- The Resources class (of a project's Properties namespace) provides access to a project's resources.
- Class ResourceManager provides methods for programmatically accessing a project's resources.
- To access an image (or any other resource) in the project's resources, you use the method Get-Object of class ResourceManager, which takes as an argument the resource name as it appears in the **Resources** tab and returns the resource as an Object.

- The Resources class provides direct access to the resources you define with expressions of the form Resources.*resourceName*.

Section 14.9 ToolTips

- Tool tips help you become familiar with a Form's features and serve as useful reminders for each control's functionality. In the **Properties** window, you can specify a tool tip for a control by setting the **ToolTip on** *componentName* entry, where *componentName* is the name of the ToolTip component.

- The ToolTip component can be used to add tool tips to your app.

- The ToolTip component is placed in the component tray—the gray region below the Form in **Design** mode.

Section 14.10 NumericUpDown Control

- At times you'll want to restrict a user's input choices to a specific range of numeric values. This is the purpose of the NumericUpDown control.

- The NumericUpDown control appears as a TextBox, with two small Buttons on the right side, one with an up arrow and one with a down arrow. By default, a user can type numeric values into this control as if it were a TextBox or click the up and down arrows to increase or decrease the value in the control, respectively.

- The largest and smallest values in the range are specified with the Maximum and Minimum properties, respectively (both are of type decimal).

- The Increment property (of type decimal) specifies by how much the current number in the control changes when the user clicks the control's up and down arrows.

- Setting a NumericUpDown control's ReadOnly property to true specifies that the user can only use the up and down arrows to modify the value in the NumericUpDown control.

Section 14.11 Mouse-Event Handling

- Mouse events, such as clicks and moves, are generated when the mouse interacts with a control.

- Mouse events can be handled for any subclass of System.Windows.Forms.Control.

- Class MouseEventArgs contains information related to the mouse event, such as the *x*- and *y*-coordinates of the mouse pointer, the mouse button pressed (Right, Left or Middle) and the number of times the mouse was clicked.

- Whenever the user holds down a mouse button, the system generates a MouseDown event.

- When the user releases the mouse button (to complete a "click" operation), the system generates a single MouseUp event.

- Whenever the mouse moves over a control, the MouseMove event for that control is raised.

Section 14.12 Keyboard-Event Handling

- Key events occur when keys on the keyboard are pressed and released.

- There are three key events—KeyPress, KeyUp and KeyDown.

- The KeyPress event occurs when the user presses a character key, or the space or backspace keys. The specific key can be determined with property KeyChar of the event handler's KeyPressEventArgs argument.

- The KeyPress event does not indicate whether modifier keys were pressed when a key event occurred. If this information is important, the KeyUp or KeyDown events should be used.

Terminology

active control
active window
anchor a control
bitwise operator
Button properties and events
Button property of class MouseEventArgs
ButtonBase class
checkbox
CheckBox class
Checked property of class CheckBox
Checked property of class RadioButton
CheckedChanged event of class CheckBox
CheckedChanged event of class RadioButton
CheckState property of class CheckBox
CheckStateChanged event of class CheckBox
Color structure
component
component tray
container
Control class
Controls property of a container
DecimalPlaces property of class NumericUpDown
default event
delegate
delegate class
delegate keyword
deselected state
DialogResult enumeration
dock a control
Dock property of class Control
Enabled property of class Control
event
event-driven programming
event handler
event handling
event multicasting
event handler
event sender
FillEllipse method of class Graphics
FlatStyle property of class Button
focus
Font class
FontStyle enumeration
GetObject method of class ResourceManager
Graphics class
GroupBox class
Height property of structure Size
IComponent interface
Increment property of class NumericUpDown

key code
key event
KeyChar property of class KeyPressEventArgs
KeyCode property of class KeyEventArgs
KeyData property of class KeyEventArgs
KeyDown event of class Control
KeyEventArgs class
KeyPress event of class Control
KeyPressEventArgs class
Keys enumeration
KeyUp event of class Control
KeyValue property of class KeyEventArgs
Maximum property of class NumericUpDown
MaximumSize property of class Control
MessageBox class
Minimum property of class NumericUpDown
MinimumSize property of class Control
modifier key
mouse click
mouse event
mouse move
mouse press
MouseDown event of class Control
MouseEventArgs class
MouseEventHandler delegate
MouseMove event of class Control
MouseUp event of class Control
multicast delegate
MulticastDelegate class
multiple document interface (MDI) window
mutual exclusion
"not-selected" state
NumericUpDown class
Padding property of class Control
Panel class
partial class
password TextBox
PictureBox class
radio button
radio button group
RadioButton class
ReadOnly property of class NumericUpDown
ResourceManager class
Resources class
Select method of class Control
selected state
Size property of class Control
Size structure
snap line

SolidBrush class
state button
Style property of class Font
TabIndex property of class Control
TabStop property of class Control
ToolTip class
ThreeState property of class CheckBox
UseSystemPasswordChar property of class
    TextBox

UpDownAlign property of class NumericUpDown
Value property of class NumericUpDown
Visible property of class Control
widget
Width property of structure Size
window gadget
Windows Form

Self-Review Exercises

14.1 State whether each of the following is *true* or *false*. If *false*, explain why.
 a) The KeyData property includes data about modifier keys.
 b) A Form is a container.
 c) All Forms, components and controls are classes.
 d) CheckBoxes are used to represent a set of mutually exclusive options.
 e) A Label displays text that a user running an app can edit.
 f) Button presses generate events.
 g) All mouse events use the same event arguments class.
 h) Visual Studio can register an event and create an empty event handler.
 i) The NumericUpDown control is used to specify a range of input values.
 j) A control's tool tip text is set with the ToolTip property of class Control.

14.2 Fill in the blanks in each of the following statements:
 a) The active control is said to have the _____.
 b) The Form acts as a(n) _____ for the controls that are added.
 c) GUIs are _____ driven.
 d) Every method that handles the same event must have the same _____.
 e) A(n) _____ TextBox masks user input with a character used repeatedly.
 f) Class _____ and class _____ help arrange controls on a GUI and provide logical groups for radio buttons.
 g) Typical mouse events include _____ and _____.
 h) _____ events are generated when a key on the keyboard is pressed or released.
 i) The modifier keys are _____, _____ and _____.
 j) A(n) _____ event or delegate can be used to call multiple methods.

Answers To Self-Review Exercises

14.1 a) True. b) True. c) True. d) False. RadioButtons are used to represent a set of mutually exclusive options. e) False. A Label's text cannot be edited by the user. f) True. g) False. Some mouse events use EventArgs, others use MouseEventArgs. h) True. i) True. j) False. A control's tool tip text is set using a ToolTip component that must be added to the app.

14.2 a) focus. b) container. c) event. d) signature. e) password. f) GroupBox, Panel. g) mouse clicks, mouse moves. h) Key. i) *Shift, Ctrl, Alt.* j) multicast.

Exercises

14.3 Extend the program in Fig. 14.26 to include a CheckBox for every font-style option. [*Hint:* Use logical exclusive OR (∧) rather than testing for every bit explicitly.]

14.4 Create the GUI in Fig. 14.41 (you do not have to provide functionality).

Fig. 14.41 | Calculator GUI.

14.5 Create the GUI in Fig. 14.42 (you do not have to provide functionality).

Fig. 14.42 | Printer GUI.

14.6 *(Temperature Conversions)* Write a temperature conversion program that converts from Fahrenheit to Celsius. The Fahrenheit temperature should be entered from the keyboard (via a TextBox). A Label should be used to display the converted temperature. Use the following formula for the conversion:

$$Celsius = (5 / 9) \times (Fahrenheit - 32)$$

14.7 *(Enhanced Painter)* Extend the program of Fig. 14.38 to include options for changing the size and color of the lines drawn. Create a GUI similar to Fig. 14.43. The user should be able to draw on the app's Panel. To retrieve a Graphics object for drawing, call method *panelName*.CreateGraphics(), substituting in the name of your Panel.

Fig. 14.43 | Drawing Panel GUI.

14.8   *(Guess the Number Game)* Write a program that plays "guess the number" as follows: Your program chooses the number to be guessed by selecting an int at random in the range 1–1000. The program then displays the following text in a label:

```
I have a number between 1 and 1000--can you guess my number?
Please enter your first guess.
```

A TextBox should be used to input the guess. As each guess is input, the background color should change to red or blue. Red indicates that the user is getting "warmer," blue that the user is getting "colder." A Label should display either "Too High" or "Too Low," to help the user zero in on the correct answer. When the user guesses the correct answer, display "Correct!" in a message box, change the Form's background color to green and disable the TextBox. Recall that a TextBox (like other controls) can be disabled by setting the control's Enabled property to false. Provide a Button that allows the user to play the game again. When the Button is clicked, generate a new random number, change the background to the default color and enable the TextBox.

14.9   *(Fuzzy Dice Order Form)* Write an app that allows users to process orders for fuzzy dice. The app should calculate the total price of the order, including tax and shipping. TextBoxes for inputting the order number, the customer name and the shipping address are provided. Initially, these fields contain text that describes their purpose. Provide CheckBoxes for selecting the fuzzy-dice color and TextBoxes for inputting the quantities of fuzzy dice to order. The app should update the total cost, tax and shipping when the user changes any one of the quantity fields' values. The app should also contain a Button that when clicked, returns all fields to their original values. Use 5% for the tax rate. Shipping charges are $1.50 for up to 20 pairs of dice. If more than 20 pairs of dice are ordered, shipping is free. All fields must be filled out, and an item must be checked for the user to enter a quantity for that item.

Making-a-Difference Exercises

14.10   *(Ecofont)* Ecofont—developed by SPRANQ (a Netherlands-based company)—is a font designed to reduce by as much as 20% the amount of ink used for printing, thus reducing also the number of ink cartridges used and the environmental impact of the manufacturing and shipping processes (using less energy, less fuel for shipping, and so on). The font, based on sans-serif Verdana, has small circular "holes" in the letters that are not visible in smaller sizes—such as the 9- or 10-point type frequently used. Download the free version of Ecofont

```
http://www.ecofont.com/en/products/green/font/download-the-ink-saving-font.html
```

then install the font file ecofont_vera_sans_regular.ttf using the instructions from the Ecofont website. Next, develop a GUI-based program that allows you to type text in a TextBox to be displayed in the Ecofont. Create **Increase Font Size** and **Decrease Font Size** buttons that allow you to scale up or down by one point at a time. Set the TextBox's Font property to 9 point Ecofont. Set the TextBox's MultiLine property to true so the user can enter multiple lines of text. As you scale up the font, you'll be able to see the holes in the letters more clearly. As you scale down, the holes will be less apparent. To change the TextBox's font programmatically, use a statement of the form:

```
inputTextBox.Font = new Font(inputTextBox.Font.FontFamily,
    inputTextBox.Font.SizeInPoints + 1);
```

This changes the TextBox's Font property to a new Font object that uses the TextBox's current font, but adds 1 to its SizeInPoints property to increase the font size. A similar statement can be used to decrease the font size. What is the smallest font size at which you begin to notice the holes?

14.11   *(Project: Typing Tutor—Tuning a Crucial Skill in the Computer Age)* Typing quickly and correctly is an essential skill for working effectively with computers and the Internet. In this exercise, you'll build an app that can help users learn to "touch type" (i.e., type correctly without looking at the keyboard). The app should display a *virtual keyboard* that mimics the one on your computer and should allow the user to watch what he or she is typing on the screen without looking at the *actual keyboard*. Use Buttons to represent the keys. As the user presses each key, the app highlights the corresponding Button and adds the character to a TextBox that shows what the user has typed so far. [*Hint:* To highlight a Button, use its BackColor property to change its background color. When the key is released, reset its original background color.]

You can test your program by typing a pangram—a phrase that contains every letter of the alphabet at least once—such as "The quick brown fox jumped over a lazy dog." You can find other pangrams on the web.

To make the program more interesting you could monitor the user's accuracy. You could have the user type specific phrases that you've prestored in your program and that you display on the screen above the virtual keyboard. You could keep track of how many keystrokes the user types correctly and how many are typed incorrectly. You could also keep track of which keys the user is having difficulty with and display a report showing those keys.

Graphical User Interfaces with Windows Forms: Part 2

15

Objectives

In this chapter you'll:

- Create menus, tabbed windows and multiple document interface (MDI) programs.

- Use the ListView and TreeView controls for displaying information.

- Create hyperlinks using the LinkLabel control.

- Display lists of information in ListBox, CheckedListBox and ComboBox controls.

- Input dates with the MonthCalendar control.

- Input date and time data with the DateTimePicker control.

- Create custom controls.

- Use visual inheritance to build upon an existing GUI.

15.1 Introduction

Here we continue our Windows `Forms` presentation. We start with menus, which present users with logically organized commands (or options). We show how to create menus in the Windows `Forms` designer. We discuss how to input and display dates and times using the `MonthCalendar` and `DateTimePicker` controls. We also introduce `LinkLabel`s that can hyperlink to a file on the current machine or a web page, simply by clicking the mouse.

We demonstrate how to manipulate lists of values via a `ListBox` and `ListView` and how to combine several checkboxes in a `CheckedListBox`. We also create drop-down lists using `ComboBox`es and display data hierarchically with a `TreeView` control. You'll learn two other important GUI elements—tab controls and multiple document interface (MDI) windows. These components enable you to create real-world programs with sophisticated GUIs. You'll use visual inheritance to build upon an existing GUI.

Visual Studio provides many GUI components, several of which are discussed in this (and the previous) chapter. You also can design custom controls and add them to the **ToolBox**, as we demonstrate in this chapter's last example. The techniques presented here form the groundwork for creating more substantial GUIs and custom controls.

15.2 Menus

Menus provide groups of related commands for Windows `Forms` apps. Although these commands depend on the program, some—such as **Open** and **Save**—are common to many apps. Menus are an integral part of GUIs, because they organize commands without "cluttering" the GUI.

In Fig. 15.1, an expanded menu from Visual Studio lists various commands (called menu items), plus submenus (menus within a menu). The top-level menus appear in the left portion of the figure, whereas any submenus or menu items are displayed to the right. The menu that contains a menu item is called that menu item's parent menu. A menu item that contains a submenu is considered to be the parent of that submenu.

Menus can have *Alt* key shortcuts (also called access shortcuts, keyboard shortcuts or hotkeys), which are accessed by pressing *Alt* and the underlined letter—for example, *Alt* + *F* typically expands the **File** menu. Menu items can have shortcut keys as well (combinations of *Ctrl, Shift, Alt, F1, F2*, letter keys, and so on). Some menu items display checkmarks, usually indicating that multiple options on the menu can be selected at once.

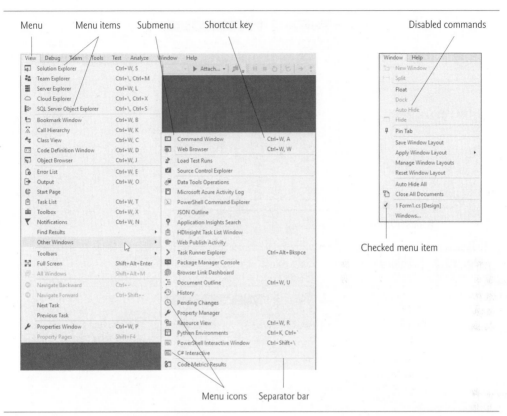

Menu   Menu items   Submenu   Shortcut key   Disabled commands

Checked menu item

Menu icons   Separator bar

Fig. 15.1 | Menus, submenus and menu items.

To create a menu, open the **Toolbox** and drag a `MenuStrip` control onto the `Form`. This creates a menu bar across the top of the `Form` (below the title bar) and places a `MenuStrip` icon in the component tray. To select the `MenuStrip`, click this icon. You can now use **Design** mode to create and edit menus for your app. Menus, like other controls, have properties and events, which can be accessed through the **Properties** window.

To add menu items to the menu, click the **Type Here** TextBox (Fig. 15.2) and type the menu item's name. This action adds an entry to the menu of type `ToolStripMenuItem`. After you press the *Enter* key, the menu item name is added to the menu. Then more **Type Here** TextBoxes appear, allowing you to add items underneath or to the side of the original menu item (Fig. 15.3).

To create an access shortcut, type an ampersand (&) before the character to be underlined. For example, to create the **File** menu item with the letter **F** underlined, type **&File**. To display an ampersand, type **&&**. To add other shortcut keys (e.g., *Ctrl + F9*) for menu items, set the `ShortcutKeys` property of the appropriate `ToolStripMenuItems`. To do this, select the down arrow to the right of this property in the **Properties** window. In the window that appears (Fig. 15.4), use the CheckBoxes and drop-down list to select the shortcut keys. When you're finished, click elsewhere on the screen. You can hide the shortcut keys by setting property `ShowShortcutKeys` to `false`, and you can modify how the shortcut keys are displayed in the menu item by modifying property `ShortcutKeyDisplayString`.

Fig. 15.2 | Editing menus in Visual Studio.

Fig. 15.3 | Adding ToolStripMenuItems to a MenuStrip.

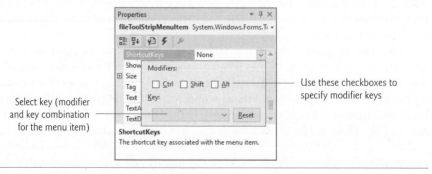

Fig. 15.4 | Setting a menu item's shortcut keys.

Look-and-Feel Observation 15.1

Buttons can have access shortcuts. Place the & symbol immediately before the desired character in the Button's text. To press the button by using its access key in the running app, the user presses Alt and the underlined character. If the underline is not visible when the app runs, press the Alt key to display the underlines.

You can remove a menu item by selecting it and pressing the *Delete* key. Menu items can be grouped logically by separator bars, which are inserted by right clicking the menu and selecting **Insert > Separator** or by typing "-" for the text of a menu item.

In addition to text, Visual Studio allows you to easily add `TextBox`es and `ComboBox`es (drop-down lists) as menu items. When adding an item in **Design** mode, you may have noticed that before you enter text for a new item, you're provided with a drop-down list. Clicking the down arrow (Fig. 15.5) allows you to select the type of item to add—**Menu-Item** (of type `ToolStripMenuItem`, the default), **ComboBox** (of type `ToolStripComboBox`) and **TextBox** (of type `ToolStripTextBox`). We focus on `ToolStripMenuItem`s. [*Note:* If you view this drop-down list for menu items that are not on the top level, a fourth option appears, allowing you to insert a separator bar.]

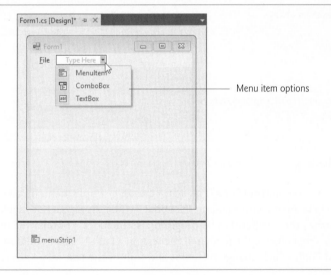

Fig. 15.5 | Menu-item options.

`ToolStripMenuItem`s generate a `Click` event when selected. To create an empty `Click` event handler, double click the menu item in **Design** mode. Common actions in response to these events include displaying dialogs and setting properties. Common menu properties and a common event are summarized in Fig. 15.6.

Look-and-Feel Observation 15.2

*It's a convention to place an ellipsis (...) after the name of a menu item (e.g., **Save As...**) that requires the user to provide more information—typically through a dialog. A menu item that produces an immediate action without prompting the user for more information (e.g., **Save**) should not have an ellipsis following its name.*

MenuStrip and ToolStripMenuItem properties and an event	Description
***MenuStrip** Properties*	
RightToLeft	Causes text to display from right to left. This is useful for languages that are read from right to left.
***ToolStripMenuItem** Properties*	
Checked	Indicates whether a menu item is checked. The default value is false, meaning that the menu item is unchecked.
CheckOnClick	Indicates that a menu item should appear checked or unchecked as it is clicked.
ShortcutKey-DisplayString	Specifies text that should appear beside a menu item for a shortcut key. If left blank, the key names are displayed. Otherwise, the text in this property is displayed for the shortcut key.
ShortcutKeys	Specifies the shortcut key for the menu item (e.g., *<Ctrl>-F9* is equivalent to clicking a specific item).
ShowShortcutKeys	Indicates whether a shortcut key is shown beside menu item text. The default is true, which displays the shortcut key.
Text	Specifies the menu item's text. To create an *Alt* access shortcut, precede a character with & (e.g., &File to specify a menu named **File** with the letter **F** underlined).
*Common **ToolStripMenuItem** Event*	
Click	Generated when an item is clicked or a shortcut key is used. This is the default event when the menu is double clicked in the designer.

Fig. 15.6 | MenuStrip and ToolStripMenuItem properties and an event.

Class MenuTestForm (Fig. 15.7) creates a simple menu on a Form. The Form has a top-level **File** menu with menu items **About** (which displays a MessageBox) and **Exit** (which terminates the program). The program also includes a **Format** menu, which contains menu items that change the format of the text on a Label. The **Format** menu has submenus **Color** and **Font**, which change the color and font of the text on a Label.

```
 1   // Fig. 15.7: MenuTestForm.cs
 2   // Using Menus to change font colors and styles.
 3   using System;
 4   using System.Drawing;
 5   using System.Windows.Forms;
 6
 7   namespace MenuTest
 8   {
 9      // our Form contains a Menu that changes the font color
10      // and style of the text displayed in Label
```

Fig. 15.7 | Using menus to change font colors and styles. (Part 1 of 5.)

```
11    public partial class MenuTestForm : Form
12    {
13       // constructor
14       public MenuTestForm()
15       {
16          InitializeComponent();
17       }
18
19       // display MessageBox when About ToolStripMenuItem is selected
20       private void aboutToolStripMenuItem_Click(
21          object sender, EventArgs e)
22       {
23          MessageBox.Show("This is an example\nof using menus.", "About",
24             MessageBoxButtons.OK, MessageBoxIcon.Information);
25       }
26
27       // exit program when Exit ToolStripMenuItem is selected
28       private void exitToolStripMenuItem_Click(object sender, EventArgs e)
29       {
30          Application.Exit();
31       }
32
33       // reset checkmarks for Color ToolStripMenuItems
34       private void ClearColor()
35       {
36          // clear all checkmarks
37          blackToolStripMenuItem.Checked = false;
38          blueToolStripMenuItem.Checked = false;
39          redToolStripMenuItem.Checked = false;
40          greenToolStripMenuItem.Checked = false;
41       }
42
43       // update Menu state and color display black
44       private void blackToolStripMenuItem_Click(
45          object sender, EventArgs e)
46       {
47          // reset checkmarks for Color ToolStripMenuItems
48          ClearColor();
49
50          // set color to Black
51          displayLabel.ForeColor = Color.Black;
52          blackToolStripMenuItem.Checked = true;
53       }
54
55       // update Menu state and color display blue
56       private void blueToolStripMenuItem_Click(object sender, EventArgs e)
57       {
58          // reset checkmarks for Color ToolStripMenuItems
59          ClearColor();
60
61          // set color to Blue
62          displayLabel.ForeColor = Color.Blue;
```

Fig. 15.7 | Using menus to change font colors and styles. (Part 2 of 5.)

```
63              blueToolStripMenuItem.Checked = true;
64          }
65
66          // update Menu state and color display red
67          private void redToolStripMenuItem_Click(
68              object sender, EventArgs e)
69          {
70              // reset checkmarks for Color ToolStripMenuItems
71              ClearColor();
72
73              // set color to Red
74              displayLabel.ForeColor = Color.Red;
75              redToolStripMenuItem.Checked = true;
76          }
77
78          // update Menu state and color display green
79          private void greenToolStripMenuItem_Click(
80              object sender, EventArgs e)
81          {
82              // reset checkmarks for Color ToolStripMenuItems
83              ClearColor();
84
85              // set color to Green
86              displayLabel.ForeColor = Color.Green;
87              greenToolStripMenuItem.Checked = true;
88          }
89
90          // reset checkmarks for Font ToolStripMenuItems
91          private void ClearFont()
92          {
93              // clear all checkmarks
94              timesToolStripMenuItem.Checked = false;
95              courierToolStripMenuItem.Checked = false;
96              comicToolStripMenuItem.Checked = false;
97          }
98
99          // update Menu state and set Font to Times New Roman
100         private void timesToolStripMenuItem_Click(
101             object sender, EventArgs e)
102         {
103             // reset checkmarks for Font ToolStripMenuItems
104             ClearFont();
105
106             // set Times New Roman font
107             timesToolStripMenuItem.Checked = true;
108             displayLabel.Font = new Font("Times New Roman", 14,
109                 displayLabel.Font.Style);
110         }
111
```

Fig. 15.7 | Using menus to change font colors and styles. (Part 3 of 5.)

```
112          // update Menu state and set Font to Courier
113          private void courierToolStripMenuItem_Click(
114             object sender, EventArgs e)
115          {
116             // reset checkmarks for Font ToolStripMenuItems
117             ClearFont();
118
119             // set Courier font
120             courierToolStripMenuItem.Checked = true;
121             displayLabel.Font = new Font("Courier", 14,
122                displayLabel.Font.Style);
123          }
124
125          // update Menu state and set Font to Comic Sans MS
126          private void comicToolStripMenuItem_Click(
127             object sender, EventArgs e)
128          {
129             // reset checkmarks for Font ToolStripMenuItems
130             ClearFont();
131
132             // set Comic Sans font
133             comicToolStripMenuItem.Checked = true;
134             displayLabel.Font = new Font("Comic Sans MS", 14,
135                displayLabel.Font.Style);
136          }
137
138          // toggle checkmark and toggle bold style
139          private void boldToolStripMenuItem_Click(object sender, EventArgs e)
140          {
141             // toggle checkmark
142             boldToolStripMenuItem.Checked = !boldToolStripMenuItem.Checked;
143
144             // use Xor to toggle bold, keep all other styles
145             displayLabel.Font = new Font(displayLabel.Font,
146                displayLabel.Font.Style ^ FontStyle.Bold);
147          }
148
149          // toggle checkmark and toggle italic style
150          private void italicToolStripMenuItem_Click(
151             object sender, EventArgs e)
152          {
153             // toggle checkmark
154             italicToolStripMenuItem.Checked =
155                !italicToolStripMenuItem.Checked;
156
157             // use Xor to toggle italic, keep all other styles
158             displayLabel.Font = new Font(displayLabel.Font,
159                displayLabel.Font.Style ^ FontStyle.Italic);
160          }
161       }
162    }
```

Fig. 15.7 | Using menus to change font colors and styles. (Part 4 of 5.)

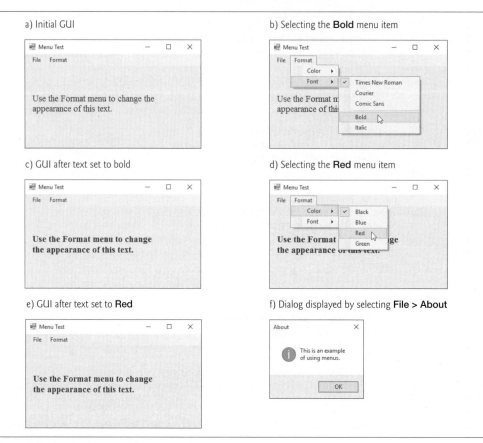

Fig. 15.7 | Using menus to change font colors and styles. (Part 5 of 5.)

Create the GUI

To create this GUI, begin by dragging the MenuStrip from the **ToolBox** onto the Form. Then use **Design** mode to create the menu structure shown in the sample outputs. The **File** menu (fileToolStripMenuItem) has menu items

- **About** (aboutToolStripMenuItem) and
- **Exit** (exitToolStripMenuItem).

The **Format** menu (formatToolStripMenuItem) has two submenus. The first submenu, **Color** (colorToolStripMenuItem), contains menu items

- **Black** (blackToolStripMenuItem),
- **Blue** (blueToolStripMenuItem),
- **Red** (redToolStripMenuItem) and
- **Green** (greenToolStripMenuItem).

The second submenu, **Font** (fontToolStripMenuItem), contains menu items

- **Times New Roman** (timesToolStripMenuItem),

- Courier (`courierToolStripMenuItem`),
- Comic Sans (`comicToolStripMenuItem`),
- a separator bar (`dashToolStripMenuItem`),
- Bold (`boldToolStripMenuItem`) and Italic (`italicToolStripMenuItem`).

Handling the `Click` Events for the About and Exit Menu Items

The **About** menu item in the **File** menu displays a `MessageBox` when clicked (lines 20–25). The **Exit** menu item closes the app through `static` method `Exit` of class `Application` (line 30). Class `Application`'s `static` methods control program execution. Method `Exit` causes our app to terminate.

Color Submenu Events

We made the items in the **Color** submenu (**Black, Blue, Red** and **Green**) *mutually exclusive*—the user can select *only one* at a time (we explain how we did this shortly). To indicate that a menu item is selected, we will set each **Color** menu item's `Checked` property to `true`. This causes a check to appear to the left of a menu item.

Each **Color** menu item has its own `Click` event handler. The method handler for color **Black** is `blackToolStripMenuItem_Click` (lines 44–53). Similarly, the event handlers for colors **Blue, Red** and **Green** are `blueToolStripMenuItem_Click` (lines 56–64), `redToolStripMenuItem_Click` (lines 67–76) and `greenToolStripMenuItem_Click` (lines 79–88), respectively. Each **Color** menu item must be *mutually exclusive*, so each event handler calls method `ClearColor` (lines 34–41) before setting its corresponding `Checked` property to `true`. Method `ClearColor` sets the `Checked` property of each color `ToolStripMenuItem` to `false`, effectively preventing more than one menu item from being selected at a time. In the designer, we initially set the **Black** menu item's `Checked` property to `true`, because at the start of the program, the text on the `Form` is black.

Software Engineering Observation 15.1

The mutual exclusion of menu items is not enforced by the `MenuStrip`, even when the `Checked` property is `true`. You must program this behavior.

Font Submenu Events

The **Font** menu contains three menu items for fonts (**Courier, Times New Roman** and **Comic Sans**) and two menu items for font styles (**Bold** and **Italic**). We added a separator bar between the font and font-style menu items to indicate that these are separate options. A `Font` object can specify only one font at a time but can *set multiple styles at once* (e.g., a font can be both *bold* and italic). We set the font menu items to display checks. As with the **Color** menu, we must enforce mutual exclusion of these items in our event handlers.

Event handlers for font menu items **Times New Roman, Courier** and **Comic Sans** are `timesToolStripMenuItem_Click` (lines 100–110), `courierToolStripMenuItem_Click` (lines 113–123) and `comicToolStripMenuItem_Click` (lines 126–136), respectively. These event handlers are similar to those of the **Color** menu items. Each clears the `Checked` properties for all font menu items by calling method `ClearFont` (lines 91–97), then sets the `Checked` property of the menu item that raised the event to `true`. This enforces the mutual exclusion of the font menu items. In the designer, we initially set the **Times New Roman** menu item's `Checked` property to `true`, because this is the original font for the text on the

Form. The event handlers for the **Bold** and **Italic** menu items (lines 139–160) use the bitwise logical exclusive OR (^) operator to combine font styles, as we discussed in Chapter 14.

15.3 MonthCalendar Control

Many apps must perform date and time calculations. The .NET Framework provides two controls that allow an app to retrieve date and time information—MonthCalendar and DateTimePicker (Section 15.4).

The MonthCalendar (Fig. 15.8) control displays a monthly calendar on the Form. The user can select a date from the currently displayed month or can use the provided arrows to navigate to another month. When a date is selected, it is highlighted. Multiple dates can be selected by clicking dates on the calendar while holding down the *Shift* key. The default event for this control is the DateChanged event, which is generated when a new date is selected. Properties are provided that allow you to modify the appearance of the calendar, how many dates can be selected at once, and the minimum date and maximum date that may be selected. MonthCalendar properties and a common MonthCalendar event are summarized in Fig. 15.9.

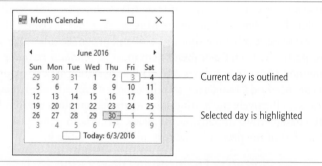

Fig. 15.8 | MonthCalendar control.

MonthCalendar properties and an event	Description
MonthCalendar *Properties*	
FirstDayOfWeek	Sets which day of the week is the first displayed for each week in the calendar.
MaxDate	The last date that can be selected.
MaxSelectionCount	The maximum number of dates that can be selected at once.
MinDate	The first date that can be selected.
MonthlyBoldedDates	An array of dates that will be displayed in bold in the calendar.
SelectionEnd	The last of the dates selected by the user.
SelectionRange	The dates selected by the user.
SelectionStart	The first of the dates selected by the user.

Fig. 15.9 | MonthCalendar properties and an event. (Part 1 of 2.)

MonthCalendar properties and an event	Description
Common MonthCalendar Event	
DateChanged	Generated when a date is selected in the calendar.

Fig. 15.9 | MonthCalendar properties and an event. (Part 2 of 2.)

15.4 DateTimePicker Control

The DateTimePicker control (see output of Fig. 15.11) is similar to the MonthCalendar control but displays the calendar when a *down arrow* is selected. The DateTimePicker can be used to retrieve date and time information from the user. A DateTimePicker's Value property stores a DateTime object, which always contains both date and time information. You can retrieve the date information from the DateTime object by using property Date, and you can retrieve only the time information by using the TimeOfDay property.

The DateTimePicker is also more customizable than a MonthCalendar control—more properties are provided to edit the look and feel of the drop-down calendar. Property Format specifies the user's selection options using the DateTimePickerFormat enumeration. The values in this enumeration are Long (displays the date in long format, as in **Thursday, July 10, 2013**), Short (displays the date in short format, as in **7/10/2013**), Time (displays a time value, as in **5:31:02 PM**) and Custom (indicates that a custom format will be used). If value Custom is used, the display in the DateTimePicker is specified using property CustomFormat. The default event for this control is ValueChanged, which occurs when the selected value (whether a date or a time) is changed. DateTimePicker properties and a common event are summarized in Fig. 15.10.

DateTimePicker properties and an event	Description
DateTimePicker Properties	
CalendarForeColor	Sets the text color for the calendar.
CalendarMonthBackground	Sets the calendar's background color.
CustomFormat	Sets the custom format string for the date and/or time displayed in the control.
Format	Sets the format of the date and/or time used for the date and/or time displayed in the control.
MaxDate	The maximum date and time that can be selected.
MinDate	The minimum date and time that can be selected.
ShowCheckBox	Indicates if a CheckBox should be displayed to the left of the selected date and time.

Fig. 15.10 | DateTimePicker properties and an event. (Part 1 of 2.)

DateTimePicker properties and an event	Description
ShowUpDown	Indicates whether the control displays up and down Buttons. Helpful when the DateTimePicker is used to select a time—the Buttons can be used to increase or decrease hour, minute and second.
Value	The data selected by the user.
Common DateTimePicker Event	
ValueChanged	Generated when the Value property changes, including when the user selects a new date or time.

Fig. 15.10 | DateTimePicker properties and an event. (Part 2 of 2.)

Figure 15.11 demonstrates using a DateTimePicker to select an item's drop-off time. Many companies use such functionality—online retailers typically specify the day a package is sent out and the estimated time that it will arrive at your home. The user selects a drop-off day, then an estimated arrival date is displayed. The date is always two days after drop-off, three days if a Sunday is reached (mail is not delivered on Sunday).

```csharp
1   // Fig. 15.11: DateTimePickerForm.cs
2   // Using a DateTimePicker to select a drop-off time.
3   using System;
4   using System.Windows.Forms;
5
6   namespace DateTimePickerTest
7   {
8      // Form lets user select a drop-off date using a DateTimePicker
9      // and displays an estimated delivery date
10     public partial class DateTimePickerForm : Form
11     {
12        // constructor
13        public DateTimePickerForm()
14        {
15           InitializeComponent();
16        }
17
18        private void dropOffDateTimePicker_ValueChanged(
19           object sender, EventArgs e)
20        {
21           DateTime dropOffDate = dropOffDateTimePicker.Value;
22
23           // add extra time when items are dropped off Sunday
24           if (dropOffDate.DayOfWeek == DayOfWeek.Friday ||
25              dropOffDate.DayOfWeek == DayOfWeek.Saturday ||
26              dropOffDate.DayOfWeek == DayOfWeek.Sunday)
27           {
```

Fig. 15.11 | Using a DateTimePicker to select a drop-off time. (Part 1 of 2.)

```
28              //estimate three days for delivery
29              outputLabel.Text = dropOffDate.AddDays(3).ToLongDateString();
30          }
31          else
32          {
33              // otherwise estimate only two days for delivery
34              outputLabel.Text = dropOffDate.AddDays(2).ToLongDateString();
35          }
36      }
37
38      private void DateTimePickerForm_Load(object sender, EventArgs e)
39      {
40          // user cannot select days before today
41          dropOffDateTimePicker.MinDate = DateTime.Today;
42
43          // user can only select days up to one year in the future
44          dropOffDateTimePicker.MaxDate = DateTime.Today.AddYears(1);
45      }
46  }
47 }
```

a) GUI when app first executes shows current date

b) Selecting a drop-off date

c) GUI after selecting drop-off date

d) GUI showing current and selected dates

Fig. 15.11 | Using a DateTimePicker to select a drop-off time. (Part 2 of 2.)

The DateTimePicker (dropOffDateTimePicker) has its Format property set to Long, so the user can select just a date in this app. When the user selects a date, the ValueChanged event occurs. The event handler for this event (lines 18–36) first retrieves the selected date from the DateTimePicker's Value property (line 21). Lines 24–26 use the DateTime structure's `DayOfWeek` property to determine the day of the week on which the selected date falls. The day values are represented using the `DayOfWeek` enumeration. Lines 29 and 34 use `Date-Time`'s `AddDays` method to increase the date by three days or two days, respectively. The resulting date is then displayed in Long format using method `ToLongDateString`.

In this app, we do not want the user to be able to select a drop-off day before the current day, or one that's more than a year into the future. To enforce this, we set the `Date-TimePicker`'s `MinDate` and `MaxDate` properties when the `Form` is loaded (lines 41 and 44). Property `Today` returns the current day, and method `AddYears` (with an argument of 1) is used to specify a date one year in the future.

Let's take a closer look at the output. This app begins by displaying the current date (Fig. 15.11(a)). In Fig. 15.11(b), we selected the 23rd of June. In Fig. 15.11(c), the estimated arrival date is displayed as the 25th of June. Figure 15.11(d) shows that the 23rd, after it is selected, is highlighted in the calendar.

15.5 LinkLabel Control

The `LinkLabel` control displays *links* to other resources, such as files or web pages (Fig. 15.12). A `LinkLabel` appears as underlined text (colored blue by default). When the mouse moves over the link, the pointer changes to a hand; this is similar to the behavior of a hyperlink in a web page. The link can change color to indicate whether it is not yet visited, previously visited or active (the mouse is over the link and a button is pressed). When clicked, the `LinkLabel` generates a `LinkClicked` event (see Fig. 15.13). Class `Link-Label` is derived from class `Label` and therefore inherits all of class `Label`'s functionality.

LinkLabel on a Form ————————   Hand image displays when mouse moves over `LinkLabel`

Fig. 15.12 | `LinkLabel` control in running program.

Look-and-Feel Observation 15.3

A `LinkLabel` is the preferred control for indicating that the user can click a link to jump to a resource such as a web page, though other controls can perform similar tasks.

LinkLabel properties and an event	Description
Common Properties	
`ActiveLinkColor`	Specifies the color of the active link when the user is in the process of clicking the link. The default color (typically red) is set by the system.
`LinkArea`	Specifies which portion of text in the `LinkLabel` is part of the link.

Fig. 15.13 | `LinkLabel` properties and an event. (Part 1 of 2.)

LinkLabel properties and an event	Description
LinkBehavior	Specifies the link's behavior, such as how the link appears when the mouse is placed over it.
LinkColor	Specifies the original color of the link before it's been visited. The default color (typically blue) is set by the system.
LinkVisited	If true, the link appears as though it has been visited (its color is changed to that specified by property VisitedLinkColor). The default value is false.
Text	Specifies the control's text.
UseMnemonic	If true, the & character in the Text property acts as a shortcut (similar to the *Alt* shortcut in menus).
VisitedLinkColor	Specifies the color of a visited link. The default color (typically purple) is set by the system.
*Common Event (Event arguments **LinkLabelLinkClickedEventArgs**)*	
LinkClicked	Generated when the link is clicked. This is the default event when the control is double clicked in **Design** mode.

Fig. 15.13 | LinkLabel properties and an event. (Part 2 of 2.)

Class LinkLabelTestForm (Fig. 15.14) uses three LinkLabels to link to the C: drive, the Deitel website (www.deitel.com) and the Notepad app, respectively. The Text properties of the LinkLabels cDriveLinkLabel, deitelLinkLabel and notepadLinkLabel describe each link's purpose.

```
1   // Fig. 15.14: LinkLabelTestForm.cs
2   // Using LinkLabels to create hyperlinks.
3   using System;
4   using System.Windows.Forms;
5
6   namespace LinkLabelTest
7   {
8      // Form using LinkLabels to browse the C:\ drive,
9      // load a web page and run Notepad
10     public partial class LinkLabelTestForm : Form
11     {
12        // constructor
13        public LinkLabelTestForm()
14        {
15           InitializeComponent();
16        }
17
18        // browse C:\ drive
19        private void cDriveLinkLabel_LinkClicked(object sender,
20           LinkLabelLinkClickedEventArgs e)
21        {
```

Fig. 15.14 | Using LinkLabels to create hyperlinks. (Part 1 of 3.)

```
22          // change LinkColor after it has been clicked
23          cDriveLinkLabel.LinkVisited = true;
24
25          System.Diagnostics.Process.Start(@"C:\");
26       }
27
28       // load www.deitel.com in web browser
29       private void deitelLinkLabel_LinkClicked(object sender,
30          LinkLabelLinkClickedEventArgs e)
31       {
32          // change LinkColor after it has been clicked
33          deitelLinkLabel.LinkVisited = true;
34
35          System.Diagnostics.Process.Start("http://www.deitel.com");
36       }
37
38       // run app Notepad
39       private void notepadLinkLabel_LinkClicked(object sender,
40          LinkLabelLinkClickedEventArgs e)
41       {
42          // change LinkColor after it has been clicked
43          notepadLinkLabel.LinkVisited = true;
44
45          // program called as if in run
46          // menu and full path not needed
47          System.Diagnostics.Process.Start("notepad");
48       }
49    }
50 }
```

Click first LinkLabel to look at contents of C: drive

Click second LinkLabel to go to Deitel website

Fig. 15.14 | Using LinkLabels to create hyperlinks. (Part 2 of 3.)

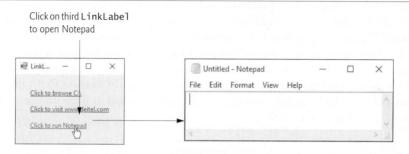

Click on third LinkLabel to open Notepad

Fig. 15.14 | Using LinkLabels to create hyperlinks. (Part 3 of 3.)

The event handlers for the LinkLabels call method Start of class Process (namespace System.Diagnostics), which allows you to execute other programs, or load documents or web sites from an app. Method Start can take one argument, the file to open, or two arguments, the app to run and its command-line arguments. Method Start's arguments can be in the same form as if they were provided for input to the Windows **Run** command (**Start > Run...**). For apps that are known to Windows, full path names are not needed, and the file extension often can be omitted. To open a file of a type that Windows recognizes (and knows how to handle), simply use the file's full path name. For example, if you a pass the method a .docx file, Windows will open it in Microsoft Word (or whatever program is registered to open .docx files, if any). The Windows operating system must be able to use the app associated with the given file's extension to open the file.

The event handler for cDriveLinkLabel's LinkClicked event browses the C: drive (lines 19–26). Line 23 sets the LinkVisited property to true, which changes the link's color from blue to purple (the LinkVisited colors can be configured through the **Properties** window in Visual Studio). The event handler then passes @"C:\" to method Start (line 25), which opens a **Windows Explorer** window. The @ symbol that we placed before "C:\" indicates that all characters in the string should be interpreted literally—this is known as a verbatim string. Thus, the backslash within the string is not considered to be the first character of an escape sequence. This simplifies strings that represent directory paths, since you do not need to use \\ for each \ character in the path.

The event handler for deitelLinkLabel's LinkClicked event (lines 29–36) opens the web page www.deitel.com in the user's default web browser. We achieve this by passing the web-page address as a string (line 35), which opens the web page in a new web browser window or tab. Line 33 sets the LinkVisited property to true.

The event handler for notepadLinkLabel's LinkClicked event (lines 39–48) opens the Notepad app. Line 43 sets the LinkVisited property to true so that the link appears as a visited link. Line 47 passes the argument "notepad" to method Start, which runs notepad.exe. In line 47, neither the full path nor the .exe extension is required—Windows automatically recognizes the argument given to method Start as an executable file.

15.6 ListBox Control

The ListBox control allows the user to view and select from multiple items in a list. ListBoxes are static GUI entities, which means that users cannot directly edit the list of items.

The user can be provided with TextBoxes and Buttons with which to specify items to be added to the list, but the actual additions must be performed in code. The CheckedList-Box control (Section 15.7) extends a ListBox by including CheckBoxes next to each item in the list. This allows users to place checks on multiple items at once, as is possible with CheckBox controls. (Users also can select multiple items from a ListBox by setting the ListBox's SelectionMode property, which is discussed shortly.) Figure 15.15 displays a ListBox and a CheckedListBox. In both controls, scrollbars appear if the number of items exceeds the ListBox's viewable area.

Fig. 15.15 | ListBox and CheckedListBox on a Form.

Figure 15.16 lists common ListBox properties and methods and a common event. The SelectionMode property determines the number of items that can be selected. This property has the possible values None, One, MultiSimple and MultiExtended (from the SelectionMode enumeration)—the differences among these settings are explained in Fig. 15.16. The SelectedIndexChanged event occurs when the user selects a new item.

ListBox properties, methods and an event	Description
Common Properties	
Items	The collection of items in the ListBox.
MultiColumn	Indicates whether the ListBox can display multiple columns. Multiple columns eliminate vertical scrollbars from the display.
SelectedIndex	Returns the index of the selected item. If no items have been selected, the property returns -1. If the user selects multiple items, this property returns only one of the selected indices. If multiple items are selected, use property SelectedIndices.
SelectedIndices	Returns a collection containing the indices for all selected items.
SelectedItem	Returns a reference to the selected item. If multiple items are selected, it can return any of the selected items.
SelectedItems	Returns a collection of the selected item(s).

Fig. 15.16 | ListBox properties, methods and an event. (Part 1 of 2.)

ListBox properties, methods and an event	Description
SelectionMode	Determines the number of items that can be selected and the means through which multiple items can be selected. Values are None, One (the default), MultiSimple (multiple selection allowed) or MultiExtended (multiple selection allowed using a combination of arrow keys or mouse clicks and *Shift* and *Ctrl* keys).
Sorted	Indicates whether items are sorted *alphabetically*. Setting this property's value to true sorts the items. The default value is false.
Common Methods	
ClearSelected	Deselects every item.
GetSelected	Returns true if the item at the specified index is selected.
Common Event	
SelectedIndexChanged	Generated when the selected index changes. This is the default event when the control is double clicked in the designer.

Fig. 15.16 | ListBox properties, methods and an event. (Part 2 of 2.)

Both the ListBox and CheckedListBox have properties Items, SelectedItem and SelectedIndex. Property **Items** returns a collection of the list items. *Collections* are a common way to manage lists of objects in the .NET framework. Many .NET GUI components (e.g., ListBoxes) use collections to expose lists of internal objects (e.g., items in a ListBox). We discuss collections further in Chapter 21. The collection returned by property Items is represented as an object of type ListBox.ObjectCollection. Property **SelectedItem** returns the ListBox's currently selected item. If the user can select multiple items, use collection **SelectedItems** to return all the selected items as a ListBox.SelectedObjectCollection. Property **SelectedIndex** returns the index of the selected item—if there could be more than one, use property **SelectedIndices**, which returns a ListBox.SelectedIndexCollection. If no items are selected, property SelectedIndex returns -1. Method **GetSelected** takes an index and returns true if the corresponding item is selected.

*Adding Items to **ListBoxes** and **CheckedListBoxes***
To add items to a ListBox or to a CheckedListBox, we must add objects to its Items collection. This can be accomplished by calling method Add to add a string to the ListBox's or CheckedListBox's Items collection. For example, we could write

```
myListBox.Items.Add(myListItem);
```

to add string *myListItem* to ListBox *myListBox*. To add multiple objects, you can either call method Add multiple times or call method AddRange to add an array of objects. Classes ListBox and CheckedListBox each call the submitted object's ToString method to determine the Label for the corresponding object's entry in the list. This allows you to add different objects to a ListBox or a CheckedListBox that later can be returned through properties SelectedItem and SelectedItems.

Alternatively, you can add items to `ListBox`es and `CheckedListBox`es visually by examining the `Items` property in the **Properties** window. Clicking the ellipsis button opens the **String Collection Editor**, which contains a text area for adding items; each item appears on a separate line (Fig. 15.17). Visual Studio then writes code to add these `string`s to the `Items` collection inside method `InitializeComponent`.

Fig. 15.17 | String Collection Editor.

Figure 15.18 uses class `ListBoxTestForm` to add, remove and clear items from `ListBox` `displayListBox`. Class `ListBoxTestForm` uses `TextBox` `inputTextBox` to allow the user to type in a new item. When the user clicks the **Add** Button, the new item appears in `displayListBox`. Similarly, if the user selects an item and clicks **Remove**, the item is deleted. When clicked, **Clear** deletes all entries in `displayListBox`. The user terminates the app by clicking **Exit**.

The `addButton_Click` event handler (lines 20–24) calls method `Add` of the `Items` collection in the `ListBox`. This method takes a `string` as the item to add to `displayListBox`. In this case, the `string` used is the user input from the `inputTextBox` (line 22). After the item is added, `inputTextBox.Text` is cleared (line 23).

The `removeButton_Click` event handler (lines 27–34) uses method `RemoveAt` to remove an item from the `ListBox`. Event handler `removeButton_Click` first uses property `SelectedIndex` to determine which index is selected. If `SelectedIndex` is not –1 (i.e., an item is selected), line 32 removes the item that corresponds to the selected index.

```
1   // Fig. 15.18: ListBoxTestForm.cs
2   // Program that adds, removes and clears ListBox items.
3   using System;
4   using System.Windows.Forms;
5
6   namespace ListBoxTest
7   {
8      // Form uses a TextBox and Buttons to add,
9      // remove, and clear ListBox items
10     public partial class ListBoxTestForm : Form
11     {
12        // constructor
13        public ListBoxTestForm()
14        {
```

Fig. 15.18 | Program that adds, removes and clears `ListBox` items. (Part 1 of 3.)

```
15                InitializeComponent();
16          }
17
18          // add new item to ListBox (text from input TextBox)
19          // and clear input TextBox
20          private void addButton_Click(object sender, EventArgs e)
21          {
22              displayListBox.Items.Add(inputTextBox.Text);
23              inputTextBox.Clear();
24          }
25
26          // remove item if one is selected
27          private void removeButton_Click(object sender, EventArgs e)
28          {
29              // check whether item is selected; if so, remove
30              if (displayListBox.SelectedIndex != -1)
31              {
32                  displayListBox.Items.RemoveAt(displayListBox.SelectedIndex);
33              }
34          }
35
36          // clear all items in ListBox
37          private void clearButton_Click(object sender, EventArgs e)
38          {
39              displayListBox.Items.Clear();
40          }
41
42          // exit app
43          private void exitButton_Click(object sender, EventArgs e)
44          {
45              Application.Exit();
46          }
47      }
48 }
```

a) GUI after adding **Dog**, **Cat** and **Chicken** and before adding **Cow**

b) GUI after adding **Cow** and before deleting **Chicken**

Fig. 15.18 | Program that adds, removes and clears ListBox items. (Part 2 of 3.)

c) GUI after deleting **Chicken**

d) GUI after clearing the `ListBox`

Fig. 15.18 | Program that adds, removes and clears `ListBox` items. (Part 3 of 3.)

The `clearButton_Click` event handler (lines 37–40) calls method `Clear` of the `Items` collection (line 39). This removes all the entries in `displayListBox`. Finally, event handler `exitButton_Click` (lines 43–46) terminates the app by calling method `Application.Exit` (line 45).

15.7 CheckedListBox Control

The `CheckedListBox` control derives from `ListBox` and displays a `CheckBox` with each item. Items can be added via methods `Add` and `AddRange` or through the **String Collection Editor**. `CheckedListBox`es allow multiple items to be checked, but item selection is more restrictive. The only values for the `SelectionMode` property are `None` and `One`. `One` allows a single selection, whereas `None` allows no selections. Because an item must be selected to be checked, you must set the `SelectionMode` to be `One` if you wish to allow users to check items. Thus, toggling property `SelectionMode` between `One` and `None` effectively switches between enabling and disabling the user's ability to check list items. Common properties, a method and an event of `CheckedListBox`es appear in Fig. 15.19.

Common Programming Error 15.1

*The IDE displays an error message if you attempt to set the `SelectionMode` property to `MultiSimple` or `MultiExtended` in the **Properties** window of a `CheckedListBox`. If this value is set programmatically, a runtime error occurs.*

Event `ItemCheck` occurs whenever a user checks or unchecks a `CheckedListBox` item. Event-argument properties `CurrentValue` and `NewValue` return `CheckState` values for the current and new state of the item, respectively. A comparison of these values allows you to determine whether the `CheckedListBox` item was checked or unchecked. The `CheckedListBox` control retains the `SelectedItems` and `SelectedIndices` properties (it inherits them from class `ListBox`). However, it also includes properties `CheckedItems` and `CheckedIndices`, which return information about the checked items and indices.

CheckedListBox properties, a method and an event	Description
Common Properties	*(All the ListBox properties, methods and events are inherited by CheckedListBox.)*
CheckedItems	Accessible only at runtime. Returns the collection of items that are checked as a CheckedListBox.CheckedItemCollection. This is distinct from the selected item, which is highlighted (but not necessarily checked). There can be at most one selected item at any given time.
CheckedIndices	Accessible only at runtime. Returns indices for all checked items as a CheckedListBox.CheckedIndexCollection.
CheckOnClick	When true and the user clicks an item, the item is both selected and checked or unchecked. By default, this property is false, which means that the user must select an item, then click it again to check or uncheck it.
SelectionMode	Determines whether items can be selected and checked. The possible values are One (the default; allows multiple checks to be placed) or None (does not allow any checks to be placed).
Common Method	
GetItemChecked	Takes an index and returns true if the corresponding item is checked.
Common Event (Event arguments ItemCheckEventArgs)	
ItemCheck	Generated when an item is checked or unchecked.
ItemCheckEventArgs Properties	
CurrentValue	Indicates whether the current item is checked or unchecked. Possible values are Checked, Unchecked and Indeterminate.
Index	Returns the zero-based index of the item that changed.
NewValue	Specifies the new state of the item.

Fig. 15.19 | CheckedListBox properties, a method and an event.

In Fig. 15.20, class CheckedListBoxTestForm uses a CheckedListBox and a ListBox to display a user's selection of books. The CheckedListBox allows the user to select multiple titles. In the **String Collection Editor**, items were added for some Deitel books: C, C++, Java, Internet & WWW, Visual Basic, Visual C++ and Visual C# (the abbreviation HTP stands for "How to Program"). The ListBox (named displayListBox) displays the user's selection. In the screenshots accompanying this example, the CheckedListBox appears to the left, the ListBox on the right.

```
1   // Fig. 15.20: CheckedListBoxTestForm.cs
2   // Using a CheckedListBox to add items to a display ListBox
3
4   using System.Windows.Forms;
```

Fig. 15.20 | Using a CheckedListBox to add items to a display ListBox. (Part 1 of 2.)

```
 5
 6    namespace CheckedListBoxTest
 7    {
 8       // Form uses a checked ListBox to add items to a display ListBox
 9       public partial class CheckedListBoxTestForm : Form
10       {
11          // constructor
12          public CheckedListBoxTestForm()
13          {
14             InitializeComponent();
15          }
16
17          // item checked or unchecked
18          // add or remove from display ListBox
19          private void itemCheckedListBox_ItemCheck(
20             object sender, ItemCheckEventArgs e)
21          {
22             // obtain reference of selected item
23             string item = itemCheckedListBox.SelectedItem.ToString();
24
25             // if item checked, add to ListBox
26             // otherwise remove from ListBox
27             if (e.NewValue == CheckState.Checked)
28             {
29                displayListBox.Items.Add(item);
30             }
31             else
32             {
33                displayListBox.Items.Remove(item);
34             }
35          }
36       }
37    }
```

Fig. 15.20 | Using a CheckedListBox to add items to a display ListBox. (Part 2 of 2.)

When the user checks or unchecks an item in itemCheckedListBox, an ItemCheck event occurs and event handler itemCheckedListBox_ItemCheck (lines 19–35) executes. An if...else statement (lines 27–34) determines whether the user checked or unchecked an item in the CheckedListBox. Line 27 uses the NewValue property to determine whether the item is being checked (CheckState.Checked). If the user checks an item, line 29 adds the checked entry to the ListBox displayListBox. If the user unchecks an item, line 33 removes the corresponding item from displayListBox. This event handler was created by selecting the CheckedListBox in **Design** mode, viewing the control's events in the **Properties** window and double clicking the ItemCheck event. The default event for a CheckedListBox is a SelectedIndexChanged event.

15.8 ComboBox Control

The ComboBox control combines TextBox features with a drop-down list—a GUI component that contains a list from which a value can be selected. A ComboBox usually appears as a TextBox with a down arrow to its right. By default, the user can enter text into the Text-Box or click the down arrow to display a list of predefined items. If a user chooses an element from this list, that element is displayed in the TextBox. If the list contains more elements than can be displayed in the drop-down list, a *scrollbar* appears. The maximum number of items that a drop-down list can display at one time is set by property MaxDrop-DownItems. Figure 15.21 shows a sample ComboBox in three different states.

Click the down arrow to display
items in the drop-down list

Selecting an item from the drop-down
list changes text in the **TextBox** portion

Fig. 15.21 | ComboBox demonstration.

As with the ListBox control, you can add objects to collection Items programmatically, using methods Add and AddRange, or visually, with the **String Collection Editor**. Figure 15.22 lists common properties and a common event of class ComboBox.

Look-and-Feel Observation 15.4

Use a ComboBox to save space on a GUI. A disadvantage is that, unlike with a ListBox, the user cannot see available items without expanding the drop-down list.

Property DropDownStyle determines the type of ComboBox and is represented as a value of the **ComboBoxStyle** enumeration, which contains values Simple, DropDown and DropDownList. Option Simple does not display a drop-down arrow. Instead, if the ComboBox is tall enough to display a list of items, they're shown vertically—possibly with a scrollbar to allow the user to view items that cannot fit in the display area. The user also can type in a selection. Style DropDown (the default) displays a drop-down list when the down arrow is clicked (or the down arrow key is pressed). The user can type a new item in the ComboBox. The last style is DropDownList, which displays a drop-down list but does not allow the user to type in the TextBox.

ComboBox properties and an event	Description
Common Properties	
DropDownStyle	Determines the type of ComboBox. Value Simple means that the text portion is editable and the list portion is always visible. Value DropDown (the default) means that the text portion is editable but the user must click an arrow button to see the list portion. Value DropDownList means that the text portion is not editable and the user must click the arrow button to see the list portion.
Items	The collection of items in the ComboBox control.
MaxDropDownItems	Specifies the maximum number of items (between 1 and 100) that the drop-down list can display. If the number of items exceeds the maximum number of items to display, a scrollbar appears.
SelectedIndex	Returns the index of the selected item, or -1 if none are selected.
SelectedItem	Returns a reference to the selected item.
Sorted	Indicates whether items are sorted alphabetically. Setting this property's value to true sorts the items. The default is false.
Common Event	
SelectedIndexChanged	Generated when the selected index changes (such as when a different item is selected). This is the default event when control is double clicked in the designer.

Fig. 15.22 | ComboBox properties and an event.

The ComboBox control has properties Items (a collection), SelectedItem and SelectedIndex, which are similar to the corresponding properties in ListBox. There can be at most one selected item in a ComboBox. If no items are selected, then SelectedIndex is -1. When the selected item changes, a SelectedIndexChanged event occurs.

Class ComboBoxTestForm (Fig. 15.23) allows users to select a shape to draw—circle, ellipse, square or pie (in both filled and unfilled versions)—by using a ComboBox. The ComboBox in this example is uneditable, so the user cannot type in the TextBox.

 Look-and-Feel Observation 15.5
Make lists (such as ComboBoxes) editable only if the app is designed to accept user-submitted elements. Otherwise, the user might try to enter a custom item that's improper for the purposes of your app.

```
1   // Fig. 15.23: ComboBoxTestForm.cs
2   // Using ComboBox to select a shape to draw.
3   using System;
4   using System.Drawing;
5   using System.Windows.Forms;
```

Fig. 15.23 | Using ComboBox to select a shape to draw. (Part 1 of 3.)

```
6
7   namespace ComboBoxTest
8   {
9       // Form uses a ComboBox to select different shapes to draw
10      public partial class ComboBoxTestForm : Form
11      {
12          // constructor
13          public ComboBoxTestForm()
14          {
15              InitializeComponent();
16          }
17
18          // get index of selected shape, draw shape
19          private void imageComboBox_SelectedIndexChanged(
20              object sender, EventArgs e)
21          {
22              // create graphics object, Pen and SolidBrush
23              using (Graphics myGraphics = base.CreateGraphics())
24
25              // create Pen using color DarkRed
26              using (Pen myPen = new Pen(Color.DarkRed))
27
28              // create SolidBrush using color DarkRed
29              using (SolidBrush mySolidBrush = new SolidBrush(Color.DarkRed))
30              {
31                  // clear drawing area, setting it to color white
32                  myGraphics.Clear(Color.White);
33
34                  // find index, draw proper shape
35                  switch (imageComboBox.SelectedIndex)
36                  {
37                      case 0: // case Circle is selected
38                          myGraphics.DrawEllipse(myPen, 50, 50, 150, 150);
39                          break;
40                      case 1: // case Rectangle is selected
41                          myGraphics.DrawRectangle(myPen, 50, 50, 150, 150);
42                          break;
43                      case 2: // case Ellipse is selected
44                          myGraphics.DrawEllipse(myPen, 50, 85, 150, 115);
45                          break;
46                      case 3: // case Pie is selected
47                          myGraphics.DrawPie(myPen, 50, 50, 150, 150, 0, 45);
48                          break;
49                      case 4: // case Filled Circle is selected
50                          myGraphics.FillEllipse(mySolidBrush, 50, 50, 150, 150);
51                          break;
52                      case 5: // case Filled Rectangle is selected
53                          myGraphics.FillRectangle(
54                              mySolidBrush, 50, 50, 150, 150);
55                          break;
56                      case 6: // case Filled Ellipse is selected
57                          myGraphics.FillEllipse(mySolidBrush, 50, 85, 150, 115);
58                          break;
```

Fig. 15.23 | Using ComboBox to select a shape to draw. (Part 2 of 3.)

```
59                        case 7: // case Filled Pie is selected
60                            myGraphics.FillPie(
61                                mySolidBrush, 50, 50, 150, 150, 0, 45);
62                            break;
63                    }
64                }
65            }
66        }
67    }
```

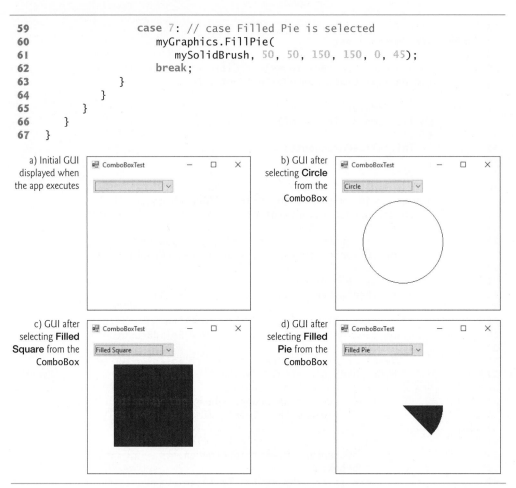

a) Initial GUI displayed when the app executes

b) GUI after selecting **Circle** from the ComboBox

c) GUI after selecting **Filled Square** from the ComboBox

d) GUI after selecting **Filled Pie** from the ComboBox

Fig. 15.23 | Using ComboBox to select a shape to draw. (Part 3 of 3.)

After creating ComboBox imageComboBox, make it uneditable by setting its DropDown-Style to DropDownList in the **Properties** window. Next, add items Circle, Square, Ellipse, Pie, Filled Circle, Filled Square, Filled Ellipse and Filled Pie to the Items collection using the **String Collection Editor**. Whenever the user selects an item from imageComboBox, a SelectedIndexChanged event occurs and event handler imageCombo-Box_SelectedIndexChanged (lines 19–65) executes. Lines 23–29 create a Graphics object, a Pen and a SolidBrush, which are used to draw on the Form—each is an IDisposable object, so a chained using statement (multiple using clauses before the opening brace at line30) ensures their Dispose methods are called at the end of the event handler. The Graphics object (line 23) allows a pen or brush to draw on a component, using one of several Graphics methods. The Pen object (line 26) is used by methods DrawEllipse, DrawRectangle and DrawPie (lines 38, 41, 44 and 47) to draw the outlines of their corresponding shapes. The SolidBrush object (line 29) is used by methods FillEllipse, FillRectangle and FillPie (lines 50, 53–54, 57 and 60–61) to fill their corresponding solid shapes. Line 32 colors the entire Form White, using Graphics method Clear.

The app draws a shape based on the selected item's index (lines 35–61). `Graphics` method `DrawEllipse` (line 38) takes a `Pen`, and the x- and y-coordinates of the upper-left corner, the width and height of the bounding box (i.e., rectangular area) in which the ellipse will be displayed. The origin of the coordinate system is in the upper-left corner of the `Form`; the x-coordinate increases to the right, and the y-coordinate increases downward. A circle is a special case of an ellipse (with the width and height equal). Line 38 draws a circle. Line 44 draws an ellipse that has different values for width and height.

Class `Graphics` method `DrawRectangle` (line 41) takes a `Pen`, the x- and y-coordinates of the upper-left corner and the width and height of the rectangle to draw. Method `DrawPie` (line 47) draws a pie as a portion of an ellipse. The ellipse is bounded by a rectangle. Method `DrawPie` takes a `Pen`, the x- and y-coordinates of the upper-left corner of the rectangle, its width and height, the start angle (in degrees) and the sweep angle (in degrees) of the pie. Angles increase clockwise. The `FillEllipse` (lines 50 and 56), `FillRectangle` (line 53–54) and `FillPie` (line 60–61) methods are similar to their unfilled counterparts, except that they take a `Brush` (e.g., `SolidBrush`) instead of a `Pen`. Some of the drawn shapes are illustrated in the screenshots of Fig. 15.23.

15.9 TreeView Control

The `TreeView` control displays nodes hierarchically in a tree. Traditionally, nodes are objects that contain values and can refer to other nodes. A parent node contains child nodes, and the child nodes can be parents to other nodes. Two child nodes that have the same parent node are considered sibling nodes. A tree is a collection of nodes, usually organized in a *hierarchical* manner. The first parent node of a tree is the root node (a `TreeView` can have multiple roots). For example, the file system of a computer can be represented as a tree. The top-level directory (perhaps `C:`) would be the root, each subfolder of `C:` would be a child node and each child folder could have its own children. `TreeView` controls are useful for displaying hierarchical information, such as the file structure that we just mentioned. We cover nodes and trees in greater detail in Chapter 19, Custom Linked Data Structures. Figure 15.24 displays a sample `TreeView` control on a `Form`.

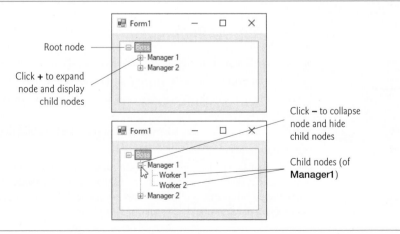

Fig. 15.24 | `TreeView` displaying a sample tree.

A parent node can be expanded or collapsed by clicking the plus box or minus box to its left. Nodes without children do not have these boxes.

The nodes in a TreeView are instances of class **TreeNode**. Each TreeNode has a **Nodes** collection (type **TreeNodeCollection**), which contains a list of other TreeNodes—known as its children. The Parent property returns a reference to the parent node (or null if the node is a root node). Figures 15.25 and 15.26 list the common properties of TreeViews and TreeNodes, common TreeNode methods and a common TreeView event.

TreeView properties and an event	Description
Common Properties	
CheckBoxes	Indicates whether CheckBoxes appear next to nodes. A value of true displays CheckBoxes. The default value is false.
ImageList	Specifies an ImageList object containing the node icons. An ImageList object is a collection that contains Image objects.
Nodes	Returns the collection of TreeNodes in the control as a TreeNodeCollection. It contains methods Add (adds a TreeNode object), Clear (deletes the entire collection) and Remove (deletes a specific node). Removing a parent node deletes all of its children.
SelectedNode	The selected node.
Common Event (Event arguments TreeViewEventArgs)	
AfterSelect	Generated after selected node changes. This is the default event when the control is double clicked in the designer.

Fig. 15.25 | TreeView properties and an event.

TreeNode properties and methods	Description
Common Properties	
Checked	Indicates whether the TreeNode is checked (CheckBoxes property must be set to true in the parent TreeView).
FirstNode	Specifies the first node in the Nodes collection (i.e., the first child in the tree).
FullPath	Indicates the path of the node, starting at the root of the tree.
ImageIndex	Specifies the index in the TreeView's ImageList of the image shown when the node is deselected.
LastNode	Specifies the last node in the Nodes collection (i.e., the last child in the tree).
NextNode	Next sibling node.
Nodes	Collection of TreeNodes contained in the current node (i.e., all the children of the current node). It contains methods Add (adds a TreeNode object), Clear (deletes the entire collection) and Remove (deletes a specific node). Removing a parent node deletes all of its children.

Fig. 15.26 | TreeNode properties and methods. (Part 1 of 2.)

TreeNode properties and methods	Description
PrevNode	Previous sibling node.
SelectedImageIndex	Specifies the index in the TreeView's ImageList of the image to use when the node is selected.
Text	Specifies the TreeNode's text.
Common Methods	
Collapse	Collapses a node.
Expand	Expands a node.
ExpandAll	Expands all the children of a node.
GetNodeCount	Returns the number of child nodes.

Fig. 15.26 | TreeNode properties and methods. (Part 2 of 2.)

To add nodes to the TreeView visually, click the ellipsis next to the Nodes property in the **Properties** window. This opens the **TreeNode Editor** (Fig. 15.27), which displays an empty tree representing the TreeView. There are Buttons to create a root and to add or delete a node. To the right are the properties of the current node. Here you can rename the node.

Fig. 15.27 | TreeNode Editor.

To add nodes programmatically, first create a root node. Create a new TreeNode object and pass it a string to display. Then call method Add to add this new TreeNode to the TreeView's Nodes collection. Thus, to add a root node to TreeView *myTreeView*, write

```
myTreeView.Nodes.Add(new TreeNode(rootLabel));
```

where *myTreeView* is the `TreeView` to which we are adding nodes, and *rootLabel* is the text to display in *myTreeView*. To add children to a root node, add new `TreeNode`s to its `Nodes` collection. We select the appropriate root node from the `TreeView` by writing

> *myTreeView*.`Nodes`[*myIndex*]

where *myIndex* is the root node's index in *myTreeView*'s `Nodes` collection. We add nodes to child nodes through the same process by which we added root nodes to *myTreeView*. To add a child to the root node at index *myIndex*, write

> *myTreeView*.`Nodes`[*myIndex*].`Nodes.Add(`**new** `TreeNode(`*ChildLabel*`));`

Class `TreeViewDirectoryStructureForm` (Fig. 15.28) uses a `TreeView` to display the contents of a directory chosen by the user. A `TextBox` and a `Button` are used to specify the directory. First, enter the full path of the directory you want to display. Then click the `Button` to set the specified directory as the root node in the `TreeView`. Each subdirectory of this directory becomes a child node. This layout is similar to that used in **Windows Explorer**. Folders can be expanded or collapsed by clicking the plus or minus boxes that appear to their left.

```
1   // Fig. 15.28: TreeViewDirectoryStructureForm.cs
2   // Using TreeView to display directory structure.
3   using System;
4   using System.Windows.Forms;
5   using System.IO;
6
7   namespace TreeViewDirectoryStructure
8   {
9      // Form uses TreeView to display directory structure
10     public partial class TreeViewDirectoryStructureForm : Form
11     {
12        string substringDirectory; // store last part of full path name
13
14        // constructor
15        public TreeViewDirectoryStructureForm()
16        {
17           InitializeComponent();
18        }
19
20        // populate current node with subdirectories
21        public void PopulateTreeView(
22           string directoryValue, TreeNode parentNode)
23        {
24           // array stores all subdirectories in the directory
25           string[] directoryArray =
26              Directory.GetDirectories(directoryValue);
27
28           // populate current node with subdirectories
29           try
30           {
```

Fig. 15.28 | Using `TreeView` to display directory structure. (Part 1 of 3.)

```
31              // check to see if any subdirectories are present
32              if (directoryArray.Length != 0)
33              {
34                  // for every subdirectory, create new TreeNode,
35                  // add as a child of current node and recursively
36                  // populate child nodes with subdirectories
37                  foreach (string directory in directoryArray)
38                  {
39                      // obtain last part of path name from the full path
40                      // name by calling the GetFileNameWithoutExtension
41                      // method of class Path
42                      substringDirectory =
43                          Path.GetFileNameWithoutExtension(directory);
44
45                      // create TreeNode for current directory
46                      TreeNode myNode = new TreeNode(substringDirectory);
47
48                      // add current directory node to parent node
49                      parentNode.Nodes.Add(myNode);
50
51                      // recursively populate every subdirectory
52                      PopulateTreeView(directory, myNode);
53                  }
54              }
55          }
56          catch (UnauthorizedAccessException)
57          {
58              parentNode.Nodes.Add("Access denied");
59          }
60      }
61
62      // handles enterButton click event
63      private void enterButton_Click(object sender, EventArgs e)
64      {
65          // clear all nodes
66          directoryTreeView.Nodes.Clear();
67
68          // check if the directory entered by user exists
69          // if it does, then fill in the TreeView,
70          // if not, display error MessageBox
71          if (Directory.Exists(inputTextBox.Text))
72          {
73              // add full path name to directoryTreeView
74              directoryTreeView.Nodes.Add(inputTextBox.Text);
75
76              // insert subfolders
77              PopulateTreeView(
78                  inputTextBox.Text, directoryTreeView.Nodes[ 0 ]);
79          }
80          // display error MessageBox if directory not found
81          else
82          {
```

Fig. 15.28 | Using TreeView to display directory structure. (Part 2 of 3.)

```
83              MessageBox.Show(inputTextBox.Text + " could not be found.",
84                 "Directory Not Found", MessageBoxButtons.OK,
85                 MessageBoxIcon.Error);
86           }
87        }
88     }
89  }
```

a) GUI after user enters a directory path

b) GUI after the user presses **Enter** to display the directory's contents

Fig. 15.28 | Using TreeView to display directory structure. (Part 3 of 3.)

When the user clicks the enterButton, all the nodes in directoryTreeView are cleared (line 66). Then, if the directory exists (line 71), the path entered in inputTextBox is used to create the root node. Line 74 adds the directory to directoryTreeView as the root node, and lines 77–78 call method PopulateTreeView (lines 21–60), which takes a directory (a string) and a parent node. Method PopulateTreeView then creates child nodes corresponding to the subdirectories of the directory it receives as an argument.

Method PopulateTreeView (lines 21–60) obtains a list of subdirectories, using method **GetDirectories** of class Directory (namespace System.IO) in lines 25–26. Method GetDirectories takes a string (the current directory) and returns an array of strings (the subdirectories). If a directory is not accessible for security reasons, an UnauthorizedAccessException is thrown. Lines 56–59 catch this exception and add a node containing "Access denied" instead of displaying the subdirectories.

If there are accessible subdirectories, lines 42–43 use method GetFileNameWithout-Extension of class Path to increase readability by shortening the full path name to just the directory name. The **Path** class provides functionality for working with strings that are file or directory paths. Next, each string in the directoryArray is used to create a new child node (line 46). We use method Add (line 49) to add each child node to the parent. Then method PopulateTreeView is called recursively on every subdirectory (line 52), which eventually populates the TreeView with the entire directory structure. Our recursive algorithm may cause a delay when the program loads large directories. However, once the folder names are added to the appropriate Nodes collection, they can be expanded and collapsed without delay. In the next section, we present an alternate algorithm to solve this problem.

15.10 ListView **Control**

The ListView control is similar to a ListBox in that both display lists from which the user can select one or more items (an example of a ListView can be found in Fig. 15.31). List-View is more versatile and can display items in different formats. For example, a ListView can display icons next to the list items (controlled by its SmallImageList, LargeImage-List or StateImageList properties) and show the details of items in columns. Property MultiSelect (a bool) determines whether multiple items can be selected. CheckBoxes can be included by setting property CheckBoxes (a bool) to true, making the ListView's appearance similar to that of a CheckedListBox. The View property specifies the layout of the ListBox. Property Activation determines the method by which the user selects a list item. The details of these properties and the Click and ItemActivate events are explained in Fig. 15.29.

ListView properties and events	Description
Common Properties	
Activation	Determines how the user activates an item. This property takes a value in the ItemActivation enumeration. Possible values are OneClick (single-click activation), TwoClick (double-click activation, item changes color when the mouse moves over the item) and Standard (the default; double-click activation, item does not change color).
CheckBoxes	Indicates whether items appear with CheckBoxes. true displays Check-Boxes. The default is false.
LargeImageList	Specifies the ImageList containing large icons for display.
Items	Returns the collection of ListViewItems in the control.
MultiSelect	Determines whether multiple selection is allowed. The default is true, which enables multiple selection.
SelectedItems	Returns the collection of selected items as a ListView.SelectedListViewItemCollection.
SmallImageList	Specifies the ImageList containing small icons for display.
View	Determines appearance of ListViewItems. Possible values are LargeIcon (the default; large icon displayed, items can be in multiple columns), SmallIcon (small icon displayed, items can be in multiple columns), List (small icons displayed, items appear in a single column), Details (like List, but multiple columns of information can be displayed per item) and Tile (large icons displayed, information provided to right of icon).
Common Events	
Click	Generated when an item is clicked. This is the default event.
ItemActivate	Generated when an item in the ListView is activated (clicked or double clicked). Does not contain the specifics of which item is activated—you can use SelectedItems or SelectedIndices to determine this.

Fig. 15.29 | ListView properties and events.

ListView allows you to define the images used as icons for ListView items. To display images, an ImageList component is required. Create one by dragging it to a Form from the **ToolBox**. Then, select the Images property in the **Properties** window to display the **Images Collection Editor** (Fig. 15.30). Here you can browse for images that you wish to add to the ImageList, which contains an array of Images. Adding images this way embeds them into the app (like resources), so they do not need to be included separately with the published app. They're not, however, part of the project. In this example, we added images to the ImageList programmatically rather than using the **Images Collection Editor** so that we could use image resources. After creating an empty ImageList, add the file and folder icon images (provided with this chapter's examples) to the project as resources. Next, set property SmallImageList of the ListView to the new ImageList object. Property Small-ImageList specifies the image list for the small icons. Property LargeImageList sets the ImageList for large icons. The items in a ListView are each of type ListViewItem. Icons for the ListView items are selected by setting the item's ImageIndex property to the appropriate index.

Fig. 15.30 | Images Collection Editor window for an ImageList component.

Class ListViewTestForm (Fig. 15.31) displays files and folders in a ListView, along with small icons representing each file or folder. If a file or folder is inaccessible because of permission settings, a MessageBox appears. The program scans the contents of the directory as it browses, rather than indexing the entire drive at once.

```
1  // Fig. 15.31: ListViewTestForm.cs
2  // Displaying directories and their contents in a ListView.
3  using System;
4  using System.Windows.Forms;
5  using System.IO;
6
7  namespace ListViewTest
8  {
```

Fig. 15.31 | Displaying directories and their contents in a ListView. (Part 1 of 4.)

```
 9        // Form contains a ListView which displays
10        // folders and files in a directory
11        public partial class ListViewTestForm : Form
12        {
13           // store current directory
14           string currentDirectory = Directory.GetCurrentDirectory();
15
16           // constructor
17           public ListViewTestForm()
18           {
19              InitializeComponent();
20           }
21
22           // browse directory user clicked or go up one level
23           private void browserListView_Click(object sender, EventArgs e)
24           {
25              // ensure an item is selected
26              if (browserListView.SelectedItems.Count != 0)
27              {
28                 // if first item selected, go up one level
29                 if (browserListView.Items[0].Selected)
30                 {
31                    // create DirectoryInfo object for directory
32                    DirectoryInfo directoryObject =
33                       new DirectoryInfo(currentDirectory);
34
35                    // if directory has parent, load it
36                    if (directoryObject.Parent != null)
37                    {
38                       LoadFilesInDirectory(directoryObject.Parent.FullName);
39                    }
40                 }
41
42                 // selected directory or file
43                 else
44                 {
45                    // directory or file chosen
46                    string chosen = browserListView.SelectedItems[0].Text;
47
48                    // if item selected is directory, load selected directory
49                    if (Directory.Exists(
50                       Path.Combine(currentDirectory, chosen)))
51                    {
52                       LoadFilesInDirectory(
53                          Path.Combine(currentDirectory, chosen));
54                    }
55                 }
56
57                 // update displayLabel
58                 displayLabel.Text = currentDirectory;
59              }
60           }
61
```

Fig. 15.31 | Displaying directories and their contents in a ListView. (Part 2 of 4.)

```
62          // display files/subdirectories of current directory
63          public void LoadFilesInDirectory(string currentDirectoryValue)
64          {
65             // load directory information and display
66             try
67             {
68                // clear ListView and set first item
69                browserListView.Items.Clear();
70                browserListView.Items.Add("Go Up One Level");
71
72                // update current directory
73                currentDirectory = currentDirectoryValue;
74                DirectoryInfo newCurrentDirectory =
75                   new DirectoryInfo(currentDirectory);
76
77                // put files and directories into arrays
78                DirectoryInfo[] directoryArray =
79                   newCurrentDirectory.GetDirectories();
80                FileInfo[] fileArray = newCurrentDirectory.GetFiles();
81
82                // add directory names to ListView
83                foreach (DirectoryInfo dir in directoryArray)
84                {
85                   // add directory to ListView
86                   ListViewItem newDirectoryItem =
87                      browserListView.Items.Add(dir.Name);
88
89                   newDirectoryItem.ImageIndex = 0;  // set directory image
90                }
91
92                // add file names to ListView
93                foreach (FileInfo file in fileArray)
94                {
95                   // add file to ListView
96                   ListViewItem newFileItem =
97                      browserListView.Items.Add(file.Name);
98
99                   newFileItem.ImageIndex = 1;  // set file image
100               }
101            }
102
103            // access denied
104            catch (UnauthorizedAccessException)
105            {
106               MessageBox.Show("Warning: Some files may not be " +
107                  "visible due to permission settings",
108                  "Attention", 0, MessageBoxIcon.Warning);
109            }
110         }
111
112         // handle load event when Form displayed for first time
113         private void ListViewTestForm_Load(object sender, EventArgs e)
114         {
```

Fig. 15.31 | Displaying directories and their contents in a ListView. (Part 3 of 4.)

```
115              // add icon images to ImageList
116              fileFolderImageList.Images.Add(Properties.Resources.folder);
117              fileFolderImageList.Images.Add(Properties.Resources.file);
118
119              // load current directory into browserListView
120              LoadFilesInDirectory(currentDirectory);
121              displayLabel.Text = currentDirectory;
122          }
123      }
124  }
```

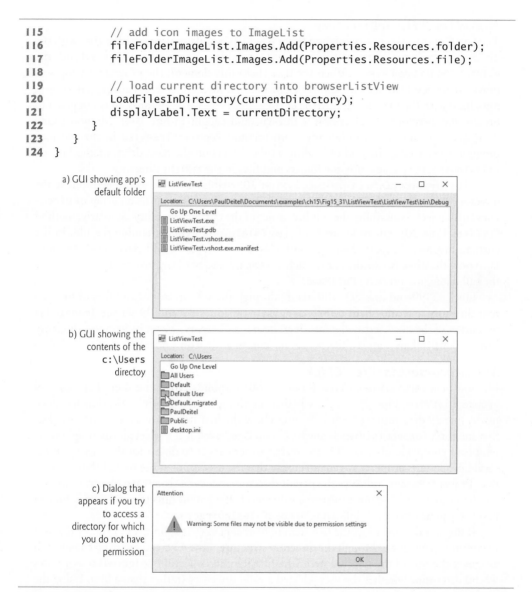

a) GUI showing app's default folder

b) GUI showing the contents of the c:\Users directoy

c) Dialog that appears if you try to access a directory for which you do not have permission

Fig. 15.31 | Displaying directories and their contents in a ListView. (Part 4 of 4.)

Method ListViewTestForm_Load

Method ListViewTestForm_Load (lines 113–122) handles the Form's Load event. When the app loads, the folder and file icon images are added to the Images collection of file-FolderImageList (lines 116–117). Since the ListView's SmallImageList property is set to this ImageList, the ListView can display these images as icons for each item. Because the folder icon was added first, it has array index 0, and the file icon has array index 1. The app also loads its home directory (obtained at line 14) into the ListView when it first loads (line 120) and displays the directory path (line 121).

Method **LoadFilesInDirectory**
The LoadFilesInDirectory method (lines 63–110) populates browserListView with the directory passed to it (currentDirectoryValue). It clears browserListView and adds the element "Go Up One Level". When the user clicks this element, the program attempts to move up one level (we see how shortly). The method then creates a DirectoryInfo object initialized with the string currentDirectory (lines 74–75). If permission is not given to browse the directory, an exception is thrown (and caught in line 104). Method Load-FilesInDirectory works differently from method PopulateTreeView in the previous program (Fig. 15.28). Instead of loading all the folders on the hard drive, method Load-FilesInDirectory loads only the folders and files in the current directory.

Class **DirectoryInfo** (namespace System.IO) enables us to browse or manipulate the directory structure easily. Method **GetDirectories** (line 79) returns an array of Direc-toryInfo objects containing the subdirectories of the current directory. Similarly, method **GetFiles** (line 80) returns an array of class **FileInfo** objects containing the files in the current directory. Property **Name** (of both class DirectoryInfo and class FileInfo) contains only the directory or file name, such as temp instead of C:\myfolder\temp. To access the full name, use property **FullName**.

Lines 83–90 and lines 93–100 iterate through the subdirectories and files of the current directory and add them to browserListView. Lines 89 and 99 set the ImageIndex properties of the newly created items. If an item is a directory, we set its icon to a directory icon (index 0); if an item is a file, we set its icon to a file icon (index 1).

Method **browserListView_Click**
Method browserListView_Click (lines 23–60) responds when the user clicks control browserListView. Line 26 checks whether anything is selected. If a selection has been made, line 29 determines whether the user chose the first item in browserListView. The first item in browserListView is always **Go Up One Level**; if it's selected, the program attempts to go up a level. Lines 32–33 create a DirectoryInfo object for the current directory. Line 36 tests property Parent to ensure that the user is not at the root of the directory tree. Property **Parent** indicates the parent directory as a DirectoryInfo object; if no parent directory exists, Parent returns the value null. If a parent directory does exist, line 38 pass the parent directory's full name to LoadFilesInDirectory.

If the user did not select the first item in browserListView, lines 43–55 allow the user to continue navigating through the directory structure. Line 46 creates string chosen and assigns it the text of the selected item (the first item in collection SelectedItems). Lines 49–50 determine whether the user selected a valid directory (rather than a file). Using the Combine method of class Path, the program combines strings currentDirectory and chosen to form the new directory path. The Combine method automatically adds a back-slash (\), if necessary, between the two pieces. This value is passed to the **Exists** method of class Directory. Method Exists returns true if its string parameter is a valid directory. If so, the program passes the string to method LoadFilesInDirectory (lines 52–53). Finally, displayLabel is updated with the new directory (line 58).

This program loads quickly, because it indexes only the files in the current directory. A small delay may occur when a new directory is loaded. In addition, changes in the directory structure can be shown by reloading a directory. The previous program (Fig. 15.28) may have a large initial delay, as it loads an entire directory structure. This type of trade-off is typical in the software world.

Software Engineering Observation 15.2

When designing apps that run for long periods of time, you might choose a large initial delay to improve performance throughout the rest of the program. However, in apps that run for only short periods, developers often prefer fast initial loading times and small delays after each action.

15.11 TabControl Control

The TabControl creates tabbed windows, such as those in Visual Studio (Fig. 15.32). This enables you to specify more information in the same space on a Form and group displayed data logically. TabControls contain **TabPage** objects, which are similar to Panels and GroupBoxes in that TabPages also can contain controls. You first add controls to the Tab-Page objects, then add the TabPages to the TabControl. Only one TabPage is displayed at a time. To add objects to the TabPage and the TabControl, write

```
myTabPage.Controls.Add(myControl);
myTabControl.TabPages.Add(myTabPage);
```

Fig. 15.32 | Tabbed windows in Visual Studio.

The preceding statements call method Add of the Controls collection and method Add of the TabPages collection. The example adds TabControl *myControl* to TabPage *myTab-Page*, then adds *myTabPage* to *myTabControl*. Alternatively, we can use method AddRange to add an array of TabPages or controls to a TabControl or TabPage, respectively. Figure 15.33 depicts a sample TabControl.

You can add TabControls visually by dragging and dropping them onto a Form in **Design** mode. To add TabPages in **Design** mode, click the top of the TabControl, open its *smart tasks menu* and select **Add Tab** (Fig. 15.34). Alternatively, click the **TabPages** property in the **Properties** window and add tabs in the dialog that appears. To change a tab label, set the **Text** property of the TabPage. Clicking the tabs selects the TabControl—to select the TabPage, click the control area underneath the tabs. You can add controls to the TabPage by dragging and dropping items from the **ToolBox**. To view different TabPages, click the appropriate tab (in either design or run mode).

Fig. 15.33 | TabControl with TabPages example.

Fig. 15.34 | TabPages added to a TabControl.

Common properties and a common event of TabControls are described in Fig. 15.35. Each TabPage generates a Click event when its tab is clicked. Event handlers for this event can be created by double clicking the body of the TabPage.

TabControl properties and an event	Description
Common Properties	
ImageList	Specifies images to be displayed on tabs.
ItemSize	Specifies the tab size.
Multiline	Indicates whether multiple rows of tabs can be displayed.
SelectedIndex	Index of the selected TabPage.
SelectedTab	The selected TabPage.
TabCount	Returns the number of tab pages.
TabPages	Returns the collection of TabPages within the TabControl as a TabControl.TabPageCollection.
Common Event	
SelectedIndexChanged	Generated when SelectedIndex changes (i.e., another TabPage is selected).

Fig. 15.35 | TabControl properties and an event.

Class UsingTabsForm (Fig. 15.36) uses a TabControl to display various options relating to the text on a label (**Color**, **Size** and **Message**). The last TabPage displays an **About** message, which describes the use of TabControls.

```
1   // Fig. 15.36: UsingTabsForm.cs
2   // Using TabControl to display various font settings.
3   using System;
4   using System.Drawing;
5   using System.Windows.Forms;
6
7   namespace UsingTabs
8   {
9      // Form uses Tabs and RadioButtons to display various font settings
10     public partial class UsingTabsForm : Form
11     {
12        // constructor
13        public UsingTabsForm()
14        {
15           InitializeComponent();
16        }
17
18        // event handler for Black RadioButton
19        private void blackRadioButton_CheckedChanged(
20           object sender, EventArgs e)
21        {
22           displayLabel.ForeColor = Color.Black; // change color to black
23        }
24
25        // event handler for Red RadioButton
26        private void redRadioButton_CheckedChanged(
27           object sender, EventArgs e)
28        {
29           displayLabel.ForeColor = Color.Red; // change color to red
30        }
31
32        // event handler for Green RadioButton
33        private void greenRadioButton_CheckedChanged(
34           object sender, EventArgs e)
35        {
36           displayLabel.ForeColor = Color.Green; // change color to green
37        }
38
39        // event handler for 12 point RadioButton
40        private void size12RadioButton_CheckedChanged(
41           object sender, EventArgs e)
42        {
43           // change font size to 12
44           displayLabel.Font = new Font(displayLabel.Font.Name, 12);
45        }
46
```

Fig. 15.36 | Using TabControl to display various font settings. (Part 1 of 2.)

```
47        // event handler for 16 point RadioButton
48        private void size16RadioButton_CheckedChanged(
49           object sender, EventArgs e)
50        {
51           // change font size to 16
52           displayLabel.Font = new Font(displayLabel.Font.Name, 16);
53        }
54
55        // event handler for 20 point RadioButton
56        private void size20RadioButton_CheckedChanged(
57           object sender, EventArgs e)
58        {
59           // change font size to 20
60           displayLabel.Font = new Font(displayLabel.Font.Name, 20);
61        }
62
63        // event handler for Hello! RadioButton
64        private void helloRadioButton_CheckedChanged(
65           object sender, EventArgs e)
66        {
67           displayLabel.Text = "Hello!"; // change text to Hello!
68        }
69
70        // event handler for Goodbye! RadioButton
71        private void goodbyeRadioButton_CheckedChanged(
72           object sender, EventArgs e)
73        {
74           displayLabel.Text = "Goodbye!"; // change text to Goodbye!
75        }
76     }
77  }
```

a) Selecting the **Red** RadioButton from the **Color** tab

b) Selecting the **20 Point** RadioButton from the **Size** tab

c) Selecting the **Goodbye!** RadioButton from the **Message** tab

d) Selecting the **About** tab

Fig. 15.36 | Using TabControl to display various font settings. (Part 2 of 2.)

The textOptionsTabControl and the colorTabPage, sizeTabPage, messageTabPage and aboutTabPage are created in the designer (as described previously):

- The colorTabPage contains three RadioButtons for the colors black (blackRadioButton), red (redRadioButton) and green (greenRadioButton). This TabPage is displayed in Fig. 15.36(a). The CheckedChanged event handler for each RadioButton updates the color of the text in displayLabel (lines 22, 29 and 36).

- The sizeTabPage (Fig. 15.36(b)) has three RadioButtons, corresponding to font sizes 12 (size12RadioButton), 16 (size16RadioButton) and 20 (size20RadioButton), which change the font size of displayLabel—lines 44, 52 and 60, respectively.

- The messageTabPage (Fig. 15.36(c)) contains two RadioButtons for the messages **Hello!** (helloRadioButton) and **Goodbye!** (goodbyeRadioButton). The two RadioButtons determine the text on displayLabel (lines 67 and 74, respectively).

- The aboutTabPage (Fig. 15.36(d)) contains a Label (messageLabel) describing the purpose of TabControls.

Software Engineering Observation 15.3

A TabPage can act as a container for a single logical group of RadioButtons, enforcing their mutual exclusivity. To place multiple RadioButton groups inside a single TabPage, you should group RadioButtons within Panels or GroupBoxes contained within the TabPage.

15.12 Multiple Document Interface (MDI) Windows

In previous chapters, we have built only single document interface (SDI) apps. Such programs (including Microsoft's Notepad and Paint) typically have one window that displays a single document at a time. To edit *multiple* documents, you must execute separate instances of the app.

Many complex apps are multiple document interface (MDI) programs, which allow users to edit multiple documents at once (e.g., Microsoft Office products). MDI programs also tend to be more complex—Paint Shop Pro and Photoshop have a greater number of image-editing features than does Paint.

An MDI program's main window is called the parent window, and each window inside the app is referred to as a child window. Although an MDI app can have many child windows, each child has only one parent window. Furthermore, a maximum of one child window can be active at once. Child windows cannot be parents themselves and cannot be moved outside their parent. Otherwise, a child window behaves like any other window (with regard to closing, minimizing, resizing, and so on). A child window's functionality can differ from that of other child windows of the parent. For example, one child window might allow the user to edit images, another might allow the user to edit text and a third might display network traffic graphically, but all could belong to the same MDI parent. Figure 15.37 depicts a sample MDI app with two child windows.

Fig. 15.37 | MDI parent window and MDI child windows.

To create an MDI Form, set a Form's `IsMdiContainer` property to `true`. The Form changes appearance, as in Fig. 15.38. Next, create a child Form class to be added to the Form. To do this, right click the project in the **Solution Explorer**, select **Project > Add Windows Form...** and name the file. Edit the Form as you like. To add the child Form to the parent, we must create a new child Form object, set its `MdiParent` property to the parent Form and call the child Form's Show method. In general, to add a child Form to a parent, write

```
ChildFormClass childForm = New ChildFormClass();
childForm.MdiParent = parentForm;
childForm.Show();
```

Fig. 15.38 | SDI and MDI forms.

In most cases, the parent Form creates the child, so the *parentForm* reference is `this`. The code to create a child usually lies inside an event handler, which creates a new window in response to a user action. Menu selections (such as **File**, followed by a submenu option of **New**, followed by a submenu option of **Window**) are common techniques for creating new child windows.

Class Form property `MdiChildren` returns an array of child Form references. This is useful if the parent window wants to check the status of all its children (for example, ensuring that all are saved before the parent closes). Property `ActiveMdiChild` returns a reference to the active child window; it returns `null` if there are no active child windows. Other features of MDI windows are described in Fig. 15.39.

MDI Form properties, a method and an event	Description
Common MDI Child Properties	
IsMdiChild	Indicates whether the Form is an MDI child. If true, Form is an MDI child (read-only property).
MdiParent	Specifies the MDI parent Form of the child.
Common MDI Parent Properties	
ActiveMdiChild	Returns the Form that's the currently active MDI child (returns null if no children are active).
IsMdiContainer	Indicates whether a Form can be an MDI parent. If true, the Form can be an MDI parent. The default value is false.
MdiChildren	Returns the MDI children as an array of Forms.
Common Method	
LayoutMdi	Determines the display of child forms on an MDI parent. The method takes as a parameter an MdiLayout enumeration with possible values ArrangeIcons, Cascade, TileHorizontal and TileVertical. Figure 15.42 depicts the effects of these values.
Common Event	
MdiChildActivate	Generated when an MDI child is closed or activated.

Fig. 15.39 | MDI Form properties, a method and an event.

Child windows can be minimized, maximized and closed independently of the parent window. Figure 15.40 shows two images: one containing two minimized child windows and a second containing a maximized child window. When the parent is minimized or closed, the child windows are minimized or closed as well.

Parent window icons: minimize, maximize and close

Maximized child window icons: minimize, restore and close

Minimized child window icons: restore, maximize and close

Parent title bar indicates maximized child

Fig. 15.40 | Minimized and maximized child windows.

Note the title bar in Fig. 15.40(b) is **Form1 - [Child1]**. When a child window is maximized, its title-bar text is inserted into the parent window's title bar. When a child window is minimized or maximized, its title bar displays a restore icon, which can be used to return the child window to its previous size (its size before it was minimized or maximized).

C# provides a property that helps track which child windows are open in an MDI container. Property `MdiWindowListItem` of class `MenuStrip` specifies which menu, if any, displays a list of open child windows that the user can select to bring the corresponding window to the foreground. When a new child window is opened, an entry is added to the end of the list (Fig. 15.41). If ten or more child windows are open, the list includes the option **More Windows...**, which allows the user to select a window from a list in a dialog.

Good Programming Practice 15.1

In an MDI app, include a menu that displays a list of the open child windows. This helps the user select a child window quickly.

MDI containers allow you to organize the placement of its child windows. The child windows in an MDI app can be arranged by calling method `LayoutMdi` of the parent `Form`. Method `LayoutMdi` takes an `MdiLayout` enumeration, which can have values `ArrangeIcons`, `Cascade`, `TileHorizontal` and `TileVertical`. Tiled windows completely fill the parent and do *not* overlap; such windows can be arranged horizontally (value `TileHorizontal`) or vertically (value `TileVertical`). Cascaded windows (value `Cascade`) overlap—each is the same size and displays a visible title bar, if possible. Value `ArrangeIcons` arranges the icons for any minimized child windows. If minimized windows are scattered around the parent window, value `ArrangeIcons` orders them neatly at the bottom-left corner of the parent window. Figure 15.42 illustrates the values of the `MdiLayout` enumeration.

Fig. 15.41 | MenuStrip property MdiWindowListItem example.

Class `UsingMDIForm` (Fig. 15.43) demonstrates MDI windows. Class `UsingMDIForm` uses three instances of child `Form` `ChildForm` (Fig. 15.44), each containing a `PictureBox` that displays an image. The parent MDI `Form` contains a menu enabling users to create and arrange child `Forms`.

Fig. 15.42 | MdiLayout enumeration values.

MDI Parent *Form*

Figure 15.43 presents class UsingMDIForm—the app's MDI parent Form. This Form, which is created first, contains two top-level menus. The first of these menus, **File** (fileToolStripMenuItem), contains both an **Exit** item (exitToolStripMenuItem) and a **New** submenu (newToolStripMenuItem) consisting of items for each type of child window. The second menu, **Window** (windowToolStripMenuItem), provides options for laying out the MDI children, plus a list of the active MDI children.

```
 1  // Fig. 15.43: UsingMDIForm.cs
 2  // Demonstrating an MDI parent and MDI child windows.
 3  using System;
 4  using System.Windows.Forms;
 5
 6  namespace UsingMDI
 7  {
 8     // Form demonstrates the use of MDI parent and child windows
 9     public partial class UsingMDIForm : Form
10     {
11        // constructor
12        public UsingMDIForm()
13        {
14           InitializeComponent();
15        }
16
```

Fig. 15.43 | · Demonstrating an MDI parent and MDI child windows. (Part 1 of 3.)

```
17      // create Lavender Flowers image window
18      private void lavenderToolStripMenuItem_Click(
19          object sender, EventArgs e)
20      {
21          // create new child
22          var child = new ChildForm(
23              "Lavender Flowers", "lavenderflowers");
24          child.MdiParent = this; // set parent
25          child.Show(); // display child
26      }
27
28      // create Purple Flowers image window
29      private void purpleToolStripMenuItem_Click(
30          object sender, EventArgs e)
31      {
32          // create new child
33          var child = new ChildForm(
34              "Purple Flowers", "purpleflowers");
35          child.MdiParent = this; // set parent
36          child.Show(); // display child
37      }
38
39      // create Yellow Flowers image window
40      private void yellowToolStripMenuItem_Click(
41          object sender, EventArgs e)
42      {
43          // create new child
44          var child = new ChildForm(
45              "Yellow Flowers", "yellowflowers");
46          child.MdiParent = this; // set parent
47          child.Show(); // display child
48      }
49
50      // exit app
51      private void exitToolStripMenuItem_Click(
52          object sender, EventArgs e)
53      {
54          Application.Exit();
55      }
56
57      // set Cascade layout
58      private void cascadeToolStripMenuItem_Click(
59          object sender, EventArgs e)
60      {
61          this.LayoutMdi(MdiLayout.Cascade);
62      }
63
64      // set TileHorizontal layout
65      private void tileHorizontalToolStripMenuItem_Click(
66          object sender, EventArgs e)
67      {
68          this.LayoutMdi(MdiLayout.TileHorizontal);
69      }
```

Fig. 15.43 | Demonstrating an MDI parent and MDI child windows. (Part 2 of 3.)

```
70
71          // set TileVertical layout
72          private void tileVerticalToolStripMenuItem_Click(
73             object sender, EventArgs e)
74          {
75             this.LayoutMdi(MdiLayout.TileVertical);
76          }
77       }
78    }
```

a) Selecting the **Lavender Flowers** menu item

b) **Lavender Flowers** ChildForm window displayed

c) Selecting the **Cascade** menu item

d) Cascaded child windows in an MDI window

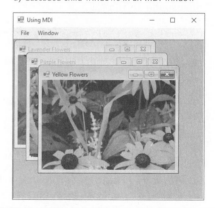

Fig. 15.43 | Demonstrating an MDI parent and MDI child windows. (Part 3 of 3.)

In the **Properties** window, we set the Form's IsMdiContainer property to true, making the Form an MDI parent. In addition, we set the MenuStrip's MdiWindowListItem property to windowToolStripMenuItem. This enables the **Window** menu to contain the list of child MDI windows.

The **Cascade** menu item (cascadeToolStripMenuItem) has an event handler (cascadeToolStripMenuItem_Click, lines 58–62) that arranges the child windows in a cascading manner. The event handler calls method LayoutMdi with the argument Cascade from the MdiLayout enumeration (line 61).

The **Tile Horizontal** menu item (tileHorizontalToolStripMenuItem) has an event handler (tileHorizontalToolStripMenuItem_Click, lines 65–69) that arranges the child windows in a horizontal manner. The event handler calls method LayoutMdi with the argument TileHorizontal from the MdiLayout enumeration (line 68).

Finally, the **Tile Vertical** menu item (tileVerticalToolStripMenuItem) has an event handler (tileVerticalToolStripMenuItem_Click, lines 72–76) that arranges the child windows in a vertical manner. The event handler calls method LayoutMdi with the argument TileVertical from the MdiLayout enumeration (line 75).

MDI Child *Form*

At this point, the app is still incomplete—we must define the MDI child class. To do this, right click the project in the **Solution Explorer** and select **Add > Windows Form....** Then name the new class in the dialog as ChildForm (Fig. 15.44). Next, we add a PictureBox (displayPictureBox) to ChildForm. In ChildForm's constructor, line 16 sets the title-bar text. Lines 19–21 retrieve the appropriate image resource, cast it to an Image and set displayPictureBox's Image property. The images that are used can be found in the Images subfolder of this chapter's examples directory.

```
 1   // Fig. 15.44: ChildForm.cs
 2   // Child window of MDI parent.
 3
 4   using System.Drawing;
 5   using System.Windows.Forms;
 6
 7   namespace UsingMDI
 8   {
 9      public partial class ChildForm : Form
10      {
11         public ChildForm(string title, string resourceName)
12         {
13            // Required for Windows Form Designer support
14            InitializeComponent();
15
16            Text = title; // set title text
17
18            // set image to display in PictureBox
19            displayPictureBox.Image =
20               (Image) (Properties.Resources.ResourceManager.GetObject(
21                  resourceName));
22         }
23      }
24   }
```

Fig. 15.44 | Child window of MDI parent.

After the MDI child class is defined, the parent MDI Form (Fig. 15.43) can create new child windows. The event handlers in lines 18–48 create a new child Form corresponding to the menu item clicked. Lines 22–23, 33–34 and 44–45 create new instances of Child-Form. Lines 24, 35 and 46 set each Child's MdiParent property to the parent Form. Lines 25, 36 and 47 call method Show to display each child Form.

15.13 Visual Inheritance

Chapter 11 discussed how to create classes via inheritance. We've also used inheritance to create Forms that display a GUI, by deriving our new Form classes from class System.Windows.Forms.Form. This is an example of visual inheritance. The derived Form class contains the functionality of its Form base class, including any base-class properties, methods, variables and controls. The derived class also inherits all visual aspects—such as sizing, component layout, spacing between GUI components, colors and fonts.

Visual inheritance enables you to achieve visual consistency. For example, you could define a base Form that contains a product's logo, a specific background color, a predefined menu bar and other elements. You then could use the base Form throughout an app for uniformity and branding. You also can create controls that inherit from other controls. For example, you might create a custom UserControl (discussed in Section 15.14) that's derived from an existing control.

*Creating a Base **Form***
Class VisualInheritanceBaseForm (Fig. 15.45) derives from Form. The output depicts how the Form works. The GUI contains two Labels with text **Bugs, Bugs, Bugs** and **Copyright 2017, by Deitel & Associates, Inc.**, as well as one Button displaying the text **Learn More**. When a user presses the **Learn More** Button, method learnMoreButton_Click (lines 18–24) is invoked. This method displays a MessageBox that provides some informative text.

```
1   // Fig. 15.45: VisualInheritanceBaseForm.cs
2   // Base Form for use with visual inheritance.
3   using System;
4   using System.Windows.Forms;
5
6   namespace VisualInheritanceBase
7   {
8      // base Form used to demonstrate visual inheritance
9      public partial class VisualInheritanceBaseForm : Form
10     {
11        // constructor
12        public VisualInheritanceBaseForm()
13        {
14           InitializeComponent();
15        }
16
17        // display MessageBox when Button is clicked
18        private void learnMoreButton_Click(object sender, EventArgs e)
19        {
20           MessageBox.Show(
21              "Bugs, Bugs, Bugs is a product of deitel.com",
22              "Learn More", MessageBoxButtons.OK,
23              MessageBoxIcon.Information);
24        }
25     }
26  }
```

Fig. 15.45 | Base Form for use with visual inheritance. (Part 1 of 2.)

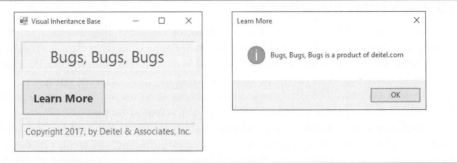

Fig. 15.45 | Base Form for use with visual inheritance. (Part 2 of 2.)

Steps for Declaring and Using a Reusable Class

Before a Form (or any class) can be used in multiple apps, it must be placed in a class library to make it reusable. The steps for creating a reusable class are:

1. Declare a public class. If the class is not public, it can be used only by other classes in the same assembly—that is, compiled into the same DLL or EXE file.

2. Choose a namespace name and add a namespace declaration to the source-code file for the reusable class declaration.

3. Compile the class into a class library.

4. Add a reference to the class library in an app.

5. Use the class.

Let's take a look at these steps in the context of this example:

Step 1: Creating a **public** Class

For *Step 1* in this discussion, we use the public class VisualInheritanceBaseForm declared in Fig. 15.45. By default, every new Form class you create is declared as a public class.

Step 2: Adding the **namespace** Declaration

For *Step 2*, we use the namespace declaration that was created for us by the IDE. By default, every new class you define is placed in a namespace with the same name as the project. In almost every example in the text, we've seen that classes from preexisting libraries, such as the .NET Framework Class Library, can be imported into a C# app. Each class belongs to a namespace that contains a group of related classes. As apps become more complex, namespaces help you manage the complexity of app components. Class libraries and namespaces also facilitate software reuse by enabling apps to add classes from other namespaces (as we've done in many examples). We removed the namespace declarations in earlier chapters because they were not necessary.

Placing a class inside a namespace declaration indicates that the class is part of the specified namespace. The namespace name is part of the fully qualified class name, so the name of class VisualInheritanceTestForm is actually VisualInheritanceBase.VisualInheritanceBaseForm. You can use this fully qualified name in your apps, or you can write a using directive and use the class's simple name (the unqualified class name—VisualInheritanceBaseForm) in the app. If another namespace also contains a class with the same name, the fully qualified class names can be used to distinguish between the classes in the app and prevent a name conflict (also called a name collision).

Step 3: Compiling the Class Library

To allow other Forms to inherit from VisualInheritanceForm, we must package VisualInheritanceForm as a class library and compile it into a .dll file. Such as file is known as a dynamically linked library—a way to package classes that you can reference from other apps. Right click the project name in the **Solution Explorer** and select **Properties**, then choose the **Application** tab. In the **Output type** drop-down list, change **Windows Application** to **Class Library**. Building the project produces the .dll. You can configure a project to be a class library when you first create it by selecting the **Class Library** template in the **New Project** dialog. [*Note:* A class library cannot execute as a stand-alone app. The screen captures in Fig. 15.45 were taken before changing the project to a class library.]

Step 4: Adding a Reference to the Class Library

Once the class is compiled and stored in the class library file, the library can be referenced from any app by indicating to Visual Studio where to find the class library file. To visually inherit from VisualInheritanceBaseForm, first create a new Windows app. Right click the **References** node in the **Solution Explorer** window and select **Add Reference...** from the pop-up menu that appears. The dialog box that appears will contain a list of class libraries from the .NET Framework. Some class libraries, like the one containing the System namespace, are so common that they're added to your app by the IDE. The ones in this list are not.

In the **Reference Manager** dialog box, click **Browse** then click the **Browse...** button. When you build a class library, Visual C# places the .dll file in the project's bin\Debug or bin\Release folder, depending on whether the **Solution Configurations** drop-down list in the IDE's toolbar is set to **Debug** or **Release**. In the **Browse** tab, you can navigate to the directory containing the class library file you created in *Step 3*, as shown in Fig. 15.46. Select the .dll file and click **Add**.

Fig. 15.46 | Using the **Reference Manager** dialog to browse for a DLL. (Part 1 of 2.)

Fig. 15.46 | Using the **Reference Manager** dialog to browse for a DLL. (Part 2 of 2.)

Step 5: Using the Class—Deriving from a Base Form

Open the file that defines the new app's GUI and modify the line that defines the class to indicate that the app's Form should inherit from class VisualInheritanceBaseForm. The class-declaration line should now appear as follows:

```
public partial class VisualInheritanceTestForm :
    VisualInheritanceBase.VisualInheritanceBaseForm
```

Unless you specify namespace VisualInheritanceBase in a using directive, you must use the fully qualified name VisualInheritanceBase.VisualInheritanceBaseForm. In **Design** view, the new app's Form should now display the controls inherited from the base Form (Fig. 15.47). We can now add more components to the Form.

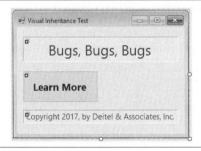

Fig. 15.47 | Form demonstrating visual inheritance.

Class VisualInheritanceTestForm

Class VisualInheritanceTestForm (Fig. 15.48) is a derived class of VisualInheritance-BaseForm. The output illustrates the functionality of the program. The components, their layouts and the functionality of base class VisualInheritanceBaseForm (Fig. 15.45) are inherited by VisualInheritanceTestForm. We added an additional Button with text **About this Program**. When a user presses this Button, method aboutButton_Click (Fig. 15.48, lines 19–25) is invoked. This method displays another MessageBox providing different informative text (lines 21–24).

```
1    // Fig. 15.48: VisualInheritanceTestForm.cs
2    // Derived Form using visual inheritance.
3    using System;
4    using System.Windows.Forms;
5
6    namespace VisualInheritanceTest
7    {
8       // derived form using visual inheritance
9       public partial class VisualInheritanceTestForm :
10         VisualInheritanceBase.VisualInheritanceBaseForm
11      {
12         // constructor
13         public VisualInheritanceTestForm()
14         {
15            InitializeComponent();
16         }
17
18         // display MessageBox when Button is clicked
19         private void aboutButton_Click(object sender, EventArgs e)
20         {
21            MessageBox.Show(
22               "This program was created by Deitel & Associates.",
23               "About This Program", MessageBoxButtons.OK,
24               MessageBoxIcon.Information);
25         }
26      }
27   }
```

Fig. 15.48 | Derived Form using visual inheritance.

If a user clicks the **Learn More** button, the event is handled by the base-class event handler learnMoreButton_Click. Because VisualInheritanceBaseForm uses a private access modifier to declare its controls, VisualInheritanceTestForm cannot modify the controls inherited from class VisualInheritanceBaseForm visually or programmatically. The IDE displays a small icon at the top left of the visually inherited controls to indicate that they're inherited and cannot be altered.

15.14 User-Defined Controls

The .NET Framework allows you to create custom controls. These custom controls appear in the user's **Toolbox** and can be added to Forms, Panels or GroupBoxes in the same way that we add Buttons, Labels and other predefined controls. The simplest way to create a custom control is to derive a class from an existing control, such as a Label. This is useful if you want to add functionality to an existing control, rather than replacing it with one that provides the desired functionality. For example, you can create a new type of Label that behaves like a normal Label but has a different appearance. You accomplish this by inheriting from class Label and overriding method OnPaint.

Method OnPaint

All controls have an OnPaint method, which the system calls when a component must be redrawn (such as when the component is resized). The method receives a PaintEventArgs object, which contains graphics information—property Graphics is the graphics object used to draw, and property ClipRectangle defines the rectangular boundary of the control. Whenever the system raises a Paint event to draw the control on the screen, the control catches the event and calls its OnPaint method. The base class's OnPaint should be called explicitly from an overridden OnPaint implementation before executing custom-paint code. In most cases, you want to do this to ensure that the original painting code executes in addition to the code you define in the custom control's class.

Creating New Controls

To create a new control composed of existing controls, use class UserControl. Controls added to a custom control are called constituent controls. For example, a programmer could create a UserControl composed of a Button, a Label and a TextBox, each associated with some functionality (for example, the Button setting the Label's text to that contained in the TextBox). The UserControl acts as a container for the controls added to it. The UserControl contains constituent controls, but it does not determine how these constituent controls are displayed. To control the appearance of each constituent control, you can handle each control's Paint event or override OnPaint. Both the Paint event handler and OnPaint are passed a PaintEventArgs object, which can be used to draw graphics (lines, rectangles, and so on) on the constituent controls.

Using another technique, a programmer can create a brand-new control by inheriting from class Control. This class does not define any specific behavior; that's left to you. Instead, class Control handles the items associated with all controls, such as events and sizing handles. Method OnPaint should contain a call to the base class's OnPaint method, which calls the Paint event handlers. You add code that draws custom graphics inside the overridden OnPaint method. This technique allows for the greatest flexibility but also requires the most planning. All three approaches are summarized in Fig. 15.49.

Custom-control techniques and PaintEventArgs properties	Description
Custom-Control Techniques	
Inherit from a Windows Forms control	You can do this to add functionality to a preexisting control. If you override method OnPaint, call the base class's OnPaint method. You only can add to the original control's appearance, not redesign it.
Create a UserControl	You can create a UserControl composed of multiple preexisting controls (e.g., to combine their functionality). You place drawing code in a Paint event handler or overridden OnPaint method.
Inherit from class Control	Define a brand new control. Override method OnPaint, then call base-class method OnPaint and add the code to draw the control. With this method you can customize both control appearance and functionality.
PaintEventArgs Properties	
Graphics	The control's graphics object, which is used to draw on the control.
ClipRectangle	Specifies the rectangle indicating the boundary of the control.

Fig. 15.49 | Custom-control creation.

Clock Control

We create a "clock" control in Fig. 15.50. This is a UserControl composed of a Label and a Timer—whenever the Timer raises an event (once per second in this example), the Label is updated to reflect the current time.

```
1   // Fig. 15.50: ClockUserControl.cs
2   // User-defined control with a Timer and a Label.
3   using System;
4   using System.Windows.Forms;
5
6   namespace ClockExample
7   {
8      // UserControl that displays the time on a Label
9      public partial class ClockUserControl : UserControl
10     {
11        // constructor
12        public ClockUserControl()
13        {
14           InitializeComponent();
15        }
```

Fig. 15.50 | User-defined control with a Timer and a Label. (Part 1 of 2.)

```
16
17          // update Label at every tick
18          private void clockTimer_Tick(object sender, EventArgs e)
19          {
20              // get current time (Now), convert to string
21              displayLabel.Text = DateTime.Now.ToLongTimeString();
22          }
23      }
24  }
```

Fig. 15.50 | User-defined control with a `Timer` and a `Label`. (Part 2 of 2.)

Timers

`Timers` (`System.Windows.Forms` namespace) are non-visual components that generate `Tick` events at a set interval. This interval is set by the `Timer`'s `Interval` property, which defines the number of milliseconds (thousandths of a second) between events. By default, timers are disabled and do not generate events.

Adding a User Control

This app contains a user control (`ClockUserControl`) and a `Form` that displays the user control. Create a Windows app, then create a `UserControl` class by selecting **Project > Add User Control…**. This displays a dialog from which we can select the type of item to add—user controls are already selected. We then name the file (and the class) `ClockUserControl`. Our empty `ClockUserControl` is displayed as a grey rectangle.

Designing the User Control

You can treat this control like a Windows `Form`, meaning that you can add controls using the **ToolBox** and set properties using the **Properties** window. However, instead of creating an app, you're simply creating a new control composed of other controls. Add a `Label` (`displayLabel`) and a `Timer` (`clockTimer`) to the `UserControl`. Set the `Timer` interval to 1000 milliseconds and set `displayLabel`'s text with each `Tick` event (lines 18–22; the default event). To generate events, `clockTimer` must be enabled by setting property `Enabled` to `true` in the **Properties** window.

Structure `DateTime` (namespace `System`) contains property `Now`, which returns the current time. Method `ToLongTimeString` converts `Now` to a `string` containing the current hour, minute and second (along with AM or PM, depending on your locale). We use this to set the time in `displayLabel` in line 21.

Once created, our clock control appears as an item in the **ToolBox** in the section titled *ProjectName* **Components**, where *ProjectName* is your project's name. *You may need to switch to the app's Form before the item appears in the **ToolBox**.* To use the control, simply drag it to the `Form` and run the Windows app. We gave the `ClockUserControl` object a white background to make it stand out in the Form. Figure 15.50 shows the output of Clock, which contains our ClockUserControl. There are no event handlers in Clock, so we show only the code for ClockUserControl.

Sharing Custom Controls with Other Developers

Visual Studio allows you to share custom controls with other developers. To create a User-Control that can be exported to other solutions, do the following:

1. Create a new **Class Library** project.

2. Delete Class1.cs, initially provided with the app.

3. Right click the project in the **Solution Explorer** and select **Add > User Control....** In the dialog that appears, name the user-control file and click **Add**.

4. Inside the project, add controls and functionality to the UserControl (Fig. 15.51).

Fig. 15.51 | Custom-control creation.

5. Build the project. Visual Studio creates a .dll file for the UserControl in the output directory (bin/Debug or bin/Release). The file is not executable; class libraries are used to define classes that are reused in other executable apps. You can give the .dll file to other developers and they can follow *Steps* 6 and 7.

6. Create a new Windows app.

7. In the new Windows app, right click the **ToolBox** and select **Choose Items....** In the **Choose Toolbox Items** dialog that appears, click **Browse....** Browse for the .dll file from the class library created in *Steps 1–5*. The item will then appear in the **.NET Framework Components** tab of the **Choose Toolbox Items** dialog. If it's not already checked, check this item. Click **OK** to add the item to the **Toolbox**. This control can now be added to the Form as if it were any other control.

15.15 Wrap-Up

Many of today's commercial apps provide GUIs that are easy to use and manipulate. Because of this demand for user-friendly GUIs, the ability to design sophisticated GUIs is an essential programming skill. Visual Studio's IDE makes GUI development quick and easy. In Chapters 14 and 15, we presented basic Windows Forms GUI development techniques. In Chapter 15, we demonstrated how to create menus, which provide users easy access to an app's functionality. You learned the DateTimePicker and MonthCalendar controls, which allow users to input date and time values. We demonstrated LinkLabels, which are used to link the user to an app or a web page. You used several controls that provide lists of data to the user—ListBoxes, CheckedListBoxes and ListViews. We used the ComboBox control to create drop-down lists, and the TreeView control to display data in hierarchical form. We then introduced complex GUIs that use tabbed windows and multiple document interfaces. The chapter concluded with demonstrations of visual inheritance and creating custom controls. In Chapter 16, we introduce string and character processing.

Summary

Section 15.2 Menus
- Menus provide groups of related commands for Windows Forms apps.
- An expanded menu lists menu items and submenus.
- A menu that contains a menu item is called that menu item's parent menu. A menu item that contains a submenu is considered to be the parent of that submenu.
- All menus and menu items can have shortcut keys.
- Some menu items display checkmarks, indicating that multiple options on the menu can be selected at once.
- The MenuStrip control is used to create menus in a GUI.
- Top-level menus and their menu items are represented using type ToolStripMenuItem.
- To create an access shortcut, type an ampersand (&) before the character to be underlined.
- To add other shortcut keys, set the ShortcutKeys property of the ToolStripMenuItem.
- You can hide shortcut keys by setting property ShowShortcutKeys to false. You can modify how shortcut keys are displayed in the menu item by modifying property ShortcutKeyDisplayString.
- A menu item's Checked property is used to display a check to the left of the menu item.

Section 15.3 MonthCalendar Control
- The MonthCalendar control displays a monthly calendar.
- The user can select a date from the currently displayed month or navigate to another month.
- A MonthCalendar's DateChanged event occurs when a new date is selected.

Section 15.4 DateTimePicker Control
- The DateTimePicker control can be used to retrieve date and/or time information from the user.
- Property Format of class DateTimePicker specifies the user's selection options.
- The DateTimePicker's ValueChanged event is raised when the selected value is changed.

Section 15.5 LinkLabel Control
- The LinkLabel control displays links to other resources, such as files or web pages.
- A LinkLabel appears as underlined text (colored blue by default). When the mouse moves over the link, the pointer changes to a hand; this is similar to a hyperlink in a web page.
- The link can change color to indicate whether the link is new, previously visited or active.
- When clicked, the LinkLabel generates a LinkClicked event.

Section 15.6 ListBox Control
- The ListBox control allows the user to view and select items in a list.

- ListBox property SelectionMode determines the number of items that can be selected.
- The SelectedIndexChanged event of class ListBox occurs when the user selects a new item.
- Property Items returns all the list items as a collection.
- Property SelectedItem returns the currently selected item.
- Use method Add to add an item to the ListBox's Items collection.
- You can add items to ListBoxes and CheckedListBoxes visually by using the Items property in the **Properties** window.

Section 15.7 CheckedListBox Control
- The CheckedListBox control extends a ListBox by including a checkbox next to each item.
- Items can be added via methods Add and AddRange or through the **String Collection Editor**.
- CheckedListBoxes imply that multiple items can be checked.
- CheckedListBox event ItemCheck occurs when a user checks or unchecks a CheckedListBox item.

Section 15.8 ComboBox Control
- The ComboBox control combines TextBox features with a drop-down list.
- Property MaxDropDownItems specifies the maximum number of items that can display at one time.
- You can add objects to collection Items programmatically, using methods Add and AddRange, or visually, with the **String Collection Editor**.
- Property DropDownStyle determines the type of ComboBox and is represented as a value of the ComboBoxStyle enumeration, which contains values Simple, DropDown and DropDownList.
- There can be at most one selected item in a ComboBox (if none, then SelectedIndex is -1).
- When the selected item changes in a ComboBox, a SelectedIndexChanged event occurs.

Section 15.9 TreeView Control
- The TreeView control displays nodes hierarchically in a tree.
- Traditionally, nodes are objects that contain values and can refer to other nodes.
- A parent node contains child nodes, and the child nodes can be parents to other nodes.
- Two child nodes that have the same parent node are considered sibling nodes.
- A tree is a collection of nodes, usually organized in a hierarchical manner. The first parent node of a tree is a root node—there can be multiple root nodes.
- TreeView controls are useful for displaying hierarchical information.
- In a TreeView, a parent node can be expanded or collapsed by clicking the plus box or minus box to its left. Nodes without children do not have these boxes.
- The nodes displayed in a TreeView are instances of class TreeNode.
- Each TreeNode has a Nodes collection (type TreeNodeCollection), containing a list of TreeNodes.
- To add nodes to a TreeView visually, click the ellipsis next to property Nodes in the **Properties** window. This opens the **TreeNode Editor**, which displays an empty tree representing the TreeView.
- To add nodes programmatically, you must create a root TreeNode object and pass it a string to display. Then call method Add to add this new TreeNode to the TreeView's Nodes collection.

Section 15.10 ListView Control
- The ListView control is similar to a ListBox in that both display lists from which the user can select one or more items. ListView is more flexible and can display items in different formats.

- Property MultiSelect (a bool) determines whether multiple items can be selected.
- To display images, an ImageList component is required.
- Property SmallImageList of class ListView sets the ImageList for the small icons.
- Property LargeImageList of class ListView sets the ImageList for large icons.
- The items in a ListView are each of type ListViewItem.

Section 15.11 *TabControl Control*
- The TabControl control creates tabbed windows.
- TabControls contain TabPage objects. Only one TabPage is displayed at a time.
- You can add TabControls visually by dragging and dropping them on a Form in **Design** mode.
- To add TabPages in **Design** mode, open the TabControl's smart tasks menu and click **Add Tab**, or click the TabPages property in the **Properties** window, and add tabs in the dialog that appears.
- Each TabPage raises a Click event when its tab is clicked.

Section 15.12 *Multiple Document Interface (MDI) Windows*
- The app window of a multiple document interface (MDI) program is called the parent window, and each window inside the app is referred to as a child window.
- Child windows cannot be parents themselves and cannot be moved outside their parent.
- To create an MDI Form, create a new Form and set its IsMdiContainer property to true.
- To add a child Form to the parent, create a new child Form object, set its MdiParent property to the parent Form and call the child Form's Show method.
- Property MdiWindowListItem of class MenuStrip specifies which menu, if any, displays a list of open child windows.
- MDI containers allow you to organize the placement of child windows. The child windows in an MDI app can be arranged by calling method LayoutMdi of the parent Form.

Section 15.13 *Visual Inheritance*
- Visual inheritance allows you to create a new Form by inheriting from an existing Form. The derived Form class contains the functionality of its base class.
- Visual inheritance also can be applied with other controls as well.
- Visual inheritance enables you to achieve visual consistency across apps by reusing code.
- A reusable class is typically placed in a class library.
- When you compile a class library, the compiler will create a .dll file, known as a dynamically linked library—a way to package classes that you can reference from other apps.

Section 15.14 *User-Defined Controls*
- The .NET Framework allows you to create custom controls.
- Custom controls can appear in the user's **Toolbox** and can be added to Forms, Panels or GroupBoxes in the same way that Buttons, Labels and other predefined controls are added.
- The simplest way to create a custom control is to derive a class from an existing control, such as a Label. This is useful if you want to add functionality to an existing control, rather than replacing it with one that provides the desired functionality.
- To create a new control composed of existing controls, use class UserControl.
- Controls added to a custom control are called constituent controls.

- A programmer can create a brand-new control by inheriting from class Control. This class does not define any specific behavior; that task is left to you.
- Timers are non-visual components that generate Tick events at a set interval. This interval is set by the Timer's Interval property, which defines the number of milliseconds (thousandths of a second) between events. Timers are disabled by default.

Terminology

access shortcut
Activation property of class ListView
ActiveMdiChild property of class Form
AddDays method of struct DateTime
AddYears method of struct DateTime
Application class
cascaded window
CheckBoxes property of class ListView
Checked property of class ToolStripMenuItem
CheckedListBox class
child node
child window
Clear method of class Graphics
Click event of class ToolStripMenuItem
ClipRectangle property of class
    PaintEventArgs
ComboBox class
ComboBoxStyle enumeration
constituent controls
CustomFormat property of class DateTimePicker
Date property of struct DateTime
DateChanged event of class MonthCalendar
DateTime struct
DateTimePicker class
DateTimePickerFormat enumeration
DayOfWeek enumeration
DayOfWeek property of struct DateTime
DirectoryInfo class
.dll file
DrawEllipse method of class Graphics
DrawPie method of class Graphics
DrawRectangle method of class Graphics
DropDownStyle property of class ComboBox
dynamically linked library
Exists method of class Directory
Exit method of class Application
FileInfo class
FillEllipse method of class Graphics
FillPie method of class Graphics
FillRectangle method of class Graphics
Format property of class DateTimePicker
FullName property of class DirectoryInfo

FullName property of class FileInfo
GetDirectories method of class DirectoryInfo
GetFiles method of class DirectoryInfo
GetSelected method of class ListBox
Graphics property of class PaintEventArgs
hotkey
ImageIndex property of class ListViewItem
ImageList class
Images property of class ImageList
Interval property of class Timer
IsMdiContainer property of class Form
ItemCheck event of class CheckedListBox
Items property of class ComboBox
Items property of class ListBox
keyboard shortcut
LargeImageList property of class ListView
LinkLabel class
ListBox class
ListView class
ListViewItem class
MaxDate property of class DateTimePicker
MaxDropDownItems property of class ComboBox
MdiChildren property of class Form
MdiParent property of class Form
MdiWindowListItem property of class MenuStrip
MenuStrip class
MinDate property of class DateTimePicker
MonthCalendar class
multiple document interface (MDI)
MultiSelect property of class ListView
Name property of class DirectoryInfo
Name property of class FileInfo
node
Nodes collection
Now property of struct DateTime
ObjectCollection class
OnPaint method of class Control
PaintEventArgs class
parent node
Parent property of class DirectoryInfo
parent window
Path class

Self-Review Exercises

15.1 State whether each of the following is *true* or *false*. If *false*, explain why.

a) Menus provide groups of related classes.

b) Menu items can display ComboBoxes, checkmarks and access shortcuts.

c) The ListBox control allows only single selection (like a RadioButton).

d) A ComboBox control typically has a drop-down list.

e) Deleting a parent node in a TreeView control deletes its child nodes.

f) The user can select only one item in a ListView control.

g) A TabPage can act as a container for RadioButtons.

h) An MDI child window can have MDI children.

i) MDI child windows can be moved outside the boundaries of their parent window.

j) There are two basic ways to create a customized control.

15.2 Fill in the blanks in each of the following statements:

a) Method _____ of class Process can open files and web pages, similar to the **Run...** command in Windows.

b) If more elements appear in a ComboBox than can fit, a(n) _____ appears.

c) The top-level node in a TreeView is the _____ node.

d) A(n) _____ and a(n) _____ can display icons contained in an ImageList control.

e) The _____ property allows a menu to display a list of active child windows.

f) Class _____ allows you to combine several controls into a single custom control.

g) The _____ saves space by layering TabPages on top of each other.

h) The _____ window layout option makes all MDI windows the same size and layers them so every title bar is visible (if possible).

i) _____ are typically used to display hyperlinks to other resources, files or web pages.

Answers to Self-Review Exercises

15.1 a) False. Menus provide groups of related commands. b) True. c) False. It can have single or multiple selection. d) True. e) True. f) False. The user can select one or more items. g) True. h) False. Only an MDI parent window can have MDI children. An MDI parent window cannot be an MDI child. i) False. MDI child windows cannot be moved outside their parent window. j) False. There are three ways: 1) Derive from an existing control, 2) use a UserControl or 3) derive from Control and create a control from scratch.

15.2 a) Start. b) scrollbar. c) root. d) ListView, TreeView. e) MdiWindowListItem. f) UserControl. g) TabControl. h) Cascade. i) LinkLabels.

Exercises

15.3 *(Using ComboBoxes)* Write an app that displays the names of 15 states in a ComboBox. When an item is selected from the ComboBox, remove it.

15.4 *(Using ComboBoxes and ListBoxes)* Modify your solution to the previous exercise to add a ListBox. When the user selects an item from the ComboBox, remove the item from the ComboBox and add it to the ListBox. Your program should check to ensure that the ComboBox contains at least one item. If it does not, display a message, using a message box, then terminate program execution when the user dismisses the message box.

15.5 *(Sorting Strings)* Write an app that allows the user to enter strings in a TextBox. Each string input is added to a ListBox. As each string is added to the ListBox, ensure that the strings are in sorted order. [*Note:* Use property Sorted.]

15.6 *(File Browser)* Create a file browser (similar to Windows Explorer) based on the programs in Figs. 15.14, 15.28 and 15.31. The file browser should have a TreeView, which allows the user to browse directories. There should also be a ListView, which displays the contents (all subdirectories and files) of the directory being browsed. Double clicking a file in the ListView should open it, and double clicking a directory in either the ListView or the TreeView should browse it. If a file or directory cannot be accessed because of its permission settings, notify the user.

15.7 *(MDI Text Editor)* Create an MDI text editor. Each child window should contain a multi-line RichTextBox. The MDI parent should have a **Format** menu, with submenus to control the size, font and color of the text in the active child window. Each submenu should have at least three options. In addition, the parent should have a **File** menu, with menu items **New** (create a new child), **Close** (close the active child) and **Exit** (exit the app). The parent should have a **Window** menu to display a list of the open child windows and their layout options.

15.8 *(Login User Control)* Create a UserControl called LoginPasswordUserControl that contains a Label (loginLabel) that displays string "Login:", a TextBox (loginTextBox), where the user inputs a login name, a Label (passwordLabel) that displays the string "Password:" and, finally, a TextBox (passwordTextBox), where a user inputs a password (set property PasswordChar to "*" in the TextBox's **Properties** window). LoginPasswordUserControl must provide public read-only properties Login and Password that allow an app to retrieve the user input from loginTextBox and passwordTextBox. The UserControl must be exported to an app that displays the values input by the user in LoginPasswordUserControl.

15.9 *(Restaurant Bill Calculator)* A restaurant wants an app that calculates a table's bill. The app should display all the menu items from Fig. 15.52 in four ComboBoxes. Each ComboBox should contain a category of food offered by the restaurant (Beverage, Appetizer, Main Course and Dessert). The user can choose from one of these ComboBoxes to add an item to a table's bill. As each item is selected in the ComboBoxes, add the price of that item to the bill. The user can click the **Clear Bill** Button to restore the **Subtotal:**, **Tax:** and **Total:** fields to $0.00.

Name	Category	Price	Name	Category	Price
Soda	Beverage	$1.95	Chicken Alfredo	Main Course	$13.95
Tea	Beverage	$1.50	Chicken Picatta	Main Course	$13.95
Coffee	Beverage	$1.25	Turkey Club	Main Course	$11.95
Mineral Water	Beverage	$2.95	Lobster Pie	Main Course	$19.95
Juice	Beverage	$2.50	Prime Rib	Main Course	$20.95
Milk	Beverage	$1.50	Shrimp Scampi	Main Course	$18.95
Buffalo Wings	Appetizer	$5.95	Turkey Dinner	Main Course	$13.95
Buffalo Fingers	Appetizer	$6.95	Stuffed Chicken	Main Course	$14.95
Potato Skins	Appetizer	$8.95	Apple Pie	Dessert	$5.95
Nachos	Appetizer	$8.95	Sundae	Dessert	$3.95
Mushroom Caps	Appetizer	$10.95	Carrot Cake	Dessert	$5.95
Shrimp Cocktail	Appetizer	$12.95	Mud Pie	Dessert	$4.95
Chips and Salsa	Appetizer	$6.95	Apple Crisp	Dessert	$5.95
Seafood Alfredo	Main Course	$15.95			

Fig. 15.52 | Food items and prices.

15.10 *(Using TabPages)* Create an app that contains three TabPages. On the first TabPage, place a CheckedListBox with six items. On the second TabPage, place six TextBoxes. On the last TabPage, place six LinkLabels. The user's selections on the first TabPage should specify which of the six LinkLabels will be displayed. To hide or display a LinkLabel's value, use its Visible property. Use the second TabPage to modify the web page that's opened by the LinkLabels.

15.11 *(MDI Drawing Programs)* Create an MDI app with child windows that each have a Panel for drawing. Add menus to the MDI app that allow the user to modify the size and color of the paintbrush. When running this app, be aware that if one of the windows overlaps another, the Panel will be cleared.

Strings and Characters: A Deeper Look

Objectives

In this chapter you'll:

- Create and manipulate immutable character-string objects of class `string` and mutable character-string objects of class `StringBuilder`.

- Use various methods of classes `string` and `StringBuilder`.

- Manipulate character objects of `struct Char`.

- Use regular-expression classes `Regex` and `Match`.

16.1 Introduction

This chapter introduces the .NET Framework Class Library's string- and character-processing capabilities and demonstrates how to use regular expressions to search for patterns in text. The techniques it presents can be employed in most kinds of applications, and particularly in text editors, word processors, page-layout software, computerized typesetting systems and other kinds of text-processing software. Previous chapters presented some basic string-processing capabilities. Now we discuss in detail the text-processing capabilities of class string and type char from the System namespace and class StringBuilder from the System.Text namespace.

We begin with an overview of the fundamentals of characters and strings in which we discuss *character constants* and *string literals*. We then provide examples of class string's many constructors and methods. The examples demonstrate how to determine the *length* of strings, *copy* strings, *access individual characters* in strings, *search* strings, obtain *substrings* from larger strings, *compare* strings, *concatenate* strings, *replace characters* in strings and convert strings to uppercase or lowercase letters.

Next, we introduce class StringBuilder, which is used to assemble strings dynamically. We demonstrate StringBuilder capabilities for determining and specifying the *size* of a StringBuilder, as well as *appending*, *inserting*, *removing* and *replacing* characters in a StringBuilder object. We then introduce the character-testing methods of struct Char that enable a program to determine whether a character is a digit, a letter, a lowercase letter, an uppercase letter, a punctuation mark or a symbol other than a punctuation mark. Such methods are useful for validating individual characters in user input. In addition, type Char provides methods for *converting* a character to *uppercase or lowercase*.

We provide an online section that discusses *regular expressions*. We present classes Regex and Match from the System.Text.RegularExpressions namespace as well as the symbols that are used to form regular expressions. We then demonstrate how to *find patterns* in a string, *match entire strings to patterns*, *replace characters* in a string that match a pattern and *split strings* at delimiters specified as a pattern in a regular expression.

16.2 Fundamentals of Characters and Strings

Characters are the fundamental building blocks of C# source code. Every program is composed of characters that, when grouped together meaningfully, create a sequence that the compiler interprets as instructions describing how to accomplish a task. A program also can contain character constants. A character constant is a character that's represented as an integer value, called a *character code*. For example, the integer value 122 corresponds to the character constant 'z'. The integer value 10 corresponds to the newline character '\n'. Character constants are established according to the Unicode character set, an international character set that contains many more symbols and letters than does the ASCII character set (listed in Appendix C). To learn more about Unicode, see our online appendix.

A string is a series of characters treated as a unit. These characters can be uppercase letters, lowercase letters, digits and various special characters: +, -, *, /, $ and others. A string is an object of type string. Just as the C# keyword object is an alias for class Object, string is an alias for class String (namespace System). We write string literals, also called string constants, as sequences of characters in double quotation marks, as follows:

```
"John Q. Doe"
"9999 Main Street"
"Waltham, Massachusetts"
"(201) 555-1212"
```

A declaration can assign a string literal to a string reference. The declaration

```
string color = "blue";
```

initializes the string color to refer to the string literal object "blue".

Performance Tip 16.1

If there are multiple occurrences of the same string literal object in an app, a single copy of it will be referenced from each location in the program that uses that string literal. It's possible to share the object in this manner, because string literal objects are implicitly constant. Such sharing conserves memory.

Verbatim strings

Recall that *backslash characters* in strings introduce escape sequences and that placing a literal backslash in a string requires \\. On occasion, a string will contain multiple literal backslash characters (this often occurs in the name of a file). To avoid excessive backslashes, it's possible to exclude escape sequences and interpret all the characters in a string literally, using the @ character to create what's known as a verbatim string. Backslashes within the double quotation marks following the @ character are not considered to be part of escape sequences. Often this simplifies programming and makes the code easier to read.

For example, consider the string in the following assignment:

```
string file = "C:\\MyFolder\\MySubFolder\\MyFile.txt";
```

Using the *verbatim string syntax*, the assignment can be altered to

```
string file = @"C:\MyFolder\MySubFolder\MyFile.txt";
```

Verbatim strings may also span multiple lines, in which case they preserve all newlines, spaces and tabs between the opening @" and closing " delimiters.

16.3 `string` Constructors

Figure 16.1 demonstrates three of class `string`'s constructors.

```
 1   // Fig. 16.1: StringConstructor.cs
 2   // Demonstrating string class constructors.
 3   using System;
 4
 5   class StringConstructor
 6   {
 7      static void Main()
 8      {
 9         // string initialization
10         char[] characterArray =
11            {'b', 'i', 'r', 't', 'h', ' ', 'd', 'a', 'y'};
12         var originalString = "Welcome to C# programming!";
13         var string1 = originalString;
14         var string2 = new string(characterArray);
15         var string3 = new string(characterArray, 6, 3);
16         var string4 = new string('C', 5);
17
18         Console.WriteLine($"string1 = \"{string1}\"\n" +
19            $"string2 = \"{string2}\"\n" +
20            $"string3 = \"{string3}\"\n" +
21            $"string4 = \"{string4}\"\n");
22      }
23   }
```

```
string1 = "Welcome to C# programming!"
string2 = "birth day"
string3 = "day"
string4 = "CCCCC"
```

Fig. 16.1 | Demonstrating `string` class constructors.

Lines 10–11 create the char array `characterArray`, which contains nine characters. Lines 12–16 declare the strings `originalString`, `string1`, `string2`, `string3` and `string4`. Line 12 assigns string literal `"Welcome to C# programming!"` to string reference `originalString`. Line 13 sets `string1` to reference the same string literal.

Line 14 assigns to `string2` a new `string`, using the `string` constructor with a character array argument. The new `string` contains a copy of the array's characters.

Line 15 assigns to `string3` a new `string`, using the `string` constructor that takes a char array and two int arguments. The second argument specifies the starting index position (the *offset*) from which characters in the array are to be copied. The third argument specifies the number of characters (the *count*) to be copied from the specified starting position in the array. The new `string` contains a copy of the specified characters in the array. If the specified offset or count indicates that the program should access an element outside the bounds of the character array, an `ArgumentOutOfRangeException` is thrown.

Line 16 assigns to `string4` a new `string`, using the `string` constructor that takes as arguments a character and an int specifying the number of times to repeat that character in the `string`.

Software Engineering Observation 16.1

In most cases, it's not necessary to make a copy of an existing string. *All strings are immutable—their character contents cannot be changed after they're created. Also, if there are one or more references to a* string *(or any reference-type object for that matter), the object cannot be reclaimed by the garbage collector.*

16.4 string Indexer, Length Property and CopyTo Method

Figure 16.2 presents

- the string *indexer* ([]) for retrieving any character in a string,
- the string property Length, which returns a string's length and
- the string method CopyTo, which copies a specified number of characters from a string into a char array.

```csharp
 1   // Fig. 16.2: StringMethods.cs
 2   // string indexer, Length property and CopyTo method.
 3
 4   using System;
 5
 6   class StringMethods
 7   {
 8      static void Main()
 9      {
10         var string1 = "hello there";
11         var characterArray = new char[5];
12
13         Console.WriteLine($"string1: \"{string1}\""); // output string1
14
15         // test Length property
16         Console.WriteLine($"Length of string1: {string1.Length}");
17
18         // loop through characters in string1 and display reversed
19         Console.Write("The string reversed is: ");
20
21         for (int i = string1.Length - 1; i >= 0; --i)
22         {
23            Console.Write(string1[i]);
24         }
25
26         // copy characters from string1 into characterArray
27         string1.CopyTo(0, characterArray, 0, characterArray.Length);
28         Console.Write("\nThe character array is: ");
29
30         foreach (var element in characterArray)
31         {
32            Console.Write(element);
33         }
```

Fig. 16.2 | string indexer, Length property and CopyTo method. (Part 1 of 2.)

```
34
35          Console.WriteLine("\n");
36     }
37 }
```

```
string1: "hello there"
Length of string1: 11
The string reversed is: ereht olleh
The character array is: hello
```

Fig. 16.2 | string indexer, Length property and CopyTo method. (Part 2 of 2.)

Line 16 uses string property Length to determine the number of characters in string1. Like arrays, strings always know their own size.

Lines 21–24 display the characters of string1 in reverse order using the string indexer ([]), which treats a string as an array of chars and returns the character at a specific index in the string. As with arrays, the first element of a string has index 0.

Common Programming Error 16.1
Attempting to access a character that's outside a string's bounds results in an Index-
OutOfRangeException.

Line 27 uses string method CopyTo to copy the characters of string1 into a character array (characterArray). The first argument given to method CopyTo is the index from which the method begins copying characters in the string. The second argument is the character array into which the characters are copied. The third argument is the index specifying the starting location at which the method begins placing the copied characters into the character array. The last argument is the number of characters that the method will copy from the string. Lines 30–33 output the char array contents one character at a time.

We used a for statement in lines 21–24 to demonstrate a string's Length property and the string indexer, using them to display the string in reverse. That loop could have been implemented with foreach and the **Reverse** extension method as in

```
foreach (var element in string1.Reverse())
{
    Console.Write(element);
}
```

Method Reverse is one of many LINQ extension methods and requires a using directive for the namespace System.Linq.

16.5 Comparing strings

The next two examples demonstrate various methods for *comparing* strings. To understand how one string can be "greater than" or "less than" another, consider the process of alphabetizing a series of last names. The reader would, no doubt, place "Jones" before "Smith", because the first letter of "Jones" comes before the first letter of "Smith" in the alphabet. The alphabet is more than just a set of 26 letters—it's an ordered list of characters in which each letter occurs in a specific position. For example, Z is more than just a letter of the alphabet; it's specifically the twenty-sixth letter of the alphabet. Computers can order characters alphabetically because they're represented internally as numeric codes and those codes are ordered according to the alphabet so, for example, 'a' is less than 'b'—see Appendix C.

Comparing *strings* with *Equals, CompareTo* and the *Equality Operator (==)*

Class `string` provides several ways to compare `strings`. Figure 16.3 demonstrates methods Equals and CompareTo and the equality operator (==).

```
1   // Fig. 16.3: StringCompare.cs
2   // Comparing strings
3   using System;
4
5   class StringCompare
6   {
7      static void Main()
8      {
9         var string1 = "hello";
10        var string2 = "good bye";
11        var string3 = "Happy Birthday";
12        var string4 = "happy birthday";
13
14        // output values of four strings
15        Console.WriteLine($"string1 = \"{string1}\"" +
16           $"\nstring2 = \"{string2}\"" +
17           $"\nstring3 = \"{string3}\"" +
18           $"\nstring4 = \"{string4}\"\n");
19
20        // test for equality using Equals method
21        if (string1.Equals("hello"))
22        {
23           Console.WriteLine("string1 equals \"hello\"");
24        }
25        else
26        {
27           Console.WriteLine("string1 does not equal \"hello\"");
28        }
29
30        // test for equality with ==
31        if (string1 == "hello")
32        {
33           Console.WriteLine("string1 equals \"hello\"");
34        }
35        else
36        {
37           Console.WriteLine("string1 does not equal \"hello\"");
38        }
39
40        // test for equality comparing case
41        if (string.Equals(string3, string4)) // static method
42        {
```

Fig. 16.3 | Comparing strings. (Part I of 2.)

```
43              Console.WriteLine("string3 equals string4");
44          }
45          else
46          {
47              Console.WriteLine("string3 does not equal string4");
48          }
49
50          // test CompareTo
51          Console.WriteLine(
52              $"\nstring1.CompareTo(string2) is {string1.CompareTo(string2)}");
53          Console.WriteLine(
54              $"string2.CompareTo(string1) is {string2.CompareTo(string1)}");
55          Console.WriteLine(
56              $"string1.CompareTo(string1) is {string1.CompareTo(string1)}");
57          Console.WriteLine(
58              $"string3.CompareTo(string4) is {string3.CompareTo(string4)}");
59          Console.WriteLine(
60              $"string4.CompareTo(string3) is {string4.CompareTo(string3)}");
61      }
62  }
```

```
string1 = "hello"
string2 = "good bye"
string3 = "Happy Birthday"
string4 = "happy birthday"

string1 equals "hello"
string1 equals "hello"
string3 does not equal string4

string1.CompareTo(string2) is 1
string2.CompareTo(string1) is -1
string1.CompareTo(string1) is 0
string3.CompareTo(string4) is 1
string4.CompareTo(string3) is -1
```

Fig. 16.3 | Comparing strings. (Part 2 of 2.)

The condition in line 21 uses string method Equals to compare string1 and literal string "hello" (the argument) to determine whether they're equal. Method Equals (inherited from object and overridden in string) tests two strings for equality (i.e., checks whether the strings have *identical contents*). The method returns true if the objects are equal and false otherwise. In this case, the condition returns true, because string1 references string literal object "hello". Method Equals uses word sorting rules that do not depend on your system's currently selected culture. Comparing "hello" with "HELLO" would return false, because the lowercase letters are different from the corresponding uppercase letters.

The condition in line 31 uses class string's *overloaded equality operator (==)* to compare string string1 with the literal string "hello" for equality. In C#, the equality operator also compares the contents of two strings. Thus, the condition in the if statement evaluates to true, because the values of string1 and "hello" are equal.

Line 41 tests whether string3 and string4 are equal to illustrate that comparisons are indeed case sensitive. Here, static method Equals is used to compare the values of two strings. "Happy Birthday" does not equal "happy birthday", so the condition fails, and the message "string3 does not equal string4" is output (line 47).

Lines 51–60 use string method CompareTo to compare strings. The method returns 0 if the strings are equal, a negative value if the string that invokes CompareTo is less than the string that's passed as an argument and a positive value if the string that invokes CompareTo is greater than the string that's passed as an argument.

Notice that CompareTo considers string3 to be greater than string4. The only difference between these two strings is that string3 contains two uppercase letters in positions where string4 contains lowercase letters. The method uses sorting rules that are case and culture sensitive.

Determining Whether a String Begins or Ends with a Specified String

Figure 16.4 tests whether a string begins or ends with a given string. Method StartsWith determines whether a string starts with the string passed to the method as an argument. Method EndsWith determines whether a string ends with the string passed to the method as an argument.

```csharp
1   // Fig. 16.4: StringStartEnd.cs
2   // Demonstrating StartsWith and EndsWith methods.
3   using System;
4
5   class StringStartEnd
6   {
7       static void Main()
8       {
9           string[] strings = {"started", "starting", "ended", "ending"};
10
11          // test every string to see if it starts with "st"
12          foreach (var element in strings)
13          {
14              if (element.StartsWith("st"))
15              {
16                  Console.WriteLine($"\"{element}\" starts with \"st\"");
17              }
18          }
19
20          Console.WriteLine();
21
22          // test every string to see if it ends with "ed"
23          foreach (var element in strings)
24          {
25              if (element.EndsWith("ed"))
26              {
27                  Console.WriteLine($"\"{element}\" ends with \"ed\"");
28              }
29          }
30
```

Fig. 16.4 | Demonstrating StartsWith and EndsWith methods. (Part 1 of 2.)

```
31          Console.WriteLine();
32       }
33    }
```

```
"started" starts with "st"
"starting" starts with "st"

"started" ends with "ed"
"ended" ends with "ed"
```

Fig. 16.4 | Demonstrating StartsWith and EndsWith methods. (Part 2 of 2.)

Line 9 defines an array of strings, which contains "started", "starting", "ended" and "ending". Line 14 uses method StartsWith, which takes a string argument. The condition in the if statement determines whether the current element starts with the characters "st". If so, the method returns true, and the element is displayed along with a message.

Line 25 uses method EndsWith to determine whether the current element ends with the characters "ed". If so, the method returns true, and the element is displayed along with a message.

16.6 Locating Characters and Substrings in strings

In many apps, it's necessary to search for a character or set of characters in a string. For example, a programmer creating a word processor would want to provide capabilities for searching through documents. Figure 16.5 demonstrates some versions of string methods IndexOf, IndexOfAny, LastIndexOf and LastIndexOfAny, which search for a specified character or substring in a string. We perform all searches in this example on the string letters (line 9).

```
 1   // Fig. 16.5: StringIndexMethods.cs
 2   // Searching for characters and substrings in strings.
 3   using System;
 4
 5   class StringIndexMethods
 6   {
 7      static void Main()
 8      {
 9         var letters = "abcdefghijklmabcdefghijklm";
10         char[] searchLetters = {'c', 'a', '$'};
11
12         // test IndexOf to locate a character in a string
13         Console.WriteLine($"First 'c' is located at index " +
14            letters.IndexOf('c'));
15         Console.WriteLine("First 'a' starting at 1 is located at index " +
16            letters.IndexOf('a', 1));
17         Console.WriteLine("First '$' in the 5 positions starting at 3 " +
18            $"is located at index " + letters.IndexOf('$', 3, 5));
19
```

Fig. 16.5 | Searching for characters and substrings in strings. (Part 1 of 3.)

```
20          // test LastIndexOf to find a character in a string
21          Console.WriteLine($"\nLast 'c' is located at index " +
22             letters.LastIndexOf('c'));
23          Console.WriteLine("Last 'a' up to position 25 is located at " +
24             "index " + letters.LastIndexOf('a', 25));
25          Console.WriteLine("Last '$' in the 5 positions ending at 15 " +
26             "is located at index " + letters.LastIndexOf('$', 15, 5));
27
28          // test IndexOf to locate a substring in a string
29          Console.WriteLine("\nFirst \"def\" is located at index " +
30             letters.IndexOf("def"));
31          Console.WriteLine("First \"def\" starting at 7 is located at " +
32             "index " + letters.IndexOf("def", 7));
33          Console.WriteLine("First \"hello\" in the 15 positions " +
34             "starting at 5 is located at index " +
35             letters.IndexOf("hello", 5, 15));
36
37          // test LastIndexOf to find a substring in a string
38          Console.WriteLine("\nLast \"def\" is located at index " +
39             letters.LastIndexOf("def"));
40          Console.WriteLine("Last \"def\" up to position 25 is located " +
41             "at index " + letters.LastIndexOf("def", 25));
42          Console.WriteLine("Last \"hello\" in the 15 positions " +
43             "ending at 20 is located at index " +
44             letters.LastIndexOf("hello", 20, 15));
45
46          // test IndexOfAny to find first occurrence of character in array
47          Console.WriteLine("\nFirst 'c', 'a' or '$' is " +
48             "located at index " + letters.IndexOfAny(searchLetters));
49          Console.WriteLine("First 'c', 'a' or '$' starting at 7 is " +
50             "located at index " + letters.IndexOfAny(searchLetters, 7));
51          Console.WriteLine("First 'c', 'a' or '$' in the 5 positions " +
52             "starting at 7 is located at index " +
53             letters.IndexOfAny(searchLetters, 7, 5));
54
55          // test LastIndexOfAny to find last occurrence of character
56          // in array
57          Console.WriteLine("\nLast 'c', 'a' or '$' is " +
58             "located at index " + letters.LastIndexOfAny(searchLetters));
59          Console.WriteLine("Last 'c', 'a' or '$' up to position 1 is " +
60             "located at index " +
61             letters.LastIndexOfAny(searchLetters, 1));
62          Console.WriteLine("Last 'c', 'a' or '$' in the 5 positions " +
63             "ending at 25 is located at index " +
64             letters.LastIndexOfAny(searchLetters, 25, 5));
65       }
66    }
```

```
First 'c' is located at index 2
First 'a' starting at 1 is located at index 13
First '$' in the 5 positions starting at 3 is located at index -1
```

Fig. 16.5 | Searching for characters and substrings in strings. (Part 2 of 3.)

```
Last 'c' is located at index 15
Last 'a' up to position 25 is located at index 13
Last '$' in the 5 positions ending at 15 is located at index -1

First "def" is located at index 3
First "def" starting at 7 is located at index 16
First "hello" in the 15 positions starting at 5 is located at index -1

Last "def" is located at index 16
Last "def" up to position 25 is located at index 16
Last "hello" in the 15 positions ending at 20 is located at index -1

First 'c', 'a' or '$' is located at index 0
First 'c', 'a' or '$' starting at 7 is located at index 13
First 'c', 'a' or '$' in the 5 positions starting at 7 is located at index -1

Last 'c', 'a' or '$' is located at index 15
Last 'c', 'a' or '$' up to position 1 is located at index 0
Last 'c', 'a' or '$' in the 5 positions ending at 25 is located at index -1
```

Fig. 16.5 | Searching for characters and substrings in `strings`. (Part 3 of 3.)

Lines 14, 16 and 18 use method `IndexOf` to locate the first occurrence of a character or substring in a `string`. If it finds a character, `IndexOf` returns the index of the specified character in the `string`; otherwise, `IndexOf` returns -1. The expression in line 16 uses a method `IndexOf` with two arguments—the character to search for and the starting index at which the search should begin. The method does not examine any characters that occur prior to the starting index (in this case, 1). The expression in line 18 uses method `IndexOf` with three arguments—the character to search for, the index at which to start searching and the number of characters to search.

Lines 22, 24 and 26 use method `LastIndexOf` to locate the last occurrence of a character in a `string`. Method `LastIndexOf` performs the search from the end to the beginning of the `string`. If it finds the character, `LastIndexOf` returns the index of the specified character in the `string`; otherwise, `LastIndexOf` returns -1. There are three versions of method `LastIndexOf`. The expression in line 22 uses the version that takes as an argument the character for which to search. The expression in line 24 uses the version that takes two arguments—the character for which to search and the highest index from which to begin searching backward for the character. The expression in line 26 uses a third version of method `LastIndexOf` that takes three arguments—the character for which to search, the starting index from which to start searching backward and the number of characters (the portion of the `string`) to search.

Lines 29–44 use versions of `IndexOf` and `LastIndexOf` that take a `string` instead of a character as the first argument. These versions of the methods perform identically to those described above except that they search for sequences of characters (or substrings) that are specified by their `string` arguments.

Lines 47–64 use methods `IndexOfAny` and `LastIndexOfAny`, which take an array of characters as the first argument. These versions of the methods also perform identically to those described above, except that they return the index of the first or last occurrence of any of the characters in the character-array argument, respectively.

Common Programming Error 16.2

In the overloaded methods `LastIndexOf` and `LastIndexOfAny` that take three parameters, the second argument must be greater than or equal to the third. This might seem counterintuitive, but remember that the search moves from the end of the string toward the start of the string.

16.7 Extracting Substrings from `strings`

Class `string` provides two `Substring` methods, which create a new `string` by copying part of an existing `string`. Each method returns a new `string`. Figure 16.6 demonstrates both methods.

```
1   // Fig. 16.6: SubString.cs
2   // Demonstrating the string Substring method.
3   using System;
4
5   class SubString
6   {
7       static void Main()
8       {
9           var letters = "abcdefghijklmabcdefghijklm";
10
11          // invoke Substring method and pass it one parameter
12          Console.WriteLine("Substring from index 20 to end is " +
13              $"\"{letters.Substring(20)}\"");
14
15          // invoke Substring method and pass it two parameters
16          Console.WriteLine("Substring from index 0 of length 6 is " +
17              $"\"{letters.Substring(0, 6)}\"");
18      }
19  }
```

```
Substring from index 20 to end is "hijklm"
Substring from index 0 of length 6 is "abcdef"
```

Fig. 16.6 | Demonstrating the string `Substring` method.

The statement in line 13 uses the `Substring` method that takes one `int` argument. The argument specifies the starting index from which the method copies characters in the original `string`. The substring returned contains a copy of the characters from the starting index to the end of the `string`. If the index specified in the argument is outside the bounds of the `string`, the program throws an `ArgumentOutOfRangeException`.

The second version of method `Substring` (line 17) takes two `int` arguments. The first argument specifies the starting index from which the method copies characters from the original `string`. The second argument specifies the length of the substring to copy. The substring returned contains a copy of the specified characters from the original `string`. If the supplied length of the substring is too large (i.e., the substring tries to retrieve characters past the end of the original `string`), an `ArgumentOutOfRangeException` is thrown.

16.8 Concatenating `strings`

The + operator is not the only way to perform `string` concatenation. The `static` method `Concat` of class `string` (Fig. 16.7) concatenates two `strings` and returns a new `string` containing the combined characters from both original `strings`. Line 15 appends the characters from `string2` to the end of a copy of `string1`, using method `Concat`. The method call in line 15 does not modify the original `strings`.

```
1   // Fig. 16.7: SubConcatenation.cs
2   // Demonstrating string class Concat method.
3   using System;
4
5   class StringConcatenation
6   {
7       static void Main()
8       {
9           var string1 = "Happy ";
10          var string2 = "Birthday";
11
12          Console.WriteLine($"string1 = \"{string1}\"");
13          Console.WriteLine($"string2 = \"{string2}\"");
14          Console.WriteLine("\nResult of string.Concat(string1, string2) = " +
15              string.Concat(string1, string2));
16          Console.WriteLine($"string1 after concatenation = {string1}");
17      }
18  }
```

```
string1 = "Happy "
string2 = "Birthday"

Result of string.Concat(string1, string2) = Happy Birthday
string1 after concatenation = Happy
```

Fig. 16.7 | Demonstrating `string` class `Concat` method.

16.9 Miscellaneous `string` Methods

Class `string` provides several methods that return modified copies of `strings`. Figure 16.8 demonstrates `string` methods `Replace`, `ToLower`, `ToUpper` and `Trim`.

```
1   // Fig. 16.8: StringMethods2.cs
2   // Demonstrating string methods Replace, ToLower, ToUpper and Trim
3
4   using System;
5
6   class StringMethods2
7   {
8       static void Main()
9       {
```

Fig. 16.8 | Demonstrating `string` methods `Replace`, `ToLower`, `ToUpper` and `Trim`. (Part 1 of 2.)

```
10          var string1 = "cheers!";
11          var string2 = "GOOD BYE ";
12          var string3 = "   spaces   ";
13
14          Console.WriteLine($"string1 = \"{string1}\"\n" +
15              $"string2 = \"{string2}\"\n" +
16              $"string3 = \"{string3}\"");
17
18          // call method Replace
19          Console.WriteLine("\nReplacing \"e\" with \"E\" in string1: " +
20              $"\"{string1.Replace('e', 'E')}\"");
21
22          // call ToLower and ToUpper
23          Console.WriteLine(
24              $"\nstring1.ToUpper() = \"{string1.ToUpper()}\"" +
25              $"\nstring2.ToLower() = \"{string2.ToLower()}\"");
26
27          // call Trim method
28          Console.WriteLine(
29              $"\nstring3 after trim = \"{string3.Trim()}\"");
30
31          Console.WriteLine($"\nstring1 = \"{string1}\"");
32      }
33  }
```

```
string1 = "cheers!"
string2 = "GOOD BYE "
string3 = "   spaces   "

Replacing "e" with "E" in string1: "chEErs!"

string1.ToUpper() = "CHEERS!"
string2.ToLower() = "good bye "

string3 after trim = "spaces"

string1 = "cheers!"
```

Fig. 16.8 | Demonstrating string methods Replace, ToLower, ToUpper and Trim. (Part 2 of 2.)

Line 20 uses string method Replace to return a new string, replacing every occurrence in string1 of character 'e' with 'E'. Method Replace takes two arguments—a char for which to search and another char with which to replace all matching occurrences of the first argument. The original string remains unchanged. If there are no occurrences of the first argument in the string, the method returns the original string. An overloaded version of this method allows you to provide two strings as arguments.

The string method ToUpper generates a new string (line 24) that replaces any *lowercase* letters in string1 with their *uppercase* equivalents (using the current culture's rules). The method returns a new string containing the converted string; the original string remains *unchanged*. If there are no characters to convert, the original string is returned. Line 25 uses string method ToLower to return a new string in which any *uppercase* letters in string2 are replaced by their *lowercase* equivalents (using the current culture's rules). The original string is *unchanged*. As with ToUpper, if there are *no* characters to convert to lowercase, method ToLower returns the *original* string.

Line 29 uses string method Trim to remove all *whitespace characters* that appear at the beginning and end of a string. Without otherwise altering the original string, the method returns a new string that contains the string, but *omits* leading and trailing *whitespace* characters. This method is particularly useful for retrieving user input (i.e., via a TextBox). Another version of method Trim takes a character array and returns a copy of the string that does not begin or end with any of the characters in the array argument.

16.10 Class StringBuilder

The string class provides many capabilities for processing strings. However a string's contents can *never* change. Operations that seem to concatenate strings are in fact creating new strings—the += operator creates a new string and assigns its reference to the variable on the left of the += operator.

The next several sections discuss the features of class StringBuilder (namespace System.Text), used to create and manipulate dynamic string information—i.e., *mutable* strings. Every StringBuilder can store a certain number of characters that's specified by its capacity. Exceeding the capacity of a StringBuilder causes the capacity to expand to accommodate the additional characters. As we'll see, members of class StringBuilder, such as methods Append and AppendFormat, can be used for *concatenation* like the operators + and += for class string—without creating any new string objects. StringBuilder is particularly useful for manipulating in place a large number of strings, as it's much more efficient than creating individual immutable strings.

Performance Tip 16.2

Objects of class string are immutable (i.e., constant strings), whereas objects of class StringBuilder are mutable. C# can perform certain optimizations involving strings (such as the sharing of one string among multiple references), because it knows these objects will not change.

StringBuilder *Constructors*

Class StringBuilder provides six overloaded constructors. Class StringBuilderConstructor (Fig. 16.9) demonstrates three of these overloaded constructors. Line 10 employs the no-parameter StringBuilder constructor to create a StringBuilder that contains no characters and has an implementation-specific *default initial capacity*. Line 11 uses the StringBuilder constructor that takes an int argument to create a StringBuilder that contains no characters and has the *initial capacity* specified in the int argument (i.e., 10). Line 12 uses the StringBuilder constructor that takes a string argument to create a StringBuilder containing the characters of the string argument—the initial capacity might differ from the string's size. Lines 14–16 implicitly use StringBuilder method ToString to obtain string representations of the StringBuilders' contents.

```
1   // Fig. 16.9: StringBuilderConstructor.cs
2   // Demonstrating StringBuilder class constructors.
3   using System;
4   using System.Text;
```

Fig. 16.9 | Demonstrating StringBuilder class constructors. (Part 1 of 2.)

```
 5
 6   class StringBuilderConstructor
 7   {
 8      static void Main()
 9      {
10         var buffer1 = new StringBuilder();
11         var buffer2 = new StringBuilder(10);
12         var buffer3 = new StringBuilder("hello");
13
14         Console.WriteLine($"buffer1 = \"{buffer1}\"");
15         Console.WriteLine($"buffer2 = \"{buffer2}\"");
16         Console.WriteLine($"buffer3 = \"{buffer3}\"");
17      }
18   }
```

```
buffer1 = ""
buffer2 = ""
buffer3 = "hello"
```

Fig. 16.9 | Demonstrating StringBuilder class constructors. (Part 2 of 2.)

16.11 Length and Capacity Properties, EnsureCapacity Method and Indexer of Class StringBuilder

Class StringBuilder provides the Length and Capacity properties to return the number of characters currently in a StringBuilder and the number of characters that a String-Builder can store without allocating more memory, respectively. These properties also can be used to increase or decrease the length or the capacity of the StringBuilder. Method EnsureCapacity allows you to reduce the number of times that a StringBuilder's capacity must be increased. The method ensures that the StringBuilder's capacity is at least the specified value. Figure 16.10 demonstrates these methods and properties.

```
 1   // Fig. 16.10: StringBuilderFeatures.cs
 2   // StringBuilder size manipulation.
 3   using System;
 4   using System.Text;
 5
 6   class StringBuilderFeatures
 7   {
 8      static void Main()
 9      {
10         var buffer = new StringBuilder("Hello, how are you?");
11
12         // use Length and Capacity properties
13         Console.WriteLine($"buffer = {buffer}" +
14            $"\nLength = {buffer.Length}" +
15            $"\nCapacity = {buffer.Capacity}");
```

Fig. 16.10 | StringBuilder size manipulation. (Part 1 of 2.)

```
16
17          buffer.EnsureCapacity(75); // ensure a capacity of at least 75
18          Console.WriteLine($"\nNew capacity = {buffer.Capacity}");
19
20          // truncate StringBuilder by setting Length property
21          buffer.Length = 10;
22          Console.Write($"New length = {buffer.Length}\n\nbuffer = ");
23
24          // use StringBuilder indexer
25          for (int i = 0; i < buffer.Length; ++i)
26          {
27              Console.Write(buffer[i]);
28          }
29
30          Console.WriteLine();
31      }
32  }
```

```
buffer = Hello, how are you?
Length = 19
Capacity = 19

New capacity = 75
New length = 10

buffer = Hello, how
```

Fig. 16.10 | StringBuilder size manipulation. (Part 2 of 2.)

The program contains one StringBuilder, called buffer. Line 10 uses the String-Builder constructor that takes a string argument to create a StringBuilder and initialize it to "Hello, how are you?". Lines 13–15 output the StringBuilder's content, length and capacity.

Line 17 expands the StringBuilder's capacity to a minimum of 75 characters. If new characters are added to a StringBuilder so that its length exceeds its capacity, the capacity *grows* to accommodate the additional characters in the same manner as if method Ensure-Capacity had been called.

Line 21 uses property Length to set the StringBuilder's length to 10—this does *not* change the Capacity. If the specified length is less than the StringBuilder's current number of characters, the contents are *truncated* to the specified length. If the specified length is greater than the current number of characters, null characters (that is, '\0' characters) are appended to the StringBuilder until the total number of characters is equal to the specified length. Lines 25–28 use StringBuilder's indexer to display each character. This for statement could be replaced with the following foreach:

```
foreach (var element in buffer)
{
    Console.Write(element);
}
```

16.12 Append and AppendFormat Methods of Class StringBuilder

Class StringBuilder provides overloaded Append methods that allow various types of values to be added to the end of a StringBuilder. The Framework Class Library provides versions for each simple type and for character arrays, strings and objects. (Remember that method ToString produces a string representation of any object.) Each method takes an argument, converts it to a string and appends it to the StringBuilder. Figure 16.11 uses several Append methods (lines 22–40) to attach the variables' string representations in lines 10–18 to the end of the StringBuilder.

```csharp
1   // Fig. 16.11: StringBuilderAppend.cs
2   // Demonstrating StringBuilder Append methods.
3   using System;
4   using System.Text;
5
6   class StringBuilderAppend
7   {
8      static void Main()
9      {
10         object objectValue = "hello";
11         var stringValue = "good bye";
12         char[] characterArray = {'a', 'b', 'c', 'd', 'e', 'f'};
13         var booleanValue = true;
14         var characterValue = 'Z';
15         var integerValue = 7;
16         var longValue = 1000000L; // L suffix indicates a long literal
17         var floatValue = 2.5F; // F suffix indicates a float literal
18         var doubleValue = 33.333;
19         var buffer = new StringBuilder();
20
21         // use method Append to append values to buffer
22         buffer.Append(objectValue);
23         buffer.Append("  ");
24         buffer.Append(stringValue);
25         buffer.Append("  ");
26         buffer.Append(characterArray);
27         buffer.Append("  ");
28         buffer.Append(characterArray, 0, 3);
29         buffer.Append("  ");
30         buffer.Append(booleanValue);
31         buffer.Append("  ");
32         buffer.Append(characterValue);
33         buffer.Append("  ");
34         buffer.Append(integerValue);
35         buffer.Append("  ");
36         buffer.Append(longValue);
37         buffer.Append("  ");
38         buffer.Append(floatValue);
39         buffer.Append("  ");
40         buffer.Append(doubleValue);
```

Fig. 16.11 | Demonstrating StringBuilder Append methods. (Part 1 of 2.)

```
41
42          Console.WriteLine($"buffer = {buffer.ToString()}");
43     }
44  }
```

```
buffer = hello  good bye  abcdef  abc  True  Z  7  1000000  2.5  33.333
```

Fig. 16.11 | Demonstrating StringBuilder Append methods. (Part 2 of 2.)

Class StringBuilder also provides method AppendFormat, which converts a string
to a specified format, then appends it to the StringBuilder. The example in Fig. 16.12
demonstrates AppendFormat.

```
1   // Fig. 16.12: StringBuilderAppendFormat.cs
2   // StringBuilder's AppendFormat method.
3   using System;
4   using System.Text;
5
6   class StringBuilderAppendFormat
7   {
8      static void Main()
9      {
10         var buffer = new StringBuilder();
11
12         // formatted string
13         var string1 = "This {0} costs: {1:C}.\n\n";
14
15         // string1 argument array
16         var objectArray = new object[2] {"car", 1234.56};
17
18         // append to buffer formatted string with argument
19         buffer.AppendFormat(string1, objectArray);
20
21         // formatted string
22         string string2 = "Number:\n{0:d3}.\n\n" +
23            "Number right aligned with spaces:\n{0,4}.\n\n" +
24            "Number left aligned with spaces:\n{0,-4}.";
25
26         // append to buffer formatted string with argument
27         buffer.AppendFormat(string2, 5);
28
29         // display formatted strings
30         Console.WriteLine(buffer.ToString());
31      }
32  }
```

```
This car costs: $1,234.56.

Number:
005.
```

Fig. 16.12 | StringBuilder's AppendFormat method. (Part 1 of 2.)

```
Number right aligned with spaces:
   5.

Number left aligned with spaces:
5   .
```

Fig. 16.12 | `StringBuilder`'s `AppendFormat` method. (Part 2 of 2.)

Line 13 declares a format `string` that consists of text and format items. Each format item in braces ({}) is a placeholder for a value. Format items also may include the same optional formatting you've seen throughout this book in interpolated `string`s. Line 16 declares and initializes an array of `object`s that will be formatted. Line 19 shows a version of `AppendFormat` that takes two parameters—a format `string` and an array of `object`s to serve as the arguments to the format `string`. The `object` at index 0 of the array is formatted by the format item "{0}", which simply produces the `object`'s `string` representation. The `object` at index 1 of the array is formatted by the format item "{1:C}", which formats the `object` as currency.

Lines 22–24 declare another format `string` with three format specifiers:

- The first—{0:d3}—formats a three-digit integer value. Any number having fewer than three digits will have leading zeros.

- The second—{0,4}—formats a `string` in a right-aligned field of four characters.

- The third—{0,-4}—formats a `string` in a left-aligned field of four characters.

Line 27 uses a version of `AppendFormat` that takes two parameters—a format `string` and an object to format. In this case, the object is the number 5, which is formatted by all three format specifiers. The output displays the result of applying these two versions of `Append-Format` with their respective arguments.

16.13 Insert, Remove and Replace Methods of Class `StringBuilder`

Class `StringBuilder` provides overloaded `Insert` methods to allow various types of data to be inserted at any position in a `StringBuilder`. The class provides versions for each simple type and for character arrays, `string`s and `object`s. Each method takes its second argument, converts it to a `string` and inserts the `string` into the `StringBuilder` in front of the character in the position specified by the first argument. The index specified by the first argument must be greater than or equal to 0 and less than the `StringBuilder`'s length; otherwise, the program throws an `ArgumentOutOfRangeException`.

Class `StringBuilder` also provides method `Remove` for deleting any portion of a `StringBuilder`. Method `Remove` takes two arguments—the index at which to begin deletion and the number of characters to delete. The sum of the starting index and the number of characters to be deleted must always be less than the `StringBuilder`'s length; otherwise, the program throws an `ArgumentOutOfRangeException`. The `Insert` and `Remove` methods are demonstrated in Fig. 16.13.

```
 1   // Fig. 16.13: StringBuilderInsertRemove.cs
 2   // Demonstrating methods Insert and Remove of the
 3   // StringBuilder class.
 4   using System;
 5   using System.Text;
 6
 7   class StringBuilderInsertRemove
 8   {
 9      static void Main()
10      {
11         object objectValue = "hello";
12         var stringValue = "good bye";
13         char[] characterArray = {'a', 'b', 'c', 'd', 'e', 'f'};
14         var booleanValue = true;
15         var characterValue = 'K';
16         var integerValue = 7;
17         var longValue = 1000000L; // L suffix indicates a long literal
18         var floatValue = 2.5F; // F suffix indicates a float literal
19         var doubleValue = 33.333;
20         var buffer = new StringBuilder();
21
22         // insert values into buffer
23         buffer.Insert(0, objectValue);
24         buffer.Insert(0, "  ");
25         buffer.Insert(0, stringValue);
26         buffer.Insert(0, "  ");
27         buffer.Insert(0, characterArray);
28         buffer.Insert(0, "  ");
29         buffer.Insert(0, booleanValue);
30         buffer.Insert(0, "  ");
31         buffer.Insert(0, characterValue);
32         buffer.Insert(0, "  ");
33         buffer.Insert(0, integerValue);
34         buffer.Insert(0, "  ");
35         buffer.Insert(0, longValue);
36         buffer.Insert(0, "  ");
37         buffer.Insert(0, floatValue);
38         buffer.Insert(0, "  ");
39         buffer.Insert(0, doubleValue);
40         buffer.Insert(0, "  ");
41
42         Console.WriteLine($"buffer after Inserts: \n{buffer}\n");
43
44         buffer.Remove(10, 1); // delete 2 in 2.5
45         buffer.Remove(4, 4);  // delete .333 in 33.333
46
47         Console.WriteLine($"buffer after Removes:\n{buffer}");
48      }
49   }
```

```
buffer after Inserts:
  33.333  2.5  10000000  7  K  True  abcdef  good bye  hello
```

Fig. 16.13 | Demonstrating methods Insert and Remove of the `StringBuilder` class. (Part 1 of 2.)

```
buffer after Removes:
  33 .5 10000000  7  K  True  abcdef  good bye  hello
```

Fig. 16.13 | Demonstrating methods Insert and Remove of the StringBuilder class. (Part 2 of 2.)

Another useful method included with StringBuilder is Replace, which searches for a specified string or character and *substitutes* another string or character all occurrences. Figure 16.14 demonstrates this method.

```
 1   // Fig. 16.14: StringBuilderReplace.cs
 2   // Demonstrating method Replace.
 3   using System;
 4   using System.Text;
 5
 6   class StringBuilderReplace
 7   {
 8      static void Main()
 9      {
10         var builder1 = new StringBuilder("Happy Birthday Jane");
11         var builder2 = new StringBuilder("goodbye greg");
12
13         Console.WriteLine($"Before replacements:\n{builder1}\n{builder2}");
14
15         builder1.Replace("Jane", "Greg");
16         builder2.Replace('g', 'G', 0, 5);
17
18         Console.WriteLine($"\nAfter replacements:\n{builder1}\n{builder2}");
19      }
20   }
```

```
Before Replacements:
Happy Birthday Jane
good bye greg

After replacements:
Happy Birthday Greg
Goodbye greg
```

Fig. 16.14 | Demonstrating method Replace.

Line 15 uses method Replace to replace all instances of "Jane" with the "Greg" in builder1. Another overload of this method takes two characters as parameters and *replaces* each occurrence of the first character with the second. Line 16 uses an overload of Replace that takes four parameters, of which the first two are both characters or both strings and the second two are ints. The method replaces all instances of the first character with the second character (or the first string with the second), beginning at the index specified by the first int and continuing for a count specified by the second int. Thus, in this case, Replace looks through only five characters, starting with the character at index 0. As the output illustrates, this version of Replace replaces g with G in the word "goodbye", but not in "greg". This is because the gs in "greg" are not in the range indicated by the int arguments (i.e., between indexes 0 and 4).

16.14 Char Methods

Section 10.13 introduced structs for representing value types. The simple types are actually aliases for struct types. For instance, an int is defined by struct System.Int32, a long by System.Int64 and so on. All struct types derive from class ValueType, which derives from object. Also, all struct types are implicitly sealed.

In the struct System.Char—which is the struct for characters and represented by C# keyword char—most methods are static, take at least one character argument and perform either a test or a manipulation on the character. We present several of these in the next example. Figure 16.15 demonstrates static methods that test characters to determine whether they're of a specific character type and static methods that perform case conversions on characters.

```csharp
 1   // Fig. 16.15: StaticCharMethods.cs
 2   // Demonstrates static character-testing and case-conversion methods
 3   // from Char struct
 4   using System;
 5
 6   class StaticCharMethods
 7   {
 8      static void Main(string[] args)
 9      {
10         Console.Write("Enter a character: ");
11         var character = char.Parse(Console.ReadLine());
12
13         Console.WriteLine($"is digit: {char.IsDigit(character)}");
14         Console.WriteLine($"is letter: {char.IsLetter(character)}");
15         Console.WriteLine(
16            $"is letter or digit: {char.IsLetterOrDigit(character)}");
17         Console.WriteLine($"is lower case: {char.IsLower(character)}");
18         Console.WriteLine($"is upper case: {char.IsUpper(character)}");
19         Console.WriteLine($"to upper case: {char.ToUpper(character)}");
20         Console.WriteLine($"to lower case: {char.ToLower(character)}");
21         Console.WriteLine(
22            $"is punctuation: {char.IsPunctuation(character)}");
23         Console.WriteLine($"is symbol: {char.IsSymbol(character)}");
24      }
25   }
```

```
Enter a character: A
is digit: False
is letter: True
is letter or digit: True
is lower case: False
is upper case: True
to upper case: A
to lower case: a
is punctuation: False
is symbol: False
```

Fig. 16.15 | Demonstrates static character-testing and case-conversion methods from Char struct. (Part 1 of 2.)

```
Enter a character: 8
is digit: True
is letter: False
is letter or digit: True
is lower case: False
is upper case: False
to upper case: 8
to lower case: 8
is punctuation: False
is symbol: False
```

```
Enter a character: @
is digit: False
is letter: False
is letter or digit: False
is lower case: False
is upper case: False
to upper case: @
to lower case: @
is punctuation: True
is symbol: False
```

```
Enter a character: m
is digit: False
is letter: True
is letter or digit: True
is lower case: True
is upper case: False
to upper case: M
to lower case: m
is punctuation: False
is symbol: False
```

```
Enter a character: +
is digit: False
is letter: False
is letter or digit: False
is lower case: False
is upper case: False
to upper case: +
to lower case: +
is punctuation: False
is symbol: True
```

Fig. 16.15 | Demonstrates static character-testing and case-conversion methods from Char struct. (Part 2 of 2.)

After the user enters a character, lines 13–23 analyze it. Line 13 uses Char method IsDigit to determine whether character is defined as a digit. If so, the method returns true; otherwise, it returns false (note that bool values are capitalized for output). Line 14 uses Char method IsLetter to determine whether character is a letter. Line 16 uses Char method IsLetterOrDigit to determine whether character character is a letter or a digit.

The methods in lines 17–20 are culture sensitive. Line 17 uses Char method IsLower to determine whether character is a *lowercase* letter. Line 18 uses Char method IsUpper to determine whether character is an *uppercase* letter.

Line 19 uses Char method ToUpper to convert character to its *uppercase* equivalent. The method returns the converted character if the it has an uppercase equivalent; otherwise, the method returns its *original* argument.

Line 20 uses Char method ToLower to convert character to its *lowercase* equivalent. The method returns the converted character if the character has a lowercase equivalent; otherwise, the method returns its *original* argument.

Line 22 uses Char method IsPunctuation to determine whether character is a punctuation mark, such as "!", ":" or ")". Line 23 uses Char method IsSymbol to determine whether character character is a symbol, such as "+", "=" or "^".

Structure type Char also contains other methods not shown in this example. Many of the static methods are similar—for instance, IsWhiteSpace is used to determine whether a certain character is a whitespace character (e.g., newline, tab or space). The struct also contains several public instance methods; many of these, such as methods ToString and Equals, are methods that we have seen before in other classes. This group includes method CompareTo, which is used to compare one character value with another.

16.15 Introduction to Regular Expressions (Online)

This online section is available via the book's Companion Website at

www.pearsonhighered.com/deitel

See the scratch card inside the book's front cover for information on how to access the Companion Website. In this section, we introduce **regular expressions**—specially formatted strings used to find patterns in text. They can be used to ensure that data is in a particular format. For example, a U.S. zip code must consist of five digits, or five digits followed by a dash followed by four more digits. Compilers use regular expressions to *validate* program syntax. If the program code does *not* match the regular expression, the compiler indicates that there's a syntax error. We discuss classes Regex and Match from the System.Text.RegularExpressions namespace as well as the symbols used to form regular expressions. We then demonstrate how to find patterns in a string, match entire strings to patterns, replace characters in a string that match a pattern and split strings at delimiters specified as a pattern in a regular expression.

16.16 Wrap-Up

This chapter presented the Framework Class Library's string- and character-processing capabilities. We overviewed the fundamentals of characters and strings. You saw how to determine the length of strings, copy strings, access the individual characters in strings, search strings, obtain substrings from larger strings, compare strings, concatenate strings, replace characters in strings and convert strings to uppercase or lowercase letters.

We showed how to use class StringBuilder to build strings dynamically. You learned how to determine and specify the size of a StringBuilder object, and how to append, insert, remove and replace characters in a `StringBuilder` object. We then introduced the character-testing methods of type `Char` that enable a program to determine whether a character is a digit, a letter, a lowercase letter, an uppercase letter, a punctuation mark or a symbol other than a punctuation mark, and the methods for converting a character to uppercase or lowercase.

In the online `Regex` section, we discussed classes `Regex`, `Match` and `MatchCollection` from namespace `System.Text.RegularExpressions` and the symbols that are used to form regular expressions. You learned how to find patterns in a `string` and match entire `string`s to patterns with `Regex` methods `Match` and `Matches`, how to replace characters in a `string` with `Regex` method `Replace` and how to split `string`s at delimiters with `Regex` method `Split`. In the next chapter, you'll learn how to read data from and write data to text files. We'll also demonstrate C#'s object-serialization mechanism that can convert objects into bytes so you can output and input objects.

Summary

Section 16.2 Fundamentals of Characters and Strings

- Characters are the fundamental building blocks of C# program code. Every program is composed of a sequence of characters that's interpreted by the compiler as a series of instructions used to accomplish a task.

- A `string` is a series of characters treated as a single unit. A `string` may include letters, digits and the various special characters: +, -, *, /, $ and others.

Section 16.3 *string* Constructors

- All `string`s are immutable—their character contents cannot be changed after they're created.

Section 16.4 *string* Indexer, **Length** Property and **CopyTo** Method

- Property `Length` determines the number of characters in a `string`.

- The `string` indexer receives an integer argument as the *position number* and returns the character at that position. The first element of a `string` is considered to be at position 0.

- Attempting to access a character that's outside a `string`'s bounds results in an `IndexOutOfRangeException`.

- Method `CopyTo` copies a specified number of characters from a `string` into a `char` array.

Section 16.5 Comparing *string*s

- Some `string`-comparison capabilities use word sorting rules that depend on the computer's currently selected culture.

- Method `Equals` and the overloaded equality operator (`==`) can each be used to compare the contents of two `string`s for equality.

- Method `CompareTo` returns 0 if the `string`s are equal, a negative number if the `string` that invokes `CompareTo` is less than the `string` passed as an argument and a positive number if the `string` that invokes `CompareTo` is greater than the `string` passed as an argument.

- `string` methods `StartsWith` and `EndsWith` determine whether a `string` starts or ends with the characters specified as an argument, respectively.

Section 16.6 Locating Characters and Substrings in *strings*

- string method IndexOf locates the first occurrence of a character or a substring in a string. Method LastIndexOf locates the last occurrence of a character or a substring in a string.

Section 16.7 Extracting Substrings from *strings*

- Class string provides two Substring methods to enable a new string to be created by copying part of an existing string.

Section 16.8 Concatenating *strings*

- The static method Concat of class string concatenates two strings and returns a new string containing the characters from both original strings.

Section 16.10 Class *StringBuilder*

- Once a string is created, its contents can never change. Class StringBuilder (namespace System.Text) is available for creating and manipulating strings that can change.

Section 16.11 *Length* and *Capacity* Properties, *EnsureCapacity* Method and Indexer of Class *StringBuilder*

- Class StringBuilder provides Length and Capacity properties to return, respectively, the number of characters currently in a StringBuilder and the number of characters that can be stored in a StringBuilder without allocating more memory. These properties also can be used to increase or decrease the StringBuilder's length or the capacity.
- Method EnsureCapacity allows you to guarantee that a StringBuilder has a minimum capacity.

Section 16.12 *Append* and *AppendFormat* Methods of Class *StringBuilder*

- Class StringBuilder provides Append and AppendFormat methods to allow various types of values to be added to the end of a StringBuilder.

Section 16.13 *Insert, Remove* and *Replace* Methods of Class *StringBuilder*

- Class StringBuilder provides many overloaded Insert methods to allow various types of values to be inserted at any position in a StringBuilder. Versions are provided for each simple type and for character arrays, strings and Objects.
- Class StringBuilder also provides method Remove for deleting any portion of a StringBuilder.
- StringBuilder method Replace searches for a specified string or character and substitutes another in its place.

Section 16.14 *Char Methods*

- The simple types are actually aliases for struct types.
- All struct types derive from class ValueType, which in turn derives from object.
- All struct types are implicitly sealed.
- Char is a struct that represents characters.
- Method Char.IsDigit determines whether a character is a defined Unicode digit.
- Method Char.IsLetter determines whether a character is a letter.
- Method Char.IsLetterOrDigit determines whether a character is a letter or a digit.
- Method Char.IsLower determines whether a character is a lowercase letter.
- Method Char.IsUpper determines whether a character is an uppercase letter.
- Method Char.ToUpper converts a lowercase character to its uppercase equivalent.

- Method `Char.ToLower` converts an uppercase character to its lowercase equivalent.
- Method `Char.IsPunctuation` determines whether a character is a punctuation mark.
- Method `Char.IsSymbol` determines whether a character is a symbol.
- Method `Char.IsWhiteSpace` determines whether a character is a whitespace character.
- Method `Char.CompareTo` compares two character values.

Terminology

@ verbatim string character	`IsSymbol` method of struct `Char`
+ operator	`IsUpper` method of struct `Char`
+= concatenation operator	`IsWhiteSpace` method of struct `Char`
== equality operator	`LastIndexOf` method of class `string`
alphabetizing	`LastIndexOfAny` method of class `string`
`Append` method of class `StringBuilder`	leading whitespace characters
`AppendFormat` method of class `StringBuilder`	`Length` property of class `string`
`Capacity` property of `StringBuilder`	`Length` property of class `StringBuilder`
char array	`Remove` method of class `StringBuilder`
`Char` struct	`Replace` method of class `string`
character	`Replace` method of class `StringBuilder`
character constant	`StartsWith` method of class `string`
`CompareTo` method of class `string`	`string` class
`CompareTo` method of struct `Char`	string literal
`Concat` method of class `string`	string reference
`CopyTo` method of class `string`	`StringBuilder` class
`EndsWith` method of class `string`	`Substring` method of class `string`
`EnsureCapacity` method of class	`System` namespace
`StringBuilder`	`System.Text` namespace
`Equals` method of class `string`	`ToLower` method of class `string`
`Equals` method of struct `Char`	`ToLower` method of struct `Char`
format string	`ToString` method of class `string`
`immutable string`	`ToString` method of `StringBuilder`
`IndexOf` method of class `string`	`ToUpper` method of class `string`
`IndexOfAny` method of class `string`	`ToUpper` method of struct `Char`
`Insert` method of class `StringBuilder`	trailing whitespace characters
`IsDigit` method of struct `Char`	`Trim` method of class `string`
`IsLetter` method of struct `Char`	Unicode character set
`IsLetterOrDigit` method of struct `Char`	`ValueType` class
`IsLower` method of struct `Char`	verbatim string syntax
`IsPunctuation` method of struct `Char`	

Self-Review Exercises

16.1 State whether each of the following is *true* or *false*. If *false*, explain why.
    a) When `strings` are compared with ==, the result is `true` if the `strings` contain the same values.
    b) A `string` can be modified after it's created.
    c) `StringBuilder` method `EnsureCapacity` sets the `StringBuilder` instance's length to the argument's value.
    d) Method `Equals` and the equality operator work the same for `strings`.
    e) Method `Trim` removes all whitespace at the beginning and the end of a `string`.

    f) It's always better to use strings, rather than StringBuilders, because strings containing the same value will reference the same object.

    g) string method ToUpper creates a new string with the first letter capitalized.

16.2   Fill in the blanks in each of the following statements:

    a) To concatenate strings, use operator _____, StringBuilder method _____ or string method _____.

    b) StringBuilder method _____ first formats the specified string, then concatenates it to the end of the StringBuilder.

    c) If the arguments to a Substring method call are out of range, a(n) _____ exception is thrown.

    d) A C in a format string means to output the number as _____.

Answers to Self-Review Exercises

16.1   a) True. b) False. strings are immutable; they cannot be modified after they're created. StringBuilder objects can be modified after they're created. c) False. EnsureCapacity simply ensures that the current capacity is at least the value specified in the method call. d) True. e) True. f) False. StringBuilder should be used if the string is to be modified. g) False. string method ToUpper creates a new string with all of its letters capitalized.

16.2   a) +, Append, Concat. b) AppendFormat c) ArgumentOutOfRangeException. d) currency.

Exercises

16.3   *(Comparing strings)* Write an app that uses string method CompareTo to compare two strings input by the user. Output whether the first string is less than, equal to or greater than the second.

16.4   *(Random Sentences and Story Writer)* Write an app that uses random-number generation to create sentences. Use four arrays of strings, called article, noun, verb and preposition. Create a sentence by selecting a word at random from each array in the following order: article, noun, verb, preposition, article, noun. As each word is picked, concatenate it to the previous words in the sentence. The words should be separated by spaces. When the sentence is output, it should start with a capital letter and end with a period. The program should generate 10 sentences and output them to a text box.

    The arrays should be filled as follows: The article array should contain the articles "the", "a", "one", "some" and "any"; the noun array should contain the nouns "boy", "girl", "dog", "town" and "car"; the verb array should contain the past-tense verbs "drove", "jumped", "ran", "walked" and "skipped"; and the preposition array should contain the prepositions "to", "from", "over", "under" and "on".

16.5   *(Pig Latin)* Write an app that encodes English-language phrases into pig Latin. Pig Latin is a form of coded language often used for amusement. Many variations exist in the methods used to form pig Latin phrases. For simplicity, use the following algorithm:

    To translate each English word into a pig Latin word, place the first letter of the English word at the end of the word and add the letters "ay." Thus, the word "jump" becomes "umpjay," the word "the" becomes "hetay" and the word "computer" becomes "omputercay." Blanks between words remain blanks. Assume the following: The English phrase consists of words separated by blanks, there are no punctuation marks and all words have two or more letters. Enable the user to input a sentence. Use techniques discussed in this chapter to divide the sentence into separate words. Method GetPigLatin should translate a single word into pig Latin. Keep a running display of all the converted sentences in a text box.

16.6   *(All Possible Three-Letter Words from a Five-Letter Word)* Write a program that reads a five-letter word from the user and produces all possible three-letter combinations that can be derived from the letters of the five-letter word. For example, the three-letter words produced from the word "bathe" include the commonly used words "ate," "bat," "bet," "tab," "hat," "the" and "tea," and the 3-letter combinations "bth," "eab," etc.

16.7   *(Capitalizing Words)* Write a program that uses regular expressions to convert the first letter of every word to uppercase. Have it do this for an arbitrary string input by the user.

Making-a-Difference Exercises

16.8   *(Project: Cooking with Healthier Ingredients)* Obesity in the United States is increasing at an alarming rate. Check the map from the Centers for Disease Control and Prevention (CDC) at http://stateofobesity.org/adult-obesity/, which shows obesity trends in the United States over the last 20 years. As obesity increases, so do occurrences of related problems (e.g., heart disease, high blood pressure, high cholesterol, type 2 diabetes). Write a program that helps users choose healthier ingredients when cooking, and helps those allergic to certain foods (e.g., nuts, gluten) find substitutes. The program should read a recipe from the user and suggest healthier replacements for some of the ingredients. For simplicity, your program should assume the recipe has no abbreviations for measures such as teaspoons, cups, and tablespoons, and uses numerical digits for quantities (e.g., 1 egg, 2 cups) rather than spelling them out (one egg, two cups). Some common substitutions are shown in Fig. 16.16. Your program should display a warning such as, "Always consult your physician before making significant changes to your diet."

Ingredient	Substitution
1 cup sour cream	1 cup yogurt
1 cup milk	1/2 cup evaporated milk and 1/2 cup water
1 teaspoon lemon juice	1/2 teaspoon vinegar
1 cup sugar	1/2 cup honey, 1 cup molasses or 1/4 cup agave nectar
1 cup butter	1 cup margarine or yogurt
1 cup flour	1 cup rye or rice flour
1 cup mayonnaise	1 cup cottage cheese or 1/8 cup mayonnaise and 7/8 cup yogurt
1 egg	2 tablespoons cornstarch, arrowroot flour or potato starch or 2 egg whites or 1/2 of a large banana (mashed)
1 cup milk	1 cup soy milk
1/4 cup oil	1/4 cup applesauce
white bread	whole-grain bread

Fig. 16.16 | Common ingredient substitutions.

Your program should take into consideration that replacements are not always one-for-one. For example, if a cake recipe calls for three eggs, it might reasonably use six egg whites instead. Conversion data for measurements and substitutes can be obtained at websites such as

```
http://chinesefood.about.com/od/recipeconversionfaqs/f/usmetricrecipes.htm
http://www.pioneerthinking.com/eggsub.html
http://www.gourmetsleuth.com/conversions.htm
```

Your program should consider the user's health concerns, such as high cholesterol, high blood pressure, weight loss, gluten allergy, and so on. For high cholesterol, the program should suggest substitutes for eggs and dairy products; if the user wishes to lose weight, low-calorie substitutes for ingredients such as sugar should be suggested.

16.9   *(Project: Spam Scanner)* Spam (or junk e-mail) costs U.S. organizations billions of dollars a year in spam-prevention software, equipment, network resources, bandwidth, and lost productivity. Research online some of the most common spam e-mail messages and words, and check your own junk e-mail folder. Create a list of 30 words and phrases commonly found in spam messages. Write an app in which the user enters an e-mail message. Then, scan the message for each of the 30 keywords or phrases. For each occurrence of one of these within the message, add a point to the message's "spam score." Next, rate the likelihood that the message is spam, based on the number of points it received.

16.10   *(Project: SMS Language)* Short Message Service (SMS) is a communications service that allows sending text messages of 160 or fewer characters between mobile phones. With the proliferation of mobile phone use worldwide, SMS is being used in many developing nations for political purposes (e.g., voicing opinions and opposition), reporting news about natural disasters, and so on. For example, check out comunica.org/radio2.0/archives/87. Since the length of SMS messages is limited, SMS Language—abbreviations of common words and phrases in mobile text messages, e-mails, instant messages, etc.—is often used. For example, "in my opinion" is "IMO" in SMS Language. Research SMS Language online. Write a program in which the user can enter a message using SMS Language, then the program translates it into English (or your own language). Also provide a mechanism to translate text written in English (or your own language) into SMS Language. One potential problem is that one SMS abbreviation could expand into a variety of phrases. For example, IMO (as used above) could also stand for "International Maritime Organization," "in memory of," etc.

Files and Streams

Objectives

In this chapter you'll:

- Create, read, write and update files.

- Use classes **File** and **Directory** to obtain information about files and directories on your computer.

- Use LINQ to search through directories.

- Become familiar with sequential-access file processing.

- Use classes **FileStream**, **StreamReader** and **StreamWriter** to read text from and write text to files.

- Use classes **FileStream** and **BinaryFormatter** to read objects from and write objects to files.

17.1 Introduction

Variables and arrays offer only *temporary* storage of data—the data is lost when a local variable "goes out of scope" or when the program terminates. By contrast, files (and databases, which we cover in Chapter 22) are used for long-term retention of large amounts of data, even after the program that created the data terminates. Data maintained in files often is called persistent data. Computers store files on secondary storage devices, such as hard drives, solid-state drives, flash drives, DVDs and tapes. In this chapter, we explain how to create, update and process data files in C# programs.

We overview some of the Framework Class Library's file-processing classes. We then create Windows Forms apps that write to and read from *text files* that are *human readable* and binary files that store entire objects in binary format. Finally, we present examples that show how you can determine information about the files and directories on your computer.

17.2 Files and Streams

C# views each file as a sequential stream of bytes (Fig. 17.1). Each file ends either with an end-of-file marker or at a specific byte number that's recorded in a system-maintained administrative data structure, because file organization is operating-system dependent. A C# program processing a stream of bytes simply receives an indication from the operating system when it reaches the end of the stream—the program does *not* need to know how the underlying platform represents files or streams.

Fig. 17.1 | C#'s view of an *n*-byte file.

Standard Streams in Console Apps
When a file is opened, an object is created and a stream is associated with the object. When a console app executes, the runtime environment creates three stream objects that are ac-

cessible via properties `Console.Out`, `Console.In` and `Console.Error`, respectively. These objects use streams to facilitate communication between a program and a particular file or device. `Console.In` refers to the standard input stream object, which enables a program to input data from the keyboard. `Console.Out` refers to the standard output stream object, which enables a program to output data to the screen. `Console.Error` refers to the standard error stream object, which enables a program to output error messages to the screen. These can be redirected to other files or devices. We've been using `Console.Out` and `Console.In` in our console apps:

- `Console` methods `Write` and `WriteLine` use `Console.Out` to perform output, and

- `Console` methods `Read` and `ReadLine` use `Console.In` to perform input.

File-Processing Classes

There are many file-processing classes in the Framework Class Library. The `System.IO` namespace includes stream classes such as `StreamReader` (for text input from a stream), `StreamWriter` (for text output to a stream) and `FileStream` (for both input from and output to a stream). These stream classes inherit from abstract classes `TextReader`, `TextWriter` and `Stream`, respectively. `Console.In` and `Console.Error` are of type `TextWriter`. `Console.In` is of type `TextReader`. The system creates objects of `TextReader` and `TextWriter` derived classes to initialize `Console` properties `Console.In` and `Console.Out`.

Abstract class `Stream` provides functionality for representing streams as bytes. Classes `FileStream`, `MemoryStream` and `BufferedStream` (all from namespace `System.IO`) inherit from class `Stream`. Class `FileStream` can be used to write data to and read data from files. Class `MemoryStream` enables the transfer of data directly to and from memory—this is much faster than reading from and writing to external devices.

Class `BufferedStream` uses buffering to transfer data to or from a stream. Buffering is an I/O performance-enhancement technique, in which each output operation is directed to a region in memory, called a buffer, that's large enough to hold the data from *many* output operations. Then actual transfer to the output device is performed in one large physical output operation each time the buffer fills. The output operations directed to the output buffer in memory often are called logical output operations. Buffering also can be used to speed input operations by initially reading more data than is required into a buffer, so subsequent reads get data from high-speed memory rather than a slower external device.

In this chapter, we use key stream classes to implement file-processing programs that create and manipulate sequential-access files.

17.3 Creating a Sequential-Access Text File

C# imposes *no* structure on files. Thus, the concept of a "record" does *not* exist in C# files. This means that you must structure files to meet the requirements of your apps. The next few examples use text and special characters to organize our own concept of a "record."

Class *BankUIForm*

The following examples demonstrate file processing in a bank-account maintenance app. These programs have similar user interfaces, so we created reusable class `BankUIForm` (Fig. 17.2) to encapsulate the common GUI (see the screen capture in Fig. 17.2). Class

BankUIForm (part of the BankLibrary project with this chapter's examples) contains four Labels and four TextBoxes. Methods ClearTextBoxes (lines 22–30), SetTextBoxValues (lines 33–51) and GetTextBoxValues (lines 54–59) clear, set the text in and get the text from the TextBoxes, respectively. Using *visual inheritance*—presented in Section 15.13—you can extend this class to create the GUIs for several examples in this chapter. Recall that to reuse class BankUIForm, you must compile the GUI into a class library, then add a reference to the new class library's DLL in each project that will reuse it (see Section 15.13).

```csharp
1   // Fig. 17.2: BankUIForm.cs
2   // A reusable Windows Form for the examples in this chapter.
3   using System;
4   using System.Windows.Forms;
5
6   namespace BankLibrary
7   {
8      public partial class BankUIForm : Form
9      {
10         protected int TextBoxCount { get; set; } = 4; // number of TextBoxes
11
12         // enumeration constants specify TextBox indices
13         public enum TextBoxIndices {Account, First, Last, Balance}
14
15         // parameterless constructor
16         public BankUIForm()
17         {
18            InitializeComponent();
19         }
20
21         // clear all TextBoxes
22         public void ClearTextBoxes()
23         {
24            // iterate through every Control on form
25            foreach (Control guiControl in Controls)
26            {
27               // if Control is TextBox, clear it
28               (guiControl as TextBox)?.Clear();
29            }
30         }
31
32         // set text box values to string-array values
33         public void SetTextBoxValues(string[] values)
34         {
35            // determine whether string array has correct length
36            if (values.Length != TextBoxCount)
37            {
38               // throw exception if not correct length
39               throw (new ArgumentException(
40                  $"There must be {TextBoxCount} strings in the array",
41                  nameof(values)));
42            }
```

Fig. 17.2 | A reusable Windows Form for the examples in this chapter. (Part 1 of 2.)

```
43              else // set array values if array has correct length
44              {
45                  // set array values to TextBox values
46                  accountTextBox.Text = values[(int) TextBoxIndices.Account];
47                  firstNameTextBox.Text = values[(int) TextBoxIndices.First];
48                  lastNameTextBox.Text = values[(int) TextBoxIndices.Last];
49                  balanceTextBox.Text = values[(int) TextBoxIndices.Balance];
50              }
51          }
52
53          // return TextBox values as string array
54          public string[] GetTextBoxValues()
55          {
56              return new string[] {
57                  accountTextBox.Text, firstNameTextBox.Text,
58                  lastNameTextBox.Text, balanceTextBox.Text};
59          }
60      }
61  }
```

Fig. 17.2 | A reusable Windows Form for the examples in this chapter. (Part 2 of 2.)

Class Record

Figure 17.3 contains class Record that Figs. 17.4, 17.6 and 17.7 use for maintaining the information in each record that's written to or read from a file. This class also belongs to the BankLibrary, so it's located in the same project as class BankUIForm.

```
 1  // Fig. 17.3: Record.cs
 2  // Class that represents a data record.
 3  namespace BankLibrary
 4  {
 5      public class Record
 6      {
 7          public int Account { get; set; }
 8          public string FirstName { get; set; }
 9          public string LastName { get; set; }
10          public decimal Balance { get; set; }
```

Fig. 17.3 | Class that represents a data record. (Part 1 of 2.)

```
11
12        // parameterless constructor sets members to default values
13        public Record() : this(0, string.Empty, string.Empty, 0M) { }
14
15        // overloaded constructor sets members to parameter values
16        public Record(int account, string firstName,
17           string lastName, decimal balance)
18        {
19           Account = account;
20           FirstName = firstName;
21           LastName = lastName;
22           Balance = balance;
23        }
24     }
25  }
```

Fig. 17.3 | Class that represents a data record. (Part 2 of 2.)

Class `Record` contains *auto-implemented properties* `Account`, `FirstName`, `LastName` and `Balance` (lines 7–10), which collectively represent all the information for a record. The parameterless constructor (line 13) sets these members by calling the four-argument constructor with 0 for the account number, `string.Empty` for the first and last name and `0.0M` for the balance. The four-argument constructor (lines 16–23) sets these members to the specified parameter values.

Using a Character Stream to Create an Output File

Class `CreateFileForm` (Fig. 17.4) uses instances of class `Record` to create a *sequential-access file* that might be used in an accounts-receivable system—i.e., a program that organizes data regarding money owed by a company's credit clients. For each client, the program obtains an account number and the client's first name, last name and balance (i.e., the amount of money that the client owes to the company for previously received goods and services). The data obtained for each client constitutes a record for that client. In this app, the account number is used as the *record key*—files are created and maintained in account-number order. This program assumes that the user enters records in account-number order. However, a comprehensive accounts-receivable system would provide a *sorting* capability, so the user could enter the records in any order. When you create a **Windows Forms Application** project for this app, be sure to add a reference to `BankLibrary.dll` and to change the base class from `Form` to `BankUIForm`. See Section 15.13 for information on adding a reference to a class library.

```
1  // Fig. 17.4: CreateFileForm.cs
2  // Creating a sequential-access file.
3  using System;
4  using System.Windows.Forms;
5  using System.IO;
6  using BankLibrary;
7
```

Fig. 17.4 | Creating a sequential-access file. (Part 1 of 5.)

```
8  namespace CreateFile
9  {
10    public partial class CreateFileForm : BankUIForm
11    {
12       private StreamWriter fileWriter; // writes data to text file
13
14       // parameterless constructor
15       public CreateFileForm()
16       {
17          InitializeComponent();
18       }
19
20       // event handler for Save Button
21       private void saveButton_Click(object sender, EventArgs e)
22       {
23          // create and show dialog box enabling user to save file
24          DialogResult result; // result of SaveFileDialog
25          string fileName; // name of file containing data
26
27          using (var fileChooser = new SaveFileDialog())
28          {
29             fileChooser.CheckFileExists = false; // let user create file
30             result = fileChooser.ShowDialog();
31             fileName = fileChooser.FileName; // name of file to save data
32          }
33
34          // ensure that user clicked "OK"
35          if (result == DialogResult.OK)
36          {
37             // show error if user specified invalid file
38             if (string.IsNullOrEmpty(fileName))
39             {
40                MessageBox.Show("Invalid File Name", "Error",
41                   MessageBoxButtons.OK, MessageBoxIcon.Error);
42             }
43             else
44             {
45                // save file via FileStream
46                try
47                {
48                   // open file with write access
49                   var output = new FileStream(fileName,
50                      FileMode.OpenOrCreate, FileAccess.Write);
51
52                   // sets file to where data is written
53                   fileWriter = new StreamWriter(output);
54
55                   // disable Save button and enable Enter button
56                   saveButton.Enabled = false;
57                   enterButton.Enabled = true;
58                }
59                catch (IOException)
60                {
```

Fig. 17.4 | Creating a sequential-access file. (Part 2 of 5.)

```
 61                             // notify user if file does not exist
 62                             MessageBox.Show("Error opening file", "Error",
 63                                 MessageBoxButtons.OK, MessageBoxIcon.Error);
 64                         }
 65                     }
 66                 }
 67             }
 68
 69             // handler for enterButton Click
 70             private void enterButton_Click(object sender, EventArgs e)
 71             {
 72                 // store TextBox values string array
 73                 string[] values = GetTextBoxValues();
 74
 75                 // determine whether TextBox account field is empty
 76                 if (!string.IsNullOrEmpty(values[(int) TextBoxIndices.Account]))
 77                 {
 78                     // store TextBox values in Record and output it
 79                     try
 80                     {
 81                         // get account-number value from TextBox
 82                         int accountNumber =
 83                             int.Parse(values[(int) TextBoxIndices.Account]);
 84
 85                         // determine whether accountNumber is valid
 86                         if (accountNumber > 0)
 87                         {
 88                             // Record containing TextBox values to output
 89                             var record = new Record(accountNumber,
 90                                 values[(int) TextBoxIndices.First],
 91                                 values[(int) TextBoxIndices.Last],
 92                                 decimal.Parse(values[(int) TextBoxIndices.Balance]));
 93
 94                             // write Record to file, fields separated by commas
 95                             fileWriter.WriteLine(
 96                                 $"{record.Account},{record.FirstName}," +
 97                                 $"{record.LastName},{record.Balance}");
 98                         }
 99                         else
100                         {
101                             // notify user if invalid account number
102                             MessageBox.Show("Invalid Account Number", "Error",
103                                 MessageBoxButtons.OK, MessageBoxIcon.Error);
104                         }
105                     }
106                     catch (IOException)
107                     {
108                         MessageBox.Show("Error Writing to File", "Error",
109                             MessageBoxButtons.OK, MessageBoxIcon.Error);
110                     }
111                     catch (FormatException)
112                     {
```

Fig. 17.4 | Creating a sequential-access file. (Part 3 of 5.)

```
113                    MessageBox.Show("Invalid Format", "Error",
114                       MessageBoxButtons.OK, MessageBoxIcon.Error);
115                }
116             }
117
118             ClearTextBoxes(); // clear TextBox values
119          }
120
121          // handler for exitButton Click
122          private void exitButton_Click(object sender, EventArgs e)
123          {
124             try
125             {
126                fileWriter?.Close(); // close StreamWriter and underlying file
127             }
128             catch (IOException)
129             {
130                MessageBox.Show("Cannot close file", "Error",
131                   MessageBoxButtons.OK, MessageBoxIcon.Error);
132             }
133
134             Application.Exit();
135          }
136       }
137    }
```

a) BankUI graphical user interface with three additional controls

b) Save File dialog

Files and directories

Fig. 17.4 | Creating a sequential-access file. (Part 4 of 5.)

c) Account 100,
"Nancy Brown",
saved with a
balance of -25.54

Fig. 17.4 | Creating a sequential-access file. (Part 5 of 5.)

Class `CreateFileForm` either creates or opens a file (depending on whether one exists), then allows the user to write records to it. The `using` directive in line 6 enables us to use the classes of the `BankLibrary` namespace; this namespace contains class `BankUI-Form`, from which class `CreateFileForm` inherits (line 10). Class `CreateFileForm`'s GUI enhances that of class `BankUIForm` with buttons **Save As**, **Enter** and **Exit**.

Method `saveButton_Click`
When the user clicks the **Save As** button, the program invokes the event handler `saveButton_Click` (lines 21–67). Line 27 instantiates an object of class `SaveFileDialog` (namespace `System.Windows.Forms`). By placing this object in a `using` statement (lines 27–32), we ensure that the dialog's `Dispose` method is called to release its resources as soon as the program has retrieved the user's input. `SaveFileDialog` objects are used for selecting files (see the second screen in Fig. 17.4). Line 29 indicates that the dialog should not check if the filename specified by the user already exists (this is actually the default). Line 30 calls `SaveFileDialog` method `ShowDialog` to display the dialog.

When displayed, a `SaveFileDialog` prevents the user from interacting with any other window in the program until the user closes the `SaveFileDialog` by clicking either **Save** or **Cancel**. Dialogs that behave in this manner are called **modal dialogs**. The user selects the appropriate drive, directory and filename, then clicks **Save**. Method `ShowDialog` returns a `DialogResult` specifying which button (**Save** or **Cancel**) the user clicked to close the dialog. This is assigned to `DialogResult` variable `result` (line 30). Line 31 gets the filename from the dialog. Line 35 tests whether the user clicked **OK** by comparing this value to `DialogResult.OK`. If the values are equal, method `saveButton_Click` continues.

You can open files to perform text manipulation by creating objects of class `FileStream`. In this example, we want the file to be opened for *output*, so lines 49–50 create a `FileStream` object. The `FileStream` constructor that we use receives three arguments—a `string` containing the path and name of the file to open, a constant describing how to open the file and a constant describing the file read-write permissions. The constant `FileMode.OpenOrCreate` (line 50) indicates that the `FileStream` object should open the file if it *exists* or create the file if it *does not exist*.

Note that the contents of an existing file are *overwritten* by the `FileStream`. To *preserve* the original contents of a file, use `FileMode.Append`. There are other `FileMode` constants describing how to open files; we introduce these constants as we use them in examples. The constant `FileAccess.Write` indicates that the program can perform only *write* operations with the `FileStream` object. There are two other constants for the third constructor parameter—`FileAccess.Read` for read-only access and `FileAccess.ReadWrite` for both read and write access.

Line 59 catches an `IOException` if there's a problem opening the file or creating the `StreamWriter`. If so, the program displays an error message (lines 62–63). If no exception occurs, the file is open for writing.

Common Programming Error 17.1

Failure to open a file before attempting to use it in a program is a logic error.

Method `enterButton_Click`

After typing information into each `TextBox`, the user clicks **Enter**, which calls `enterButton_Click` (lines 70–119) to save the data from the `TextBox`es into the user-specified file. If the user entered a *valid* account number (i.e., an integer greater than zero), lines 89–92 create a `Record` containing the `TextBox` values. If the user entered *invalid* data in one of the `TextBox`es (such as nonnumeric characters in the **Balance** field), the program throws a `FormatException`. The `catch` block in lines 111–115 handles such exceptions by notifying the user (via a `MessageBox`) of the improper format.[1]

If the user entered *valid* data, lines 95–97 write the record to the file by invoking method `WriteLine` of the `StreamWriter` object that was created at line 53. Method `WriteLine` writes a sequence of characters to a file. The `StreamWriter` object is constructed with a `FileStream` argument that specifies the file to which the `StreamWriter` will output text. Class `StreamWriter` (like most of the classes we discuss in this chapter) belongs to the `System.IO` namespace. Finally, the `TextBox`es are cleared so the user can begin typing the next record's data.

Method `exitButton_Click`

When the user clicks **Exit**, `exitButton_Click` (lines 122–135) executes. Line 126 closes the `StreamWriter` (if it is not `null`), which automatically closes the underlying `FileStream`. Then, line 134 terminates the program. Note that method `Close` is called in a `try` block. Method `Close` throws an `IOException` if the file or stream cannot be closed properly. In this case, it's important to notify the user that the information in the file or stream might be *corrupted*.

Performance Tip 17.1

Releasing resources explicitly when they're no longer needed makes them immediately available for reuse by other programs, thus improving resource utilization.

---

1. We could prevent these exceptions by using `int.TryParse` in line 83 and `decimal.TryParse`—we chose not to in this chapter's apps, because doing so adds many lines of logic to the apps (which are already long). However, it's considered better practice to prevent such exceptions.

Sample Data

To test the program, we entered information for the accounts shown in Fig. 17.5. The program does not depict how the data records are stored in the file. To verify that the file has been created successfully, we create a program in the next section to read and display the file. Since this is a *text file*, you can actually open it in any *text editor* to see its contents.

Account number	First name	Last name	Balance
100	Nancy	Brown	-25.54
200	Stacey	Dunn	314.33
300	Doug	Barker	0.00
400	Dave	Smith	258.34
500	Sam	Stone	34.98

Fig. 17.5 | Sample data for the program of Fig. 17.4.

17.4 Reading Data from a Sequential-Access Text File

The previous section demonstrated how to create a file for use in sequential-access apps. In this section, we discuss how to read (or retrieve) data sequentially from a file. Class `ReadSequentialAccessFileForm` (Fig. 17.6) reads records from the file created by the program in Fig. 17.4, then displays the contents of each record. Much of the code in this example is similar to that of Fig. 17.4, so we discuss only the unique aspects of the app.

```
1   // Fig. 17.6: ReadSequentialAccessFileForm.cs
2   // Reading a sequential-access file.
3   using System;
4   using System.Windows.Forms;
5   using System.IO;
6   using BankLibrary;
7
8   namespace ReadSequentialAccessFile
9   {
10     public partial class ReadSequentialAccessFileForm : BankUIForm
11     {
12        private StreamReader fileReader; // reads data from a text file
13
14        // parameterless constructor
15        public ReadSequentialAccessFileForm()
16        {
17           InitializeComponent();
18        }
19
```

Fig. 17.6 | Reading a sequential-access file. (Part 1 of 4.)

```
20          // invoked when user clicks the Open button
21          private void openButton_Click(object sender, EventArgs e)
22          {
23             // create and show dialog box enabling user to open file
24             DialogResult result; // result of OpenFileDialog
25             string fileName; // name of file containing data
26
27             using (OpenFileDialog fileChooser = new OpenFileDialog())
28             {
29                result = fileChooser.ShowDialog();
30                fileName = fileChooser.FileName; // get specified name
31             }
32
33             // ensure that user clicked "OK"
34             if (result == DialogResult.OK)
35             {
36                ClearTextBoxes();
37
38                // show error if user specified invalid file
39                if (string.IsNullOrEmpty(fileName))
40                {
41                   MessageBox.Show("Invalid File Name", "Error",
42                      MessageBoxButtons.OK, MessageBoxIcon.Error);
43                }
44                else
45                {
46                   try
47                   {
48                      // create FileStream to obtain read access to file
49                      FileStream input = new FileStream(
50                         fileName, FileMode.Open, FileAccess.Read);
51
52                      // set file from where data is read
53                      fileReader = new StreamReader(input);
54
55                      openButton.Enabled = false; // disable Open File button
56                      nextButton.Enabled = true; // enable Next Record button
57                   }
58                   catch (IOException)
59                   {
60                      MessageBox.Show("Error reading from file",
61                         "File Error", MessageBoxButtons.OK,
62                         MessageBoxIcon.Error);
63                   }
64                }
65             }
66          }
67
68          // invoked when user clicks Next button
69          private void nextButton_Click(object sender, EventArgs e)
70          {
71             try
72             {
```

Fig. 17.6 | Reading a sequential-access file. (Part 2 of 4.)

```
73              // get next record available in file
74              var inputRecord = fileReader.ReadLine();
75
76              if (inputRecord != null)
77              {
78                  string[] inputFields = inputRecord.Split(',');
79
80                  // copy string-array values to TextBox values
81                  SetTextBoxValues(inputFields);
82              }
83              else
84              {
85                  // close StreamReader and underlying file
86                  fileReader.Close();
87                  openButton.Enabled = true; // enable Open File button
88                  nextButton.Enabled = false; // disable Next Record button
89                  ClearTextBoxes();
90
91                  // notify user if no records in file
92                  MessageBox.Show("No more records in file", string.Empty,
93                      MessageBoxButtons.OK, MessageBoxIcon.Information);
94              }
95          }
96          catch (IOException)
97          {
98              MessageBox.Show("Error Reading from File", "Error",
99                  MessageBoxButtons.OK, MessageBoxIcon.Error);
100         }
101     }
102   }
103 }
```

a) BankUI graphical user interface with an Open File button

Fig. 17.6 | Reading a sequential-access file. (Part 3 of 4.)

b) `OpenFileDialog` window

c) Reading account 100

d) User is shown a messagebox when all records have been read

Fig. 17.6 | Reading a sequential-access file. (Part 4 of 4.)

Method *openButton_Click*

When the user clicks **Open File**, the program calls event handler openButton_Click (lines 21–66). Line 27 creates an `OpenFileDialog`, and line 29 calls its ShowDialog method to display the **Open** dialog (see the second screenshot in Fig. 17.6). The behavior and GUI for the **Save** and **Open** dialog types are identical, except that **Save** is replaced by **Open**. If the user selects a *valid* filename, lines 49–50 create a FileStream object and assign it to reference input. We pass constant FileMode.Open as the second argument to the FileStream constructor to indicate that the FileStream should open the file if it exists or throw a `FileNotFoundException` if it does not. (In this example, the FileStream constructor will *not* throw a FileNotFoundException, because the OpenFileDialog is configured to check that the file exists.) In the last example (Fig. 17.4), we wrote text to the file using a FileStream object with *write-only access*. In this example (Fig. 17.6), we specify *read-only access* to the file by passing constant FileAccess.Read as the third argument to the FileStream constructor. This FileStream object is used to create a StreamReader object in line 53. The FileStream object specifies the file from which the StreamReader object will read text.

Error-Prevention Tip 17.1

Open a file with the `FileAccess.Read` *file-open mode if its contents should not be modified. This prevents unintentional modification of the contents.*

Method **nextButton_Click**

When the user clicks the **Next Record** button, the program calls event handler `nextButton_Click` (lines 69–101), which reads the next record from the user-specified file. (The user must click **Next Record** after opening the file to view the first record.) Line 74 calls `StreamReader` method `ReadLine` to read the next record. If an error occurs while reading the file, an `IOException` is thrown (caught at line 96), and the user is notified (lines 98–99). Otherwise, line 76 determines whether `StreamReader` method `ReadLine` returned `null` (i.e., there's no more text in the file). If not, line 78 uses `string` method `Split` to separate the stream of characters that was read from the file into tokens (`string`s) that represent the `Record`'s properties—the second argument indicates that the tokens are delimited by commas in this file. Line 81 displays the `Record` values in the `TextBox`es. If `ReadLine` returns `null`, the program closes the `StreamReader` object (line 86), automatically closing the `FileStream` object, then notifies the user that there are no more records (lines 92–93).

17.5 Case Study: Credit-Inquiry Program

To retrieve data *sequentially* from a file, programs normally start from the *beginning* of the file, reading consecutively until the desired data is found. It sometimes is necessary to process a file *sequentially* several times (from the *beginning* of the file) during the execution of a program. A `FileStream` object can *reposition* its file-position pointer (which contains the byte number of the next byte to be read from or written to the file) to *any* position in the file. When a `FileStream` object is opened, its *file-position pointer* is set to *byte position 0* (i.e., the *beginning* of the file).

We now present a program that builds on the concepts employed in Fig. 17.6. Class `CreditInquiryForm` (Fig. 17.7) is a credit-inquiry program that enables a credit manager to search for and display account information for those customers with credit balances (i.e., customers to whom the company owes money), zero balances (i.e., customers who do not owe the company money) and debit balances (i.e., customers who owe the company money for previously received goods and services). We use a `RichTextBox` in the program to display the account information. `RichTextBox`es provide more functionality than regular `TextBox`es—for example, `RichTextBox`es offer method `Find` for searching individual strings and method `LoadFile` for displaying file contents. Classes `RichTextBox` and `TextBox` both inherit from `abstract` class `System.Windows.Forms.TextBoxBase`. In this example, we chose a `RichTextBox`, because it displays multiple lines of text by default, whereas a regular `TextBox` displays only one. Alternatively, we could have specified that a `TextBox` object display *multiple* lines of text by setting its `Multiline` property to `true`.

The program displays buttons that enable a credit manager to obtain credit information. The **Open File** button opens a file for gathering data. The **Credit Balances** button displays a list of accounts that have credit balances, the **Debit Balances** button displays a list of accounts that have debit balances and the **Zero Balances** button displays a list of accounts that have zero balances. The **Done** button exits the app.

```csharp
1   // Fig. 17.7: CreditInquiryForm.cs
2   // Read a file sequentially and display contents based on
3   // account type specified by user (credit, debit or zero balances).
4   using System;
5   using System.Windows.Forms;
6   using System.IO;
7   using BankLibrary;
8
9   namespace CreditInquiry
10  {
11     public partial class CreditInquiryForm : Form
12     {
13        private FileStream input; // maintains the connection to the file
14        private StreamReader fileReader; // reads data from text file
15
16        // parameterless constructor
17        public CreditInquiryForm()
18        {
19           InitializeComponent();
20        }
21
22        // invoked when user clicks Open File button
23        private void openButton_Click(object sender, EventArgs e)
24        {
25           // create dialog box enabling user to open file
26           DialogResult result;
27           string fileName;
28
29           using (OpenFileDialog fileChooser = new OpenFileDialog())
30           {
31              result = fileChooser.ShowDialog();
32              fileName = fileChooser.FileName;
33           }
34
35           // exit event handler if user clicked Cancel
36           if (result == DialogResult.OK)
37           {
38              // show error if user specified invalid file
39              if (string.IsNullOrEmpty(fileName))
40              {
41                 MessageBox.Show("Invalid File Name", "Error",
42                    MessageBoxButtons.OK, MessageBoxIcon.Error);
43              }
44              else
45              {
46                 // create FileStream to obtain read access to file
47                 input = new FileStream(fileName,
48                    FileMode.Open, FileAccess.Read);
49
50                 // set file from where data is read
51                 fileReader = new StreamReader(input);
52
```

Fig. 17.7 | Credit-inquiry program. (Part 1 of 5.)

```
53                      // enable all GUI buttons, except for Open File button
54                      openButton.Enabled = false;
55                      creditButton.Enabled = true;
56                      debitButton.Enabled = true;
57                      zeroButton.Enabled = true;
58                   }
59                }
60             }
61
62          // invoked when user clicks credit balances,
63          // debit balances or zero balances button
64          private void getBalances_Click(object sender, System.EventArgs e)
65          {
66             // convert sender explicitly to object of type button
67             Button senderButton = (Button) sender;
68
69             // get text from clicked Button, which stores account type
70             string accountType = senderButton.Text;
71
72             // read and display file information
73             try
74             {
75                // go back to the beginning of the file
76                input.Seek(0, SeekOrigin.Begin);
77
78                displayTextBox.Text =
79                   $"Accounts with {accountType}{Environment.NewLine}";
80
81                // traverse file until end of file
82                while (true)
83                {
84                   // get next Record available in file
85                   string inputRecord = fileReader.ReadLine();
86
87                   // when at the end of file, exit method
88                   if (inputRecord == null)
89                   {
90                      return;
91                   }
92
93                   // parse input
94                   string[] inputFields = inputRecord.Split(',');
95
96                   // create Record from input
97                   var record =
98                      new Record(int.Parse(inputFields[0]), inputFields[1],
99                         inputFields[2], decimal.Parse(inputFields[3]));
100
101                  // determine whether to display balance
102                  if (ShouldDisplay(record.Balance, accountType))
103                  {
```

Fig. 17.7 | Credit-inquiry program. (Part 2 of 5.)

```csharp
104                   // display record
105                   displayTextBox.AppendText($"{record.Account}\t" +
106                       $"{record.FirstName}\t{record.LastName}\t" +
107                       $"{record.Balance:C}{Environment.NewLine}");
108               }
109           }
110       }
111       catch (IOException)
112       {
113           MessageBox.Show("Cannot Read File", "Error",
114               MessageBoxButtons.OK, MessageBoxIcon.Error);
115       }
116   }
117
118   // determine whether to display given record
119   private bool ShouldDisplay(decimal balance, string accountType)
120   {
121       if (balance > 0M && accountType == "Credit Balances")
122       {
123           return true; // should display credit balances
124       }
125       else if (balance < 0M && accountType == "Debit Balances")
126       {
127           return true; // should display debit balances
128       }
129       else if (balance == 0 && accountType == "Zero Balances")
130       {
131           return true; // should display zero balances
132       }
133
134       return false;
135   }
136
137   // invoked when user clicks Done button
138   private void doneButton_Click(object sender, EventArgs e)
139   {
140       // close file and StreamReader
141       try
142       {
143           fileReader?.Close(); // close StreamReader and underlying file
144       }
145       catch (IOException)
146       {
147           // notify user of error closing file
148           MessageBox.Show("Cannot close file", "Error",
149               MessageBoxButtons.OK, MessageBoxIcon.Error);
150       }
151
152       Application.Exit();
153   }
154 }
155 }
```

Fig. 17.7 | Credit-inquiry program. (Part 3 of 5.)

a) GUI when the app first executes

b) Opening the clients.txt file

c) Displaying accounts with credit balances

d) Displaying accounts with debit balances

Fig. 17.7 | Credit-inquiry program. (Part 4 of 5.)

e) Displaying accounts with
zero balances

Fig. 17.7 | Credit-inquiry program. (Part 5 of 5.)

When the user clicks the **Open File** button, the program calls the event handler openButton_Click (lines 23–60). Line 29 creates an OpenFileDialog, and line 31 calls its ShowDialog method to display the **Open** dialog, in which the user selects the file to open. Lines 47–48 create a FileStream object with *read-only file access* and assign it to reference input. Line 51 creates a StreamReader object that we use to read text from the FileStream.

When the user clicks **Credit Balances**, **Debit Balances** or **Zero Balances**, the program invokes method getBalances_Click (lines 64–116). Line 67 casts the sender parameter, which is an object reference to the control that generated the event, to a Button object. Line 70 extracts the Button object's text, which the program uses to determine which type of accounts to display. Line 76 uses FileStream method Seek to reset the *file-position pointer* back to the *beginning* of the file. FileStream method Seek allows you to reset the *file-position pointer* by specifying the number of bytes it should be *offset* from the file's *beginning, end* or *current* position. The part of the file you want to be *offset* from is chosen using constants from the SeekOrigin enumeration. In this case, our stream is offset by 0 bytes from the file's *beginning* (SeekOrigin.Begin). Line 102 uses private method ShouldDisplay (lines 119–135) to determine whether to display each record in the file. The while loop obtains each record by repeatedly calling StreamReader method ReadLine (line 85) and splitting the text into *tokens* (line 94) that are used to initialize object record (lines 97–99). Line 88 determines whether the *file-position pointer* has reached the end of the file, in which case ReadLine returns null. If so, the program returns from method getBalances_Click (line 90).

17.6 Serialization

Section 17.3 demonstrated how to write the individual fields of a Record object to a text file, and Section 17.4 demonstrated how to read those fields from a file and place their values in a Record object in memory. In the examples, Record was used to *aggregate* the information for one record. When the instance variables for a Record were output to a disk file as text, certain information was lost, such as the type of each value. For instance, if the value "3" is read from a text file, there's no way to tell if the value came from an int, a string or a decimal. We have only data, not type information, on disk. If the program that's going to read this data "knows" what object type the data corresponds to, then the data can be read directly into objects of that type.

In Fig. 17.6, we know that we're inputting an int account number, followed by first name and last name strings and a decimal balance. We also know that these values are separated by commas, with only one record on each line. So, we are able to parse the strings and convert the account number to an int and the balance to a decimal. Sometimes it would be easier to read or write entire objects. C# provides such a mechanism, called **object serialization**. A serialized object is an object represented as a sequence of bytes that includes the *object's data*, as well as information about the *object's type* and the *types of data stored in the object*. After a *serialized object* has been written to a file, it can be read from the file and deserialized—that is, the type information and bytes that represent the object and its data can be used to *recreate* the object in memory.

Class **BinaryFormatter** (namespace **System.Runtime.Serialization.Formatters. Binary**) enables entire objects to be written to or read from a stream in binary format. BinaryFormatter method **Serialize** writes an object's representation to a file. Binary-Formatter method **Deserialize** reads this representation from a file and *reconstructs* the original object. Both methods throw a **SerializationException** if an error occurs during *serialization* or *deserialization*. Both methods require a Stream object (e.g., the FileStream) as a parameter so that the BinaryFormatter can access the correct stream.

In Sections 17.7–17.8, we create and manipulate *sequential-access files* using *object serialization*. Object serialization is performed with *byte-based streams*, so the sequential files created and manipulated will be *binary files*. Binary files are not human-readable. For this reason, we write a separate app that reads and displays *serialized objects*. Other serialization formats are available that are both human- and machine-readable. For example,

- the XmlSerializer class (namespace System.Xml.Serialization) can read and write objects in XML (Extensible Markup Language) format and

- the DataContractJsonSerializer class (namespace System.Runtime.Serialization.Json) can read and write objects in JSON (JavaScript Object Notation) format.

XML and JSON are popular formats for transferring data over the Internet.

17.7 Creating a Sequential-Access File Using Object Serialization

We begin by creating and writing *serialized objects* to a *sequential-access file*. In this section, we reuse much of the code from Section 17.3, so we focus only on the new features.

Defining the RecordSerializable Class

Let's modify class Record (Fig. 17.3) so that objects of this class can be *serialized*. Class RecordSerializable (Fig. 17.8; part of the BankLibrary project) is marked with what is-known as an attribute—[Serializable] (line 7)—this attribute indicates to the CLR that RecordSerializable objects can be *serialized*. Classes that represent serializable types must include this attribute in their declarations or must implement *interface* ISerializable.

```
I    // Fig. 17.8: RecordSerializable.cs
2    // Serializable class that represents a data record.
3    using System;
4
5    namespace BankLibrary
6    {
7       [Serializable]
8       public class RecordSerializable
9       {
10         public int Account { get; set; }
11         public string FirstName { get; set; }
12         public string LastName { get; set; }
13         public decimal Balance { get; set; }
14
15         // default constructor sets members to default values
16         public RecordSerializable()
17            : this(0, string.Empty, string.Empty, 0M) {}
18
19         // overloaded constructor sets members to parameter values
20         public RecordSerializable(int account, string firstName,
21            string lastName, decimal balance)
22         {
23            Account = account;
24            FirstName = firstName;
25            LastName = lastName;
26            Balance = balance;
27         }
28      }
29   }
```

Fig. 17.8 | Serializable class that represents a data record.

In a class that's marked with the [Serializable] attribute or that implements interface ISerializable, you must ensure that every instance variable of the class is also *serializable*. All simple-type variables and strings are *serializable*. For variables of *reference types*, you must check the class declaration (and possibly its base classes) to ensure that the type is *serializable*. By default, array objects are serializable. However, if the array contains references to other objects, those objects may or may not be serializable.

Using a Serialization Stream to Create an Output File
Next, we'll create a sequential-access file with *serialization* (Fig. 17.9). To test this program, we used the sample data from Fig. 17.5 to create a file named clients.ser—we chose the extension .ser to indicate that the file stores serialized objects. Since the sample screen captures are the same as Fig. 17.4, they are not shown here. Line 15 creates a BinaryFormatter for writing *serialized objects*. Lines 55–56 open the FileStream to which this program writes the *serialized objects*. The string argument that's passed to the FileStream's constructor represents the name and path of the file to be opened. This specifies the file to which the *serialized objects* will be written.

```
 1   // Fig. 17.9: CreateFileForm.cs
 2   // Creating a sequential-access file using serialization.
 3   using System;
 4   using System.Windows.Forms;
 5   using System.IO;
 6   using System.Runtime.Serialization.Formatters.Binary;
 7   using System.Runtime.Serialization;
 8   using BankLibrary;
 9
10   namespace CreateFile
11   {
12      public partial class CreateFileForm : BankUIForm
13      {
14         // object for serializing RecordSerializables in binary format
15         private BinaryFormatter formatter = new BinaryFormatter();
16         private FileStream output; // stream for writing to a file
17
18         // parameterless constructor
19         public CreateFileForm()
20         {
21            InitializeComponent();
22         }
23
24         // handler for saveButton_Click
25         private void saveButton_Click(object sender, EventArgs e)
26         {
27            // create and show dialog box enabling user to save file
28            DialogResult result;
29            string fileName; // name of file to save data
30
31            using (SaveFileDialog fileChooser = new SaveFileDialog())
32            {
33               fileChooser.CheckFileExists = false; // let user create file
34
35               // retrieve the result of the dialog box
36               result = fileChooser.ShowDialog();
37               fileName = fileChooser.FileName; // get specified file name
38            }
39
40            // ensure that user clicked "OK"
41            if (result == DialogResult.OK)
42            {
43               // show error if user specified invalid file
44               if (string.IsNullOrEmpty(fileName))
45               {
46                  MessageBox.Show("Invalid File Name", "Error",
47                     MessageBoxButtons.OK, MessageBoxIcon.Error);
48               }
49               else
50               {
51                  // save file via FileStream if user specified valid file
52                  try
53                  {
```

Fig. 17.9 | Creating a sequential-access file using serialization. (Part 1 of 3.)

```
54                        // open file with write access
55                        output = new FileStream(fileName,
56                            FileMode.OpenOrCreate, FileAccess.Write);
57
58                        // disable Save button and enable Enter button
59                        saveButton.Enabled = false;
60                        enterButton.Enabled = true;
61                    }
62                    catch (IOException)
63                    {
64                        // notify user if file could not be opened
65                        MessageBox.Show("Error opening file", "Error",
66                            MessageBoxButtons.OK, MessageBoxIcon.Error);
67                    }
68                }
69            }
70        }
71
72        // handler for enterButton Click
73        private void enterButton_Click(object sender, EventArgs e)
74        {
75            // store TextBox values string array
76            string[] values = GetTextBoxValues();
77
78            // determine whether TextBox account field is empty
79            if (!string.IsNullOrEmpty(values[(int) TextBoxIndices.Account]))
80            {
81                // store TextBox values in RecordSerializable and serialize it
82                try
83                {
84                    // get account-number value from TextBox
85                    int accountNumber = int.Parse(
86                        values[(int) TextBoxIndices.Account]);
87
88                    // determine whether accountNumber is valid
89                    if (accountNumber > 0)
90                    {
91                        // RecordSerializable to serialize
92                        var record = new RecordSerializable(accountNumber,
93                            values[(int) TextBoxIndices.First],
94                            values[(int) TextBoxIndices.Last],
95                            decimal.Parse(values[(int) TextBoxIndices.Balance]));
96
97                        // write Record to FileStream (serialize object)
98                        formatter.Serialize(output, record);
99                    }
100                   else
101                   {
102                       // notify user if invalid account number
103                       MessageBox.Show("Invalid Account Number", "Error",
104                           MessageBoxButtons.OK, MessageBoxIcon.Error);
105                   }
106               }
```

Fig. 17.9 | Creating a sequential-access file using serialization. (Part 2 of 3.)

```
107                    catch (SerializationException)
108                    {
109                        MessageBox.Show("Error Writing to File", "Error",
110                            MessageBoxButtons.OK, MessageBoxIcon.Error);
111                    }
112                    catch (FormatException)
113                    {
114                        MessageBox.Show("Invalid Format", "Error",
115                            MessageBoxButtons.OK, MessageBoxIcon.Error);
116                    }
117                }
118
119                ClearTextBoxes(); // clear TextBox values
120            }
121
122            // handler for exitButton Click
123            private void exitButton_Click(object sender, EventArgs e)
124            {
125                // close file
126                try
127                {
128                    output?.Close(); // close FileStream
129                }
130                catch (IOException)
131                {
132                    MessageBox.Show("Cannot close file", "Error",
133                        MessageBoxButtons.OK, MessageBoxIcon.Error);
134                }
135
136                Application.Exit();
137            }
138        }
139    }
```

Fig. 17.9 | Creating a sequential-access file using serialization. (Part 3 of 3.)

This program assumes that data is input correctly and in record-number order. Method enterButton_Click (lines 73–120) performs the write operation. Lines 92–95 create and initialize a RecordSerializable object. Line 98 calls Serialize to write the RecordSerializable object to the output file. Method Serialize takes the FileStream object as the first argument so that the BinaryFormatter can write its second argument to the correct file. The app does not specify how to format the objectfor output—Serialize handles these details. If a problem occurs during *serialization*, a SerializationException occurs.

In the sample execution (Fig. 17.9), we entered five accounts—the same as in Fig. 17.5. The program does not show how the data records actually appear in the file. Remember that we are now using *binary files*, which are *not* human readable. To verify that the file was created successfully, the next section presents a program to read the file's contents.

17.8 Reading and Deserializing Data from a Binary File

The preceding section showed how to create a *sequential-access file* using *object serialization*. In this section, we discuss how to read serialized objects sequentially from a file.

Figure 17.10 reads and displays the contents of the clients.ser file created by the program in Fig. 17.9. The sample screen captures are identical to those of Fig. 17.6, so they are not shown here. Line 15 creates the BinaryFormatter that will be used to read objects. The program opens the file for input by creating a FileStream object (lines 51–52). The name of the file to open is specified as the first argument to the FileStream constructor.

The program reads objects from a file in event handler nextButton_Click (lines 61–93). We use method Deserialize (of the BinaryFormatter created in line 15) to read the data (lines 67–68). Note that we cast the result of Deserialize to type RecordSerializable (line 67)—Deserialize returns a reference of type object, so we must perform this cast to access properties that belong to class RecordSerializable. If an error occurs during *deserialization* or the end of the file is reached, a SerializationException is thrown, and the FileStream object is closed (line 83).

```csharp
1   // Fig. 17.10: ReadSequentialAccessFileForm.cs
2   // Reading a sequential-access file using deserialization.
3   using System;
4   using System.Windows.Forms;
5   using System.IO;
6   using System.Runtime.Serialization.Formatters.Binary;
7   using System.Runtime.Serialization;
8   using BankLibrary;
9
10  namespace ReadSequentialAccessFile
11  {
12     public partial class ReadSequentialAccessFileForm : BankUIForm
13     {
14        // object for deserializing RecordSerializable in binary format
15        private BinaryFormatter reader = new BinaryFormatter();
16        private FileStream input; // stream for reading from a file
17
18        // parameterless constructor
19        public ReadSequentialAccessFileForm()
20        {
21           InitializeComponent();
22        }
23
24        // invoked when user clicks the Open button
25        private void openButton_Click(object sender, EventArgs e)
26        {
27           // create and show dialog box enabling user to open file
28           DialogResult result; // result of OpenFileDialog
29           string fileName; // name of file containing data
30
31           using (OpenFileDialog fileChooser = new OpenFileDialog())
32           {
33              result = fileChooser.ShowDialog();
34              fileName = fileChooser.FileName; // get specified name
35           }
36
```

Fig. 17.10 | Reading a sequential-access file using deserialization. (Part 1 of 3.)

```
37          // ensure that user clicked "OK"
38          if (result == DialogResult.OK)
39          {
40              ClearTextBoxes();
41
42              // show error if user specified invalid file
43              if (string.IsNullOrEmpty(fileName))
44              {
45                  MessageBox.Show("Invalid File Name", "Error",
46                      MessageBoxButtons.OK, MessageBoxIcon.Error);
47              }
48              else
49              {
50                  // create FileStream to obtain read access to file
51                  input = new FileStream(
52                      fileName, FileMode.Open, FileAccess.Read);
53
54                  openButton.Enabled = false; // disable Open File button
55                  nextButton.Enabled = true;  // enable Next Record button
56              }
57          }
58      }
59
60      // invoked when user clicks Next button
61      private void nextButton_Click(object sender, EventArgs e)
62      {
63          // deserialize RecordSerializable and store data in TextBoxes
64          try
65          {
66              // get next RecordSerializable available in file
67              RecordSerializable record =
68                  (RecordSerializable) reader.Deserialize(input);
69
70              // store RecordSerializable values in temporary string array
71              var values = new string[] {
72                  record.Account.ToString(),
73                  record.FirstName.ToString(),
74                  record.LastName.ToString(),
75                  record.Balance.ToString()
76              };
77
78              // copy string-array values to TextBox values
79              SetTextBoxValues(values);
80          }
81          catch (SerializationException)
82          {
83              input?.Close(); // close FileStream
84              openButton.Enabled = true; // enable Open File button
85              nextButton.Enabled = false; // disable Next Record button
86
87              ClearTextBoxes();
88
```

Fig. 17.10 | Reading a sequential-access file using deserialization. (Part 2 of 3.)

```
89              // notify user if no RecordSerializables in file
90              MessageBox.Show("No more records in file", string.Empty,
91                 MessageBoxButtons.OK, MessageBoxIcon.Information);
92          }
93       }
94    }
95 }
```

Fig. 17.10 | Reading a sequential-access file using deserialization. (Part 3 of 3.)

17.9 Classes File and Directory

Files are organized in directories (also called folders). Classes File and Directory enable programs to manipulate files and directories on disk. Class File can determine information about files and can be used to open files for reading or writing. We discussed techniques for writing to and reading from files in previous sections.

Figure 17.11 lists several of class File's static methods for manipulating and determining information about files. We demonstrate several of these methods in Fig. 17.13.

static Method	Description
AppendText	Returns a StreamWriter that appends text to an existing file or creates a file if one does not exist.
Copy	Copies a file to a new file.
Create	Creates a file and returns its associated FileStream.
CreateText	Creates a text file and returns its associated StreamWriter.
Delete	Deletes the specified file.
Exists	Returns true if the specified file exists and false otherwise.
GetCreationTime	Returns a DateTime object representing when the file/directory was created.
GetLastAccessTime	Returns a DateTime object representing when the file/directory was last accessed.
GetLastWriteTime	Returns a DateTime object representing when the file/directory was last modified.
Move	Moves the specified file to a specified location.
Open	Returns a FileStream associated with the specified file and equipped with the specified read/write permissions.
OpenRead	Returns a read-only FileStream associated with the specified file.
OpenText	Returns a StreamReader associated with the specified file.
OpenWrite	Returns a write FileStream associated with the specified file.

Fig. 17.11 | File class static methods (partial list).

Class Directory provides capabilities for manipulating directories. Figure 17.12 lists some of class Directory's static methods for directory manipulation. Figure 17.13 demonstrates several of these methods, as well. The DirectoryInfo object returned by method

`CreateDirectory` contains information about a directory. Much of the information contained in class `DirectoryInfo` also can be accessed via the methods of class `Directory`.

static Method	Description
CreateDirectory	Creates a directory and returns its associated `DirectoryInfo` object.
Delete	Deletes the specified directory.
Exists	Returns `true` if the specified directory exists and `false` otherwise.
GetDirectories	Returns a `string` array containing the names of the subdirectories in the specified directory.
GetFiles	Returns a `string` array containing the names of the files in the specified directory.
GetCreationTime	Returns a `DateTime` object representing when the directory was created.
GetLastAccessTime	Returns a `DateTime` object representing when the directory was last accessed.
GetLastWriteTime	Returns a `DateTime` object representing when items were last written to the directory.
Move	Moves the specified directory to a specified location.

Fig. 17.12 | `Directory` class `static` methods.

17.9.1 Demonstrating Classes `File` and `Directory`

Class `FileTestForm` (Fig. 17.13) uses `File` and `Directory` methods to access file and directory information. The `Form` contains the `inputTextBox`, in which the user enters a file or directory name. For each key that the user presses while typing in the `TextBox`, the program calls `inputTextBox_KeyDown` (lines 19–76). If the user presses the *Enter* key (line 22), this method displays either the file's or directory's contents, depending on the text the user input. (If the user does not press the *Enter* key, this method returns without displaying any content.)

```
1   // Fig. 17.13: FileTestForm.cs
2   // Using classes File and Directory.
3   using System;
4   using System.Windows.Forms;
5   using System.IO;
6
7   namespace FileTest
8   {
9      // displays contents of files and directories
10     public partial class FileTestForm : Form
11     {
12        // parameterless constructor
13        public FileTestForm()
14        {
```

Fig. 17.13 | Using classes `File` and `Directory`. (Part 1 of 4.)

```
15                InitializeComponent();
16          }
17
18          // invoked when user presses key
19          private void inputTextBox_KeyDown(object sender, KeyEventArgs e)
20          {
21              // determine whether user pressed Enter key
22              if (e.KeyCode == Keys.Enter)
23              {
24                  // get user-specified file or directory
25                  string fileName = inputTextBox.Text;
26
27                  // determine whether fileName is a file
28                  if (File.Exists(fileName))
29                  {
30                      // get file's creation date, modification date, etc.
31                      GetInformation(fileName);
32
33                      // display file contents through StreamReader
34                      try
35                      {
36                          // obtain reader and file contents
37                          using (var stream = new StreamReader(fileName))
38                          {
39                              outputTextBox.AppendText(stream.ReadToEnd());
40                          }
41                      }
42                      catch (IOException)
43                      {
44                          MessageBox.Show("Error reading from file",
45                              "File Error", MessageBoxButtons.OK,
46                              MessageBoxIcon.Error);
47                      }
48                  }
49                  // determine whether fileName is a directory
50                  else if (Directory.Exists(fileName))
51                  {
52                      // get directory's creation date,
53                      // modification date, etc.
54                      GetInformation(fileName);
55
56                      // obtain directory list of specified directory
57                      string[] directoryList =
58                          Directory.GetDirectories(fileName);
59
60                      outputTextBox.AppendText("Directory contents:\n");
61
62                      // output directoryList contents
63                      foreach (var directory in directoryList)
64                      {
65                          outputTextBox.AppendText($"{directory}\n");
66                      }
67                  }
```

Fig. 17.13 | Using classes File and Directory. (Part 2 of 4.)

```
68              else
69              {
70                  // notify user that neither file nor directory exists
71                  MessageBox.Show(
72                      $"{inputTextBox.Text} does not exist", "File Error",
73                      MessageBoxButtons.OK, MessageBoxIcon.Error);
74              }
75          }
76      }
77
78      // get information on file or directory,
79      // and output it to outputTextBox
80      private void GetInformation(string fileName)
81      {
82          outputTextBox.Clear();
83
84          // output that file or directory exists
85          outputTextBox.AppendText($"{fileName} exists\n");
86
87          // output when file or directory was created
88          outputTextBox.AppendText(
89              $"Created: {File.GetCreationTime(fileName)}\n" +
90              Environment.NewLine);
91
92          // output when file or directory was last modified
93          outputTextBox.AppendText(
94              $"Last modified: {File.GetLastWriteTime(fileName)}\n" +
95              Environment.NewLine);
96
97          // output when file or directory was last accessed
98          outputTextBox.AppendText(
99              $"Last accessed: {File.GetLastAccessTime(fileName)}\n" +
100             Environment.NewLine);
101     }
102   }
103 }
```

a) Viewing the contents of file **"quotes.txt"**   b) Viewing all directories in **C:\Program Files**

Fig. 17.13 | Using classes File and Directory. (Part 3 of 4.)

c) User gives invalid input

d) Error message is displayed

Fig. 17.13 | Using classes File and Directory. (Part 4 of 4.)

Line 28 uses File method Exists to determine whether the user-specified text is the name of an existing file. If so, line 31 invokes private method GetInformation (lines 80–101), which calls File methods GetCreationTime (line 89), GetLastWriteTime (line 94) and GetLastAccessTime (line 99) to access file information. When method GetInformation returns, line 37 instantiates a StreamReader for reading text from the file. The StreamReader constructor takes as an argument a string containing the name and path of the file to open. Line 39 calls StreamReader method **ReadToEnd** to read the entire contents of the file as a string, then appends the string to outputTextBox. Once the file has been read, the using block disposes of the corresponding object, which closes the file.

If line 28 determines that the user-specified text is not a file, line 50 determines whether it's a directory using Directory method **Exists**. If the user specified an *existing* directory, line 54 invokes method GetInformation to access the directory information. Lines 57–58 call Directory method **GetDirectories** to obtain a string array containing the names of the subdirectories in the specified directory. Lines 63–66 display each element in the string array. Note that, if line 50 determines that the user-specified text is *not* a directory name, lines 71–73 notify the user that the name the user entered does not exist as a file or directory.

17.9.2 Searching Directories with LINQ

We now consider another example that uses file- and directory-manipulation capabilities. Class LINQToFileDirectoryForm (Fig. 17.14) uses LINQ with classes File, Path and Directory to report the number of files of each file type that exist in the specified directory path. The program also serves as a "clean-up" utility—when it finds a file that has the .bak filename extension (i.e., a *backup* file), the program displays a MessageBox asking the user whether that file should be removed, then responds appropriately to the user's input. This example also uses *LINQ to Objects* to help delete the backup files.

When the user clicks **Search Directory**, the program invokes searchButton_Click (lines 23–62), which searches recursively through the directory path specified by the user. If the user inputs text in the TextBox, line 27 calls Directory method Exists to determine whether that text is a valid directory. If it's not, lines 30–31 notify the user of the error.

```
1   // Fig. 17.14: LINQToFileDirectoryForm.cs
2   // Using LINQ to search directories and determine file types.
3   using System;
4   using System.Collections.Generic;
5   using System.Linq;
6   using System.Windows.Forms;
7   using System.IO;
8
9   namespace LINQToFileDirectory
10  {
11     public partial class LINQToFileDirectoryForm : Form
12     {
13        // store extensions found, and number of each extension found
14        Dictionary<string, int> found = new Dictionary<string, int>();
15
16        // parameterless constructor
17        public LINQToFileDirectoryForm()
18        {
19           InitializeComponent();
20        }
21
22        // handles the Search Directory Button's Click event
23        private void searchButton_Click(object sender, EventArgs e)
24        {
25           // check whether user specified path exists
26           if (!string.IsNullOrEmpty(pathTextBox.Text) &&
27              !Directory.Exists(pathTextBox.Text))
28           {
29              // show error if user does not specify valid directory
30              MessageBox.Show("Invalid Directory", "Error",
31                 MessageBoxButtons.OK, MessageBoxIcon.Error);
32           }
33           else
34           {
35              // directory to search; if not specified use current directory
36              string currentDirectory =
37                 (!string.IsNullOrEmpty(pathTextBox.Text)) ?
38                    pathTextBox.Text : Directory.GetCurrentDirectory();
39
40              directoryTextBox.Text = currentDirectory; // show directory
41
42              // clear TextBoxes
43              pathTextBox.Clear();
44              resultsTextBox.Clear();
45
46              SearchDirectory(currentDirectory); // search the directory
47
48              // allow user to delete .bak files
49              CleanDirectory(currentDirectory);
50
51              // summarize and display the results
52              foreach (var current in found.Keys)
53              {
```

Fig. 17.14 | Using LINQ to search directories and determine file types. (Part 1 of 3.)

```
54              // display the number of files with current extension
55              resultsTextBox.AppendText(
56                 $"* Found {found[current]} {current} files." +
57                 Environment.NewLine);
58           }
59
60           found.Clear(); // clear results for new search
61        }
62     }
63
64     // search directory using LINQ
65     private void SearchDirectory(string folder)
66     {
67        // files contained in the directory
68        string[] files = Directory.GetFiles(folder);
69
70        // subdirectories in the directory
71        string[] directories = Directory.GetDirectories(folder);
72
73        // find all file extensions in this directory
74        var extensions =
75           from file in files
76           group file by Path.GetExtension(file);
77
78        foreach (var extension in extensions)
79        {
80           if (found.ContainsKey(extension.Key))
81           {
82              found[extension.Key] += extension.Count(); // update count
83           }
84           else
85           {
86              found[extension.Key] = extension.Count(); // add count
87           }
88        }
89
90        // recursive call to search subdirectories
91        foreach (var subdirectory in directories)
92        {
93           SearchDirectory(subdirectory);
94        }
95     }
96
97     // allow user to delete backup files (.bak)
98     private void CleanDirectory(string folder)
99     {
100       // files contained in the directory
101       string[] files = Directory.GetFiles(folder);
102
103       // subdirectories in the directory
104       string[] directories = Directory.GetDirectories(folder);
105
```

Fig. 17.14 | Using LINQ to search directories and determine file types. (Part 2 of 3.)

```
106         // select all the backup files in this directory
107         var backupFiles =
108             from file in files
109             where Path.GetExtension(file) == ".bak"
110             select file;
111
112         // iterate over all backup files (.bak)
113         foreach (var backup in backupFiles)
114         {
115             DialogResult result = MessageBox.Show(
116                 $"Found backup file {Path.GetFileName(backup)}. Delete?",
117                 "Delete Backup", MessageBoxButtons.YesNo,
118                 MessageBoxIcon.Question);
119
120             // delete file if user clicked 'yes'
121             if (result == DialogResult.Yes)
122             {
123                 File.Delete(backup); // delete backup file
124                 --found[".bak"]; // decrement count in Dictionary
125
126                 // if there are no .bak files, delete key from Dictionary
127                 if (found[".bak"] == 0)
128                 {
129                     found.Remove(".bak");
130                 }
131             }
132         }
133
134         // recursive call to clean subdirectories
135         foreach (var subdirectory in directories)
136         {
137             CleanDirectory(subdirectory);
138         }
139     }
140   }
141 }
```

a) GUI after entering a directory to search and pressing **Search Directory**

b) Dialog that appears to confirm deletion of a `.bak` file

Fig. 17.14 | Using LINQ to search directories and determine file types. (Part 3 of 3.)

Method *SearchDirectory*

Lines 36–38 get the current directory (if the user did not specify a path) or the specified directory. Line 46 passes the directory name to *recursive* method SearchDirectory (lines 65–95). Line 68 calls Directory method GetFiles to get a string array containing filenames in the specified directory. Line 71 calls Directory method GetDirectories to get a string array containing the subdirectory names in the specified directory.

Lines 74–76 use LINQ to get the filename extensions in the files array. **Path** method GetExtension obtains the extension for the specified filename. We use the LINQ **group by** clause to group the results by filename extension. For each filename-extension group returned by the LINQ query, lines 78–88 use LINQ method Count to determine the number of occurrences of that extension in the files array.

Class LINQToFileDirectoryForm uses a Dictionary (declared in line 14) to store each filename extension and the corresponding number of filenames with that extension. A Dictionary (namespace System.Collections.Generic) is a collection of *key–value pairs*, in which each *key* has a corresponding *value*. Class Dictionary is a *generic class* like class List (presented in Section 9.4). Line 14 indicates that the Dictionary found contains pairs of strings and ints, which represent the filename extensions and the number of files with those extensions, respectively. Line 80 uses Dictionary method ContainsKey to determine whether the specified filename extension has been placed in the Dictionary previously. If this method returns true, line 82 adds the count of the number of files with a given extention to the current total for that extension that's stored in the Dictionary. Otherwise, line 86 inserts a new *key–value pair* into the Dictionary for the new filename extension and its extension count. Lines 91–94 recursively call SearchDirectory for each subdirectory in the current directory—depending on the number of files and folders, this operation could take substantial time to complete.

Method *CleanDirectory*

When method SearchDirectory returns, line 49 calls CleanDirectory (lines 98–139) to search for all files with extension .bak. Lines 101 and 104 obtain the list of filenames and list of directory names in the current directory, respectively. The LINQ query in lines 107–110 locates all filenames in the current directory that have the .bak extension. Lines 113–132 iterate through the results and ask the user whether each file should be deleted. If the user clicks **Yes** in the dialog, line 123 uses File method Delete to remove the file from disk, and line 124 subtracts 1 from the total number of .bak files. If the number of .bak files remaining is 0, line 129 uses Dictionary method Remove to delete the key–value pair for .bak files from the Dictionary. Lines 135–138 recursively call CleanDirectory for each subdirectory in the current directory. After each subdirectory has been checked for .bak files, method CleanDirectory returns, and lines 52–58 display the summary of filename extensions and the number of files with each extension. Line 52 uses Dictionary property Keys to get all the keys. Line 56 uses the Dictionary's indexer to get the value for the current key. Finally, line 60 uses Dictionary method Clear to delete the contents of the Dictionary.

17.10 Wrap-Up

In this chapter, you used file processing to manipulate persistent data. We overviewed several file-processing classes from the System.IO namespace. We showed how to use sequential-access file processing to manipulate records in text files. We then discussed the differences between text-file processing and object serialization, and used serialization to store entire objects in and retrieve entire objects from files. Finally, you used class File to manipulate files, and classes Directory and DirectoryInfo to manipulate directories.

In Chapter 18, we begin our four-chapter discussion of algorithms and data structures. Chapter 18 presents various searching algorithms for locating items in arrays and sorting algorithms for arranging the elements in arrays into ascending order. We also use Big O notation to represent the worst-case runtime for an algorithm.

Summary

Section 17.1 Introduction
- Files are used for long-term retention of large amounts of data.
- Data stored in files often is called persistent data.
- Computers store files on secondary storage devices.

Section 17.2 Files and Streams
- C# views each file as a sequential stream of bytes.
- Files are opened by creating an object that has a stream associated with it.
- Streams provide communication channels between files and programs.
- File processing in C# requires the System.IO namespace.
- Class Stream provides functionality for representing streams as bytes. This class is abstract, so objects of this class cannot be instantiated.
- Classes FileStream, MemoryStream and BufferedStream inherit from class Stream.
- Class FileStream can be used to read data to and write data from sequential-access files.
- Class MemoryStream enables the transfer of data directly to and from memory—this is much faster than other types of data transfer (e.g., to and from disk).
- Class BufferedStream uses buffering to transfer data to or from a stream. Buffering enhances I/O performance by directing each output operation to a buffer large enough to hold the data from many outputs. Then the actual transfer to the output device is performed in one large physical output operation each time the buffer fills. Buffering also can be used to speed input operations.

Section 17.3 Creating a Sequential-Access Text File
- C# imposes no structure on files. You must structure files to meet your app's requirements.
- A SaveFileDialog is a modal dialog—the user must interact with the dialog to dismiss it.
- A StreamWriter's constructor receives a FileStream that specifies the file in which to write text.

Section 17.4 Reading Data from a Sequential-Access Text File
- Data is stored in files so that it can be retrieved for processing when it's needed.
- To retrieve data sequentially from a file, programs normally start from the beginning of the file, reading consecutively until the desired data is found. It sometimes is necessary to process a file sequentially several times during the execution of a program.
- An OpenFileDialog allows a user to select files to open. Method ShowDialog displays the dialog.

Section 17.5 Case Study: Credit-Inquiry Program

- Stream method Seek moves the file-position pointer in a file. You specify the number of bytes it should be offset from the file's beginning, end or current position. The part of the file you want to be offset from is chosen using constants from the SeekOrigin enumeration.

Section 17.6 Serialization

- A serialized object is represented as a sequence of bytes that includes the object's data, as well as information about the object's type and the types of data stored in the object.
- After a serialized object has been written to a file, it can be read from the file and deserialized (recreated in memory).
- Class BinaryFormatter (namespace System.Runtime.Serialization.Formatters.Binary), which supports the ISerializable interface, enables entire objects to be read from or written to a stream.
- BinaryFormatter methods Serialize and Deserialize write objects to and read objects from streams, respectively.
- Both method Serialize and method Deserialize require a Stream object (e.g., the FileStream) as a parameter so that the BinaryFormatter can access the correct file.

Section 17.7 Creating a Sequential-Access File Using Object Serialization

- Classes that are marked with the Serializable attribute or implement the ISerializable interface indicate to the CLR that objects of the class can be serialized. Objects that we wish to write to or read from a stream must include this attribute or implement the ISerializable interface in their class definitions.
- In a serializable class, you must ensure that every instance variable of the class is also serializable. By default, all simple-type variables are serializable. For reference-type variables, you must check the declaration of the class (and possibly its superclasses) to ensure that the type is serializable.

Section 17.8 Reading and Deserializing Data from a Binary File

- Method Deserialize (of class BinaryFormatter) reads a serialized object from a stream and reforms the object in memory.
- Method Deserialize returns a reference of type object which must be cast to the appropriate type to manipulate the object.
- If an error occurs during deserialization, a SerializationException is thrown.

Section 17.9 Classes **File** and **Directory**

- Information on computers is stored in files, which are organized in directories. Classes File and Directory enable programs to manipulate files and directories on disk.
- Class File provides static methods for determining information about files and can be used to open files for reading or writing.
- Class Directory provides static methods for manipulating directories.
- The DirectoryInfo object returned by Directory method CreateDirectory contains information about a directory. Much of the information contained in class DirectoryInfo also can be accessed via the methods of class Directory.
- File method Exists determines whether a string is the name and path of an existing file.
- An overloaded StreamReader constructor takes a string containing the name of the file to open and its path. StreamReader method ReadToEnd reads the entire contents of a file.
- Directory method Exists determines whether a string is the name of an existing directory.

- `Directory` method `GetDirectories` obtains a `string` array containing the names of subdirectories in the specified directory.
- `Directory` method `GetFiles` returns a `string` array containing filenames in the specified directory.
- `Path` method `GetExtension` obtains the extension for the specified filename.
- A `Dictionary` (namespace `System.Collections.Generic`) is a collection of key–value pairs, in which each key has a corresponding value. Class `Dictionary` is a generic class like class `List`.
- `Dictionary` method `ContainsKey` determines whether the specified key exists in the `Dictionary`.
- `Dictionary` method `Add` inserts a key–value pair into a `Dictionary`.
- `File` method `Delete` removes the specified file from disk.
- `Dictionary` property `Keys` returns all the keys in a `Dictionary`.
- `Dictionary` method `Clear` deletes the contents of a `Dictionary`.
- LINQ's group by clause enables you to group query results into collections.

Terminology

Add method of class `Dictionary`
`BinaryFormatter` class
buffer
`BufferedStream` class
buffering
`Close` method of class `StreamWriter`
closing a file
`ContainsKey` method of class `Dictionary`
`Copy` method of class `File`
`Create` method of class `File`
`CreateDirectory` method of class `Directory`
`CreateText` method of class `File`
`Delete` method of class `Directory`
`Delete` method of class `File`
`Deserialize` method of class `BinaryFormatter`
deserialized object
`Dictionary` class
`Directory` class
`DirectoryInfo` class
end-of-file marker
`Error` property of class `Console`
`Exists` method of class `Directory`
`Exists` method of class `File`
`File` class
file-processing programs
`FileAccess` enumeration
`FileNotFoundException` class
file-position pointer
`FileStream` class
`GetCreationTime` method of class `Directory`
`GetCreationTime` method of class `File`
`GetDirectories` method of class `Directory`
`GetExtension` method of class `Path`

`GetFiles` method of class `Directory`
`GetLastAccessTime` method of class `Directory`
`GetLastAccessTime` method of class `File`
`GetLastWriteTime` method of class `Directory`
`GetLastWriteTime` method of class `File`
`In` property of class `Console`
`IOException`
`ISerializable` interface
logical output operation
`MemoryStream` class
modal dialog
`Move` method of class `Directory`
`Move` method of class `File`
object serialization
`Open` method of class `File`
`OpenFileDialog` class
`OpenRead` method of class `File`
`OpenText` method of class `File`
`OpenWrite` method of class `File`
`Out` property of class `Console`
`Path` class
persistent data
physical output operation
`Read` method of class `Console`
`ReadLine` method of class `Console`
`ReadLine` method of class `StreamReader`
`SaveFileDialog` class
`Seek` method of class `Stream`
`SeekOrigin` enumeration
sequential-access file
`Serializable` attribute
`SerializationException`
`Serialize` method of class `BinaryFormatter`

ShowDialog method of class `SaveFileDialog`
standard error stream object
standard input stream object
standard output stream object
Stream class
stream of bytes
StreamReader class
StreamWriter class

`System.IO` namespace
`System.Runtime.Serialization.`
    `Formatters.Binary` namespace
TextReader class
TextWriter class
transaction-processing system
Write method of class `StreamWriter`
WriteLine method of class `StreamWriter`

Self-Review Exercises

17.1 State whether each of the following is *true* or *false*. If *false*, explain why.
   a) You cannot instantiate objects of type `Stream`.
   b) Typically, a sequential file stores records in order by the record-key field.
   c) Class `StreamReader` inherits from class `Stream`.
   d) Any class can be serialized to a file.
   e) Method `Seek` of class `FileStream` always seeks relative to the beginning of a file.
   f) Classes `StreamReader` and `StreamWriter` are used with sequential-access files.

17.2 Fill in the blanks in each of the following statements:
   a) The _____ namespace contains the `BinaryFormatter` class.
   b) `StreamReader` method _____ reads a line of text from a file.
   c) `StreamWriter` method _____ writes a line of text to a file.
   d) Method `Serialize` of class `BinaryFormatter` takes a(n) _____ and a(n) _____ as arguments.
   e) The _____ namespace contains most of C#'s file-processing classes.

Answers to Self-Review Exercises

17.1 a) True. b) True. c) False. Class `StreamReader` inherits from class `TextReader`. d) False. Only classes that implement interface `ISerializable` or are declared with the `Serializable` attribute can be serialized. e) False. It seeks relative to the `SeekOrigin` enumeration member that's passed as one of the arguments. f) True.

17.2 a) `System.Runtime.Serialization.Formatters.Binary`.   b) `ReadLine`.   c) `WriteLine`. d) `Stream`, `object`. e) `System.IO`.

Exercises

17.3 *(File of Student Grades)* Create a program that stores student grades in a text file. The file should contain the name, ID number, class taken and grade of every student. Allow the user to load a grade file and display its contents in a read-only `TextBox`. The entries should be displayed in the following format:

```
LastName, FirstName: ID# Class  Grade
```

We list some sample data below:

```
Jones, Bob: 1 "Introduction to Computer Science" "A-"
Johnson, Sarah: 2 "Data Structures" "B+"
Smith, Sam: 3 "Data Structures" "C"
```

17.4 *(Serializing and Deserializing)* Modify the previous program to use objects of a class that can be serialized to and deserialized from a file.

17.5 *(Extending `StreamReader` and `StreamWriter`)* Extend classes `StreamReader` and `StreamWriter`. Make the class that derives from `StreamReader` have methods `ReadInteger`, `ReadBoolean` and `ReadString`. Make the class that derives from `StreamWriter` have methods `WriteInteger`, `WriteBoolean` and `WriteString`. Think about how to design the writing methods so that the reading methods will be able to read what was written. Design `WriteInteger` and `WriteBoolean` to write strings of uniform size so that `ReadInteger` and `ReadBoolean` can read those values accurately. Make sure `ReadString` and `WriteString` use the same character(s) to separate `strings`.

17.6   *(Reading and Writing Account Information)* Create a program that combines the ideas of Fig. 17.4 and Fig. 17.6 to allow a user to write records to and read records from a file. Add an extra field of type `bool` to the record to indicate whether the account has overdraft protection.

17.7   *(Telephone-Number Word Generator)* Standard telephone keypads contain the digits zero through nine. The numbers two through nine each have three letters associated with them (Fig. 17.15). Many people find it difficult to memorize phone numbers, so they use the correspondence between digits and letters to develop seven-letter words that correspond to their phone numbers. For example, a person whose telephone number is 686-2377 might use the correspondence indicated in Fig. 17.15 to develop the seven-letter word "NUMBERS." Every seven-letter word corresponds to exactly one seven-digit telephone number. A restaurant wishing to increase its takeout business could surely do so with the number 825-3688 (i.e., "TAKEOUT").

Every seven-letter phone number corresponds to many different seven-letter words. Unfortunately, most of these words represent unrecognizable juxtapositions of letters. It's possible, however, that the owner of a barbershop would be pleased to know that the shop's telephone number, 424-7288, corresponds to "HAIRCUT." The owner of a liquor store would no doubt be delighted to find that the store's number, 233-7226, corresponds to "BEERCAN." A veterinarian with the phone number 738-2273 would be pleased to know that the number corresponds to the letters "PETCARE." An automotive dealership would be pleased to know that its phone number, 639-2277, corresponds to "NEWCARS."

Digit	Letter	Digit	Letter
2	A B C	6	M N O
3	D E F	7	P R S
4	G H I	8	T U V
5	J K L	9	W X Y Z

Fig. 17.15 | Letters that correspond to the numbers on a telephone keypad .

Write a GUI program that, given a seven-digit number, uses a `StreamWriter` object to write to a file every possible seven-letter word combination corresponding to that number. There are 2,187 (3^7) such combinations. Avoid phone numbers with the digits 0 and 1.

17.8   *(Student Poll)* Figure 8.9 contains an array of survey responses that's hard-coded into the program. Suppose we wish to process survey results that are stored in a file. First, create a Windows `Form` that prompts the user for survey responses and outputs each response to a file. Use `StreamWriter` to create a file called `numbers.txt`. Each integer should be written using method `Write`. Then add a `TextBox` that will output the frequency of survey responses. You should modify the code in Fig. 8.9 to read the survey responses from `numbers.txt`. The responses should be read from the file by using a `StreamReader`. Class `string`'s `Split` method should be used to split the input string into separate responses, then each response should be converted to an integer. The program should continue to read responses until it reaches the end of file. The results should be output to the `TextBox`.

Making a Difference Exercise

17.9 *(Phishing Scanner)* Phishing is a form of identity theft in which, in an e-mail, a sender posing as a trustworthy source attempts to acquire private information, such as your user names, passwords, credit-card numbers and social security number. Phishing e-mails claiming to be from popular banks, credit-card companies, auction sites, social networks and online payment services may look quite legitimate. These fraudulent messages often provide links to spoofed (fake) websites where you're asked to enter sensitive information.

Visit www.snopes.com and other websites to find lists of the top phishing scams. Also check out the Anti-Phishing Working Group

```
www.antiphishing.org/
```

and the FBI's Cyber Investigations website

```
https://www.fbi.gov/about-us/investigate/cyber/cyber
```

where you'll find information about the latest scams and how to protect yourself.

Create a list of 30 words, phrases and company names commonly found in phishing messages. Assign a point value to each based on your estimate of its likeliness to be in a phishing message (e.g., one point if it's somewhat likely, two points if moderately likely, or three points if highly likely). Write a program that scans a file of text for these terms and phrases. For each occurrence of a keyword or phrase within the text file, add the assigned point value to the total points for that word or phrase. For each keyword or phrase found, output one line with the word or phrase, the number of occurrences and the point total. Then show the point total for the entire message. Does your program assign a high point total to some actual phishing e-mails you've received? Does it assign a high point total to some legitimate e-mails you've received?

18

Searching and Sorting

18.1 Introduction

Searching data involves determining whether a value (referred to as the search key) is present in the data and, if so, finding the value's location. This chapter presents two popular search algorithms—the simple *linear search* and the faster, but more complex, *binary search*. Sorting places data in order, based on one or more sort keys. A list of names could be sorted alphabetically, bank accounts could be sorted by account number, employee payroll records could be sorted by social security number and so on. This chapter introduces two simple sorting algorithms, the *selection sort* and the *insertion sort*, and the more efficient, but more complex, *merge sort*. Figure 18.1 summarizes the searching and sorting capabilities in this book. We include this chapter for the benefit of computer-science students. Most programmers will use the .Net Framework's built-in searching and sorting capabilities, such as class Array's BinarySearch and Sort methods and similar capabilities in .NET collections (Chapter 21).

Chapter	Algorithm	Location
Searching Algorithms:		
18	Linear Search	Section 18.2.1
	Binary Search	Section 18.2.2
	Recursive Linear Search	Exercise 18.8
	Recursive Binary Search	Exercise 18.9
21	BinarySearch method of class Array	Fig. 21.3
	ContainsKey method of class Dictionary<K, T>	Fig. 21.4
Sorting Algorithms:		
18	Selection Sort	Section 18.3.1
	Insertion Sort	Section 18.3.2
	Recursive Merge Sort	Section 18.3.3
	Bubble Sort	Exercises 18.5–18.6
	Bucket Sort	Exercise 18.7
	Recursive Quicksort	Exercise 18.10
18, 21	Sort method of classes Array	Figs. 18.3 and 21.3

Fig. 18.1 | Searching and sorting capabilities in this text.

18.2 Searching Algorithms

Looking up a phone number, accessing a website and checking the definition of a word in a dictionary all involve searching large amounts of data. The next two sections discuss two common search algorithms—one that is easy to program yet relatively inefficient and one that is relatively efficient but more complex to program.

18.2.1 Linear Search

The linear search algorithm searches each element in an array sequentially. If the search key does not match an element in the array, the algorithm tests each element and, when the end of the array is reached, informs the user that the search key is not present. If the search key is in the array, the algorithm tests each element until it finds one that matches the search key and returns the index of that element.

As an example, consider an array containing the following values

34	56	2	10	77	51	93	30	5	52

and a method that is searching for 51. Using the linear search algorithm, the method first checks whether 34 (at index 0) matches the search key. It does not, so the algorithm checks whether 56 (at index 1) matches the search key. The method continues moving through the array sequentially, testing 2 (at index 2), then 10 (at index 3), then 77 (at index 4). When the method tests 51 (at index 5), which matches the search key, the method returns 51's location (5) in the array. If, after checking every array element, the method determines that the search key does not match any element in the array, the method returns -1. If there are duplicate values in the array, linear search returns the index of the first element in the array that matches the search key.

Performing a Linear Search
Figure 18.2 implements the linear search algorithm. Method Main declares as local variables a Random object (line 10) to produce random int values and the int array data (line 11) to store randomly generated ints. Lines 14–17 store in data random ints in the range 10–99. Line 19 displays the array using string method Join to create a string with the array's elements separated by spaces. Join's first argument is a delimiter that's placed between each pair of elements and the second argument is the array. Lines 22–23 prompt for and input the search key. Lines 26–45 loop until the user enters -1. Line 29 calls method LinearSearch to determine whether searchInt is in the array. If so, LinearSearch returns the element's index, which is displayed in lines 33–34. If not, LinearSearch returns -1, and lines 38–39 notify the user. Lines 43–44 prompt for and input the next search key.

```
1   // Fig. 18.2: LinearSearchTest.cs
2   // Class that contains an array of random integers and a method
3   // that searches that array sequentially.
4   using System;
5
6   public class LinearSearchTest
7   {
```

Fig. 18.2 | Class that contains an array of random integers and a method that searches that array sequentially. (Part 1 of 3.)

```
8      static void Main()
9      {
10         var generator = new Random();
11         var data = new int[10]; // create space for array
12
13         // fill array with random ints in range 10-99
14         for (var i = 0; i < data.Length; ++i)
15         {
16            data[i] = generator.Next(10, 100);
17         }
18
19         Console.WriteLine(string.Join(" ", data) + "\n"); // display array
20
21         // input first int from user
22         Console.Write("Enter an integer value (-1 to quit): ");
23         var searchInt = int.Parse(Console.ReadLine());
24
25         // repeatedly input an integer; -1 terminates the app
26         while (searchInt != -1)
27         {
28            // perform linear search
29            int position = LinearSearch(data, searchInt);
30
31            if (position != -1) // integer was found
32            {
33               Console.WriteLine($"The integer {searchInt} was found in " +
34                  $"position {position}.\n");
35            }
36            else // integer was not found
37            {
38               Console.WriteLine(
39                  $"The integer {searchInt} was not found.\n");
40            }
41
42            // input next int from user
43            Console.Write("Enter an integer value (-1 to quit): ");
44            searchInt = int.Parse(Console.ReadLine());
45         }
46      }
47
48      // perform a linear search on the data
49      public static int LinearSearch(int[] values, int searchKey)
50      {
51         // loop through array sequentially
52         for (var index = 0; index < values.Length; ++index)
53         {
54            if (values[index] == searchKey)
55            {
56               return index; // return the element's index
57            }
58         }
```

Fig. 18.2 | Class that contains an array of random integers and a method that searches that array sequentially. (Part 2 of 3.)

```
59
60          return -1; // integer was not found
61     }
62  }
```

```
64 90 84 62 28 68 55 27 78 73

Enter an integer value (-1 to quit): 78
The integer 78 was found in position 8.

Enter an integer value (-1 to quit): 64
The integer 64 was found in position 0.

Enter an integer value (-1 to quit): 65
The integer 65 was not found.

Enter an integer value (-1 to quit): -1
```

Fig. 18.2 | Class that contains an array of random integers and a method that searches that array sequentially. (Part 3 of 3.)

Method LinearSearch

Lines 49–61 perform the linear search. The search key is passed to parameter searchKey. Lines 52–58 loop through the elements in the array. Line 54 compares the current element in the array with searchKey. If the values are equal, line 56 returns the index of the element. If the loop ends without finding the value, line 60 returns -1.

Efficiency of Linear Search

Searching algorithms all accomplish the same goal—finding an element that matches a given search key, if such an element exists. Many things, however, differentiate search algorithms from one another. The major difference is the amount of effort required to complete the search. One way to describe this effort is with **Big O notation**, which is a measure of the *worst-case runtime* for an algorithm—that is, *how hard an algorithm may have to work* to solve a problem. For searching and sorting algorithms, this is particularly dependent on *how many elements* there are in the data set and the algorithm used.

Constant Runtime

Suppose an algorithm is designed to test whether the first element of an array is equal to the second element. If the array has 10 elements, this algorithm requires one comparison. If the array has 1,000 elements, this algorithm still requires one comparison. In fact, this algorithm is completely independent of the number of elements in the array, and is thus said to have a **constant runtime**, which is represented in Big O notation as $O(1)$. An algorithm that is $O(1)$ does not necessarily require only one comparison. $O(1)$ just means that the number of comparisons is *constant*—it *does not grow as the size of the array increases*. An algorithm that tests whether the first element of an array is equal to any of the next three elements is still $O(1)$, even though it requires three comparisons.

Linear Runtime

An algorithm that tests whether the first element of an array is equal to *any* of the other elements of the array will require at most $n - 1$ comparisons, where n is the number of elements in the array. If the array has 10 elements, this algorithm requires up to nine comparisons. If the array has 1,000 elements, this algorithm requires up to 999 comparisons. As n grows larger, the n part of the expression *dominates*, and subtracting one becomes inconsequential. Big O is designed to highlight these dominant terms and ignore terms that become unimportant as n grows. For this reason, an algorithm that requires a total of $n - 1$ comparisons (such as the one we described earlier) is said to be $O(n)$. An $O(n)$ algorithm is referred to as having a linear runtime. $O(n)$ is often pronounced "on the order of n" or more simply "order n."

Quadratic Runtime

Now suppose you have an algorithm that tests whether *any* element of an array is duplicated elsewhere in the array. The first element must be compared with every other element in the array. The second element must be compared with every other element except the first (it was already compared to the first). The third element must be compared with every other element except the first two. In the end, this algorithm will end up making $(n - 1)$ $+ (n - 2) + \ldots + 2 + 1$ or $n^2/2 - n/2$ comparisons. As n increases, the n^2 term dominates and the n term becomes inconsequential. Again, Big O notation highlights the n^2 term, leaving $n^2/2$. But as we'll soon see, constant factors are omitted in Big O notation.

Big O is concerned with how an algorithm's runtime grows in relation to the number of items processed. Suppose an algorithm requires n^2 comparisons. With four elements, the algorithm will require 16 comparisons; with eight elements, the algorithm will require 64 comparisons. With this algorithm, doubling the number of elements quadruples the number of comparisons. Consider a similar algorithm requiring $n^2/2$ comparisons. With four elements, the algorithm will require eight comparisons; with eight elements, 32 comparisons. Again, *doubling* the number of elements *quadruples* the number of comparisons. Both of these algorithms grow as the square of n, so Big O ignores the constant, and both algorithms are considered to be $O(n^2)$, referred to as quadratic runtime and pronounced "on the order of n-squared" or more simply "order n-squared."

When n is small, $O(n^2)$ algorithms (running on today's billions-of-operations-per-second personal computers) will not noticeably affect performance. But as n grows, you'll start to notice the performance degradation. An $O(n^2)$ algorithm running on a million-element array would require a trillion "operations" (where each could actually require several machine instructions to execute). This could require many minutes to execute. A billion-element array would require a quintillion operations, a number so large that the algorithm could take decades! $O(n^2)$ algorithms are easy to write, as you'll see shortly. You'll also see algorithms with more favorable Big O measures. These efficient algorithms often take more cleverness and effort to create, but their superior performance can be well worth the extra effort, especially as n gets large.

Linear Search Runtime

The linear search algorithm runs in $O(n)$ time. The worst case in this algorithm is that every element must be checked to determine whether the search item exists in the array. If the size of the array is doubled, the number of comparisons that the algorithm must perform is also doubled. Linear search can provide outstanding performance if the element matching the search key happens to be at or near the front of the array. But we seek algorithms that perform well, on average, across *all* searches, including those where the element matching the search key is near the end of the array.

Linear search is the easiest search algorithm to program, but it can be slow compared to other search algorithms. If an app needs to perform many searches on large arrays, it may be better to implement a different, more efficient algorithm, such as the binary search, which we present in the next section.

> **Performance Tip 18.1**
>
> *Sometimes the simplest algorithms perform poorly. Their virtue is that they're easy to program, test and debug. Sometimes more complex algorithms are required to realize maximum performance.*

18.2.2 Binary Search

The binary search algorithm is more efficient than the linear search algorithm, but it requires that the array first be *sorted*. The first iteration of this algorithm tests the middle element in the array. If this matches the search key, the algorithm ends. Assuming the array is sorted in ascending order, if the search key is less than the middle element, the search key cannot match any element in the second half of the array and the algorithm continues with only the first half of the array (i.e., the first element up to, but not including, the middle element). If the search key is greater than the middle element, the search key cannot match any element in the first half of the array, and the algorithm continues with only the second half of the array (i.e., the element after the middle element through the last element). Each iteration tests the middle value of the remaining portion of the array, called a *subarray*. A subarray can have no elements, or it can encompass the entire array. If the search key does not match the element, the algorithm eliminates half of the remaining elements. The algorithm ends by either finding an element that matches the search key or reducing the subarray to zero size.

As an example, consider the sorted 15-element array

2	3	5	10	27	30	34	51	56	65	77	81	82	93	99

and a search key of 65. The binary search algorithm would first check whether 51 is the search key, because 51 is the array's middle element. The search key 65 is larger than 51, so 51 is "discarded" (i.e., eliminated from consideration) along with the first half of the array (all elements smaller than 51), leaving the following subarray to be searched:

56	65	77	81	82	93	99

Next, the algorithm checks whether the subarray's middle element (81) matches the search key—65 is smaller than 81, so 81 is discarded along with the elements larger than 81, leaving the following subarray to be searched:

56	65	77

After just two tests, the algorithm has narrowed the search from 15 elements to three. The algorithm then checks 65 (which indeed matches the search key) and returns that array element's index. This algorithm required just three comparisons to determine whether the search key matched an element in the array. Using a linear search algorithm would have required 10 comparisons. [*Note:* In this example, we have chosen to use an array with 15 elements so that there will always be an obvious middle element in the array. With an even number of elements, the middle of the array lies between two elements. We implement the algorithm to choose the higher of the two elements.]

Implementing Binary Search

Figure 18.3 declares class BinarySearchTest, which contains static methods Main, BinarySearch and DisplayElements (which helps visualize the binary search algorithm). Method Main has as local variables a Random object named generator (line 10) to produce random int values and the int array data (line 11) to store randomly generated ints. Lines 14–17 generate random ints in the range 10–99 and store them in data. Recall that a binary search requires an array's elements to be sorted. For this reason, line 19 calls class Array's static method Sort for the array data—this sorts the elements in an array in *ascending* order. Line 20 outputs the array's contents by calling method DisplayElements (lines 86–98). Lines 23–24 prompt the user for the search key and store it in searchInt. Lines 27–46 loop until the user enters -1. Line 30 calls method BinarySearch to determine whether searchInt is in the array. If searchInt is found, BinarySearch returns the element's index, which is displayed in lines 34–35. If searchInt is not in the array, BinarySearch returns -1, and lines 39–40 notify the user. Lines 44–45 prompt for and retrieve the next integer from the user.

```
 1   // Fig. 18.3: BinarySearchTest.cs
 2   // Class that contains an array of random integers and a method
 3   // that uses binary search to find an integer.
 4   using System;
 5
 6   public class BinarySearchTest
 7   {
 8      static void Main()
 9      {
10         var generator = new Random();
11         var data = new int[15]; // create space for array
12
13         // fill array with random ints in range 10-99
14         for (var i = 0; i < data.Length; ++i)
15         {
16            data[i] = generator.Next(10, 100);
17         }
18
19         Array.Sort(data); // elements must be sorted in ascending order
20         DisplayElements(data, 0, data.Length - 1); // display array
21
22         // input first int from user
23         Console.Write("\nPlease enter an integer value (-1 to quit): ");
24         int searchInt = int.Parse(Console.ReadLine());
25
26         // repeatedly input an integer; -1 terminates the app
27         while (searchInt != -1)
28         {
29            // perform binary search
30            int position = BinarySearch(data, searchInt);
31
32            if (position != -1) // integer was found
33            {
```

Fig. 18.3 | Class that contains an array of random integers and a method that uses binary search to find an integer. (Part 1 of 3.)

```
34              Console.WriteLine($"The integer {searchInt} was found in " +
35                  $"position {position}.\n");
36          }
37          else // integer was not found
38          {
39              Console.WriteLine(
40                  $"The integer {searchInt} was not found.\n");
41          }
42
43          // input next int from user
44          Console.Write("Please enter an integer value (-1 to quit): ");
45          searchInt = int.Parse(Console.ReadLine());
46      }
47  }
48
49  // perform a binary search on the data
50  public static int BinarySearch(int[] values, int searchElement)
51  {
52      var low = 0; // low end of the search area
53      var high = values.Length - 1; // high end of the search area
54      var middle = (low + high + 1) / 2; // middle element
55
56      do // loop to search for element
57      {
58          // display remaining elements of array
59          DisplayElements(values, low, high);
60
61          // indicate current middle; pad left with spaces for alignment
62          Console.WriteLine("-- ".PadLeft((middle + 1) * 3));
63
64          // if the element is found at the middle
65          if (searchElement == values[middle])
66          {
67              return middle; // search key found, so return its index
68          }
69          // middle element is too high
70          else if (searchElement < values[middle])
71          {
72              high = middle - 1; // eliminate the higher half
73          }
74          else // middle element is too low
75          {
76              low = middle + 1; // eliminate the lower half
77          }
78
79          middle = (low + high + 1) / 2; // recalculate the middle
80      } while (low <= high);
81
82      return -1; // search key was not found
83  }
84
```

Fig. 18.3 | Class that contains an array of random integers and a method that uses binary search to find an integer. (Part 2 of 3.)

```
85        // method to output certain values in array
86        public static void DisplayElements(int[] values, int low, int high)
87        {
88            // output three spaces for each element up to low for alignment
89            Console.Write(string.Empty.PadLeft(low * 3));
90
91            // output elements left in array
92            for (var i = low; i <= high; ++i)
93            {
94                Console.Write($"{values[i]} ");
95            }
96
97            Console.WriteLine();
98        }
99    }
```

```
12 17 22 25 30 39 40 52 56 72 76 82 84 91 93

Please enter an integer value (-1 to quit): 72
12 17 22 25 30 39 40 52 56 72 76 82 84 91 93
                          *
                          56 72 76 82 84 91 93
                                   *
                          56 72 76
                               *
The integer 72 was found in position 9.

Please enter an integer value (-1 to quit): 13
12 17 22 25 30 39 40 52 56 72 76 82 84 91 93
                     *
12 17 22 25 30 39 40
          *
12 17 22
    *
12
*
The integer 13 was not found.

Please enter an integer value (-1 to quit): -1
```

Fig. 18.3 | Class that contains an array of random integers and a method that uses binary search to find an integer. (Part 3 of 3.)

The first line of output from this app is the array of ints, in increasing order. When the user instructs the app to search for 72, the app first tests the middle element (indicated by -- below the element in the output), which is 52. The search key is greater than 52, so the app eliminates from consideration the first half of the array and tests the middle element from the second half. The search key is smaller than 82, so the app eliminates from consideration the second half of the subarray, leaving only three elements. Finally, the app checks 72 (which matches the search key) and returns the index 9. string method PadLeft (lines 62 and 89) adds the specified number of spaces to the beginning of the string on which the method is called and returns a new string containing the results.

*Method **BinarySearch***

Lines 50–83 declare method `BinarySearch`, which receives as parameters the array to search and the search key. Lines 52–54 calculate the `low` end index, `high` end index and `middle` index of the portion of the array being searched. When the method is first called, the `low` index is 0, the `high` index is the length of the array minus 1 and the `middle` is the average of these two values. Lines 56–80 loop until `low` is greater than `high` (this occurs when the element is not found). Line 65 tests whether the value in the `middle` element is equal to `searchElement`. If this is `true`, line 67 returns `middle`—the search key's location—to the caller. Each iteration of the loop tests a single value (line 65 and 70) and eliminates half of the remaining values in the array (line 72 or 76), then adjusts the `middle` index (line 79) for the next iteration of the loop. Lines 59 and 62 in this program—and similar statements in the chapters' remaining programs—help visualize the algorithm's operation. Actual searching and sorting implementations (and other time-critical algorithms) should not include output statements.

Efficiency of Binary Search

In the worst-case scenario, searching a sorted array of 1,023 elements causes `Binary-Search`'s loop to iterate only 10 times. Repeatedly dividing 1,023 by 2 (because each iteration, eliminates half of the array) and rounding down (because we also remove the middle element) yields the values 511, 255, 127, 63, 31, 15, 7, 3, 1 and 0. The number 1023 ($2^{10} - 1$) is divided by 2 only 10 times to get the value 0, which indicates that there are no more elements to test. Dividing by 2 is equivalent to one loop iteration in the binary search algorithm. Thus, an array of 1,048,575 ($2^{20} - 1$) elements takes a maximum of 20 iterations to find the key, and an array of one billion elements (which is less than $2^{30} - 1$) takes a maximum of 30 iterations. This is a tremendous improvement in performance over the linear search. For a one-billion-element array, this is a difference between an average of 500 million iterations for the linear search and a maximum of only 30 iterations for the binary search! The maximum number of iterations needed for the binary search of any sorted array is the exponent of the first power of 2 greater than the number of elements in the array, which is represented as $\log_2 n$. All logarithms grow at roughly the same rate, so in Big O notation the base can be omitted. This results in a big O of *O(log n)* for a binary search, which is also known as logarithmic runtime.

18.3 Sorting Algorithms

Sorting data (i.e., placing the data in some particular order, such as *ascending* or *descending*) is one of the most important computing applications. A bank sorts all checks by account number so that it can prepare individual bank statements at the end of each month. Telephone companies sort their lists of accounts by last name and, further, by first name to make it easy to find phone numbers. Virtually every organization must sort some data—often, massive amounts of it. Sorting data is an intriguing, compute-intensive problem that has attracted substantial research efforts.

   It's important to understand about sorting that the *end result*—the sorted array—will be the *same* no matter which (correct) algorithm you use to sort the array. The choice of algorithm affects only the *runtime* and *memory use* of the app. The rest of the chapter introduces three common sorting algorithms. The first two—*selection sort* and *insertion sort*—are simple to program, but inefficient. The last—*merge sort*—is much faster than selection sort and insertion sort but more difficult to program. We focus on sorting arrays of simple-type data, namely `int`s. It's possible to sort arrays of objects as well—we discuss this in Chapter 21, Generic Collections; Functional Programming with LINQ/PLINQ.

Sorting Visualizations
In the text, we add output statements to help you visualize how each sort works. The web is loaded with visual animations that show these sorts in action. Simply search for the algorithm name and "animation."

18.3.1 Selection Sort

Selection sort is a simple, but inefficient, sorting algorithm. The first iteration of the algorithm selects the *smallest element* in the array and swaps it with the first element. The second iteration selects the *second-smallest element* (which is the smallest remaining element) and swaps it with the second element. The algorithm continues until the last iteration selects the *second-largest element* and, if necessary, swaps it with the *second-to-last element*, leaving the *largest element* in the *last* position. After the ith iteration, the smallest i elements of the array will be sorted in increasing order in the first i positions of the array.

For the following discussion, we higlight the smallest element in bold and italic, and the element with which it will be swapped in bold. Consider the array

34	56	***4***	10	77	51	93	30	5	52

A selection sort begins from index 0 and determines the smallest element (4). The app then swaps 4 with the element at index 0 (34), resulting in

4	**56**	34	10	77	51	93	30	***5***	52

The second iteration begins from index 1 and determines the smallest value of the *remaining* elements (5). The app then swaps 5 with the element at index 1 (56), resulting in

4	5	**34**	***10***	77	51	93	30	56	52

The third iteration begins from index 2 and determines the next smallest value (10). The app then swaps 10 with the element at index 2 (34), resulting in

4	5	10	**34**	77	51	93	***30***	56	52

The process continues until the array is fully sorted:

4	5	10	30	34	51	52	56	77	93

After the first iteration, the smallest element is in the first position. After the second iteration, the two smallest elements are in order in the first two positions. After the third iteration, the three smallest elements are in order in the first three positions.

Implementing Selection Sort
In Fig. 18.4, `Main` declares as local variables a `Random` object named `generator` (line 10) to produce random `int` values and the `int` array `data` (line 11) to store randomly generated `int`s. Lines 14–17 generate random `int`s in the range 10–99 and store them in `data`. Line 20 outputs the array's unsorted contents. Line 22 calls method `SelectionSort` to sort array `data`'s contents in ascending order, then lines 24–25 display the sorted array. Method `SelectionSort` calls method `PrintPass` (defined in lines 59–86) to help visualize the sorting algorithm. The output uses dashes to indicate the portion of the array that is sorted after each pass of the algorithm. An asterisk is placed next to the position of the element that was

swapped with the smallest element on that pass. On each pass, the element next to the aster-isk and the element above the rightmost set of dashes were the two values that were swapped.

```
1   // Fig. 18.4: SelectionSortTest.cs
2   // Class that creates an array filled with random integers.
3   // Provides a method to sort the array with selection sort.
4   using System;
5
6   public class SelectionSortTest
7   {
8      static void Main()
9      {
10        var generator = new Random();
11        var data = new int[10]; // create space for array
12
13        // fill array with random ints in range 10-99
14        for (var i = 0; i < data.Length; ++i)
15        {
16           data[i] = generator.Next(10, 100);
17        }
18
19        Console.WriteLine("Unsorted array:");
20        Console.WriteLine(string.Join(" ", data) + "\n"); // display array
21
22        SelectionSort(data); // sort array
23
24        Console.WriteLine("Sorted array:");
25        Console.WriteLine(string.Join(" ", data) + "\n"); // display array
26     }
27
28     // sort array using selection sort
29     public static void SelectionSort(int[] values)
30     {
31        // loop over data.Length - 1 elements
32        for (var i = 0; i < values.Length - 1; ++i)
33        {
34           var smallest = i; // first index of remaining array
35
36           // loop to find index of smallest element
37           for (var index = i + 1; index < values.Length; ++index)
38           {
39              if (values[index] < values[smallest])
40              {
41                 smallest = index;
42              }
43           }
44
45           Swap(ref values[i], ref values[smallest]); // swap elements
46           PrintPass(values, i + 1, smallest); // output pass of algorithm
47        }
48     }
```

Fig. 18.4 | Class that creates an array filled with random integers. Provides a method to sort the array with selection sort. (Part 1 of 3.)

```
49
50      // helper method to swap values in two elements
51      public static void Swap(ref int first, ref int second)
52      {
53          var temporary = first; // store first in temporary
54          first = second; // replace first with second
55          second = temporary; // put temporary in second
56      }
57
58      // display a pass of the algorithm
59      public static void PrintPass(int[] values, int pass, int index)
60      {
61          Console.Write($"after pass {pass}: ");
62
63          // output elements through the selected item
64          for (var i = 0; i < index; ++i)
65          {
66              Console.Write($"{values[i]}  ");
67          }
68
69          Console.Write($"{values[index]}* "); // indicate swap
70
71          // finish outputting array
72          for (var i = index + 1; i < values.Length; ++i)
73          {
74              Console.Write($"{values[i]}  ");
75          }
76
77          Console.Write("\n                    "); // for alignment
78
79          // indicate amount of array that is sorted
80          for(var j = 0; j < pass; ++j)
81          {
82              Console.Write("--  ");
83          }
84
85          Console.WriteLine("\n"); // skip a line in output
86      }
87  }
```

```
Unsorted array:
86  97  83  45  19  31  86  13  57  61

after pass 1: 13  97  83  45  19  31  86  86* 57  61
              --

after pass 2: 13  19  83  45  97* 31  86  86  57  61
              --  --

after pass 3: 13  19  31  45  97  83* 86  86  57  61
              --  --  --
```

Fig. 18.4 | Class that creates an array filled with random integers. Provides a method to sort the array with selection sort. (Part 2 of 3.)

```
after pass 4: 13  19  31  45* 97  83  86  86  57  61
              --  --  --  --

after pass 5: 13  19  31  45  57  83  86  86  97* 61
              --  --  --  --  --

after pass 6: 13  19  31  45  57  61  86  86  97  83*
              --  --  --  --  --  --

after pass 7: 13  19  31  45  57  61  83  86  97  86*
              --  --  --  --  --  --  --

after pass 8: 13  19  31  45  57  61  83  86* 97  86
              --  --  --  --  --  --  --  --

after pass 9: 13  19  31  45  57  61  83  86  86  97*
              --  --  --  --  --  --  --  --  --

Sorted array:
13  19  31  45  57  61  83  86  86  97
```

Fig. 18.4 | Class that creates an array filled with random integers. Provides a method to sort the array with selection sort. (Part 3 of 3.)

Method SelectionSort

Lines 29–48 declare method SelectionSort. Lines 32–47 loop data.Length - 1 times. Line 29 initializes smallest to the index of the current item. Lines 37–43 loop over the remaining elements in the array. For each of these elements, line 39 compares its value to the value of the smallest element. If the current element is smaller than the element at index smallest, line 41 assigns the current element's index to smallest. When this loop finishes, smallest contains the index of the smallest element in the remaining array. Line 45 calls method Swap (lines 51–56) to place the smallest remaining element in the next spot in the array.

Efficiency of Selection Sort

The selection sort algorithm runs in $O(n^2)$ time. Method SelectionSort, which implements the selection sort algorithm, contains *nested for loops*. The outer for loop (lines 32–47) iterates over the first $n - 1$ elements in the array, swapping the smallest remaining element to its sorted position. The inner for loop (lines 37–43) iterates over each element in the remaining array, searching for the smallest. This loop executes $n - 1$ times during the first iteration of the outer loop, $n - 2$ times during the second iteration, then $n - 3$, …, 3, 2, 1. This inner loop will iterate a total of $n(n - 1) / 2$ or $(n^2 - n)/2$. In Big O notation, smaller terms drop out and constants are ignored, leaving a final Big O of $O(n^2)$.

18.3.2 Insertion Sort

Insertion sort is another *simple*, but *inefficient*, sorting algorithm. Its first iteration takes the second element in the array and, if it's less than the first, swaps them. The second iteration looks at the third element and inserts it in the correct position with respect to the first two elements (moving them as necessary), so all three elements are in order. At the ith iteration of this algorithm, the first i elements in the original array will be sorted.

Consider as an example the following array:

34	56	4	10	77	51	93	30	5	52

An app that implements the insertion sort algorithm first looks at the first two elements of the array, 34 and 56. These are already in order, so the app continues (if they were out of order, it would swap them).

In the next iteration, the app looks at the third value, 4. This value is less than 56, so the app stores 4 in a temporary variable and moves 56 one element to the right. The app then checks and determines that 4 is less than 34, so it moves 34 one element to the right. The app has now reached the beginning of the array, so it places 4 in the zeroth position. The array now is

4	34	56	10	77	51	93	30	5	52

In the next iteration, the app stores the value 10 in a temporary variable. Then the app compares 10 to 56 and moves 56 one element to the right because it's larger than 10. The app then compares 10 to 34, moving 34 one element to the right. When the app compares 10 to 4, it observes that 10 is larger than 4 and places 10 in element 1. The array now is

4	10	34	56	77	51	93	30	5	52

Using this algorithm, at the ith iteration, the original array's first i elements are sorted, but they may not be in their final locations—smaller values may be located later in the array.

Implementing Insertion Sort

Figure 18.5 declares the `InsertionSortTest` class. Lines 29–51 declare method `InsertionSort`. Lines 32–50 loop through `data.Length - 1` items in the array. In each iteration, line 35 stores in variable `insert` the value of the element that will be inserted in the sorted portion of the array. Line 38 declares and initializes variable `moveItem`, which keeps track of where to insert the element. Lines 41–46 loop to locate the correct position to insert the element. The loop will terminate either when the app reaches the front of the array or when it reaches an element that is less than the value to be inserted. Line 44 moves an element to the right, and line 45 decrements the position at which to insert the next element. After the loop ends, line 48 inserts the element in place—it's possible that no movements will need to me made. Method `InsertionSort` calls method `PrintPass` (defined in lines 54–81) to help visualize the sorting algorithm. The output uses dashes to indicate the portion of the array that is sorted after each pass of the algorithm. An asterisk is placed next to the element that was inserted in place on that pass.

```
1   // Fig. 18.5: InsertionSortTest.cs
2   // Class that creates an array filled with random integers.
3   // Provides a method to sort the array with insertion sort.
4   using System;
5
6   public class InsertionSortTest
7   {
```

Fig. 18.5 | Class that creates an array filled with random integers. Provides a method to sort the array with insertion sort. (Part 1 of 4.)

```csharp
 8     static void Main()
 9     {
10        var generator = new Random();
11        var data = new int[10]; // create space for array
12
13        // fill array with random ints in range 10-99
14        for (var i = 0; i < data.Length; ++i)
15        {
16           data[i] = generator.Next(10, 100);
17        }
18
19        Console.WriteLine("Unsorted array:");
20        Console.WriteLine(string.Join(" ", data) + "\n"); // display array
21
22        InsertionSort(data); // sort array
23
24        Console.WriteLine("Sorted array:");
25        Console.WriteLine(string.Join(" ", data) + "\n"); // display array
26     }
27
28     // sort array using insertion sort
29     public static void InsertionSort(int[] values)
30     {
31        // loop over data.Length - 1 elements
32        for (var next = 1; next < values.Length; ++next)
33        {
34           // store value in current element
35           var insert = values[next];
36
37           // initialize location to place element
38           var moveItem = next;
39
40           // search for place to put current element
41           while (moveItem > 0 && values[moveItem - 1] > insert)
42           {
43              // shift element right one slot
44              values[moveItem] = values[moveItem - 1];
45              moveItem--;
46           }
47
48           values[moveItem] = insert; // place inserted element
49           PrintPass(values, next, moveItem); // output pass of algorithm
50        }
51     }
52
53     // display a pass of the algorithm
54     public static void PrintPass(int[] values, int pass, int index)
55     {
56        Console.Write($"after pass {pass}: ");
57
```

Fig. 18.5 | Class that creates an array filled with random integers. Provides a method to sort the array with insertion sort. (Part 2 of 4.)

```
58          // output elements till swapped item
59          for (var i = 0; i < index; ++i)
60          {
61              Console.Write($"{values[i]}   ");
62          }
63
64          Console.Write($"{values[index]}* "); // indicate swap
65
66          // finish outputting array
67          for (var i = index + 1; i < values.Length; ++i)
68          {
69              Console.Write($"{values[i]}   ");
70          }
71
72          Console.Write("\n                    "); // for alignment
73
74          // indicate amount of array that is sorted
75          for(var i = 0; i <= pass; ++i)
76          {
77              Console.Write("--  ");
78          }
79
80          Console.WriteLine("\n"); // skip a line in output
81      }
82  }
```

```
Unsorted array:
12  27  36  28  33  92  11  93  59  62

after pass 1: 12  27* 36  28  33  92  11  93  59  62
              --  --

after pass 2: 12  27  36* 28  33  92  11  93  59  62
              --  --  --

after pass 3: 12  27  28* 36  33  92  11  93  59  62
              --  --  --  --

after pass 4: 12  27  28  33* 36  92  11  93  59  62
              --  --  --  --  --

after pass 5: 12  27  28  33  36  92* 11  93  59  62
              --  --  --  --  --  --

after pass 6: 11* 12  27  28  33  36  92  93  59  62
              --  --  --  --  --  --  --

after pass 7: 11  12  27  28  33  36  92  93* 59  62
              --  --  --  --  --  --  --  --

after pass 8: 11  12  27  28  33  36  59* 92  93  62
              --  --  --  --  --  --  --  --  --
```

Fig. 18.5 | Class that creates an array filled with random integers. Provides a method to sort the array with insertion sort. (Part 3 of 4.)

```
after pass 9: 11  12  27  28  33  36  59  62* 92  93
              --  --  --  --  --  --  --  --  --  --

Sorted array:
11  12  27  28  33  36  59  62  92  93
```

Fig. 18.5 | Class that creates an array filled with random integers. Provides a method to sort the array with insertion sort. (Part 4 of 4.)

Efficiency of Insertion Sort

The insertion sort algorithm also runs in $O(n^2)$ time. Like selection sort, the implementation of insertion sort (lines 29–51 of Fig. 18.5) contains *nested loops*. The for loop (lines 32–50) iterates data.Length - 1 times, inserting an element in the appropriate position in the elements sorted so far. For the purposes of this app, data.Length - 1 is equivalent to $n-1$ (as data.Length is the size of the array). The while loop (lines 41–46) iterates over the elements that precede the one that will be inserted. In the *worst case*, this while loop will require $n-1$ comparisons. Each individual loop runs in $O(n)$ time. In Big O notation, *nested loops* mean that you must *multiply* the number of iterations of each loop. For each iteration of an outer loop, there will be a certain number of iterations of the inner loop. In this algorithm, for each $O(n)$ iterations of the outer loop, there will be $O(n)$ iterations of the inner loop. Multiplying these values results in a Big O of $O(n^2)$.

18.3.3 Merge Sort

Merge sort is an *efficient* sorting algorithm but is conceptually more *complex* than selection sort and insertion sort. The merge sort algorithm sorts an array by *splitting* it into two equal-sized subarrays, *sorting* each subarray and *merging* them in one larger array. With an odd number of elements, the algorithm creates the two subarrays such that one has one more element than the other.

The implementation of merge sort in this example is *recursive*. The base case is an array with one element. A one-element array is, of course, sorted, so merge sort immediately returns when it's called with a one-element array. The *recursion step splits* an array in two approximately equal-length pieces, recursively *sorts* them and *merges* the two sorted arrays in one larger, sorted array.

Suppose the algorithm has already merged smaller arrays to create sorted arrays A:

	4	10	34	56	77

and B:

	5	30	51	52	93

Merge sort combines these two arrays in one larger, sorted array. The smallest element in A is 4 (located in element 0 of A). The smallest element in B is 5 (located in element 0 of B). To determine the smallest element in the merged array, the algorithm compares 4 and 5. The value from A is smaller, so 4 becomes the merged array's first element. The algorithm continues by comparing 10 (located in element 1 in A) to 5 (located in element 0 in B). The value from B is smaller, so 5 becomes the second element in the larger array.

The algorithm continues by comparing 10 to 30, with 10 becoming the third element in the array, and so on.

Implementing Merge Sort
Lines 29–32 of Fig. 18.6 declare the MergeSort method. Line 31 calls private method SortArray with 0 and data.Length - 1 as the arguments—these are the beginning and ending indices of the array to be sorted. These values tell SortArray to operate on the entire array. Method SubArray (lines 116–127)—which is called from methods SortArray (35–56) and Merge (59–113)—produces a string representation of a portion of the array. The program displays these strings to help visualize the sort algorithm—the output shows the splits and merges performed by MergeSort as the algorithm progresses.

```
1    // Fig. 18.6: MergeSortTest.cs
2    // Class that creates an array filled with random integers.
3    // Provides a method to sort the array with merge sort.
4    using System;
5
6    public class MergeSortTest
7    {
8       static void Main()
9       {
10          var generator = new Random();
11          var data = new int[10]; // create space for array
12
13          // fill array with random ints in range 10-99
14          for (var i = 0; i < data.Length; ++i)
15          {
16             data[i] = generator.Next(10, 100);
17          }
18
19          Console.WriteLine("Unsorted array:");
20          Console.WriteLine(string.Join(" ", data) + "\n"); // display array
21
22          MergeSort(data); // sort array
23
24          Console.WriteLine("Sorted array:");
25          Console.WriteLine(string.Join(" ", data) + "\n"); // display array
26       }
27
28       // calls recursive SortArray method to begin merge sorting
29       public static void MergeSort(int[] values)
30       {
31          SortArray(values, 0, values.Length - 1); // sort entire array
32       }
33
34       // splits array, sorts subarrays and merges subarrays into sorted array
35       private static void SortArray(int[] values, int low, int high)
36       {
```

Fig. 18.6 | Class that creates an array filled with random integers. Provides a method to sort the array with merge sort. (Part 1 of 5.)

```
37          // test base case; size of array equals 1
38          if ((high - low) >= 1) // if not base case
39          {
40              int middle1 = (low + high) / 2; // calculate middle of array
41              int middle2 = middle1 + 1; // calculate next element over
42
43              // output split step
44              Console.WriteLine($"split:    {Subarray(values, low, high)}");
45              Console.WriteLine($"          {Subarray(values, low, middle1)}");
46              Console.WriteLine($"          {Subarray(values, middle2, high)}");
47              Console.WriteLine();
48
49              // split array in half; sort each half (recursive calls)
50              SortArray(values, low, middle1); // first half of array
51              SortArray(values, middle2, high); // second half of array
52
53              // merge two sorted arrays after split calls return
54              Merge(values, low, middle1, middle2, high);
55          }
56      }
57
58      // merge two sorted subarrays into one sorted subarray
59      private static void Merge(int[] values, int left, int middle1,
60          int middle2, int right)
61      {
62          int leftIndex = left; // index into left subarray
63          int rightIndex = middle2; // index into right subarray
64          int combinedIndex = left; // index into temporary working array
65          int[] combined = new int[values.Length]; // working array
66
67          // output two subarrays before merging
68          Console.WriteLine($"merge:    {Subarray(values, left, middle1)}");
69          Console.WriteLine($"          {Subarray(values, middle2, right)}");
70
71          // merge arrays until reaching end of either
72          while (leftIndex <= middle1 && rightIndex <= right)
73          {
74              // place smaller of two current elements into result
75              // and move to next space in arrays
76              if (values[leftIndex] <= values[rightIndex])
77              {
78                  combined[combinedIndex++] = values[leftIndex++];
79              }
80              else
81              {
82                  combined[combinedIndex++] = values[rightIndex++];
83              }
84          }
85
```

Fig. 18.6 | Class that creates an array filled with random integers. Provides a method to sort the array with merge sort. (Part 2 of 5.)

```
86          // if left array is empty
87          if (leftIndex == middle2)
88          {
89              // copy in rest of right array
90              while (rightIndex <= right)
91              {
92                  combined[combinedIndex++] = values[rightIndex++];
93              }
94          }
95          else // right array is empty
96          {
97              // copy in rest of left array
98              while (leftIndex <= middle1)
99              {
100                 combined[combinedIndex++] = values[leftIndex++];
101             }
102         }
103
104         // copy values back into original array
105         for (int i = left; i <= right; ++i)
106         {
107             values[i] = combined[i];
108         }
109
110         // output merged array
111         Console.WriteLine($"            {Subarray(values, left, right)}");
112         Console.WriteLine();
113     }
114
115     // method to output certain values in array
116     public static string Subarray(int[] values, int low, int high)
117     {
118         string temporary = string.Empty.PadLeft(low * 3);
119
120         // output elements left in array
121         for (int i = low; i <= high; ++i)
122         {
123             temporary += $" {values[i]}";
124         }
125
126         return temporary;
127     }
128 }
```

```
Unsorted:   36 38 81 93 85 72 31 11 33 74

split:      36 38 81 93 85 72 31 11 33 74
            36 38 81 93 85
                          72 31 11 33 74
```

Fig. 18.6 | Class that creates an array filled with random integers. Provides a method to sort the array with merge sort. (Part 3 of 5.)

```
split:     36 38 81 93 85
           36 38 81
                    93 85

split:     36 38 81
           36 38
                 81

split:     36 38
           36
              38

merge:     36
              38
           36 38

merge:     36 38
                 81
           36 38 81

split:              93 85
                    93
                       85

merge:              93
                       85
                    85 93

merge:     36 38 81
                    85 93
           36 38 81 85 93

split:                   72 31 11 33 74
                         72 31 11
                                  33 74

split:                   72 31 11
                         72 31
                               11

split:                   72 31
                         72
                            31

merge:                   72
                            31
                         31 72

merge:                   31 72
                               11
                         11 31 72
```

Fig. 18.6 | Class that creates an array filled with random integers. Provides a method to sort the array with merge sort. (Part 4 of 5.)

```
split:                          33 74
                                33
                                   74

merge:                          33
                                   74
                                33 74

merge:                 11 31 72
                                33 74
                       11 31 33 72 74

merge:      36 38 81 85 93
                       11 31 33 72 74
            11 31 33 36 38 72 74 81 85 93

Sorted:    11 31 33 36 38 72 74 81 85 93
```

Fig. 18.6 | Class that creates an array filled with random integers. Provides a method to sort the array with merge sort. (Part 5 of 5.)

Method SortArray

Method SortArray is declared in lines 35–56. Line 38 tests the base case. When the array's size is 1, the array is *already sorted*, so the method simply returns immediately. If the array size is greater than 1, the method

- splits the array in two,
- recursively calls method SortArray to sort the two subarrays and
- merges them.

Lines 50–51 recursively call method SortArray on the array's first half and second half, respectively. When these two method calls return, the array's two halves have been sorted. Line 54 calls method Merge (lines 59–113) to combine the two sorted halves of the array into one larger sorted array.

Method Merge

Lines 72–84 in method Merge loop until the app reaches the end of either subarray. Line 76 tests which element at the beginning of the subarrays is smaller. If the element in the left array is smaller or equal, line 78 places it in position in the combined array. If the element in the right array is smaller, line 82 places it in position in the combined array. When the loop completes, one entire subarray is placed in the combined array, but the other subarray still contains data. Line 87 tests whether the left array has reached the end. If so, lines 90–93 fill the combined array with the remaining elements of the right array. If the left array has not reached the end, then the right array has, and lines 98–101 fill the combined array with the remaining elements of the left array. Finally, lines 105–108 copy the combined array into the original array.

Efficiency of Merge Sort

Merge sort is a *far more efficient* algorithm than either insertion sort or selection sort when sorting *large* sets of data. Consider the first (*nonrecursive*) call to method SortArray. This results in two *recursive* calls to method SortArray with subarrays each approximately *half* the size of the original array, and a single call to method Merge. This call to method Merge requires, at worst, $n - 1$ comparisons to fill the original array, which is $O(n)$. (Recall that each element in the array can be chosen by comparing one element from each of the subarrays.) The two calls to method SortArray result in four more *recursive* calls to SortArray, each with a subarray approximately a quarter the size of the original array, along with two calls to method Merge. These two calls to method Merge each require, at worst, $n/2 - 1$ comparisons for a total number of comparisons of $(n/2 - 1) + (n/2 - 1) = n - 2$, which is $O(n)$. This process continues, each call to SortArray generating two additional calls to method SortArray and a call to Merge, until the algorithm has split the array into one-element subarrays. At each level, $O(n)$ comparisons are required to merge the subarrays. Each level *splits* the size of the arrays in half, so *doubling* the size of the array requires only *one* more level. *Quadrupling* the size of the array requires only *two* more levels. This pattern is *logarithmic* and results in *log2 n levels*. This results in a total efficiency of $O(n \log n)$.

Performance Tip 18.2
As you may have noticed, the key to achieving the high efficiency of the merge sort is cleverly using additional memory. This is another example of the space/time trade-off—if you have more space you can get your algorithm to run in less time and if you have less space your algorithm may require more time. In industry, you might create apps for memory constrained devices, which might prevent you from using the merge sort algorithm.

18.4 Summary of the Efficiency of Searching and Sorting Algorithms

Figure 18.7 summarizes some of the searching and sorting algorithms covered in this book and lists the Big O of each. Figure 18.8 lists the Big O expressions covered in this chapter, along with a number of values for n to highlight the differences in the growth rates.

Algorithm	Location	Big O
Searching Algorithms:		
Linear Search	Section 18.2.1	$O(n)$
Binary Search	Section 18.2.2	$O(\log n)$
Recursive Linear Search	Exercise 18.8	$O(n)$
Recursive Binary Search	Exercise 18.9	$O(\log n)$
Sorting Algorithms:		
Selection Sort	Section 18.3.1	$O(n^2)$
Insertion Sort	Section 18.3.2	$O(n^2)$
Merge Sort	Section 18.3.3	$O(n \log n)$
Bubble Sort	Exercises 18.5–18.6	$O(n^2)$

Fig. 18.7 | Searching and sorting algorithms with Big O values.

$n =$	$O(\log n)$	$O(n)$	$O(n \log n)$	$O(n^2)$
1	0	1	0	1
2	1	2	2	4
3	1	3	3	9
4	1	4	4	16
5	1	5	5	25
10	1	10	10	100
100	2	100	200	10000
1,000	3	1000	3000	10^6
1,000,000	6	1000000	6000000	10^{12}
1,000,000,000	9	1000000000	9000000000	10^{18}

Fig. 18.8 | Number of comparisons for common Big O notations.

18.5 Wrap-Up

In this chapter, you learned how to search for items in arrays and how to sort arrays so that their elements are arranged in order. We discussed linear search and binary search, and selection sort, insertion sort and merge sort. You learned that linear search can operate on any set of data, but that binary search requires the data to be sorted first. You also learned that the simplest searching and sorting algorithms can exhibit poor performance. We introduced Big O notation—a measure of the efficiency of algorithms—and used it to compare the efficiency of the algorithms we discussed. In the next chapter, you'll learn about dynamic data structures that can grow or shrink at execution time.

Summary

Section 18.1 Introduction
- Searching involves determining if a search key is present in the data and, if so, finding its location.
- Sorting involves arranging data in order.

Section 18.2.1 Linear Search
- The linear search algorithm searches an array's elements sequentially until it finds one that matches the search key. If the search key is not in the array, the algorithm tests every element and returns an indication (such as a sentinel value) that the search key was not found.
- One way to describe the efficiency of an algorithm is with Big O notation (O), which indicates how hard an algorithm may have to work to solve a problem.
- In searching and sorting algorithms, Big O is dependent on how many elements are in the data.
- An $O(n)$ algorithm is referred to as having a linear runtime.
- Big O is designed to highlight dominant factors and ignore terms that become unimportant with high n values. Big O notation is concerned with the growth rate of algorithm runtimes, so constants are ignored.
- The linear search algorithm runs in $O(n)$ time.

- The worst case in linear search is that every element must be checked to determine whether the search item exists. This occurs if the search key is the last element in the array or is not present.

Section 18.2.2 Binary Search
- The binary search algorithm is more efficient than the linear search algorithm, but it requires that the array be sorted.
- The first iteration of binary search tests the middle array element. If this is the search key, the algorithm returns its location. If the search key is less than the middle element, the search continues with the array's first half. If the search key is greater than the middle element, the search continues with the array's second half. Each iteration of binary search tests the middle value of the remaining array and, if the element is not found, eliminates half of the remaining elements.
- Binary search is a more efficient searching algorithm than linear search because with each comparison it eliminates from consideration half of the elements in the array.
- Binary search runs in $O(\log n)$ time, because each step removes half of the remaining elements.

Section 18.3.1 Selection Sort
- The selection sort is a simple, but inefficient, sorting algorithm.
- The first iteration of the selection sort selects the smallest element in the array and swaps it with the first element. The second iteration selects the second-smallest element (which is the smallest remaining element) and swaps it with the second element. Selection sort continues until the largest element is in the last position. After the ith iteration of selection sort, the smallest i elements of the whole array are sorted into the first i positions.
- The selection sort algorithm runs in $O(n^2)$ time.

Section 18.3.2 Insertion Sort
- The first iteration of insertion sort takes the second element in the array and, if it's less than the first, swaps them. The second iteration looks at the third element and inserts it in the correct position with respect to the first two. After the ith iteration of insertion sort, the first i elements in the original array are sorted.
- The insertion sort algorithm runs in $O(n^2)$ time.

Section 18.3.3 Merge Sort
- Merge sort is a sorting algorithm that is faster, but more complex to implement, than selection sort and insertion sort.
- The merge sort algorithm sorts an array by splitting it into two equal-sized subarrays, sorting each recursively and merging them into one larger array.
- Merge sort's base case is an array with one element. A one-element array is already sorted.
- Merge sort performs the merge by looking at the first element in each array, which is also the smallest. Merge sort takes the smallest of these and places it in the first element of the larger array. If there are still elements in the subarray, merge sort looks at the second element in that subarray (which is now the smallest element remaining) and compares it to the first element in the other subarray. Merge sort continues this process until the larger array is filled.
- In the worst case, the first call to merge sort has to make $O(n)$ comparisons to fill the n slots in the final array.
- The merging portion of the merge sort algorithm is performed on two subarrays, each of approximately size $n/2$. Creating each of these subarrays requires $n/2 - 1$ comparisons for each subarray, or $O(n)$ comparisons total. This pattern continues as each level works on twice as many arrays, but each is half the size of the previous array. Similar to binary search, this halving results in log n levels for a total efficiency of $O(n \log n)$.

Terminology

Big O notation	$O(n)$
binary search	$O(n^2)$
constant runtime	search key
efficiency of algorithms	quadratic runtime
insertion sort	search key
linear runtime	searching
linear search	selection sort
logarithmic runtime	sort key
merge sort	Sort method of class Array
$O(1)$	sorting
$O(\log n)$	swapping values
$O(n \log n)$	

Self-Review Exercises

18.1   Fill in the blanks in each of the following statements:

a)   A selection sort app would take approximately _____ times as long to run on a 128-element array as on a 32-element array.

b)   The efficiency of merge sort is _____.

18.2   What key aspect of both the binary search and the merge sort accounts for the logarithmic portion of their respective Big Os?

18.3   In what sense is the insertion sort superior to the merge sort? In what sense is the merge sort superior to the insertion sort?

18.4   In the text, we say that after the merge sort splits the array into two subarrays, it then sorts these two subarrays and merges them. Why might someone be puzzled by our statement that "it then sorts these two subarrays"?

Answers to Self-Review Exercises

18.1   a) 16, because an $O(n^2)$ algorithm takes 16 times as long to sort four times as much information. b) $O(n \log n)$.

18.2   Both of these algorithms incorporate "halving"—somehow reducing something by half. The binary search eliminates from consideration one half of the array after each comparison. The merge sort splits the array in half each time it's called.

18.3   The insertion sort is easier to understand and to program than the merge sort. The merge sort is far more efficient ($O(n \log n)$) than the insertion sort ($O(n^2)$).

18.4   In a sense, it does not really sort these two subarrays. It simply keeps splitting the original array in half until it provides a one-element subarray, which is, of course, sorted. It then builds up the original two subarrays by merging these one-element arrays to form larger subarrays, which are then merged until the whole array has been sorted.

Exercises

18.5   *(Bubble Sort)* Implement the bubble sort—another simple, yet inefficient, sorting technique. It's called bubble sort or sinking sort because smaller values gradually "bubble" their way to the top of the array (i.e., toward the first element) like air bubbles rising in water, while the larger values sink to the bottom (end) of the array. The technique uses *nested loops* to make several passes through the array. Each pass compares successive overlapping pairs of elements (i.e., elements 0 and

1, 1 and 2, 2 and 3, etc.). If a pair is in increasing order (or the values are equal), the bubble sort leaves the values as they are. If a pair is in decreasing order, the bubble sort swaps their values in the array.

The first pass compares the first two elements of the array and swaps them if necessary. It then compares the second and third elements. The end of this pass compares the last two elements in the array and swaps them if necessary. After one pass, the largest element will be in the last position. After two passes, the largest two elements will be in the last two positions. Explain why bubble sort is an $O(n^2)$ algorithm.

18.6 *(Enhanced Bubble Sort)* Make the following simple modifications to improve the performance of the bubble sort you developed in Exercise 18.5:

    a) After the first pass, the largest number is guaranteed to be in the highest-numbered element of the array (for an array being sorted in ascending order); after the second pass, the two highest numbers are "in place"; and so on. Instead of making nine comparisons on every pass of a 10-element array, modify the bubble sort to make eight comparisons on the second pass, seven on the third pass and so on.

    b) The data in the array may already be in the proper order or near-proper order, so why make nine passes of a 10-element array if fewer will suffice? Modify the sort to check at the end of each pass whether any swaps have been made. If none have been made, the data must already be in the proper order, so the app should terminate. If swaps have been made, at least one more pass is needed.

18.7 *(Bucket Sort)* A bucket sort begins with a one-dimensional array of positive integers to be sorted and a two-dimensional array of integers with rows indexed from 0 to 9 and columns indexed from 0 to $n-1$, where n is the number of values to be sorted. Each row of the two-dimensional array is referred to as a *bucket*. Write a class named BucketSort containing a method called Sort that operates as follows:

    a) Place each value of the one-dimensional array into a row of the bucket array, based on the value's "ones" (rightmost) digit. For example, 97 is placed in row 7, 3 is placed in row 3 and 100 is placed in row 0. This procedure is called a *distribution pass*.

    b) Loop through the bucket array row by row, and copy the values back to the original array. This procedure is called a *gathering pass*. The new order of the preceding values in the one-dimensional array is 100, 3 and 97.

    c) Repeat this process for each subsequent digit position (tens, hundreds, thousands, etc.).

On the second (tens digit) pass, 100 is placed in row 0, 3 is placed in row 0 (because 3 has no tens digit) and 97 is placed in row 9. After the gathering pass, the order of the values in the one-dimensional array is 100, 3 and 97. On the third (hundreds digit) pass, 100 is placed in row 1, 3 is placed in row 0 and 97 is placed in row 0. After the last gathering pass, the original array is in sorted order.

The two-dimensional array of buckets is 10 times the length of the integer array being sorted. This sorting technique provides better performance than a bubble sort, but requires much more memory—the bubble sort requires space for only one additional element of data. This comparison is an example of the space/time trade-off: The bucket sort uses more memory than the bubble sort, but performs better. This version of the bucket sort requires copying all the data back to the original array on each pass. Another possibility is to create a second two-dimensional bucket array and repeatedly swap the data between the two bucket arrays.

18.8 *(Recursive Linear Search)* Modify Fig. 18.2 to use recursive method RecursiveLinearSearch to perform a linear search of the array. The method should receive the search key and starting index as arguments. If the search key is found, return its index in the array; otherwise, return -1. Each call to the recursive method should check one index in the array.

18.9 *(Recursive Binary Search)* Modify Fig. 18.3 to use recursive method RecursiveBinarySearch to perform a binary search of the array. The method should receive the search key, starting index and ending index as arguments. If the search key is found, return its index in the array. If the search key is not found, return -1.

18.10   *(Quicksort)* The recursive sorting technique called quicksort uses the following basic algorithm for a one-dimensional array of values:

    a) *Partitioning Step*: Take the first element of the unsorted array and determine its final location in the sorted array (i.e., all values to the left of the element in the array are less than the element, and all values to the right of the element in the array are greater than the element—we show how to do this below). We now have one element in its proper location and two unsorted subarrays.

    b) *Recursive Step*: Perform *Step a* on each unsorted subarray.

Each time *Step a* is performed on a subarray, another element is placed in its final location in the sorted array, and two unsorted subarrays are created. When a subarray consists of one element, that element is in its final location (because a one-element array is already sorted).

    The basic algorithm seems simple enough, but how do we determine the final position of the first element of each subarray? As an example, consider the following set of values (the element in bold is the partitioning element—it will be placed in its final location in the sorted array):

        37   2   6   4   89   8   10   12   68   45

    a) Starting from the rightmost element of the array, compare each element with 37 until an element less than 37 is found, then swap 37 and that element. The first element less than 37 is 12, so 37 and 12 are swapped. The new array is

        12   2   6   4   89   8   10   **37**   68   45

    Element 12 is in italics to indicate that it was just swapped with 37.

    b) Starting from the left of the array, but beginning with the element after 12, compare each element with 37 until an element greater than 37 is found—then swap 37 and that element. The first element greater than 37 is 89, so 37 and 89 are swapped. The new array is

        12   2   6   4   **37**   8   10   *89*   68   45

    c) Starting from the right, but beginning with the element before 89, compare each element with 37 until an element less than 37 is found—then swap 37 and that element. The first element less than 37 is 10, so 37 and 10 are swapped. The new array is

        12   2   6   4   *10*   8   **37**   89   68   45

    d) Starting from the left, but beginning with the element after 10, compare each element with 37 until an element greater than 37 is found—then swap 37 and that element. There are no more elements greater than 37, so when we compare 37 with itself, we know that 37 has been placed in its final location of the sorted array. Every value to the left of 37 is smaller than it, and every value to the right of 37 is larger than it.

Once the partition has been applied on the previous array, there are two unsorted subarrays. The subarray with values less than 37 contains 12, 2, 6, 4, 10 and 8. The subarray with values greater than 37 contains 89, 68 and 45. The sort continues recursively, with both subarrays being partitioned in the same manner as the original array.

    Based on the preceding discussion, write recursive method QuickSortHelper to sort a one-dimensional integer array—a QuickSort method should receive the array as an argument, then call QuickSortHelper. The method should receive as arguments a starting index and an ending index in the original array being sorted.

19

Custom Linked Data Structures

Objectives

In this chapter you'll:

- Form linked data structures using references, self-referential classes and recursion.

- Learn how boxing and unboxing enable simple-type values to be used where `object`s are expected in a program.

- Create and manipulate dynamic data structures, such as linked lists, queues, stacks and binary trees.

- Learn various important applications of linked data structures.

- Create reusable data structures with classes, inheritance and composition.

19.1 Introduction

This chapter continues our four-chapter treatment of algorithms and data structures. Most of the data structures that we have studied thus far have had fixed sizes, such as one- and two-dimensional arrays. Previously, we also introduced the dynamically resizable List<T> collection (Chapter 9). This chapter enhances our discussion of *dynamic data structures* that grow and shrink at execution time. *Linked lists* are collections of data items "lined up in a row" or "chained together"—users can make insertions and deletions anywhere in a linked list. As you recall from Section 7.11, *stacks* are important in compilers and operating systems; insertions and deletions are made at only one end—its *top*. *Queues* represent waiting lines; insertions are made at the back (also referred to as the *tail*) of a queue, and deletions are made from the front (also referred to as the *head*) of a queue. *Binary trees* facilitate high-speed searching and sorting of data, efficient elimination of duplicate data items, representation of file-system directories and compilation of expressions into machine language. These data structures have many other interesting applications as well.

We'll discuss each of these major types of data structures and implement programs that create and manipulate them. We use classes, inheritance and composition to create and package these data structures for reusability and maintainability. In Chapter 20, we introduce *generics*, which allow you to declare data structures that can be automatically adapted to contain data of a specific type. In Chapter 21, we discuss C#'s predefined *collection classes* that implement various data structures.

The chapter examples are practical programs that will be useful in more advanced courses and in industrial applications. The programs focus on reference manipulation. The exercises offer a rich collection of useful applications.

19.2 Simple-Type `struct`s, Boxing and Unboxing

The data structures we discuss in this chapter store `object` references. As you'll soon see, we're able to store both simple- and reference-type values in these data structures. This section discusses the mechanisms that enable simple-type values to be manipulated as objects.

Simple-Type `struct`s

Each simple type (see Appendix B) has a corresponding `struct` in namespace System that defines the simple type. These `struct`s are called `Boolean`, `Byte`, `SByte`, `Char`, `Decimal`, `Double`, `Single`, `Int16`, `UInt16` `Int32`, `UInt32`, `Int64` and `UInt64`. Types declared with keyword `struct` are *value types*.

Simple types are actually *aliases* for their corresponding structs, so a variable of a simple type can be declared using either the keyword for that simple type or the struct name—e.g., int and Int32 are interchangeable. The methods related to a simple type are located in the corresponding struct (e.g., method Parse, which converts a string to an int value, is located in struct Int32). Refer to the documentation for the corresponding struct type to see the methods available for manipulating values of that type.

Boxing and Unboxing Conversions
Simple types and other structs inherit from class ValueType in namespace System. Class ValueType inherits from class object. Thus, any simple-type value can be assigned to an object variable; this is referred to as a boxing conversion and enables simple types to be used anywhere objects are expected. In a boxing conversion, the simple-type value is copied into an object so that the simple-type value can be manipulated as an object. Boxing conversions can be performed either *explicitly* or *implicitly* as shown in the following statements:

```
int i = 5; // create an int value
object object1 = (object) i; // explicitly box the int value
object object2 = i; // implicitly box the int value
```

After executing the preceding code, both object1 and object2 refer to two different objects that contain a copy of the integer value in int variable i.

An unboxing conversion can be used to explicitly convert an object reference to a simple value, as shown in the following statement:

```
int int1 = (int) object1; // explicitly unbox the int value
```

Explicitly attempting to unbox an object reference that does not refer to the correct simple value type causes an InvalidCastException.

In Chapters 20 and 21, we discuss C#'s *generics* and *generic collections* where you'll see that you can create data structures of specific value types so that you do not need boxing and unboxing conversions.

19.3 Self-Referential Classes

A self-referential class contains a reference member that refers to an object of the same class type. For example, the class declaration in Fig. 19.1 defines the shell of a self-referential class named Node. This type has two properties—Data (an int) and Next (a Node). Next references another Node object—that is, an object of the *same type* as the one being declared here, hence the term "self-referential class." Next is referred to as a link (like the links in a chain).

```
1   // Fig. 19.1
2   // Self-referential Node class declaration.
3   class Node
4   {
5       public int Data { get; set; } // store integer data
6       public Node Next { get; set; } // store reference to next Node
```

Fig. 19.1 | Self-referential Node class declaration. (Part 1 of 2.)

```
 7
 8     public Node(int data)
 9     {
10         Data = data;
11     }
12 }
```

Fig. 19.1 | Self-referential `Node` class declaration. (Part 2 of 2.)

Self-referential objects can be linked together to form useful data structures, such as lists, queues, stacks and trees. Figure 19.2 illustrates two self-referential objects *linked together* to form a linked list. A backslash (representing a `null` reference) is placed in the link member of the second self-referential object to indicate that the link does not refer to another object. The backslash is for illustration purposes; it does *not* correspond to the backslash character in C#. A `null` link normally indicates the *end* of a data structure.

Common Programming Error 19.1

Not setting the link in the last node of a list to `null` is a logic error.

Fig. 19.2 | Self-referential class objects linked together.

Creating and maintaining dynamic data structures requires dynamic memory allocation—a program's ability to obtain more memory space at execution time to hold new nodes and to release space no longer needed. As you learned in Section 10.8, C# programs do not *explicitly* release dynamically allocated memory—rather, the CLR performs automatic *garbage collection*.

The `new` operator is essential to dynamic memory allocation. Operator `new` takes as an operand the type of the object being dynamically allocated and returns a reference to an object of that type. For example, the statement

```
var nodeToAdd = new Node(10);
```

allocates the appropriate amount of memory to store a `Node`, initializes it and stores a reference to this object in `nodeToAdd`. If no memory is available, `new` throws an `OutOfMemoryException`. The constructor argument 10 specifies the `Node` object's data.

The following sections discuss lists, stacks, queues and trees. These data structures are created and maintained with dynamic memory allocation and self-referential classes.

19.4 Linked Lists

A linked list is a *linear collection* (i.e., a sequence) of self-referential class objects, called nodes, connected by reference links—hence, the term "linked" list. A program accesses a linked list via a reference to the first node of the list. Each subsequent node is accessed via the link-reference member stored in the previous node. By convention, the link reference in the *last* node of a list is set to null to mark the end of the list. Data is stored in a linked list dynamically—that is, each node is created as necessary. A node can contain data of any type, including references to objects of other classes. Stacks and queues are also linear data structures—in fact, they may be viewed as constrained versions of linked lists. Trees are nonlinear data structures.

Lists of data can be stored in arrays, but linked lists provide several advantages. A linked list is appropriate when the number of data elements to be represented in the data structure is unpredictable. Unlike a linked list, the size of a conventional C# array cannot be altered, because the array size is *fixed* at creation time. Conventional arrays can become full, but linked lists become full only when the system has insufficient memory to satisfy dynamic memory allocation requests.

Performance Tip 19.1

An array can be declared to contain more elements than the number of items expected, possibly wasting memory. Linked lists provide better memory utilization in these situations, because they can grow and shrink at execution time.

Programmers can maintain linked lists in sorted order simply by inserting each new element at the proper point in the list (locating the proper insertion point does take time). They do not need to move existing list elements.

Performance Tip 19.2

The elements of an array are stored contiguously in memory to allow immediate access to any array element—the address of any element can be calculated directly from its index. Linked lists do not afford such immediate access to their elements—an element can be accessed only by traversing the list.

Normally linked-list nodes are *not* stored contiguously in memory. Rather, the nodes are logically contiguous. Figure 19.3 illustrates a linked list with several nodes. Note that the reference lastNode is not required to implement a linked list—it's an optimization that enables fast access to a linked list's last element.

Performance Tip 19.3

Using linked data structures and dynamic memory allocation (instead of arrays) for data structures that grow and shrink at execution time can save memory. Keep in mind, however, that reference links occupy space, and dynamic memory allocation incurs the overhead of method calls.

Fig. 19.3 | Linked list graphical representation.

Linked-List Implementation

Figures 19.4–19.5 use an object of our List class to manipulate a list of miscellaneous object types. Class ListTest's Main method (Fig. 19.5) creates a list of objects, inserts objects at the beginning of the list using List method InsertAtFront, inserts objects at the end of the list using List method InsertAtBack, deletes objects from the front of the list using List method RemoveFromFront and deletes objects from the end of the list using List method RemoveFromBack. After each insert and delete operation, the program invokes List method Display to output the current list contents. If an attempt is made to remove an item from an empty list, an EmptyListException occurs. A detailed discussion of the program follows.

Performance Tip 19.4

Insertion and deletion in a sorted array can be time consuming—all the elements following the inserted or deleted element must be shifted appropriately.

The program consists of four classes—ListNode (Fig. 19.4, lines 8–27), List (lines 30–161), EmptyListException (lines 164–176) and ListTest (Fig. 19.5). The classes in Fig. 19.4 create a linked-list library (defined in namespace LinkedListLibrary) that can be reused throughout this chapter. You should place the code of Fig. 19.4 in its own class library project, as we described in Section 15.13.

```
1   // Fig. 19.4: LinkedListLibrary.cs
2   // ListNode, List and EmptyListException class declarations.
3   using System;
4
5   namespace LinkedListLibrary
6   {
7      // class to represent one node in a list
8      class ListNode
9      {
10        // automatic read-only property Data
11        public object Data { get; private set; }
12
13        // automatic property Next
14        public ListNode Next { get; set; }
15
16        // constructor to create ListNode that refers to dataValue
17        // and is last node in list
18        public ListNode(object dataValue) : this(dataValue, null) { }
19
20        // constructor to create ListNode that refers to dataValue
21        // and refers to next ListNode in List
22        public ListNode(object dataValue, ListNode nextNode)
23        {
24           Data = dataValue;
25           Next = nextNode;
26        }
27     }
28
```

Fig. 19.4 | ListNode, List and EmptyListException class declarations. (Part 1 of 4.)

```
29    // class List declaration
30    public class List
31    {
32        private ListNode firstNode;
33        private ListNode lastNode;
34        private string name; // string like "list" to display
35
36        // construct empty List with specified name
37        public List(string listName)
38        {
39            name = listName;
40            firstNode = lastNode = null;
41        }
42
43        // construct empty List with "list" as its name
44        public List() : this("list") { }
45
46        // Insert object at front of List. If List is empty,
47        // firstNode and lastNode will refer to same object.
48        // Otherwise, firstNode refers to new node.
49        public void InsertAtFront(object insertItem)
50        {
51            if (IsEmpty())
52            {
53                firstNode = lastNode = new ListNode(insertItem);
54            }
55            else
56            {
57                firstNode = new ListNode(insertItem, firstNode);
58            }
59        }
60
61        // Insert object at end of List. If List is empty,
62        // firstNode and lastNode will refer to same object.
63        // Otherwise, lastNode's Next property refers to new node.
64        public void InsertAtBack(object insertItem)
65        {
66            if (IsEmpty())
67            {
68                firstNode = lastNode = new ListNode(insertItem);
69            }
70            else
71            {
72                lastNode = lastNode.Next = new ListNode(insertItem);
73            }
74        }
75
76        // remove first node from List
77        public object RemoveFromFront()
78        {
79            if (IsEmpty())
80            {
```

Fig. 19.4 | ListNode, List and EmptyListException class declarations. (Part 2 of 4.)

```
81                  throw new EmptyListException(name);
82              }
83
84          object removeItem = firstNode.Data; // retrieve data
85
86          // reset firstNode and lastNode references
87          if (firstNode == lastNode)
88          {
89              firstNode = lastNode = null;
90          }
91          else
92          {
93              firstNode = firstNode.Next;
94          }
95
96          return removeItem; // return removed data
97      }
98
99      // remove last node from List
100     public object RemoveFromBack()
101     {
102         if (IsEmpty())
103         {
104             throw new EmptyListException(name);
105         }
106
107         object removeItem = lastNode.Data; // retrieve data
108
109         // reset firstNode and lastNode references
110         if (firstNode == lastNode)
111         {
112             firstNode = lastNode = null;
113         }
114         else
115         {
116             ListNode current = firstNode;
117
118             // loop while current.Next is not lastNode
119             while (current.Next != lastNode)
120             {
121                 current = current.Next; // move to next node
122             }
123
124             // current is new lastNode
125             lastNode = current;
126             current.Next = null;
127         }
128
129         return removeItem; // return removed data
130     }
131
```

Fig. 19.4 | ListNode, List and EmptyListException class declarations. (Part 3 of 4.)

```
132        // return true if List is empty
133        public bool IsEmpty()
134        {
135           return firstNode == null;
136        }
137
138        // output List contents
139        public void Display()
140        {
141           if (IsEmpty())
142           {
143              Console.WriteLine($"Empty {name}");
144           }
145           else
146           {
147              Console.Write($"The {name} is: ");
148
149              ListNode current = firstNode;
150
151              // output current node data while not at end of list
152              while (current != null)
153              {
154                 Console.Write($"{current.Data} ");
155                 current = current.Next;
156              }
157
158              Console.WriteLine("\n");
159           }
160        }
161     }
162
163     // class EmptyListException declaration
164     public class EmptyListException : Exception
165     {
166        // parameterless constructor
167        public EmptyListException() : base("The list is empty") { }
168
169        // one-parameter constructor
170        public EmptyListException(string name)
171           : base($"The {name} is empty") { }
172
173        // two-parameter constructor
174        public EmptyListException(string exception, Exception inner)
175           : base(exception, inner) { }
176     }
177  }
```

Fig. 19.4 | ListNode, List and EmptyListException class declarations. (Part 4 of 4.)

Class *ListNode*

Encapsulated in each List is a linked list of ListNode objects. Class ListNode (Fig. 19.4, lines 8–27) contains two properties—Data and Next. Data can refer to any object. [*Note:* Typically, a data structure will contain data of only *one* type, or data of any type derived from one base type.] In this example, we use data of various types derived from object to demonstrate that our List class can store data of any type—normally a data structure's elements are all of the *same* type. Next stores a reference to the next ListNode object in the linked list. The ListNode constructors (lines 18 and 22–26) enable us to initialize a ListNode that will be placed at the end of a List or before a specific ListNode in a List, respectively. ListNode is not a public class, because only class List needs to manipulate ListNodes.

Class *List*

Class List (lines 30–161) contains private instance variables firstNode and lastNode—references to the first and last ListNodes in a List, respectively. The constructors (lines 37–41 and 44) initialize both references to null and enable us to specify the List's name for output purposes. InsertAtFront (lines 49–59), InsertAtBack (lines 64–74), RemoveFrom-Front (lines 77–97) and RemoveFromBack (lines 100–130) are the primary methods of class List. Method IsEmpty (lines 133–136) is a predicate method—such a method checks a condition and returns a bool value without modifying the object on which it's called. In this case, the method determines whether the list is empty (i.e., firstNode is null). (IsEmpty also could have been implemented as a getter-only property.) If the list is empty, method IsEmpty returns true; otherwise, it returns false. Method Display (lines 139–160) displays the list's contents. A detailed discussion of class List's methods follows Fig. 19.5.

Class *EmptyListException*

Class EmptyListException (lines 164–176) defines an exception class that we use to indicate illegal operations on an empty List.

Class *ListTest*

Class ListTest (Fig. 19.5) uses the linked-list library to create and manipulate a linked list. [*Note:* In the project containing Fig. 19.5, you must add a reference to the class library containing the classes in Fig. 19.4.] Line 11 creates a new List object and assigns it to variable list. Lines 14–17 create data to add to the list. Lines 20–27 use List insertion methods to insert these values and use List method Display to output the contents of list after each insertion. The values of the simple-type variables are implicitly boxed in lines 20, 22 and 24 where object references are expected. The code inside the try block (lines 32–46) removes objects via List deletion methods, outputs each removed object and outputs list after every deletion. If there's an attempt to remove an object from an *empty* list, the catch at lines 48–51 catches the EmptyListException and displays an error message.

```
 1   // Fig. 19.5: ListTest.cs
 2   // Testing class List.
 3   using System;
 4   using LinkedListLibrary;
 5
 6   // class to test List class functionality
 7   class ListTest
 8   {
 9      static void Main()
10      {
11         var list = new List(); // create List container
```

Fig. 19.5 | Testing class List. (Part 1 of 3.)

```
12
13         // create data to store in List
14         bool aBoolean = true;
15         char aCharacter = '$';
16         int anInteger = 34567;
17         string aString = "hello";
18
19         // use List insert methods
20         list.InsertAtFront(aBoolean);
21         list.Display();
22         list.InsertAtFront(aCharacter);
23         list.Display();
24         list.InsertAtBack(anInteger);
25         list.Display();
26         list.InsertAtBack(aString);
27         list.Display();
28
29         // remove data from list and display after each removal
30         try
31         {
32            object removedObject = list.RemoveFromFront();
33            Console.WriteLine($"{removedObject} removed");
34            list.Display();
35
36            removedObject = list.RemoveFromFront();
37            Console.WriteLine($"{removedObject} removed");
38            list.Display();
39
40            removedObject = list.RemoveFromBack();
41            Console.WriteLine($"{removedObject} removed");
42            list.Display();
43
44            removedObject = list.RemoveFromBack();
45            Console.WriteLine($"{removedObject} removed");
46            list.Display();
47         }
48         catch (EmptyListException emptyListException)
49         {
50            Console.Error.WriteLine($"\n{emptyListException}");
51         }
52      }
53   }
```

```
The list is: True

The list is: $ True

The list is: $ True 34567

The list is: $ True 34567 hello

$ removed
The list is: True 34567 hello
```

Fig. 19.5 | Testing class List. (Part 2 of 3.)

```
True removed
The list is: 34567 hello

hello removed
The list is: 34567

34567 removed
Empty list
```

Fig. 19.5 | Testing class List. (Part 3 of 3.)

Method *InsertAtFront*

Over the next several pages, we discuss each of the methods of class List in detail. Method InsertAtFront (Fig. 19.4, lines 49–59) places a new node at the front of the list. The method consists of three steps:

1. Call IsEmpty to determine whether the list is empty (line 51).

2. If the list is empty, set both firstNode and lastNode to refer to a new ListNode initialized with insertItem (line 53). The ListNode constructor at line 18 calls the ListNode constructor at lines 22–26, which sets property Data to refer to the object passed as the first argument and sets the Next property's reference to null.

3. If the list is not empty, the new node is "linked" into the list by setting firstNode to refer to a new ListNode object initialized with insertItem and firstNode (line 57). When the ListNode constructor (lines 22–26) executes, it sets property Data to refer to the object passed as the first argument and performs the insertion by setting the Next reference to the ListNode passed as the second argument.

In Fig. 19.6, part (a) shows a list and a new node during the InsertAtFront operation before the new node is linked into the list. The dashed lines and arrows in part (b) illustrate *Step 3* of the InsertAtFront operation, which enables the node containing 12 to become the new list front.

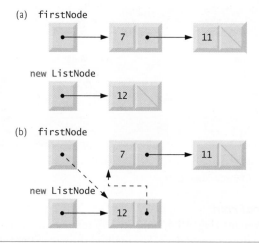

Fig. 19.6 | InsertAtFront operation.

Performance Tip 19.5

After locating the insertion point for a new item in a sorted linked list, inserting an element in the list is fast—only two references have to be modified. All existing nodes remain at their current locations in memory.

Method *InsertAtBack*

Method `InsertAtBack` (Fig. 19.4, lines 64–74) places a new node at the back of the list. The method consists of three steps:

1. Call `IsEmpty` to determine whether the list is empty (line 66).

2. If the list is empty, set both `firstNode` and `lastNode` to refer to a new `ListNode` initialized with `insertItem` (line 68). The `ListNode` constructor at line 18 calls the `ListNode` constructor at lines 22–26, which sets property `Data` to refer to the object passed as the first argument and sets the `Next` reference to `null`.

3. If the list is not empty, link the new node into the list by setting `lastNode` and `lastNode.Next` to refer to a new `ListNode` object initialized with `insertItem` (line 72)—setting `lastNode.Next` that the *previous* last node links to the new last node. When the `ListNode` constructor (line 18) executes, it calls the constructor at lines 22–26, which sets property `Data` to refer to the `object` passed as an argument and sets the `Next` reference to `null`.

In Fig. 19.7, part (a) shows a list and a new node during the `InsertAtBack` operation before the new node has been linked into the list. The dashed lines and arrows in part (b) illustrate *Step 3* of method `InsertAtBack`, which enables a new node to be added to the end of a list that is not empty.

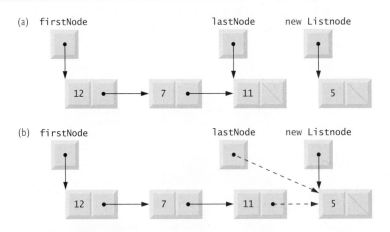

Fig. 19.7 | InsertAtBack operation.

Method *RemoveFromFront*

Method `RemoveFromFront` (Fig. 19.4, lines 77–97) removes the front node of the list and returns a reference to the removed data. The method throws an `EmptyListException` (line 81) if the programmer tries to remove a node from an empty list. Otherwise, the method returns a reference to the removed data. After determining that a List is not empty, the method consists of four steps to remove the first node:

1. Assign firstNode.Data (the data being removed from the list) to variable removeItem (line 84).

2. If the objects to which firstNode and lastNode refer are the *same* object, the list has only one element, so the method sets firstNode and lastNode to null (line 89) to remove the node from the list (leaving the list empty).

3. If the list has more than one node, the method leaves reference lastNode as is and assigns firstNode.Next to firstNode (line 93). Thus, firstNode references the node that was previously the second node in the List.

4. Return the removeItem reference (line 96).

In Fig. 19.8, part (a) illustrates a list before a removal operation. The dashed lines and arrows in part (b) show the reference manipulations.

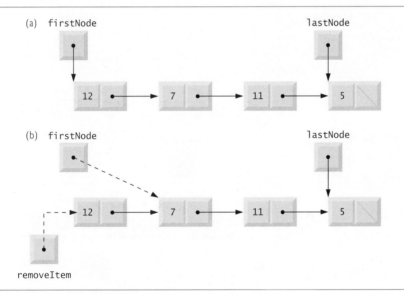

Fig. 19.8 | RemoveFromFront operation.

Method RemoveFromBack

Method RemoveFromBack (Fig. 19.4, lines 100–130) removes the last node of a list and returns a reference to the removed data. The method throws an EmptyListException (line 104) if the program attempts to remove a node from an empty list. The method consists of several steps:

1. Assign lastNode.Data (the data being removed from the list) to variable removeItem (line 107).

2. If firstNode and lastNode refer to the *same* object (line 110), the list has only one element, so the method sets firstNode and lastNode to null (line 112) to remove that node from the list (leaving the list empty).

3. If the list has more than one node, create `ListNode` variable `current` and assign it `firstNode` (line 116).

4. Now "walk the list" with `current` until it references the node before the last node. The `while` loop (lines 119–122) assigns `current.Next` to `current` as long as `current.Next` is not equal to `lastNode`.

5. After locating the second-to-last node, assign `current` to `lastNode` (line 125) to update which node is last in the list.

6. Set `current.Next` to `null` (line 126) to remove the last node from the list and terminate the list at the current node.

7. Return the `removeItem` reference (line 129).

In Fig. 19.9, part (a) illustrates a list before a removal operation. The dashed lines and arrows in part (b) show the reference manipulations.

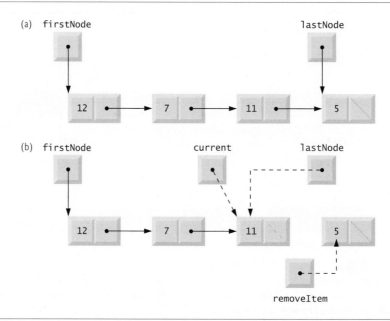

Fig. 19.9 | RemoveFromBack operation.

Method `Display`

Method `Display` (Fig. 19.4, lines 139–161) first determines whether the list is empty (line 141). If so, `Display` displays a `string` consisting of the string `"Empty "` and the list's name, then returns control to the calling method. Otherwise, `Display` outputs the data in the list. The method writes a `string` consisting of the string `"The "`, the list's name and the string `" is: "`. Then line 149 creates `ListNode` variable `current` and initializes it with `firstNode`. While `current` is not `null`, there are more items in the list. Therefore, the method repeatedly displays `current.Data` (line 154), then assigns `current.Next` to `current` (line 155) to move to the next node in the list.

Linear and Circular Singly Linked and Doubly Linked Lists

The kind of linked list we have been discussing is a singly linked list—it begins with a reference to the first node, and each node contains a reference to the next node "in sequence." This list terminates with a node whose reference member has the value null. A singly linked list may be traversed in *only* one direction.

A circular, singly linked list (Fig. 19.10) begins with a reference to the first node, and each node contains a reference to the next node. The "last node" does not contain a null reference; rather, the reference in the last node points back to the first node, thus closing the "circle."

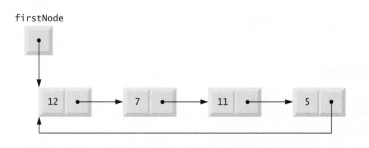

Fig. 19.10 | Circular, singly linked list.

A doubly linked list (Fig. 19.11) allows traversals both forward and backward. Such a list is often implemented with two "start references"—one that refers to the *first* element of the list to allow *front-to-back traversal* of the list and one that refers to the *last* element to allow *back-to-front traversal*. Each node has both a forward reference to the next node in the list and a backward reference to the previous node. If your list contains an alphabetized telephone directory, for example, a search for someone whose name begins with a letter near the front of the alphabet might begin from the front of the list. A search for someone whose name begins with a letter near the end of the alphabet might begin from the back.

Fig. 19.11 | Doubly linked list.

In a circular, doubly linked list (Fig. 19.12), the forward reference of the last node refers to the first node, and the backward reference of the first node refers to the last node, thus closing the "circle."

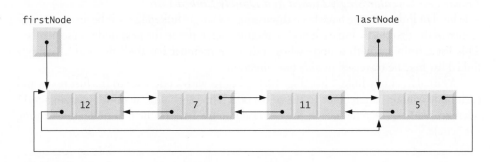

firstNode   lastNode

Fig. 19.12 | Circular, doubly linked list.

19.5 Stacks

A stack may be viewed as a constrained version of a linked list—it receives new nodes and releases nodes only at the top. For this reason, a stack is referred to as a last-in, first-out (LIFO) data structure.

The primary operations to manipulate a stack are push and pop. Operation push adds a new node to the top of the stack. Operation pop removes a node from the top of the stack and returns the data item from the popped node.

Stacks have many interesting applications. For example, when a program calls a method, the called method must know how to return to its caller, so the return address is pushed onto the method-call stack. If a series of method calls occurs, the successive return values are pushed onto the stack in last-in, first-out order so that each method can return to its caller. Stacks support recursive method calls in the same manner that they do conventional nonrecursive method calls.

In our next example, we take advantage of the close relationship between lists and stacks to implement a stack class by reusing a list class. We demonstrate two different forms of reusability. First, we implement the stack class by inheriting from class List of Fig. 19.4. Then we implement an identically performing stack class through composition by including a List object as a private member of a stack class. The System.Collections.Generic namespace contains class Stack for implementing and manipulating stacks that can grow and shrink during program execution.

Stack Class That Inherits from List

The code in Fig. 19.13 creates a stack class by inheriting from class List of Fig. 19.4 (line 8 of Fig. 19.13). We want the stack to have methods Push, Pop, IsEmpty and Display. Essentially, these are the methods InsertAtFront, RemoveFromFront, IsEmpty and Display of class List. Of course, class List contains other methods (such as InsertAtBack and RemoveFromBack) that we would rather not make accessible through the public interface of the stack. It's important to remember though that all methods in the public interface of class List are also public methods of the derived class StackInheritance (Fig. 19.13).

```
 1   // Fig. 19.13: StackInheritanceLibrary.cs
 2   // Implementing a stack by inheriting from class List.
 3   using LinkedListLibrary;
 4
 5   namespace StackInheritanceLibrary
 6   {
 7      // class StackInheritance inherits class List's capabilities
 8      public class StackInheritance : List
 9      {
10         // pass name "stack" to List constructor
11         public StackInheritance() : base("stack") { }
12
13         // place dataValue at top of stack by inserting
14         // dataValue at front of linked list
15         public void Push(object dataValue)
16         {
17            InsertAtFront(dataValue);
18         }
19
20         // remove item from top of stack by removing
21         // item at front of linked list
22         public object Pop()
23         {
24            return RemoveFromFront();
25         }
26      }
27   }
```

Fig. 19.13 | Implementing a stack by inheriting from class List.

The implementation of each StackInheritance method calls the appropriate List method—method Push calls InsertAtFront, method Pop calls RemoveFromFront. Class StackInheritance does not define methods IsEmpty and Display, because StackInheritance inherits these methods from class List into StackInheritance's public interface. Class StackInheritance uses namespace LinkedListLibrary (Fig. 19.4); thus, the class library that defines StackInheritance must have a reference to the LinkedListLibrary class library.

StackInheritanceTest's Main method (Fig. 19.14) uses class StackInheritance to create a stack of objects called stack (line 12). Lines 15–18 define four values that will be pushed onto the stack and popped off it. The program pushes onto the stack (lines 21, 23, 25 and 27) a bool containing true, a char containing '$', an int containing 34567 and a string containing "hello". An infinite while loop (lines 33–38) pops the elements from the stack. When the stack is empty, method Pop throws an EmptyListException, and the program displays the exception's stack trace, which shows the program-execution stack at the time the exception occurred. The program uses method Display (inherited by StackInheritance from class List) to output the contents of the stack after each operation. Class StackInheritanceTest uses namespace LinkedListLibrary (Fig. 19.4) and namespace StackInheritanceLibrary (Fig. 19.13); thus, the solution for class StackInheritanceTest must have references to both class libraries.

```
1   // Fig. 19.14: StackInheritanceTest.cs
2   // Testing class StackInheritance.
3   using System;
4   using StackInheritanceLibrary;
5   using LinkedListLibrary;
6
7   // demonstrate functionality of class StackInheritance
8   class StackInheritanceTest
9   {
10      static void Main()
11      {
12         StackInheritance stack = new StackInheritance();
13
14         // create objects to store in the stack
15         bool aBoolean = true;
16         char aCharacter = '$';
17         int anInteger = 34567;
18         string aString = "hello";
19
20         // use method Push to add items to stack
21         stack.Push(aBoolean);
22         stack.Display();
23         stack.Push(aCharacter);
24         stack.Display();
25         stack.Push(anInteger);
26         stack.Display();
27         stack.Push(aString);
28         stack.Display();
29
30         // remove items from stack
31         try
32         {
33            while (true)
34            {
35               object removedObject = stack.Pop();
36               Console.WriteLine($"{removedObject} popped");
37               stack.Display();
38            }
39         }
40         catch (EmptyListException emptyListException)
41         {
42            // if exception occurs, write stack trace
43            Console.Error.WriteLine(emptyListException.StackTrace);
44         }
45      }
46   }
```

```
The stack is: True
The stack is: $ True
The stack is: 34567 $ True
The stack is: hello 34567 $ True
```

Fig. 19.14 | Testing class StackInheritance. (Part 1 of 2.)

```
hello popped
The stack is: 34567 $ True

34567 popped
The stack is: $ True

$ popped
The stack is: True

True popped
Empty stack
   at LinkedListLibrary.List.RemoveFromFront() in C:\Users\PaulDeitel\
      Documents\examples\ch19\Fig19_04\LinkedListLibrary\
      LinkedListLibrary\LinkedListLibrary.cs:line 81
   at StackInheritanceLibrary.StackInheritance.Pop() in C:\Users\
      PaulDeitel\Documents\examples\ch19\Fig19_13\StackInheritanceLibrary\
      StackInheritanceLibrary\StackInheritance.cs:line 24
   at StackInheritanceTest.Main(String[] args) in C:\Users\PaulDeitel\
      Documents\examples\ch19\Fig19_14\StackInheritanceTest\
      StackInheritanceTest\StackInheritanceTest.cs:line 35
```

Fig. 19.14 | Testing class StackInheritance. (Part 2 of 2.)

Stack Class That Contains a Reference to a *List*

Another way to implement a stack class is by reusing a list through *composition*. Class StackComposition (Fig. 19.15) uses a private object of class List (line 10). Composition enables us to *hide* the methods of class List that should not be in our stack's public interface by providing public interface methods only to the required List methods. This class implements each stack method by *delegating* its work to an appropriate List method. StackComposition's methods call List methods Insert-AtFront, RemoveFromFront, IsEmpty and Display. In this example, we do not show class StackCompositionTest, because the only differences in this example are that we change the name of the stack class from StackInheritance to StackComposition and update a using directive.

```
1   // Fig. 19.15: StackCompositionLibrary.cs
2   // StackComposition class encapsulates functionality of class List.
3   using LinkedListLibrary;
4
5   namespace StackCompositionLibrary
6   {
7      // class StackComposition encapsulates List's capabilities
8      public class StackComposition
9      {
10         private List stack;
11
12         // construct empty stack
13         public StackComposition()
14         {
15            stack = new List("stack");
16         }
```

Fig. 19.15 | StackComposition class encapsulates functionality of class List. (Part 1 of 2.)

```
17
18          // add object to stack
19          public void Push(object dataValue)
20          {
21              stack.InsertAtFront(dataValue);
22          }
23
24          // remove object from stack
25          public object Pop()
26          {
27              return stack.RemoveFromFront();
28          }
29
30          // determine whether stack is empty
31          public bool IsEmpty()
32          {
33              return stack.IsEmpty();
34          }
35
36          // output stack contents
37          public void Display()
38          {
39              stack.Display();
40          }
41      }
42  }
```

Fig. 19.15 | StackComposition class encapsulates functionality of class List. (Part 2 of 2.)

19.6 Queues

Another commonly used data structure is the *queue*. A queue is similar to a checkout line in a supermarket—the cashier services the person at the beginning of the line first. Other customers enter the line only at the end and wait for service. Queue nodes are removed only from the *head* (or *front*) of the queue and are inserted only at the *tail* (or *end*). For this reason, a queue is a first-in, first-out (FIFO) data structure. The insert and remove operations are known as enqueue and dequeue.

Queues have many uses in computer systems. Computers with only a single processor can service only one app at a time. Each app requiring processor time is placed in a queue. The app at the front of the queue is the next to receive service. Each app gradually advances to the front as the apps before it receive service.

Queues are also used to support print spooling. For example, a single printer might be shared by all users of a network. Many users can send print jobs to the printer, even when the printer is already busy. These print jobs are placed in a queue until the printer becomes available. A program called a spooler manages the queue to ensure that as each print job completes, the next one is sent to the printer.

Information packets also wait in queues in computer networks. Each time a packet arrives at a network node, it must be routed to the next node along the path to the packet's final destination. The routing node routes one packet at a time, so additional packets are enqueued until the router can route them.

   A file server in a computer network handles file-access requests from many clients throughout the network. Servers have a limited capacity to service requests from clients. When that capacity is exceeded, client requests wait in queues.

Queue Class That Inherits from List

The code in Fig. 19.16 creates a queue class by inheriting from a list class. We want the QueueInheritance class (Fig. 19.16) to have methods Enqueue, Dequeue, IsEmpty and Display. Essentially, these are the methods InsertAtBack, RemoveFromFront, IsEmpty and Display of class List. Of course, the list class contains other methods (such as InsertAtFront and RemoveFromBack) that we would rather not make accessible through the public interface to the queue class. Remember that all methods in the public interface of the List class are also public methods of the derived class QueueInheritance.

   The implementation of each QueueInheritance method calls the appropriate List method—method Enqueue calls InsertAtBack and method Dequeue calls RemoveFromFront. Calls to IsEmpty and Display invoke the base-class versions that were inherited from class List into QueueInheritance's public interface. Class QueueInheritance uses namespace LinkedListLibrary (Fig. 19.4); thus, the class library for QueueInheritance must have a reference to the LinkedListLibrary class library. Just as we demonstrated with stacks, we could use composition to implement a queue class that does not expose the unwanted methods of class List.

```
1    // Fig. 19.16: QueueInheritanceLibrary.cs
2    // Implementing a queue by inheriting from class List.
3    using LinkedListLibrary;
4
5    namespace QueueInheritanceLibrary
6    {
7       // class QueueInheritance inherits List's capabilities
8       public class QueueInheritance : List
9       {
10          // pass name "queue" to List constructor
11          public QueueInheritance() : base("queue") { }
12
13          // place dataValue at end of queue by inserting
14          // dataValue at end of linked list
15          public void Enqueue(object dataValue)
16          {
17             InsertAtBack(dataValue);
18          }
19
20          // remove item from front of queue by removing
21          // item at front of linked list
22          public object Dequeue()
23          {
24             return RemoveFromFront();
25          }
26       }
27    }
```

Fig. 19.16 | Implementing a queue by inheriting from class List.

Class QueueTest's Main method (Fig. 19.17) creates a QueueInheritance object called queue. Lines 15–18 define four values that will be enqueued and dequeued. The program enqueues (lines 21, 23, 25 and 27) a bool containing true, a char containing '$', an int containing 34567 and a string containing "hello". Class QueueTest uses namespace LinkedListLibrary and namespace QueueInheritanceLibrary; thus, the solution for class QueueTest must have references to both class libraries.

```
1   // Fig. 19.17: QueueTest.cs
2   // Testing class QueueInheritance.
3   using System;
4   using QueueInheritanceLibrary;
5   using LinkedListLibrary;
6
7   // demonstrate functionality of class QueueInheritance
8   class QueueTest
9   {
10      static void Main()
11      {
12         QueueInheritance queue = new QueueInheritance();
13
14         // create objects to store in the queue
15         bool aBoolean = true;
16         char aCharacter = '$';
17         int anInteger = 34567;
18         string aString = "hello";
19
20         // use method Enqueue to add items to queue
21         queue.Enqueue(aBoolean);
22         queue.Display();
23         queue.Enqueue(aCharacter);
24         queue.Display();
25         queue.Enqueue(anInteger);
26         queue.Display();
27         queue.Enqueue(aString);
28         queue.Display();
29
30         // use method Dequeue to remove items from queue
31         object removedObject = null;
32
33         // remove items from queue
34         try
35         {
36            while (true)
37            {
38               removedObject = queue.Dequeue();
39               Console.WriteLine($"{removedObject} dequeued");
40               queue.Display();
41            }
42         }
43         catch (EmptyListException emptyListException)
44         {
```

Fig. 19.17 | Testing class QueueInheritance. (Part 1 of 2.)

```
45              // if exception occurs, write stack trace
46              Console.Error.WriteLine(emptyListException.StackTrace);
47          }
48      }
49  }
```

```
The queue is: True

The queue is: True $

The queue is: True $ 34567

The queue is: True $ 34567 hello

True dequeued
The queue is: $ 34567 hello

$ dequeued
The queue is: 34567 hello

34567 dequeued
The queue is: hello

hello dequeued
Empty queue
    at LinkedListLibrary.List.RemoveFromFront() in C:\Users\PaulDeitel\
        Documents\examples\ch19\Fig19_04\LinkedListLibrary\
        LinkedListLibrary\LinkedListLibrary.cs:line 81
    at QueueInheritanceLibrary.QueueInheritance.Dequeue() in C:\Users\
        PaulDeitel\Documents\examples\ch19\Fig19_16\QueueInheritanceLibrary\
        QueueInheritanceLibrary\QueueInheritance.cs:line 24
    at QueueTest.Main(String[] args) in C:\Users\PaulDeitel\Documents\
        examples\ch19\Fig19_17\QueueTest\QueueTest\QueueTest.cs:line 38
```

Fig. 19.17 | Testing class `QueueInheritance`. (Part 2 of 2.)

An infinite `while` loop (lines 36–41) dequeues the elements from the queue in FIFO order. When there are no objects left to dequeue, method `Dequeue` throws an `EmptyListException`, and the program displays the exception's stack trace, which shows the program-execution stack at the time the exception occurred. The program uses method `Display` (inherited from class `List`) to output the contents of the queue after each operation.

19.7 Trees

Linked lists, stacks and queues are **linear data structures** (i.e., **sequences**). A **tree** is a nonlinear, two-dimensional data structure with special properties. Tree nodes contain two or more links.

Basic Terminology
With binary trees (Fig. 19.18), each tree node contains two links (none, one or both of which may be `null`). The **root node** is the first node in a tree. Each link in the root node refers to a **child**. The **left child** is the first node in the **left subtree**, and the **right child** is the first node in the **right subtree**. The children of a specific node are called **siblings**. A

node with no children is called a leaf node. Computer scientists normally draw trees from the root node down—the opposite of the way most trees grow in nature.

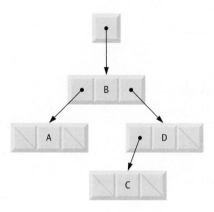

Fig. 19.18 | Binary-tree graphical representation.

Binary Search Trees

In our binary-tree example, we create a special binary tree called a binary search tree. A binary search tree (with no duplicate node values) has the characteristic that the values in any left subtree are less than the value in the subtree's parent node, and the values in any right subtree are greater than the value in the subtree's parent node. Figure 19.19 illustrates a binary search tree with 9 integer values. The shape of the binary search tree that corresponds to a set of data can depend on the order in which the values are inserted into the tree.

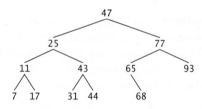

Fig. 19.19 | Binary search tree containing 9 values.

19.7.1 Binary Search Tree of Integer Values

The app of Figs. 19.20 and 19.21 creates a binary search tree of integers and *traverses* it (i.e., walks through all its nodes) in three ways—using recursive inorder, preorder and postorder traversals. The program generates 10 random numbers and inserts each into the tree. Figure 19.20 defines class Tree in namespace BinaryTreeLibrary for reuse purposes. Figure 19.21 defines class TreeTest to demonstrate class Tree's functionality. Method Main of class TreeTest instantiates an empty Tree object, then randomly generates 10 integers and inserts each value in the binary tree by calling Tree method InsertNode. The program then performs *preorder*, *inorder* and *postorder* traversals of the tree. We'll discuss these traversals shortly.

```
1   // Fig. 19.20: BinaryTreeLibrary.cs
2   // Declaration of class TreeNode and class Tree.
3   using System;
4
5   namespace BinaryTreeLibrary
6   {
7      // class TreeNode declaration
8      class TreeNode
9      {
10        // automatic property LeftNode
11        public TreeNode LeftNode { get; set; }
12
13        // automatic property Data
14        public int Data { get; private set; }
15
16        // automatic property RightNode
17        public TreeNode RightNode { get; set; }
18
19        // initialize Data and make this a leaf node
20        public TreeNode(int nodeData)
21        {
22           Data = nodeData;
23        }
24
25        // insert TreeNode into Tree that contains nodes;
26        // ignore duplicate values
27        public void Insert(int insertValue)
28        {
29           if (insertValue < Data) // insert in left subtree
30           {
31              // insert new TreeNode
32              if (LeftNode == null)
33              {
34                 LeftNode = new TreeNode(insertValue);
35              }
36              else // continue traversing left subtree
37              {
38                 LeftNode.Insert(insertValue);
39              }
40           }
41           else if (insertValue > Data) // insert in right subtree
42           {
43              // insert new TreeNode
44              if (RightNode == null)
45              {
46                 RightNode = new TreeNode(insertValue);
47              }
48              else // continue traversing right subtree
49              {
```

Fig. 19.20 | Declaration of class TreeNode and class Tree. (Part 1 of 3.)

```
50                    RightNode.Insert(insertValue);
51                }
52            }
53        }
54    }
55
56    // class Tree declaration
57    public class Tree
58    {
59        private TreeNode root;
60
61        // Insert a new node in the binary search tree.
62        // If the root node is null, create the root node here.
63        // Otherwise, call the insert method of class TreeNode.
64        public void InsertNode(int insertValue)
65        {
66            if (root == null)
67            {
68                root = new TreeNode(insertValue);
69            }
70            else
71            {
72                root.Insert(insertValue);
73            }
74        }
75
76        // begin preorder traversal
77        public void PreorderTraversal()
78        {
79            PreorderHelper(root);
80        }
81
82        // recursive method to perform preorder traversal
83        private void PreorderHelper(TreeNode node)
84        {
85            if (node != null)
86            {
87                // output node Data
88                Console.Write($"{node.Data} ");
89
90                // traverse left subtree
91                PreorderHelper(node.LeftNode);
92
93                // traverse right subtree
94                PreorderHelper(node.RightNode);
95            }
96        }
97
98        // begin inorder traversal
99        public void InorderTraversal()
100        {
101            InorderHelper(root);
102        }
```

Fig. 19.20 | Declaration of class TreeNode and class Tree. (Part 2 of 3.)

```
103
104        // recursive method to perform inorder traversal
105        private void InorderHelper(TreeNode node)
106        {
107           if (node != null)
108           {
109              // traverse left subtree
110              InorderHelper(node.LeftNode);
111
112              // output node data
113              Console.Write($"{node.Data} ");
114
115              // traverse right subtree
116              InorderHelper(node.RightNode);
117           }
118        }
119
120        // begin postorder traversal
121        public void PostorderTraversal()
122        {
123           PostorderHelper(root);
124        }
125
126        // recursive method to perform postorder traversal
127        private void PostorderHelper(TreeNode node)
128        {
129           if (node != null)
130           {
131              // traverse left subtree
132              PostorderHelper(node.LeftNode);
133
134              // traverse right subtree
135              PostorderHelper(node.RightNode);
136
137              // output node Data
138              Console.Write($"{node.Data} ");
139           }
140        }
141     }
142 }
```

Fig. 19.20 | Declaration of class TreeNode and class Tree. (Part 3 of 3.)

```
 1  // Fig. 19.21: TreeTest.cs
 2  // Testing class Tree with a binary tree.
 3  using System;
 4  using BinaryTreeLibrary;
 5
 6  // class TreeTest declaration
 7  class TreeTest
 8  {
```

Fig. 19.21 | Testing class Tree with a binary tree. (Part 1 of 2.)

```
 9     // test class Tree
10     static void Main()
11     {
12        Tree tree = new Tree();
13
14        Console.WriteLine("Inserting values: ");
15        Random random = new Random();
16
17        // insert 10 random integers from 0-99 in tree
18        for (var i = 1; i <= 10; i++)
19        {
20           int insertValue = random.Next(100);
21           Console.Write($"{insertValue} ");
22
23           tree.InsertNode(insertValue);
24        }
25
26        // perform preorder traversal of tree
27        Console.WriteLine("\n\nPreorder traversal");
28        tree.PreorderTraversal();
29
30        // perform inorder traversal of tree
31        Console.WriteLine("\n\nInorder traversal");
32        tree.InorderTraversal();
33
34        // perform postorder traversal of tree
35        Console.WriteLine("\n\nPostorder traversal");
36        tree.PostorderTraversal();
37        Console.WriteLine();
38     }
39  }
```

```
Inserting values:
39 69 94 47 50 72 55 41 97 73

Preorder traversal
39 69 47 41 50 55 94 72 73 97

Inorder traversal
39 41 47 50 55 69 72 73 94 97

Postorder traversal
41 55 50 47 73 72 97 94 69 39
```

Fig. 19.21 | Testing class Tree with a binary tree. (Part 2 of 2.)

Class TreeNode (lines 8–54 of Fig. 19.20) is a self-referential class containing three properties—LeftNode and RightNode of type TreeNode and Data of type int. TreeNode is not a public class, because only class List needs to manipulate TreeNodes. Initially, every TreeNode is a leaf node—by default LeftNode and RightNode are initialized to null. We discuss TreeNode method Insert (lines 27–53) shortly.

Class Tree (lines 57–141) manipulates objects of class TreeNode. Class Tree has as private data root (line 59)—a reference to the root node of the tree—which is null by default. The class contains `public` method `InsertNode` (lines 64–74) to insert a new node in the tree and `public` methods `PreorderTraversal` (lines 77–80), `InorderTraversal` (lines 99–102) and `PostorderTraversal` (lines 121–127) to begin traversals of the tree. Each of these methods calls a separate *recursive utility method* to perform the traversal operations on the internal representation of the tree.

Tree method `InsertNode` (lines 64–74) first determines whether the tree is empty. If so, line 68 allocates a new `TreeNode`, initializes the node with the integer being inserted in the tree and assigns the new node to `root`. If the tree is not empty, `InsertNode` calls `TreeNode` method `Insert` (lines 27–53), which recursively determines the location for the new node in the tree and inserts the node at that location. *A node can be inserted only as a leaf node in a binary search tree.*

The `TreeNode` method `Insert` compares the value to insert with the `data` value in the specified node. If the insert value is less than the specified node's, the program determines whether the left subtree is empty (line 32). If so, line 34 allocates a new `TreeNode`, initializes it with the integer being inserted and assigns the new node to reference `LeftNode`. Otherwise, line 38 recursively calls `Insert` for the left subtree to insert the value into the left subtree. If the insert value is greater than the specified node's data, the program determines whether the right subtree is empty (line 44). If so, line 46 allocates a new `TreeNode`, initializes it with the integer being inserted and assigns the new node to reference `Right-Node`. Otherwise, line 50 recursively calls `Insert` for the right subtree to insert the value in the right subtree. If the insert value matches an existing node value, the insert value is *ignored.*

Methods `PreorderTraversal`, `InorderTraversal` and `PostorderTraversal` call helper methods `PreorderHelper` (lines 83–96), `InorderHelper` (lines 105–118) and `PostorderHelper` (lines 127–140), respectively, to traverse the tree and display the node values. The purpose of the helper methods in class `Tree` is to allow the programmer to start a traversal without needing to obtain a reference to the `root` node first, then call the recursive method with that reference. Methods `InorderTraversal`, `PreorderTraversal` and `PostorderTraversal` simply take `private` instance variable `root` and pass it to the appropriate helper method to initiate a traversal of the tree. For the following discussion, we use the binary search tree shown in Fig. 19.22.

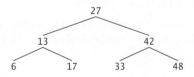

Fig. 19.22 | Binary search tree.

Inorder Traversal Algorithm
Method `InorderHelper` (lines 105–118) defines the steps for an *inorder traversal*. Those steps are as follows:

1. If the argument is `null`, do not process the tree.

2. Recursively traverse the left subtree with a call to `InorderHelper` (line 110).

3. Process the value in the node (line 113).

4. Recursively traverse the right subtree with a call to `InorderHelper` (line 116).

The inorder traversal does not process the value in a node until the values in that node's left subtree are processed. The inorder traversal of the tree in Fig. 19.22 is

```
6 13 17 27 33 42 48
```

The inorder traversal of a binary search tree displays the node values in ascending order. The process of creating a binary search tree actually sorts the data (when coupled with an inorder traversal)—thus, this process is called the binary-tree sort.

Preorder Traversal Algorithm

Method `PreorderHelper` (lines 83–96) defines the steps for a *preorder traversal*. Those steps are as follows:

1. If the argument is `null`, do not process the tree.

2. Process the value in the node (line 88).

3. Recursively traverse the left subtree with a call to `PreorderHelper` (line 91).

4. Recursively traverse the right subtree with a call to `PreorderHelper` (line 94).

The preorder traversal processes the value in each node as the node is visited. After processing the value in a given node, the preorder traversal processes the values in the left subtree, then the values in the right subtree. The preorder traversal of the tree in Fig. 19.22 is

```
27 13 6 17 42 33 48
```

Postorder Traversal Algorithm

Method `PostorderHelper` (lines 127–140) defines the steps for a *postorder traversal*. Those steps are as follows:

1. If the argument is `null`, do not process the tree.

2. Recursively traverse the left subtree with a call to `PostorderHelper` (line 132).

3. Recursively traverse the right subtree with a call to `PostorderHelper` (line 135).

4. Process the value in the node (line 138).

The postorder traversal processes the value in each node after the values of all that node's children are processed. The postorder traversal of the tree in Fig. 19.22 is

```
6 17 13 33 48 42 27
```

Duplicate Elimination

A binary search tree facilitates duplicate elimination. While building a tree, the insertion operation recognizes attempts to insert a duplicate value, because a duplicate follows the same "go left" or "go right" decisions on each comparison as the original value did. Thus, the insertion operation eventually compares the duplicate with a node containing the same value. At this point, the insertion operation might simply discard the duplicate value.

Searching a binary tree for a value that matches a key value is fast, especially for tightly packed binary trees. In a tightly packed binary tree, each level contains about twice as many elements as the previous level. Figure 19.22 is a tightly packed binary tree. A tightly packed binary search tree with n elements has a minimum of $\log_2 n$ levels. For such a tree, at most $\log_2 n$ comparisons are required either to find a match or to determine that no match exists. Searching a (tightly packed) 1000-element binary search tree requires at most 10 comparisons, because $2^{10} > 1000$. Searching a (tightly packed) 1,000,000-element binary search tree requires at most 20 comparisons, because $2^{20} > 1,000,000$.

Overview of the Level-Order Binary-Tree Exercise

The chapter exercises present the algorithm for a level-order traversal of a binary tree, which visits the nodes of the tree row by row, starting at the root-node level. On each level of the tree, a level-order traversal visits the nodes from left to right.

19.7.2 Binary Search Tree of IComparable Objects

The binary-tree example in Section 19.7.1 works nicely when all the data is of type int. Suppose that you want to manipulate a binary tree of doubles. You could rewrite the TreeNode and Tree classes with different names and customize the classes to manipulate doubles. Similarly, for each data type you could create customized versions of classes TreeNode and Tree. This proliferates code, and can become difficult to manage and maintain.

Ideally, we'd like to define the binary tree's functionality once and *reuse* it for *many* types. Languages like C# provide capabilities that enable all objects to be manipulated in a uniform manner. Using such capabilities enables us to design a more flexible data structure. C# provides these capabilities with *generics* (Chapter 20).

In our next example, we take advantage of C#'s polymorphic capabilities by implementing TreeNode and Tree classes that manipulate objects of *any* type that implements interface IComparable (namespace System). It is imperative that we be able to compare objects stored in a binary search tree, so we can determine the path to the insertion point of a new node. Classes that implement IComparable define method CompareTo, which compares the object that invokes the method with the object that the method receives as an argument. The method returns an int value less than zero if the calling object is less than the argument object, zero if the objects are equal and a positive value if the calling object is greater than the argument object. Also, both the calling and argument objects must be of the *same* data type; otherwise, the method throws an ArgumentException.

Figures 19.23–19.24 enhance the program of Section 19.7.1 to manipulate IComparable objects. One restriction on the new versions of classes TreeNode and Tree is that each Tree object can contain objects of only one type (e.g., all strings or all doubles). If a program attempts to insert multiple types in the same Tree object, ArgumentExceptions will occur. We modified only five lines of code in class TreeNode (lines 14, 20, 27, 29 and 41 of Fig. 19.23) and one line of code in class Tree (line 64) to enable processing of IComparable objects. Except for lines 30 and 42, all other changes simply replaced int with IComparable. Lines 30 and 42 previously used the < and > operators to compare the value being inserted with the value in a given node. These lines now compare IComparable objects via the interface's CompareTo method, then test the method's return value to determine whether it's less than zero (the calling object is less than the argument object) or greater than zero (the calling object is greater than the argument object), respectively. [Note: If this class were written using generics (Chapter 20), the type of data, int or

IComparable, could be replaced at compile time by any other type that implements the
necessary operators and methods.]

```csharp
1   // Fig. 19.23: BinaryTreeLibrary2.cs
2   // Declaration of class TreeNode and class Tree.
3   using System;
4
5   namespace BinaryTreeLibrary2
6   {
7      // class TreeNode declaration
8      class TreeNode
9      {
10        // automatic property LeftNode
11        public TreeNode LeftNode { get; set; }
12
13        // automatic property Data
14        public IComparable Data { get; private set; }
15
16        // automatic property RightNode
17        public TreeNode RightNode { get; set; }
18
19        // initialize Data and make this a leaf node
20        public TreeNode(IComparable nodeData)
21        {
22           Data = nodeData;
23        }
24
25        // insert TreeNode into Tree that contains nodes;
26        // ignore duplicate values
27        public void Insert(IComparable insertValue)
28        {
29           if (insertValue.CompareTo(Data) < 0) // insert in left subtree
30           {
31              // insert new TreeNode
32              if (LeftNode == null)
33              {
34                 LeftNode = new TreeNode(insertValue);
35              }
36              else // continue traversing left subtree
37              {
38                 LeftNode.Insert(insertValue);
39              }
40           }
41           else if (insertValue.CompareTo(Data) > 0) // insert in right
42           {
43              // insert new TreeNode
44              if (RightNode == null)
45              {
46                 RightNode = new TreeNode(insertValue);
47              }
48              else // continue traversing right subtree
49              {
```

Fig. 19.23 | Declaration of class TreeNode and class Tree. (Part 1 of 3.)

```
50                        RightNode.Insert(insertValue);
51                     }
52                 }
53             }
54         }
55
56         // class Tree declaration
57         public class Tree
58         {
59             private TreeNode root;
60
61             // Insert a new node in the binary search tree.
62             // If the root node is null, create the root node here.
63             // Otherwise, call the insert method of class TreeNode.
64             public void InsertNode(IComparable insertValue)
65             {
66                 if (root == null)
67                 {
68                     root = new TreeNode(insertValue);
69                 }
70                 else
71                 {
72                     root.Insert(insertValue);
73                 }
74             }
75
76             // begin preorder traversal
77             public void PreorderTraversal()
78             {
79                 PreorderHelper(root);
80             }
81
82             // recursive method to perform preorder traversal
83             private void PreorderHelper(TreeNode node)
84             {
85                 if (node != null)
86                 {
87                     // output node Data
88                     Console.Write($"{node.Data} ");
89
90                     // traverse left subtree
91                     PreorderHelper(node.LeftNode);
92
93                     // traverse right subtree
94                     PreorderHelper(node.RightNode);
95                 }
96             }
97
98             // begin inorder traversal
99             public void InorderTraversal()
100            {
101                InorderHelper(root);
102            }
```

Fig. 19.23 | Declaration of class TreeNode and class Tree. (Part 2 of 3.)

```
103
104            // recursive method to perform inorder traversal
105            private void InorderHelper(TreeNode node)
106            {
107               if (node != null)
108               {
109                  // traverse left subtree
110                  InorderHelper(node.LeftNode);
111
112                  // output node data
113                  Console.Write($"{node.Data} ");
114
115                  // traverse right subtree
116                  InorderHelper(node.RightNode);
117               }
118            }
119
120            // begin postorder traversal
121            public void PostorderTraversal()
122            {
123               PostorderHelper(root);
124            }
125
126            // recursive method to perform postorder traversal
127            private void PostorderHelper(TreeNode node)
128            {
129               if (node != null)
130               {
131                  // traverse left subtree
132                  PostorderHelper(node.LeftNode);
133
134                  // traverse right subtree
135                  PostorderHelper(node.RightNode);
136
137                  // output node Data
138                  Console.Write($"{node.Data} ");
139               }
140            }
141      }
142  }
```

Fig. 19.23 | Declaration of class `TreeNode` and class `Tree`. (Part 3 of 3.)

Class `TreeTest` (Fig. 19.24) creates three `Tree` objects to store `int`, `double` and `string` values, all of which the .NET Framework defines as `IComparable` types. The program populates the trees with the values in arrays `intArray` (line 12), `doubleArray` (line 13) and `stringArray` (lines 14–15), respectively.

```
1   // Fig. 19.24: TreeTest.cs
2   // Testing class Tree with IComparable objects.
3   using System;
```

Fig. 19.24 | Testing class `Tree` with `IComparable` objects. (Part 1 of 3.)

```csharp
4    using BinaryTreeLibrary2;
5
6    // class TreeTest declaration
7    public class TreeTest
8    {
9       // test class Tree
10      static void Main()
11      {
12         int[] intArray = {8, 2, 4, 3, 1, 7, 5, 6};
13         double[] doubleArray = {8.8, 2.2, 4.4, 3.3, 1.1, 7.7, 5.5, 6.6};
14         string[] stringArray =
15            {"eight", "two", "four","three", "one", "seven", "five", "six"};
16
17         // create int Tree
18         Tree intTree = new Tree();
19         PopulateTree(intArray, intTree, nameof(intTree));
20         TraverseTree(intTree, nameof(intTree));
21
22         // create double Tree
23         Tree doubleTree = new Tree();
24         PopulateTree(doubleArray, doubleTree, nameof(doubleTree));
25         TraverseTree(doubleTree, nameof(doubleTree));
26
27         // create string Tree
28         Tree stringTree = new Tree();
29         PopulateTree(stringArray, stringTree, nameof(stringTree));
30         TraverseTree(stringTree, nameof(stringTree));
31      }
32
33      // populate Tree with array elements
34      private static void PopulateTree(Array array, Tree tree, string name)
35      {
36         Console.WriteLine($"\n\n\nInserting into {name}:");
37
38         foreach (IComparable data in array)
39         {
40            Console.Write($"{data} ");
41            tree.InsertNode(data);
42         }
43      }
44
45      // perform traversals
46      private static void TraverseTree(Tree tree, string treeType)
47      {
48         // perform preorder traversal of tree
49         Console.WriteLine($"\n\nPreorder traversal of {treeType}");
50         tree.PreorderTraversal();
51
52         // perform inorder traversal of tree
53         Console.WriteLine($"\n\nInorder traversal of {treeType}");
54         tree.InorderTraversal();
55
```

Fig. 19.24 | Testing class Tree with IComparable objects. (Part 2 of 3.)

```
56          // perform postorder traversal of tree
57          Console.WriteLine($"\n\nPostorder traversal of {treeType}");
58          tree.PostorderTraversal();
59      }
60  }
```

```
Inserting into intTree:
8 2 4 3 1 7 5 6

Preorder traversal of intTree
8 2 1 4 3 7 5 6

Inorder traversal of intTree
1 2 3 4 5 6 7 8

Postorder traversal of intTree
1 3 6 5 7 4 2 8


Inserting into doubleTree:
8.8 2.2 4.4 3.3 1.1 7.7 5.5 6.6

Preorder traversal of doubleTree
8.8 2.2 1.1 4.4 3.3 7.7 5.5 6.6

Inorder traversal of doubleTree
1.1 2.2 3.3 4.4 5.5 6.6 7.7 8.8

Postorder traversal of doubleTree
1.1 3.3 6.6 5.5 7.7 4.4 2.2 8.8


Inserting into stringTree:
eight two four three one seven five six

Preorder traversal of stringTree
eight two four five three one seven six

Inorder traversal of stringTree
eight five four one seven six three two

Postorder traversal of stringTree
five six seven one three four two eight
```

Fig. 19.24 | Testing class Tree with IComparable objects. (Part 3 of 3.)

Method PopulateTree (lines 34–43) receives as arguments an Array containing the initializer values for the Tree, a Tree in which the array elements will be placed and a string representing the Tree name, then inserts each Array element into the Tree. Method TraverseTree (lines 46–59) receives as arguments a Tree and a string representing the Tree name, then outputs the preorder, inorder and postorder traversals of the Tree. The inorder traversal of each Tree outputs the data in *sorted order* regardless of the data type stored in the Tree. Our polymorphic implementation of class Tree invokes the appropriate data type's CompareTo method to determine the path to each value's insertion point by using the standard binary-search-tree insertion rules. Also, notice that the Tree of strings appears in alphabetical order.

19.8 Wrap-Up

In this chapter, you learned that simple types are value-type `struct`s but can still be used anywhere `object`s are expected in a program due to boxing and unboxing conversions. You learned that linked lists are collections of data items that are "linked together in a chain." You also learned that a program can perform insertions and deletions anywhere in a linked list (though our implementation performed insertions and deletions only at the ends of the list). We demonstrated that the stack and queue data structures are constrained versions of lists. For stacks, you saw that insertions and deletions are made only at the top—so stacks are known as last-in, first out (LIFO) data structures. For queues, which represent waiting lines, you saw that insertions are made at the tail and deletions are made from the head—so queues are known as first-in, first out (FIFO) data structures. We also presented the binary tree data structure. You saw a binary search tree that facilitated high-speed searching and sorting of data and efficient duplicate elimination. In the next chapter, we introduce *generics*, which allow you to declare a family of classes and methods that implement the same functionality on *any* type.

Summary

Section 19.1 Introduction
- Dynamic data structures can grow and shrink at execution time.

Section 19.2 Simple-Type `struct`s, Boxing and Unboxing
- All simple-type names are aliases for corresponding `struct`s in namespace `System`.
- Each simple type `struct` declares methods for manipulating the corresponding simple-type values.
- Each `struct` that represents a simple type inherits from class `ValueType` in namespace `System`.
- A boxing conversion creates an object that contains a copy of a simple-type value.
- An unboxing conversion retrieves a simple-type value from an object.

Section 19.3 Self-Referential Classes
- A self-referential class contains a data member that refers to an object of the same class type. Self-referential objects can be linked to form data structures, such as lists, queues, stacks and trees.
- Creating and maintaining dynamic data structures requires dynamic memory allocation—a program's ability to obtain more memory at execution time (to hold new nodes) and to release memory no longer needed.
- Operator `new` takes as an operand the type of the object being dynamically allocated, calls the appropriate constructor to initialize the object and returns a reference to the new object. If no memory is available, `new` throws an `OutOfMemoryException`.

Section 19.4 Linked Lists
- A linked list is a linear collection (i.e., a sequence) of self-referential class objects called nodes, connected by reference links.
- A node can contain properties of any type, including references to objects of other classes.
- A linked list is accessed via a reference to the first node of the list. Each subsequent node is accessed via the link-reference member stored in the previous node.

- By convention, the link reference in the last node of a list is set to `null` to mark the end of the list.

- A circular, singly linked list begins with a reference to the first node, and each node contains a reference to the next node. The "last node" does not contain a null reference; rather, the reference in the last node points back to the first node, thus closing the "circle."

- A doubly linked list allows traversals both forward and backward. Such a list is often implemented with two "start references"—one that refers to the first element of the list to allow front-to-back traversal of the list and one that refers to the last element to allow back-to-front traversal. Each node has both a forward reference to the next node in the list and a backward reference to the previous node.

- In a circular, doubly linked list, the forward reference of the last node refers to the first node, and the backward reference of the first node refers to the last node, thus closing the "circle."

Section 19.5 Stacks

- Stacks are important in compilers and operating systems.

- A stack is a constrained version of a linked list—new nodes can be added to and removed from a stack only at the top. A stack is referred to as a last-in, first-out (LIFO) data structure.

- The primary stack operations are push and pop. Operation push adds a new node to the top of the stack. Operation pop removes a node from the top of the stack and returns the data object from the popped node.

Section 19.6 Queues

- Queues represent waiting lines. Insertions occur at the back (also referred to as the tail) of a queue, and deletions occur from the front (also referred to as the head) of a queue.

- A queue is similar to a checkout line in a supermarket: The first person in line is served first; other customers enter the line at the end and wait to be served.

- Queue nodes are removed only from the head of the queue and are inserted only at the tail of the queue. For this reason, a queue is referred to as a first-in, first-out (FIFO) data structure.

- The insert and remove operations for a queue are known as enqueue and dequeue.

Section 19.7 Trees

- Binary trees facilitate high-speed searching and sorting of data.

- Tree nodes contain two or more links.

- A binary tree is a tree whose nodes all contain two links (each of which can be `null`). The root node is the first node in a tree.

- Each link in the root node refers to a child. The left child is the root node of the left subtree, and the right child is the root node of the right subtree.

- The children of a node are called siblings. A node with no children is called a leaf node.

- A binary search tree (with no duplicate node values) has the characteristic that the values in any left subtree are less than the value in that subtree's parent node, and the values in any right subtree are greater than the value in that subtree's parent node.

- A node can be inserted only as a leaf node in a binary search tree.

- In a preorder traversal, the value in each node is processed as the node is visited. After the value in a given node is processed, the values in the left subtree are processed, then the values in the right subtree are processed.

- In a postorder traversal, the value in each node is processed after the node's left and right subtrees are processed.

- In an inorder traversal, the value in each node is processed after the node's left subtree is processed and before the node's right subtree is processed.
- The inorder traversal of a binary search tree processes the node values in ascending order. The process of creating a binary search tree actually sorts the data (when coupled with an inorder traversal)—thus, this process is called the binary-tree sort.
- The binary search tree facilitates duplicate elimination. As the tree is created, attempts to insert a duplicate value are recognized because a duplicate follows the same "go left" or "go right" decisions on each comparison that the original value did. Thus, the duplicate eventually is compared with a node containing the same value. The duplicate value may simply be discarded at this point.

Terminology

ArgumentException
binary search tree
binary tree
binary-tree sort
boxing conversion
child node
circular, doubly linked list
circular, singly linked list
collection
CompareTo method of interface IComparable
data structures
dequeue
doubly linked list
duplicate elimination
dynamic data structures
enqueue
first-in, first-out (FIFO) data structure
head of a queue
IComparable interface
inorder traversal
InvalidCastException
last-in, first-out (LIFO) data structure
leaf node
left child node
left subtree
level-order traversal of a binary tree
linear data structure
link

linked list
node
OutOfMemoryException
parent node
pop on a stack
postorder traversal
predicate method
preorder traversal
print spooling
push on a stack
queue
right child node
right subtree
root node
searching
self-referential class
sibling node
simple type
singly linked list
sorting
spooler
stack
struct
tail of a queue
top of a stack
tightly packed binary tree
unboxing conversion
ValueType class

Self-Review Exercises

19.1 State whether each of the following is *true* or *false*. If *false*, explain why.
 a) In a queue, the first item to be added is the last item to be removed.
 b) Trees can have no more than two child nodes per node.
 c) A tree node with no children is called a leaf node.
 d) Linked-list nodes are stored contiguously in memory.
 e) The primary operations of the stack data structure are enqueue and dequeue.
 f) Lists, stacks and queues are linear data structures.

19.2 Fill in the blanks in each of the following statements:

a) A(n) _____ class is used to define nodes that form dynamic data structures, which can grow and shrink at execution time.

b) Operator _____ allocates memory dynamically; this operator returns a reference to the allocated memory.

c) A(n) _____ is a constrained version of a linked list in which nodes can be inserted and deleted only from the start of the list; this data structure returns node values in last-in, first-out order.

d) A queue is a(n) _____ data structure, because the first nodes inserted are the first nodes removed.

e) A(n) _____ is a constrained version of a linked list in which nodes can be inserted only at the end of the list and deleted only from the start of the list.

f) A(n) _____ is a nonlinear, two-dimensional data structure that contains nodes with two or more links.

g) The nodes of a(n) _____ tree contain two link members.

h) The tree-traversal algorithm that processes the node then processes all the nodes to its left followed by all the nodes to its right is called _____.

Answers to Self-Review Exercises

19.1 a) False. A queue is a first-in, first-out data structure—the first item added is the first item removed. b) False. In general, trees may have as many child nodes per node as is necessary. Only binary trees are restricted to no more than two child nodes per node. c) True. d) False. Linked-list nodes are logically contiguous, but they need not be stored in a physically contiguous memory space. e) False. Those are the primary operations of a queue. The primary operations of a stack are push and pop. f) True.

19.2 a) self-referential. b) new. c) stack. d) first-in, first-out (FIFO). e) queue. f) tree. g) binary. h) preorder.

Exercises

19.3 *(Merging Ordered-List Objects)* Write a program that merges two ordered-list objects of integers into a single ordered-list object of integers. Method Merge of class ListMerge should receive references to each of the list objects to be merged and should return a reference to the merged-list object.

19.4 *(Reversing a Line of Text with a Stack)* Write a program that inputs a line of text and uses a stack object to display the line reversed.

19.5 *(Palindromes)* Write a program that uses a stack to determine whether a string is a palindrome (i.e., the string is spelled identically backward and forward). The program should ignore capitalization, spaces and punctuation.

19.6 *(Evaluating Expressions with a Stack)* Stacks are used by compilers to evaluate expressions and generate machine-language code. In this and the next exercise, we investigate how compilers evaluate arithmetic expressions consisting only of constants, operators and parentheses.

Humans generally write expressions like 3 + 4 and 7 / 9, in which the operator (+ or / here) is written between its operands—this is called *infix notation*. Computers "prefer" *postfix notation*, in which the operator is written to the right of its two operands. The preceding infix expressions would appear in postfix notation as 3 4 + and 7 9 /, respectively.

To evaluate a complex infix expression, a compiler would first convert the expression to postfix notation, then evaluate the postfix version of the expression. Each of these algorithms requires only a single left-to-right pass of the expression. Each algorithm uses a stack object in support of its operation, and in each algorithm the stack is used for a different purpose. Here, you'll implement the infix-to-postfix conversion algorithm. In the next exercise, you'll implement the postfix-expression evaluation algorithm.

Write class `InfixToPostfixConverter` to convert an ordinary infix arithmetic expression (assume a valid expression is entered), with single-digit integers, such as

```
(6 + 2) * 5 - 8 / 4
```

to a postfix expression. The postfix version of the preceding infix expression is

```
6 2 + 5 * 8 4 / -
```

The program should read the expression into `StringBuilder infix`, then use class `StackInheritance` (implemented in Fig. 19.13) to help create the postfix expression in `StringBuilder postfix`. The algorithm for creating a postfix expression is as follows:

a) Push a left parenthesis `'('` on the stack.
b) Append a right parenthesis `')'` to the end of `infix`.
c) While the stack is not empty, read `infix` from left to right and do the following:
  If the current character in `infix` is a digit, append it to `postfix`.
  If the current character in `infix` is a left parenthesis, push it onto the stack.
  If the current character in `infix` is an operator:
    Pop operators (if there are any) at the top of the stack while they have equal or higher precedence than the current operator, and append the popped operators to `postfix`.
    Push the current character in `infix` onto the stack.
  If the current character in `infix` is a right parenthesis:
    Pop operators from the top of the stack and append them to `postfix` until a left parenthesis is at the top of the stack.
    Pop (and discard) the left parenthesis from the stack.

The following arithmetic operations are allowed in an expression:

  + addition
  - subtraction
  * multiplication
  / division
  ∧ exponentiation
  % modulus

Some of the methods you may want to provide in your program follow:

a) Method `ConvertToPostfix`, which converts the infix expression to postfix notation.
b) Method `IsOperator`, which determines whether `c` is an operator.
c) Method `Precedence`, which determines whether the precedence of `operator1` (from the infix expression) is less than, equal to or greater than the precedence of `operator2` (from the stack). The method returns `true` if `operator1` has lower precedence than or equal precedence to `operator2`. Otherwise, `false` is returned.

19.7 *(Evaluating a Postfix Expression with a Stack)* Write class `PostfixEvaluator`, which evaluates a postfix expression (assume it is valid) such as

```
6 2 + 5 * 8 4 / -
```

The program should read a postfix expression consisting of digits and operators into a `StringBuilder`. Using the stack class from Exercise 19.6, the program should scan the expression and evaluate it. The algorithm (for single-digit numbers) is as follows:

a) Append a right parenthesis `')'` to the end of the postfix expression. When the right-parenthesis character is encountered, no further processing is necessary.

b) When the right-parenthesis character has not been encountered, read the expression from left to right.

> If the current character is a digit, do the following:
>
>> Push its integer value on the stack (the integer value of a digit character is its value in the computer's character set minus the value of '0' in Unicode).
>
> Otherwise, if the current character is an *operator*:
>
>> Pop the two top elements of the stack into variables x and y.
>>
>> Calculate y *operator* x.
>>
>> Push the result of the calculation onto the stack.

c) When the right parenthesis is encountered in the expression, pop the top value of the stack. This is the result of the postfix expression.

[*Note:* In *Part b* above (based on the sample expression at the beginning of this exercise), if the operator is '/', the top of the stack is 4 and the next element in the stack is 8, then pop 4 into x, pop 8 into y, evaluate y / x and push the result, 2, back on the stack. This note also applies to operator '-'.] The arithmetic operations allowed in an expression are:

+   addition
-   subtraction
*   multiplication
/   division
∧   exponentiation
%   modulus

You may want to provide the following methods:

a) Method EvaluatePostfixExpression, which evaluates the postfix expression.

b) Method Calculate, which evaluates the expression op1 *operator* op2.

19.8   (*Level-Order Binary Tree-Traversal*) The program of Fig. 19.21 illustrated three recursive methods of traversing a binary tree—inorder, preorder, and postorder traversals. This exercise presents the *level-order traversal* of a binary tree, in which the node values are displayed level by level, starting at the root-node level. The nodes on each level are displayed from left to right. The level-order traversal is not a recursive algorithm. It uses a queue object to control the output of the nodes. The algorithm is as follows:

a) Insert the root node in the queue.

b) While there are nodes left in the queue, do the following:

> Get the next node in the queue.
>
> Display the node's value.
>
> If the reference to the left child of the node is not null:
>
>> Insert the left child node in the queue.
>
> If the reference to the right child of the node is not null:
>
>> Insert the right child node in the queue.

Write method LevelOrderTraversal to perform a level-order traversal of a binary-tree object. Modify the program of Fig. 19.21 to use this method. [*Note:* You also will need to use the queue-processing methods of Fig. 19.16 in this program.]

Special Section: Building Your Own Compiler

In Exercises 8.31–8.33, we introduced Simpletron Machine Language (SML), and you implemented a Simpletron computer simulator to execute SML programs. In Exercises 19.9–19.13, we build a compiler that converts programs written in a high-level programming language to SML. This section "ties" together the entire programming process. You'll write programs in this new high-level language, compile them on the compiler you build and run them on the simulator you built in Exercise 8.32. [*Note:* Due to the size of the descriptions for Exercises 19.29–19.33, we've posted them in a PDF document located at http://www.deitel.com/books/VCSharpHTP6.]

Generics

20

Objectives

In this chapter you'll:

- Create generic methods that perform identical tasks on arguments of different types.

- Create a generic **Stack** class that can be used to store objects of a specific type.

- Understand how to overload generic methods with nongeneric methods or with other generic methods.

- Understand the kinds of constraints that can be applied to a type parameter.

- Apply multiple constraints to a type parameter.

20.1 Introduction

Chapter 19 presented data structures that store and manipulate references to `objects`. Here we continue our multi-chapter data-structures discussion.

`object`-Based Data Structure Disadvantages

You can store any `object` in our data structures. One inconvenient aspect of storing object references occurs when retrieving them from a collection. An app normally needs to process specific types of objects. As a result, the `object` references obtained from a collection typically need to be *downcast* to an appropriate type to allow the app to process the objects correctly. In addition, data of value types (e.g., `int` and `double`) must be *boxed* to be manipulated with `object` references, which increases the overhead of processing such data. Most importantly, processing all data as type `object` limits the C# compiler's ability to perform type checking.

Compile-Time Type Safety

Though we can easily create data structures that manipulate any type of data as `objects` (as we did in Chapter 19), it would be nice if we could detect type mismatches at compile time—this is known as compile-time type safety. For example, if a `Stack` should store only `int` values, attempting to push a `string` onto that `Stack` should cause a compile-time error. Similarly, a `Sort` method should be able to compare elements that are all guaranteed to have the same type. If we create type-specific versions of class `Stack` and method `Sort`, the C# compiler would certainly be able to ensure compile-time type safety. However, this would require that we create many copies of the same basic code.

Generics

This chapter discusses generics, which provide the means to create the general models mentioned above. Generic methods enable you to specify, with a *single method declaration*, *a set of related methods*. Generic classes enable you to specify, with a *single class declaration*, *a set of related classes*. Similarly, generic interfaces enable you to specify, with a *single interface declaration, a set of related interfaces*. Generics provide *compile-time type safety*. [*Note:* You also can implement generic `structs` and `delegates`.] So far in this book, we've used the generic types `List` (Chapter 9) and `Dictionary` (Chapter 17).

    We can write a generic method for sorting an array, then invoke the generic method separately with an `int` array, a `double` array, a `string` array and so on, to sort each different type of array. The compiler performs type checking to ensure that the array passed to the sorting method contains only elements of the correct type. We can write a single generic Stack class, then instantiate Stack objects for a stack of ints, a stack of doubles, a stack of strings and so on. The compiler performs *type checking* to ensure that the Stack stores *only* elements of the correct type.

This chapter presents examples of generic methods and generic classes. Chapter 21, Generic Collections; Functional Programming with LINQ/PLINQ, discusses the .NET Framework's generic collections classes. A *collection* is a data structure that maintains a group of related objects or values. The .NET Framework collection classes use generics to allow you to specify the exact types of object that a particular collection will store.

20.2 Motivation for Generic Methods

Overloaded methods are often used to perform similar operations on different types of data. To understand the motivation for generic methods, let's begin with an example (Fig. 20.1) that contains three overloaded DisplayArray methods (lines 23–31, lines 34–42 and lines 45–53). These methods display the elements of an int array, a double array and a char array, respectively. Soon, we'll reimplement this program more concisely and elegantly using a *single* generic method.

```csharp
 1   // Fig. 20.1: OverloadedMethods.cs
 2   // Using overloaded methods to display arrays of different types.
 3   using System;
 4
 5   class OverloadedMethods
 6   {
 7      static void Main(string[] args)
 8      {
 9         // create arrays of int, double and char
10         int[] intArray = {1, 2, 3, 4, 5, 6};
11         double[] doubleArray = {1.1, 2.2, 3.3, 4.4, 5.5, 6.6, 7.7};
12         char[] charArray = {'H', 'E', 'L', 'L', 'O'};
13
14         Console.Write("Array intArray contains: ");
15         DisplayArray(intArray); // pass an int array argument
16         Console.Write("Array doubleArray contains: ");
17         DisplayArray(doubleArray); // pass a double array argument
18         Console.Write("Array charArray contains: ");
19         DisplayArray(charArray); // pass a char array argument
20      }
21
22      // output int array
23      private static void DisplayArray(int[] inputArray)
24      {
25         foreach (var element in inputArray)
26         {
27            Console.Write($"{element} ");
28         }
29
30         Console.WriteLine();
31      }
```

Fig. 20.1 | Using overloaded methods to display arrays of different types. (Part 1 of 2.)

```
32
33      // output double array
34      private static void DisplayArray(double[] inputArray)
35      {
36         foreach (var element in inputArray)
37         {
38            Console.Write($"{element} ");
39         }
40
41         Console.WriteLine();
42      }
43
44      // output char array
45      private static void DisplayArray(char[] inputArray)
46      {
47         foreach (var element in inputArray)
48         {
49            Console.Write($"{element} ");
50         }
51
52         Console.WriteLine();
53      }
54   }
```

```
Array intArray contains: 1 2 3 4 5 6
Array doubleArray contains: 1.1 2.2 3.3 4.4 5.5 6.6 7.7
Array charArray contains: H E L L O
```

Fig. 20.1 | Using overloaded methods to display arrays of different types. (Part 2 of 2.)

The program begins by declaring and initializing three arrays—six-element int array intArray (line 10), seven-element double array doubleArray (line 11) and five-element char array charArray (line 12). Then, lines 14–19 output the arrays.

When the compiler encounters a method call, it attempts to locate a method declaration that has the *same* method name and parameters that *match* the argument types in the method call. In this example, each DisplayArray call exactly matches one of the DisplayArray method declarations. For example, line 15 calls DisplayArray with intArray as its argument. At compile time, the compiler determines argument intArray's type (i.e., int[]), attempts to locate a method named DisplayArray that specifies a single int[] parameter (which it finds at lines 23–31) and sets up a call to that method. Similarly, when the compiler encounters the DisplayArray call at line 17, it determines argument doubleArray's type (i.e., double[]), then attempts to locate a method named DisplayArray that specifies a single double[] parameter (which it finds at lines 34–42) and sets up a call to that method. Finally, when the compiler encounters the DisplayArray call at line 19, it determines argument charArray's type (i.e., char[]), then attempts to locate a method named DisplayArray that specifies a single char[] parameter (which it finds at lines 45–53) and sets up a call to that method.

Study each DisplayArray method. Note that the array element type (int, double or char) appears in *one* location in each method—the method header (lines 23, 34 and 45). Each foreach statement header (lines 25, 36 and 47) uses var to infer the element type from the method's parameter. If we were to replace the element types in each method's header with a generic name (such as T for "type"), then all three methods would look like the one in Fig. 20.2. It appears that if we can replace the array element type in each of the three methods with a single "generic type parameter," then we should be able to declare one DisplayArray method that can display the elements of *any* array. The method in Fig. 20.2 *will not compile*, because its syntax is not correct. We declare a generic DisplayArray method with the proper syntax in Fig. 20.3.

```
1   private static void DisplayArray(T[] inputArray)
2   {
3      foreach (var element in inputArray)
4      {
5         Console.Write($"{element} ");
6      }
7
8      Console.WriteLine();
9   }
```

Fig. 20.2 | DisplayArray method in which actual type names have been replaced by convention with the generic name T. Again, this code will *not* compile.

20.3 Generic-Method Implementation

If the operations performed by several overloaded methods are identical for each argument type, the overloaded methods can be more compactly and conveniently coded using a generic method. You can write a single generic-method declaration that can be called at different times with arguments of different types. Based on the types of the arguments passed to the generic method, the compiler handles each method call appropriately.

Figure 20.3 reimplements the app of Fig. 20.1 using a generic DisplayArray method (lines 24–32). Note that the DisplayArray method calls in lines 15, 17 and 19 are identical to those of Fig. 20.1, the outputs of the two apps are identical and the code in Fig. 20.3 is 22 lines *shorter* than that in Fig. 20.1. As illustrated in Fig. 20.3, generics enable us to create and test our code once, then *reuse* it for many different types of data. This effectively demonstrates the expressive power of generics.

```
1    // Fig. 20.3: GenericMethod.cs
2    // Using a generic method to display arrays of different types.
3    using System;
4
5    class GenericMethod
6    {
7       static void Main()
8       {
9          // create arrays of int, double and char
10         int[] intArray = {1, 2, 3, 4, 5, 6};
11         double[] doubleArray = {1.1, 2.2, 3.3, 4.4, 5.5, 6.6, 7.7};
12         char[] charArray = {'H', 'E', 'L', 'L', 'O'};
```

Fig. 20.3 | Using a generic method to display arrays of different types. (Part 1 of 2.)

```
13
14          Console.Write("Array intArray contains: ");
15          DisplayArray(intArray); // pass an int array argument
16          Console.Write("Array doubleArray contains: ");
17          DisplayArray(doubleArray); // pass a double array argument
18          Console.Write("Array charArray contains: ");
19          DisplayArray(charArray); // pass a char array argument
20      }
21
22      // output array of all types
23      private static void DisplayArray<T>(T[] inputArray)
24      {
25          foreach (var element in inputArray)
26          {
27              Console.Write($"{element} ");
28          }
29
30          Console.WriteLine();
31      }
32  }
```

```
Array intArray contains: 1 2 3 4 5 6
Array doubleArray contains: 1.1 2.2 3.3 4.4 5.5 6.6 7.7
Array charArray contains: H E L L O
```

Fig. 20.3 | Using a generic method to display arrays of different types. (Part 2 of 2.)

Line 23 begins method DisplayArray's declaration, which is static so that Main can call DisplayArray. All generic method declarations have a type-parameter list delimited by angle brackets (<T> in this example) that follows the method's name. Each type-parameter list contains one or more type parameters, separated by commas (e.g., Dictionary<K, V>). A type parameter is an identifier that's used in place of actual type names. The type parameters can be used to declare the return type, the parameter types and local variable types in a generic method declaration; the type parameters act as placeholders for type arguments that represent the types of data that will be passed to the generic method.

The type-parameter names throughout the method declaration (if any) must match those declared in the type-parameter list. Also, a type parameter can be declared *only once* in the type-parameter list but can appear *more than once* in the method's parameter list. Type-parameter names need *not* be unique among separate generic methods.

Common Programming Error 20.1

If you forget to include the type-parameter list when declaring a generic method, the compiler will not recognize the type-parameter names when they're encountered in the method. This results in compilation errors.

Method DisplayArray's type-parameter list (line 23) declares type parameter T as the placeholder for the array-element type that DisplayArray will output. Note that T appears in the parameter list as the array-element type (line 23). This is the same location where the overloaded DisplayArray methods of Fig. 20.1 specified int, double or char as the element type. The remainder of DisplayArray is identical to the version presented in

Fig. 20.1. In this example though, the foreach statement infers element's type from the array type passed to the method.

As in Fig. 20.1, the program of Fig. 20.3 begins by declaring and initializing six-element int array intArray (line 10), seven-element double array doubleArray (line 11) and five-element char array charArray (line 12). Then each array is output by calling DisplayArray (lines 15, 17 and 19)—once with argument intArray, once with argument doubleArray and once with argument charArray.

When the compiler encounters a method call such as line 15, it analyzes the set of methods (both nongeneric and generic) that might match the method call, looking for a method that best matches the call. If there's no matching method, or if there's more than one best match, the compiler generates an error.

In the case of line 15, the compiler determines that the best match occurs if the type parameter T in line 23 of method DisplayArray's declaration is replaced with the type of the elements in the method call's argument intArray (i.e., int). Then the compiler sets up a call to DisplayArray with int as the type argument for the type parameter T. This is known as the type-inferencing process. The same process is repeated for the calls to method DisplayArray in lines 17 and 19.

 Common Programming Error 20.2
If the compiler cannot find a single nongeneric or generic method declaration that's a best match for a method call, or if there are multiple best matches, a compilation error occurs.

For each variable declared with a type parameter, the compiler checks whether the operations performed on the variable are allowed for all types that the type parameter can assume. By default, a type parameter can assume any type, but we'll show in Section 20.4 that you can restrict this to specific types. The only operation performed on each array element in this example is to output its string representation. Line 27 performs an *implicit* ToString call on the current array element. Since all objects have a ToString method, the compiler is satisfied that line 27 performs a valid operation for *any* array element.

By declaring DisplayArray as a generic method in Fig. 20.3, we eliminated the need for the overloaded methods of Fig. 20.1, saving 22 lines of code and creating a *reusable* method that can output the string representations of the elements in *any* one-dimensional array, not just arrays of int, double or char elements.

Value Types vs. Reference Types in Generics
The compiler handles value and reference types differently in generic method calls. When a value-type argument is used for a given type parameter, the compiler generates a version of the method that's specific to the value type—if one has been generated previously, the compiler reuses that one. So in Fig. 20.3, the compiler generates three versions of method DisplayArray—one each for types int, double and char. If DisplayArray were called with a reference type, the compiler would also generate a *single* version of the method that's used by all reference types.

Explicit Type Arguments
You also can use explicit type arguments to indicate the exact type that should be used to call a generic function. For example, line 15 could be written as

```
DisplayArray<int>(intArray); // pass an int array argument
```

The preceding method call explicitly provides the type argument (int) that should be used to replace type parameter T in line 23. Though not required here, an explicit type argument would be required if the compiler cannot infer the type from the method's argument(s).

20.4 Type Constraints

In this section, we present a generic Maximum method that determines and returns the largest of its three arguments (all of the same type). The generic method in this example uses the type parameter to declare *both* the method's return type *and* its parameters. Normally, when comparing values to determine which one is greater, you would use the > operator. However, this operator is not overloaded for use with every type that's built into the Framework Class Library or that might be defined by extending those types. By default, generic code is restricted to performing operations that are guaranteed to work for every possible type. Thus, an expression like value1 < value2 is not allowed unless the compiler can ensure that the operator < is provided for every type that will ever be used in the generic code. Similarly, you cannot call a method or access a property on a generic-type variable unless the compiler can ensure that all types that will ever be used in the generic code support that method. For this reason, generic code supports only the methods of class object by default.

20.4.1 IComparable<T> Interface

It's possible to compare two objects of the *same* type if that type implements the generic interface IComparable<T> (of namespace System)—the generic version of interface IComparable that we introduced in Section 19.7.2. A benefit of implementing this interface is that such objects can be used with the *sorting* and *searching* methods of classes in the System.Collections.Generic namespace—we discuss those methods in Chapter 21.

C#'s simple types *all* implement IComparable<T> via their .NET Framework Class Library types. For example, the Double value type (for simple type double) implements IComparable<Double>, and the Int32 value type (for simple type int) implements IComparable<Int32>. Types that implement IComparable<T> *must* declare a CompareTo method for comparing objects. For example, if we have two ints, int1 and int2, they can be compared with the expression:

```
int1.CompareTo(int2)
```

Method CompareTo must return

- 0 if the objects are equal,
- a negative integer if int1 is less than int2 or
- a positive integer if int1 is greater than int2.

20.4.2 Specifying Type Constraints

Even though IComparable<T> objects can be compared, by default they cannot be used with generic code, because *not* all types implement interface IComparable<T>. However, we can restrict the types that can be used with a generic method or class to ensure that the types meet the method's or class's requirements. This is accomplished with **type constraints**.

Figure 20.4 declares method Maximum (lines 18–35) with a type constraint that requires each of the method's arguments to be of type IComparable<T>. This restriction is important, because *not* all objects can be compared via a CompareTo method. However, all IComparable<T> objects are *guaranteed* to have a CompareTo method, which we use in method Maximum to determine the largest of its three arguments. In addition, because there's only one type parameter, all three arguments must be of the same type.

```
 1   // Fig. 20.4: MaximumTest.cs
 2   // Generic method Maximum returns the largest of three objects.
 3   using System;
 4
 5   class MaximumTest
 6   {
 7      static void Main()
 8      {
 9         Console.WriteLine($"Maximum of 3, 4 and 5 is {Maximum(3, 4, 5)}\n");
10         Console.WriteLine(
11            $"Maximum of 6.6, 8.8 and 7.7 is {Maximum(6.6, 8.8, 7.7)}\n");
12         Console.WriteLine("Maximum of pear, apple and orange is " +
13            $"{Maximum("pear", "apple", "orange")}\n");
14      }
15
16      // generic function determines the
17      // largest of the IComparable<T> objects
18      private static T Maximum<T>(T x, T y, T z) where T : IComparable<T>
19      {
20         var max = x; // assume x is initially the largest
21
22         // compare y with max
23         if (y.CompareTo(max) > 0)
24         {
25            max = y; // y is the largest so far
26         }
27
28         // compare z with max
29         if (z.CompareTo(max) > 0)
30         {
31            max = z; // z is the largest
32         }
33
34         return max; // return largest object
35      }
36   }
```

```
Maximum of 3, 4 and 5 is 5
Maximum of 6.6, 8.8 and 7.7 is 8.8
Maximum of pear, apple and orange is pear
```

Fig. 20.4 | Generic method Maximum returns the largest of three objects.

*Specifying the Type Constraint with a **where** Clause*

Generic method Maximum uses type parameter T as the return type of the method (line 18), as the type of method parameters x, y and z (line 18), and as the inferred type of local variable max (line 20). The **where** clause (after the parameter list in line 18) specifies the type constraint for type parameter T. In this case, the type constraint

```
where T : IComparable<T>
```

indicates that this method requires the type argument to implement interface IComparable<T>. If no type constraint is specified, the default type constraint is object. If you pass to Maximum a value of a type that does not match the type constraint, the compiler generates an error. Note once again, that we declared Maximum static so Main can call it—generic methods are not required to be static in every case.

Kinds of Type Constraints

C# provides several kinds of type constraints:

- A **class constraint** indicates that the type argument must be an object of a specific base class or one of its subclasses.

- An **interface constraint** indicates that the type argument's class must implement a specific interface. The type constraint in line 18 is an interface constraint, because IComparable<T> is an interface.

- You can specify that the type argument must be a reference type or a value type by using the **reference-type constraint** (**class**) or the **value-type constraint** (**struct**), respectively.

- Finally, you can specify a **constructor constraint**—**new()**—to indicate that the generic code can use operator new to create new objects of the type represented by the type parameter. If a type parameter is specified with a constructor constraint, the type argument's class must provide a public parameterless or default constructor to ensure that objects of the class can be created without passing constructor arguments; otherwise, a compilation error occurs.

Applying Multiple Type Constraints

It's possible to apply **multiple constraints** to a type parameter. To do so, simply provide a comma-separated list of constraints in the where clause. If you have a class constraint, reference-type constraint or value-type constraint, it must be listed first—only one of these types of constraints can be used for each type parameter. Interface constraints (if any) are listed next. The constructor constraint is listed last (if there is one).

Analyzing the Code

Method Maximum assumes that its first argument (x) is the largest and assigns it to local variable max (line 20). Next, the if statement at lines 23–26 determines whether y is greater than max. The condition invokes y.CompareTo(max). If y is greater than max—that is, CompareTo returns a value greater than 0—then y is assigned to variable max (line 25). Similarly, the statement at lines 29–32 determines whether z is greater than max. If so, line 31 assigns z to max. Then, line 34 returns max to the caller.

In Main (lines 7–14), line 9 calls Maximum with the integers 3, 4 and 5. Generic method Maximum is a match for this call, but its arguments must implement interface IComparable<T> to ensure that they can be compared. Type int is a synonym for Int32, which implements interface IComparable<int>. Thus, ints (and other simple types) are valid arguments to method Maximum.

Line 11 passes three `double` arguments to `Maximum`. Again, this is allowed because `double` is a synonym for `Double`, which implements `IComparable<double>`. Line 13 passes `Maximum` three `string`s, which are also `IComparable<string>` objects. We intentionally placed the largest value in a different position in each method call (lines 9, 11 and 13) to show that the generic method always finds the maximum value, regardless of its position in the argument list and regardless of the inferred type argument.

Value Types vs. Reference Types in Generics

In this example, the compiler generates three versions of method `Maximum`, based on the calls in `Main`. Customized `Maximum` methods are generated for types `int` and `double` and, because `string` is a class, a third version of `Maximum` is generated for all reference types—the runtime then determines the reference type argument from the method call. For more details on how the runtime handles generics for value and reference types, see

```
https://msdn.microsoft.com/library/f4a6ta2h
```

20.5 Overloading Generic Methods

A generic method may be overloaded. Each overloaded method must have a unique signature (as discussed in Chapter 7). A class can provide two or more generic methods with the *same* name but *different* method parameters. For example, we could provide a second version of generic method `DisplayArray` (Fig. 20.3) with the additional parameters `lowIndex` and `highIndex` that specify the portion of the array to output (see Exercise 20.8).

A generic method can be overloaded by nongeneric methods with the same method name. When the compiler encounters a method call, it searches for the method declaration that best matches the method name and the argument types specified in the call. For example, generic method `DisplayArray` of Fig. 20.3 could be overloaded with a version specific to `string`s that outputs the `string`s in tabular format (see Exercise 20.9)—the non-generic version of a method takes precedence over a generic version. If the compiler cannot match a method call to either a nongeneric method or a generic method, or if there's ambiguity due to multiple possible matches, the compiler generates an error.

20.6 Generic Classes

The concept of a data structure (e.g., a stack) that contains data elements can be understood independently of the element type it manipulates. A generic class provides a means for describing a class in a *type-independent* manner. We can then instantiate type-specific versions of the generic class. This capability is an opportunity for software reusability.

With a generic class, you can use a simple, concise notation to indicate the actual type(s) that should be used in place of the class's type parameter(s). At compilation time, the compiler ensures your code's type safety, and the runtime system replaces type parameters with type arguments to enable your client code to interact with the generic class.

One generic `Stack` class, for example, could be the basis for creating many `Stack` classes (e.g., "Stack of `double`," "Stack of `int`," "Stack of `char`," "Stack of `Employee`"). Figure 20.5 presents a generic `Stack` class declaration. This class should not be confused with the class `Stack` from namespace `System.Collections.Generics`. A generic class declaration is similar to a nongeneric class declaration, except that the class name is followed by a type-parameter list (line 5) and, optionally, one or more constraints on its type parameter. Type parameter T represents the element type the Stack will manipulate. As with generic methods, the type-parameter list of a generic class can have one or more type parameters separated by commas. (You'll create a generic class with two type parameters in Exercise 20.11.) Type parameter T is used throughout the Stack class declaration (Fig. 20.5) to represent the element type. Class Stack declares variable elements as an array of type T (line 8). This array (created at line 25) will store the Stack's elements. [*Note:* This example implements a Stack as an array. As you've seen in Chapter 19, Stacks also are commonly implemented as constrained versions of linked lists.]

```
 1   // Fig. 20.5: Stack.cs
 2   // Generic class Stack.
 3   using System;
 4
 5   public class Stack<T>
 6   {
 7      private int top; // location of the top element
 8      private T[] elements; // array that stores stack elements
 9
10      // parameterless constructor creates a stack of the default size
11      public Stack()
12         : this(10) // default stack size
13      {
14         // empty constructor; calls constructor at line 18 to perform init
15      }
16
17      // constructor creates a stack of the specified number of elements
18      public Stack(int stackSize)
19      {
20         if (stackSize <= 0) // validate stackSize
21         {
22            throw new ArgumentException("Stack size must be positive.");
23         }
24
25         elements = new T[stackSize]; // create stackSize elements
26         top = -1; // stack initially empty
27      }
28
29      // push element onto the stack; if unsuccessful,
30      // throw FullStackException
31      public void Push(T pushValue)
32      {
33         if (top == elements.Length - 1) // stack is full
34         {
35            throw new FullStackException(
36               $"Stack is full, cannot push {pushValue}");
37         }
38
39         ++top; // increment top
40         elements[top] = pushValue; // place pushValue on stack
41      }
```

Fig. 20.5 | Generic class Stack. (Part 1 of 2.)

```
42
43    // return the top element if not empty,
44    // else throw EmptyStackException
45    public T Pop()
46    {
47        if (top == -1) // stack is empty
48        {
49            throw new EmptyStackException("Stack is empty, cannot pop");
50        }
51
52        --top; // decrement top
53        return elements[top + 1]; // return top value
54    }
55 }
```

Fig. 20.5 | Generic class Stack. (Part 2 of 2.)

As with generic methods, when a generic class is compiled, the compiler performs type checking on the class's type parameters to ensure that they can be used with the code in the generic class. For value-types, the compiler generates a custom version of the class for each unique value type used to create a new Stack object, and for reference types, the compiler generates a single additional custom Stack. The constraints determine the operations that can be performed on the type parameters. For reference types, the runtime system replaces the type parameters with the actual types. For class Stack, no type constraint is specified, so the default type constraint, object, is used. The scope of a generic class's type parameter is the entire class.

Stack *Constructors*
Class Stack has two constructors. The parameterless constructor (lines 11–15) passes the default stack size (10) to the one-argument constructor, using the syntax this (line 12) to invoke another constructor in the same class. The one-argument constructor (lines 18–27) validates the stackSize argument and creates an array of the specified stackSize (if it's greater than 0) or throws an exception, otherwise.

Stack *Method* Push
Method Push (lines 31–41) first determines whether an attempt is being made to push an element onto a full Stack. If so, line 35–36 throw a FullStackException (declared in Fig. 20.6). If the Stack is not full, line 39 increments the top counter to indicate the new top position, and line 40 places the argument in that location of array elements.

Stack *Method* Pop
Method Pop (lines 45–54) first determines whether an attempt is being made to pop an element from an empty Stack. If so, line 49 throws an EmptyStackException (declared in Fig. 20.7). Otherwise, line 52 decrements the top counter to indicate the new top position, and line 53 returns the original top element of the Stack.

Classes *FullStackException and EmptyStackException*
Classes FullStackException (Fig. 20.6) and EmptyStackException (Fig. 20.7) each provide a parameterless constructor, a one-argument constructor of exception classes (as dis-

cussed in Section 13.8) and a two-argument constructor for creating a new exception using an existing one. The parameterless constructor sets the default error message while the other two constructors set custom error messages.

```
1   // Fig. 20.6: FullStackException.cs
2   // FullStackException indicates a stack is full.
3   using System;
4
5   public class FullStackException : Exception
6   {
7      // parameterless constructor
8      public FullStackException() : base("Stack is full")
9      {
10        // empty constructor
11     }
12
13     // one-parameter constructor
14     public FullStackException(string exception) : base(exception)
15     {
16        // empty constructor
17     }
18
19     // two-parameter constructor
20     public FullStackException(string exception, Exception inner)
21        : base(exception, inner)
22     {
23        // empty constructor
24     }
25  }
```

Fig. 20.6 | FullStackException indicates a stack is full.

```
1   // Fig. 20.7: EmptyStackException.cs
2   // EmptyStackException indicates a stack is empty.
3   using System;
4
5   public class EmptyStackException : Exception
6   {
7      // parameterless constructor
8      public EmptyStackException() : base("Stack is empty")
9      {
10        // empty constructor
11     }
12
13     // one-parameter constructor
14     public EmptyStackException(string exception) : base(exception)
15     {
16        // empty constructor
17     }
18
```

Fig. 20.7 | EmptyStackException indicates a stack is empty. (Part 1 of 2.)

```
19      // two-parameter constructor
20      public EmptyStackException(string exception, Exception inner)
21          : base(exception, inner)
22      {
23          // empty constructor
24      }
25  }
```

Fig. 20.7 | EmptyStackException indicates a stack is empty. (Part 2 of 2.)

Demonstrating Class *Stack*

Now, let's consider an app (Fig. 20.8) that uses our generic Stack class. Lines 13–14 declare variables of type Stack<double> (pronounced "Stack of double") and Stack<int> (pronounced "Stack of int"). The types double and int are the Stack's type arguments. The compiler replaces the type parameters in the generic class and performs type checking. Method Main instantiates objects doubleStack of size 5 (line 18) and intStack of size 10 (line 19), then calls methods TestPushDouble (declared in lines 28–47), TestPopDouble (declared in lines 50–71), TestPushInt (declared in lines 74–93) and TestPopInt (declared in lines 96–117) to manipulate the two Stacks in this example.

```
1   // Fig. 20.8: StackTest.cs
2   // Testing generic class Stack.
3   using System;
4
5   class StackTest
6   {
7      // create arrays of doubles and ints
8      private static double[] doubleElements =
9          {1.1, 2.2, 3.3, 4.4, 5.5, 6.6};
10     private static int[] intElements =
11         {1, 2, 3, 4, 5, 6, 7, 8, 9, 10, 11};
12
13     private static Stack<double> doubleStack; // stack stores doubles
14     private static Stack<int> intStack; // stack stores ints
15
16     static void Main()
17     {
18         doubleStack = new Stack<double>(5); // stack of doubles
19         intStack = new Stack<int>(10); // stack of ints
20
21         TestPushDouble(); // push doubles onto doubleStack
22         TestPopDouble(); // pop doubles from doubleStack
23         TestPushInt(); // push ints onto intStack
24         TestPopInt(); // pop ints from intStack
25     }
26
27     // test Push method with doubleStack
28     private static void TestPushDouble()
29     {
```

Fig. 20.8 | Testing generic class Stack. (Part 1 of 4.)

```csharp
30         // push elements onto stack
31         try
32         {
33             Console.WriteLine("\nPushing elements onto doubleStack");
34
35             // push elements onto stack
36             foreach (var element in doubleElements)
37             {
38                 Console.Write($"{element:F1} ");
39                 doubleStack.Push(element); // push onto doubleStack
40             }
41         }
42         catch (FullStackException exception)
43         {
44             Console.Error.WriteLine($"\nMessage: {exception.Message}");
45             Console.Error.WriteLine(exception.StackTrace);
46         }
47     }
48
49     // test Pop method with doubleStack
50     private static void TestPopDouble()
51     {
52         // pop elements from stack
53         try
54         {
55             Console.WriteLine("\nPopping elements from doubleStack");
56
57             double popValue; // store element removed from stack
58
59             // remove all elements from stack
60             while (true)
61             {
62                 popValue = doubleStack.Pop(); // pop from doubleStack
63                 Console.Write($"{popValue:F1} ");
64             }
65         }
66         catch (EmptyStackException exception)
67         {
68             Console.Error.WriteLine($"\nMessage: {exception.Message}");
69             Console.Error.WriteLine(exception.StackTrace);
70         }
71     }
72
73     // test Push method with intStack
74     private static void TestPushInt()
75     {
76         // push elements onto stack
77         try
78         {
79             Console.WriteLine("\nPushing elements onto intStack");
80
```

Fig. 20.8 | Testing generic class Stack. (Part 2 of 4.)

```
81              // push elements onto stack
82              foreach (var element in intElements)
83              {
84                  Console.Write($"{element} ");
85                  intStack.Push(element); // push onto intStack
86              }
87          }
88          catch (FullStackException exception)
89          {
90              Console.Error.WriteLine($"\nMessage: {exception.Message}");
91              Console.Error.WriteLine(exception.StackTrace);
92          }
93      }
94
95      // test Pop method with intStack
96      private static void TestPopInt()
97      {
98          // pop elements from stack
99          try
100         {
101             Console.WriteLine("\nPopping elements from intStack");
102
103             int popValue; // store element removed from stack
104
105             // remove all elements from stack
106             while (true)
107             {
108                 popValue = intStack.Pop(); // pop from intStack
109                 Console.Write($"{popValue:F1} ");
110             }
111         }
112         catch (EmptyStackException exception)
113         {
114             Console.Error.WriteLine($"\nMessage: {exception.Message}");
115             Console.Error.WriteLine(exception.StackTrace);
116         }
117     }
118 }
```

```
Pushing elements onto doubleStack
1.1 2.2 3.3 4.4 5.5 6.6
Message: Stack is full, cannot push 6.6
   at Stack`1.Push(T pushValue) in C:\Users\PaulDeitel\Documents\
      examples\ch20\Fig20_05_08\Stack\Stack\Stack.cs:line 35
   at StackTest.TestPushDouble() in C:\Users\PaulDeitel\Documents\
      examples\ch20\Fig20_05_08\Stack\Stack\StackTest.cs:line 39

Popping elements from doubleStack
5.5 4.4 3.3 2.2 1.1
Message: Stack is empty, cannot pop
   at Stack`1.Pop() in C:\Users\PaulDeitel\Documents\
      examples\ch20\Fig20_05_08\Stack\Stack\Stack.cs:line 49
   at StackTest.TestPopDouble() in C:\Users\PaulDeitel\Documents\
      examples\ch20\Fig20_05_08\Stack\Stack\StackTest.cs:line 62
```

Fig. 20.8 | Testing generic class Stack. (Part 3 of 4.)

```
Pushing elements onto intStack
1 2 3 4 5 6 7 8 9 10 11
Message: Stack is full, cannot push 11
   at Stack`1.Push(T pushValue) in C:\Users\PaulDeitel\Documents\
      examples\ch20\Fig20_05_08\Stack\Stack\Stack.cs:line 35
   at StackTest.TestPushInt() in C:\Users\PaulDeitel\Documents\
      examples\ch20\Fig20_05_08\Stack\Stack\StackTest.cs:line 85

Popping elements from intStack
10 9 8 7 6 5 4 3 2 1
Message: Stack is empty, cannot pop
   at Stack`1.Pop() in C:\Users\PaulDeitel\Documents\
      examples\ch20\Fig20_05_08\Stack\Stack\Stack.cs:line 49
   at StackTest.TestPopInt() in C:\Users\PaulDeitel\Documents\
      examples\ch20\Fig20_05_08\Stack\Stack\StackTest.cs:line 109
```

Fig. 20.8 | Testing generic class Stack. (Part 4 of 4.)

Method TestPushDouble

Method TestPushDouble (lines 28–47) invokes method Push to place the double values 1.1, 2.2, 3.3, 4.4 and 5.5 stored in array doubleElements onto doubleStack. The for-each statement terminates when the test program attempts to Push a sixth value onto doubleStack (which is full, because doubleStack can store only five elements). In this case, the method throws a FullStackException (Fig. 20.6) to indicate that the Stack is full. Lines 42–46 of Fig. 20.8 catch this exception and display the message and stack-trace information. The stack trace indicates the exception that occurred and shows that Stack method Push generated the exception at line 35 of the file Stack.cs (Fig. 20.5). The trace also shows that method Push was called by StackTest method TestPushDouble at line 39 of StackTest.cs. This information enables you to determine the methods that were on the method-call stack at the time that the exception occurred. Because the program catches the exception, the C# runtime environment considers the exception to have been handled, and the program can continue executing.

Method TestPopDouble

Method TestPopDouble (Fig. 20.8, lines 50–71) invokes Stack method Pop in an infinite while loop to remove all the values from the stack. Note in the output that the values are popped off in *last-in, first-out order*—this, of course, is the defining characteristic of stacks. The while loop (lines 60–64) continues until the stack is empty. An EmptyStackException occurs when an attempt is made to pop from the empty stack. This causes the program to proceed to the catch block (lines 66–70) and handle the exception, so the program can continue executing. When the test program attempts to Pop a sixth value, the doubleStack is empty, so method Pop throws an EmptyStackException.

Methods TestPushInt *and* TestPopInt

Method TestPushInt (lines 74–93) invokes Stack method Push to place values onto intStack until it's full. Method TestPopInt (lines 96–117) invokes Stack method Pop to remove values from intStack until it's empty. Again, values pop in last-in, first-out order.

Creating Generic Methods to Test Class Stack<T>

Note that the code in methods TestPushDouble and TestPushInt is virtually identical for pushing values onto Stacks. Similarly the code in methods TestPopDouble and TestPopInt is virtually identical for popping values from Stacks. This presents another opportunity to use generic methods. Figure 20.9 declares generic method TestPush (lines 33–53) to perform the same tasks as TestPushDouble and TestPushInt in Fig. 20.8—that is, Push values onto a Stack<T>. Similarly, generic method TestPop (lines 56–77) performs the same tasks as TestPopDouble and TestPopInt in Fig. 20.8—that is, Pop values off a Stack<T>.

```
1   // Fig. 20.9: StackTest.cs
2   // Testing generic class Stack.
3   using System;
4   using System.Collections.Generic;
5
6   class StackTest
7   {
8      // create arrays of doubles and ints
9      private static double[] doubleElements =
10        {1.1, 2.2, 3.3, 4.4, 5.5, 6.6};
11     private static int[] intElements =
12        {1, 2, 3, 4, 5, 6, 7, 8, 9, 10, 11};
13
14     private static Stack<double> doubleStack; // stack stores doubles
15     private static Stack<int> intStack; // stack stores int objects
16
17     static void Main()
18     {
19        doubleStack = new Stack<double>(5); // stack of doubles
20        intStack = new Stack<int>(10); // stack of ints
21
22        // push doubles onto doubleStack
23        TestPush(nameof(doubleStack), doubleStack, doubleElements);
24        // pop doubles from doubleStack
25        TestPop(nameof(doubleStack), doubleStack);
26        // push ints onto intStack
27        TestPush(nameof(doubleStack), intStack, intElements);
28        // pop ints from intStack
29        TestPop(nameof(doubleStack), intStack);
30     }
31
32     // test Push method
33     private static void TestPush<T>(string name, Stack<T> stack,
34        IEnumerable<T> elements)
35     {
36        // push elements onto stack
37        try
38        {
39           Console.WriteLine($"\nPushing elements onto {name}");
40
41           // push elements onto stack
42           foreach (var element in elements)
43           {
```

Fig. 20.9 | Testing generic class Stack. (Part 1 of 3.)

```
44                    Console.Write($"{element} ");
45                    stack.Push(element); // push onto stack
46                }
47            }
48            catch (FullStackException exception)
49            {
50                Console.Error.WriteLine($"\nMessage: {exception.Message}");
51                Console.Error.WriteLine(exception.StackTrace);
52            }
53        }
54
55        // test Pop method
56        private static void TestPop<T>(string name, Stack<T> stack)
57        {
58            // pop elements from stack
59            try
60            {
61                Console.WriteLine($"\nPopping elements from {name}");
62
63                T popValue; // store element removed from stack
64
65                // remove all elements from stack
66                while (true)
67                {
68                    popValue = stack.Pop(); // pop from stack
69                    Console.Write($"{popValue} ");
70                }
71            }
72            catch (EmptyStackException exception)
73            {
74                Console.Error.WriteLine($"\nMessage: {exception.Message}");
75                Console.Error.WriteLine(exception.StackTrace);
76            }
77        }
78    }
```

```
Pushing elements onto doubleStack
1.1 2.2 3.3 4.4 5.5 6.6
Message: Stack is full, cannot push 6.6
   at Stack`1.Push(T pushValue) in C:\Users\PaulDeitel\Documents\
      examples\ch20\Fig20_09\Stack\Stack\Stack.cs:line 35
   at StackTest.TestPush[T](String name, Stack`1 stack, IEnumerable`1
      elements) in C:\Users\PaulDeitel\Documents\examples\ch20\Fig20_09\
      Stack\Stack\StackTest.cs:line 45

Popping elements from doubleStack
5.5 4.4 3.3 2.2 1.1
Message: Stack is empty, cannot pop
   at Stack`1.Pop() in C:\Users\PaulDeitel\Documents\
      examples\ch20\Fig20_09\Stack\Stack\Stack.cs:line 49
   at StackTest.TestPop[T](String name, Stack`1 stack) in
      C:\Users\PaulDeitel\Documents\examples\ch20\Fig20_09\Stack\
      Stack\StackTest.cs:line 68
```

Fig. 20.9 | Testing generic class Stack. (Part 2 of 3.)

```
Pushing elements onto intStack
1 2 3 4 5 6 7 8 9 10 11
Message: Stack is full, cannot push 11
    at Stack`1.Push(T pushValue) in C:\Users\PaulDeitel\Documents\
      examples\ch20\Fig20_09\Stack\Stack\Stack.cs:line 35
    at StackTest.TestPush[T](String name, Stack`1 stack, IEnumerable`1
      elements) in C:\Users\PaulDeitel\Documents\examples\ch20\Fig20_09\
      Stack\Stack\StackTest.cs:line 45

Popping elements from intStack
10 9 8 7 6 5 4 3 2 1
Message: Stack is empty, cannot pop
    at Stack`1.Pop() in C:\Users\PaulDeitel\Documents\
      examples\ch20\Fig20_09\Stack\Stack\Stack.cs:line 49
    at StackTest.TestPop[T](String name, Stack`1 stack) in
      C:\Users\PaulDeitel\Documents\examples\ch20\Fig20_09\Stack\
      Stack\StackTest.cs:line 68
```

Fig. 20.9 | Testing generic class Stack. (Part 3 of 3.)

Method Main (Fig. 20.9, lines 17–30) creates the Stack<double> (line 19) and Stack<int> (line 20) objects. Lines 23–29 invoke generic methods TestPush and TestPop to test the Stack objects.

Generic method TestPush (lines 33–53) uses type parameter T (specified at line 33) to represent the data type stored in the Stack. The generic method takes three arguments—a string that represents the name of the Stack object for output purposes, an object of type Stack<T> and an IEnumerable<T> that contains the elements that will be Pushed onto Stack<T>. The compiler enforces consistency between the type of the Stack and the elements that will be pushed onto the Stack when Push is invoked, which is the type argument of the generic method call. Generic method TestPop (lines 56–77) takes two arguments—a string that represents the name of the Stack object for output purposes and an object of type Stack<T>.

20.7 Wrap-Up

This chapter introduced generics. We discussed how generics ensure compile-time type safety by checking for type mismatches at compile time. You learned that the compiler will allow generic code to compile only if all operations performed on the type parameters in the generic code are supported for all types that could be used with the generic code. You also learned how to declare generic methods and classes using type parameters. We demonstrated how to use a type constraint to specify the requirements for a type parameter—a key component of compile-time type safety. We discussed several kinds of type constraints, including reference-type constraints, value-type constraints, class constraints, interface constraints and constructor constraints. We also discussed how to implement multiple type constraints for a type parameter. Finally, we showed how generics improve code reuse. In the next chapter, we demonstrate the .NET Framework Class Library's collection classes, interfaces and algorithms. Collection classes are pre-built data structures that you can reuse in your apps, saving you time.

Summary

Section 20.1 Introduction

- Generic methods enable you to specify, with a single method declaration, a set of related methods.

- Generic classes enable you to specify, with a single class declaration, a set of related classes.

- Generic interfaces enable you to specify, with a single interface declaration, a set of related interfaces.

- Generics provide compile-time type safety.

Section 20.2 Motivation for Generic Methods

- Overloaded methods are often used to perform similar operations on different types of data.

- When the compiler encounters a method call, it attempts to locate a method declaration that has the same method name and parameters that match the argument types in the method call.

Section 20.3 Generic-Method Implementation

- If the operations performed by several overloaded methods are identical for each argument type, the overloaded methods can be more compactly and conveniently coded using a generic method.

- You can write a single generic-method declaration that can be called at different times with arguments of different types. Based on the types of the arguments passed to the generic method, the compiler handles each method call appropriately.

- All generic-method declarations have a type-parameter list delimited by angle brackets that follows the method's name. Each type-parameter list contains one or more type parameters, separated by commas.

- A type parameter is used in place of actual type names. The type parameters can be used to declare the return type, parameter types and local variable types in a generic-method declaration; the type parameters act as placeholders for type arguments that represent the types of that data that will be passed to the generic method.

- A generic method's body is declared like that of any other method. The type-parameter names throughout the method declaration must match those declared in the type-parameter list.

- A type parameter can be declared only once in the type-parameter list but can appear more than once in the method's parameter list. Type-parameter names need not be unique among different generic methods.

- When the compiler encounters a method call, it analyzes the set of methods (both nongeneric and generic) that might match the method call, looking for a method that best matches the call. If there are no matching methods, or if there's more than one best match, the compiler generates an error.

- You can use explicit type arguments to indicate the exact type that should be used to call a generic function. For example, the method call `DisplayArray<int>(intArray);` explicitly provides the type argument (`int`) that should be used to replace type parameter `T` in the `DisplayArray` method's declaration.

- For each variable declared with a type parameter, the compiler also determines whether the operations performed on such a variable are allowed for all types that the type parameter can assume.

Section 20.4 Type Constraints

- Generic code is restricted to performing operations that are guaranteed to work for every possible type. Thus, an expression like `variable1 < variable2` is not allowed unless the compiler can ensure that the operator `<` is provided for every type that will ever be used in the generic code. Similarly, you cannot call a method on a generic-type variable unless the compiler can ensure that all types that will ever be used in the generic code support that method.

- It's possible to compare two objects of the same type if that type implements the generic interface IComparable<T> (of namespace System), which declares method CompareTo.

- IComparable<T> objects can be used with the sorting and searching methods of classes in the System.Collections.Generic namespace.

- Simple types all implement interface IComparable<T>.

- It's the responsibility of the programmer who declares a type that implements IComparable<T> to provide method CompareTo such that it compares the contents of two objects of that type and returns 0 if they're equal, a negative value if the first is less than the second and a positive value if the first is greater than the second.

- You can restrict the types that can be used with a generic method or class to ensure that they meet certain requirements. This feature—known as a type constraint—restricts the type of the argument supplied to a particular type parameter. For example, the clause where T : IComparable<T> indicates that the type arguments must implement interface IComparable<T>. If no type constraint is specified, the default type constraint is object.

- A class constraint indicates that the type argument must be an object of a specific base class or one of its subclasses.

- An interface constraint indicates that the type argument's class must implement a specific interface.

- You can specify that the type argument must be a reference type or a value type by using the reference-type constraint (class) or the value-type constraint (struct), respectively.

- You can specify a constructor constraint—new()—to indicate that the generic code can use operator new to create new objects of the type represented by the type parameter. If a type parameter is specified with a constructor constraint, the type argument's class must provide a public parameterless or default constructor to ensure that objects of the class can be created without passing constructor arguments; otherwise, a compilation error occurs.

- It's possible to apply multiple constraints to a type parameter by providing a comma-separated list of constraints in the where clause.

- If you have a class constraint, reference-type constraint or value-type constraint, it must be listed first—only one of these types of constraints can be used for each type parameter. Interface constraints (if any) are listed next. The constructor constraint is listed last (if there is one).

Section 20.5 Overloading Generic Methods
- A generic method may be overloaded. All methods must contain a unique signature.

- A generic method can be overloaded by nongeneric methods with the same method name. When the compiler encounters a method call, it searches for the method declaration that most precisely matches the method name and the argument types specified in the call.

Section 20.6 Generic Classes
- A generic class provides a means for describing a class in a type-independent manner.

- Once you have a generic class, you can use a simple, concise notation to indicate the actual type(s) that should be used in place of the class's type parameter(s). At compilation time, the compiler ensures the type safety of your code, and the runtime system replaces type parameters with actual arguments to enable your client code to interact with the generic class.

- A generic class declaration is similar to a nongeneric class declaration, except that the class name is followed by a type-parameter list and optional constraints on its type parameters.

- As with generic methods, the type-parameter list of a generic class can have one or more type parameters separated by commas, and each type parameter can have type constraints.
- When a generic class is compiled, the compiler performs type checking on the class's type parameters to ensure that they can be used with the code in the generic class. The constraints determine the operations that can be performed on the variables declared with type parameters.

Terminology

class constraint
CompareTo method of interface IComparable<T>
compile-time type safety
constructor constraint (new())
default type constraint (object) of a type
    parameter
explicit type argument
generic class
generic interface
generic method
generics
IComparable<T> interface
interface constraint

multiple constraints
new() (constructor) constraint
overloading generic methods
reference-type constraint (class)
scope of a type parameter
type argument
type checking
type constraint
type inference
type parameter
type-parameter list
value type constraint (struct)
where clause

Self-Review Exercises

20.1 State whether each of the following is *true* or *false*. If *false*, explain why.
  a) A generic method cannot have the same method name as a nongeneric method.
  b) All generic method declarations have a type-parameter list that immediately precedes the method name.
  c) A generic method can be overloaded by another generic method with the same method name but a different number of type parameters.
  d) A type parameter can be declared only once in the type-parameter list but can appear more than once in the method's parameter list.
  e) Type-parameter names among different generic methods must be unique.
  f) The scope of a generic class's type parameter is the entire class.
  g) A type parameter can have at most one interface constraint, but multiple class constraints.

20.2 Fill in the blanks in each of the following:
  a) _____ enable you to specify, with a single method declaration, a set of related methods; _____ enable you to specify, with a single class declaration, a set of related classes.
  b) A type-parameter list is delimited by _____.
  c) The _____ of a generic method can be used to specify the types of the arguments to the method, to specify the return type of the method and to declare variables within the method.
  d) The statement "Stack<int> myStack = new Stack<int>();" indicates that myStack stores _____.
  e) In a generic class declaration, the class name is followed by a(n) _____.
  f) The _____ constraint requires that the type argument must have a public parameterless constructor.

Answers to Self-Review Exercises

20.1 a) False. A generic method can be overloaded by nongeneric methods. b) False. All generic method declarations have a type-parameter list that immediately follows the method's name. c) True. d) True. e) False. Type-parameter names among different generic methods need not be unique. f) True. g) False. A type parameter can have at most one class constraint, but multiple interface constraints.

20.2 a) Generic methods, generic classes. b) angle brackets. c) type parameters. d) `ints`. e) type-parameter list. f) `new`.

Exercises

20.3 *(Generic Notation)* Explain the use of the following notation in a C# program:

```
public class Array<T>
```

20.4 *(Overloading Generic Methods)* How can generic methods be overloaded?

20.5 *(Determining Which Method to Call)* The compiler performs a matching process to determine which method to call when a method is invoked. Under what circumstances does an attempt to make a match result in a compile-time error?

20.6 *(What Does This Statement Do?)* Explain why a C# program might use the statement

```
var workerlist = new Array<Employee>();
```

20.7 *(Generic Linear Search Method)* Write a generic method, `Search`, that searches an array using the linear-search algorithm. Method `Search` should compare the search key with each element in its array parameter until the search key is found or until the end of the array is reached. If the search key is found, return its location in the array; otherwise, return -1. Write a test app that inputs and searches an `int` array and a `double` array. Provide buttons that the user can click to randomly generate `int` and `double` values. Display the generated values in a `TextBox`, so the user knows what values they can search for [*Hint:* Use (`T : IComparable<T>`) in the `where` clause for method `Search` so that you can use method `CompareTo` to compare the search key to the elements in the array.]

20.8 *(Overloading a Generic Method)* Overload generic method `DisplayArray` of Fig. 20.3 so that it takes two additional `int` arguments: `lowIndex` and `highIndex`. A call to this method displays only the designated portion of the array. Validate `lowIndex` and `highIndex`. If either is out of range, or if `highIndex` is less than or equal to `lowIndex`, the overloaded `DisplayArray` method should throw an `ArgumentException`; otherwise, `DisplayArray` should return the number of elements displayed. Then modify `Main` to exercise both versions of `DisplayArray` on arrays `intArray`, `doubleArray` and `charArray`. Test all capabilities of both versions of `DisplayArray`.

20.9 *(Overloading a Generic Method with a Non-Generic Method)* Overload generic method `DisplayArray` of Fig. 20.3 with a nongeneric version that displays an array of strings in neat, tabular format, as shown in the sample output that follows:

```
Array stringArray contains:
one     two     three   four
five    six     seven   eight
```

20.10 *(Generic Method `IsEqualTo`)* Write a simple generic version of method `IsEqualTo` that compares its two arguments with the `Equals` method, and returns `true` if they're equal and `false` otherwise. Use this generic method in a program that calls `IsEqualTo` with a variety of simple types, such as `object` or `int`. What result do you get when you attempt to run this program?

20.11 *(Generic Class Pair)* Write a generic class Pair which has two type parameters, F and S, representing the type of the first and second element of the pair, respectively. Add properties for the first and second elements of the pair. [*Hint:* The class header should be public class Pair<F, S>.]

20.12 *(Generic Classes TreeNode and Tree)* Convert classes TreeNode and Tree from Fig. 19.20 into generic classes. To insert an object in a Tree, the object must be compared to the objects in existing TreeNodes. For this reason, classes TreeNode and Tree should specify IComparable<T> as the interface constraint of each class's type parameter. After modifying classes TreeNode and Tree, write a test app that creates three Tree objects—one that stores ints, one that stores doubles and one that stores strings. Insert 10 values into each tree. Then output the preorder, inorder and postorder traversals for each Tree.

20.13 *(Generic Method TestTree)* Modify your test program from Exercise 20.12 to use generic method TestTree to test the three Tree objects. The method should be called three times—once for each Tree object.

Generic Collections; Functional Programming with LINQ/PLINQ

21

Objectives

In this chapter you'll:

- Learn about additional .NET generic collections.
- Manipulate arrays with class Array's static methods.
- Provide a using static directive to access a class's static members without fully qualifying their names.
- Iterate through a collection with enumerators.
- Use generic collections SortedDictionary and LinkedList.
- Use the C# 6 null-conditional ?[] operator to access array or collection elements.
- Use C# 6 index initializers to initialize a dictionary.
- Store method references in delegate variables, then use those variables to invoke the corresponding methods.
- Use lambda expressions to create anonymous methods and refer to those methods via delegate variables.
- Use LINQ method-call syntax and lambdas to demonstrate functional programming techniques.
- Parallelize LINQ operations with PLINQ for multicore performance.
- Learn covariance and contravariance for generic types.

21.1 Introduction

Chapter 19 showed how to create and manipulate custom data structures. The discussion was "low level," in the sense that we painstakingly created each element of each data structure dynamically with new and modified the data structures by directly manipulating their elements and references to their elements. For the vast majority of apps, there's no need to build custom data structures. Instead, you can use the *prepackaged* data-structure classes provided by the .NET Framework. These are known as **collection classes**—they store collections of data. Each instance of one of these classes is a **collection** of items. Some examples of collections are the cards you hold in a card game, the songs stored in your computer, the real-estate records in your local registry of deeds (which map book numbers and page numbers to property owners), and the players on your favorite sports team.

Use the Existing Collection Classes Rather Than Building Your Own
Collection classes enable you to store sets of items by using *existing* data structures, without concern for how they're implemented. This is a nice example of code reuse. You can code faster and expect excellent performance, maximizing execution speed and minimizing memory consumption. In this chapter, we discuss

- the collection interfaces that declare each collection type's capabilities
- the implementation classes
- the **enumerators** that iterate through collections (these are like iterators in languages like C++ and Java).

Collections Namespaces

The .NET Framework provides several namespaces dedicated to collections:

- `System.Collections` contains collections that store objects—similar to the data structures we defined in Chapter 19. Such collections can store objects of many different types at the same time, because all C# types derive directly or indirectly from object. You might encounter this namespace's classes, such as `ArrayList`, `Stack` and `Hashtable`, in C# legacy code prior to the introduction of generics in C# 2.0 (2005). Legacy code uses older programming techniques—possibly including language and library features that a programming language no longer supports or that have been superseded by newer capabilities.

- `System.Collections.Generic` contains generic collections, such as the `List<T>` (Section 9.4) and `Dictionary<K, V>` (Section 17.9) classes, that store objects of types you specify when you create the collection. You should use the generic collections—rather than the object-based legacy collections—to take advantage of compile-time type checking of your collection-processing code.

- `System.Collections.Concurrent` contains so-called thread-safe generic collections for use in multithreaded applications.

- `System.Collections.Specialized` contains collections that are optimized for specific scenarios, such as manipulating collections of bits.

Delegates and Lambda Expressions

In Section 14.3.3, we introduced the concept of a *delegate*—an object that holds a reference to a method. Delegates enable apps to store methods as data and to pass a method as an argument to another method. In event handling, a delegate stores a reference to the event-handler method that will be called when a user interacts with a GUI control. In this chapter, we'll discuss delegates in more detail and introduce lambda expressions, which allow you to define **anonymous methods** that can be used with delegates. Here we'll focus on using lambdas to pass method references to methods that specify delegate parameters.

Introduction to Functional Programming

So far, we've demonstrated three programming paradigms:

- structured programming (also known as procedural programming)
- object-oriented programming
- generic programming (which we'll continue discussing in this chapter).

Sections 21.10–21.11 define and introduce functional programming, showing how to use it with LINQ to Objects to write code more concisely and with fewer bugs than programs written with other techniques. In Section 21.12, with one additional method call, we'll demonstrate how *PLINQ (Parallel LINQ)* can improve LINQ to Objects performance substantially on multicore systems. In the exercises, we'll also ask you to revisit earlier examples and implement them using functional-programming techniques.

21.2 Collections Overview

All collection classes in the .NET Framework implement some combination of the collection interfaces that declare the operations to be performed on various types of collections. Figure 21.1 lists some of the collection interfaces in namespace System.Collections.Generic, which also have legacy object-based analogs in System.Collections. Many collection classes implement these interfaces. You may also provide implementations specific to your own requirements.

Interface	Description
IEnumerable<T>	An object that can be enumerated—for example, a foreach loop can iterate over such an object's elements. This interface contains one method, GetEnumerator, which returns an IEnumerator<T> object, which (as you'll see in Section 21.3) can be used manually to iterate through a collection. In fact, foreach uses a collection's IEnumerator<T> object behind the scenes. ICollection<T> extends IEnumerable<T> so all collection classes implement IEnumerable directly or indirectly.
ICollection<T>	The interface from which interfaces IList<T> and IDictionary<K,V> inherit. Contains a Count property to determine the size of a collection and a CopyTo method for copying a collection's contents to a traditional array, and an IsReadOnly property.
IList<T>	An ordered collection that can be manipulated like an array. Provides a [] operator (known as an *indexer*) for accessing elements with an int index. Also has methods for searching and modifying a collection, including Add, Remove, Contains and IndexOf.
IDictionary<K,V>	A collection of values, indexed by an arbitrary "key" object of type K. Provides an indexer ([]) for accessing elements by key and methods for modifying the collection (e.g., Add, Remove). IDictionary<K,V> property Keys contains all the keys, and property Values contains all the stored values.

Fig. 21.1 | Some common generic collection interfaces.

Namespace **System.Collections.Generic**
With the collections of the System.Collections.Generic namespace, you can specify the exact type that will be stored in a collection. This provides two key benefits over the object-based legacy collections:

- *Compile-time type checking* ensures that you're using appropriate types with your collection and, if not, the compiler issues error messages.

- Any item you retrieve from a generic collection will have the correct type. With object-based collections, any item you retrieve is returned as an object. Then, you must *explicitly cast* the object to the type that your program manipulates. This could lead to InvalidCastExceptions at execution time if the referenced object does not have the appropriate type.

Generic collections are especially useful for storing value types, since they eliminate the overhead of boxing and unboxing required with object-based legacy collections.

In this chapter, we continue our discussion of data structures and collections with additional built-in array capabilities, as well as the generic SortedDictionary and LinkedList classes. Namespace System.Collections.Generic provides many other data structures, including Stack<T>, Queue<T> and SortedList<K,V> (a collection of *key–value* pairs that are sorted by key and can be accessed either by key or by index). Figure 21.2 summarizes many of the collection classes—for a complete list, visit

https://msdn.microsoft.com/library/system.collections.generic

The collection classes have many common capabilities specified by the interfaces they implement. Once you know how to use a few collections (like List, Dictionary, LinkedList and SortedDictionary), you can figure out how to use the others via their online documentation, which includes sample code.

Class	Implements interface	Description
System namespace		
Array	IList	The base class of all conventional arrays. See Section 21.3.
System.Collections.Generic namespace		
Dictionary<K, V>	IDictionary<K, V>	A generic, unordered collection of key–value pairs that can be accessed rapidly by key. See Section 17.9.2.
LinkedList<T>	ICollection<T>	A generic doubly linked list. See Section 21.5.
List<T>	IList<T>	A generic array-based list. See Section 9.4.
Queue<T>	ICollection<T>	A generic first-in, first-out (FIFO) collection. See Section 19.6 for information on queues.
SortedDictionary<K, V>	IDictionary<K, V>	A Dictionary that sorts the data by the keys in a binary tree. See Section 21.4.
SortedList<K, V>	IDictionary<K, V>	Similar to a SortedDictionary, but uses arrays internally. If the data already exists and is sorted before insertion in a collection, then inserting in a SortedList is faster than a SortedDictionary. If the data is not sorted, insertion in a SortedDictionary is faster.
Stack<T>	ICollection<T>	A generic last-in, first-out (LIFO) collection. See Section 19.5 for information on stacks.
Legacy collections of the System.Collections namespace		
ArrayList	IList	Mimics conventional arrays, but will grow or shrink as needed to accommodate the number of elements.

Fig. 21.2 | Some .NET Framework collection classes. (Part 1 of 2.)

Class	Implements interface	Description
BitArray	ICollection	A memory-efficient array of bits in which each bit's 0 or 1 value represents the bool value false or true. Exercise 21.14 asks you to use a BitArray to implement the Sieve of Eratosthenes algorithm for finding prime numbers.
Hashtable	IDictionary	An unordered collection of key–value pairs that can be accessed rapidly by key.
Queue	ICollection	A first-in, first-out (FIFO) collection. See Section 19.6 for information on queues.
SortedList	IDictionary	A collection of key–value pairs that are sorted by key and can be accessed either by key or by index.
Stack	ICollection	A last-in, first-out (LIFO) collection. See Section 19.5 for information on stacks.

Fig. 21.2 | Some .NET Framework collection classes. (Part 2 of 2.)

We also discuss the IEnumerator<T> interface. Each collection class's enumerator allows you to iterate through the collection. Although these enumerators have different implementations, they all implement the IEnumerator<T> interface so that an app can iterate through a collection's elements (e.g., with a foreach statement). In the next section, we begin our discussion by examining enumerators and the capabilities for array manipulation. Collection classes directly or indirectly implement ICollection<T> and IEnumerable<T> (or their object-based equivalents ICollection and IEnumerable for legacy collections).

21.3 Class Array and Enumerators

Chapter 8 presented basic array-processing capabilities. All arrays implicitly inherit from abstract base class Array (namespace System); this class defines property Length, which specifies the number of elements in the array. In addition, class Array provides static methods that provide algorithms for processing arrays. Typically, class Array overloads these methods—for example, Array method Reverse can reverse the order of the elements in an entire array or in a specified range of elements. For a complete list of class Array's static methods visit

```
https://msdn.microsoft.com/library/system.array
```

Figure 21.3 demonstrates several static methods of class Array.

```
1   // Fig. 21.3: UsingArray.cs
2   // Array class static methods for common array manipulations.
3   using System;
4   using static System.Array;
```

Fig. 21.3 | Array class static methods for common array manipulations. (Part 1 of 3.)

```
 5   using System.Collections;
 6
 7   // demonstrate algorithms of class Array
 8   class UsingArray
 9   {
10      private static int[] intValues = {1, 2, 3, 4, 5, 6};
11      private static double[] doubleValues = {8.4, 9.3, 0.2, 7.9, 3.4};
12      private static int[] intValuesCopy;
13
14      // method Main demonstrates class Array's methods
15      static void Main()
16      {
17         intValuesCopy = new int[intValues.Length]; // defaults to zeroes
18
19         Console.WriteLine("Initial array values:\n");
20         PrintArrays(); // output initial array contents
21
22         // sort doubleValues
23         Sort(doubleValues); // unqualified call to Array static method Sort
24
25         // copy intValues into intValuesCopy
26         Array.Copy(intValues, intValuesCopy, intValues.Length);
27
28         Console.WriteLine("\nArray values after Sort and Copy:\n");
29         PrintArrays(); // output array contents
30         Console.WriteLine();
31
32         // search for 5 in intValues
33         int result = Array.BinarySearch(intValues, 5);
34         Console.WriteLine(result >= 0 ?
35            $"5 found at element {result} in intValues" :
36            "5 not found in intValues");
37
38         // search for 8763 in intValues
39         result = Array.BinarySearch(intValues, 8763);
40         Console.WriteLine(result >= 0 ?
41            $"8763 found at element {result} in intValues" :
42            "8763 not found in intValues");
43      }
44
45      // output array content with enumerators
46      private static void PrintArrays()
47      {
48         Console.Write("doubleValues: ");
49
50         // iterate through the double array with an enumerator
51         IEnumerator enumerator = doubleValues.GetEnumerator();
52
53         while (enumerator.MoveNext())
54         {
55            Console.Write($"{enumerator.Current} ");
56         }
57
```

Fig. 21.3 | Array class static methods for common array manipulations. (Part 2 of 3.)

```
58          Console.Write("\nintValues: ");
59
60          // iterate through the int array with an enumerator
61          enumerator = intValues.GetEnumerator();
62
63          while (enumerator.MoveNext())
64          {
65              Console.Write($"{enumerator.Current} ");
66          }
67
68          Console.Write("\nintValuesCopy: ");
69
70          // iterate through the second int array with a foreach statement
71          foreach (var element in intValuesCopy)
72          {
73              Console.Write($"{element} ");
74          }
75
76          Console.WriteLine();
77      }
78  }
```

```
Initial array values:

doubleValues: 8.4 9.3 0.2 7.9 3.4
intValues: 1 2 3 4 5 6
intValuesCopy: 0 0 0 0 0 0

Array values after Sort and Copy:

doubleValues: 0.2 3.4 7.9 8.4 9.3
intValues: 1 2 3 4 5 6
intValuesCopy: 1 2 3 4 5 6

5 found at element 4 in intValues
8763 not found in intValues
```

Fig. 21.3 | Array class `static` methods for common array manipulations. (Part 3 of 3.)

21.3.1 C# 6 using static Directive

The `using` directives in lines 3 and 5 include the namespaces `System` (for classes `Array` and `Console`) and `System.Collections` (for interface `IEnumerator`, which we discuss shortly). Line 4 introduces C# 6's **using static** directive for accessing a type's `static` members without fully qualifying their names—in this case, class `Array`'s `static` members. Line 23

```
Sort(doubleValues); // unqualified call to Array static method Sort
```

shows an *unqualified call* to `Array` static method `Sort`, which is equivalent to

```
Array.Sort(doubleValues); // call to Array static method Sort
```

Though we could use unqualified calls for all of class `Array`'s `static` members in this example (e.g., `Copy` in line 26 and `BinarySearch` in lines 33 and 39), the code is easier to read with the fully qualified method calls, which make it absolutely clear which class contains a given `static` method.

21.3.2 Class UsingArray's static Fields

Our test class declares three static array variables (lines 10–12). The first two lines initialize intValues and doubleValues to an int and double array, respectively. static variable intValuesCopy is intended to demonstrate the Array's Copy method—it's initially null, so it does not yet refer to an array.

Line 17 initializes intValuesCopy to an int array with the same length as array intValues. Line 20 calls the PrintArrays method (lines 46–77) to output the initial contents of all three arrays. We discuss the PrintArrays method shortly. The output of Fig. 21.3 shows that each element of array intValuesCopy is initialized to the default value 0.

21.3.3 Array Method Sort

Line 23 uses static Array method Sort to sort array doubleValues in ascending order. The elements in the array must implement the IComparable interface (as all simple types do), which enables method Sort to compare elements to determine their order.

21.3.4 Array Method Copy

Line 26 uses static Array method Copy to copy elements from array intValues to array intValuesCopy. The first argument is the array to copy (intValues), the second argument is the destination array (intValuesCopy) and the third argument is an int representing the number of elements to copy (in this case, intValues.Length specifies all elements). Class Array also provides overloads for copying portions of arrays.

21.3.5 Array Method BinarySearch

Lines 33 and 39 invoke static Array method BinarySearch to perform binary searches on array intValues. Method BinarySearch receives the *sorted* array in which to search and the key for which to search. The method returns the index in the array at which it finds the key (or a negative number if the key was not found). BinarySearch assumes that it receives a sorted array. Its behavior on an *unsorted* array is *undefined*. Chapter 18 discussed binary searching in detail.

21.3.6 Array Method GetEnumerator and Interface IEnumerator

Method PrintArrays (lines 46–77) uses class Array's methods to iterate over the elements of the arrays. Class Array implements the IEnumerable interface (the non-generic version of IEnumerable<T>). All arrays inherit implicitly from Array, so both the int[] and double[] array types implement IEnumerable interface method GetEnumerator, which returns an enumerator that can *iterate* over the collection—this method always returns an enumerator positioned *before the first element*. Interface IEnumerator (which all enumerators implement) defines methods MoveNext and Reset and property Current:

- MoveNext moves the enumerator to the next element in the collection. The first call to MoveNext positions the enumerator at the *first* element of the collection—if there is an element, MoveNext returns true; otherwise, the method returns false.

- Method Reset positions the enumerator before the first element of the collection.

- Read-only property Current returns the object at the current location in the collection (determined by the last call to MoveNext).

Enumerators cannot be used to *modify* the contents of collections, only to obtain the contents.

Common Programming Error 21.1

If a collection is modified after an enumerator is created for that collection, the enumerator immediately becomes invalid—for this reason, enumerators are said to be "fail fast." Any calls to the enumerator's Reset or MoveNext methods after this point throw Invalid-OperationExceptions. This is true for collections, but not for arrays.

When an enumerator is returned by the GetEnumerator method in line 51, it's initially positioned *before* the first element in Array doubleValues. Then when line 53 calls MoveNext in the first iteration of the while loop, the enumerator advances to the first element in doubleValues. The while statement in lines 53–56 iterates over each element until the enumerator passes the end of doubleValues and MoveNext returns false. In each iteration, we use the enumerator's Current property to obtain and output the current array element. Lines 63–66 iterate over array intValues.

21.3.7 Iterating Over a Collection with foreach

Lines 71–74 use a foreach statement to iterate over the collection. Both foreach and an enumerator loop over the elements of an array one by one in consecutive order. Neither allows you to modify the elements during the iteration. This is not a coincidence. Every foreach statement implicitly obtains an enumerator via the GetEnumerator method and uses the enumerator's MoveNext method and Current property to traverse the collection, just as we did explicitly in lines 51–56 and 61–66. For this reason, you should use the foreach statement to iterate over *any* collection that implements IEnumerable or IEnumerable<T>—as you saw for class List<T> in Section 9.4. Even class string implements IEnumerable<char> so you can iterate over a string's characters.

21.3.8 Array Methods Clear, IndexOf, LastIndexOf and Reverse

Other static Array methods include:

- Clear which sets a range of elements to 0, false or null, as appropriate.
- IndexOf which locates the first occurrence of an object in an array or portion of an array.
- LastIndexOf which locates the last occurrence of an object in an array or portion of an array.
- Reverse which reverses the contents of an array or portion of an array.

21.4 Dictionary Collections

A dictionary is the general term for a collection of key–value pairs. Section 17.9.2 introduced the generic Dictionary collection. In this section, we discuss fundamentals of how a Dictionary works, then demonstrate the related SortedDictionary collection.

21.4.1 Dictionary Fundamentals

When an app creates objects of new or existing types, it needs to manage those objects efficiently. This includes sorting and retrieving objects. Sorting and retrieving information with arrays is efficient if some aspect of your data directly matches the key value and if those keys are *unique* and *tightly packed*. If you have 100 employees with nine-digit social security numbers and you want to store and retrieve employee data by using the social security number as a key, it would nominally require an array with 1,000,000,000 elements, because there are 1,000,000,000 unique nine-digit numbers. If you have an array that large, you could get high performance storing and retrieving employee records by simply using the social security number as the array index, but it would be a huge waste of memory. Many apps have this problem—either the keys are of the wrong type (i.e., not non-negative integers), or they're of the right type but are sparsely spread over a large range.

Hashing

What's needed is a high-speed scheme for converting keys such as social security numbers and inventory part numbers to unique array indices. Then, when an app needs to store something, the scheme could convert the key rapidly to an index and the record of information could be stored at that location in the array. Retrieval occurs the same way—once the app has a key for which it wants to retrieve the data record, the app simply applies the conversion to the key, which produces the array index where the data resides in the array and retrieves the data.

The scheme we describe here is the basis of a technique called hashing. Why the name? Because, when we convert a key into an array index, we literally *scramble* the bits, making a "hash" of the number. The number actually has no real significance beyond its usefulness in storing and retrieving this particular data record. Data structures that use hashing are commonly called hash tables (like class `Hashtable` in the `System.Collections` namespace). A hash table is one way to implement a dictionary—class `Dictionary<K,V>` in the `System.Collections.Generic` namespace is implemented as a hash table.

Collisions

A glitch in the scheme occurs when there are collisions (i.e., two different keys "hash into" the same cell, or element, in the array). Since we cannot sort two different data records to the *same* space, we need to find an alternative home for all records beyond the first that hash to a particular array index. One scheme for doing this is to "hash again" (i.e., to reapply the hashing transformation to the key to provide a next candidate cell in the array). The hashing process is designed so that with just a few hashes, an available cell will be found.

Another scheme uses one hash to locate the first candidate cell. If the cell is occupied, successive cells are searched linearly until an available cell is found. Retrieval works the same way—the key is hashed once, the resulting cell is checked to determine whether it contains the desired data. If it does, the search is complete. If it does not, successive cells are searched linearly until the desired data is found.

The most popular solution to hash-table collisions is to have each cell of the table be a hash "bucket"—typically, a linked list of all the key–value pairs that hash to that cell. This is the solution that the .NET Framework's `Dictionary` class implements.

Load Factor

The load factor affects the performance of hashing schemes. The load factor is the ratio of the number of objects stored in the hash table to the total number of cells of the hash table. As this ratio gets *higher*, the chance of collisions tends to *increase*.

Performance Tip 21.1

The load factor in a hash table is a classic example of a space/time trade-off: By increasing the load factor, we get better memory utilization, but the app runs slower due to increased hashing collisions. By decreasing the load factor, we get better speed because of reduced hashing collisions, but we get poorer memory utilization because a larger portion of the hash table remains empty.

Hash Function

A hash function performs a calculation that determines where to place data in the hash table. The hash function is applied to the key in a key–value pair of objects. Any `object` can be used as a key. For this reason, class `object` defines method `GetHashCode`, which all objects inherit. Most classes that are candidates to be used as keys in a hash table, such as `string`, override this method to provide one that performs efficient hash-code calculations for a specific type.

21.4.2 Using the SortedDictionary Collection

The .NET Framework provides several implementations of dictionaries that implement the `IDictionary<K,V>` interface (described in Fig. 21.1). The app in Fig. 21.4 demonstrates the generic class `SortedDictionary`. Unlike class `Dictionary`—which is implemented as a hash table—class `SortedDictionary` stores its key–value pairs in a binary search tree (introduced in Section 19.7). As the class name suggests, the entries in `SortedDictionary` are sorted by key. For key types that implement `IComparable<T>`, the `SortedDictionary` uses the results of `IComparable<T>` method `CompareTo` to sort the keys. Despite these implementation details, we use the same `public` methods, properties and indexers with classes `Dictionary` and `SortedDictionary`. In many scenarios, these classes are interchangeable—this is the beauty of object-oriented programming.

Performance Tip 21.2

Because class `SortedDictionary` keeps its elements sorted in a binary tree, obtaining or inserting a key–value pair takes O(log n) time, which is fast compared to linear searching, then inserting.

```
1   // Fig. 21.4: SortedDictionaryTest.cs
2   // App counts the number of occurrences of each word in a string
3   // and stores them in a generic sorted dictionary.
4   using System;
5   using System.Text.RegularExpressions;
6   using System.Collections.Generic;
7
```

Fig. 21.4 | App counts the number of occurrences of each word in a `string` and stores them in a generic sorted dictionary. (Part 1 of 3.)

```
 8  class SortedDictionaryTest
 9  {
10     static void Main()
11     {
12        // create sorted dictionary based on user input
13        SortedDictionary<string, int> dictionary = CollectWords();
14
15        DisplayDictionary(dictionary); // display sorted dictionary content
16     }
17
18     // create sorted dictionary from user input
19     private static SortedDictionary<string, int> CollectWords()
20     {
21        // create a new sorted dictionary
22        var dictionary = new SortedDictionary<string, int>();
23
24        Console.WriteLine("Enter a string: "); // prompt for user input
25        string input = Console.ReadLine(); // get input
26
27        // split input text into tokens
28        string[] words = Regex.Split(input, @"\s+");
29
30        // processing input words
31        foreach (var word in words)
32        {
33           var key = word.ToLower(); // get word in lowercase
34
35           // if the dictionary contains the word
36           if (dictionary.ContainsKey(key))
37           {
38              ++dictionary[key];
39           }
40           else
41           {
42              // add new word with a count of 1 to the dictionary
43              dictionary.Add(key, 1);
44           }
45        }
46
47        return dictionary;
48     }
49
50     // display dictionary content
51     private static void DisplayDictionary<K, V>(
52        SortedDictionary<K, V> dictionary)
53     {
54        Console.WriteLine(
55           $"\nSorted dictionary contains:\n{"Key",-12}{"Value",-12}");
56
```

Fig. 21.4 | App counts the number of occurrences of each word in a string and stores them in a generic sorted dictionary. (Part 2 of 3.)

```
57              // generate output for each key in the sorted dictionary
58              // by iterating through the Keys property with a foreach statement
59              foreach (var key in dictionary.Keys)
60              {
61                  Console.WriteLine($"{key,-12}{dictionary[key],-12}");
62              }
63
64              Console.WriteLine($"\nsize: {dictionary.Count}");
65          }
66      }
```

```
Enter a string:
We few, we happy few, we band of brothers

Sorted dictionary contains:
Key          Value
band         1
brothers     1
few,         2
happy        1
of           1
we           3

size: 6
```

Fig. 21.4 | App counts the number of occurrences of each word in a `string` and stores them in a generic sorted dictionary. (Part 3 of 3.)

Lines 4–6 contain using directives for namespaces `System` (for class `Console`), `System.Text.RegularExpressions` (for class `Regex`) and `System.Collections.Generic` (for class `SortedDictionary`). The generic class `SortedDictionary` takes two type arguments:

- the first specifies the type of key (i.e., `string`) and
- the second the type of value (i.e., `int`).

Class `SortedDictionaryTest` declares three `static` methods:

- Method `CollectWords` (lines 19–48) inputs a sentence and returns a `SortedDictionary<string, int>` in which the keys are the words in the sentence and the values are the number of times each word appears in the sentence.

- Method `DisplayDictionary` (lines 51–65) displays the `SortedDictionary` passed to it in column format.

- Method `Main` (lines 10–16) simply invokes `CollectWords` (line 13), then passes the `SortedDictionary<string, int>` returned by `CollectWords` to `Display-Dictionary` in line 15.

Method `CollectWords`

Method `CollectWords` (lines 19–48) begins by initializing local variable `dictionary` with a new `SortedDictionary<string, int>` (line 22). Lines 24–25 prompt the user and input a sentence as a `string`. We use `static` method `Split` of class `Regex` (introduced in the online section of Chapter 16) in line 28 to divide the string by its whitespace characters. In the regular expression \s+, \s means *whitespace* and + means one or more of the expression to its left—so the words are separated by one or more whitespace characters, which are discarded. This creates an array of "words," which we then store in local variable words.

SortedDictionary *Methods* ContainsKey *and* Add

Lines 31–45 iterate through the array words. Each word is converted to lowercase with string method ToLower, then stored in variable key (line 33). Next, line 36 calls Sorted-Dictionary method **ContainsKey** to determine whether the word is in the dictionary. If so, that word occurred previously in the sentence. If the SortedDictionary does *not* contain an entry for the word, line 43 uses SortedDictionary method **Add** to create a new entry in the dictionary, with the lowercase word as the key and 1 as the value.

Common Programming Error 21.2
Using the Add *method to add a key that already exists in the hash table causes an* Argu-mentException.

SortedDictionary *Indexer*

If the word is already a key in the hash table, line 38 uses the SortedDictionary's indexer to obtain and set the key's associated value (the word count) in the dictionary. Using the set accessor with a key that does not exist in the hash table creates a new entry, as if you had used the Add method, so line 43 could have been written as

```
dictionary[key] = 1;
```

Common Programming Error 21.3
Invoking the get *accessor of a* SortedDictionary *indexer with a key that does not exist in the collection causes a* KeyNotFoundException.

Method DisplayDictionary

Line 47 returns the dictionary to the Main method, which then passes it to method DisplayDictionary (lines 51–65), which displays all the key–value pairs. This method uses read-only property **Keys** (line 59) to get an ICollection<T> that contains all the keys. Because the interface ICollection<T> extends IEnumerable<T>, we can use this collection in the foreach statement in lines 59–62 to iterate over the keys. This loop accesses and outputs each key and its corresponding value using the iteration variable and the SortedDictionary indexer's get accessor. Each key and value is displayed *left aligned* in a field width of 12 positions. Because a SortedDictionary stores its key–value pairs in a binary search tree, the key–value pairs are displayed with the keys in sorted order. Line 64 uses SortedDictionary property **Count** to get the number of key–value pairs in the dictionary.

Iterating Over a SortedDictionary's KeyValuePairs

Lines 59–62 could have also used the foreach statement with the SortedDictionary object itself, instead of using the Keys property. If you use a foreach statement with a SortedDictionary object, the iteration variable will be of type **KeyValuePair<K,V>**. The enumerator of a SortedDictionary uses the KeyValuePair<K,V> struct value type to store key–value pairs. KeyValuePair<K,V> provides properties Key and Value for retrieving the key and value of the current element.

SortedDictionary's Values Property

If you do not need the keys, class SortedDictionary also provides a read-only Values property that gets an ICollection<T> of all the values stored in the SortedDictionary. You could use this property to iterate through the values stored in the SortedDictionary without regard for their corresponding keys.

21.5 Generic LinkedList Collection

Section 9.4 introduced the generic List<T> collection, which defines an array-based list implementation. Here, we discuss class LinkedList<T>, which defines a doubly linked list that an app can navigate both forwards and backwards. A LinkedList<T> contains nodes of generic class LinkedListNode<T>. Each node contains property Value and read-only properties Previous and Next. The Value property's type matches LinkedList<T>'s single type parameter because it contains the data stored in the node. Previous gets a reference to the preceding node in the linked list (or null if the node is the first of the list). Similarly, Next gets a reference to the subsequent reference in the linked list (or null if the node is the last of the list). We demonstrate a few linked-list manipulations in Fig. 21.5.

```csharp
1   // Fig. 21.5: LinkedListTest.cs
2   // Using LinkedLists.
3   using System;
4   using System.Collections.Generic;
5
6   class LinkedListTest
7   {
8      private static readonly string[] colors =
9         {"black", "yellow", "green", "blue", "violet", "silver"};
10     private static readonly string[] colors2 =
11        {"gold", "white", "brown", "blue", "gray"};
12
13     // set up and manipulate LinkedList objects
14     static void Main()
15     {
16        var list1 = new LinkedList<string>();
17
18        // add elements to first linked list
19        foreach (var color in colors)
20        {
21           list1.AddLast(color);
22        }
23
24        // add elements to second linked list via constructor
25        var list2 = new LinkedList<string>(colors2);
26
27        Concatenate(list1, list2); // concatenate list2 onto list1
28        PrintList(list1); // display list1 elements
29
30        Console.WriteLine("\nConverting strings in list1 to uppercase\n");
31        ToUppercaseStrings(list1); // convert to uppercase string
```

Fig. 21.5 | Using LinkedLists. (Part 1 of 3.)

```csharp
32          PrintList(list1); // display list1 elements
33
34          Console.WriteLine("\nDeleting strings between BLACK and BROWN\n");
35          RemoveItemsBetween(list1, "BLACK", "BROWN");
36
37          PrintList(list1); // display list1 elements
38          PrintReversedList(list1); // display list in reverse order
39       }
40
41       // display list contents
42       private static void PrintList<T>(LinkedList<T> list)
43       {
44          Console.WriteLine("Linked list: ");
45
46          foreach (var value in list)
47          {
48             Console.Write($"{value} ");
49          }
50
51          Console.WriteLine();
52       }
53
54       // concatenate the second list on the end of the first list
55       private static void Concatenate<T>(
56          LinkedList<T> list1, LinkedList<T> list2)
57       {
58          // concatenate lists by copying element values
59          // in order from the second list to the first list
60          foreach (var value in list2)
61          {
62             list1.AddLast(value); // add new node
63          }
64       }
65
66       // locate string objects and convert to uppercase
67       private static void ToUppercaseStrings(LinkedList<string> list)
68       {
69          // iterate over the list by using the nodes
70          LinkedListNode<string> currentNode = list.First;
71
72          while (currentNode != null)
73          {
74             string color = currentNode.Value; // get value in node
75             currentNode.Value = color.ToUpper(); // convert to uppercase
76             currentNode = currentNode.Next; // get next node
77          }
78       }
79
80       // delete list items between two given items
81       private static void RemoveItemsBetween<T>(
82          LinkedList<T> list, T startItem, T endItem)
83       {
```

Fig. 21.5 | Using LinkedLists. (Part 2 of 3.)

```
84            // get the nodes corresponding to the start and end item
85            LinkedListNode<T> currentNode = list.Find(startItem);
86            LinkedListNode<T> endNode = list.Find(endItem);
87
88            // remove items after the start item
89            // until we find the last item or the end of the linked list
90            while ((currentNode.Next != null) && (currentNode.Next != endNode))
91            {
92                list.Remove(currentNode.Next); // remove next node
93            }
94        }
95
96        // display reversed list
97        private static void PrintReversedList<T>(LinkedList<T> list)
98        {
99            Console.WriteLine("Reversed List:");
100
101            // iterate over the list by using the nodes
102            LinkedListNode<T> currentNode = list.Last;
103
104            while (currentNode != null)
105            {
106                Console.Write($"{currentNode.Value} ");
107                currentNode = currentNode.Previous; // get previous node
108            }
109
110            Console.WriteLine();
111        }
112    }
```

```
Linked list:
black yellow green blue violet silver gold white brown blue gray

Converting strings in list1 to uppercase

Linked list:
BLACK YELLOW GREEN BLUE VIOLET SILVER GOLD WHITE BROWN BLUE GRAY

Deleting strings between BLACK and BROWN

Linked list:
BLACK BROWN BLUE GRAY
Reversed List:
GRAY BLUE BROWN BLACK
```

Fig. 21.5 | Using LinkedLists. (Part 3 of 3.)

Lines 16–25 create LinkedLists of strings named list1 and list2 and fill them with the contents of arrays colors and colors2, respectively. LinkedList is a *generic class* that has one type parameter for which we specify the type argument string in this example (lines 16 and 25).

LinkedList Methods AddLast and AddFirst
We demonstrate two ways to fill the lists. Lines 19–22 use the foreach statement and method AddLast to fill list1. The AddLast method creates a new LinkedListNode (with

the node's value available via the Value property) and appends this node to the end of the list. There's also an **AddFirst** method that inserts a node at the beginning of the list.

Line 25 invokes the constructor that takes an IEnumerable<T> parameter. All arrays implement the generic interfaces IList<T> and IEnumerable<T> with the array's element type as the type argument, so a string array implements IEnumerable<string>. Thus, colors2 is an IEnumerable<string> and can be passed to the List<string> constructor to initialize the List. This constructor copies array colors2's contents into list2.

Methods That Test Class *LinkedList*

Line 27 calls *generic method* Concatenate (lines 55–64) to append all elements of list2 to the end of list1. Line 28 calls method PrintList (lines 42–52) to output list1's contents. Line 31 calls method ToUppercaseStrings (lines 67–78) to convert each string element to uppercase, then line 32 calls PrintList again to display the modified strings. Line 35 calls method RemoveItemsBetween (lines 81–94) to remove the elements between "BLACK" and "BROWN"—not including either. Line 37 outputs the list again, then line 38 invokes method PrintReversedList (lines 97–111) to display the list in *reverse* order.

Generic Method *Concatentate*

Generic method Concatenate (lines 55–64) iterates over its second parameter (list2) with a foreach statement and calls method AddLast to append each value to the end of its first parameter (list1). The LinkedList class's enumerator loops over the values of the nodes, not the nodes themselves, so the iteration variable is inferred to be of the LinkedList's element type T. Notice that this creates a new node in list1 for each node in list2. One LinkedListNode cannot be a member of more than one LinkedList. If you want the same data to belong to more than one LinkedList, you must make a copy of the node for each list to avoid InvalidOperationExceptions.

Generic Method *PrintList* and Method *ToUppercaseStrings*

Generic method PrintList (lines 42–52) similarly uses a foreach statement to iterate over the values in a LinkedList, and outputs them. Method ToUppercaseStrings (lines 67–78) takes a linked list of strings and converts each string value to uppercase. This method replaces the strings stored in the list, so we cannot use a foreach statement as in the previous two methods. Instead, we obtain the first LinkedListNode via the First property (line 70) and use a sentinel-controlled while statement to loop through the list (lines 72–77). Each iteration of the while statement obtains and updates the contents of currentNode via property Value (line 74), using string method ToUpper to create an uppercase version of the string (line 75). Then line 76 moves to the next node in the list by assigning to currentNode the value of currentNode.Next, which refers to the LinkedList's next node. The Next property of the LinkedList's last node is null, so when the while statement iterates past the end of the list, the loop exits.

Method *ToUppercaseStrings* is not a Generic Method

It does not make sense to declare ToUppercaseStrings as a generic method, because it uses the string-specific methods of the values in the nodes.

Software Engineering Observation 21.1

For maximal code reuse, define methods with generic type parameters whenever possible.

Generic Method **RemoveItemsBetween**

Generic method RemoveItemsBetween (lines 81–94) removes a range of items between two nodes. Lines 85–86 obtain the two "boundary" nodes of the range by using method Find, which performs a linear search on the list and returns the first node that contains a value equal to Find's argument, or null if the value is not found. We store the node preceding the range in local variable currentNode and the node following the range in endNode.

Lines 90–93 remove all the elements between currentNode and endNode. Each iteration of the loop removes the node following currentNode by invoking method Remove (line 92), which takes a LinkedListNode, splices it out of the LinkedList, and fixes the references of the surrounding nodes. After the Remove call, currentNode's Next property now refers to the node *following* the node just removed, and that node's Previous property refers to currentNode. The while statement continues to loop until there are no nodes left between currentNode and endNode, or until currentNode is the last node in the list. An overloaded version of method Remove performs a linear search for a specified value and removes the first node in the list that contains it.

Method **PrintReversedList**

Method PrintReversedList (lines 97–111) displays the list backwards by navigating the nodes manually. Line 102 obtains the last element of the list via the Last property and stores it in currentNode. The while statement in lines 104–108 iterates through the list backwards by assigning to currentNode the value of currentNode.Previous (the previous node in the list). The loop terminates when currentNode.Previous is null. Note how similar this code is to lines 70–77, which iterated through the list from the beginning to the end.

21.6 C# 6 Null Conditional Operator ?[]

Section 13.9 introduced nullable types and C# 6's null-conditional operator (?.), which checks whether a reference is null before using it to call a method or access a property. C# 6 provides another null-conditional operator, ?[], for arrays and for collections that support the [] indexing operator.

Assume that a class Employee has a decimal Salary property and that an app defines a List<Employee> named employees. The statement

```
decimal? salary = employees?[0]?.Salary;
```

uses both null-conditional operators and executes as follows:

- First the ?[] operator determines whether employees is null. If so, the expression employees?[0]?.Salary short circuits—that is, it terminates immediately—and the expression evaluates to null. In the preceding statement, this is assigned to the nullable decimal variable salary. If employees is not null, employees?[0] accesses the element at position 0 of the List<Employee>.

- Element 0 could be null or a reference to an Employee object, so we use the ?. operator to check whether employees?[0] is null. If so, once again the entire expression evaluates to null, which is assigned to the nullable decimal variable salary; otherwise, the property Salary's value is assigned to salary.

Note in the preceding statement that salary *must* be declared as a nullable type, because the expression employees?[0]?.Salary can return null or a decimal value.

21.7 C# 6 Dictionary Initializers and Collection Initializers

6

C# 6 supports two new features with respect to initializing collections—index initializers and using collection initializers with collections that have an Add extension method.

C# 6 Index Initializers

Prior to C# 6, you could use a fully braced collection initializer to initialize a Dictionary's key–value pairs. For example, if you have a Dictionary<string, int> named toolInventory, you could create and initialize it as follows:

```
var toolInventory = new Dictionary<string, int>{
    {"Hammer", 13},
    {"Saw", 17},
    {"Screwdriver", 7}
};
```

This is shorthand for creating the Dictionary then using its Add method to add each key–value pairs.

C# 6 introduces the index initializers, which enable you to clearly indicate the key and the value in each key–value pair as follows:

6

```
var toolInventory = new Dictionary<string, int>{
    ["Hammer"] = 13,
    ["Saw"] = 17,
    ["Screwdriver"] = 7
};
```

C# 6 Collection Initializers Now Support Collections with **Add** Extension Methods

Prior to C# 6, any collection that defined an Add instance method could be initialized with a collection initializer. As of C# 6, the compiler also supports collection initializers for any collection that has an Add extension method.

6

21.8 Delegates

In Section 14.3.3, we introduced the concept of a *delegate*—an object that holds a reference to a method.[1] You can call a method through a variable of a delegate type—thus *delegating* to the referenced method the responsibilty of performing a task. Delegates also allow you to pass methods to and from other methods. We introduced delegates in the context of GUI event handlers, but they're used in many areas of the .NET Framework. For example, in Chapter 9, we introduced LINQ query syntax. The compiler converts such LINQ queries into calls to extension methods—many of which have delegate parameters. Figure 21.6 declares and uses a delegate type. In Section 21.11, we'll use delegates in the context of LINQ extension methods.

---

1. This is similar to function pointers and function objects (also called functors) in C++.

```
 1    // Fig. 21.6: Delegates.cs
 2    // Using delegates to pass functions as arguments.
 3    using System;
 4    using System.Collections.Generic;
 5
 6    class Delegates
 7    {
 8       // delegate for a function that receives an int and returns a bool
 9       public delegate bool NumberPredicate(int number);
10
11       static void Main()
12       {
13          int[] numbers = {1, 2, 3, 4, 5, 6, 7, 8, 9, 10};
14
15          // create an instance of the NumberPredicate delegate type
16          NumberPredicate evenPredicate = IsEven;
17
18          // call IsEven using a delegate variable
19          Console.WriteLine(
20             $"Call IsEven using a delegate variable: {evenPredicate(4)}");
21
22          // filter the even numbers using method IsEven
23          List<int> evenNumbers = FilterArray(numbers, evenPredicate);
24
25          // display the result
26          DisplayList("Use IsEven to filter even numbers: ", evenNumbers);
27
28          // filter the odd numbers using method IsOdd
29          List<int> oddNumbers = FilterArray(numbers, IsOdd);
30
31          // display the result
32          DisplayList("Use IsOdd to filter odd numbers: ", oddNumbers);
33
34          // filter numbers greater than 5 using method IsOver5
35          List<int> numbersOver5 = FilterArray(numbers, IsOver5);
36
37          // display the result
38          DisplayList("Use IsOver5 to filter numbers over 5: ", numbersOver5);
39       }
40
41       // select an array's elements that satisfy the predicate
42       private static List<int> FilterArray(int[] intArray,
43          NumberPredicate predicate)
44       {
45          // hold the selected elements
46          var result = new List<int>();
47
48          // iterate over each element in the array
49          foreach (var item in intArray)
50          {
51             // if the element satisfies the predicate
52             if (predicate(item)) // invokes method referenced by predicate
53             {
```

Fig. 21.6 | Using delegates to pass functions as arguments. (Part 1 of 2.)

```
54                    result.Add(item); // add the element to the result
55              }
56          }
57
58          return result; // return the result
59      }
60
61      // determine whether an int is even
62      private static bool IsEven(int number) => number % 2 == 0;
63
64      // determine whether an int is odd
65      private static bool IsOdd(int number) => number % 2 == 1;
66
67      // determine whether an int is greater than 5
68      private static bool IsOver5(int number) => number > 5;
69
70      // display the elements of a List
71      private static void DisplayList(string description, List<int> list)
72      {
73          Console.Write(description); // display the output's description
74
75          // iterate over each element in the List
76          foreach (var item in list)
77          {
78              Console.Write($"{item} "); // print item followed by a space
79          }
80
81          Console.WriteLine(); // add a new line
82      }
83  }
```

```
Call IsEven using a delegate variable: True
Use IsEven to filter even numbers: 2 4 6 8 10
Use IsOdd to filter odd numbers: 1 3 5 7 9
Use IsOver5 to filter numbers over 5: 6 7 8 9 10
```

Fig. 21.6 | Using delegates to pass functions as arguments. (Part 2 of 2.)

21.8.1 Declaring a Delegate Type

Line 9 defines a delegate type named NumberPredicate. A variable of this type can store a reference to any method that takes one int argument and returns a bool. A delegate type is declared by preceding a method header with keyword delegate (placed after any access specifiers, such as public or private) and following the method header with a semicolon. A delegate type declaration includes the method header only—the header describes a set of methods with specific parameters and a specific return type.

21.8.2 Declaring a Delegate Variable

Line 16 declares evenPredicate as a NumberPredicate variable and initializes it with a reference to the expression-bodied IsEven method (line 62). Since method IsEven's signature matches the NumberPredicate delegate's signature, IsEven can be referenced by a variable of type NumberPredicate. Variable evenPredicate can now be used as an alias for method IsEven. A NumberPredicate variable can hold a reference to any method that receives an int and returns a bool. Lines 19–20 use variable evenPredicate to call method IsEven, then display the result. The method referenced by the delegate is called using the delegate variable's name in place of the method's name, as in

```
    evenPredicate(4)
```

21.8.3 Delegate Parameters

The real power of delegates is in passing method references as arguments to methods, as we do in this example with method FilterArray (lines 42–59). The method takes as arguments

- an int array and
- a NumberPredicate that references a method used to filter the array elements.

The method returns a List<int> containing only the ints that satisfy the condition specified by the NumberPredicate. FilterArray returns a List, because we don't know in advance how many elements will be included in the result.

The foreach statement (lines 49–56) calls the method referenced by the NumberPredicate delegate (line 52) once for each element of the array. If the method call returns true, the element is included in result. The NumberPredicate is guaranteed to return either true or false, because any method referenced by a NumberPredicate must return a bool—as specified by the definition of the NumberPredicate delegate type (line 9). Line 23 passes to FilterArray the int array (numbers) and the NumberPredicate that references the IsEven method (evenPredicate). FilterArray then calls the NumberPredicate delegate on each array element. Line 23 assigns the List returned by FilterArray to variable evenNumbers and line 26 calls method DisplayList (lines 71–82) to display the results.

21.8.4 Passing a Method Name Directly to a Delegate Parameter

Line 29 calls method FilterArray to select the odd numbers in the array. In this case, we pass the method name IsOdd (defined in line 65) as FilterArray's second argument, rather than creating a NumberPredicate variable. Line 32 displays the results showing only the odd numbers. Line 35 calls method FilterArray to select the numbers greater than 5 in the array, using method IsOver5 (defined in line 68) as FilterArray's second argument. Line 38 displays the elements that are greater than 5.

21.9 Lambda Expressions

Lambda expressions allow you to define simple, anonymous methods—that is, methods that do not have names and that are defined where they are assigned to a delegate or passed to a delegate parameter. In many cases, working with lambda expressions can reduce the size of your code and the complexity of working with delegates. As you'll see in later examples, lambda expressions are particularly powerful when combined with the where clause in LINQ queries. Figure 21.7 reimplements the example of Fig. 21.6 using lambda expressions rather than explicitly declared methods IsEven, IsOdd and IsOver5.

```
1   // Fig. 21.7: Lambdas.cs
2   // Using lambda expressions.
3   using System;
4   using System.Collections.Generic;
5
6   class Lambdas
7   {
8      // delegate for a function that receives an int and returns a bool
9      public delegate bool NumberPredicate(int number);
10
11     static void Main(string[] args)
12     {
13        int[] numbers = {1, 2, 3, 4, 5, 6, 7, 8, 9, 10};
14
15        // create an instance of the NumberPredicate delegate type using an
16        // implicit lambda expression
17        NumberPredicate evenPredicate = number => number % 2 == 0;
18
19        // call a lambda expression through a variable
20        Console.WriteLine(
21           $"Use a lambda-expression variable: {evenPredicate(4)}");
22
23        // filter the even numbers using a lambda expression
24        List<int> evenNumbers = FilterArray(numbers, evenPredicate);
25
26        // display the result
27        DisplayList("Use a lambda expression to filter even numbers: ",
28           evenNumbers);
29
30        // filter the odd numbers using an explicitly typed lambda
31        // expression
32        List<int> oddNumbers =
33           FilterArray(numbers, (int number) => number % 2 == 1);
34
35        // display the result
36        DisplayList("Use a lambda expression to filter odd numbers: ",
37           oddNumbers);
38
39        // filter numbers greater than 5 using an implicit lambda statement
40        List<int> numbersOver5 =
41           FilterArray(numbers, number => {return number > 5;});
42
43        // display the result
44        DisplayList("Use a lambda expression to filter numbers over 5: ",
45           numbersOver5);
46     }
47
48     // select an array's elements that satisfy the predicate
49     private static List<int> FilterArray(
50        int[] intArray, NumberPredicate predicate)
51     {
52        // hold the selected elements
53        var result = new List<int>();
```

Fig. 21.7 | Using lambda expressions. (Part 1 of 2.)

```
54
55          // iterate over each element in the array
56          foreach (var item in intArray)
57          {
58              // if the element satisfies the predicate
59              if (predicate(item))
60              {
61                  result.Add(item); // add the element to the result
62              }
63          }
64
65          return result; // return the result
66      }
67
68      // display the elements of a List
69      private static void DisplayList(string description, List<int> list)
70      {
71          Console.Write(description); // display the output's description
72
73          // iterate over each element in the List
74          foreach (int item in list)
75          {
76              Console.Write($"{item} "); // print item followed by a space
77          }
78
79          Console.WriteLine(); // add a new line
80      }
81  }
```

```
Use a lambda expression variable: True
Use a lambda expression to filter even numbers: 2 4 6 8 10
Use a lambda expression to filter odd numbers: 1 3 5 7 9
Use a lambda expression to filter numbers over 5: 6 7 8 9 10
```

Fig. 21.7 | Using lambda expressions. (Part 2 of 2.)

21.9.1 Expression Lambdas

A lambda expression (line 17)

```
number => number % 2 == 0
```

begins with a parameter list (number in this case). The parameter list is followed by the =>
lambda operator (read as "goes to") and an expression that represents the lambda's body.
The lambda expression in line 17 uses the % operator to determine whether the parameter's
number value is an even int. The value produced by the expression—true if the int is
even, false otherwise—is implicitly returned by the lambda expression. The lambda in
line 17 is called an expression lambda, because it has a single expression to the right of the
lambda operator. Note that we do not specify a return type for the lambda expression—
the return type is inferred from the return value or, in some cases, from a delegate's return
type. The lambda expression in line 17 is equivalent to the IsEven method in Fig. 21.6.
Note that C# 6's expression-bodied methods use a similar syntax to expression lambdas,
including the lambda operator (=>).

21.9.2 Assigning Lambdas to Delegate Variables

In line 17 of Fig. 21.7, the lambda expression is assigned to a variable of type `NumberPredicate`—the delegate type declared in line 9. A delegate can hold a reference to a lambda expression. As with traditional methods, a method defined by a lambda expression must have a signature that's compatible with the delegate type. The `NumberPredicate` delegate can hold a reference to any method that receives an `int` and returns a `bool`. Based on this, the compiler is able to infer that the lambda expression in line 17 defines a method that implicitly takes an `int` as an argument and returns the `bool` result of the expression in its body.

Lines 20–21 display the result of calling the lambda expression defined in line 17. The lambda expression is called via the variable that references it (`evenPredicate`). Line 24 passes `evenPredicate` to method `FilterArray` (lines 49–66), which is identical to the method used in Fig. 21.6—it uses the `NumberPredicate` delegate to determine whether an array element should be included in the result. Lines 27–28 display the filtered results.

21.9.3 Explicitly Typed Lambda Parameters

Lambda expressions often are used as arguments to methods with delegate-type parameters, rather than defining and referencing a separate method or defining a delegate variable that references a lambda. Lines 32–33 select the odd array elements with the lambda

```
(int number) => number % 2 == 1
```

In this case, the lambda is passed directly to method `FilterArray` and is implicitly stored in the `NumberPredicate` delegate parameter.

The lambda expression's input parameter `number` is explicitly typed as an `int` here—sometimes this is necessary to avoid ambiguity that would lead to compilation errors (though that is not the case here). When specifying a lambda parameter's type and/or when a lambda has more than one parameter, you must enclose the parameter list in parentheses as in line 33. The lambda expression in line 33 is equivalent to the `IsOdd` method defined in Fig. 21.6. Lines 36–37 of Fig. 21.7 display the filtered results.

21.9.4 Statement Lambdas

Lines 40–41 use the lambda

```
number => {return number > 5;}
```

to find the `int`s greater than 5 in the array and store the results. This lambda is equivalent to the `IsOver5` method in Fig. 21.6.

The preceding lambda is called a statement lambda, because it contains a statement block—one or more statements enclosed in braces (`{}`)—to the right of the lambda operator. This lambda's signature is compatible with the `NumberPredicate` delegate, because the parameter `number`'s type is inferred to be `int` and the statement in the lambda returns a `bool`. For additional information on lambdas, visit

```
https://msdn.microsoft.com/library/bb397687
```

21.10 Introduction to Functional Programming

So far, you've learned structured, object-oriented and generic programming techniques. Though you often used .NET Framework classes and interfaces to perform various tasks, you typically determined *what* you wanted to accomplish in a task, then specified precisely *how* to accomplish it.

For example, let's assume that *what* you'd like to accomplish is to sum the elements of an int array named values (the *data source*). You might use the following code:

```
var sum = 0;

for (var counter = 0; counter < values.Length; ++counter)
{
    sum += values[counter];
}
```

This loop specifies precisely *how* to add each array element's value to the sum—with a for iteration statement that processes each element one at a time, adding its value to the sum. This technique is known as external iteration—because *you* specify how to iterate, not the library—and requires you to access the elements sequentially from beginning to end in a single thread of execution. To perform the preceding task, you also create two variables (sum and counter) that are *mutated* repeatedly—their values *change* as the iteration is performed. You performed many similar array and collection tasks, such as displaying the elements of an array, summarizing the faces of a die that was rolled 60,000,000 times, calculating the average of an array's elements and more.

External Iteration Is Error Prone
The problem with external iteration is that even in this simple loop, there are many opportunities for error. You could, for example,

- initialize variable sum incorrectly,

- initialize control variable counter incorrectly,

- use the wrong loop-continuation condition,

- increment control variable counter incorrectly or

- incorrectly add each value in the array to the sum.

Internal Iteration
In functional programming, you specify *what* you want to accomplish in a task, but *not how* to accomplish it. As you'll see, to sum a numeric data source's elements (such as those in an array or collection), you can use LINQ capabilities that allow you to say, "Here's a data source, give me the sum of its elements." You do *not* need to specify *how* to iterate through the elements or declare and use *any* mutable (that is, modifiable) variables. This is known as internal iteration, because the *library* code (behind the scenes) iterates through all the elements to perform the task.[2]

---

2. Systems developers have been familiar with the "*what* vs. *how*" distinction for decades. They begin a systems development effort by defining a *requirements document* that specifies *what* the system is supposed to do. Then, they use tools, such as the UML, to design the system, which specifies *how* the system should be built to meet the requirements. In the online chapters, we build the software for a very simple ATM. We begin with a requirements document that specifies *what* the software is supposed to do, then we use the UML to specify *how* the software should do it. We specify the final details of *how* by writing the actual C# code.

A key aspect of functional programming is immutability—not modifying the data source being processed or any other program state, such as counter-control variables in loops. By using internal iteration, you eliminate from your programs common errors that are caused by modifying data incorrectly. This makes it easier to write correct code.

Filter, Map and Reduce
Three common functional-programming operations that you'll perform on collections of data are *filter*, *map* and *reduce*:

- A filter operation results in a *new* collection containing only the elements that satisfy a condition. For example, you might filter a collection of ints to locate only the even integers, or you might filter a collection of Employee's to locate people in a specific department of a large company. Filter operations *do not modify* the original collection.

- A map operation results in a *new* collection in which each element of the original collection is mapped to a new value (possibly of a different type)—e.g., mapping numeric values to the squares of the numeric values. The new collection has the same number of elements as the collection that was mapped. Map operations *do not modify* the original collection.

- A reduce operation combines the elements of a collection into a single new value typically using a lambda that specifies how to combine the elements. For example, you might reduce a collection of int grades from zero to 100 on an exam to the number of students who passed with a grade greater than or equal to 60. Reduce operations *do not modify* the original collection.

In the next section, we'll demonstrate filter, map and reduce operations using class Enumerable's LINQ to Objects extension methods Where, Select and Aggregate, respectively. The extension methods defined by class Enumerable operate on collections that implement the interface IEnumerable<T>.

C# and Functional Programming
Though C# was not originally designed as a functional-programming language, C#'s LINQ query syntax and LINQ extension methods support functional-programming techniques, such as internal iteration and immutability. In addition, C# 6's getter-only, auto-implemented properties make it easier to define immutable types. We expect future versions of C# and most other popular programming languages to include more functional-programming capabilities that make implementing programs with a functional style more natural.

21.11 Functional Programming with LINQ Method-Call Syntax and Lambdas

In Chapter 9, we introduced LINQ, demonstrated LINQ query syntax and introduced some LINQ extension methods. The same tasks you can perform with LINQ query syntax can also be performed with various LINQ extension methods and lambdas. In fact, the compiler translates LINQ query syntax into calls to LINQ extension methods that receive lambdas as arguments. For example, lines 21–24 of Fig. 9.2

```
    var filtered =
        from value in values // data source is values
        where value > 4
        select value;
```

can be written as

```
    var filtered = values.Where(value => value > 4);
```

Figure 21.8 demonstrates simple functional programming techniques using a list of integers.

```
 1   // Fig. 21.8: FunctionalProgramming.cs
 2   // Functional programming with LINQ extension methods and lambdas.
 3   using System;
 4   using System.Collections.Generic;
 5   using System.Linq;
 6
 7   namespace FilterMapReduce
 8   {
 9       class FunctionalProgramming
10       {
11           static void Main()
12           {
13               var values = new List<int> {3, 10, 6, 1, 4, 8, 2, 5, 9, 7};
14
15               Console.Write("Original values: ");
16               values.Display(); // call Display extension method
17
18               // display the Min, Max, Sum and Average
19               Console.WriteLine($"\nMin: {values.Min()}");
20               Console.WriteLine($"Max: {values.Max()}");
21               Console.WriteLine($"Sum: {values.Sum()}");
22               Console.WriteLine($"Average: {values.Average()}");
23
24               // sum of values via Aggregate
25               Console.WriteLine("\nSum via Aggregate method: " +
26                   values.Aggregate(0, (x, y) => x + y));
27
28               // sum of squares of values via Aggregate
29               Console.WriteLine("Sum of squares via Aggregate method: " +
30                   values.Aggregate(0, (x, y) => x + y * y));
31
32               // product of values via Aggregate
33               Console.WriteLine("Product via Aggregate method: " +
34                   values.Aggregate(1, (x, y) => x * y));
35
36               // even values displayed in sorted order
37               Console.Write("\nEven values displayed in sorted order: ");
38               values.Where(value => value % 2 == 0) // find even integers
39                   .OrderBy(value => value) // sort remaining values
40                   .Display(); // show results
41
```

Fig. 21.8 | Functional programming with LINQ extension methods and lambdas. (Part 1 of 2.)

```
42              // odd values multiplied by 10 and displayed in sorted order
43              Console.Write(
44                  "Odd values multiplied by 10 displayed in sorted order: ");
45              values.Where(value => value % 2 != 0) // find odd integers
46                  .Select(value => value * 10) // multiply each by 10
47                  .OrderBy(value => value) // sort the values
48                  .Display(); // show results
49
50              // display original values again to prove they were not modified
51              Console.Write("\nOriginal values: ");
52              values.Display(); // call Display extension method
53          }
54      }
55
56      // declares an extension method
57      static class Extensions
58      {
59          // extension method that displays all elements separated by spaces
60          public static void Display<T>(this IEnumerable<T> data)
61          {
62              Console.WriteLine(string.Join(" ", data));
63          }
64      }
65  }
```

```
Original values: 3 10 6 1 4 8 2 5 9 7

Min: 1
Max: 10
Sum: 55
Average: 5.5

Sum via Aggregate method: 55
Sum of squares via Aggregate method: 385
Product via Aggregate method: 3628800

Even values displayed in sorted order: 2 4 6 8 10
Odd values multiplied by 10 displayed in sorted order: 10 30 50 70 90

Original values: 3 10 6 1 4 8 2 5 9 7
```

Fig. 21.8 | Functional programming with LINQ extension methods and lambdas. (Part 2 of 2.)

Extension Method Display

Throughout this example, we display the results of various operations by calling our own extension method named Display, which is defined in the static class Extensions (lines 57–64). The method uses string method Join to concatenate the IEnumerable<T> argument's elements separated by spaces.

Note at the beginning and end of Main that when we call Display directly on the values collection (lines 16 and 52) the same values are displayed in the same order. These outputs confirm that the functional-programming operations performed throughout Main (which we discuss in Sections 21.11.1–21.11.4) do not modify the contents of the original values collection.

21.11.1 LINQ Extension Methods Min, Max, Sum and Average

Class Enumerable (namespace System.Linq) defines various LINQ extension methods for performing common *reduction* operations including:

- Min (line 19) returns the smallest value in the collection.
- Max (line 20) returns the largest value in the collection.
- Sum (line 21) returns the sum of all the values in the collection.
- Average (line 22) returns the average of all the values in the collection.

Iteration and Mutation Are Hidden from You

Note in lines 19–22 that for each of these reduction operations:

- We simply say *what* we want to accomplish, not *how* to accomplish it—there are no iteration details in the app.
- *No mutable variables* are used in the app to perform these operations.
- The values collection is *not modified* (confirmed by the output of line 52).

In fact, the LINQ operations have no *side effects* that modify the original collection or any other variables in the app—a key aspect of functional programming.

Of course, behind the scenes iteration and mutable variables *are* required:

- All four extension methods iterate through the collection and must keep track of the current element they're processing.
- While iterating through the collection, Min and Max must store the current smallest and largest items, respectively, and Sum and Average must keep track of the total of the elements processed so far—all of these require mutating a local variable that's hidden from you.

The other operations in Sections 21.11.2–21.11.4 also require iteration and mutable variables, but the *library*—which has already been thoroughly debugged and tested—handles these details for you. To see how LINQ extension methods like Min, Max, Sum and Average implement these concepts, check out class Enumerable in the .NET source code at

```
https://github.com/dotnet/corefx/tree/master/src/System.Linq/src/
    System/Linq
```

Class Enumerable is divided into many partial classes—you can find methods Min, Max, Sum and Average in the files Min.cs, Max.cs, Sum.cs and Average.cs.

21.11.2 Aggregate Extension Method for Reduction Operations

You can define your own *reductions* with the Aggregate LINQ extension method. For example, the call to Aggregate in lines 25–26 sums the elements of values. The version of Aggregate used here receives two arguments:

- The first argument (0) is a value that helps you begin the reduction operation. When summing the elements of a collection, we begin with the value 0. Shortly, we'll use 1 to begin calculating the *product* of the elements.
- The second argument is a delegate of type Func (namespace System) that represents a method which receives two arguments of the same type and returns a value— there are many versions of type Func that specify from 0 to 16 arguments of any

type. In this case, we pass the following lambda expression, which returns the sum of its two arguments:

```
(x, y) => x + y
```

Once for each element in the collection, Aggregate calls this lambda expression.

- On the first call to the lambda, parameter x's value is Aggregate's first argument (0) and parameter y's value is the first int in values (3), producing the value 3 (0 + 3).

- Each subsequent call to the lambda uses the result of the previous call as the lambda's first argument and the next element of the collection as the second. On the second call to the lambda, parameter x's value is the result of the first calculation (3) and parameter y's value is the *second* int in values (10), producing the sum 13 (3 + 10).

- On the third call to the lambda, parameter x's value is the result of the previous calculation (13) and parameter y's value is the *third* int in values (6), producing the sum 19 (13 + 6).

This process continues producing a running total of the values until they've all been used, at which point the final sum is returned by Aggregate. Note again that *no mutable variables* are used to reduce the collection to the sum of its elements and that the original values collection is *not* modified.

Summing the Squares of the Values with Method Aggregate

Lines 29–30 use Aggregate to calculate the sums of the squares of values' elements. The lambda in this case,

```
(x, y) => x + y * y
```

adds the *square* of the current value to the running total. Evaluation of the reduction proceeds as follows:

- On the first call to the lambda, parameter x's value is Aggregate's first argument (0) and parameter y's value is the first int in values (3), producing the value 9 ($0 + 3^2$).

- On the next call to the lambda, parameter x's value is the result of the first calculation (9) and parameter y's value is the *second* int in values (10), producing the sum 109 ($9 + 10^2$).

- On the next call to the lambda, parameter x's value is the result of the previous calculation (109) and parameter y's value is the *third* int in values (6), producing the sum 145 ($109 + 6^2$).

This process continues producing a running total of the squares of the elements until they've all been used, at which point the final sum is returned by Aggregate. Note again that *no mutable variables* are used to reduce the collection to the sum of its squares and that the original values collection is *not* modified.

Calculating the Product of the Values with Method Aggregate

Lines 33–34 use Aggregate to calculate the product of values' elements. The lambda

```
(x, y) => x * y
```

multiplies its two arguments. Because we're producing a product, we begin with the value 1 in this case. Evaluation of the reduction proceeds as follows:

- On the first call to the lambda, parameter x's value is Aggregate's first argument (1) and parameter y's value is the *first* int in values (3), producing the value 3 (1 * 3).

- On the next call to the lambda, parameter x's value is the result of the first calculation (3) and parameter y's value is the *second* int in values (10), producing the sum 30 (3 * 10).

- On the next call to the lambda, parameter x's value is the result of the previous calculation (30) and parameter y's value is the *third* int in values (6), producing the sum 180 (30 * 6).

This process continues producing a running product of the elements until they've all been used, at which point the final product is returned. Note again that *no mutable variables* are used to reduce the collection to the product of its elements and that the original values collection is *not* modified.

21.11.3 The Where Extension Method for Filtering Operations

Lines 38–40 *filter* the even integers in values, *sort* them in ascending order and display the results. You *filter* elements to produce a *new* collection of results that match a condition known as a *predicate*. LINQ extension method Where (line 38) receives as its argument a Func delegate for a method that receives one argument and returns a bool indicating whether a given element should be included in the collection returned by Where.

The lambda in line 38:

```
value => value % 2 == 0
```

receives a value and returns a bool indicating whether the value satisfies the predicate—in this case, if the value it receives is divisible by 2.

Sorting the Results

The OrderBy extension method receives as its argument a Func delegate representing a method that receives one parameter and returns a value that's used to order the results. In this case (line 39), the lambda expression

```
value => value
```

simply returns its argument, which OrderBy uses to sort the values in ascending order—for descending order you'd use OrderByDescending. Note again that *no mutable variables* are used to filter or sort the collection and that the original values collection is *not* modified.

Deferred Execution

Calls to Where and OrderBy use the same *deferred execution* we discussed in Section 9.5.2—they aren't evaluated until you iterate over the results. In lines 38–40, this occurs when our Display extension method is called (line 40). This means you can save the operation into a variable for future execution, as in

```
var evenIntegers =
    values.Where(value => value % 2 == 0) // find even integers
        .OrderBy(value => value); // sort remaining values
```

You can execute the operation by iterating over evenIntegers later. Each time you execute the operation, the current elements in values will be filtered and sorted. So, if you modify values by adding more even integers to the collection, these will appear in the results when you iterate over evenIntegers.

21.11.4 Select Extension Method for Mapping Operations

Lines 45–48 *filter* the odd integers in values, *multiply* each odd integer by 10, *sort* the values in ascending order and display the results. The new feature here is the *mapping* operation that takes each value and multiplies it by 10. Mapping transforms a collection's elements to new values, which sometimes are of different types from the original elements.

LINQ extension method Select receives as its argument a Func delegate for a method that receives one argument and maps it to a new value (possibly of another type) that's included in the collection returned by Select. The lambda in line 46:

```
value => value * 10
```

multiplies its value argument by 10, thus mapping it to a new value. Line 47 sorts the results. Calls to Select are *deferred* until you iterate over the results—in this case, when our Display extension method is called (line 48). Note again that *no mutable variables* are used to map the collection's elements and that the original values collection is *not* modified.

21.12 PLINQ: Improving LINQ to Objects Performance with Multicore

Today's computers are likely to have multicore processors with four or eight cores. One vendor already offers a 61-core processor[3] and future processors are likely to have many more cores. Your computer's operating system shares the cores among operating system tasks and the apps running at a given time.

Threads

A concept called *threads* enables the operating system to run parts of an app concurrently—for example, while the *user-interface thread* (commonly called the *GUI thread*) waits for the user to interact with a GUI control, separate threads in the same app could be performing other tasks like complex calculations, downloading a video, playing music, sending an e-mail, etc. Though all of these tasks can make progress concurrently, they may do so by sharing one processor core.

Sharing Processors

With multicore processors, apps can operate truly in parallel (that is, simultaneously) on separate cores. In addition, the operating system can allow one app's threads to operate truly in parallel on separate cores, possibly increasing the app's performance substantially. Parallelizing apps and algorithms to take advantage of multiple cores is difficult and highly error prone, especially if those tasks share data that can be modified by one or more of the tasks.

PLINQ (Parallel LINQ)

In Section 21.10, we mentioned that a benefit of functional programming and internal iteration is that the library code (behind the scenes) iterates through all the elements of a

---

3.   The website http://processors.specout.com shows a range of processors with 1 to 61 cores.

collection to perform a task. Another benefit is that you can easily ask the library to perform a task with *parallel processing* to take advantage of a processor's multiple cores. This is the purpose of PLINQ (Parallel LINQ)—an implementation of the LINQ to Objects extension methods that parallelizes the operations for increased performance. PLINQ handles for you the error-prone aspects of breaking tasks into smaller pieces that can execute in *parallel* and coordinating the results of those pieces, making it easier for you to write high-performance apps that take advantage of multicore processors.

Demonstrating PLINQ

Figure 21.9 demonstrates the LINQ to Objects and PLINQ extension methods Min, Max and Average operating on a 10,000,000-element array of random int values (created in lines 13–15). As with LINQ to Objects, the PLINQ versions of these operations *do not modify* the original collection. We time the operations to show the substantial performance improvements of PLINQ (using multiple cores) over LINQ to Objects (using a single core). For the remainder of this discussion we refer to LINQ to Objects simply as LINQ.

```
1   // Fig. 21.9: ParallelizingWithPLINQ.cs
2   // Comparing performance of LINQ and PLINQ Min, Max and Average methods.
3   using System;
4   using System.Linq;
5
6   class ParallelizingWithPLINQ
7   {
8      static void Main()
9      {
10         var random = new Random();
11
12         // create array of random ints in the range 1-999
13         int[] values = Enumerable.Range(1, 10000000)
14                             .Select(x => random.Next(1, 1000))
15                             .ToArray();
16
17         // time the Min, Max and Average LINQ extension methods
18         Console.WriteLine(
19            "Min, Max and Average with LINQ to Objects using a single core");
20         var linqStart = DateTime.Now; // get time before method calls
21         var linqMin = values.Min();
22         var linqMax = values.Max();
23         var linqAverage = values.Average();
24         var linqEnd = DateTime.Now; // get time after method calls
25
26         // display results and total time in milliseconds
27         var linqTime = linqEnd.Subtract(linqStart).TotalMilliseconds;
28         DisplayResults(linqMin, linqMax, linqAverage, linqTime);
29
30         // time the Min, Max and Average PLINQ extension methods
31         Console.WriteLine(
32            "\nMin, Max and Average with PLINQ using multiple cores");
```

Fig. 21.9 | Comparing performance of LINQ and PLINQ Min, Max and Average methods. (Part 1 of 2.)

```
33          var plinqStart = DateTime.Now; // get time before method calls
34          var plinqMin = values.AsParallel().Min();
35          var plinqMax = values.AsParallel().Max();
36          var plinqAverage = values.AsParallel().Average();
37          var plinqEnd = DateTime.Now; // get time after method calls
38
39          // display results and total time in milliseconds
40          var plinqTime = plinqEnd.Subtract(plinqStart).TotalMilliseconds;
41          DisplayResults(plinqMin, plinqMax, plinqAverage, plinqTime);
42
43          // display time difference as a percentage
44          Console.WriteLine("\nPLINQ took " +
45             $"{((linqTime - plinqTime) / linqTime):P0}" +
46             " less time than LINQ");
47       }
48
49       // displays results and total time in milliseconds
50       static void DisplayResults(
51          int min, int max, double average, double time)
52       {
53          Console.WriteLine($"Min: {min}\nMax: {max}\n" +
54             $"Average: {average:F}\nTotal time in milliseconds: {time:F}");
55       }
56    }
```

```
Min, Max and Average with LINQ to Objects using a single core
Min: 1
Max: 999
Average: 499.96
Total time in milliseconds: 179.03

Min, Max and Average with PLINQ using multiple cores
Min: 1
Max: 999
Average: 499.96
Total time in milliseconds: 80.99

PLINQ took 55 % less time than LINQ
```

```
Min, Max and Average with LINQ to Objects using a single core
Min: 1
Max: 999
Average: 500.07
Total time in milliseconds: 152.13

Min, Max and Average with PLINQ using multiple cores
Min: 1
Max: 999
Average: 500.07
Total time in milliseconds: 89.05

PLINQ took 41 % less time than LINQ
```

Fig. 21.9 | Comparing performance of LINQ and PLINQ Min, Max and Average methods. (Part 2 of 2.)

Generating a Range of ints *with Enumerable Method* **Range**

Using functional techniques, lines 13–15 create an array of 10,000,000 random ints. Class Enumerable provides static method **Range** to produce an IEnumerable<int> containing integer values. The expression

```
Enumerable.Range(1, 10000000)
```

produces an IEnumerable<int> containing the values 1 through 10,000,000—the first argument specifies the starting value in the range and the second specifies the number of values to produce. Next, line 14 uses LINQ extension method Select to *map* every element to a random integer in the range 1–999. The lambda

```
x => random.Next(1, 1000)
```

ignores its parameter (x) and simply returns a random value that becomes part of the IEnumerable<int> returned by Select. Finally, line 15 calls extension method **ToArray**, which returns an array of ints containing the elements produced by the Select operation. Note that class Enumerable also provides extension method **ToList** to obtain a List<T> rather than an array.

Min, Max and Average with LINQ

To calculate the total time required for the LINQ Min, Max and Average extension-method calls, we use type DateTime's Now property to get the current time before (line 20) and after (line 24) the LINQ operations. Lines 21–23 perform Min, Max and Average on the array values. Line 27 uses DateTime method **Subtract** to compute the difference between the end and start times, which is returned as a **TimeSpan**. We then store the TimeSpan's **TotalMilliseconds** value for use in a later calculation showing PLINQ's percentage improvement over LINQ.

Min, Max and Average with PLINQ

Lines 33–41 perform the same tasks as lines 20–28, but use PLINQ Min, Max and Average extension-method calls to demonstrate the performance improvement over LINQ. To initiate parallel processing, lines 34–36 invoke IEnumerable<T> extension method **AsParallel** (from class **ParallelEnumerable**), which returns a **ParallelQuery<T>** (in this example, T is int). An object that implements ParallelQuery<T> can be used with PLINQ's parallelized versions of the LINQ extension methods. Class ParallelEnumerable defines the ParallelQuery<T> (PLINQ) parallelized versions as well as several PLINQ-specific extension methods. For more information on the extension methods defined in class ParallelEnumerable, visit

```
https://msdn.microsoft.com/library/system.linq.parallelenumerable
```

Performance Difference

Lines 44–46 calculate and display the percentage improvement in processing time of PLINQ over LINQ. As you can see from the sample outputs, the simple choice of PLINQ (via AsParallel) decreased the total processing time substantially—55% and 41% less time in the two sample outputs. We ran the app many more times (using up to three cores) and processing-time savings were generally within the 41–55% range—though we did have a 61% savings on one sample execution. The overall savings will be affected by your processor's number of cores and by what else is running on your computer.

21.13 (Optional) Covariance and Contravariance for Generic Types

C# supports *covariance* and *contravariance* of generic interface and delegate types. We'll consider these concepts in the context of arrays, which have always been covariant and contravariant in C#.

Covariance in Arrays

Recall our `Employee` class hierarchy from Section 12.5, which consisted of the base class `Employee` and the derived classes `SalariedEmployee`, `HourlyEmployee`, `CommissionEmployee` and `BasePlusCommissionEmployee`. Assuming the declarations

```
SalariedEmployee[] salariedEmployees = {
    new SalariedEmployee("Bob", "Blue", "111-11-1111", 800M),
    new SalariedEmployee("Rachel", "Red", "222-22-2222", 1234M) };
Employee[] employees;
```

we can write the following statement:

```
employees = salariedEmployees;
```

Even though the array type `SalariedEmployee[]` does *not* derive from the array type `Employee[]`, the preceding assignment *is* allowed because class `SalariedEmployee` is a derived class of `Employee`.

Similarly, suppose we have the following method, which displays the string representation of each `Employee` in its employees array parameter:

```
void PrintEmployees(Employee[] employees)
```

We can call this method with the array of `SalariedEmployees`, as in

```
PrintEmployees(salariedEmployees);
```

and the method will correctly display the string representation of each `SalariedEmployee` object in the argument array. Assigning an array of a derived-class type to an array variable of a base-class type is an example of covariance.

Covariance in Generic Types

Covariance works with several *generic interface and delegate types*, including `IEnumerable<T>`. Arrays and generic collections implement the `IEnumerable<T>` interface. Using the `salariedEmployees` array declared previously, consider the following statement:

```
IEnumerable<Employee> employees = salariedEmployees;
```

In earlier versions of C#, this generated a compilation error. Interface `IEnumerable<T>` is now covariant, so the preceding statement *is* allowed. If we modify method `PrintEmployees`, as in

```
void PrintEmployees(IEnumerable<Employee> employees)
```

we can call `PrintEmployees` with the array of `SalariedEmployee` objects, because that array implements the interface `IEnumerable<SalariedEmployee>` and because a `SalariedEmployee` *is an* `Employee` and because `IEnumerable<T>` is covariant. Covariance like this works *only* with *reference* types that are related by a class hierarchy.

Contravariance in Arrays

Previously, we showed that an array of a derived-class type (salariedEmployees) can be assigned to an array variable of a base-class type (employees). Now, consider the following statement, which has *always* compiled in C#:

```
SalariedEmployee[] salariedEmployees2 =
    (SalariedEmployee[]) employees;
```

Based on the previous statements, we know that the Employee array variable employees currently refers to an array of SalariedEmployees. Using a cast operator to assign employees—an array of base-class-type elements—to salariedEmployees2—an array of derived-class-type elements—is an example of contravariance. The preceding cast will fail at runtime if employees is *not* an array of SalariedEmployees.

Contravariance in Generic Types

To understand contravariance in generic types, consider a SortedSet of SalariedEmployees. Class SortedSet<T> maintains a set of objects in sorted order—no duplicates are allowed. The objects placed in a SortedSet must implement the IComparable<T> interface. For classes that do not implement this interface, you can still compare their objects using an object that implements the IComparer<T> interface. This interface's Compare method compares its two arguments and returns 0 if they're equal, a negative integer if the first object is less than the second, or a positive integer if the first object is greater than the second.

Our Employee hierarchy classes do not implement IComparable<T>. Let's assume we wish to sort Employees by social security number. We can implement the following class to compare any two Employees:

```
class EmployeeComparer : IComparer<Employee>
{
    int IComparer<Employee>.Compare(Employee a, Employee b)
    {
        return a.SocialSecurityNumber.CompareTo(
            b.SocialSecurityNumber);
    }
}
```

Method Compare returns the result of comparing the two Employees' social security numbers using string method CompareTo.

Now consider the following statement, which creates a SortedSet:

```
SortedSet<SalariedEmployee> set =
    new SortedSet<SalariedEmployee>(new EmployeeComparer());
```

When the type argument does *not* implement IComparable<T>, you must supply an appropriate IComparer<T> object to compare the objects that will be placed in the SortedSet. Since, we're creating a SortedSet of SalariedEmployees, the compiler expects the IComparer<T> object to implement the IComparer<SalariedEmployee>. Instead, we provided an object that implements IComparer<Employee>. The compiler allows us to provide an IComparer for a base-class type where an IComparer for a derived-class type is expected because interface IComparer<T> supports contravariance.

Web Resources

For a list of covariant and contravariant interface types, visit

```
https://msdn.microsoft.com/library/dd799517#VariantList
```

It's also possible to create your own types that support covariance and contravariance. For information, visit

```
https://msdn.microsoft.com/library/mt654058
```

21.14 Wrap-Up

This chapter introduced the prepackaged collection classes provided by the .NET Framework. We presented the hierarchy of interfaces that many of the collection classes implement, overviewed many of the implementation classes and introduced enumerators that enable programs to iterate through collections.

We discussed the .NET Framework namespaces dedicated to collections, including `System.Collections` for object-based collections and `System.Collections.Generic` for generic collections—such as the `List<T>`, `LinkedList<T>`, `Dictionary<K,V>` and `Sorted-Dictionary<K,V>` classes—that store objects of types you specify when you create the collection. We also mentioned the namespace `System.Collections.Concurrent` containing so-called thread-safe generic collections for use in multithreaded applications, and `System.Collections.Specialized` containing collections that are optimized for specific scenarios, such as manipulating collections of bits.

You saw how to use class `Array` to perform array manipulations. We continued our discussion of delegates that hold references to methods and introduced lambda expressions, which allow you to define anonymous methods that can be used with delegates. We focused on using lambdas to pass method references to methods that specify delegate parameters.

We provided a brief introduction to functional programming, showing how to use it to write code more concisely and with fewer bugs than programs written with previous techniques. In particular, we used LINQ extension methods and lambdas to implement functional operations that manipulated lists of values.

In Chapter 22, we begin our discussion of databases, which organize data in such a way that the data can be selected and updated quickly. We introduce the ADO.NET Entity Framework and LINQ to Entities, which allow you to write LINQ queries that are used to query databases.

Summary

Section 21.1 Introduction

- The prepackaged data-structure classes provided by the .NET Framework are known as collection classes—they store collections of data.
- With collection classes, instead of creating data structures to store these sets of items, you simply use existing data structures, without concern for how they're implemented.

Section 21.2 Collections Overview

- The .NET Framework collections provide high-performance, high-quality implementations of common data structures and enable effective software reuse.

- In earlier versions of C#, the .NET Framework primarily provided the collection classes in the System.Collections namespace to store and manipulate object references.

- The .NET Framework's System.Collections.Generic namespace contains collection classes that take advantage of .NET's generics capabilities.

Section 21.3 Class **Array** and Enumerators

- All arrays implicitly inherit from abstract base class Array (namespace System).

Section 21.3.1 C# 6 **using static** Directive

- C# 6's using static directive allows access to a class's static members without fully qualifying their names.

Section 21.3.3 **Array** Method **Sort**

- The static Array method Sort sorts an array.

Section 21.3.4 **Array** Method **Copy**

- The static Array method Copy copies elements from one array to another.

Section 21.3.5 **Array** Method **BinarySearch**

- The static Array method BinarySearch performs binary searches on an array. This method assumes that it receives a sorted array.

Section 21.3.6 **Array** Method **GetEnumerator** and Interface **IEnumerator**

- A collection's GetEnumerator method returns an enumerator that can iterate over the collection.

- All enumerators have methods MoveNext and Reset and property Current.

- MoveNext moves the enumerator to the next element in the collection. MoveNext returns true if there's at least one more element in the collection; otherwise, the method returns false.

- Read-only property Current returns the object at the current location in the collection.

Section 21.3.7 Iterating Over a Collection with **foreach**

- The foreach statement implicitly obtains an enumerator via the GetEnumerator method and uses the enumerator's MoveNext method and Current property to traverse the collection. This can be done with any collection that implements the IEnumerable interface—not just arrays.

Section 21.3.8 **Array** Methods **Clear, IndexOf, LastIndexOf** and **Reverse**

- The static Array method Clear sets a range of elements to 0, false or null, as appropriate.

- The static Array method IndexOf locates the first occurrence of an object in an array or portion of an array.

- The static Array method LastIndexOf locate the last occurrence of an object in an array or portion of an array.

- The static Array method Reverse reverses the contents of an array or portion of an array.

Section 21.4 **Dictionary** Collections

- A dictionary is a collection of key–value pairs. A hash table is one way to implement a dictionary.

Section 21.4.1 **Dictionary** Fundamentals

- Hashing is a high-speed scheme for converting keys to unique array indices.

Section 21.4.2 Using the **SortedDictionary** *Collection*

- Generic class SortedDictionary does not use a hash table, but instead stores its key–value pairs in a binary search tree.
- Generic class SortedDictionary takes two type arguments—the first specifies the type of key and the second the type of value.
- Method ContainsKey determines whether a key is in a dictionary.
- SortedDictionary method Add creates a new entry in the dictionary, with the first argument as the key and the second as the value.
- SortedDictionary's indexer can be used to get or set a key's corresponding value.
- SortedDictionary property Keys gets an ICollection<T> that contains all the keys.
- If you use a foreach statement with a SortedDictionary, the iteration variable is of type KeyValuePair, which has properties Key and Value for retrieving the current pair's key and value.
- Invoking the get accessor of a SortedDictionary indexer with a key that does not exist in the collection causes a KeyNotFoundException.

Section 21.5 Generic **LinkedList** *Collection*

- The LinkedList class is a doubly linked list—we can navigate the list both backwards and forwards with nodes of generic class LinkedListNode.
- Each node contains property Value and read-only properties Previous and Next.
- The LinkedList class's enumerator loops over the values of the nodes, not the nodes themselves.
- One LinkedListNode cannot be a member of more than one LinkedList. Any attempt to add a node from one LinkedList to another generates an InvalidOperationException.
- Method Find performs a linear search on the list and returns the first node that contains a value equal to the passed argument.
- Method Remove deletes a node from a LinkedList.

Section 21.6 C# 6 Null Conditional Operator ?[]

- C# 6 also provides a null-conditional operator, ?[], for arrays and for collections that support the [] indexing operator.
- The ?[] operator determines whether the array or collection reference is null before accessing an element.

Section 21.7 C# 6 **Dictionary** *Initializers and Collection Initializers*

- C# 6's index initializer syntax enables you to initialize a Dictionary's key–value pairs as in

```
var variableName = new Dictionary<TypeOfKey, TypeOfValue>{
    [key1] = value1,
    [key2] = value2,
    [key3] = value3
};
```

- As of C# 6, the compiler also supports collection initializers for any collection that has an Add extension method.

Section 21.8 Delegates

- A delegate is an object that holds a reference to a method.
- Via delegates, you can assign methods to variables, and pass methods to and from other methods. You also can call methods through variables of delegate types.

- The compiler converts LINQ queries into calls to extension methods—many of which have delegate parameters.

Section 21.8.1 Declaring a Delegate Type

- A delegate type is declared by preceding a method header with keyword `delegate` (placed after any access specifiers, such as `public` or `private`) and following the method header with a semicolon.
- A delegate type declaration includes the method header only—the header describes a set of methods with specific parameters and a specific return type.

Section 21.8.2 Declaring a Delegate Variable

- A delegate variable can hold a reference to any method with a matching signature.

Section 21.8.3 Delegate Parameters

- The real power of delegates is in passing method references as arguments to methods.

Section 21.8.4 Passing a Method Name Directly to a Delegate Parameter

- A method name can be passed directly to a delegate parameter, rather than first assigning it to a delegate variable.

Section 21.9 Lambda Expressions

- Lambda expressions allow you to define simple, anonymous methods—that is, methods that do not have names and that are defined where they are assigned to a delegate or passed to a delegate parameter.
- Working with lambda expressions can reduce the size of your code and the complexity of working with delegates.

Section 21.9.1 Expression Lambdas

- A lambda expression begins with a parameter list and is followed by the => lambda operator and an expression that represents the lambda's body.
- The value produced by the expression is implicitly returned by the lambda expression.
- An expression lambda has a single expression to the right of the lambda operator.
- A lambda's return type is inferred from the return value or, in some cases, from a delegate's return type.

Section 21.9.2 Assigning Lambdas to Delegate Variables

- A delegate can hold a reference to a lambda expression that has a signature that's compatible with the delegate type.
- A lambda expression is called via a variable that references it.

Section 21.9.3 Explicitly Typed Lambda Parameters

- Lambda expressions often are used as arguments to methods with delegate-type parameters, rather than defining and referencing a separate method or defining a delegate variable that references a lambda.
- You can explicitly type a lambda expression's parameters.
- When specifying a lambda parameter's type and/or when a lambda has more than one parameter, you must enclose the parameter list in parentheses.

Section 21.9.4 Statement Lambdas
- A statement lambda contains a statement block—one or more statements enclosed in braces ({})—to the right of the lambda operator.

Section 21.10 Introduction to Functional Programming
- With external iteration, you specify how to iterate, not the library. Also, you must access the elements sequentially from beginning to end in a single thread of execution.

- External iteration requires variables that are mutated repeatedly as the iteration is performed.

- External iteration is error prone.

- In functional programming, you specify what you want to accomplish in a task, but not how to accomplish it.

- You do not need to specify how to iterate through the elements or declare and use any mutable (that is, modifiable) variables. This is known as internal iteration, because the library code (behind the scenes) iterates through all the elements to perform the task.

- A key aspect of functional programming is immutability—not modifying the data source being processed or any other program state, such as counter-control variables in loops. This eliminates common errors that are caused by modifying data incorrectly.

- Three common functional-programming operations that you'll perform on collections of data are filter, map and reduce.

- A filter operation results in a new collection containing only the elements that satisfy a condition.

- A map operation results in a new collection in which each element of the original collection is mapped to a new value (possibly of a different type). The new collection has the same number of elements as the collection that was mapped.

- A reduce operation combines the elements of a collection into a single new value, typically using a lambda that specifies how to combine the elements.

- Though C# was not originally designed as a functional-programming language, C#'s LINQ query syntax and LINQ extension methods support functional-programming techniques, such as internal iteration and immutability.

Section 21.11 Functional Programming with LINQ Method-Call Syntax and Lambdas
- The same tasks you can perform with LINQ query syntax can also be performed with various LINQ extension methods and lambdas.

- The compiler translates LINQ query syntax into calls to LINQ extension methods that receive lambdas as arguments.

Section 21.11.1 LINQ Extension Methods Min, Max, Sum and Average
- Class Enumerable (namespace System.Linq) defines the LINQ to Objects extension methods.

- Min returns the smallest value in the collection.

- Max returns the largest value in the collection.

- Sum returns the sum of all the values in the collection.

- Average returns the average of all the values in the collection.

Section 21.11.2 Aggregate Extension Method for Reduction Operations
- You can define your own reductions with the Aggregate LINQ extension method.

- The version of Aggregate demonstrated in the chapter receives two arguments—a value that helps you begin the reduction operation and a Func delegate (namespace System) representing a method that receives two arguments and returns a value and specifies how to reduce the arguments. Once for each element in the collection, Aggregate calls this lambda expression.

- On the first call to the lambda, Aggregate's first argument and the first element of the collection are passed. Each subsequent call to the lambda uses the result of the previous call as the lambda's first argument and the next element of the collection as the second. This continues until all elements of the collection have been processed to reduce the collection to a single value.

Section 21.11.3 The **Where** Extension Method for Filtering Operations

- You filter elements to produce a collection of results that match a condition—known as a predicate.

- LINQ extension method Where receives as its argument a Func delegate for a method that receives one argument and returns a bool indicating whether a given element should be included in the collection returned by Where.

- The OrderBy extension method receives as its argument a Func delegate representing a method that receives one parameter (an element in the collection) and returns a value that's used to order the results.

- Calls to Where and OrderBy use deferred execution—they aren't evaluated until you iterate over the results.

Section 21.11.4 **Select** Extension Method for Mapping Operations

- Mapping transforms a collection's elements to new values, which sometimes are of different types from the original elements.

- LINQ extension method Select receives as its argument a Func delegate for a method that receives one argument (an element in the collection) and maps it to a new value (possibly of another type) that's included in the collection returned by Select.

Section 21.12 PLINQ: Improving LINQ to Objects Performance with Multicore

- A concept called threads enables the operating system to run parts of an app concurrently.

- Though all of these tasks can make progress concurrently, they may do so by sharing one processor core.

- With multicore processors, apps can operate truly in parallel on separate cores.

- The operating system can allow one app's threads to operate truly in parallel on separate cores, possibly increasing the app's performance substantially.

- Parallelizing apps and algorithms to take advantage of multiple cores is difficult and highly error prone, especially if those tasks share data that can be modified by one or more of the tasks.

- Another benefit of functional programming is that you can easily ask the library to perform a task with parallel processing to take advantage of a processor's multiple cores. This is the purpose of PLINQ (Parallel LINQ)—an implementation of the LINQ to Objects extension methods that parallelizes the operations for increased performance.

- Class Enumerable provides static method Range to produce an IEnumerable<int> containing integer values in sequence. The first argument specifies the starting value in the range and the second specifies the number of values to produce.

- Extension method ToArray returns an array representation of an IEnumerable<T>'s contents. Class Enumerable also provides method ToList to obtain a List<T> rather than an array.

- DateTime's Now property gets the current time.

- `DateTime` method `Subtract` compute the difference between two `DateTimes`, which is returned as a `TimeSpan`.

- `TimeSpan`'s `TotalMilliseconds` returns the number of milliseconds represented by the `TimeSpan`.

- To initiate parallel processing, invoke `IEnumerable<T>` extension method `AsParallel` (from class `ParallelEnumerable`), which returns a `ParallelQuery<T>`.

- An object that implements `ParallelQuery<T>` can be used with PLINQ's parallelized versions of the LINQ extension methods.

- Class `ParallelEnumerable` defines the `ParallelQuery<T>` (PLINQ) parallelized versions of LINQ to Objects extension methods as well as several PLINQ-specific extension methods.

Section 21.13 (Optional) Covariance and Contravariance for Generic Types

- C# supports covariance and contravariance of generic interface and delegate types.

- Assigning an array of a derived-class type to an array variable of a base-class type is an example of covariance.

- Covariance now works with several generic interface types, including `IEnumerable<T>`.

- Covariance in generic collections works *only* with reference types in the same class hierarchy.

- Using a cast operator to assign an array variable of a base-class type to an array variable of a derived-class type is an example of contravariance.

- Class `SortedSet` maintains a set of objects in sorted order—no duplicates are allowed.

- The objects placed in a `SortedSet` must be comparable to determine their sorting order. Objects are comparable if their classes implement the `IComparable<T>` interface.

- For classes that do not implement `IComparable<T>`, you can compare the objects using an object that implements the `IComparer<T>` interface. This interface's `Compare` method compares its two arguments and returns 0 if they are equal, a negative integer if the first object is less than the second, or a positive integer if the first object is greater than the second.

- Providing an `IComparer` for a base-class type where an `IComparer` for a derived-class type is expected is allowed because interface `IComparer<T>` supports contravariance.

Terminology

`?[]` null-conditional operator
`=>` lambda operator
Add method of class `SortedDictionary<K,V>`
AddFirst method of class `LinkedList<T>`
AddLast method of class `LinkedList<T>`
Aggregate `IEnumerable<T>` extension method
anonymous method
AsParallel `IEnumerable<T>` extension method
Average `IEnumerable<T>` extension method
Average `ParallelQuery<T>` extension method
BinarySearch method of class `Array`
Clear method of class `Array`
collection
collection class
collision in a hash table
ContainsKey method of class
    `SortedDictionary<K,V>`
contravariance

Copy method of class `Array`
Count property of class `SortedDictionary<K,V>`
covariance
CreateInstance method of class `Array`
Current property of interface `IEnumerator<T>`
dictionary
`Dictionary<K,V>` collection
Enumerable class
enumerator
expression lambda
Find method of class `LinkedList<T>`
external iteration
filter operation in functional programming
Func delegate
functional programming
GetEnumerator method of interface `IEnumerable<T>`
GetHashCode method of class object

hash function
hash table
hashing
IComparer<T> interface
IEnumerable<T> interface
IEnumerator<T> interface
immutability
index initializer
indexer of class SortedDictionary<K,V>
IndexOf method of class Array
internal iteration
Keys property of class SortedDictionary<K,V>
KeyValuePair<K,V> type
lambda
lambda expression
Last property of class LinkedList<T>
LastIndexOf method of class Array
LinkedList<T> collection
LinkedListNode<T> class
load factor in a hash table
map operation in functional programming
Max IEnumerable<T> extension method
Max ParallelQuery<T> extension method
Min IEnumerable<T> extension method
Min ParallelQuery<T> extension method
MoveNext method of interface IEnumerator<T>
Next property of a LinkedListNode<T>
Now property of type DateTime
OrderBy IEnumerable<T> extension method
ParallelEnumerable class
ParallelQuery<T> interface

PLINQ (Parallel LINQ)
Previous property of a LinkedListNode<T>
Queue<T> collection
Range method of class Enumerable
reduce operation in functional programming
Remove method of class LinkedList<T>
Reset method of interface IEnumerator<T>
Reverse method of class Array
Select IEnumerable<T> extension method
Sort method of class Array
SortedDictionary<K,V> collection
SortedList<K,V> collection
SortedSet<T> collection
Stack<T> collection
statement lambda
Subtract method of type DateTime
Sum IEnumerable<T> extension method
System.Collections namespace
System.Collections.Concurrent namespace
System.Collections.Generic namespace
System.Collections.Specialized namespace
TimeSpan type
ToArray method of class Enumerable
ToList method of class Enumerable
TotalMilliseconds property of type TimeSpan
using static directive
Value property of a LinkedListNode<T>
Values property of class
    SortedDictionary<K,V>
Where IEnumerable<T> extension method

Self-Review Exercises

21.1 Fill in the blanks in each of the following statements:

a) A(n) _____ is used to iterate through a collection but cannot remove elements from the collection during the iteration.

b) IEnumerator method _____ advances the enumerator to the next item.

c) If the collection it references has been altered since the enumerator's creation, calling method Reset will cause a(n) _____.

d) C# 6's _____ directive allows access to a class's static members without fully qualifying their names.

e) The _____ statement implicitly obtains an enumerator via the GetEnumerator method and uses the enumerator's MoveNext method and Current property to traverse the collection.

f) A(n) _____ is a collection of key–value pairs.

g) _____ allow you to define simple, anonymous methods—that is, methods that do not have names and that are defined where they are assigned to a delegate or passed to a delegate parameter.

h) With _____ you specify how to iterate, not the library.

i) With _____ the library determines how to iterate through a collection.

j) In functional programming, a(n) _____ operation results in a new collection containing only the elements that satisfy a condition.

k) In functional programming, a(n) _____ operation results in a new collection in which each element of the original collection is mapped to a new value (possibly of a different type). The new collection has the same number of elements as the collection that was mapped.

l) In functional programming, a(n) _____ operation combines the elements of a collection into a single new value, typically using a lambda that specifies how to combine the elements.

m) To initiate parallel processing with PLINQ, invoke IEnumerable<T> extension method _____ (from class ParallelEnumerable), which returns a(n) _____.

21.2 State whether each of the following is *true* or *false*. If *false*, explain why.

a) Functional programming's filter, map and reduce operations correspond to the IEnumerable<T> extension methods Where, Select and Aggregate.

b) A Hashtable stores key–value pairs.

c) A class implementing interface IEnumerator<T> must define only methods MoveNext and Reset, and no properties.

d) A SortedDictionary<K,V> can contain duplicate keys.

e) A LinkedList<T> can contain duplicate values.

f) Dictionary is an interface.

g) Enumerators can change the values of elements but cannot remove them.

h) With hashing, as the load factor increases, the chance of collisions decreases.

i) Elements in an array must be sorted in ascending order before a BinarySearch may be performed.

j) Class Array provides static method Sort for sorting array elements.

k) A hash table is one way to implement a dictionary.

l) The ?. operator determines whether an array or collection is null before accessing an element of the array or collection.

m) A lambda expression begins with a parameter list and is followed by the => lambda operator and an expression that represents the lambda's body.

n) An expression lambda contains a statement block—one or more statements enclosed in braces ({})—to the right of the lambda operator.

o) The parentheses surrounding a lambda's parameter list are optional.

p) A key aspect of functional programming is immutability—not modifying the data source being processed or any other program state, such as counter-control variables in loops. This eliminates common errors that are caused by modifying data incorrectly.

Answers to Self-Review Exercises

21.1 a) enumerator (or foreach statement). b) MoveNext. c) InvalidOperationException. d) using static. e) foreach. f) dictionary. g) Lambda expressions. h) external iteration. i) internal iteration. j) filter. k) map. l) reduce. m) AsParallel, ParallelQuery<T>.

21.2 a) True. b) True. c) False. The class must also implement property Current. d) False. A SortedDictionary cannot contain duplicate keys. e) True. f) False. Dictionary is a class; IDictionary is an interface. g) False. An enumerator cannot be used to change the values of elements. h) False. With hashing, as the load factor increases, there are fewer available slots relative to the total number of slots, so the chance of selecting an occupied slot (a collision) with a hashing operation increases. i) True. j) True. k) True. l) False. The ?[] determines whether an array or collection is null before accessing an element of the array or collection. m) True. n) False. A statement lambda contains a statement block—one or more statements enclosed in braces ({})—to the right of the lambda operator. o) False. When specifying a lambda parameter's type and/or when a lambda has more than one parameter, you must enclose the parameter list in parentheses. p) True.

Exercises

21.3 *(Collections Terminology)* Describe each of the following:
  a) `ICollection`
  b) `Array`
  c) `IList`
  d) load factor
  e) hash-table collision
  f) space/time trade-off in hashing
  g) dictionary

21.4 *(Enumerator Members)* Explain briefly the operation of each of the following enumerator-related methods:
  a) `GetEnumerator`
  b) `Current`
  c) `MoveNext`

21.5 *(`IDictionary<K,V>` Methods and Properties)* Explain briefly the operation of each of the following methods and properties of interface `IDictionary<K,V>`, which both `Dictionary` and `SortedDictionary` implement:
  a) `Add`
  b) `Keys`
  c) `Values`
  d) `ContainsKey`

21.6 *(`LinkedList` without Duplicates)* Write an app that reads in a series of first names and stores them in a `LinkedList`. Do not store duplicate names. Allow the user to search for a first name.

21.7 *(Summarizing Characters with `SortedDictionary`)* Modify the app in Fig. 21.4 to count the number of occurrences of each letter rather than of each word. For example, the string "HELLO THERE" contains two Hs, three Es, two Ls, one O, one T and one R. Display the results.

21.8 *(`SortedDictionary` of Colors)* Use a `SortedDictionary` to create a reusable class for choosing from some of the predefined colors in class `Color` (in the `System.Drawing` namespace). The names of the colors should be used as keys, and the predefined `Color` objects should be used as values. Place this class in a class library that can be referenced from any C# app. Use your new class in a Windows app that allows the user to select a color, then changes the background color of the `Form`.

21.9 *(Duplicate Words in a Sentence)* Write an app that determines and displays the number of duplicate words in a sentence. Treat uppercase and lowercase letters the same. Ignore punctuation.

21.10 *(Using a `List`)* Write an app that inserts 25 random integers from 0 to 100 in order into an object of class `List`. The app should calculate the sum of the elements and the floating-point average of the elements. Use loops to help perform the calculations.

21.11 *(Reversing a `LinkedList`)* Write an app that creates a `LinkedList` object of 10 characters, then creates a second list object containing a copy of the first list, but in reverse order. Do not call `LinkedList` method `Reverse`.

21.12 *(Prime Numbers and Prime Factorization)* Write an app that takes a whole-number input from a user and determines whether it's prime. If the number is not prime, display the unique prime factors of the number (use a `List<int>` to store the factors). Remember that a prime number's factors are only 1 and the prime number itself. Every number that's not prime has a unique prime factorization. For example, consider the number 54. The prime factors of 54 are 2, 3, 3 and 3. When the values are multiplied together, the result is 54. For the number 54, the prime factors output should be 2 and 3.

21.13 *(Bucket Sort with LinkedList<int>)* In Exercise 18.7, you performed a bucket sort of ints by using a two-dimensional array, where each row of the array represented a bucket. If you use a dynamically expanding data structure to represent each bucket, you do not have to write code that keeps track of the number of ints in each bucket. Rewrite your solution to use a one-dimensional array of LinkedList<int> buckets.

21.14 *(Sieve of Eratosthenes with BitArray)* Investigate class BitArray in namespace System.Collections.Specialized, then use it to reimplement Exercise 8.27's Sieve of Eratosthenes algorithm. Measure the performance of this version vs. the one in Exercise 8.27. Which is faster?

Functional-Programming Exercises

Sections 21.11–21.12 presented several functional programming examples with LINQ and PLINQ—showing simpler ways to implement tasks that you programmed in earlier chapters. The following exercises ask you to reimplement some other of the book's earlier examples with LINQ extension methods, lambdas and functional-programming techniques.

21.15 *(Generating the Values in an Array)* Figure 8.4 filled an array with the even integers from 2 to 10. Use the technique shown in lines 13–15 of Fig. 21.9 to create an array containing the even integers from 2 to 10.

21.16 *(Generating the Values in an Array)* Modify Exercise 21.15 to fill an array of 20,000,000 elements. Perform the task using both LINQ and PLINQ and display the percentage difference in processing time as we did in Fig. 21.9.

21.17 *(Processing Employees)* Use LINQ to map the List<Employee> in Fig. 12.9 to a List of anonymous objects in which each object contains an Employee's name and earning. When a BasePlusCommissionEmployee is encountered, give a 10% base-salary increase without modifying the original BasePlusCommissionEmployee object. Display the names and earnings.

21.18 *(Credit-Inquiry Program)* The class File provides static method ReadLines, which returns an IEnumerable<string> representing the lines of text in a file. Reimplement the credit-inquiry program of Fig. 17.7 to use functional-programming techniques to separately filter the accounts that have credit, debit or zero balances.

21.19 *(Advanced: Rolling a Die 60,000,000 Times)* Figure 8.8 rolled a die 60,000,000 times and used an array to summarize the frequencies of each face. Use the technique shown in lines 13–15 of Fig. 21.9 to generate 60,000,000 random numbers from 1–6 representing the faces on a six-sided die. Rather than converting the IEnumerable<T> to an array, use the GroupBy extension method to summarize the results.

GroupBy's argument is a Func delegate that receives one argument and returns a value, which GroupBy uses to create a collection of all elements with that value. For this exercise, you'll group the elements by their random values, so use the lambda

```
value => value
```

GroupBy returns an IEnumerable containing IGrouping objects for each group. Each IGrouping is an IEnumerable (so you can iterate through all the elements in that group) and also has a Key property representing the unique value that was used to group the elements in that IGrouping. For the random die values, there will be a total of six IGrouping objects for the values 1–6.

Use the OrderBy extension method to order the IGroupings by Key. Then iterate over the results and display them in tabular format as in Fig. 8.8. To determine the number of occurrences of each face, simply call the Count extension method for the current IGrouping.

21.20 *(Advanced: Rolling a Die 60,000,000 Times)* Modify Exercise 21.19 to map each IGrouping to a new object that contains Face and Frequency properties where the Face is the IGrouping's Key and the Frequency is the Count of elements in the IGrouping.

21.21 *(Advanced: Summarizing Survey Results)* Use the techniques of Exercise 21.19 to reimplement the student-poll analysis app of Fig. 8.9.

Databases and LINQ

22

22.1 Introduction

A **database** is an organized collection of data. A **database management system** (DBMS) provides mechanisms for storing, organizing, retrieving and modifying data. Many of today's most popular DBMSs manage *relational databases*, which organize data simply as tables with *rows* and *columns*.

Some popular proprietary DBMSs are Microsoft SQL Server, Oracle, Sybase and IBM DB2. PostgreSQL, MariaDB and MySQL are popular *open-source* DBMSs that can be downloaded and used *freely* by anyone. In this chapter, we use a version of Microsoft's SQL Server that's installed with Visual Studio. It also can be downloaded separately from

```
https://www.microsoft.com/en-us/server-cloud/products/sql-server-
    editions/sql-server-express.aspx
```

SQL Server Express
SQL Server Express provides many features of Microsoft's full (fee-based) SQL Server product, but has some limitations, such as a maximum database size of 10GB. A SQL Server Express database file can be easily migrated to a full version of SQL Server. You can learn more about the SQL Server versions at

```
https://www.microsoft.com/en-us/server-cloud/products/sql-server-
    editions/overview.aspx
```

The version of SQL Server bundled with Visual Studio Community is called SQL Server Express LocalDB. It's meant for development and testing of apps on your computer.

Structured Query Language (SQL)
A language called Structured Query Language (SQL)—pronounced "sequel"—is an international standard used with relational databases to perform queries (that is, to request information that satisfies given criteria) and to manipulate data. For years, programs that

accessed a relational database passed SQL queries as `strings` to the database management system, then processed the results.

LINQ to Entities and the ADO.NET Entity Framework

A logical extension of querying and manipulating data in databases is to perform similar operations on *any* sources of data, such as arrays, collections (like the `Items` collection of a `ListBox`) and files. Chapter 9 introduced *LINQ to Objects* and used it to manipulate data stored in arrays. LINQ to Entities allows you to manipulate data stored in a relational database—in our case, a SQL Server Express database. As with LINQ to Objects, the IDE provides *IntelliSense* for your LINQ to Entities queries.

The ADO.NET Entity Framework (EF) enables apps to interact with data in various forms, including data stored in relational databases. You'll use the ADO.NET Entity Framework and Visual Studio to create a so-called *entity data model* that represents the database, then use LINQ to Entities to manipulate objects in the entity data model. Though you'll manipulate data in a *SQL Server Express* database in this chapter, the ADO.NET Entity Framework works with *most* popular database management systems. Behind the scenes, the ADO.NET Entity Framework generates SQL statements that interact with a database.

This chapter introduces general concepts of relational databases, then implements several database apps using the ADO.NET Entity Framework, LINQ to Entities and the IDE's tools for working with databases. In later chapters, you'll see other practical database and LINQ to Entities apps, such as a web-based guestbook and a web-based bookstore. Databases are at the heart of most "industrial strength" apps.

22.2 Relational Databases

A relational database organizes data in tables. Figure 22.1 illustrates a sample `Employees` table that might be used in a personnel system. The table stores the attributes of employees. Tables are composed of rows (also called records) and columns (also called fields) in which values are stored. This table consists of six rows (one per employee) and five columns (one per attribute). The attributes are the employee's

- ID,
- name,
- department,
- salary and
- location.

The `ID` column of each row is the table's primary key—a column (or group of columns) requiring a *unique* value that cannot be duplicated in other rows. This guarantees that each primary-key value can be used to identify *one* row. A primary key composed of two or more columns is known as a composite key—in this case, every combination of column values in the composite key must be unique. Good examples of primary-key columns in other apps are a book's ISBN number in a book information system or a part number in an inventory system—values in each of these columns must be unique. We show an example of a composite primary key in Section 22.3. LINQ to Entities *requires every table to have a primary key* to support updating the data in tables. The rows in

	Number	Name	Department	Salary	Location
	23603	Jones	413	1100	New Jersey
	24568	Kerwin	413	2000	New Jersey
Row	34589	Larson	642	1800	Los Angeles
	35761	Myers	611	1400	Orlando
	47132	Neumann	413	9000	New Jersey
	78321	Stephens	611	8500	Orlando
	Primary key		Column		

Fig. 22.1 | Employees table sample data.

Fig. 22.1 are displayed in *ascending order* by primary key. But they could be listed in *descending order* or in no particular order at all.

Each *column* represents a different data *attribute*. Some column values may be duplicated between rows. For example, three different rows in the Employees table's Department column contain the number 413, indicating that these employees work in the same department.

Selecting Data Subsets

You can use LINQ to Entities to define queries that *select subsets* of the data from a table. For example, a program might select data from the Employees table to create a query result that shows where each department is located, in ascending order by Department number (Fig. 22.2).

Department	Location
413	New Jersey
611	Orlando
642	Los Angeles

Fig. 22.2 | Distinct Department and Location data from the Employees table.

22.3 A Books Database

We now consider a simple Books database that stores information about some Deitel books. First, we overview the database's tables. A database's tables, their fields and the relationships among them are collectively known as a database schema. The ADO.NET Entity Framework uses a database's schema to define classes that enable you to interact with the database. Sections 22.5–22.8 show how to manipulate the Books database. The database file—Books.mdf—is provided with this chapter's examples. SQL Server database files have the .mdf ("master data file") filename extension.

Authors Table

The database consists of three tables: Authors, Titles and AuthorISBN. The Authors table (described in Fig. 22.3) consists of three columns that maintain each author's unique

ID number, first name and last name, respectively. Figure 22.4 contains the sample data from the Authors table.

Column	Description
AuthorID	Author's ID number in the database. In the Books database, this integer column is defined as an identity column, also known as an autoincremented column—for each row inserted in the table, the AuthorID value is increased by 1 automatically to ensure that each row has a unique AuthorID. This is the *primary key*.
FirstName	Author's first name (a string).
LastName	Author's last name (a string).

Fig. 22.3 | Authors table of the Books database.

AuthorID	FirstName	LastName
1	Paul	Deitel
2	Harvey	Deitel
3	Abbey	Deitel
4	Sue	Green
4	John	Purple

Fig. 22.4 | Data from the Authors table.

Titles *Table*

The Titles table (described in Fig. 22.5) consists of four columns that maintain information about each book in the database, including its ISBN, title, edition number and copyright year. Figure 22.6 contains the data from the Titles table.

Column	Description
ISBN	ISBN of the book (a string). The table's primary key. ISBN is an abbreviation for "International Standard Book Number"—a numbering scheme that publishers worldwide use to give every book a *unique* identification number.
Title	Title of the book (a string).
EditionNumber	Edition number of the book (an integer).
Copyright	Copyright year of the book (a string).

Fig. 22.5 | Titles table of the Books database.

ISBN	Title	EditionNumber	Copyright
0132151006	Internet & World Wide Web How to Program	5	2012
0133807800	Java How to Program	10	2015
0132575655	Java How to Program, Late Objects Version	10	2015
0133976890	C How to Program	8	2016
0133406954	Visual Basic 2012 How to Program	6	2014
0134601548	Visual C# How to Program	6	2017
0134448235	C++ How to Program	10	2016
0134444302	Android How to Program	3	2016
0134289366	Android 6 for Programmers: An App-Driven Approach	3	2016
0133965260	iOS 8 for Programmers: An App-Driven Approach with Swift	3	2015
0134021363	Swift for Programmers	1	2015

Fig. 22.6 | Data from the Titles table of the Books database.

AuthorISBN *Table of the* Books *Database*

The AuthorISBN table (described in Fig. 22.7) consists of two columns that maintain ISBNs for each book and their corresponding authors' ID numbers. This table associates authors with their books. The AuthorID column is a foreign key—a column in this table that matches the primary-key column in another table (that is, AuthorID in the Authors table). The ISBN column is also a *foreign key*—it matches the primary-key column (that is, ISBN) in the Titles table. A database might consist of many tables. A goal of a database's designer is to minimize the amount of duplicated data among the database's tables. Foreign keys, which are specified when a database table is created in the database, link the data in multiple tables. Together the AuthorID and ISBN columns in this table form a *composite primary key*. Every row in this table *uniquely* matches *one* author to *one* book's ISBN. Figure 22.8 contains the data from the AuthorISBN table of the Books database.

Column	Description
AuthorID	The author's ID number, a foreign key to the Authors table.
ISBN	The ISBN for a book, a foreign key to the Titles table.

Fig. 22.7 | AuthorISBN table of the Books database.

AuthorID	ISBN	AuthorID	ISBN
1	0132151006	1	0132575655
1	0133807800	1	0133976890

Fig. 22.8 | Data from the AuthorISBN table of the Books database. (Part 1 of 2.)

AuthorID	ISBN	AuthorID	ISBN
1	0133406954	2	0133406954
1	0134601548	2	0134601548
1	0134448235	2	0134448235
1	0134444302	2	0134444302
1	0134289366	2	0134289366
1	0133965260	2	0133965260
1	0134021363	2	0134021363
2	0132151006	3	0132151006
2	0133807800	3	0133406954
2	0132575655	4	0134289366
2	0133976890	5	0134289366

Fig. 22.8 | Data from the AuthorISBN table of the Books database. (Part 2 of 2.)

Every foreign-key value must appear as another table's primary-key value so the DBMS can ensure that the foreign key value is valid. For example, the DBMS ensures that the AuthorID value for any particular row of the AuthorISBN table (Fig. 22.8) is valid by checking that there is a row in the Authors table with that AuthorID as the primary key.

Foreign keys also allow related data in multiple tables to be selected from those tables—this is known as joining the data. There's a one-to-many relationship between a primary key and a corresponding foreign key—e.g., an author can write many books and a book can be written by many authors. So a foreign key can appear many times in its own table but only *once* (as the primary key) in another table. For example, the ISBN 0132151006 can appear in several rows of AuthorISBN but only once in Titles, where ISBN is the primary key.

*Entity-Relationship Diagram for the **Books** Database*
Figure 22.9 is an entity-relationship (ER) diagram for the Books database. This diagram shows the tables in the database and the relationships among them.

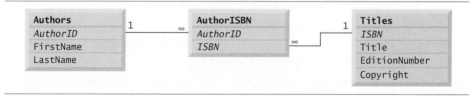

Fig. 22.9 | Entity-relationship diagram for the Books database.

Primary Keys
The first compartment in each box contains the table's name. The names in italic font are *primary keys*—*AuthorID* in the Authors table, AuthorID and ISBN in the AuthorISBN table, and ISBN in the Titles table. Every row *must* have a value in the primary-key column (or group of columns), and the value of the key must be *unique* in the table; otherwise, the DBMS will report an error. The names AuthorID and ISBN in the AuthorISBN table are both italic—together these form a *composite primary key* for the AuthorISBN table.

Relationships Between Tables
The lines connecting the tables in Fig. 22.9 represent the *relationships* among the tables. Consider the line between the Authors and AuthorISBN tables. On the Authors end of the line, there's a 1, and on the AuthorISBN end, an infinity symbol (∞). This indicates a *one-to-many relationship*—for each author in the Authors table, there can be an arbitrary number of ISBNs for books written by that author in the AuthorISBN table (that is, an author can write any number of books). Note that the relationship line links the AuthorID column in the Authors table (where AuthorID is the primary key) to the AuthorID column in the AuthorISBN table (where AuthorID is a foreign key)—the line between the tables links the primary key to the matching foreign key.

The line between the Titles and AuthorISBN tables illustrates a *one-to-many relationship*—one book can be written by many authors. Note that the line between the tables links the *primary key* ISBN in the Titles table to the corresponding *foreign key* in the AuthorISBN table. Figure 22.9 illustrates that the sole purpose of the AuthorISBN table is to provide a many-to-many relationship between the Authors and Titles tables—an author can write many books, and a book can have many authors.

22.4 LINQ to Entities and the ADO.NET Entity Framework

When using the ADO.NET Entity Framework, you interact with the database via classes that the IDE generates from the database schema. You'll initiate this process by adding a new ADO.NET Entity Data Model to your project (as you'll see in Section 22.5.1).

Classes Generated in the Entity Data Model
For the Authors and Titles tables in the Books database, the IDE creates two classes each in the data model:

- The first class represents a row of the table and contains properties for each column in the table. Objects of this class—called row objects—store the data from individual rows of the table. The IDE uses the singular version of a table's plural name as the row class's name. For the Books database's Authors table, the row class's name is Author, and for the Titles table, it's Title.

- The second class represents the table itself. An object of this class stores a collection of row objects that correspond to all of the rows in the table. The table classes for the Books database are named Authors and Titles.

Once generated, the entity data model classes have full *IntelliSense* support in the IDE. Section 22.7 demonstrates queries that use the relationships among the Books database's tables to join data.

Relationships Between Tables in the Entity Data Model
You'll notice that we did not mention the Books database's AuthorISBN table. Recall that this table links

- each author in the Authors table to that author's books in the Titles table, and
- each book in the Titles table to the book's authors in the Authors table.

The entity data model's generated classes include the relationships between tables. For example, the Author row class contains a navigation property named Titles which provides access to the Title objects representing all the books written by that author. The IDE automatically adds the "s" to "Title" to indicate that this property represents a collection of Title objects. Similarly, the Title row class contains a navigation property named Authors, which provides access to the Author objects representing a given book's authors.

DbContext Class

A DbContext (namespace System.Data.Entity) manages the data flow between the program and the database. When the IDE generates the *entity data model's* row and table classes, it also creates a derived class of DbContext that's specific to the database being manipulated. For the Books database, this derived class has properties for the Authors and Titles tables. As you'll see, these can be used as data sources for manipulating data in LINQ queries and in GUIs. Any changes made to the data managed by the DbContext can be saved back to the database using the DbContext's SaveChanges method.

IQueryable<T> Interface

LINQ to Entities works through interface IQueryable<T>, which inherits from interface IEnumerable<T> introduced in Chapter 9. When a LINQ to Entities query on an IQueryable<T> object executes against the database, the results are loaded into objects of the corresponding entity data model classes for convenient access in your code.

Using Extension Methods to Manipulate IQueryable<T> Objects

Recall that extension methods add functionality to an existing class without modifying the class's source code. In Chapter 9, we introduced several LINQ extension methods, including First, Any, Count, Distinct, ToArray and ToList. These methods, which are defined as static methods of class Enumerable (namespace System.Linq), can be applied to any object that implements the IEnumerable<T> interface, such as arrays, collections and the results of LINQ to Objects queries.

In this chapter, we use a combination of the LINQ query syntax and LINQ extension methods to manipulate database contents. The extension methods we use are defined as static methods of class Queryable (namespace System.Linq) and can be applied to any object that implements the IQueryable<T> interface—these include various entity data model objects and the results of LINQ to Entities queries.

22.5 Querying a Database with LINQ

In this section, we demonstrate how to

- *connect* to a database,
- *query* it and
- *display* the results of the query.

There is little code in this section—the IDE provides *visual programming* tools and *wizards* that simplify accessing data in apps. These tools establish database connections and create the objects necessary to view and manipulate the data through Windows Forms GUI controls—a technique known as data binding.

For the examples in Sections 22.5–22.8, we'll create one solution that contains *several* projects. One will be a reusable class library containing the ADO.NET Entity Data Model for interacting with the Books database. The other projects will be Windows Forms apps that use the ADO.NET Entity Data Model in the class library to manipulate the database.

Our first example performs a simple query on the Books database from Section 22.3. We retrieve the entire Authors table, ordered by the authors' last name, then first name. We then use data binding to display the data in a **DataGridView**—a control from namespace System.Windows.Forms that can display data from a data source in tabular format. The basic steps we'll perform are:

- Create the ADO.NET entity data model classes for manipulating the database.
- Add the entity data model object that represents the Authors table as a data source.
- Drag the Authors table data source onto the **Design** view to create a GUI for displaying the table's data.
- Add code that allows the app to interact with the database.

The GUI for the program is shown in Fig. 22.10. All of the controls in this GUI are automatically generated when we drag a *data source* that represents the Authors table onto the Form in **Design** view. The **BindingNavigator** toolbar at the top of the window is a collection of controls that allow you to navigate through the records in the DataGridView that fills the rest of the window.

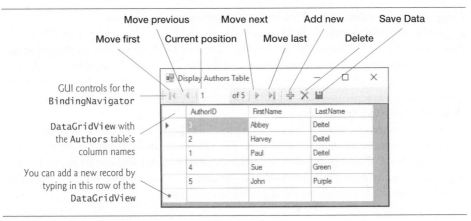

Fig. 22.10 | GUI for the **Display Authors Table** app.

The BindingNavigator's controls help you add records, delete records, modify existing records and save your changes to the database. You can add a new record by pressing the **Add new** button

then entering the new author's first and last name in the DataGridView. You can delete an existing record by selecting an author (either in the DataGridView or via the controls on the BindingNavigator) and pressing the **Delete** button

You can edit an existing record by clicking the first-name or last-name field for that record and typing the new value. To save your changes to the database, click the **Save Data** button

Empty values are not allowed in the Authors table of the Books database, so if you attempt to save a record that does not contain a value for both the first name and last name, an exception occurs.

22.5.1 Creating the ADO.NET Entity Data Model Class Library

This section presents the steps required to create the entity data model from an existing database. A *model* describes the data that you'll be manipulating—in our case, the data represented by the tables in the Books database.

Step 1: Creating a Class Library Project for the ADO.NET Entity Data Model
Select **File > New > Project…** to display the **New Project** dialog, then select **Class Library** from the **Visual C#** templates and name the project BooksExamples. Click **OK** to create the project, then delete the Class1.cs file from the **Solution Explorer**.

Step 2: Adding the ADO.NET Entity Data Model to the Class Library
To interact with the database, you'll add an ADO.NET entity data model to the class library project. This will also configure the connection to the database.

1. *Adding the ADO.NET Entity Data Model.* Right click the BooksExamples project in the **Solution Explorer**, then select **Add > New Item…** to display the **Add New Item** dialog (Fig. 22.11). From the **Data** category select **ADO.NET Entity Data Model** and name the model BooksModel—this will be the name of a file (with the filename extension .edmx) that configures the entity data model. Click **Add** to add the entity data model to the class library and display the **Entity Data Model Wizard** dialog.

Fig. 22.11 | Selecting **ADO.NET Entity Data Model** in the **Add New Item** Dialog.

2. *Choosing the Model Contents.* The **Choose Model Contents** step in the **Entity Data Model Wizard** dialog (Fig. 22.12) enables you to specify the entity data model's contents. The model in these examples will consist of data from the Books database, so select **EF Designer from database** and click **Next >** to display the **Choose Your Data Connection** step.

Fig. 22.12 | Entity Data Model Wizard dialog's Choose Model Contents step.

3. *Choosing the Data Connection.* In the **Choose Your Data Connection** step, click **New Connection...** to display the **Connection Properties** dialog (Fig. 22.13). (If

Fig. 22.13 | Connection Properties dialog.

the IDE displays a **Choose Data Source** dialog, select **Microsoft SQL Server Database File** and click **Continue**.) For the **Data source** field, if **Microsoft SQL Server Database File (SqlClient)** is not displayed, click **Change...**, select **Microsoft SQL Server Database File (SqlClient)** and click **OK**. Next, click **Browse...** to the right of the **Database file name** field to locate and select the Books.mdf file in the Databases directory included with this chapter's examples. You can click **Test Connection** to verify that the IDE can connect to the database through SQL Server Express. Click **OK** to create the connection. Figure 22.14 shows the **Connection string** for the Books.mdf database. This contains the information that the ADO.NET Entity Framework requires to connect to the database at runtime. Click **Next >**. A dialog will appear asking if you'd like to add the database file to your project. Click **Yes** to move to the next step.

Fig. 22.14 | Choose Your Data Connection step after selecting Books.mdf.

4. *Choosing the Entity Framework Version.* In the **Choose Your Version** step, select the **Entity Framework 6.x** (Fig. 22.15), then click **Next >**. This adds the latest version of the Entity Framework to your project.

5. *Choosing the Database Objects to Include in the Model.* In the **Choose Your Database Objects and Settings** step, you'll specify the parts of the database that should be used in the ADO.NET Entity Data Model. Select the **Tables** node as shown in Fig. 22.16, then click **Finish**. At this point, the IDE will download the Entity Framework 6.x templates you need and add them to your project. You may see one or more **Security Warning** dialogs—Visual Studio displays these when you attempt to use downloaded content in your projects. Click **OK** to dismiss each dialog. These warnings are intended primarily for cases in which a Visual Studio template is downloaded from an untrusted website.

Fig. 22.15 | Choosing the Entity Framework version to use in the project.

Fig. 22.16 | Selecting the database's tables to include in the ADO.NET Entity Data Model.

6. *Viewing the Entity Data Model Diagram in the Model Designer.* At this point, the IDE creates the entity data model and displays a diagram (Fig. 22.17) in the *model designer*. The diagram contains **Author** and **Title** *entities*—these represent

authors and titles in the database and the properties of each. Notice that the IDE renamed the Title column of the Titles table as Title1 to avoid a naming conflict with the class Title that represents a row in the table. The line between the entities indicates a relationship between authors and titles—this relationship is implemented in the Books database as the AuthorISBN table. The asterisk (*) at each end of the line indicates a *many-to-many relationship*—each author can author many titles and each title can have many authors. The **Navigation Properties** section in the **Author** entity contains the **Titles** property, which connects an author to all titles written by that author. Similarly, the **Navigation Properties** section in the **Title** entity contains the **Authors** property, which connects a title to all of its authors.

Fig. 22.17 | Entity data model diagram for the **Author** and **Title** entities.

7. *Building the Class Library.* Select **Build > Build Solution** to build the class library that you'll reuse in the next several examples—this will compile the entity data model classes that were generated by the IDE.[1] When you build the class library, the IDE generates the classes that you can use to interact with the database. These include a class for each table you selected from the database and a derived class of DbContext named BooksEntities that enables you to programmatically interact with the database—the IDE created the name BooksEntities (Fig. 22.14) by adding Entities to the database file's base name (Books in Books.mdf). Building the project causes the IDE to execute a script that creates and compiles the entity data model classes.

22.5.2 Creating a Windows Forms Project and Configuring It to Use the Entity Data Model

Recall that the next several examples will all be part of *one* solution containing several projects—the class library project with our reusable model and individual Windows Forms apps for each example. In this section, you'll create a new Windows Forms app and configure it to be able to use the entity data model that you created in the preceding section.

Step 1: Creating the Project
To add a new Windows Forms project to the existing solution:

---

1. If you get an error message indicating that the IDE can't copy the .mdf file to the bin\Debug folder because it's in use, close Visual Studio, then reopen the project and try to build the solution again.

1. Right click **Solution 'BooksExamples'** (the solution name) in **Solution Explorer** and select **Add > New Project...** to display the **Add New Project** dialog.

2. Select **Windows Forms Application** from the **Visual C# > Windows > Classic Desktop** category, name the project `DisplayTable` and click **OK**.

3. Change the name of the `Form1.cs` source file to `DisplayAuthorsTable.cs`. The IDE updates the `Form`'s class name to match the source file. Set the `Form`'s **Text** property to `Display Authors Table`.

4. Right click the `DisplayTable` project's name in the **Solution Explorer**, then select **Set as Startup Project** to configure the solution so that project `DisplayTable` will execute when you select **Debug > Start Debugging** (or press *F5*).

Step 2: Adding a Reference to the *BooksExamples* Class Library
To use the entity data model classes for data binding, you must first add a reference to the class library you created in Section 22.5.1—this allows the new project to use that class library. Each project you create typically contains references to several .NET class libraries (called *assemblies*) by default—for example, a Windows Forms project contains a reference to the `System.Windows.Forms` library. When you compile a class library, the IDE creates a `.dll` file containing the library's components. To add a reference to the class library containing the entity data model's classes:

1. Right click the `DisplayTable` project's **References** node in the **Solution Explorer** and select **Add Reference....**

2. In the left column of the **Reference Manager** dialog that appears, select **Projects** to display the other projects in this solution, then in center of the dialog ensure that the checkbox next to `BooksExamples` is checked and click **OK**. `BooksExamples` should now appear in the projects **References** node.

Step 3: Adding a Reference to *EntityFramework*
You'll also need a reference to the `EntityFramework` library to use the ADO.NET Entity Framework. This library was added by the IDE to the `BooksExamples` class library project when we created the entity data model, but you also must add the `EntityFramework` library to each app that will use the entity data model. To add an `EntityFramework` library reference to a project:

1. Right click the project's name in the **Solution Explorer** and select **Manage NuGet Packages...** to display the **NuGet** tab in Visual Studio's editors area. NuGet is a tool (known as a *package manager*) that that helps you download and manage libraries (known as *packages*) used by your projects.

2. In the dialog that appears, click **Browse**, then select the **EntityFramework by Microsoft** and click **Install** (Fig. 22.18).

3. The IDE will ask you to review the changes. Click **OK**.

4. The IDE will ask you to accept the `EntityFramework` license. Click **I Accept** to complete the installation.

`EntityFramework` should now appear in the projects **References** node. You can now close the **NuGet** tab.

Fig. 22.18 | Selecting and installing the **EntityFramework** in the **NuGet** tab.

Step 4: Adding the Connection String to the Windows Forms App
Each app that will use the entity data model also requires the *connection string* that tells the Entity Framework how to connect to the database. The connection string is stored in the BooksExamples class library's App.Config file. In the **Solution Explorer**, open the BooksExamples class library's App.Config file, then copy the connectionStrings element (lines 7–9 in our file), which has the format:

```
<connectionStrings>
    Connection string information appears here
</connectionStrings>
```

Next, open the App.Config file in the DisplayTable project and paste the connection string information *after* the line containing </entityFramework> and *before* the line containing </configuration>. Save, then close the App.Config file.

22.5.3 Data Bindings Between Controls and the Entity Data Model
You'll now use the IDE's drag-and-drop GUI design capabilities to create the GUI for interacting with the Books database. You must write a small amount of code to enable the autogenerated GUI to interact with the entity data model. You'll now perform the steps to display the contents of the Authors table in a GUI.

*Step 1: Adding a Data Source for the **Authors** Table*
To use the entity data model classes for data binding, you must first add them as a *data source*. To do so:

1. Select **View > Other Windows > Data Sources** to display the **Data Sources** window at the left side of the IDE, then in that window click the **Add New Data Source...** link to display the **Data Source Configuration Wizard**.

2. The Entity Data Model classes are used to create *objects* representing the tables in the database, so we'll use an **Object** data source. In the dialog, select **Object** and

click **Next >**. Expand the tree view as shown in Fig. 22.19 and ensure that **Author** is checked. An object of this class will be this app's *data source*.

3. Click **Finish**.

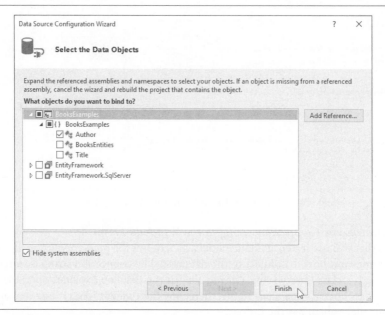

Fig. 22.19 | Selecting the Entity Data Model class `Author` as the data source.

The `Authors` table in the database is now a data source that can be bound to a GUI control that obtains author data automatically. In the **Data Sources** window (Fig. 22.20), you can see the `Author` class that you added in the previous step. We expanded the node to show `Author`'s properties, representing columns of the database's `Authors` table, as well as the `Titles` navigation property, representing the relationship between the database's `Authors` and `Titles` tables.

Fig. 22.20 | **Data Sources** window showing the expanded `Author` class as a data source.

Step 2: Creating GUI Elements

Next, you'll use the **Design** view to create a `DataGridView` control that can display the `Authors` table's data. To do so:

1. Switch to **Design** view for the `DisplayAuthorsTable` class.

2. Click the **Author** node in the **Data Sources** window—it should change to a drop-down list. Open the drop-down by clicking the down arrow and ensure that the `DataGridView` option is selected—this is the GUI control that will be used to display and interact with the data.

3. Drag the **Author** node from the **Data Sources** window onto the `Form` in **Design** view. You'll need to resize the `Form` to fit the `DataGridView`.

The IDE creates a `DataGridView` (Fig. 22.21) with column names representing all the properties for an `Author`, including the `Titles` navigation property.

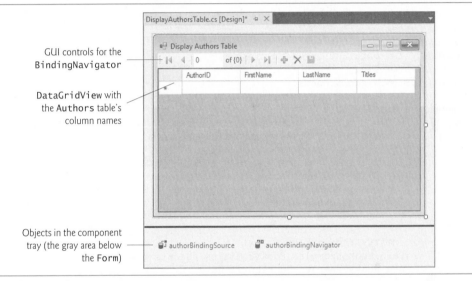

Fig. 22.21 | Component tray holds nonvisual components in **Design** view.

The IDE also creates a `BindingNavigator` that contains `Buttons` for

- moving between entries,
- adding entries,
- deleting entries and
- saving changes to the database.

In addition, the IDE generates a `BindingSource` (`authorBindingSource`), which handles the transfer of data between the *data source* and the *data-bound controls* on the `Form`. Nonvisual components such as the `BindingSource` and the nonvisual aspects of the `BindingNavigator` appear in the *component tray*—the gray region below the `Form` in **Design** view. The IDE names the `BindingNavigator` and `BindingSource` (`authorBindingNavigator` and `authorBindingSource`, respectively) based on the data source's name (`Author`). We use the default names for automatically generated components throughout this chapter to show exactly what the IDE creates.

To make the `DataGridView` occupy the *entire* window below the `BindingNavigator`, select the `DataGridView`, then use the **Properties** window to set the `Dock` property to `Fill`. You can stretch the window horizontally to see all the `DataGridView` columns. We do not use the Titles column in this example, so right click the DataGridView and select **Edit Columns...** to display the **Edit Columns** dialog. Select **Titles** in the **Selected Columns** list, click **Remove** to remove that column, then click **OK**.

Step 3: Connecting the Data Source to the authorBindingSource
The final step is to connect the data source to the authorBindingSource, so that the app can interact with the database. Figure 22.22 shows the code needed to obtain data from the database and to save any changes that the user makes to the data back into the database.

```
1  // Fig. 22.22: DisplayAuthorsTable.cs
2  // Displaying data from a database table in a DataGridView.
3  using System;
4  using System.Data.Entity;
5  using System.Data.Entity.Validation;
6  using System.Linq;
7  using System.Windows.Forms;
8
9  namespace DisplayTable
10 {
11    public partial class DisplayAuthorsTable : Form
12    {
13       // constructor
14       public DisplayAuthorsTable()
15       {
16          InitializeComponent();
17       }
18
19       // Entity Framework DbContext
20       private BooksExamples.BooksEntities dbcontext =
21          new BooksExamples.BooksEntities();
22
23       // load data from database into DataGridView
24       private void DisplayAuthorsTable_Load(object sender, EventArgs e)
25       {
26          // load Authors table ordered by LastName then FirstName
27          dbcontext.Authors
28             .OrderBy(author => author.LastName)
29             .ThenBy(author => author.FirstName)
30             .Load();
31
32          // specify DataSource for authorBindingSource
33          authorBindingSource.DataSource = dbcontext.Authors.Local;
34       }
35
36       // click event handler for the Save Button in the
37       // BindingNavigator saves the changes made to the data
38       private void authorBindingNavigatorSaveItem_Click(
39          object sender, EventArgs e)
40       {
41          Validate(); // validate the input fields
42          authorBindingSource.EndEdit(); // complete current edit, if any
```

Fig. 22.22 | Displaying data from a database table in a DataGridView. (Part 1 of 2.)

```
43
44          // try to save changes
45          try
46          {
47              dbcontext.SaveChanges(); // write changes to database file
48          }
49          catch(DbEntityValidationException)
50          {
51              MessageBox.Show("FirstName and LastName must contain values",
52                  "Entity Validation Exception");
53          }
54      }
55   }
56 }
```

Fig. 22.22 | Displaying data from a database table in a DataGridView. (Part 2 of 2.)

Creating the *DbContext* Object

As mentioned in Section 22.4, a DbContext object interacts with the database on the app's behalf. The BooksEntities class (a derived class of DbContext) was automatically generated by the IDE when you created the entity data model classes to access the Books database (Section 22.5.1). Lines 20–21 create an object of this class named dbcontext.

DisplayAuthorsTable_Load Event Handler

You can create the Form's Load event handler (lines 24–34) by double clicking the Form's title bar in **Design** view. In this app, we allow data to move between the DbContext and the database by using LINQ to Entities extension methods to extract data from the BooksEntities's Authors property (lines 27–30), which corresponds to the Authors table in the database. The expression

```
    dbcontext.Authors
```

indicates that we wish to get data from the Authors table.

The OrderBy extension method call

```
        .OrderBy(author => author.LastName)
```

indicates that the rows of the table should be retrieved in ascending order by the authors' last names. Extension method OrderBy receives as its argument a Func delegate (namespace System) representing a method that receives one parameter and returns a value that's used to order the results. In this case, we pass a lambda expression that defines an anonymous method in which

- the parameter author (an object of the Author entity data model class) is passed to the method, and
- the expression to the right of the lambda operator (=>)—the author's LastName in this case—is implicitly returned by the method.

The lambda expression infers author's type from dbcontext.Authors—which contains Author objects—and infers the lambda's return type (string) from author.LastName.

When there are multiple authors with the same last name, we'd like them to be listed in ascending order by first name as well. The **ThenBy** extension method call

```
.ThenBy(author => author.FirstName)
```

enables you to order results by an additional column. This is applied to the Author objects that have already been ordered by last name. Like OrderBy, ThenBy also receives a Func delegate that's used to order the results.

Finally, line 30 calls the **Load** extension method (defined in class **DbExtensions** from the namespace System.Data.Entity). This method executes the LINQ to Entities query and loads the results into memory. This data is tracked by the BookEntities DbContext in local memory so that any changes made to the data can eventually be saved into the database. Lines 27–30 are equivalent to using the following statement:

```
(from author in dbcontext.Authors
 orderby author.LastName, author.FirstName
 select author).Load();
```

Line 33 sets the authorBindingSource's **DataSource** property to the Local property of the dbcontext.Authors object. In this case, the Local property is an ObservableCollection<Author> that represents the query results that were loaded into memory by lines 27–30. When a BindingSource's DataSource property is assigned an **ObservableCollection<T>** (namespace System.Collections.ObjectModel), the GUI that's bound to the BindingSource is notified of any changes to the data so the GUI can be updated accordingly. In addition, changes made by the user to the data in the GUI will be tracked so the DbContext can eventually save those changes to the database.

authorBindingNavigatorSaveItem_Click Event Handler: Saving Modifications to the Database

If the user modifies the data in the DataGridView, we'd also like to save the modifications in the database. By default, the BindingNavigator's **Save Data** Button

is disabled. To enable it, right click this Button's icon in the BindingNavigator and select **Enabled**. Then, double click the icon to create its Click event handler and add the code in the method's body (lines 41–53).

Saving the data entered in the DataGridView back to the database is a three-step process. First, the Form's controls are validated (line 41) by calling the inherited Validate method—if any control has an event handler for the Validating event, it executes. You typically handle this event to determine whether a control's contents are valid. Next, line

42 calls `EndEdit` on the `authorBindingSource`, which forces it to save any pending changes into the `BooksEntities` model in memory. Finally, line 47 calls `SaveChanges` on the `BooksEntities` object `dbcontext` to store any changes into the database. We placed this call in a `try` statement, because the `Authors` table does not allow empty values for the first name and last name—these rules were configured when we originally created the database. When `SaveChanges` is called, any changes stored into the `Authors` table must satisfy the table's rules. If any do not, a `DBEntityValidationException` occurs.

22.6 Dynamically Binding Query Results

Next we show how to perform several different queries and display the results in a `DataGridView`. This app only reads data from the entity data model, so we disabled the buttons in the `BindingNavigator` that enable the user to add and delete records—simply select each button and set its **Enabled** property to `False` in the **Properties** window. You also could delete these buttons from the `BindingNavigator`. Later, we'll explain why we do not support modifying the database in this example.

The **Display Query Results** app (Figs. 22.23–22.25) allows the user to select a query from the `ComboBox` at the bottom of the window, then displays the results of the query.

ISBN	Title1	EditionNumber	Copyright
0134289366	Android 6 for Programmers: An App-Driven Approach	3	2016
0134444302	Android How to Program	3	2016
0133976890	C How to Program	8	2016
0134448235	C++ How to Program	10	2016
0132151006	Internet & World Wide Web How to Program	5	2012
0133965260	iOS 8 for Programmers: An App-Driven Approach with Swift	3	2015
0133807800	Java How to Program	10	2015
0132575655	Java How to Program, Late Objects Version	10	2015
0134021363	Swift for Programmers	1	2015
0133406954	Visual Basic 2012 How to Program	6	2014
0134601548	Visual C# How to Program	6	2017

Fig. 22.23 | Results of the **Display Query Results** app's **All titles** query, which shows the contents of the `Titles` table ordered by the book titles.

ISBN	Title1	EditionNumber	Copyright
0134289366	Android 6 for Programmers: An App-Driven Approach	3	2016
0134444302	Android How to Program	3	2016
0133976890	C How to Program	8	2016
0134448235	C++ How to Program	10	2016

Fig. 22.24 | Results of the **Display Query Results** app's **Titles with 2016 copyright** query.

Fig. 22.25 | Results of the Display Query Results app's Titles ending with "How to Program" query.

22.6.1 Creating the Display Query Results GUI

Perform the following steps to build the **Display Query Results** app's GUI.

Step 1: Creating the Project
Perform the steps in Section 22.5.2 to create a new **Windows Forms Application** project named `DisplayQueryResult` in the same solution as the `DisplayTable` app. Rename the `Form1.cs` source file to `TitleQueries.cs`. Set the Form's **Text** property to `Display Query Results`. Be sure to add references to the `BooksExamples` and `EntityFramework` libraries, add the connection string to the project's `App.Config` file and set the `DisplayQuery-Result` project as the startup project.

Step 2: Creating a `DataGridView` to Display the `Titles` Table
Follow *Steps 1* and *2* in Section 22.5.3 to create the data source and the `DataGridView`. For this example, select the `Title` class (rather than `Author`) as the data source, and drag the `Title` node from the **Data Sources** window onto the form. Remove the `Authors` column from the `DataGridView`, as it will not be used in this example.

Step 3: Adding a `ComboBox` to the Form
In **Design** view, add a `ComboBox` named `queriesComboBox` below the `DataGridView` on the Form. Users will select which query to execute from this control. Set the `ComboBox`'s **Dock** property to `Bottom` and the `DataGridView`'s **Dock** property to `Fill`.

Next, you'll add the names of the queries to the `ComboBox`. Open the `ComboBox`'s **String Collection Editor** by right clicking the `ComboBox` and selecting **Edit Items...**. You also can access the **String Collection Editor** from the `ComboBox`'s *smart tag menu*. A smart tag menu provides you with quick access to common properties you might set for a control (such as the `Multiline` property of a `TextBox`), so you can set these properties directly in **Design** view, rather than in the **Properties** window. You can open a control's *smart tag menu* by clicking the small arrowhead

that appears in the control's upper-right corner in **Design** view when the control is selected. In the **String Collection Editor**, add the following three items to `queriesComboBox`—one for each of the queries we'll create:

1. All titles

2. Titles with 2016 copyright

3. Titles ending with "How to Program"

22.6.2 Coding the Display Query Results App

Next you'll create the code for this app (Fig. 22.26).

```
1   // Fig. 22.26: TitleQueries.cs
2   // Displaying the result of a user-selected query in a DataGridView.
3   using System;
4   using System.Data.Entity;
5   using System.Linq;
6   using System.Windows.Forms;
7
8   namespace DisplayQueryResult
9   {
10     public partial class TitleQueries : Form
11     {
12        public TitleQueries()
13        {
14           InitializeComponent();
15        }
16
17        // Entity Framework DbContext
18        private BooksExamples.BooksEntities dbcontext =
19           new BooksExamples.BooksEntities();
20
21        // load data from database into DataGridView
22        private void TitleQueries_Load(object sender, EventArgs e)
23        {
24           dbcontext.Titles.Load(); // load Titles table into memory
25
26           // set the ComboBox to show the default query that
27           // selects all books from the Titles table
28           queriesComboBox.SelectedIndex = 0;
29        }
30
31        // loads data into titleBindingSource based on user-selected query
32        private void queriesComboBox_SelectedIndexChanged(
33           object sender, EventArgs e)
34        {
35           // set the data displayed according to what is selected
36           switch (queriesComboBox.SelectedIndex)
37           {
38              case 0: // all titles
39                 // use LINQ to order the books by title
40                 titleBindingSource.DataSource =
41                    dbcontext.Titles.Local.OrderBy(book => book.Title1);
42                 break;
```

Fig. 22.26 | Displaying the result of a user-selected query in a DataGridView. (Part 1 of 2.)

```
43                  case 1: // titles with 2016 copyright
44                      // use LINQ to get titles with 2016
45                      // copyright and sort them by title
46                      titleBindingSource.DataSource =
47                          dbcontext.Titles.Local
48                              .Where(book => book.Copyright == "2016")
49                              .OrderBy(book => book.Title1);
50                      break;
51                  case 2: // titles ending with "How to Program"
52                      // use LINQ to get titles ending with
53                      // "How to Program" and sort them by title
54                      titleBindingSource.DataSource =
55                          dbcontext.Titles.Local
56                              .Where(
57                                  book => book.Title1.EndsWith("How to Program"))
58                              .OrderBy(book => book.Title1);
59                      break;
60              }
61
62          titleBindingSource.MoveFirst(); // move to first entry
63      }
64  }
65 }
```

Fig. 22.26 | Displaying the result of a user-selected query in a DataGridView. (Part 2 of 2.)

*Customizing the **Form**'s **Load** Event Handler*
Create the TitleQueries_Load event handler (lines 22–29) by double clicking the title bar in **Design** view. When the Form loads, it should display the complete list of books from the Titles table, sorted by title. Line 24 calls the Load extension method on the BookEntities DbContext's Titles property to load the Titles table's contents into memory. Rather than defining the same LINQ query as in lines 40–41, we can programmatically cause the queriesComboBox_SelectedIndexChanged event handler to execute simply by setting the queriesComboBox's SelectedIndex to 0 (line 28).

queriesComboBox_SelectedIndexChanged Event Handler
Next you must write code that executes the appropriate query each time the user chooses a different item from queriesComboBox. Double click queriesComboBox in **Design** view to generate a queriesComboBox_SelectedIndexChanged event handler (lines 32–63) in the TitleQueries.cs file. In the event handler, add a switch statement (lines 36–60). Each case in the switch will change the titleBindingSource's DataSource property to the results of a query that returns the correct set of data. The data bindings created by the IDE *automatically* update the titleDataGridView *each time* we change its DataSource. The BindingSource maintains a **Position** property that represents the current item in the data source. The **MoveFirst method** of the BindingSource (line 62) sets the Position property to 0 to move to the first row of the result each time a query executes. The results of the queries in lines 40–41, 46–49 and 54–58 are shown in Figs. 22.23–22.25, respectively. Because we do not modify the data in this app, each of the queries is performed on the in-memory representation of the Titles table, which is accessible through dbcontext.Titles.Local.

Ordering the Books By Title

Lines 40–41 invoke the `OrderBy` extension method on `dbcontext.Titles.Local` to order the `Title` objects by their `Title1` property values. As we mentioned previously, the IDE renamed the `Title` column of the database's `Titles` table as `Title1` in the generated `Title` entity data model class to avoid a naming conflict with the class's name. Recall that `Local` returns an `ObservableCollection<T>` containing the row objects of the specified table—in this case, `Local` returns an `ObservableCollection<Title>`. When you invoke `OrderBy` on an `ObservableCollection<T>`, the method returns an `IOrderedEnumerable<T>`. We assign that object to the `titleBindingSource`'s `DataSource` property. When the `DataSource` property changes, the `DataGridView` iterates through the contents of the `IEnumerable<T>` and displays the data.

Selecting Books with 2016 Copyright

Lines 46–49 filter the titles displayed by using the **Where** extension method with the lambda expression

```
book => book.Copyright == "2016"
```

as an argument. The `Where` extension method expects as its parameter a `Func` delegate representing a method that receives one parameter and returns a `bool` indicating whether the method's argument matches the specified criteria. The lambda expression used here takes one `Title` object (named book) as its parameter and uses it to check whether the given `Title`'s `Copyright` property (a `string` in the database) is equal to 2014. A lambda expression that's used with the `Where` extension method must return a `bool` value. Only `Title` objects for which this lambda expression returns `true` will be selected. We use `OrderBy` to order the results by the `Title1` property so the books are displayed in ascending order by title. The type of the lambda's book parameter is *inferred* from `dbcontext.Titles.Local`, which contains `Title` objects. As soon as the `titleBindingSource`'s `DataSource` property changes, the `DataGridView` is updated with the query results.

Selecting Books with Titles That End in "How to Program"

Lines 54–58 filter the titles displayed by using the `Where` extension method with the lambda expression

```
book => book.Title1.EndsWith("How to Program")
```

as an argument. This lambda expression takes one `Title` object (named book) as its parameter and uses it to check whether the given `Title`'s `Title1` property value ends with `"How to Program"`. The expression `books.Title1` returns the `string` stored in that property, then we use the string class's `EndsWith` method to perform the test. We order the results by the `Title1` property so the books are displayed in ascending order by title.

22.7 Retrieving Data from Multiple Tables with LINQ

In this section, you'll perform LINQ to Entities queries using the LINQ query syntax that was introduced in Chapter 9. In particular, you'll learn how to obtain query results that combine data from multiple tables (Figs. 22.27–22.29). The **Joining Tables with LINQ** app uses LINQ to Entities to combine and organize data from multiple tables, and shows the results of queries that perform the following tasks:

- Get a list of all the authors and the ISBNs of the books they've authored, sorted by last name, then first name (Fig. 22.27).

- Get a list of all the authors and the titles of the books they've authored, sorted by last name, then first name; for each author sort the titles alphabetically (Fig. 22.28).

- Get a list of all the book titles grouped by author, sorted by last name, then first name; for a given author sort the titles alphabetically (Fig. 22.29).

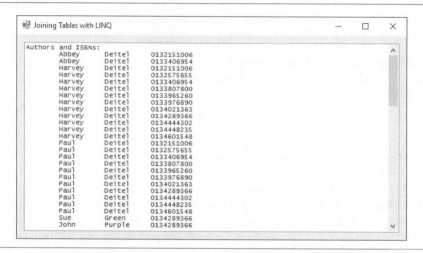

Fig. 22.27 | Joining Tables with LINQ app showing the list of authors and the ISBNs of the books they've authored. The authors are sorted by last name, then first name.

```
Authors and titles:
        Abbey       Deitel      Internet & World Wide Web How to Program
        Abbey       Deitel      Visual Basic 2012 How to Program
        Harvey      Deitel      Android 6 for Programmers: An App-Driven Approach
        Harvey      Deitel      Android How to Program
        Harvey      Deitel      C How to Program
        Harvey      Deitel      C++ How to Program
        Harvey      Deitel      Internet & World Wide Web How to Program
        Harvey      Deitel      iOS 8 for Programmers: An App-Driven Approach with Swift
        Harvey      Deitel      Java How to Program
        Harvey      Deitel      Java How to Program, Late Objects Version
        Harvey      Deitel      Swift for Programmers
        Harvey      Deitel      Visual Basic 2012 How to Program
        Harvey      Deitel      Visual C# How to Program
        Paul        Deitel      Android 6 for Programmers: An App-Driven Approach
        Paul        Deitel      Android How to Program
        Paul        Deitel      C How to Program
        Paul        Deitel      C++ How to Program
        Paul        Deitel      Internet & World Wide Web How to Program
        Paul        Deitel      iOS 8 for Programmers: An App-Driven Approach with Swift
        Paul        Deitel      Java How to Program
        Paul        Deitel      Java How to Program, Late Objects Version
        Paul        Deitel      Swift for Programmers
        Paul        Deitel      Visual Basic 2012 How to Program
        Paul        Deitel      Visual C# How to Program
        Sue         Green       Android 6 for Programmers: An App-Driven Approach
        John        Purple      Android 6 for Programmers: An App-Driven Approach
```

Fig. 22.28 | Joining Tables with LINQ app showing the list of authors and the titles of the book's they've authored. The authors are sorted by last name, then first name, and the titles for a given author are sorted alphabetically.

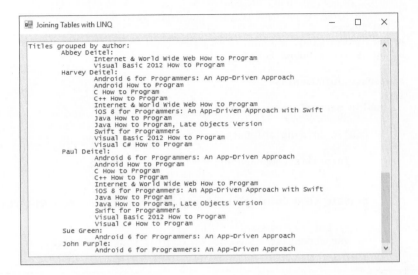

```
Joining Tables with LINQ                                       —   □   ×

Titles grouped by author:
        Abbey Deitel:
                Internet & World Wide Web How to Program
                Visual Basic 2012 How to Program
        Harvey Deitel:
                Android 6 for Programmers: An App-Driven Approach
                Android How to Program
                C How to Program
                C++ How to Program
                Internet & World Wide Web How to Program
                iOS 8 for Programmers: An App-Driven Approach with Swift
                Java How to Program
                Java How to Program, Late Objects Version
                Swift for Programmers
                Visual Basic 2012 How to Program
                Visual C# How to Program
        Paul Deitel:
                Android 6 for Programmers: An App-Driven Approach
                Android How to Program
                C How to Program
                C++ How to Program
                Internet & World Wide Web How to Program
                iOS 8 for Programmers: An App-Driven Approach with Swift
                Java How to Program
                Java How to Program, Late Objects Version
                Swift for Programmers
                Visual Basic 2012 How to Program
                Visual C# How to Program
        Sue Green:
                Android 6 for Programmers: An App-Driven Approach
        John Purple:
                Android 6 for Programmers: An App-Driven Approach
```

Fig. 22.29 | Joining Tables with LINQ app showing the list of titles grouped by author. The authors are sorted by last name, then first name, and the titles for a given author are sorted alphabetically.

GUI for the *Joining Tables with LINQ App*

For this example (Fig. 22.30–Fig. 22.33), perform the steps in Section 22.5.2 to create a new **Windows Forms Application** project named JoinQueries in the same solution as the previous examples. Rename the Form1.cs source file to JoiningTableData.cs. Set the Form's **Text** property to Joining Tables with LINQ. Be sure to add references to the Books-Examples and EntityFramework libraries, add the connection string to the project's App.Config file and set the JoinQueries project as the startup project. We set the following properties for the outputTextBox:

- Font property: Set to Lucida Console to display the output in a fixed-width font.

- Multiline property: Set to True so that multiple lines of text can be displayed.

- Anchor property: Set to Top, Bottom, Left, Right so that you can resize the window and the outputTextBox will resize accordingly.

- Scrollbars property: Set to Vertical, so that you can scroll through the output.

Creating the **DbContext**

The code uses the entity data model classes to combine data from the tables in the Books database and display the relationships between the authors and books in three different ways. We split the code for class JoiningTableData into several figures (Figs. 22.30–22.33) for presentation purposes. As in previous examples, the DbContext object (Fig. 22.30, line 19) allows the program to interact with the database.

```
1   // Fig. 22.30: JoiningTableData.cs
2   // Using LINQ to perform a join and aggregate data across tables.
3   using System;
4   using System.Linq;
5   using System.Windows.Forms;
6
7   namespace JoinQueries
8   {
9      public partial class JoiningTableData : Form
10     {
11        public JoiningTableData()
12        {
13           InitializeComponent();
14        }
15
16        private void JoiningTableData_Load(object sender, EventArgs e)
17        {
18           // Entity Framework DbContext
19           var dbcontext = new BooksExamples.BooksEntities();
20
```

Fig. 22.30 | Creating the `BooksEntities` for querying the Books database.

Combining Author Names with the ISBNs of the Books They've Written

The first query (Fig. 22.31, lines 22–26) *joins* data from two tables and returns a list of author names and the ISBNs representing the books they've written, sorted by `LastName`, then `FirstName`. The query takes advantage of the properties in the entity data model classes that were created based on foreign-key relationships between the database's tables. These properties enable you to easily combine data from related rows in multiple tables.

```
21        // get authors and ISBNs of each book they co-authored
22        var authorsAndISBNs =
23           from author in dbcontext.Authors
24           from book in author.Titles
25           orderby author.LastName, author.FirstName
26           select new {author.FirstName, author.LastName, book.ISBN};
27
28        outputTextBox.AppendText("Authors and ISBNs:");
29
30        // display authors and ISBNs in tabular format
31        foreach (var element in authorsAndISBNs)
32        {
33           outputTextBox.AppendText($"\r\n\t{element.FirstName,-10} " +
34              $"{element.LastName,-10} {element.ISBN,-10}");
35        }
36
```

Fig. 22.31 | Getting a list of authors and the ISBNs of the books they've authored.

The first `from` clause (line 23) gets each author from the `Authors` table. The second `from` clause (line 24) uses the `Author` class's `Titles` property to get the ISBNs for the current author. The entity data model uses the foreign-key information stored in the database's `AuthorISBN` table to get the appropriate ISBNs. The combined result of the two `from` clauses is a collection of all the authors and the ISBNs of the books they've authored. The two `from` clauses introduce *two* range variables into the scope of this query—other clauses can access both range variables to combine data from multiple tables. Line 25 orders the results by the author's `LastName`, then `FirstName`. Line 26 creates a new anonymous type containing an author's `FirstName` and `LastName` from the `Authors` table and the `ISBN` for one of that author's books from the `Titles` table.

Anonymous Types
Recall from Section 9.3.5 that a LINQ query's `select` clause can create an anonymous type with the properties specified in the initializer list— in this case, `FirstName`, `LastName` and `ISBN` (line 26). Note that all properties of an anonymous type are `public` and *read-only*. Because the type has no name, you must use *implicitly typed local variables* to store references to objects of anonymous types (e.g., line 31). Also, in addition to the `ToString` method in an anonymous type, the compiler provides an `Equals` method, which compares the properties of the anonymous object that calls the method and the anonymous object that it receives as an argument.

Combining Author Names with the Titles of the Books They've Written
The second query (Fig. 22.32, lines 38–42) gives similar output, but uses the foreign-key relationships to get the title of each book that an author wrote.

```
37        // get authors and titles of each book they co-authored
38        var authorsAndTitles =
39           from book in dbcontext.Titles
40           from author in book.Authors
41           orderby author.LastName, author.FirstName, book.Title1
42           select new {author.FirstName, author.LastName, book.Title1};
43
44        outputTextBox.AppendText("\r\n\r\nAuthors and titles:");
45
46        // display authors and titles in tabular format
47        foreach (var element in authorsAndTitles)
48        {
49           outputTextBox.AppendText($"\r\n\t{element.FirstName,-10} " +
50              $"{element.LastName,-10} {element.Title1}");
51        }
52
```

Fig. 22.32 | Getting a list of authors and the titles of the books they've authored.

The first `from` clause (line 39) gets each book from the `Titles` table. The second `from` clause (line 40) uses the generated `Authors` property of the `Title` class to get only the authors for the current book. The entity data model uses the foreign-key information stored in the database's `AuthorISBN` table to get the appropriate authors. The `author` objects give us access to the names of the current book's authors. The `select` clause (line 42) uses the `author` and `book` range variables to get the `FirstName` and `LastName` of each author from the `Authors` table and the title of one of the author's books from the `Titles` table.

Organizing Book Titles by Author

Most queries return results with data arranged in a relational-style table of rows and columns. The last query (Fig. 22.33, lines 55–62) returns hierarchical results. Each element in the results contains the name of an Author and a list of Titles that the author wrote. The LINQ query does this by using a *nested query* in the select clause. The outer query iterates over the authors in the database. The inner query takes a specific author and retrieves all titles that the author wrote. The select clause (lines 58–62) creates an anonymous type with two properties:

- The property Name (line 58) is initialized with a string that separates the author's first and last names by a space.

- The property Titles (lines 59–62) is initialized with the result of the nested query, which returns the title of each book written by the current author.

In this case, we're providing names for each property in the new anonymous type. When you create an anonymous type, you can specify the name for each property by using the format *name = value*.

```
53      // get authors and titles of each book
54      // they co-authored; group by author
55      var titlesByAuthor =
56          from author in dbcontext.Authors
57          orderby author.LastName, author.FirstName
58          select new {Name = author.FirstName + " " + author.LastName,
59              Titles =
60                  from book in author.Titles
61                  orderby book.Title1
62                  select book.Title1};
63
64      outputTextBox.AppendText("\r\n\r\nTitles grouped by author:");
65
66      // display titles written by each author, grouped by author
67      foreach (var author in titlesByAuthor)
68      {
69          // display author's name
70          outputTextBox.AppendText($"\r\n\t{author.Name}:");
71
72          // display titles written by that author
73          foreach (var title in author.Titles)
74          {
75              outputTextBox.AppendText($"\r\n\t\t{title}");
76          }
77      }
78  }
79  }
80  }
```

Fig. 22.33 | Getting a list of titles grouped by authors.

The range variable book in the nested query iterates over the current author's books using the Titles property. The Title1 property of a given book returns the Title column from that row of the Titles table in the database.

The nested `foreach` statements (lines 67–77) use the anonymous type's properties to output the hierarchical results. The outer loop displays the author's name and the inner loop displays the titles of all the books written by that author.

22.8 Creating a Master/Detail View App

Figure 22.34 shows a so-called master/detail view—one part of the GUI (the master) allows you to select an entry, and another part (the details) displays detailed information about that entry. When the app first loads, it displays the name of the first author in the data source and shows that author's books in the `DataGridView`. When you use the buttons on the `BindingNavigator` to change authors, the app displays the details of the books written by the corresponding author—Fig. 22.34 shows the second author's books. This app only reads data from the entity data model, so we disabled the buttons in the `BindingNavigator` that enable the user to add and delete records. When you run the app, experiment with the `BindingNavigator`'s controls. The DVD-player-like buttons of the `BindingNavigator` allow you to change the currently displayed row.

Fig. 22.34 | Master/Detail app displaying books for an author in the data source.

22.8.1 Creating the Master/Detail GUI

You've seen that the IDE can automatically generate the `BindingSource`, `BindingNavigator` and GUI elements when you drag a data source onto the Form. You'll now use two `BindingSources`—one for the master list of authors and one for the titles associated with a given author. Both will be generated by the IDE. The completed GUI that you'll now build is shown in Fig. 22.35.

Step 1: Creating the Project
Follow the instructions in Section 22.5.2 to create and configure a new **Windows Forms Application** project called `MasterDetail`. Name the source file `Details.cs` and set the Form's Text property to **Master/Detail**. Be sure to add references to the `BooksExamples` and `EntityFramework` libraries, add the connection string to the project's `App.Config` file and set the `MasterDetail` project as the startup project.

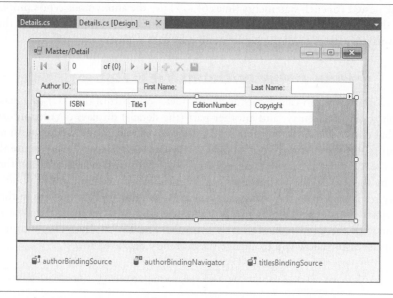

Fig. 22.35 | Finished design of the **Master/Detail** app.

Step 2: Adding a Data Source for the **Authors** Table

Follow the steps in Section 22.5.3 to add a data source for the Authors table. Although you'll be displaying records from the Titles table for each author, you do not need to add a data source for that table. The title information will be obtained from the Titles navigation property in the Author entity data model class.

Step 3: Creating GUI Elements

Next, you'll use the **Design** view to create the GUI components by dragging-and-dropping items from the **Data Sources** window onto the Form. In the earlier sections, you dragged an object from the **Data Sources** window to the Form to create a DataGridView. The IDE allows you to specify the type of control(s) that it will create when you drag-and-drop an object from the **Data Sources** window onto a Form. To do so:

1. Switch to **Design** view for the Details class.

2. Click the **Author** node in the **Data Sources** window—it should change to a drop-down list. Open the drop-down by clicking the down arrow and select the **Details** option—this indicates that we'd like to generate Label–TextBox pairs that represent each column of the Authors table.

3. Drag the **Author** node from the **Data Sources** window onto the Form in **Design** view. This creates the authorBindingSource, the authorBindingNavigator and the Label–TextBox pairs that represent each column in the table. Initially, the controls appear as shown in Fig. 22.36. We rearranged the controls as shown in Fig. 22.35.

4. By default, the Titles navigation property is implemented in the entity data model classes as a HashSet<Title>. To bind the data to GUI controls properly, you must change this to an ObservableCollection<Title>. To do this, expand

Fig. 22.36 | Details representation of an Author.

the class library project's BooksModel.edmx node in the **Solution Explorer**, then expand the BooksModel.tt node and open Author.cs in the editor. Add a using statement for the namespace System.Collections.ObjectModel. Then, in the Author constructor change HashSet to ObservableCollection, and in the Titles property's declaration, change ICollection to ObservableCollection. Right click the class library project in the **Solution Explorer** and select **Build** to recompile the class.

5. Select the MasterDetail project in the **Solution Explorer**. Next, click the **Titles** node that's nested in the **Author** node in the **Data Sources** window—it should change to a drop-down list. Open the drop-down by clicking the down arrow and ensure that the DataGridView option is selected—this is the GUI control that will be used to display the data from the Titles table that corresponds to a given author.

6. Drag the **Titles** node onto the Form in **Design** view. This creates the titlesBindingSource and the DataGridView. This control is only for *viewing* data, so set its ReadOnly property to True using the **Properties** window. Because we dragged the **Titles** node from the **Author** node in the **Data Sources** window, the DataGridView will automatically display the books for the currently selected author once we bind the author data to the authorBindingSource.

We used the DataGridView's Anchor property to anchor it to all four sides of the Form. We also set the Form's Size and MinimumSize properties to 550, 300 to set the Form's initial size and minimum size, respectively.

22.8.2 Coding the Master/Detail App

The code to display an author and the corresponding books (Fig. 22.37) is straightforward. Lines 18–19 create the DbContext. The Form's Load event handler (lines 22–32) orders the Author objects by LastName (line 26) and FirstName (line 27), then loads them into memory (line 28). Next, line 31 assigns dbcontext.Authors.Local to the authorBindingSource's DataSource property. At this point:

*   the BindingNavigator displays the number of Author objects and indicates that the first one in the results is selected,

*   the TextBoxes display the currently selected Author's AuthorID, FirstName and LastName property values, and

*   the currently selected Author's titles are automatically assigned to the titlesBindingSource's DataSource, which causes the DataGridView to display those titles.

Now, when you use the BindingNavigator to change the selected Author, the corresponding titles are displayed in the DataGridView.

```
1   // Fig. 22.37: Details.cs
2   // Using a DataGridView to display details based on a selection.
3   using System;
4   using System.Data.Entity;
5   using System.Linq;
6   using System.Windows.Forms;
7
8   namespace MasterDetail
9   {
10      public partial class Details : Form
11      {
12         public Details()
13         {
14            InitializeComponent();
15         }
16
17         // Entity Framework DbContext
18         BooksExamples.BooksEntities dbcontext =
19            new BooksExamples.BooksEntities();
20
21         // initialize data sources when the Form is loaded
22         private void Details_Load(object sender, EventArgs e)
23         {
24            // load Authors table ordered by LastName then FirstName
25            dbcontext.Authors
26               .OrderBy(author => author.LastName)
27               .ThenBy(author => author.FirstName)
28               .Load();
29
30            // specify DataSource for authorBindingSource
31            authorBindingSource.DataSource = dbcontext.Authors.Local;
32         }
33      }
34   }
```

Fig. 22.37 | Using a DataGridView to display details based on a selection.

22.9 Address Book Case Study

Our final example implements a simple AddressBook app (with sample outputs in (Figs. 22.38–22.40) that enables users to perform the following tasks on the database AddressBook.mdf (which is included in the directory with this chapter's examples):

- Insert new contacts.
- Find contacts whose last names begin with the specified letters.
- Update existing contacts.
- Delete contacts.

We populated the database with six fictional contacts.

Fig. 22.38 | Use the BindingNavigator's controls to navigate through the contacts.

Fig. 22.39 | Type a search string in the **Last Name** TextBox, then press **Find** to locate contacts whose last names begin with that string. Only two names start with **Br**, so the BindingNavigator shows the first of two matching records.

Fig. 22.40 | Click **Browse All Entries** to clear a search and return to browsing all contacts.

Rather than displaying a database table in a `DataGridView`, this app presents the details of one contact at a time in several `TextBox`es. The `BindingNavigator` at the top of the window allows you to control which *row* of the table is displayed at any given time. The `BindingNavigator` also allows you to *add* a contact and *delete* a contact—but only when browsing the complete contact list. When you filter the contacts by last name, the app disables the **Add new**

and **Delete**

buttons (we'll explain why shortly). Clicking **Browse All Entries** enables these buttons again. Adding a row clears the `TextBox`es and sets the `TextBox` to the right of **Address ID** to zero to indicate that the `TextBox`es now represent a new record. When you save a new entry, the **Address ID** field is automatically changed from zero to a unique ID number by the database. No changes are made to the underlying database unless you click the **Save Data** button:

22.9.1 Creating the Address Book App's GUI

We discuss the app's code momentarily. First you'll set up a new solution containing the entity data model and a Windows `Forms` app. Close the `BooksExamples` solution you used in this chapter's previous examples.

Step 1: Creating a Class Library Project for the Entity Data Model
Perform the steps in Section 22.5.1 to create a **Class Library** project named `AddressExample` that contains an entity data model for the `AddressBook.mdf` database, which contains only an `Addresses` table with `AddressID`, `FirstName`, `LastName`, `Email` and `PhoneNumber` columns. Name the entity data model `AddressModel`. The `AddressBook.mdf` database is located in the `Databases` folder with this chapter's examples.

Step 2: Creating a Windows Forms Application Project for the AddressBook App
Perform the steps in Section 22.5.2 to create a new **Windows Forms Application** project named `AddressBook` in the `AddressExample` solution. Set the Form's filename to `Contacts.cs`, then set the Form's **Text** property to `Address Book`. Set the `AddressBook` project as the solution's startup project.

Step 3: Adding the Address Object as a Data Source
Add the entity data model's `Address` object as a data source, as you did with the `Author` object in *Step 1* of Section 22.5.3.

Step 4: Displaying the Details of Each Row
In **Design** view, select the **Address** node in the **Data Sources** window. Click the **Address** node's down arrow and select the **Details** option to indicate that the IDE should create a set of `Label`–`TextBox` pairs to show the details of a single record at a time.

Step 5: Dragging the *Address Data-Source Node to the* **Form**

Drag the Address node from the **Data Sources** window to the Form. This automatically creates a BindingNavigator and the Labels and TextBoxes corresponding to the columns of the database table. The fields are placed in alphabetical order. Reorder the components, using **Design** view, so they're in the order shown in Fig. 22.38. You'll also want to change the tab order of the controls. To do so, select **View > Tab Order**, then click the TextBoxes from top to bottom in the order they appear in Fig. 22.38.

Step 5: Making the **AddressID** *TextBox* **ReadOnly**

The AddressID column of the Addresses table is an *autoincremented identity column*, so users should *not* be allowed to edit the values in this column. Select the TextBox for the AddressID and set its ReadOnly property to True using the **Properties** window.

Step 6: Adding Controls to Allow Users to Specify a Last Name to Locate

While the BindingNavigator allows you to browse the address book, it would be more convenient to be able to find a specific entry by last name. To add this functionality to the app, we must create controls to allow the user to enter a last name and provide event handlers to perform the search.

Add a Label named findLabel, a TextBox named findTextBox, and a Button named findButton. Place these controls in a GroupBox named findGroupBox, then set its Text property to **Find an entry by last name**. Set the Text property of the Label to Last Name: and set the Text property of the Button to Find.

Step 7: Allowing the User to Return to Browsing All Rows of the Database

To allow users to return to browsing all the contacts after searching for contacts with a specific last name, add a Button named browseAllButton below the findGroupBox. Set the Text property of browseAllButton to **Browse All Entries**.

22.9.2 Coding the Address Book App

The Contacts.cs code-behind file is split into several figures (Figs. 22.41–22.45) for presentation purposes.

Method **RefreshContacts**

As we showed in previous examples, we must connect the addressBindingSource that controls the GUI with the DbContext that interacts with the database. In this example, we declare the AddressEntities DbContext object at line 20 of Fig. 22.41, but create it and initiate the data binding in the RefreshContacts method (lines 23–45), which is called from several other methods in the app. When this method is called, if dbcontext is not null, we call its Dispose method, then create a new AddressEntities DbContext at line 32. We do this so we can re-sort the data in the entity data model. If we maintained one dbcontext.Addresses object in memory for the duration of the program and the user changed a person's last name or first name, the records would still remain in their original order in the dbcontext.Addresses object, even if that order is incorrect. Lines 36–39 order the Address objects by LastName, then FirstName and load the objects into memory. Then line 42 sets the addressBindingSource's DataSource property to dbcontext.Addresses.Local to bind the data in memory to the GUI.

```
 1   // Fig. 22.41: Contact.cs
 2   // Manipulating an address book.
 3   using System;
 4   using System.Data;
 5   using System.Data.Entity;
 6   using System.Data.Entity.Validation;
 7   using System.Linq;
 8   using System.Windows.Forms;
 9
10   namespace AddressBook
11   {
12      public partial class Contacts : Form
13      {
14         public Contacts()
15         {
16            InitializeComponent();
17         }
18
19         // Entity Framework DbContext
20         private AddressExample.AddressBookEntities dbcontext = null;
21
22         // fill our addressBindingSource with all rows, ordered by name
23         private void RefreshContacts()
24         {
25            // Dispose old DbContext, if any
26            if (dbcontext != null)
27            {
28               dbcontext.Dispose();
29            }
30
31            // create new DbContext so we can reorder records based on edits
32            dbcontext = new AddressExample.AddressBookEntities();
33
34            // use LINQ to order the Addresses table contents
35            // by last name, then first name
36            dbcontext.Addresses
37               .OrderBy(entry => entry.LastName)
38               .ThenBy(entry => entry.FirstName)
39               .Load();
40
41            // specify DataSource for addressBindingSource
42            addressBindingSource.DataSource = dbcontext.Addresses.Local;
43            addressBindingSource.MoveFirst(); // go to first result
44            findTextBox.Clear(); // clear the Find TextBox
45         }
46
```

Fig. 22.41 | Creating the BooksEntities and defining method RefreshContacts for use in other methods.

Method Contacts_Load

Method Contacts_Load (Fig. 22.42) calls RefreshContacts (line 50) so that the first record is displayed when the app starts. As before, you create the Load event handler by double clicking the Form's title bar.

```
47          // when the form loads, fill it with data from the database
48          private void Contacts_Load(object sender, EventArgs e)
49          {
50             RefreshContacts(); // fill binding with data from database
51          }
52
```

Fig. 22.42 | Calling `RefreshContacts` to fill the `TextBoxes` when the app loads.

Method *addressBindingNavigatorSaveItem_Click*

Method addressBindingNavigatorSaveItem_Click (Fig. 22.43) saves the changes to the database when the BindingNavigator's **Save Data** Button is clicked. (Remember to enable this button.) The AddressBook database requires values for the first name, last name, phone number and e-mail. If a field is empty when you attempt to save, a DbEntityVal-idationException exception occurs. We call RefreshContacts (line 72) after saving to re-sort the data and move back to the first element.

```
53          // Click event handler for the Save Button in the
54          // BindingNavigator saves the changes made to the data
55          private void addressBindingNavigatorSaveItem_Click(
56             object sender, EventArgs e)
57          {
58             Validate(); // validate input fields
59             addressBindingSource.EndEdit(); // complete current edit, if any
60
61             // try to save changes
62             try
63             {
64                dbcontext.SaveChanges(); // write changes to database file
65             }
66             catch (DbEntityValidationException)
67             {
68                MessageBox.Show("Columns cannot be empty",
69                   "Entity Validation Exception");
70             }
71
72             RefreshContacts(); // change back to updated unfiltered data
73          }
74
```

Fig. 22.43 | Saving changes to the database when the user clicks **Save Data**.

Method *findButton_Click*

Method findButton_Click (Fig. 22.44) uses LINQ query syntax (lines 81–85) to select only people whose last names start with the characters in the findTextBox. The query sorts the results by last name, then first name. In LINQ to Entities, you *cannot* bind a LINQ query's results directly to a BindingSource's DataSource. So, line 88 calls the query object's ToList method to get a List representation of the filtered data and assigns the List to the BindingSource's DataSource. When you convert the query result to a List, only changes to *existing* records in the DbContext are tracked by the DbContext—any records that you add or remove while viewing the filtered data would be lost. For this reason we disabled the **Add new** and **Delete** buttons when the data is filtered. When you enter a last name and click **Find**, the BindingNavigator allows the user to browse only the rows containing the matching last names. This is because the data source bound to the Form's controls (the result of the LINQ query) has changed and now contains only a limited number of rows.

```
75        // use LINQ to create a data source that contains only people
76        // with last names that start with the specified text
77        private void findButton_Click(object sender, EventArgs e)
78        {
79            // use LINQ to filter contacts with last names that
80            // start with findTextBox contents
81            var lastNameQuery =
82                from address in dbcontext.Addresses
83                where address.LastName.StartsWith(findTextBox.Text)
84                orderby address.LastName, address.FirstName
85                select address;
86
87            // display matching contacts
88            addressBindingSource.DataSource = lastNameQuery.ToList();
89            addressBindingSource.MoveFirst(); // go to first result
90
91            // don't allow add/delete when contacts are filtered
92            bindingNavigatorAddNewItem.Enabled = false;
93            bindingNavigatorDeleteItem.Enabled = false;
94        }
95
```

Fig. 22.44 | Finding the contacts whose last names begin with a specified String.

Method *browseAllButton_Click*
Method browseAllButton_Click (Fig. 22.45) allows users to return to browsing all the rows after searching for specific rows. Double click browseAllButton to create a Click event handler. The event handler enables the **Add new** and **Delete** buttons, then calls RefreshContacts to restore the data source to the full list of people (in sorted order) and clear the findTextBox.

```
96        // reload addressBindingSource with all rows
97        private void browseAllButton_Click(object sender, EventArgs e)
98        {
99            // allow add/delete when contacts are not filtered
100           bindingNavigatorAddNewItem.Enabled = true;
101           bindingNavigatorDeleteItem.Enabled = true;
102           RefreshContacts(); // change back to initial unfiltered data
103        }
104    }
105 }
```

Fig. 22.45 | Allowing the user to browse all contacts.

22.10 Tools and Web Resources

Our LINQ Resource Center at www.deitel.com/LINQ contains many links to additional information, including blogs by Microsoft LINQ team members, sample chapters, tutorials, videos, downloads, FAQs, forums, webcasts and other resource sites.

A useful tool for learning LINQ is LINQPad

```
http://www.linqpad.net
```

which allows you to execute and view the results of any C# or Visual Basic expression, including LINQ queries. It also supports the ADO.NET Entity Framework and LINQ to Entities.

This chapter is meant as an introduction to databases, the ADO.NET Entity Framework and LINQ to Entities. Microsoft's Entity Framework site

```
https://msdn.microsoft.com/en-us/data/aa937723
```

provides lots of additional information on working with the ADO.NET Entity Framework and LINQ to Entities, including tutorials, videos and more.

22.11 Wrap-Up

This chapter introduced the relational database model, the ADO.NET Entity Framework, LINQ to Entities and Visual Studio's visual programming tools for working with databases. You examined the contents of a simple Books database and learned about the relationships among the tables in the database. You used LINQ to Entities and the entity data model classes generated by the IDE to retrieve data from, add new data to, delete data from and update data in a SQL Server Express database.

We discussed the entity data model classes automatically generated by the IDE, such as the DbContext class that manages an app's interactions with a database. You learned how to use the IDE's tools to connect to databases and to generate entity data model classes based on an existing database's schema. You then used the IDE's drag-and-drop capabilities to automatically generate GUIs for displaying and manipulating database data. In the next chapter, we'll show how to use asynchronous programming with C#'s async modifier and await operator to take advantage of multicore architectures.

Summary

Section 22.1 Introduction
- A database is an organized collection of data.
- A database management system (DBMS) provides mechanisms for storing, organizing, retrieving and modifying data.
- SQL Server Express provides most of the features of Microsoft's full (fee-based) SQL Server product, but has some limitations, such as a maximum database size.
- A SQL Server Express database can be easily migrated to a full version of SQL Server.
- The ADO.NET Entity Framework and LINQ to Entities allow you to manipulate relational data stored in a relational database, such as a SQL Server Express database.

Section 22.2 Relational Databases

- A relational database organizes data simply in tables.
- Tables are composed of rows and columns (also called fields) in which values are stored.
- A column (or group of columns) of each row is the table's primary key—a column (or group of columns) requiring a unique value that cannot be duplicated in other rows. This guarantees that a primary-key value can be used to uniquely identify a row.
- A primary key composed of two or more columns is known as a composite key.
- Each column represents a different data attribute.
- Rows are unique (by primary key) within a table, but some column values may be duplicated between rows.

Section 22.3 A Books Database

- A database's tables, their fields and the relationships between them are collectively known as a database schema.
- A foreign key is a column in one table that matches the primary-key column in another table.
- Foreign keys, which are specified when a database table is created, link the data in multiple tables.
- Every foreign-key value must appear as another table's primary-key value so the DBMS can ensure that the foreign-key value is valid.
- Foreign keys also allow related data in multiple tables to be selected from those tables—this is known as joining the data.
- There's a one-to-many relationship between a primary key and a corresponding foreign key—a foreign key can appear many times in its own table but only once (as the primary key) in another table.
- An entity-relationship (ER) diagram shows the tables in a database and their relationships.
- Every row must have a value in the primary-key column, and the value of the key must be unique in the table.

Section 22.4 LINQ to Entities and the ADO.NET Entity Framework

- With the ADO.NET Entity Framework, you interact with the database via classes that the IDE generates from the database schema when you add a new ADO.NET Entity Data Model to your project.
- The IDE creates two classes for a table. The first class represents a row of the table and contains properties for each table column. Objects of this class are called row objects and store the data from individual rows of the table. The IDE uses the singular version of a table's plural name as the row class's name. The second class represents the table itself. An object of this class stores a collection of row objects that correspond to all of the rows in the table.
- The entity data model classes have full *IntelliSense* support in the IDE.
- Navigation properties in row classes represent the relationships between tables.
- A DbContext (namespace System.Data.Entity) manages the data flow between the program and the database. When the IDE generates the entity data model's row and table classes, it also creates a derived class of DbContext that is specific to the database being manipulated. This class contains properties that represent the database's tables.These can be used as data sources for manipulating data in LINQ queries and in GUIs.
- Changes made to the data managed by a DbContext can be saved back to the database using the DbContext's SaveChanges method.

- LINQ to Entities works through the IQueryable<T> interface, which inherits from the interface IEnumerable<T>. When a LINQ to Entities query on an IQueryable<T> object executes against the database, the results are loaded into objects of the corresponding entity data model classes for convenient access in your code.

- The extension methods used with LINQ to Entities are defined as static methods of class Queryable (namespace System.Linq) and can be applied to any object that implements the IQueryable<T> interface—these include various entity data model objects and the results of LINQ to Entities queries.

Section 22.5 Querying a Database with LINQ

- The IDE provides visual programming tools and wizards that simplify accessing data in your projects. These tools establish database connections and create the objects necessary to view and manipulate the data through the GUI—a technique known as data binding.

- A DataGridView (namespace System.Windows.Forms) displays data from a data source in tabular format.

- A BindingNavigator is a collection of controls that allow you to navigate through the records displayed in a GUI. The BindingNavigator controls also allow you to add records, delete records and save your changes to the database.

Section 22.5.1 Creating the ADO.NET Entity Data Model Class Library

- An entity data model describes as C# classes the data that you'll be manipulating.

- To interact with a database, you add an ADO.NET entity data model to the project (typically a class library project for reuse). This will also configure the connection to the database.

- The ADO.NET entity data model's .edmx file contains information about the entity data model.

- When configuring the model, you create a connection to the database and choose the model's contents from the database.

- The entity connection string contains the information that the ADO.NET Entity Framework requires to connect to the database at runtime.

- The entity data model diagram contains the selected database objects and shows the relationships between them.

Section 22.5.2 Creating a Windows Forms Project and Configuring It to Use the Entity Data Model

- To use the entity data model classes from a class library for data binding, you must first add a reference to the class library to your project. You'll also need to add a reference to the EntityFramework library.

- The EntityFramework library is required in each app that will use an entity data model.

- Each app that will use an entity data model also requires the connection string that tells the Entity Framework how to connect to the database. The connection string is stored in the App.Config file of the project in which the entity data model is defined and must be copied into the App.Config file of any project that uses the entity data model.

Section 22.5.3 Data Bindings Between Controls and the Entity Data Model

- You must write code to enable the autogenerated GUI to interact with the entity data model.

- To use the entity data model classes for data binding, first add them as a data source via Visual Studio's **Data Sources** window. The entity data model classes are used to create objects representing the tables in the database, so use an **Object** data source.

- The default GUI for a table is a `DataGridView` with column names representing all the properties of the data source object. The IDE also creates a `BindingNavigator` that contains `Button`s for moving between entries, adding entries, deleting entries and saving changes to the database. The IDE also generates a `BindingSource`, which handles the transfer of data between the data source and the data-bound controls on the `Form`.

- Nonvisual components such as the `BindingSource` and the nonvisual aspects of the `BindingNavigator` appear in the component tray—the gray region below the `Form` in **Design** view.

- The IDE names the `BindingNavigator` and `BindingSource` based on the data source's name.

- To edit the columns displayed in a `DataGridView`, right click it, then select **Edit Columns...** to display the **Edit Columns** dialog.

- To complete the data binding, you must create an object of the entity data model's `DbContext` derived class and use it to obtain data.

- The `OrderBy` extension method receives a `Func` delegate and orders rows in ascending order by the value returned by the delegate.

- The `ThenBy` extension method receives a `Func` delegate and enables you to order results by an additional column.

- The `Load` extension method (defined in class `DBExtensions` from the namespace `System.Data.Entity`) loads data into memory. This data is tracked by the `DbContext` in local memory so that any changes made to the data can eventually be saved into the database.

- The `Local` property of a `DbContext` property is an `ObservableCollection<T>` that represents the data in memory.

- When a `BindingSource`'s `DataSource` property is assigned an `ObservableCollection<T>` (namespace `System.Collections.ObjectModel`), the GUI that's bound to the `BindingSource` is notified of any changes to the data so the GUI can be updated accordingly. In addition, changes made by the user to the data in the GUI will be tracked so the `DbContext` can eventually save those changes to the database.

- Calling `EndEdit` on the `BindingSource` forces it to save any pending changes into the `DbContext` model in memory.

- Calling `SaveChanges` on the `DbContext` object stores any changes into the database.

Section 22.6 Dynamically Binding Query Results
- The data bindings created by the IDE automatically update a `DataGridView` each time its `BindingSource`'s `DataSource` changes.

- The `MoveFirst` method of the `BindingSource` sets the `Position` property to 0 to move to the first row of the data source.

- Invoking `OrderBy` on an `ObservableCollection<T>` returns an `IOrderedEnumerable<T>`.

- A `Func` delegate that's used with the `Where` extension method must return a `bool` value indicating whether the delegate's argument matches the specified criteria.

Section 22.7 Retrieving Data from Multiple Tables with LINQ
- To join data from multiple tables you use the properties that the entity data model contains based on foreign-key relationships between the database's tables. These properties enable you to easily access related rows in other tables.

- Most queries return result with data arranged in relational-style rows and columns. With LINQ to Entities you can create queries that return hierarchical results in which each item in the result contains a collection of other items.

- All properties of an anonymous type are public and read-only.

- You refer to objects of anonymous types via implicitly typed local variables.

- An anonymous type's autogenerated Equals method compares the properties of the anonymous object that calls the method and the anonymous object that it receives as an argument.

Section 22.8 Creating a Master/Detail View App

- In a master/detail view, one part of the GUI (the master) allows you to select an entry, and another part (the details) displays detailed information about that entry.

- The IDE allows you to specify the type of control(s) that it will create when you drag-and-drop an object from the **Data Sources** window onto a Form. To do so, click a data source object's node in the **Data Sources** window—it should change to a drop-down list from which you can select the controls to use on the GUI. The **Details** option indicates that the IDE should generate Label–TextBox pairs that represent each column of the data source object.

- Dragging a navigation property from a data source object in the **Data Sources** window creates a BindingSource and a GUI for the items in another table that are associated with the data source object. The items in this second BindingSource will automatically update based on the currently selected master object.

Section 22.9 Address Book Case Study

- You cannot bind a LINQ to Entities query's results directly to a BindingSource's DataSource.

- When you convert a query result to a List, only changes to existing records in the DbContext are tracked by the DbContext—any records that you add or remove while viewing the filtered data in a List would be lost.

Terminology

ADO.NET Entity Framework
autoincremented database column
BindingNavigator class
BindingSource class
column of a database table
composite key
connection to a database
data binding
Data Sources window
Data Source Configuration Wizard window
database
database management system (DBMS)
database schema
database table
DataGridView class
DataSource property of class BindingSource
DbContext class
EndEdit method of class BindingSource
entity data model
entity-relationship (ER) diagram
Enumerable class
field in a database table
foreign key

Func delegate
identity column in a database table
IQueryable<T> interface
joining database tables
LINQ to Entities
Load extension method of class DBExtensions
many-to-many relationship
master/detail view
Microsoft SQL Server Express
MoveFirst method of class BindingSource
navigation property
Object data source
ObservableCollection<T> class
one-to-many relationship
OrderBy extension method of class Queryable
primary key
query
Queryable class
relational database
row object
row of a database table
SaveChanges method of a DbContext
smart tag menu

Structured Query Language (SQL)
System.Data.Entity
table in a database

ThenBy extension method of class Queryable
Where extension method of class Queryable

Self-Review Exercises

22.1 Fill in the blanks in each of the following statements:
a) A table in a relational database consists of _____ and _____ in which values are stored.
b) The _____ uniquely identifies each row in a relational database table.
c) A relational database can be manipulated with the ADO.NET Entity Framework via an object of a derived class of _____, which contains properties for accessing each table in the database.
d) The _____ control (presented in this chapter) displays data in rows and columns that correspond to the rows and columns of a data source.
e) Merging data from multiple relational database tables is called _____ the data.
f) A(n) _____ is a column (or group of columns) in a relational database table that matches the primary-key column (or group of columns) in another table.
g) A(n) _____ object serves as an intermediary between a data source and its corresponding data-bound GUI control.
h) The _____ property of a control specifies where it gets the data it displays.

22.2 State whether each of the following is *true* or *false*. If *false*, explain why.
a) Providing the same value for a foreign key in multiple rows causes the DBMS to report an error.
b) Providing a foreign-key value that does not appear as a primary-key value in another table is an error.
c) The result of a query can be sorted in ascending or descending order.
d) A BindingNavigator object can extract data from a database.
e) A DbContext automatically saves changes made back to the database.

Answers to Self-Review Exercises

22.1 a) rows, columns. b) primary key. c) DbContext. d) DataGridView. e) joining. f) foreign key. g) BindingSource. h) DataSource.

22.2 a) False. Multiple rows can have the same value for a foreign key. Providing the same value for the primary key in multiple rows causes the DBMS to report an error, because duplicate primary keys would prevent each row from being identified uniquely. b) True. c) True. d) False. A BindingNavigator allows users to browse and manipulate data displayed by another GUI control. A DbContext can extract data from a database. e) False. You must call the SaveChanges method of the DbContext to save the changes made back to the database.

Exercises

22.3 *(Display Authors Table App Modification)* Modify the app in Section 22.5 to contain a TextBox and a Button that allow the user to search for specific authors by last name. Include a Label to identify the TextBox. Using the techniques presented in Section 22.9, create a LINQ query and change the DataSource property of authorBindingSource to contain only the specified authors. Also, provide a Button that enables the user to return to browsing the complete set of authors.

22.4 *(Display Query Results App Modification)* Modify the app in Section 22.6 to contain a TextBox and a Button that allow the user to perform a search of the book titles in the Titles table of the

Books database. Use a Label to identify the TextBox. When the user clicks the Button, the app should execute and display the result of a query that selects all the rows in which the search term entered by the user in the TextBox appears anywhere in the Title column. For example, if the user enters the search term "Visual," the DataGridView should display the rows for *Visual Basic 2012 How to Program* and *Visual C# How to Program*. If the user enters "Swift," the DataGridView should display only the rows for *iOS 8 for Programmers: An App-Driven Approach with Swift* and *Swift for Programmers*. [*Hint:* Use the Contains method of the String class.] Also, provide a Button that enables the user to return to browsing the complete set of titles.

22.5   *(Joining Tables with LINQ App Modification)* Create an app like the one in Section 22.7 that uses the Books database and displays the results of the following queries:
    a) Get a list of all the titles and the authors who wrote them. Sort the results by title.
    b) Get a list of all the titles and the authors who wrote them. Sort the results by title. For each title sort the authors alphabetically by last name, then first name.
    c) Get a list of all the authors grouped by title, sorted by title; for a given title sort the author names alphabetically by last name then first name.

22.6   *(Baseball Database App)* Build an app that executes a query against the Players table of the Baseball database included in the Databases folder with this chapter's examples. Display the table in a DataGridView, and add a TextBox and Button to allow the user to search for a specific player by last name. Use a Label to identify the TextBox. Clicking the Button should execute the appropriate query. Also, provide a Button that enables the user to return to browsing the complete set of players.

22.7   *(Baseball Database App Modification)* Modify Exercise 22.6 to allow the user to locate players with batting averages in a specific range. Add a minimumTextBox for the minimum batting average (0.000 by default) and a maximumTextBox for the maximum batting average (1.000 by default). Use a Label to identify each TextBox. Add a Button for executing a query that selects rows from the Players table in which the BattingAverage column is greater than or equal to the specified minimum value and less than or equal to the specified maximum value.

23

Asynchronous Programming with async and await

Objectives

In this chapter you'll:

- Understand what asynchronous programming is and how it can improve the performance of your apps.

- Use the `async` modifier to indicate that a method is asynchronous.

- Use an `await` expression to wait for an asynchronous task to complete execution so that an `async` method can continue its execution.

- Take advantage of multicore processors by executing tasks asynchronously via Task Parallel Library (TPL) features.

- Use `Task` method `WhenAll` to wait for multiple tasks to complete before an `async` method continues.

- Time multiple tasks running on a single-core system and a dual-core system (all with the same processor speeds) to determine the performance improvement when these tasks are run on the dual-core system.

- Use an `HttpClient` to invoke a web service asynchronously.

- Show an asynchronous task's progress and intermediate results,

23.1 Introduction

It would be nice if we could focus our attention on performing only one task at a time and doing it well. That's usually difficult to do in a complex world in which there's so much going on at once. This chapter presents C#'s capabilities for developing programs that create and manage multiple tasks. As we'll demonstrate, this can greatly improve program performance, especially on multicore systems.

Concurrency

When we say that two tasks are operating concurrently, we mean that they're both *making progress* at once. Until recently, most computers had only a single processor. Operating systems on such computers execute tasks concurrently by rapidly switching between them, doing a small portion of each before moving on to the next, so that all tasks keep progressing. For example, it's common for personal computers to compile a program, send a file to a printer, receive electronic mail messages over a network and more, concurrently. Tasks like these that proceed independently of one another are said to execute asynchronously and are referred to as asynchronous tasks.

Parallelism

When we say that two tasks are operating in parallel, we mean that they're executing *simultaneously*. In this sense, parallelism is a subset of concurrency. The human body performs a great variety of operations in parallel. Respiration, blood circulation, digestion, thinking and walking, for example, can occur in parallel, as can all the senses—sight, hearing, touch, smell and taste. It's believed that this parallelism is possible because the human brain is thought to contain billions of "processors." Today's multicore computers have multiple processors that can perform tasks in parallel.

Multithreading

C# makes concurrency available to you through the language and APIs. C# programs can have multiple threads of execution, where each thread has its own method-call stack, allowing it to execute concurrently with other threads while sharing with them application-wide resources such as memory and files. This capability is called multithreading.

> **Performance Tip 23.1**
>
> *A problem with single-threaded applications that can lead to poor responsiveness is that lengthy activities must complete before others can begin. In a multithreaded application, threads can be distributed across multiple cores (if available) so that multiple tasks execute in parallel and the application can operate more efficiently. Multithreading can also increase performance on single-processor systems—when one thread cannot proceed (because, for example, it's waiting for the result of an I/O operation), another can use the processor.*

Multithreading Is Difficult

People find it difficult to jump between concurrent trains of thought. To see why multithreaded programs can be difficult to write and understand, try the following experiment: Open three books to page 1, and try reading the books concurrently. Read a few words from the first book, then a few from the second, then a few from the third, then loop back and read the next few words from the first book, the second and so on. After this experiment, you'll appreciate many of the challenges of multithreading—switching between the books, reading briefly, remembering your place in each book, moving the book you're reading closer so that you can see it and pushing the books you're not reading aside—and, amid all this chaos, trying to comprehend the content of the books!

Asynchronous Programming, `async` and `await`

To take full advantage of multicore architectures you need to write applications that can process tasks *asynchronously*. Asynchronous programming is a technique for writing apps containing tasks that can execute asynchronously, which can improve app performance and GUI responsiveness in apps with long-running or compute-intensive tasks. Before languages like C#, such apps were implemented with operating-system primitives available only to experienced systems programmers. Then C# and other programming languages began enabling app developers to specify concurrent operations. Initially, these capabilities were complex to use, which led to frequent and subtle bugs.

The async modifier and await operator greatly simplify asynchronous programming, reduce errors and enable your apps to take advantage of the processing power in today's multicore computers, smartphones and tablets. Many .NET classes for web access, file processing, networking, image processing and more have methods that return Task objects for use with async and await, so you can take advantage of asynchronous programming model. This chapter presents a simple introduction to asynchronous programming with async and await.

23.2 Basics of `async` and `await`

Before `async` and `await`, it was common for a method that was called *synchronously* (i.e., performing tasks one after another in order) in the calling thread to launch a long-running task *asynchronously* and to provide that task with a *callback method* (or, in some cases, register an event handler) that would be invoked once the asynchronous task completed. This style of coding is simplified with `async` and `await`.

23.2.1 async Modifier

The `async` modifier indicates that a method or lambda expression contains at least one `await` expression. An `async` method executes its body in the same thread as the calling method. (Throughout the remainder of this discussion, we'll use the term "method" to mean "method or lambda expression.")

23.2.2 await Expression

An `await` expression, which can appear *only* in an async method, consists of the `await` operator followed by an expression that returns an *awaitable entity*—typically a Task object (as you'll see in Section 23.3), though it is possible to create your own awaitable entities. Creating awaitable entities is beyond the scope of our discussion. For more information, see

```
http://blogs.msdn.com/b/pfxteam/archive/2011/01/13/10115642.aspx
```

When an async method encounters an `await` expression:

- If the asynchronous task has already completed, the `async` method simply continues executing.

- Otherwise, program control returns to the async method's caller until the asynchronous task completes execution. This allows the caller to perform other work that does not depend on the results of the asynchronous task.

When the asynchronous task completes, control returns to the async method and continues with the next statement after the `await` expression.

Software Engineering Observation 23.1

The mechanisms for determining whether to return control to an async *method's caller or continue executing an* async *method, and for continuing an* async *method's execution when the asynchronous task completes, are handled entirely by code that's written for you by the compiler.*

23.2.3 async, await and Threads

The `async` and `await` mechanism does *not* create new threads. If any threads are required, the method that you call to start an asynchronous task on which you `await` the results is responsible for creating the threads that are used to perform the asynchronous task. For example, we'll show how to use class Task's Run method in several examples to start new threads of execution for executing tasks asynchronously. Task method Run returns a Task on which a method can `await` the result.

23.3 Executing an Asynchronous Task from a GUI App

This section demonstrates the benefits of executing compute-intensive tasks asynchronously in a GUI app.

23.3.1 Performing a Task Asynchronously

Figure 23.1 demonstrates executing an asynchronous task from a GUI app. Consider the GUI at the end of Fig. 23.1. In the GUI's top half, you can enter an integer, then click **Calculate** to calculate that integer's Fibonacci value (discussed momentarily) using a compute-intensive recursive implementation (Section 23.3.2). Starting with integers in the 40s (on our test computer), the recursive calculation can take seconds or even minutes to calculate. If this calculation were to be performed *synchronously*, the GUI would *freeze* for that amount of time and the user would not be able to interact with the app (as we'll demonstrate in Fig. 23.2). We launch the calculation *asynchronously* and have it execute on a *separate* thread so the GUI remains *responsive*. To demonstrate this, in the GUI's bottom half, you can click **Next Number** repeatedly to calculate the next Fibonacci number by simply adding the two previous numbers in the sequence. For the screen captures in Fig. 23.1, we used the top half of the GUI to calculate `Fibonacci(45)`, which took over a minute on our test computer. While that calculation proceeded in a separate thread, we clicked **Next Number** repeatedly to demonstrate that we could still interact with the GUI and that the iterative Fibonacci calculation is much more efficient.

A Compute-Intensive Algorithm: Calculating Fibonacci Numbers Recursively
The powerful technique of recursion was introduced in Section 7.16. The examples in this section and in Sections 23.4–23.5 each perform a compute-intensive *recursive* Fibonacci calculation (defined in the `Fibonacci` method at lines 53–63). The Fibonacci series

$$0, 1, 1, 2, 3, 5, 8, 13, 21, \ldots$$

begins with 0 and 1, and each subsequent Fibonacci number is the sum of the previous two Fibonacci numbers. The Fibonacci series can be defined *recursively* as follows:

$$\text{Fibonacci}(0) = 0$$
$$\text{Fibonacci}(1) = 1$$
$$\text{Fibonacci}(n) = \text{Fibonacci}(n-1) + \text{Fibonacci}(n-2)$$

```
1   // Fig. 23.1: FibonacciForm.cs
2   // Performing a compute-intensive calculation from a GUI app
3   using System;
4   using System.Threading.Tasks;
5   using System.Windows.Forms;
6
7   namespace FibonacciTest
8   {
9      public partial class FibonacciForm : Form
10     {
11        private long n1 = 0; // initialize with first Fibonacci number
12        private long n2 = 1; // initialize with second Fibonacci number
```

Fig. 23.1 | Performing a compute-intensive calculation from a GUI app. (Part 1 of 3.)

```csharp
13          private int count = 1; // current Fibonacci number to display
14
15          public FibonacciForm()
16          {
17             InitializeComponent();
18          }
19
20          // start an async Task to calculate specified Fibonacci number
21          private async void calculateButton_Click(object sender, EventArgs e)
22          {
23             // retrieve user's input as an integer
24             int number = int.Parse(inputTextBox.Text);
25
26             asyncResultLabel.Text = "Calculating...";
27
28             // Task to perform Fibonacci calculation in separate thread
29             Task<long> fibonacciTask = Task.Run(() => Fibonacci(number));
30
31             // wait for Task in separate thread to complete
32             await fibonacciTask;
33
34             // display result after Task in separate thread completes
35             asyncResultLabel.Text = fibonacciTask.Result.ToString();
36          }
37
38          // calculate next Fibonacci number iteratively
39          private void nextNumberButton_Click(object sender, EventArgs e)
40          {
41             // calculate the next Fibonacci number
42             long temp = n1 + n2; // calculate next Fibonacci number
43             n1 = n2; // store prior Fibonacci number in n1
44             n2 = temp; // store new Fibonacci
45             ++count;
46
47             // display the next Fibonacci number
48             displayLabel.Text = $"Fibonacci of {count}:";
49             syncResultLabel.Text = n2.ToString();
50          }
51
52          // recursive method Fibonacci; calculates nth Fibonacci number
53          public long Fibonacci(long n)
54          {
55             if (n == 0 || n == 1)
56             {
57                return n;
58             }
59             else
60             {
61                return Fibonacci(n - 1) + Fibonacci(n - 2);
62             }
63          }
64       }
65    }
```

Fig. 23.1 | Performing a compute-intensive calculation from a GUI app. (Part 2 of 3.)

a) GUI after `Fibonacci(45)` began executing in a separate thread

b) GUI while `Fibonacci(45)` was still executing in a separate thread

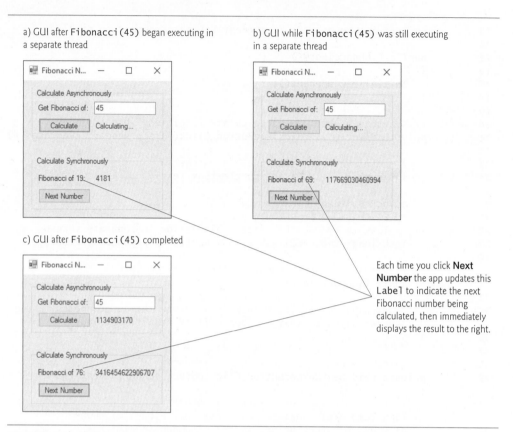

c) GUI after `Fibonacci(45)` completed

Each time you click **Next Number** the app updates this `Label` to indicate the next Fibonacci number being calculated, then immediately displays the result to the right.

Fig. 23.1 | Performing a compute-intensive calculation from a GUI app. (Part 3 of 3.)

Exponential Complexity

A word of caution is in order about recursive methods like the one we use here to generate Fibonacci numbers. The number of recursive calls that are required to calculate the nth Fibonacci number is on the order of 2^n. This rapidly gets out of hand as n gets larger. Calculating only the 20th Fibonacci number would require on the order of 2^{20} or about a million calls, calculating the 30th Fibonacci number would require on the order of 2^{30} or about a billion calls, and so on. This exponential complexity can humble even the world's most powerful computers! Calculating just Fibonacci(47) recursively—even on today's most recent desktop and notebook computers—can take minutes.

23.3.2 Method `calculateButton_Click`

The **Calculate** button's event handler (lines 21–36) initiates the call to method `Fibonacci` in a separate thread and displays the results when the call completes. The method is declared `async` (line 21) to indicate to the compiler that the method will initiate an asynchronous task and `await` the results. In an `async` method, you write code that looks as if it executes sequentially, and the compiler handles the complicated issues of managing asynchronous execution. This makes your code easier to write, debug, modify and maintain, and reduces errors.

23.3.3 Task Method Run: Executing Asynchronously in a Separate Thread

Line 29 creates and starts a `Task<TResult>` (namespace `System.Threading.Tasks`), which *promises* to return a result of generic type TResult *at some point* in the future. Class Task is part of .NET's *Task Parallel Library (TPL)* for parallel and asynchronous programming. The version of class Task's `static` method `Run` used in line 29 receives a `Func<TResult>` *delegate* (delegates were introduced in Section 14.3.3) as an argument and executes a method in a *separate thread*. The delegate Func<TResult> represents any method that takes *no arguments* and returns a *result* of the type specified by the TResult type parameter. The return type of the method you pass to Run is used by the compiler as the type argument for Run's Func delegate and for the Task that Run returns.

Method Fibonacci requires an argument, so line 29 passes the *lambda expression*

```
() => Fibonacci(number)
```

which takes *no arguments*—this labmda encapsulates the call to Fibonacci with the argument number (the value entered by the user). The lambda expression *implicitly* returns the Fibonacci call's result (a long), so it meets the Func<TResult> delegate's requirements. In this example, Task's `static` method Run creates and returns a Task<long>. The compiler *infers* the type long from the return type of method Fibonacci. We could declare local variable fibonacciTask (line 29) with var—we explicitly used the type Task<long> for clarity, because Task method Run's return type is not obvious from the call.

23.3.4 awaiting the Result

Next, line 32 `awaits` the result of the fibonacciTask that's executing asynchronously. If the fibonacciTask is *already complete*, execution continues with line 35. Otherwise, control returns to calculateButton_Click's caller (the GUI event-handling thread) until the result of the fibonacciTask is available. This allows the GUI to remain *responsive* while the Task executes. Once the Task completes, calculateButton_Click continues execution at line 35, which uses Task property `Result` to get the value returned by Fibonacci and display it on asyncResultLabel.

An async method can perform statements between those that launch an asynchronous Task and await the results. In such a case, the method continues executing those statements after launching the asynchronous Task until it reaches the await expression.

Lines 29 and 32 can be written more concisely as

```
long result = await Task.Run(() => Fibonacci(number));
```

In this case, the await operator unwraps and returns the Task's result—the long returned by method Fibonacci. You can then use the long value directly without accessing the Task's Result property.

23.3.5 Calculating the Next Fibonacci Value Synchronously

When you click **Next Number**, the event handler nextNumberButton_Click (lines 39–50) executes. Lines 42–45 add the previous two Fibonacci numbers stored in instance variables n1 and n2 to determine the next number in the sequence, update instance variables n1 and n2 to their new values and increment instance variable count. Then lines 48–49 update the GUI to display the Fibonacci number that was just calculated.

The code in the **Next Number** event handler is performed in the GUI thread of execution that processes user interactions with controls. Handling such short computations in this thread does *not* cause the GUI to become unresponsive. Because the longer Fibonacci computation is performed in a *separate thread*, it's possible to get the next Fibonacci number *while the recursive computation is still in progress.*

23.4 Sequential Execution of Two Compute-Intensive Tasks

Figure 23.2 uses the recursive Fibonacci method that we introduced in Section 23.3. The example sequentially performs the calculations Fibonacci(46) (line 22) and Fibonacci(45) (line 35) when the user clicks the **Start Sequential Fibonacci Calls** Button. Note that once you click the Button, the app becomes nonresponsive. This occurs because the Fibonacci calculations are performed in the GUI thread—once the calculations complete, you'll be able to interact with the app again. Before and after each Fibonacci call, we capture the time (as a DateTime; Section 15.4) so that we can calculate the total time required for *that* calculation and the total time required for *both* calculations. In this app, we used DateTime's overloaded minus (-) operator to calculate the differences between DateTimes (lines 27, 40 and 45)—like method Subtract introduced previously, the minus (-) operator returns a TimeSpan.

The first two outputs show the results of executing the app on a *dual-core* Windows 10 computer. The last two outputs show the results of executing the app on a single-core Windows 10 computer. In all cases, the cores operated at the same speed. The app *always* took longer to execute (in our testing) on the single-core computer, because the processor was being *shared* between this app and all the others that happened to be executing on the computer at the same time. On the dual-core system, one of the cores could have been handling the "other stuff" executing on the computer, reducing the demand on the core performing the synchronous calculation. Results may vary across systems based on processor speeds, the number of cores, apps currently executing and the chores the operating system is performing.

```csharp
1   // Fig. 23.2: SynchronousTestForm.cs
2   // Fibonacci calculations performed sequentially
3   using System;
4   using System.Windows.Forms;
5
6   namespace FibonacciSynchronous
7   {
8      public partial class SynchronousTestForm : Form
9      {
10        public SynchronousTestForm()
11        {
12           InitializeComponent();
13        }
```

Fig. 23.2 | Fibonacci calculations performed sequentially. (Part 1 of 3.)

```
14
15        // start sequential calls to Fibonacci
16        private void startButton_Click(object sender, EventArgs e)
17        {
18           // calculate Fibonacci (46)
19           outputTextBox.Text = "Calculating Fibonacci(46)\r\n";
20           outputTextBox.Refresh(); // force outputTextBox to repaint
21           DateTime startTime1 = DateTime.Now; // time before calculation
22           long result1 = Fibonacci(46); // synchronous call
23           DateTime endTime1 = DateTime.Now; // time after calculation
24
25           // display results for Fibonacci(46)
26           outputTextBox.AppendText($"Fibonacci(46) = {result1}\r\n");
27           double minutes = (endTime1 - startTime1).TotalMinutes;
28           outputTextBox.AppendText(
29              $"Calculation time = {minutes:F6} minutes\r\n\r\n");
30
31           // calculate Fibonacci (45)
32           outputTextBox.AppendText("Calculating Fibonacci(45)\r\n");
33           outputTextBox.Refresh(); // force outputTextBox to repaint
34           DateTime startTime2 = DateTime.Now;
35           long result2 = Fibonacci(45); // synchronous call
36           DateTime endTime2 = DateTime.Now;
37
38           // display results for Fibonacci(45)
39           outputTextBox.AppendText($"Fibonacci(45) = {result2}\r\n");
40           minutes = (endTime2 - startTime2).TotalMinutes;
41           outputTextBox.AppendText(
42              $"Calculation time = {minutes:F6} minutes\r\n\r\n");
43
44           // show total calculation time
45           double totalMinutes = (endTime2 - startTime1).TotalMinutes;
46           outputTextBox.AppendText(
47              $"Total calculation time = {totalMinutes:F6} minutes\r\n");
48        }
49
50        // Recursively calculates Fibonacci numbers
51        public long Fibonacci(long n)
52        {
53           if (n == 0 || n == 1)
54           {
55              return n;
56           }
57           else
58           {
59              return Fibonacci(n - 1) + Fibonacci(n - 2);
60           }
61        }
62     }
63  }
```

Fig. 23.2 | Fibonacci calculations performed sequentially. (Part 2 of 3.)

a) Outputs on a Dual-Core Windows 10 Computer

b) Outputs on a Single-Core Windows 10 Computer

Fig. 23.2 | Fibonacci calculations performed sequentially. (Part 3 of 3.)

23.5 Asynchronous Execution of Two Compute-Intensive Tasks

When you run any program, its tasks compete for processor time with the operating system, other programs and other activities that the operating system is running on your behalf. When you execute the next example, the time to perform the Fibonacci calculations can vary based on your computer's processor speed, number of cores and what else is running on your computer. It's like a drive to the supermarket—the time it takes can vary based on traffic conditions, weather, timing of traffic lights and other factors.

Figure 23.3 also uses the recursive Fibonacci method, but the two initial calls to Fibonacci execute in *separate threads*. The first two outputs show the results on a *dual-core* computer. Though execution times varied, the total time to perform both Fibonacci calculations (in our tests) was typically *significantly less* than the total sequential-execution time in Fig. 23.2. Dividing the compute-intensive calculations into threads and running them on a dual-core system does *not* perform the calculations *twice* as fast, but they'll typically run *faster* than when performed *in sequence* on one core. Though the total time was the compute time for the longer calculation, this is not always the case, as there's overhead inherent in using threads to perform separate Tasks.

The last two outputs show that executing calculations in multiple threads on a single-core processor can actually take *longer* than simply performing them synchronously, due to the overhead of sharing *one* processor among the app's threads, all the other apps executing on the computer and the chores the operating system was performing.

```
1   // Fig. 23.3: AsynchronousTestForm.cs
2   // Fibonacci calculations performed in separate threads
3   using System;
4   using System.Threading.Tasks;
5   using System.Windows.Forms;
6
7   namespace FibonacciAsynchronous
8   {
9      public partial class AsynchronousTestForm : Form
10     {
11        public AsynchronousTestForm()
12        {
13           InitializeComponent();
14        }
15
16        // start asynchronous calls to Fibonacci
17        private async void startButton_Click(object sender, EventArgs e)
18        {
19           outputTextBox.Text =
20              "Starting Task to calculate Fibonacci(46)\r\n";
21
22           // create Task to perform Fibonacci(46) calculation in a thread
23           Task<TimeData> task1 = Task.Run(() => StartFibonacci(46));
24
25           outputTextBox.AppendText(
26              "Starting Task to calculate Fibonacci(45)\r\n");
27
28           // create Task to perform Fibonacci(45) calculation in a thread
29           Task<TimeData> task2 = Task.Run(() => StartFibonacci(45));
30
31           await Task.WhenAll(task1, task2); // wait for both to complete
32
33           // determine time that first thread started
34           DateTime startTime =
35              (task1.Result.StartTime < task2.Result.StartTime) ?
36              task1.Result.StartTime : task2.Result.StartTime;
37
38           // determine time that last thread ended
39           DateTime endTime =
40              (task1.Result.EndTime > task2.Result.EndTime) ?
41              task1.Result.EndTime : task2.Result.EndTime;
42
```

Fig. 23.3 | Fibonacci calculations performed in separate threads. (Part 1 of 3.)

```
43          // display total time for calculations
44          double totalMinutes = (endTime - startTime).TotalMinutes;
45          outputTextBox.AppendText(
46             $"Total calculation time = {totalMinutes:F6} minutes\r\n");
47       }
48
49       // starts a call to Fibonacci and captures start/end times
50       TimeData StartFibonacci(int n)
51       {
52          // create a TimeData object to store start/end times
53          var result = new TimeData();
54
55          AppendText($"Calculating Fibonacci({n})");
56          result.StartTime = DateTime.Now;
57          long fibonacciValue = Fibonacci(n);
58          result.EndTime = DateTime.Now;
59
60          AppendText($"Fibonacci({n}) = {fibonacciValue}");
61          double minutes =
62             (result.EndTime - result.StartTime).TotalMinutes;
63          AppendText($"Calculation time = {minutes:F6} minutes\r\n");
64
65          return result;
66       }
67
68       // Recursively calculates Fibonacci numbers
69       public long Fibonacci(long n)
70       {
71          if (n == 0 || n == 1)
72          {
73             return n;
74          }
75          else
76          {
77             return Fibonacci(n - 1) + Fibonacci(n - 2);
78          }
79       }
80
81       // append text to outputTextBox in UI thread
82       public void AppendText(String text)
83       {
84          if (InvokeRequired) // not GUI thread, so add to GUI thread
85          {
86             Invoke(new MethodInvoker(() => AppendText(text)));
87          }
88          else // GUI thread so append text
89          {
90             outputTextBox.AppendText(text + "\r\n");
91          }
92       }
93    }
94 }
```

Fig. 23.3 | Fibonacci calculations performed in separate threads. (Part 2 of 3.)

a) Outputs on a Dual-Core Windows 10 Computer

b) Outputs on a Single-Core Windows 10 Computer

Fig. 23.3 | Fibonacci calculations performed in separate threads. (Part 3 of 3.)

23.5.1 awaiting Multiple Tasks with Task Method WhenAll

In method startButton_Click, lines 23 and 29 use Task method Run to create and start Tasks that execute method StartFibonacci (lines 50–66)—one to calculate Fibonacci(46) and one to calculate Fibonacci(45). To show the total calculation time, the app must wait for *both* Tasks to complete *before* executing lines 34–46. You can wait for *multiple* Tasks to complete by awaiting the result of Task static method WhenAll (line 31), which returns a Task that waits for *all* of WhenAll's argument Tasks to complete and places *all* the results in an array. In this app, the Task's Result is a TimeData[], because both of WhenAll's argument Tasks execute methods that return TimeData objects. Class TimeData is defined as follows in this project's TimeData.cs file:

```
class TimeData
{
    public DateTime StartTime { get; set; }
    public DateTime EndTime { get; set; }
}
```

We use objects of this class to store the time just before and immediately after the call to Fibonacci—we use these properties to perform time calculations. The `TimeData` array can be used to iterate through the results of the `await`ed `Task`s. In this example, we have only two `Task`s, so we interact with the `task1` and `task2` objects directly in the remainder of the event handler.

23.5.2 Method `StartFibonacci`

Method `StartFibonacci` (lines 50–66) specifies the task to perform—in this case, to call `Fibonacci` (line 57) to perform the recursive calculation, to time the calculation (lines 56 and 58), to display the calculation's result (line 60) and to display the time the calculation took (lines 61–63). The method returns a `TimeData` object that contains the time before and after each thread's call to `Fibonacci`.

23.5.3 Modifying a GUI from a Separate Thread

Lines 55, 60 and 63 in `StartFibonacci` call method `AppendText` (lines 82–92) to append text to the `outputTextBox`. GUI controls are designed to be manipulated *only* by the GUI thread—all GUI event handlers are invoked in the GUI thread automatically. Modifying GUI controls one from a non-GUI thread can corrupt the GUI, making it unreadable or unusable. When updating a control from a non-GUI thread, you *must schedule* that update to be performed by the GUI thread. To do so in Windows `Forms`, check the inherited `Form` property `InvokeRequired` (line 84). If this property is `true`, the code is executing in a non-GUI thread and *must not* update the GUI directly. Instead, you call the inherited `Form` method `Invoke` method (line 86), which receives as an argument a `Delegate` representing the update to perform in the GUI thread. In this example, we pass a `MethodInvoker` (namespace `System.Windows.Forms`)—a `Delegate` that invokes a method with no arguments and a `void` return type. We initialize the `MethodInvoker` with a *lambda expression* that calls `AppendText`. Line 86 *schedules* this `MethodInvoker` to execute in the GUI thread. When the method is called from the GUI thread, line 90 updates the `outputTextBox`. Similar concepts also apply to WPF and Universal Windows Platform GUIs.

23.5.4 `await`ing One of Several Tasks with Task Method WhenAny

Similar to `WhenAll`, class `Task` also provides `static` method `WhenAny`, which enables you to wait for any one of several `Task`s specified as arguments to complete. `WhenAny` returns the `Task` that completes first. One use of `WhenAny` might be to initiate several `Task`s that perform the same complex calculation on computers around the Internet, then wait for any one of those computers to send results back. This would allow you to take advantage of computing power that's available to you to get the result as fast as possible. In this case, it's up to you to decide whether to cancel the remaining `Task`s or allow them to continue executing. For details on how to do this, see

```
https://msdn.microsoft.com/library/jj155758
```

Another use of `WhenAny` might be to download several large files—one per `Task`. In this case, you might want all the results eventually, but you'd like to start processing immediately the results from the first `Task` that returns. You could then call `WhenAny` again for the remaining `Task`s that are still executing.

23.6 Invoking a Flickr Web Service Asynchronously with HttpClient

In this section, we present a **Flickr Viewer** app that allows you to search for photos on Flickr (flickr.com)—one of the first photo-sharing websites—then browse through the results. The app uses an asynchronous method to invoke a Flickr web service—that is, a software component that can receive method calls over the Internet using standard web technologies.

XML and LINQ to XML
Many web services return data in XML (Extensible Markup Language) format. XML is a widely supported standard for describing data that is commonly used to exchange that data between applications over the Internet. XML describes data in a way that both human beings and computers can understand.

The Flickr web-service method we use in this example returns XML by default. We'll use LINQ to XML, which is built into the .NET platform, to process the data returned by Flickr. We'll explain in Section 23.6.3 the small amount of XML and LINQ to XML needed—in the online LINQ to XML chapter, we explain these technologies in detail.

REST Web Service
Flickr provides a so-called REST web service that can receive method calls via standard web technologies. As you'll see, the app invokes the a Flickr web-service method via a URL, just as you'd use to access a web page from a web browser. REST—which stands for Representational State Transfer—is discussed in our online REST Web Services chapter.

Asynchronously Invoking a Web Service
Because there can be unpredictably long delays while awaiting a web-service response, asynchronous Tasks are frequently used in GUI apps that invoke web services (or perform network communication in general) to ensure that the apps remain responsive to their users.

A Flickr API Key Is Required
To run this example on your computer, *you must obtain your own Flickr API key* at

```
https://www.flickr.com/services/apps/create/apply
```

and use it to replace the words YOUR API KEY HERE inside the quotes in line 18 of Fig. 23.4. This key is a unique string of characters and numbers that enables Flickr to track your usage of its APIs. Be sure to read the Flickr API's Terms of Use carefully.

Flicker Viewer App
Our **Flickr Viewer** app (Fig. 23.4) allows you to search by tag for photos that users worldwide have uploaded to Flickr. Tagging—or labeling content—is part of the collaborative nature of social media. A tag is any user-supplied word or phrase that helps organize web content. Tagging items with meaningful words or phrases creates a strong identification of the content. Flickr uses the tags to improve its photo-search service, giving users better results.

```
 1    // Fig. 23.4: FickrViewerForm.cs
 2    // Invoking a web service asynchronously with class HttpClient
 3    using System;
 4    using System.Drawing;
 5    using System.IO;
 6    using System.Linq;
 7    using System.Net.Http;
 8    using System.Threading.Tasks;
 9    using System.Windows.Forms;
10    using System.Xml.Linq;
11
12    namespace FlickrViewer
13    {
14       public partial class FickrViewerForm : Form
15       {
16          // Use your Flickr API key here--you can get one at:
17          // https://www.flickr.com/services/apps/create/apply
18          private const string KEY = "YOUR API KEY HERE";
19
20          // object used to invoke Flickr web service
21          private static HttpClient flickrClient = new HttpClient();
22
23          Task<string> flickrTask = null; // Task<string> that queries Flickr
24
25          public FickrViewerForm()
26          {
27             InitializeComponent();
28          }
29
30          // initiate asynchronous Flickr search query;
31          // display results when query completes
32          private async void searchButton_Click(object sender, EventArgs e)
33          {
34             // if flickrTask already running, prompt user
35             if (flickrTask?.Status != TaskStatus.RanToCompletion)
36             {
37                var result = MessageBox.Show(
38                   "Cancel the current Flickr search?",
39                   "Are you sure?", MessageBoxButtons.YesNo,
40                   MessageBoxIcon.Question);
41
42                // determine whether user wants to cancel prior search
43                if (result == DialogResult.No)
44                {
45                   return;
46                }
47                else
48                {
49                   flickrClient.CancelPendingRequests(); // cancel search
50                }
51             }
```

Fig. 23.4 | Invoking a web service asynchronously with class `HttpClient`. (Part I of 3.)
[Photos used in this example ©Paul Deitel. All rights reserved.]

```
52
53         // Flickr's web service URL for searches
54         var flickrURL = "https://api.flickr.com/services/rest/?method=" +
55             $"flickr.photos.search&api_key={KEY}&" +
56             $"tags={inputTextBox.Text.Replace(" ", ",")}" +
57             "&tag_mode=all&per_page=500&privacy_filter=1";
58
59         imagesListBox.DataSource = null; // remove prior data source
60         imagesListBox.Items.Clear(); // clear imagesListBox
61         pictureBox.Image = null; // clear pictureBox
62         imagesListBox.Items.Add("Loading..."); // display Loading...
63
64         // invoke Flickr web service to search Flickr with user's tags
65         flickrTask = flickrClient.GetStringAsync(flickrURL);
66
67         // await flickrTask then parse results with XDocument and LINQ
68         XDocument flickrXML = XDocument.Parse(await flickrTask);
69
70         // gather information on all photos
71         var flickrPhotos =
72             from photo in flickrXML.Descendants("photo")
73             let id = photo.Attribute("id").Value
74             let title = photo.Attribute("title").Value
75             let secret = photo.Attribute("secret").Value
76             let server = photo.Attribute("server").Value
77             let farm = photo.Attribute("farm").Value
78             select new FlickrResult
79             {
80                 Title = title,
81                 URL = $"https://farm{farm}.staticflickr.com/" +
82                     $"{server}/{id}_{secret}.jpg"
83             };
84         imagesListBox.Items.Clear(); // clear imagesListBox
85
86         // set ListBox properties only if results were found
87         if (flickrPhotos.Any())
88         {
89             imagesListBox.DataSource = flickrPhotos.ToList();
90             imagesListBox.DisplayMember = "Title";
91         }
92         else // no matches were found
93         {
94             imagesListBox.Items.Add("No matches");
95         }
96     }
97
98     // display selected image
99     private async void imagesListBox_SelectedIndexChanged(
100        object sender, EventArgs e)
101    {
```

Fig. 23.4 | Invoking a web service asynchronously with class `HttpClient`. (Part 2 of 3.)

```
102             if (imagesListBox.SelectedItem != null)
103             {
104                 string selectedURL =
105                     ((FlickrResult) imagesListBox.SelectedItem).URL;
106
107                 // use HttpClient to get selected image's bytes asynchronously
108                 byte[] imageBytes =
109                     await flickrClient.GetByteArrayAsync(selectedURL);
110
111                 // display downloaded image in pictureBox
112                 MemoryStream memoryStream = new MemoryStream(imageBytes);
113                 pictureBox.Image = Image.FromStream(memoryStream);
114             }
115         }
116     }
117 }
```

Fig. 23.4 | Invoking a web service asynchronously with class `HttpClient`. (Part 3 of 3.)
[Photos used in this example ©Paul Deitel. All rights reserved.]

As shown in the Fig. 23.4, you can type one or more tags (e.g., "pdeitel flowers") into the TextBox. When you click the **Search** Button, the application invokes the Flickr web service that searches for photos, which returns an XML document containing links to the first 500 (or fewer if there are not 500) results that match the tags you specify. We use LINQ to XML to parse the results and display a list of photo titles in a ListBox. When you select an image's title in the ListBox, the app uses another asynchronous Task to download the full-size image from Flickr and display it in a PictureBox.

23.6.1 Using Class HttpClient to Invoke a Web Service

This app uses class HttpClient (namespace System.Net.Http) to interact with Flickr's web service and retrieve photos that match the search tags. Line 21 creates the static HttpClient object flickrClient that's used in this app to download data from Flickr. Class HttpClient is one of many .NET classes that support asynchronous programming with async and await. In searchButton_Click (lines 32–96), we use class HttpClient's GetStringAsync method to start a new Task (line 65). When we create that Task, we assign it to instance variable flickrTask (declared in line 23) so that we can test whether the Task is still executing when the user initiates a new search.

Software Engineering Observation 23.2
An HttpClient object is typically declared static so it can be used by all of an app's threads. According to the HttpClient documentation, a static HttpClient object can be used from multiple threads of execution.

23.6.2 Invoking the Flickr Web Service's flickr.photos.search Method

Method searchButton_Click (lines 32–96) initiates the *asynchronous* Flickr search, so it's declared as an async method. First, lines 35–51 check whether you started a search previously and, if so, whether that search has already completed (lines 34–35). If an existing search is still being performed, we display a dialog asking if you wish to cancel the search (lines 37–40). If you click **No**, the event handler simply returns. Otherwise, we call the HttpClient's CancelPendingRequests method to terminate the search (line 49).

Lines 54–57 create the URL that invokes Flickr's flickr.photos.search web-service method, which searches for photos, based on the provided parameters. You can learn more about this method's parameters and the format of the URL for invoking the method at

https://www.flickr.com/services/api/flickr.photos.search.html

In this example, we specify values for the following flickr.photos.search parameters:

- api_key—Your Flickr API key. Remember that you must obtain your own key from https://www.flickr.com/services/apps/create/apply.

- tags—A comma-separated list of the tags for which to search. In our sample executions it was "pdeitel,flowers". If the user separates the tags with spaces, the app replaces the spaces with commas.

- tag_mode—We use the all mode to get results that match *all* the tags specified in the search. You also can use any to get results that match *one or more* of the tags.

- per_page—The maximum number of results to return (up to 500). If this parameter is omitted, the default is 100.

- privacy_filter—1 indicates only *publicly accessible* photos should be returned.

Line 65 calls class `HttpClient`'s `GetStringAsync` method, which uses the URL specified as the `string` argument to request information from a web server. Because this URL represents a call to a web-service method, calling `GetStringAsync` will invoke the Flickr web service to perform the search. `GetStringAsync` returns a `Task<string>` representing a *promise* to eventually return a `string` containing the search results. Line 68 then `await`s the `Task`'s result. At this point, if the `Task` is complete, method `searchButton_Click`'s execution continues at line 71; otherwise, program control returns to method `searchButton_Click`'s caller until the results are received. This allows the GUI thread of execution to handle other events, so the GUI remains *responsive* while the search is ongoing. Thus, you could decide to start a *different* search at any time (which cancels the original search in this app).

23.6.3 Processing the XML Response

When the `Task` completes, program control continues in method `searchButton_Click` at line 68 where the app begins processing the XML returned by the web service. A sample of the XML is shown in Fig. 23.5.

```
 1   <rsp stat="ok">
 2      <photos page="1" pages="1" perpage="500" total="5">
 3         <photo id="8708146820" owner="8832668@N04" secret="40fabab966"
 4            server="8130" farm="9" title="fuchsiaflowers" ispublic="1"
 5            isfriend="0" isfamily="0"/>
 6         <photo id="8707026559" owner="8832668@N04" secret="97be93bb05"
 7            server="8115" farm="9" title="redflowers" ispublic="1"
 8            isfriend="0" isfamily="0"/>
 9         <photo id="8707023603" owner="8832668@N04" secret="54db053efd"
10            server="8263" farm="9" title="yellowflowers" ispublic="1"
11            isfriend="0" isfamily="0"/>
12      </photos>
13   </rsp>
```

Fig. 23.5 | Sample XML response from the Flickr APIs.

XML Elements and Attributes

XML represents data as elements, attributes and text. XML delimits elements with start tags and end tags. A start tag consists of the element name, possibly followed by *attributeName=value* pairs, all enclosed in angle brackets. For example, line 1 in the sample XML

```
    <rsp stat="ok">
```

is the start tag for an `rsp` element containing the entire web-service *response*. This tag also contains the attribute `stat` (for "status")—the value `"ok"` indicates that the Flickr web-service request was successful. An end tag consists of the element name preceded by a forward slash (/) in angle brackets (for example, `</rsp>` in line 19, which denotes "end of response").

An element's start and end tags enclose

- text that represents a piece of data or

- other nested elements—for example, the rsp element contains one photos element (lines 2–12) and the photos element contains three photo elements (lines 3–11) representing photos that were found by the web service.

An element is *empty* if it does not contain text or nested elements between its start and end tags. Such an element can be represented by a start tag that ends with />. For example, lines 3–5 define an empty photo element with several *attribute=value* pairs in the start tag.

Class *XDocument* and LINQ to XML

Namespace System.Xml.Linq contains the classes used to manipulate XML using LINQ to XML—we use several of these classes to process the Flickr response. Once the app receives the XML search results, line 68 (Fig. 23.4) uses **XDocument** method **Parse** to convert into an XDocument object the string of XML returned by the await expression. LINQ to XML can query an XDocument to extract data from the XML.

Lines 71–83 use LINQ to XML to gather from each photo element in the XDocument the attributes required to locate the corresponding photo on Flickr:

- XDocument method **Descendants** (line 72) returns a list of **XElement** objects representing the elements with the name specified as an argument—in this case, the photo elements.

- Lines 73–77 use XElement method **Attribute** to extract **XAttributes** representing the element's id, title, secret, server and farm attributes from the current photo XElement.

- XAttribute property **Value** (lines 73–77) returns the value of a given attribute.

For each photo, we create an object of class FlickrResult (located in this project's FlickrResult.cs file) containing:

- A Title property—initialized with the photo element's title attribute and used to display the photo's title in the app's ListBox.

- A URL property—assembled from the photo element's id, secret, server and farm (a *farm* is a collection of servers on the Internet) attributes. The format of the URL for each image is specified at

```
http://www.flickr.com/services/api/misc.urls.html
```

We use a FlickrResult's URL in imagesListBox_SelectedIndexChanged (Section 23.6.5) to download the corresponding photo when the user selects it in the ListBox.

23.6.4 Binding the Photo Titles to the `ListBox`

If there are any results (line 87), lines 89–90 *bind* the results' titles to the ListBox. You cannot bind a LINQ query's result directly to a ListBox, so line 89 invokes LINQ method ToList on the flickrPhotos LINQ query to convert it to a List first, then assigns the result to the ListBox's DataSource property. This indicates that the List's data should be used to populate the ListBox's Items collection. The List contains FlickrResult objects, so line 90 sets the ListBox's DisplayMember property to indicate that each FlickrResult's Title property should be displayed in the ListBox.

23.6.5 Asynchronously Downloading an Image's Bytes

Method `imagesListBox_SelectedIndexChanged` (lines 99–115) is declared `async` because it awaits an *asynchronous* download of a photo. Lines 104–105 get the URL property of the selected `ListBox` item. Then lines 108–109 invoke `HttpClient`'s `GetByteArray-Async` method, which gets a byte array containing the photo. The method uses the URL specified as the method's `string` argument to request the photo from Flickr and returns a `Task<byte[]>`—a *promise* to return a `byte[]` once the task completes execution. The event handler then awaits the result. When the `Task` completes, the await expression returns the `byte[]`. Line 112 creates a `MemoryStream` from the `byte[]` (which allows reading bytes as a stream from an array in memory), then line 113 uses the `Image` class's `static` `FromStream` method to create an `Image` from the byte array and assign it to the `Picture-Box`'s `Image` property to display the selected photo.

23.7 Displaying an Asynchronous Task's Progress

Our last example shows how to display an asynchronous task's progress and intermediate results. Figure 23.6 presents class `FindPrimes`, which asynchronously determines whether each value from 2 up to a user-entered value is a prime number. During the asynchronous testing of each value, we update a `TextBox` with each prime that's found and update a `ProgressBar` and `Label` to show the percentage of the testing that has been completed so far.

```
1   // Fig. 23.6: FindPrimes.cs
2   // Displaying an asynchronous task's progress and intermediate results
3   using System;
4   using System.Linq;
5   using System.Threading.Tasks;
6   using System.Windows.Forms;
7
8   namespace FindPrimes
9   {
10     public partial class FindPrimesForm : Form
11     {
12        // used to enable cancelation of the async task
13        private bool Canceled { get; set; } = false;
14        private bool[] primes; // array used to determine primes
15
16        public FindPrimesForm()
17        {
18           InitializeComponent();
19           progressBar.Minimum = 2; // 2 is the smallest prime number
20           percentageLabel.Text = $"{0:P0}"; // display 0 %
21        }
22
23        // handles getPrimesButton's click event
24        private async void getPrimesButton_Click(object sender, EventArgs e)
25        {
26           // get user input
27           var maximum = int.Parse(maxValueTextBox.Text);
```

Fig. 23.6 | Displaying an asynchronous task's progress and intermediate results. (Part 1 of 3.)

```
28
29          // create array for determining primes
30          primes = Enumerable.Repeat(true, maximum).ToArray();
31
32          // reset Canceled and GUI
33          Canceled = false;
34          getPrimesButton.Enabled = false; // disable getPrimesButton
35          cancelButton.Enabled = true; // enable cancelButton
36          primesTextBox.Text = string.Empty; // clear primesTextBox
37          statusLabel.Text = string.Empty; // clear statusLabel
38          percentageLabel.Text = $"{0:P0}"; // display 0 %
39          progressBar.Value = progressBar.Minimum; // reset progressBar min
40          progressBar.Maximum = maximum; // set progressBar max
41
42          // show primes up to maximum
43          int count = await FindPrimes(maximum);
44          statusLabel.Text = $"Found {count} prime(s)";
45       }
46
47       // displays prime numbers in primesTextBox
48       private async Task<int> FindPrimes(int maximum)
49       {
50          var primeCount = 0;
51
52          // find primes less than maximum
53          for (var i = 2; i < maximum && !Canceled; ++i)
54          {
55             // if i is prime, display it
56             if (await Task.Run(() => IsPrime(i)))
57             {
58                ++primeCount; // increment number of primes found
59                primesTextBox.AppendText($"{i}{Environment.NewLine}");
60             }
61
62             var percentage = (double)progressBar.Value /
63                (progressBar.Maximum - progressBar.Minimum + 1);
64             percentageLabel.Text = $"{percentage:P0}";
65             progressBar.Value = i + 1; // update progress
66          }
67
68          // display message if operation was canceled
69          if (Canceled)
70          {
71             primesTextBox.AppendText($"Canceled{Environment.NewLine}");
72          }
73
74          getPrimesButton.Enabled = true; // enable getPrimesButton
75          cancelButton.Enabled = false; // disable cancelButton
76          return primeCount;
77       }
78
```

Fig. 23.6 | Displaying an asynchronous task's progress and intermediate results. (Part 2 of 3.)

```
79              // check whether value is a prime number
80              // and mark all multiples as not prime
81              public bool IsPrime(int value)
82              {
83                 // if value is prime, mark all of multiples
84                 // as not prime and return true
85                 if (primes[value])
86                 {
87                    // mark all multiples of value as not prime
88                    for (var i = value + value; i < primes.Length; i += value)
89                    {
90                       primes[i] = false; // i is not prime
91                    }
92
93                    return true;
94                 }
95                 else
96                 {
97                    return false;
98                 }
99              }
100
101             // if user clicks Cancel Button, stop displaying primes
102             private void cancelButton_Click(object sender, EventArgs e)
103             {
104                Canceled = true;
105                getPrimesButton.Enabled = true; // enable getPrimesButton
106                cancelButton.Enabled = false; // disable cancelButton
107             }
108          }
109       }
```

Fig. 23.6 | Displaying an asynchronous task's progress and intermediate results. (Part 3 of 3.)

Sieve of Eratosthenes

Line 14 declares the `bool` array `primes`, which we use with the Sieve of Eratosthenes algorithm (described in Exercise 8.27) to find all prime numbers less than a maximum value. The Sieve of Eratosthenes takes a list of integers and, beginning with the first prime, filters out all multiples of that prime. It then moves to the next number not yet filtered out, which is the next prime, then eliminates all of its multiples. It continues until all nonprimes have been filtered out. Algorithmically, we begin with element 2 of the bool array (ignoring elements 0 and 1) and set the elements at all indices that are multiples of 2 to false to indicate that they're divisible by 2 and thus not prime. We then move to the next array element, check whether it's true, and if so set all of its multiples to false to indicate that they're divisible by the current index. When the algorithm completes, all indices that contain true are prime, as they have no divisors. The Sieve of Eratosthenes in this example is implemented by methods FindPrimes (lines 48–77) and IsPrime (lines 81–99). Each time IsPrime determines that a specific number is prime, it immediately eliminates all multiples of that number. As implemented, the algorithm in this example is intentionally inefficient. Exercise 23.10 discusses why and asks you to modify the program.

Constructor

Class FindPrimesForm's constructor (lines 16–21) sets progressBar's Minimum property to 2—the first prime number—and sets the percentageLabel's Text to 0 formatted as a whole-number percentage. In the format specifier P0, P indicates that the value should be formatted as a percentage and 0 indicates zero decimal places.

async *Method* getPrimesButton_Click

When the user enters a number in the maxValueTextBox and presses the **Get Primes** Button, method getPrimesButton_Click (lines 24–45) is called. This method is declared async because it will await the results of the FindPrimes method. Line 27 gets the maximum value entered by the user, then line 30 creates a bool array with that number of elements and fills it with true values. The elements with indices that are not prime numbers will eventually be set to false. Enumerable static method Repeat creates a list of elements containing its first argument's value. The second argument specifies the length of the list. We then call ToArray on the result to get an array representation of the elements. Repeat is a *generic* method—the type of the list it returns is determined by the first argument's type.

Lines 33–40 reset the Canceled property to false and reset the GUI to prepare to determine the prime numbers. Lines 39–40 reset the progressBar's Value to the Minimum value and set Maximum to the new value entered by the user. As we test each number from 2 to the maximum to determine whether its prime, we'll set the progressBar's Value property to the current number being tested. As this number increases, the progressBar will fill proportionally with color to show the asynchronous task's progress.

Line 43 calls async method FindPrimes to begin the process of finding prime numbers. Upon completion, FindPrimes returns the number of primes less than the maximum value entered by the user, which the app then displays at line 44.

async *Method* FindPrimes

The async method FindPrimes implements the Sieve of Eratosthenes algorithm, displays the primes that are found and updates the progressBar and percentage completion. Line 50 initially sets primeCount to 0 to indicate that no primes have been found yet. Lines 53–66 iterate through the values from 2 up to, but not including, the maximum entered by the user. For each value, line 56 launches an async Task to determine whether that value is prime and awaits the Task's result. When that result is returned, if it's true, line 58 increments primeCount to indicate that a prime number was found and line 59 appends that number's `string` representation to the `primesTextBox`'s text—thus displaying one of the intermediate results. Regardless of whether a value is prime, lines 62–64 calculate the percentage of the loop that has completed so far and display that percentage, and line 65 updates the `progressBar`'s `Value`.

At any point during the execution of `FindPrimes`, the user could click the app's **Cancel** Button, in which case property `Canceled` will be set to `true` and the loop will terminate early. If this occurs, lines 69–72 display `"Canceled"` in the `primesTextBox`.

Method *IsPrime*
Method `IsPrime` (lines 81–99) is called by `async` method `FindPrimes` to perform part of the Sieve of Eratosthenes. `IsPrime` tests whether its `value` argument is prime by checking the corresponding element in array `primes` (line 85). If `value` is prime, lines 88–91 set to `false` the `primes` elements at all indices that are multiples of `value`, then line 93 returns `true` to indicate that `value` is prime; otherwise, the method returns `false`.

Method *cancelButton_Click*
When the user clicks the **Cancel** Button, method `cancelButton_Click` (lines 102–107) sets property `Canceled` to `true`, then enables the **Get Primes** Button and disables the **Cancel** Button. When the condition at line 53 is evaluated next, the loop in method `FindPrimes` terminates.

23.8 Wrap-Up

In this chapter, you learned how to use the `async` modifier, `await` operator and `Tasks` to perform long-running or compute-intensive tasks asynchronously. You learned that tasks that proceed independently of one another are said to execute asynchronously and are referred to as asynchronous tasks.

We showed that multithreading enables threads to execute concurrently with other threads while sharing application-wide resources such as memory and processors. To take full advantage of multicore architecture, we wrote applications that processed tasks asynchronously. You learned that asynchronous programming is a technique for writing apps containing tasks that can execute asynchronously, which can improve app performance and GUI responsiveness in apps with long-running or compute-intensive tasks.

To provide a convincing demonstration of asynchronous programming, we presented several apps:

- The first showed how to execute a compute-intensive calculation asynchronously in a GUI app so that the GUI remained responsive while the calculation executed.
- The second app performed two compute-intensive calculations synchronously (sequentially). When that app executed, the GUI froze because the calculations were performed in the GUI thread. The third app executed the same compute-intensive calculations asynchronously. We executed these two apps on single-core and dual-core computers to demonstrate the performance of each program in each scenario.
- The fourth app used class `HttpClient` to interact with the Flickr website to search for photos. You learned that class `HttpClient` is one of many built-in .NET Framework classes that can initiate asynchronous tasks for use with `async` and `await`.

- The last app demonstrated how to show an asynchronous task's progress in a ProgressBar.

In the online chapters, we begin with an introduction to ASP.NET for building web-based applications in C# and .NET. The ASP.NET chapter is the first of several bonus online chapters. See your book's inside front cover for information on accessing these via the book's Companion Website. For a list of the online chapters, visit the book's web page at

```
http://www.deitel.com/books/VCSharpHTP6
```

Summary

Section 23.1 Introduction
- Computers can perform operations concurrently.
- Tasks that proceed independently of one another are said to execute asynchronously and are referred to as asynchronous tasks.
- Only computers that have multiple processors or cores can truly execute multiple asynchronous tasks concurrently.
- Visual C# apps can have multiple threads of execution, where each thread has its own method-call stack, allowing it to execute concurrently with other threads while sharing with them application-wide resources such as memory and processors. This capability is called multithreading.
- Operating systems on single-core computers create the illusion of concurrent execution by rapidly switching between activities (threads).
- Today's multicore computers, smartphones and tablets enable computers to perform tasks truly concurrently.
- Asynchronous programming is a technique for writing apps containing tasks that can execute asynchronously, which can improve app performance and GUI responsiveness in apps with long-running or compute-intensive tasks.
- The async modifier and await operator greatly simplify asynchronous programming, reduce errors and enable your apps to take advantage of the processing power in today's multicore computers, smartphones and tablets.
- In .NET, many classes for web access, file processing, networking, image processing and more provide methods that return Task objects for use with async and await, so you can take advantage of this new asynchronous programming model.

Section 23.2.1 async Modifier
- The async modifier indicates that a method or lambda expression contains at least one await expression.
- An async method executes its body in the same thread as the calling method.

Section 23.2.2 await Expression
- When an async method encounters an await expression: If the asynchronous task has already completed, the async method simply continues executing. Otherwise, program control returns to the async method's caller until the asynchronous task completes execution. When the asynchronous task completes, control returns to the async method and continues with the next statement after the await expression.

- The mechanisms for determining whether to return control to the async method's caller or continue executing the async method, and for continuing the async method's execution when the asynchronous task completes, are handled entirely by code that's written for you by the compiler.

Section 23.2.3 `async`, `await` and Threads
- The async and await mechanism does not create new threads. The method that you call to start an asynchronous task on which you await the results is responsible for creating any threads that are used to perform the asynchronous task (e.g., Task method Run).

Section 23.3.1 Performing a Task Asynchronously
- If a long-running calculation were to be performed synchronously in a GUI app, the GUI would freeze until the calculation completed and the user would not be able to interact with the app.
- Launching a calculation asynchronously and executing it on a separate thread keeps the GUI responsive.
- The recursive implementation of the Fibonacci calculation is a compute-intensive calculation.

Section 23.3.2 Method `calculateButton_Click`
- A method is declared async to indicate to the compiler that the method will await an asynchronous task.
- In effect, an async method allows you to write code that looks as if it executes sequentially, while the compiler deals with the complicated issues of managing asynchronous execution.

Section 23.3.3 `Task` Method `Run`: Executing Asynchronously in a Separate Thread
- A Task promises to return a result at some point in the future.
- Class Task is part of .NET's Task Parallel Library (TPL) for parallel and asynchronous programming.
- Task static method Run receives a Func<TResult> delegate as an argument and executes a method in a separate thread. The method returns a Task<TResult>, where TResult represents the type of value returned by the method being executed.
- The Func<TResult> delegate represents any method that takes no arguments and returns a result of generic type TResult.

Section 23.3.4 `await`ing the Result
- Task property Result returns the value returned by a Task.
- An async method can perform other statements between those that launch an asynchronous Task and await the Task's results. In such a case, the method continues executing those statements after launching the asynchronous Task until it reaches the await expression.
- You can place the await expression on the right side of an assignment. The await operator unwraps and returns the Task's result so you can use it directly without accessing the Task's Result property.

Section 23.3.5 Calculating the Next Fibonacci Value Synchronously
- Handling short computations in the GUI thread does not cause the GUI to become unresponsive.

Section 23.4 Sequential Execution of Two Compute-Intensive Tasks
- An app that performs synchronous tasks on a single-core computer often takes longer to execute than on a multicore computer, because the processor is shared between the app and all the other apps that happened to be executing on the computer at the same time. On the dual-core system,

one of the cores could have been handling the "other stuff" executing on the computer, reducing the demand on the core that's doing the synchronous calculation.

Section 23.5 Asynchronous Execution of Two Compute-Intensive Tasks

• When you run any program, your program's tasks compete for processor time with the operating system, other programs and other activities that the operating system is running on your behalf. In any app, the time to perform the app's tasks can vary based on your computer's processor speed, number of cores and what else is running on your computer.

• Executing asynchronous methods in separate threads on a dual-core computer typically takes less time than executing the same tasks sequentially.

• Executing asynchronous methods in multiple threads on a single-core processor can actually take longer than simply performing them synchronously, due to the overhead of sharing one processor among the app's threads, all the other apps executing on the computer at the same time and the chores the operating system was performing.

Section 23.5.1 *awaiting Multiple* Tasks *with* Task *Method* WhenAll

• You can wait for multiple Tasks to complete by awaiting the result of Task static method WhenAll, which returns a Task that waits for all of WhenAll's argument Tasks to complete and places all the results in an array. This array can be used to iterate through the results of the awaited Tasks.

Section 23.5.3 *Modifying a GUI from a Separate Thread*

• GUI controls are designed to be manipulated only by the GUI thread—modifying a control from a non-GUI thread can corrupt the GUI, making it unreadable or unusable.

• When updating a control from a non-GUI thread, you must schedule that update to be performed by the GUI thread. To do so in Windows Forms, you check the InvokeRequired property of class Form. If this property's value is true, the code is executing in a non-GUI thread and must not update the GUI directly. Instead, you call the Invoke method of class Form, which receives as an argument a Delegate representing the update to perform in the GUI thread.

• A MethodInvoker (namespace System.Windows.Forms) is a Delegate that invokes a method with no arguments and a void return type.

Section 23.5.4 *awaiting One of Several Tasks with* Task *Method* WhenAny

• Task static method WhenAny enables you to wait for any one of several Tasks specified as arguments to complete. WhenAny returns the Task that completes first.

Section 23.6 *Invoking a Flickr Web Service Asynchronously with* HttpClient

• A web service is software that can receive method calls over a network using standard web technologies. Because there can be unpredictably long delays while awaiting a web-service response, asynchronous Tasks are frequently used in GUI apps that invoke web services (or perform network communication in general) to ensure that the apps remain responsive.

Section 23.6.1 *Using Class* HttpClient *to Invoke a Web Service*

• Class HttpClient (namespace System.Net.Http) can invoke a web service. Class HttpClient is one of many .NET classes that support asynchronous programming with async and await.

Section 23.6.2 *Invoking the Flickr Web Service's* flickr.photos.search *Method*

• HttpClient's CancelPendingRequests method terminates its executing asynchronous tasks.

- Class `HttpClient`'s `GetStringAsync` method uses the URL specified as the method's `string` argument to request information from a web server and returns a `Task<string>` representing a promise to eventually return a `string`.

Section 23.6.3 Processing the XML Response
- XML represents data as elements, attributes and text.
- XML delimits elements with start tags and end tags.
- A start tag consists of the element name, possibly followed by *attributeName=value* pairs, all enclosed in angle brackets.
- An end tag consists of the element name preceded by a forward slash (/) in angle brackets.
- An element's start and end tags enclose text that represents a piece of data or other nested elements.
- If an element is empty—that is, it does not contain text or nested elements between its start and end tags—then the element can be represented by a start tag that ends with /> rather than >.
- Namespace `System.Xml.Linq` contains the classes used to manipulate XML using LINQ to XML.
- `XDocument` method `Parse` converts into an `XDocument` object a `string` of XML.
- LINQ to XML can query an `XDocument` to extract data from the XML.
- `XDocument` method `Descendants` returns a list of `XElement` objects representing the elements with the name specified as an argument.
- `XElement` method `Attribute` extracts `XAttributes` representing an element's attributes.
- `XAttribute` property `Value` returns the value of a given attribute.

Section 23.6.4 Binding the Photo Titles to the `ListBox`
- You cannot bind a LINQ query's result directly to a `ListBox`. You must first convert the results to a `List` with method `ToList` or to an array with `ToArray`.
- A `ListBox`'s `DataSource` property indicates the source of the data that populates the `ListBox`'s `Items` collection. A `ListBox`'s `DisplayMember` property indicates which property of each item in the data source should be displayed in the `ListBox`.

Section 23.6.5 Asynchronously Downloading an Image's Bytes
- `HttpClient`'s `GetByteArrayAsync` method launches in a separate thread a `Task<byte[]>` that gets a `byte[]` from the URL specified as the method's `string` argument.

Section 23.7 Displaying an Asynchronous Task's Progress
- `ProgressBar` property `Minimum` gets or sets a `ProgressBar`'s minimum value.
- `ProgressBar` property `Maximum` gets or sets a `ProgressBar`'s maximum value.
- `ProgressBar` property `Value` gets or sets a `ProgressBar`'s current value. As this number increases, a `ProgressBar` fills with color.
- `Enumerable` `static` method `Repeat` creates a list of elements containing the first argument's value. The length of the list is specified by the second argument. `Repeat` is a generic method—the type of the list it returns is determined by the first argument's type.

Terminology

async modifier	Attribute method of class `XElement`
asynchronous call	`await` expression
asynchronous programming	`await` multiple Tasks
asynchronous task	`await` operator

awaitable entity
block a calling method
callback method
CancelPendingRequests method of class Http-
    Client
concurrency
concurrent operations
Descendants method of class XDocument
exponential complexity
Fibonacci series
Func<TResult> delegate
GetByteArrayAsync method of class HttpClient
GetStringAsync method of class HttpClient
HttpClient class
Invoke method of class Control
InvokeRequired property of class Control
MethodInvoker delegate
Maximum property of class ProgressBar
Minimum property of class ProgressBar
multithreading
parallel operations

Parse method of class XDocument
performing operations concurrently
ProgressBar class
responsive GUI
REST web service
Result property of class Task
Run method of class Task
System.Net.Http namespace
System.Threading.Tasks namespace
Task class
Task Parallel Library
thread of execution
Value property of class XAttribute
Value property of class ProgressBar
web service
WhenAll method of class Task
WhenAny method of class Task
XAttribute class
XDocument class
XElement class

Self-Review Exercises

23.1   What does it mean to process tasks asynchronously?

23.2   What is the key advantage of programming your apps for multicore systems?

23.3   Suppose you program an app with two compute-intensive tasks that run on one core of a dual-core system. Then, suppose you program the app so that the two compute-intensive tasks run asynchronously in separate threads on a dual-core system. Should you expect the latter program to run in half the time? Why?

23.4   Does the async and await mechanism create new threads?

23.5   (True/False) You can update a GUI from any thread of execution. If *false*, explain why.

Answers to Self-Review Exercises

23.1   It means that the tasks can proceed independently of one another.

23.2   In multicore systems, the hardware can put multiple cores to work simultaneously, thereby enabling faster completion of programs that can be implemented with asynchronous tasks.

23.3   No. There's overhead inherent in using threads to perform separate tasks. Simply performing the tasks asynchronously on a dual-core system does not complete the tasks in half the time, though they'll often run faster than if you perform the tasks in sequence.

23.4   No. The method that you call to start an asynchronous task on which you await the result is responsible for creating any new threads.

23.5   False. When updating a control from a non-GUI thread, you must schedule that update to be performed by the GUI thread. To do so, you check the Form's inherited InvokeRequired property. If this property's value is true, the code is executing in a non-GUI thread and must not update the GUI directly. Instead, you call Form's inherited Invoke method, which receives as an argument a Delegate representing a method to invoke.

Exercises

23.6   Investigate other compute-intensive calculations, then modify the example of Fig. 23.1 to perform a different compute-intensive calculation asynchronously.

23.7   Modify the example of Fig. 23.3 to process the results by using the array returned by the `Task` produced by `Task` method `WhenAll`.

23.8   Investigate other web services at a site like `http://www.programmableweb.com`. Locate a REST web service that returns XML, then modify the example of Fig. 23.4 to invoke the web service asynchronously using the methods of class `HttpClient`. Parse the results using LINQ to XML, then display the results as appropriate for the type of data returned.

23.9   You may have noticed that the prime-number example in Fig. 23.6 produces prime numbers rapidly. The asynchronous task in the example is probably not compute bound, but rather I/O bound—that is, the speed of displaying the results on the screen slows the program down, not the ability of the processor to determine the prime numbers. Reimplement the example of Fig. 23.6 with a compute bound algorithm such as the recursive Fibonacci calculation of Fig. 23.1. Try calculating all the Fibonacci values from 0 to 47. When you run the app, observe that as the Fibonacci numbers get higher, the calculation speed slows dramatically, slowing the updates of the `Progress-Bar` and the `TextBox` that shows the calculation results. Because this calculation is compute bound, the overall speed of the app will depend on your computer's processor—you may want to decrease or increase the largest Fibonacci number the app calculates accordingly. For example, on our computer the Fibonacci of 47 takes a couple of minutes to calculate.

23.10   Visit `https://en.wikipedia.org/wiki/Sieve_of_Eratosthenes` to learn more about the Sieve of Eratosthenes. The algorithm as implemented in Fig. 23.6 is inefficient, because it keeps eliminating multiples of primes even after the array already represents all primes up to the maximum entered by the user. The algorithm is complete once it eliminates the multiples of all primes that are less than or equal to the square root of the maximum value. Make the following modifications to Fig. 23.6:

   a) Update the algorithm to eliminate multiples of primes that are less than or equal to the square root of the maximum value.

   b) Modify the code that updates the `ProgressBar` and percentage `Label` so that they indicate the progress of the Sieve of Eratosthenes algorithm, rather than the progress of checking whether each number in the range is prime.

Chapters on the Web

Additional chapters are available as PDF documents[1] on this book's Companion Website:

```
http://www.pearsonhighered.com/deitel
```

Once at this site, select Visual C# How to Program, 6/e to view links to the book's Companion Website and code examples.

New copies of this book come with a Companion Website access code that is located on the book's inside front cover. If the access code is already visible or there is no card, you purchased a used book or an edition that does not come with an access code. In this case, you can purchase access directly from the Companion Website.

---

1. These files can be viewed in Adobe® Reader® (`http://get.adobe.com/reader`).

Operator Precedence Chart

Operators are shown in decreasing order of precedence from top to bottom with each level of precedence separated by a horizontal line. The associativity of the operators is shown in the right column.

Operator	Type	Associativity
.	member access	left-to-right
?.	null-conditional member access	
()	method call	
[]	element access	
?[]	null-conditional element access	
++	postfix increment	
--	postfix decrement	
nameof	string representation of an identifier	
new	object creation	
typeof	get System.Type object for a type	
sizeof	get size in bytes of a type	
checked	checked evaluation	
unchecked	unchecked evaluation	
+	unary plus	right-to-left
-	unary minus	
!	logical negation	
~	bitwise complement	
++	prefix increment	
--	prefix decrement	
(*type*)	cast	
*	multiplication	left-to-right
/	division	
%	remainder	

Fig. A.1 | Operator precedence chart (Part 1 of 2.).

Operator	Type	Associativity
+	addition	left-to-right
-	subtraction	
>>	right shift	left-to-right
<<	left shift	
<	less than	left-to-right
>	greater than	
<=	less than or equal to	
>=	greater than or equal to	
is	type comparison	
as	type conversion	
!=	is not equal to	left-to-right
==	is equal to	
&	logical AND	left-to-right
^	logical XOR	left-to-right
|	logical OR	left-to-right
&&	conditional AND	left-to-right
||	conditional OR	left-to-right
??	null coalescing	right-to-left
?:	conditional	right-to-left
=	assignment	right-to-left
*=	multiplication assignment	
/=	division assignment	
%=	remainder assignment	
+=	addition assignment	
-=	subtraction assignment	
<<=	left shift assignment	
>>=	right shift assignment	
&=	logical AND assignment	
^=	logical XOR assignment	
|=	logical OR assignment	

Fig. A.1 | Operator precedence chart (Part 2 of 2.).

B

Simple Types

Type	Size in bits	Value range	Standard
bool	8	true or false	
byte	8	0 to 255, inclusive	
sbyte	8	−128 to 127, inclusive	
char	16	'\u0000' to '\uFFFF' (0 to 65535), inclusive	Unicode
short	16	−32768 to 32767, inclusive	
ushort	16	0 to 65535, inclusive	
int	32	−2,147,483,648 to 2,147,483,647, inclusive	
uint	32	0 to 4,294,967,295, inclusive	
float	32	*Approximate negative range:* −3.4028234663852886E+38 to −1.40129846432481707E−45 *Approximate positive range:* 1.40129846432481707E−45 to 3.4028234663852886E+38 *Other supported values:* positive and negative zero positive and negative infinity not-a-number (NaN)	IEEE 754 IEC 60559
long	64	−9,223,372,036,854,775,808 to 9,223,372,036,854,775,807, inclusive	
ulong	64	0 to 18,446,744,073,709,551,615, inclusive	

Fig. B.1 | Simple types. (Part 1 of 2.)

Type	Size in bits	Value range	Standard
double	64	*Approximate negative range:* −1.7976931348623157E+308 to −4.94065645841246544E−324 *Approximate positive range:* 4.94065645841246544E−324 to 1.7976931348623157E+308 *Other supported values:* positive and negative zero positive and negative infinity not-a-number (NaN)	IEEE 754 IEC 60559
decimal	128	*Negative range:* −79,228,162,514,264,337,593,543,950,335 (−7.9E+28) to −1.0E−28 *Positive range:* 1.0E−28 to 79,228,162,514,264,337,593,543,950,335 (7.9E+28)	

Fig. B.1 | Simple types. (Part 2 of 2.)

Additional Simple Type Information

- This appendix is based on information from the **Types** section of Microsoft's C# 6 specification. A draft of this document can be found at:

    `http://msdn.microsoft.com/vcsharp/aa336809`

- Values of type `float` have seven digits of precision.

- Values of type `double` have 15–16 digits of precision.

- Values of type `decimal` are represented as integer values that are scaled by a power of 10. Values between −1.0 and 1.0 are represented exactly to 28 digits.

- For more information on IEEE 754 visit `http://grouper.ieee.org/groups/754/`.

- For more information on Unicode, visit `http://unicode.org`.

C

ASCII Character Set

	0	1	2	3	4	5	6	7	8	9
0	nul	soh	stx	etx	eot	enq	ack	bel	bs	ht
1	nl	vt	ff	cr	so	si	dle	dc1	dc2	dc3
2	dc4	nak	syn	etb	can	em	sub	esc	fs	gs
3	rs	us	sp	!	"	#	$	%	&	'
4	(	)	*	+	,	-	.	/	0	1
5	2	3	4	5	6	7	8	9	:	;
6	<	=	>	?	@	A	B	C	D	E
7	F	G	H	I	J	K	L	M	N	O
8	P	Q	R	S	T	U	V	W	X	Y
9	Z	[	\	]	^	_	'	a	b	c
10	d	e	f	g	h	i	j	k	l	m
11	n	o	p	q	r	s	t	u	v	w
12	x	y	z	{			}	~	del		

Fig. C.1 | ASCII Character Set.

The digits at the left of the table are the left digits of the decimal equivalent (0–127) of the character code, and the digits at the top of the table are the right digits of the character code. For example, the character code for "F" is 70, and the character code for "&" is 38.

Most users of this book are interested in the ASCII character set used to represent English characters on many computers. The ASCII character set is a subset of the Unicode character set used by C# to represent characters from most of the world's languages. For more information on the Unicode character set, see http://unicode.org.

Appendices on the Web

Additional appendices are available as PDF documents[1] on this book's Companion Website:

```
http://www.pearsonhighered.com/deitel
```

Once at this site, select Visual C# How to Program, 6/e to view links to the book's Companion Website and code examples.

New copies of this book come with a Companion Website access code that is located on the book's inside front cover. If the access code is already visible or there is no card, you purchased a used book or an edition that does not come with an access code. In this case, you can purchase access directly from the Companion Website.

---

1. These files can be viewed in Adobe® Reader® (`http://get.adobe.com/reader`).

Index

uperbly clear, and the huge selection of exercises for each chapter is amazing! Excellent intro to
ning! A very gentle, well-rounded introduction to programming in C#—great set of exercises.
w C# 6 string interpolation feature. Introducing UML class diagrams in parallel with the
idea. Excellent chapter on algorithm development and control statements! The discussion
uge plus. I like the early introduction of exception handling. Brings students up to speed fast
ation, and event-driven programming. Nice example demonstrating the method call stack and
ase chapter perfectly explains LINQ to Entities and UI binding."
ez, Microsoft Certified Solution Developer (MCSD), Principal Software Engineer at Advanced Bionics

e perfect amount of material for introducing Visual Studio and GUI elements—I wish I had this chapter when
getting back into computers. Students feel comfortable using the book. A great start to the C# language and the
studio environment. I liked the examples for formulating algorithms. Everything felt just right in the methods chapter.
cursion will warp anyone's brain—the stack discussion really helps students understand what is going on. A good discussion
of when to use for, while and foreach. I really like the deck of cards example, being a former casino gaming programmer.
Multidimensional arrays are handled well. Great 'Making a Difference' exercises. I like the attention to detail and the UML.
Thank you for showing correct code formatting conventions. I like the description of the recursive evaluation of a factorial.
Pretty thorough display of all the 'pass-by' types. The card shuffling and dealing simulation is a great example for bringing
together many concepts. Good use of overloaded functions for rectangular arrays and jagged arrays. The LINQ chapter is
perfect—so much more will be revealed in later chapters but students will remember this, especially after doing the problems
in the homework section. The collections are a nice addition as well—a chapter that is important to get a taste of now so
the later material can be feasted upon. Describes inheritance perfectly—we implement most of your shapes inheritance
hierarchy in class." **—Bradley Sward, College of Dupage**

"This new edition solidifies it as the fundamental tool for learning C# updated to the latest C# 6 features. It covers from the
fundamentals of OOP to the most advanced topics (web and mobile development, cloud computing, asynchronous programming,
etc.), all in a very easily accessible way thanks to its crystal-clear explanations. Very polished introductory chapter on computers
and the Internet. A good job explaining such a complex topic as asynchronous programming."
—José Antonio González Seco, Parliament of Andalusia, Spain

"I wish I were a student again so I could experience the joy of discovery and invention as I work through the thrilling exercises—
they're so inventive that they really grab your attention, intrigue you and inspire you to learn the language so you can solve
them. Building GUIs is an awesome hook for beginner students—the exercises at the end of this chapter are empowering and
exciting. I loved Chapter 3—great intro to coding. I liked the natural use of C# 6 string interpolation. The exercises range from
fun math puzzlers like calculating pi, to fun coding exercises like printing ASCII art, to fun 'be a better-informed citizen of
our democracy' exercises by using code to think critically about what politicians and media tell us. Seriously, if civics/politics/
media students and professionals were able to do the Making A Difference exercises, they'd be able to do their studies/jobs
so much better. The 'code.org' project has a concrete civic benefit, and this book exemplifies it. A good clear explanation of
LINQ query syntax. GUI apps are where coding starts to become fun—you've handled it well and covered all the bases.
Great exercises creating the GUIs for a notepad, a calendar and a calculator. The Game of Craps is an awesome example—
the modification exercise that adds betting is fun. I love that you're paying attention to formats and using them well.
Great Enhanced Painter exercise! The Random Sentences Story Writer and Pig Latin exercises are entertaining."
—Lucian Wischik, C# Language Design Team, Microsoft

"In the Windows forms chapter, cool how the message box will be customized to the clicked buttons—I really like this example.
I love the Paint example—this is so much fun! Your descriptions in the strings chapter are great. A good overall look at files
and directories—generally we teach text mode because it's easier to see what's going on—binary mode is much more efficient
so it's good to see it here. You show error checking in GUI and files/streams very well. The file chooser functionality was a nice
touch. Good example of serialization. The recursive directory searching was a nice touch since students hardly ever see recursion
outside Fibonacci and factorials. This book is an excellent resource to tame the beast that is C#. I like the chapter on asynchronous
programming with async and await—this is the future of programming, and making these types of tasks "easy" to program is
going to be key to any programming language. The introduction to multi-threading was interesting. It was good to see synchronous
versus asynchronous programming head-to-head. The flickr demo was awesome."
—Bradley Sward, College of Dupage